## DATE DUE

|  |  |  |  |
|---|---|---|---|
|  |  |  |  |
|  |  |  |  |
|  |  |  |  |
|  |  |  |  |
|  |  |  |  |
|  |  |  |  |
|  |  |  |  |
|  |  |  |  |
|  |  |  |  |
|  |  |  |  |
|  |  |  |  |
|  |  |  |  |
|  |  |  |  |
|  |  |  |  |
|  |  |  |  |
|  |  |  |  |
|  |  |  |  |
|  |  |  |  |

DEMCO 38-297

# ANNUAL REVIEW OF PHYSIOLOGY

# ANNUAL REVIEW OF PHYSIOLOGY

## VOLUME 59, 1997

JOSEPH F. HOFFMAN, *Editor*
Yale University School of Medicine

PAUL De WEER, *Associate Editor*
University of Pennsylvania School of Medicine

http://annurev.org                    science@annurev.org                    415-493-4400

ANNUAL REVIEW INC.   4139 EL CAMINO WAY,   P.O. BOX 10139   PALO ALTO, CALIFORNIA 04303-0139

R ANNUAL REVIEWS INC.
Palo Alto, California, USA

# PREFACE

This is the second time in three years that I have written in this space about the dramatic changes occurring in the accessibility of the literature of our science. In 1995 I wrote about some of the consequences that have been imposed on the biomedical community by the 1966 (soon to be 1964) cutoff of MEDLINE. The new concern is about the impact of electronic publishing on our use of the journal literature of science. There is now ample evidence that digital information will be the primary form of scientific communication. I am told that user searches on MEDLINE and the Internet are and have been increasing at a rapid rate. Many journals are already on-line, with many others soon to follow. Some will evidently only be accessible electronically, with no hard copies printed. Obviously, the current state of the art is one in transition, both from the library/user side as well as for the publishers. What form the shakeout will take is still to be defined, but questions to be answered include the archival storage of journals, access and downloading costs, and copyright laws. The driving force behind these changes is, of course, the rising costs of journal subscriptions. Most libraries have been, because of limited budgets, reducing steadily the numbers of their journal subscriptions. Although the economics of journal costs may be inversely related to the number of subscriptions (whether paper or electronic), journal size and their number is influenced by the scientists themselves driven by their needs for research grants, jobs, promotions, and so forth. Change usually generates problems, but there is every reason to be optimistic about the future. Just as we can expect to see new developments in electronic networking in increasing the speed and efficiency of literature access, we can also watch with interest to see how the interaction between publishers and libraries/users will be sorted out.

However, the main message of this preface is to emphasize the emerging new responsibility, as well as importance, for critical reviews highlighting the advances of our science such as those published in the Annual Review's series, as well as in related journals. This is because use of the network (or MED-LINE) necessarily is limited if it is to be workable. That is, searches are usually narrowly directed (but fortunately not always), which diminishes browsing and

*(continued)*     v

thwarts curiosity in exploring complementary fields or more general aspects of our science. It has been said (Bennett 1996) that "An investigator who ordinarily first discovers key information for his or her work in the published literature of science is arguably out of touch. The commonplace observation is that published journals are now little more than the archives of science, while most of the vital work of scholarly communication is carried elsewhere." It is difficult to imagine that the foregoing quotation describes any current state or pursuit of biomedical science, but if it is a descriptive harbinger of the future, then it accentuates the need for access to broader commentaries that provide different perspectives and insights. It is the hope that reviews such as those appearing in the *Annual Review of Physiology* will contribute to if not subserve this purpose. We can, by the way, be contacted at http:/www.annurev.org.

JOSEPH F. HOFFMAN
EDITOR

Bennett S. 1996. Re-engineering scholarly communication; Thoughts addressed to authors. *J. Schol. Pub.* July, pp. 185–96

Annual Review of Physiology
Volume 59, 1997

# CONTENTS

OTHER REVIEWS OF INTEREST TO PHYSIOLOGISTS

From the *Annual Review of Biochemistry*, Volume 65 (1996):

Protein Prenylation: Molecular Mechanisms and Functional Consequences, *F. L. Zhang, P. J. Casey*

Protein Transport Across the Eukaryotic Endoplasmic Reticulum and Bacterial Inner Membranes, *T. A. Rapoport, B. Jungnickel, U. Kutay*

Molecular Biology of Mammalian Amino Acid Transporters, *M. S. Malandro, M. S. Kilberg*

Molecular Genetics of Signal Transduction in *Dictyostelium*, *C. A. Parent, P. N. Devreotes*

Connexins, Connexons, and Intercellular Communication, *D. A. Goodenough, J. A. Goliger, D. L. Paul*

From the *Annual Review of Cell and Developmental Biology*, Volume 12 (1996):

Actin: General Principles from Studies in Yeast, *K. R. Ayscough, D. G. Drubin*

Signaling by Extracellular Nucleotides, *A. J. Brake, D. Julius*

Structure-Function Analysis of the Motor Domain of Myosin, *K. M. Ruppel, J. A. Spudich*

From the *Annual Review of Medicine*, Volume 47 (1996):

Gene Transfer into Hematopoietic Stem Cells: Implications for Gene Therapy of Human Disease, *C. E. Dunbar*

How Does Lithium Work on Manic Depression?   Clinical and Psychological Correlates of the Inositol Theory, *R. H. Belmaker, Y. Bersudsky, G. Agam, J. Levine, O. Kofman*

The Cardiac Ion Channels: Relevance to Management of Arrhythmias, *D. M. Roden, A. L. George, Jr.*

Nitiric Oxide Synthase: Role as a Transmitter/Mediator in the Brain and Endocrine System, *T. M. Dawson, V. L. Dawson*

High-Altitude Pulmonary Edema: Current Concepts, *H. N. Hultgren*

Genetics of Non-Insulin-Dependent (Type II) Diabetes Mellitus, *C. R. Kahn, D. Vicent, A. Doria*

From the *Annual Review of Neuroscience*, Volume 20 (1997):

The Role of Vesicular Transport Proteins in Synaptic Transmission and Neural Degeneration, *Y. Liu, R. H. Edwards*

Cloned Potassium Channels from Eukaryotes and Prokaryotes, *L. Y. Jan, Y. N. Jan*

ARIA: A Neuromuscular Junction Neuregulin, *G. D. Fischbach, & K. M. Rosen*

Molecular Genetic Analysis of Synaptic Plasticity, Activity-Dependent Neural Development, Learning, and Memory in the Mammalian Brain, *C. Chen, S. Tonegawa*

Mechanisms of Olfactory Discrimination: Converging Evidence for Common Principles Across Phyla, *J. G. Hildebrand, G. M. Shepherd*

Functional and Structural Complexity of Signal Transduction via G Protein-Coupled Receptors, *T. Gudermann, T. Schönberg, G. Schultz*

The Molecules of Mechanosensation, *J. Garcíia-Añoveros, D. P. Corey*

From the *Annual Review of Nutrition*, Volume 16 (1996):

Peptide Transporters in the Intestine and Kidney, *F. H. Leibach, V. Ganapathy*

Structure, Function, and Regulation of the Mammalian Facilitative Glucose Transporter Gene Family, *A. L. Olson, J. E. Pessin*

Molecular Biology of Mineralocorticoid Metabolism, *C. E. Fardella, W. L. Miller*

From the *Annual Review of Pharmacology & Toxicology*, Volume 37 (1997):

G Protein Beta-Gamma Subunits of G Proteins as Regulators of Agonist Action, *D. E. Clapham, E. J. Neer*

Structure-Function Aspects in the Nitric Oxide Synthases, *D. J. Stuehr*

Determinants of Drug Binding and Action on L-Type Calcium Channels, *G. H. Hockerman, B. Z. Peterson, B. D. Johnson, W. A. Catterall*

Structure-Based Drug Design: Computational Advances, *T. J. Marrone, J. M. Briggs, J. A. McCammon*

Pharmacology and Functions of Metabotropic Glutamate Receptors, *P. J. Conn, J.-P. Pin*

Transgenic Animals as New Approaches in Pharmacological Studies, *L.-N. Wei*

John A. Clements

*Annu. Rev. Physiol. 1997. 59:1–21*

# LUNG SURFACTANT: A Personal Perspective

*John A. Clements*

Cardiovascular Research Institute and Department of Pediatrics, University of California, San Francisco, California 94143-0130

KEY WORDS: pulmonary surface tension, phospholipid, lipoprotein, respiratory distress syndrome, autobiography

## ABSTRACT

This perspective tells the story of the discovery, characterization, and understanding of the surfactant system of the lung; of how investigators from many disciplines studied the system, stimulated by the demonstration of surfactant deficiency in respiratory distress syndrome of the newborn; and of how the resulting knowledge formed a basis for highly successful surfactant substitution treatment for this syndrome. The chapter includes personal reminiscences and reflections of the author and ends with a few thoughts about the present status and future prospects of this field of research.

## Prologue

When the editor of the *Annual Review of Physiology* invited me to write a perspective on lung surfactant, I had serious misgivings. I had just finished preparing a historical chapter on the subject for the American Physiological Society's series *People and Ideas* (18), and I was also a bit concerned about intruding my own story. I decided finally to write a perspective that would include information and commentary on the development of the field and some autobiographical material. This chapter is not intended to be prefatory to other chapters on respiratory physiology in this volume. Because the *People and Ideas* chapter treated the background and early history of the field at length, this one covers those aspects in less detail.

## Discovery of Lung Surfactant and Its Clinical Significance

For over a century, students of physiology were taught that breathing consists of an alternating balance between the force of the respiratory muscles and the elastic recoil of the chest wall and lung tissue. During quiet breathing, the

1

0066-4278/97/0315-0001$08.00

muscles work to expand the alveoli, bringing in fresh air, and when the muscles relax, the chest wall and airspaces contract, expelling stale air. It was not until the 1920s that the Swiss physician Kurt von Neergaard began to question the correctness of this simple concept. He came to the conclusion that the alveoli normally have a wet lining and therefore the force of surface tension must add to their elastic recoil. He did a clever experiment to prove his idea and published it in 1929 (71). Unfortunately, his work was largely ignored for the next 20 years until Jere Mead and his colleagues at the Harvard School of Public Health got interested in the subject. When they started out, they did not know about von Neergaard's results. They were working on a research contract with the Medical Laboratories of the Army Chemical Center in Maryland, trying to understand how certain chemical agents caused pulmonary edema and how accumulating liquid foams up and blocks the airways. This problem led them to think about the actions of surface tension on lung mechanics (52).

As it happened, I was serving my two years of military duty as a medical officer at the Medical Laboratories, and one of my assignments was to monitor the Harvard contract. That may sound like a dull job, but it turned out to be pure joy. The research was so fine, and Jere Mead was such a wonderful, enthusiastic, open kind of scientist, that I was in heaven discussing the work with him and his colleagues. Here was I, a neophyte in respiratory physiology, admitted into the inner council of leaders in the field. I knew their thinking long before it was published, and it was they who first aroused my interest in the problem of surface tension in the pulmonary alveoli. Before I could understand it, though, I had to study some fundamental concepts, such as the nature of surface tension, the operation of surfactants, and the meaning of Laplace's relationship.

Surface tension is the tendency of a liquid surface to contract due to the cohesive forces between the molecules in and near the surface. These forces are enormous, about 13 orders of magnitude greater than the force of the earth's gravity on the molecules. Unlike gravity, which acts over huge distances, cohesive forces are significant only between molecules that are almost touching. The stronger the attractive forces, the greater the tendency of the surface to shrink. If the system permits shrinkage, the interface can do work on the adjacent bulk phases and the tension measures the mechanical free energy of the surface. When the surface is curved, as in a bubble of air in water, surface tension raises the pressure inside, and the smaller the bubble the higher the pressure. This is an example of the familiar Law of Laplace, which states that the pressure difference across the surface is directly proportional to the tension and inversely proportional to the radius of curvature. If a bubble is blown on a tube, the same law holds, but the bubble collapses as air flows out through the tube unless enough pressure is applied to keep it in. This model is often used to explain the effect of surface tension in the alveoli, with the bubble representing the wet surface of the airspaces and the tube standing for the airways.

When a liquid contains dissolved material, the molecules of the solute may accumulate spontaneously at the surface of the liquid, lowering its surface tension. Substances that act in this way are called surfactants. Some surfactants have such small solubility in the liquid that once their molecules have entered the surface, they do not leave easily. These have the additional important property that if the surface area of the liquid is decreased, the surfactant molecules get crowded together and lower the surface tension to very small values. Surface tension is then a function of surface area. Lung surfactant falls into this category.

When I first learned about surface forces in the lungs from Mead, my interest was casual. My military research assignments received most of my attention. That changed after Radford joined Mead's group and began doing experiments like those von Neergaard had done in the 1920s. Radford was unaware of von Neergaard's work when he began, but his results were similar (63). Both compared the pressure-volume curve of lungs filled with air to that obtained with an aqueous solution in order to reveal the effect of alveolar surface tension. The theory was that when air was in the airspaces an interface existed that had tension, but when the airspaces were filled with solution, the interface and tension were eliminated. The difference between the pressure-volume curves, then, reflected the magnitude of the surface tension or surface free energy. Using a value of surface tension similar to that of serum in the Laplace relation, von Neergaard calculated a pressure arising from surface tension in the alveoli that agreed with his experimental measurements, and he appeared satisfied with that result. Radford's objective was different. He wanted to estimate the surface area of the alveoli, and to do this, he divided their surface free energy, measured from the pressure-volume curves, by their surface tension (which is numerically equal to the surface free energy per unit area). As did von Neergaard, he assumed the surface tension of serum for his calculation. His estimate of area came out 10 times smaller than prevailing histologic estimates. He noted this discrepancy but seemed to think that the morphologic area method was wrong.

As I pondered Radford's results, I became more and more dissatisfied with his interpretation. I couldn't believe that the anatomical estimates of area were really 10 times too high. When I calculated the diffusion capacity of the lungs using Radford's area, it was much lower than the observed one. When I looked at the pressure-volume curves, I could see that the pressure difference between air and saline filling got less as the lungs were emptied. That meant that according to the Laplace relation, if surface tension were constant as von Neergaard and Radford assumed, the airspace radius of curvature would have to become larger as the lungs got smaller, and that seemed strange. Turning the logic backwards, if the size of the airspaces did not get larger, the surface tension would have to decrease with volume. I made a back-of-the-envelope calculation, assuming that airspace radius would vary as the cube root of volume, that showed surface tension falling with volume. This result implied that the alveoli contained surface-active material, an idea that seemed magical at the time. Today these thoughts are obvious, but when Radford published his paper in the fall of 1954, the concepts were new to me. I worried about experimental artifacts; I had doubts about the theory; I wondered whether I really understood it, and because of such distractions these insights were slow in coming. Complicating matters further was the fact that in those days physicians and biologists were taught almost nothing about surface tension. We had to pull ourselves up by our bootstraps, reading the literature of surface chemistry and physics, finding virtually nobody to discuss it with, and trying to apply it to pulmonary physiology ourselves.

The scene was about to change. In June 1955, Richard Pattle published a paper in *Nature* in which he suggested that the airspaces are lined by an "insoluble protein layer which can abolish the tension of the alveolar surface" (56). I did not fully believe Pattle's conclusion because the data of von Neergaard and Radford indicated significant surface tension in the airspaces. Within a month, Elwyn Brown, an anesthesiologist who had been trained as an engineer and physical chemist, was posted to my laboratory for his two years of military service, and it was my responsibility to assign him a research problem. We immediately discussed the Radford and Pattle papers and decided that Brown would try to repeat the Radford experiments with improved methods and calculate a surface tension-area curve by assuming that alveolar area varied as the two-thirds power of volume, and that I would attempt to extract surface active material from lung tissue and measure it in a Langmuir-Wilhelmy balance. Brown's experiments were quickly successful, and he gave a paper at the spring 1956 meeting of the American Physiological Society, reporting that calculated alveolar surface tension fell as the lung was deflated and that calculated alveolar area matched the anatomical estimates (6).

My experiments on extracts took longer. The unusual properties of the surface-active material in lung tissue required changes in the design of the Langmuir-Wilhelmy balance, but by spring 1956, I had enough reliable data to submit an abstract for the fall APS meeting. I reported evidence that lung extracts contained material that could lower surface tension to less than 10 dynes/cm and stabilize alveoli against collapse. The low compressibility of the surfactant film explained why surface tension depended so strongly on area, which made it possible to harmonize the observations of Pattle with those of von Neergaard and Radford and Mead (15).

Much to my disappointment, my presentation evoked little interest. Mead appreciated it and discussed the meaning of the results, but others did not seem to understand them. Probably that was because of the poor background of most biologists of that era in the physics and chemistry of interfaces. I was sure that the findings were important and wrote them up for *Science*, only to have the paper rejected. It was a very painful time for me. After several months of grieving, I decided that the work had to be published and asked a colleague to introduce it into *Proc Soc*, an unreviewed journal, where it finally appeared in 1957 (16). Years later the Institute for Scientific Information determined, despite the location of the article in a déclassé rag, that it had become a Citation Classic. For the moment, however, Pattle and Brown and I were alone with our delusions.

In December of 1957, Mary Ellen Avery visited my laboratory to see my methods at first hand. She had a special interest in respiratory diseases of babies and had gone to Harvard for postdoctoral training in pediatrics and pulmonary physiology. She and Mead postulated that a lack of surfactant might be the cause of respiratory distress syndrome, the commonest cause of death in the newborn, and they planned to examine extracts of lungs of infants who had died shortly after birth. They set up a surface balance and in a few months were getting interesting results. By December 1958, they were able to submit a paper reporting that surfactant could not be demonstrated in the lungs of infants that had died with respiratory distress syndrome but that it was found in infants who had died without pulmonary disease, provided that their birth weight was more than about 1000 grams (1).

## Development of the Science of Lung Surfactant and Its Clinical Application

With this proof of clinical relevance, surfactant research became socially acceptable, and many investigators were drawn into it. The field expanded quantitatively and qualitatively, producing a literature of thousands of papers with hundreds now being added each year, incorporating the disciplines of biochemistry, morphology, cell biology, molecular biology, and macromolecular structure and therapeutics, in addition to the physics and chemistry and physiology that were part of it from the beginning. It is obvious that such a large body of information can be treated only briefly in this short perspective, and I apologize to many colleagues for whose work there is not space. For convenience I have organized the following precis around some questions that arose at the start and have persisted throughout the development of the subject.

The most basic of these questions is whether the tension of the alveolar surface really falls to tiny values when the lung is deflated to residual volume, as theory suggests. Interestingly, surfactant research went on for 20 years before direct measurements in the alveoli settled this issue. Schürch et al invented a technique in 1976 that used critical spreading of droplets of immiscible liquids deposited by micropipette right on the alveolar surface to map the changes in tension with volume. The theoretical values were fully confirmed (65). With the exception of a few authors (2, 36, 64), present day students of the subject accept this conclusion.

The chemical composition of the surfactant has interested investigators since it was discovered. After initially being mistaken as a protein (56) or mucoid (8) layer, its true nature as a phospholipid-rich, membrane-like, lipid-protein complex emerged (41, 43, 57). The multiplicity of components, their assembly and stabilization largely by noncovalent interactions, and the variation in composition of surfactants among vertebrate species led to much confusion over the years. Although this delayed progress somewhat, the more serious misunderstandings and disagreements have been resolved, and I believe that no profound lessons would be taught here by rehashing the arguments. The central facts that came out of the chemical analysis are the preponderance of dipalmitoylphosphatidylcholine (DPPC) and phosphatidylglycerol (PG), which are unusual molecules in other mammalian membrane and serum lipoproteins; the paucity of unsaturated acyl chains and neutral lipids; and the presence of four apoproteins that are apparently lung specific.

Isolation, purification, and characterization of these apoproteins progressed slowly until methods of molecular biology became available and then accelerated smartly, so that most of the current information has developed in the last 10 years. Two of the surfactant-associated proteins, designated SP-A and SP-D, are large, water-soluble molecules belonging to the collectin family that contain long collagen-like N-terminal regions, and C-terminal regions with calcium ion- and carbohydrate-binding domains (5, 58). Apoproteins SP-B and SP-C are small, hydrophobic molecules that bind strongly to lipids and, in fact, dissolve in organic solvents rather than in water (20, 31, 32, 35, 60). Trying to deduce the biological functions of these lipid and protein components is the longest-running and to me the most entertaining game in the field of lung surfactant research, and it continues unabated today.

Before discussing the functions of the surfactant and its components, however, it is well to review its structure. The complex can take a bewildering variety of forms by electron microscopy, but over the years it has become clear that they all are permutations of bilayer or monolayer structures. In the secretory granules (lamellar bodies) of the alveolar type II epithelial cells, which synthesize and secrete surfactant components, the material presents as closely stacked bilayers (75). When secreted into the alveolar liquid, the lamellar body contents hydrate and rearrange into the remarkable tubular myelin form that, in cross section, resembles a pile of square hot dogs lying underneath the liquid surface (73). Occasionally, an electron micrograph shows continuity between an osmiophilic layer in the tubular myelin and the layer at the air-liquid interface (30), suggesting that the surface film can form from tubular myelin. In freeze-fracture images (50), the alveolar liquid shows many small unilamellar vesicles that may represent material shed from the surface and on its way to removal by alveolar macrophages and by recycling into type II cells. Results of tracer labeling of surfactant components to measure their turnover (33, 34, 49) are compatible with this description.

Why does the surfactant have so many components, and what are their functions? Probably the most important property of the surfactant is to lower surface tension quickly; that is to form a stable film rapidly when the surface area is increased. When alveoli are inflated from the gas-free state, for example when a newborn baby takes its first breath, only a few tenths of a second is available before the infant exhales. If too little material has entered the surface or if the film is too compressible, the alveoli collapse on the next expiration. The lack of an adequate end-expiratory volume of gas in the airspaces seriously impedes oxygen and carbon dioxide exchange and leads to respiratory failure. This is how infants with untreated respiratory distress syndrome used to die.

In early fractionation experiments, it was found that the characteristic surface activity was associated with phospholipids (7, 10, 43). In particular, DPPC spread from organic solvent gave a stable, low-compressibility film, but if it was suspended in buffer, it adsorbed at rates far less than those required by the normal lung (41). Adsorption was faster with total lipids of the surfactant but not as fast as with whole, protein-containing material (41). The temperature-dependence of the first-cycle deflation pressure-volume curves of the lung, expressed as a thermal transition of the surface tension component, matched the DPPC gel-to-liquid crystal transition but was not at all like that of whole, purified surfactant (17). These results implied that DPPC was ferried by the complex into the interface where it could stabilize the alveoli. A cottage industry sprang up over the next two decades of isolating and recombining surfactant components in many permutations and combinations in order to elucidate the molecular mechanisms (reviewed in 39). When the small, hydrophobic apoproteins SP-B and SP-C were isolated and characterized (74), it became clear that they accelerate adsorption substantially. Soon it was shown that SP-A greatly enhances this effect (35) and together with DPPC, PG, SP-B, and calcium ions can generate tubular myelin in vitro (67, 76). The precise details of these molecular interactions remain uncertain today, but the observations suggest a picture of cooperation between apoproteins and lipids to speed film formation

(19, 38) and to catalyze selection of DPPC. There is evidence that SP-A promotes low film compressibility in spontaneously adsorbed films, and this has been interpreted as enrichment in DPPC (66). Direct chemical analysis of the film is needed to support this interpretation because low film compressibility might be generated in other ways.

As soon as pulmonary surfactant was discovered, one had to ask what cells synthesize and secrete it, how long it stays in the alveolar lining, and how it is removed. The questions were easy to ask but difficult to answer, because the surfactant is not one molecule but rather a complex of many components, each of which has its own metabolic pathways, and because lung tissue contains dozens of different cell types that must be separated away before unambiguous experiments can be done with the cells that process the surfactant. The connection between the surfactant and the lamellar bodies of the type II alveolar epithelial cells was appreciated very early (11, 42), but it was a decade before respectable lamellar body fractions (29) and type II cell preparations were achieved (40, 51), and yet another decade before extracellular surfactant was resolved into meaningful subfractions (33, 49, 68). With these tools in hand, many studies have been done revealing the pathways and control points of synthesis of phospholipid components (summarized in 4). These results give a general idea of the regulation of such processes and their development in the fetal lung and suggest that lipid composition is adjusted to maintain a proper fluidity (45). The signaling mechanisms involved remain to be demonstrated. Early autoradiographic studies using labeled precursors indicated that the complex lipids and proteins of surfactant are synthesized in type II cell endoplasmic reticulum and transported via Golgi apparatus and multivesicular bodies to lamellar bodies for storage (12). How the components are assembled into the lamellae characteristic of lamellar bodies has not been worked out. More recently the application of methods of molecular biology has shown that the apoproteins are synthesized as proproteins and are processed by the same organelles to the mature secreted forms (reviewed in 72). In addition, SP-A may be constitutively secreted via a pathway not involving lamellar bodies (26). In 1993, Nogee et al (54) identified a rare mutation in the human SP-B gene associated with fatal respiratory failure in infants. At autopsy, SP-B was undetectible in the lungs, lamellar body structure was deranged, airspaces showed an alveolar proteinosis-like picture, and SP-C was found only as proSP-C. A nearly identical result followed in mice in which the SP-B gene was knocked out (14), thus raising the question of how SP-B affects the synthesis, assembly, secretion, and clearance of surfactant components.

Secretion of surfactant has been increased both in vivo and in vitro by mechanical and pharmacological stimuli (22, 55, 77), and it can be inhibited to a remarkable extent in vitro by SP-A (23). Tracer experiments indicate that the turnover time of surfactant components in the alveolar spaces is normally five to ten hours (37), but with vigorous breathing, transport can be greatly accelerated (53). Clearance from the airspaces seems to involve phagocytosis by alveolar macrophages and recycling into type II cells, but virtually none occurs directly by way of airways or lymphatics (3, 21). The division of clearance between the cells is altered by physiological state and drugs (37). Interestingly, SP-A enhances uptake of surfactant lipids in vitro by alveolar macrophages and type II cells (78). The possible in vivo roles of SP-A and of the other apoproteins in surfactant turnover are not clear. Overall, the large body of information that exists about surfactant metabolism depicts a robust system that tunes itself rapidly to changes in the physiological state of the lungs, but much more needs to be known about the detailed mechanisms by which it responds.

When does surfactant appear in the fetal lung? Even in the early years of lung surfactant research there was evidence that the system does not mature until late in gestation (1), and this was confirmed by studies of morphology, phospholipid content, surface activity, and mechanical stability of fetal lungs (9). These results did not show how the development is controlled. That insight arose from experiments that Liggins was doing to understand how the fetus participates in determining the onset of parturition. It was known that delivery of anencephalic infants is sometimes delayed for weeks, and the involvement of the pituitary in the malformation led to speculation that fetal hormones might contribute to the initiation of delivery. In the course of his experiments, Liggins found that infusion of ACTH or glucocorticoid into fetal lambs caused premature delivery (46). When he arrived at the laboratory one morning, he found a glucocorticoid-treated animal that had been born very prematurely during the night. To his astonishment, the lamb was breathing, albeit with some difficulty, and survived until observation was stopped an hour or so later. Histological examination of the lungs in this animal and five others in the series revealed expanded airspaces, and Liggins concluded that the hormone had accelerated the maturation of the surfactant system as well as promoting parturition. This seminal finding intrigued investigators everywhere and led to many studies of glucocorticoid and other hormones in lung maturation and in induction of surfactant function in fetal animals (reviewed in 61) and to use of antenatal steroid therapy for prevention of respiratory distress syndrome in high-risk pregnancies (47). An immense amount of information about the effects of exogenous hormones and mediators on the several surfactant components and on the related genes has come out of such studies, but the role of these agents in normal development is yet to be fully defined. The field has moved on to second-generation investigations of multiple hormone interactions in the hope of better imitating the complexity of the *milieu interne*. Their outcome is as yet uncertain.

When lung surfactant was discovered, the questions arose whether any diseases might be associated with its lack and if so whether they could be ameliorated by surfactant replacement. The first question was soon answered by the observations of Avery & Mead (1), but the second answer took longer. It required isolation and characterization of surfactant. Shortly after DPPC was found to be the principal component, attempts were made to treat respiratory distress syndrome of the newborn with aerosols of this substance. The results were unsatisfactory (13), probably for several reasons. Aerosol administration was an inefficient way to deliver material to the alveoli, clinical management of the patients was relatively primitive, and the adsorption and spreading of DPPC particles into the interface was slow. Possibly due in part to the failure of those early trials, there was a hiatus of about 10 years before systematic evaluation of surfactant treatment was resumed. During that interval, research accelerated on basic aspects of the surfactant system, and understanding of its properties leaped ahead. Meanwhile, instillation of extracted surfactant was being tried in premature animals that were delivered before the lungs had made their own (25, 27). The results of these experiments were very promising and led Fujiwara and his colleagues to try a surfactant prepared from cow lungs in infants with respiratory distress syndrome. The number of cases was small, but the effects were dramatic (28). The successful outcome of this courageous undertaking generated enormous interest around the world, and soon the modern era of surfactant trials was under way.

My clinical colleagues in San Francisco decided to join the fray, and they asked me what surfactant preparation they should use. I did not like the idea of putting cow lung extract into premature babies, and so I volunteered to design a surfactant that would use only synthetic components and thus avoid the potential problems of variable composition of material extracted from animals, sensitivity to foreign proteins, and contamination with infectious agents. That was even before mad cow disease had come into the limelight. Of course, I was proposing to do in a few weeks what God, or evolution, or both had taken millions of years to accomplish, but that realization did not stop me. In fact, 25 years of experience in the physical chemistry of lung surfactant stood me in good stead, and I was able to produce a synthetic that worked quite well (69). It gave very low surface tension in the captive bubble surfactometer. It expanded the lungs well and prevented ventilator damage in prematurely delivered animals. When I calculated the surface tension in the lungs of these animals with the formula I had used back in the 1950s, the synthetic lowered it nicely. The treated animals survived longer (24).

These results were sufficiently promising that a feasibility study of the synthetic in infants with respiratory distress syndrome was carried out (59), followed by a large scale controlled trial (48). The outcome was striking. There were very few complications and survival rates increased significantly. These changes translated into a decrease in mortality of more than 50%. The data were so compelling that the Food and Drug Administration approved the material for general use in record time. Treatment of neonatal respiratory distress syndrome with this and other surfactant preparations is now standard around the world (62). This therapy is clearly cost effective, with annual savings estimated at several hundreds of millions of dollars in the United States alone. Life in the intensive care nursery today is very different from what it was just a few years ago. To the skeptics who long doubted the importance of pulmonary surfactant, this denouement is perhaps the most telling proof. To the pioneers who kept the faith for four decades, the most difficult aspect is that the story is now old hat. In the words of the epigram: When a thing was new people said, "It isn't true." When its truth was shown people said, "It isn't important." And when at long last its importance was proven beyond doubt people said, "Well anyhow, it isn't new!" Maybe so, but the field of research on lung surfactant, like any other field, is forever new. A field plays out only when our imagination fails and we can no longer think of good questions to ask.

## The Protagonist

What of the protagonist of this perspective? Where did his scientific curiosity come from? What luck led to discovering one of Nature's important secrets? Was it an anomaly not likely to be repeated? Why would anyone spend four decades investigating a tiny branch of science? Are there useful lessons in this story? Although modesty should forbid it, I will try to answer these questions.

I was born in 1923 in Auburn, New York. Seat of an agricultural county situated in the beautiful Finger Lakes district, Auburn was then a city of 40,000 inhabitants. Founded in 1793 it had a prosperous history and remarkable cultural traditions. It had its own museum, community orchestra and chorus, and a theological seminary. It was home to the distinguished Seward family (William was secretary of state for Abraham Lincoln). It was on a spur line of the New York Central Railway and boasted a series of concerts and lectures by the leading lights of the day. It had a first-rate public school system. With half a dozen factories down at the west end, it had a good tax base, and its pretty, broad, elm-canopied streets were spotlessly maintained despite harsh winters and hot summers. Hoopes Park, the municipal rose garden, had a pond decorated in summer with graceful swans and ducks, and swept clear of snow in winter for ice skating. Twenty minutes away by bicycle was Owasco lake, which had wonderful sandy beaches, clear spring-fed water that you could drink without fear, and mild breezes perfect for sailing. There was virtually no crime. Burglary was rare, and residents mostly did not bother to lock up at night. On weekends there were church services and Sunday dinner, followed by a ride to the country to visit Uncle Allie's farm, or a stroll in the park and a nap. It was an idyllic place for a child. Those were the days when Norman Rockwell's covers for the *Saturday Evening Post* were still considered art; you knew that George Washington never told a lie; Abe Lincoln actually did free the slaves; and only one of your high school classmates got pregnant.

My parents believed and lived according to the virtues of that time, and they expected their children to do the same although they were not domineering in enforcing compliance. When we reached age sixteen, for instance, we didn't have to go to church if we didn't want to. Good behavior was taught more by example than by discipline, reinforced by the clear understanding that we owed it to ourselves to be above the common herd. Crude manners, sloppy thinking, and shoddy homework were not encouraged. Nonetheless, my parents created a tolerant, intellectual atmosphere in the home. They were voracious readers, devoted to classical music, politics, history, and art, and they often discussed such matters at the dinner table.

Born in 1880 to a merchant family that was prominent in Auburn, my mother was a proper Victorian lady, who could trace her ancestry back to General Jonathan Stark, an aide to George Washington. Five feet two inches in height, she was a human dynamo, giving the impression of a much larger person. Although accustomed to servants in her youth, she addressed herself without complaint, when the Great Depression struck, to the tasks of maintaining a household for her husband and four children and her ailing maiden sister, doing shopping, cooking, housecleaning, laundry, and mending, and still finding time to sing solos at church, present recitals at the Old Ladies' Home, read voluminously, write literary papers, visit the sick and elderly, and take part in political activities. There was no time left for self-pity. I remember as a child staring in wonderment at her speed in peeling a potato or dicing a carrot, all the time regaling me with lively tales of her youth and family. At age 90, eight years before her death, she wrote out from memory the genealogy of her family going back to revolutionary times, complete with dates of birth and death of the relatives. To me she was a heroine, a liberated woman 50 years ahead of her time, but still committed to the old values. With a mother like that, you don't need a father.

But I had a father and a very fine one too. He came from plainer stock. His father was a molder in the local foundry, descended from English and Irish forebears who had settled in New England and Pennsylvania during the previous century and had moved slightly west. My father was born in 1881 and before long showed his true colors as a nineteenth century nerd. He is supposed to have devoured Gibbon's *Decline and Fall of the Roman Empire* by the age of 10, at which time he had already decided on his vocation, attorney at law, a decision he never regretted. Brought up in working-class, possibly even anti-intellectual, surroundings, mild to the point of pacifism, he nonetheless marched to his own drummer. Alone among his siblings he managed to go to college and then law school, surviving whole semesters mainly on beans, and finally achieving his dream of graduating and joining a law firm in 1904. Except for a short, unhappy, stint as a municipal judge, he continued in the general practice of law until his death in 1951. He became well-known in the county as a fine lawyer, highly respected for his absolute integrity, and admired for his astonishing memory. He was a pillar of his church, acting as treasurer for thirty-three years. Many a time I helped him count the collection of a Sunday afternoon, learning at first hand the meaning of fiduciary responsibility. But first there was dinner at which my father, uplifted by the morning service and gratified by my mother's cooking, would display his gifts as a raconteur and humorist. We children would laugh till our sides ached and our eyes streamed tears. I thought he was the funniest man who ever lived. It was only later that I realized that his humor was jolly, it had no sharp edge. It seemed all the more hilarious because he was such a quiet man at other times. He took his civic duties and family obligations seriously. Generous to a fault, he accepted countless charity cases in his practice, even during the Depression when small-town lawyers barely scraped by. I remember most his kindness, his keen analytical mind, his willingness to listen, and his ability to resolve differences of opinion without confrontation. And his aphorisms. "Just because some fool asks a question doesn't mean you have to answer it." " There's always someone who can't tell when the argument is over." Useful folk wisdom.

I must have been a trial to my parents as a small child. I was the youngest of four and separated by four years. The older three were close together and they largely ignored me. I was isolated, pathologically shy, and peculiar, and the disdain of my siblings intensified my feelings of worthlessness. My parents were not given to psychologizing. It would have been a confession of weakness in those days. They just hoped I would "grow out of it." Later, when she was not so rushed, my mother would always have time for me, but during my second to sixth years it was my maiden aunt who rescued me. We were wounded birds together, I because of my isolation, she because of hypochondriasis and lack of stamina. She was a piano teacher, the best in town and a superb player, but she would have starved in those depression years if she had not been invited to live with her sister's family. She had time on her hands and that was what I needed. We grew very close, and she poured her love and poetical soul and hope for the future into me. We went on countless nature walks together. She taught me the alphabet before I was three. She gave me piano lessons from the age of five. At last I had become a person.

There was a price, of course. To my aunt, music was serious business, and if I accepted lessons, only my best effort was good enough. Her standards were unattainable. Until her health failed she had studied for a career as a concert pianist with Albert Ross Parsons, America's foremost piano teacher at the turn of the century. He had trained in Germany with the greatest musicians, Tausig in Berlin, Moscheles in Leipzig, and he had been a good friend of Wagner. I did not realize it at the time, but I was learning from the latest in a direct line of pedagogues that stretched back through Liszt, Czerny, and Beethoven to Papa Bach; and through Thalberg to the Mozarts and Papa Haydn. I worked reasonably hard, and there was enough music in my bones that I became fairly proficient. But by the time I turned thirteen, when my aunt died, I had realized that my talent was of a lesser order and had given up hope of a career in music. It was a disappointment to her, no doubt, but she knew she had done her work well. I was part-way out of my shell, I had a sense of worth, I had some self-discipline, I had an appreciation of music that would sustain me throughout life (and draw me into marriage and musical partnership with an opera singer), and I had a skill that would come in handy at parties and later on help form bonds with my daughters.

The schools in Auburn were excellent, but I was an indifferent pupil. Suddenly, at about age eleven, I woke up to the fact that learning was really fun and incidentally that good marks would make my parents happy. I became a committed student thenceforth and ultimately graduated as covaledictorian with two other students. All three of us had four-year averages over 99% in the New York State Regents Examinations and thereby won much-needed scholarships for college. During the intervening years, I had developed a consuming interest in science and mathematics and indulged in the horseplay with huge Tesla coils, catapults, explosives, and harmless (?) pranks so dear to the hearts of adolescent boys. Chemistry enthralled me.

The time for college arrived, and I thought I wanted to be a chemical engineer. My father was not convinced that I knew my own mind and arranged for me to visit several industrial laboratories. Wise father was right. I did not like what I saw and promptly changed my registration from chemical engineering to pre-med. My love of chemistry won out, though, and I took the chemical engineers' chemistry courses instead of the bonehead pre-med chemistry courses. Cornell University at Ithaca was a dream campus, with its superb teachers, its gorgeous views, its grand buildings, its carillon sounding the hours plus fifteen minutes of evensong, its free concerts and lectures, and its coeds. I enjoyed all but the latter—I wasn't that far out of my shell. Yet, I felt myself expanding in all directions. I was away from home. I was surrounded by a delicious ocean of knowledge, there for the taking. It was glorious, but I would only get to enjoy two and a quarter years of it. The United States entered World War II in December 1941, three months after I arrived on campus, and our curriculum was accelerated so we could go off and fight sooner. I did not go because I was deferred as a pre-med student. I learned too that if one enlisted in the army, it would pay all expenses of one's medical education. So I volunteered for service in December 1943 and the next month found myself enrolled in the ASTAP (Army Specialized Training Advanced Program) at Cornell University Medical College. Another phase of my enlightenment had begun.

Again I found the teaching excellent despite having four years of school packed into three. The subject matter was voluminous and fascinating. At last I got to know how my insides worked, superficially anyhow, and that was thrilling. Also, living in the big, bad city of New York widened my horizons considerably, what with ethnic restaurants, foreign language films, and beer busts. I could be the life of the party at the piano in spite of my shyness. However, the thrill of learning began to pall as I came to appreciate how shallow the understanding of biological processes and diseases was in those days. The mindless, rote answers to questions of why and how began to gall me. The teachers were good, but they were limited by the ignorance of the period. The idea of trying to practice medicine with my mind constantly full of unanswered questions and therefore doubts about the completeness of diagnoses and the correctness of treatments became intolerable, and I decided before the "fourth" year that I would do research instead. Meanwhile, the war ended, and I was free to join the Department of Physiology at Cornell as a Research Assistant (postdoctoral fellow). No internship was needed and I didn't take one.

What a breath of fresh air! One was encouraged to ponder, to question. The unknown became friend rather than foe, a challenge for exploration. Thoughtfulness was admired. At long last I was in my proper milieu. The independence of thought and the analytical frame of mind that my parents had taught me were not only accepted, they were rewarded. Curiosity was a virtue. Eugene DuBois, the department chairman, proudly traced his scientific lineage back to Laplace and Lavoisier, and he encouraged his staff to think in grand terms but also to mind the significant figures. As I struggled to encompass this combination of synthetic and reductionist philosophy, I realized that I needed remedial reading. My accelerated education had left me short of analytical geometry, calculus, differential equations, and physical chemistry and weak in physics. Fortunately, just across town Columbia University had a marvelous night school, and I was able to take these courses in my spare time. These plus carrying out a research problem in tissue metabolism and reading of books like Höber's *Physical Chemistry of Cells and Tissues*, Schrödinger's *What is Life?*, and Poincaré's *Foundations of Science* made me think I might actually become a scientist one day. My excitement in learning was doubled by debates with my peers on current topics, by lunchtime discussions with Vince du Vigneaud, Cornell's (subsequent) Nobelist in chemistry, and by seminars at the Rockefeller Institute just across the street, where cell biology was being born.

In 1949 came the doctor draft. The armed services were short of physicians and those of us who had enjoyed the benefits of the ASTAP would be first in line. Once again I volunteered and was lucky enough to be given my choice of assignments. I chose the Medical Laboratories of the Army Chemical Center in Maryland because William Summerson, who had supervised my senior research problem in medical school, had become head of the Biochemistry Division there, and I thought I could work for him. Fate had a surprise in store for me. I donned my first lieutenant's uniform and reported to the Commanding Officer for duty. He returned my salute with a wave, listened to my respectful request to work with Summerson and then, like Uncle Sam in the recruiting poster, pointed his finger at me and said, "We don't need any more biochemists. You're a physiologist!" At that moment I became one, and I've been one ever since. My assignment was to carry out physiological studies of the mechanisms by which anticholinesterase agents cause respiratory failure and to devise treatments that would save the lives of soldiers exposed to them. I was mighty lucky to have that assignment and I knew it. Because I had not interned, my alternative would have been inspecting latrines, of which the army had many, some of them in most undesirable places.

I was luckier than I realized, though, because my assignment meant that I had to learn respiratory physiology from the ground up. I knew almost nothing about it, and I read the textbooks to start, which did not help much. So I plunged into the literature, which helped more; but what helped the most was consulting with experts. That was made easy by two things. One was the contract with Harvard, which I mentioned at the beginning of this chapter, and the other was the day-a-week that the Commanding Officer encouraged medical officers to spend at the Johns Hopkins Hospital. I used mine to join in the activities of Richard Riley's division of respiratory diseases. In typical fashion, he welcomed me with open arms, and I began a productive dialogue with him and the members of his group. This was highly educational for me, and ultimately I was able to bring new thoughts to them. In those days, the only chemistry in respiratory physiology concerned blood gases and acid-base balance. The idea of the lungs as a biologically active, metabolizing organ was only remotely in people's minds. Back in the 1920s, Lovatt-Evans had not even been able to measure the oxygen uptake of the lungs, and Comroe's Harvey

Lecture of 1952 only mentioned their clearance functions. They were mere bags for gas exchange then, but the surfactant story brought in biochemistry, and after that cell biology and after that molecular biology—three reincarnations of real chemistry. That is why I ended up spending four decades on a tiny corner of science.

As for the role of luck in the discovery of lung surfactant, it was manifested in my arbitrary appointment as a military physiologist and the resulting unplanned fusion of chemistry with respiratory mechanics. What could have been less likely? Yet, every time scientists are forced to look outside their disciplines such cross-fertilization of minds can happen. The consequences are often unexpected and sometimes wonderful.

It is a truism that curiosity is the stock in trade of the researcher. Curiosity is a natural state for the child's mind, and it persists into adulthood if it isn't squashed by dogma or so-called education. To quote words I heard from Margaret Dawes, wife of a famous Oxford don, "Scientists are like dirty little boys, forever peeking under Nature's skirts." There is nothing like a Victorian upbringing to fan the fire of curiosity to white heat. I can testify.

Does the story of lung surfactant teach us any unique lesson? I don't think so in principle. It is, however, one of the best examples I can adduce of research that was originally driven by pure curiosity about a theory being translated through years of collaborative effort between laboratory scientists and clinicians into innovative, lifesaving therapy. The pundits who set policy for funding of research could well ponder it. I once heard my old boss Julius Comroe speak on this subject. He said, "There is no such thing as basic research or applied research. There's only good research and **bad** research." And then he looked straight at me. He was almost as funny as my father.

## The Future of Research on Lung Surfactant

The *Annual Review of Physiology* is not an appropriate venue for soothsaying, but I will make a few comments that seem justified here on the current status and future directions of this field. I have the global impression of a mature field full of new ideas and methods and of accelerating progress. We have a glimmering of a synthesis of the functions of airspace components in alveolar homeostasis and perhaps the beginning of an understanding of broncho-alveolar balance. The relationship of the surfactant system to respiratory distress syndrome in the newborn is clear, and its role in other pulmonary diseases is under scrutiny. For reductionists, however, there is a lot to do, and I will mention just a few examples. Apoprotein-lipid interactions are not yet clearly understood at the molecular level. Structure-activity correlations need much refinement. There is fertile ground here for application of the methods of macromolecular structure determination, such as nuclear magnetic resonance, X-ray diffraction, and molecular dynamics calculations. The nature of the critical steps in surfactant adsorption and spreading is unclear, especially as they may foster molecular sorting. The ventilation-dependent interconversion of forms in the alveoli is only beginning to be understood. The clearance of surfactant components from the airspaces is still mysterious; perhaps the GMCSF knockout mouse will help clarify these processes. The nonmechanical functions of surfactant components have come of age, as illustrated by effects of SP-A and SP-D on alveolar macrophages and type II cells in vitro (44, 70, 79). Much work will be needed to delineate these phenomena in vivo and to exhibit their true roles in host defense. In all these issues, genetic methods will offer exciting possibilities, provided that investigators remember the weaknesses as well as the strengths of these techniques and insist on putting the results into the proper context of organ and system physiology. To do this efficiently will require adherents of different disciplines to get together, learn to speak each others' scientific languages, respect each other, and work hand-in-hand.

## Epilogue

It is difficult for me to imagine that anyone could experience more joy and fulfillment in a scientific career than I have in my four and a half decades of work on the lung surfactant system. It has brought me lasting intellectual stimulation, perennial learning, world-wide friendships, the means to make a useful contribution to medicine, a comfortable lifestyle, and heart-warming recognition. For all this I owe profound thanks to my many colleagues whose achievements have formed the main substance of our field. However, we have only (pardon the pun) scratched the surface. There are many fascinating problems that beg for investigation by the next generation of pulmonary alveolar biologists, and I wish them all success.

ACKNOWLEDGMENT

I thank John Goerke for reading this manuscript and offering helpful suggestions.

*Literature Cited*

1. Avery ME, Mead J. 1959. Surface properties in relation to atelectasis and hyaline membrane disease. *Am. J. Dis. Child.* 97:517–23
2. Bangham AD. 1992. "Surface tension" in the lungs [letter]. *Nature* 359:110
3. Baritussio AG, Magoon MW, Goerke J, Clements JA. 1981. Precursor-product re-

lationship between rabbit type II cell lamellar bodies and alveolar surface-active material. *Biochim. Biophys. Acta* 666:382–93
4. Batenburg JJ. 1992. Biosynthesis of surfactant lipids. See Reference 63a, pp. 255–81
5. Benson B, Hawgood S, Schilling J,

Clements J, Damm D, et al. 1985. Structure of canine pulmonary surfactant apoprotein: cDNA and complete amino acid sequence. *Proc. Natl. Acad. Sci. USA* 82:6379–83

6. Brown ES. 1956. Lung area from surface tension effects. *Fed. Proc.* 15:26

7. Brown ES. 1964. Isolation and assay of dipalmitoyl lecithin in lung extracts. *Am. J. Physiol.* 207:402–6

8. Brown ES, Johnson RP, Clements JA. 1959. Pulmonary surface tension. *J. Appl. Physiol.* 14:717–20

9. Brumley GW, Chernick V, Hodson WA, Normand C, Fenner A, Avery ME. 1967. Correlations of mechanical stability, morphology, pulmonary surfactant, and phospholipid content in the developing lamb lung. *J. Clin. Invest.* 46:863–73

10. Buckingham S. 1961. Studies on the identification of an antiatelectasis factor in normal sheep lung. *Am. J. Dis. Child.* 102:521–22

11. Buckingham S, Avery ME. 1962. Time of appearance of lung surfactant in the foetal mouse. *Nature* 193:688–89

12. Chevalier G, Collet AJ. 1972. In vivo incorporation of choline-3H, leucine-3H and galactose-3H in alveolar type II pneumocytes in relation to surfactant synthesis. A quantitative radioautographic study in mouse by electron microscopy. *Anat. Rec.* 174:289–310

13. Chu J, Clements JA, Cotton EK, Klaus MH, Sweet AY, et al. 1967. Neonatal pulmonary ischemia. I. Clinical and physiological studies. *Pediatrics* 40:709–82 (Suppl.)

14. Clark JC, Wert SE, Bachurski CJ, Stahlman MT, Stripp BR, et al. 1995. Targeted disruption of the surfactant protein B gene disrupts surfactant homeostasis, causing respiratory failure in newborn mice. *Proc. Natl. Acad. Sci. USA* 92:7794–98

15. Clements JA. 1956. Dependence of pressure-volume characteristics of lungs on intrinsic surface-active material. *Am. J. Physiol.* 187:592–92

16. Clements JA. 1957. Surface tension of lung extracts. *Proc. Soc. Exp. Biol. Med.* 95:170–72

17. Clements JA. 1977. Functions of the alveolar lining. *Am Rev Respir Dis* 115:67–71

18. Clements J. 1996. Lung surface tension and surfactant: the early years. In *History of Respiratory Physiology*, ed. J West, New York: Oxford Univ. Press. pp. 208–29.

19. Cochrane CG, Revak SD. 1991. Pulmonary surfactant protein B (SP-B): structure-function relationships. *Science* 254:566–68

20. Curstedt T, Jörnvall H, Robertson B, Bergman T, Berggren P. 1987. Two hydrophobic low-molecular-mass protein fractions of pulmonary surfactant. Characterization and biophysical activity. *Eur. J. Biochem.* 168:255–62

21. Davis PA, Gunther RA, Cross CE. 1987. Clearance of instilled surfactant lipid from the lungs of unanesthetized sheep: lipids are differentially transported by nonlymphatic pathways. *J. Lab. Clin. Med.* 109:191–200

22. Dobbs LG, Mason RJ. 1978. Stimulation of secretion of disaturated phosphatidylcholine from isolated alveolar type II cells by 12-O-tetradecanoyl-13-phorbol acetate. *Am. Rev. Respir. Dis.* 118:705–33

23. Dobbs LG, Wright JR, Hawgood S, Gonzalez R, Venstrom K, Nellenbogen J. 1987. Pulmonary surfactant and its components inhibit secretion of phosphatidylcholine from cultured rat alveolar type II cells. *Proc. Natl. Acad. Sci. USA* 84:1010–14

24. Durand DJ, Clyman RI, Heymann MA, Clements JA, Mauray F, et al. 1985. Effects of a protein-free, synthetic surfactant on survival and pulmonary function in preterm lambs. *J. Pediatr.* 107:775–80

25. Enhorning G, Robertson B. 1972. Lung expansion in the premature rabbit fetus after tracheal deposition of surfactant. *Pediatrics* 50:58–66

26. Froh D, Gonzales LW, Ballard PL. 1993. Secretion of surfactant protein A and phosphatidylcholine from type II cells of human fetal lung. *Am. J. Respir. Cell. Mol. Biol.* 8:556–61

27. Fujiwara T, Maeta H, Chida S, Morita T. 1979. Improved lung-thorax compliance and prevention of neonatal pulmonary lesion in prematurely delivered rabbit neonates subjected to IPPV after tracheal instillation of artificial surfactant. *IRCS Med. Sci.* 7:313

28. Fujiwara T, Maeta H, Chida S, Morita T, Watabe Y, Abe T. 1980. Artificial surfactant therapy in hyaline membrane disease. *Lancet* 1:55–59

29. Gil J, Reiss OK. 1973. Isolation and characterization of lamellar bodies and tubular myelin from rat lung homogenates. *J. Cell Biol.* 58:152–71

30. Gil J, Weibel ER. 1969. Improvement in demonstration of lining layer of lung alveoli by electron microscopy. *Respir. Physiol.* 8:13–36

31. Glasser SW, Korfhagen TR, Perme CM, Pilot MT, Kister SE, Whitsett JA. 1988. Two SP-C genes encoding human pulmonary surfactant proteolipid. *J. Biol. Chem.* 263:10326–31

32. Glasser SW, Korfhagen TR, Weaver T, Pilot-Matias T, Fox JL, Whitsett JA. 1987. cDNA and deduced amino acid sequence of human pulmonary surfactant-associated proteolipid SPL(Phe). *Proc. Natl. Acad. Sci. USA* 84:4007–11

33. Gross NJ, Narine KR. 1989. Surfactant subtypes in mice: metabolic relationships and conversion in vitro. *J. Appl. Physiol.* 67:414–21

34. Hallman M, Epstein BL, Gluck L. 1981. Analysis of labeling and clearance of lung surfactant phospholipids in rabbit. Evidence of bi-directional surfactant flux between lamellar bodies and alveolar lavage. *J. Clin. Invest.* 68:742–51

35. Hawgood S, Benson BJ, Schilling J, Damm D, Clements JA, White RT. 1987. Nucleotide and amino acid sequences of pulmonary surfactant protein SP 18 and evidence for cooperation between SP 18 and SP 28–36 in surfactant lipid adsorption. *Proc. Natl. Acad. Sci. USA* 84:66–70

36. Hills BA. 1981. What is the true role of surfactant in the lung? *Thorax* 36:1–4

37. Jobe AH, Rider ED. 1992. Catabolism and recycling of surfactant. See Reference 63a, pp. 313–37

38. Johansson J, Szyperski T, Wuthrich K. 1995. Pulmonary surfactant-associated polypeptide SP-C in lipid micelles: CD studies of intact SP-C and NMR secondary structure determination of depalmitoyl-SP-C(1–17). *FEBS. Lett* 362:261–65

39. Keough KMW. 1992. Physical chemistry of pulmonary surfactant in the terminal air spaces. See Reference 63a, pp. 109–64

40. Kikkawa Y, Yoneda K. 1974. The type II epithelial cell of the lung. I. Method of isolation. *Lab. Invest.* 30:76–84

41. King RJ. 1974. The surfactant system of the lung. *Fed. Proc.* 33:2238–47

42. Klaus M, Reiss OK, Tooley WH, Piel C, Clements JA. 1962. Alveolar epithelial cell mitochondria as source of the surface-active lung lining. *Science* 137:750–51

43. Klaus MH, Clements JA, Havel RJ. 1961. Composition of surface-active material isolated from beef lung. *Proc. Natl. Acad. Sci. USA* 47:1858–59

44. Kuroki Y. 1992. Surfactant protein SP-D. See Reference 63a, pp. 77–85

45. Lau MJ, Keough KMW. 1981. Lipid composition of lung and lung lavage fluid from map turtles maintained at different environmental temperatures. *Can. J. Biochem.* 59:208–19

46. Liggins GC. 1969. Premature delivery of foetal lambs infused with glucocorticoids. *J. Endocrinol.* 45:515–23

47. Liggins GC, Howie RN. 1972. A controlled trial of antepartum glucocorticoid treatment for prevention of the respiratory distress syndrome in premature infants. *Pediatrics* 50:515–25

48. Long W, Thompson T, Sundell H, Schumacher R, Volberg F, Guthrie R. 1991. Effects of two rescue doses of a synthetic surfactant on mortality rate and survival without bronchopulmonary dysplasia in 700- to 1350-gram infants with respiratory distress syndrome. The American Exosurf Neonatal Study Group I. *J. Pediatr.* 118:595–605

49. Magoon MW, Wright JR, Baritussio A, Williams MC, Goerke J, et al. 1983. Subfractionation of lung surfactant. Implications for metabolism and surface activity. *Biochim. Biophys. Acta* 750:18–31

50. Manabe T. 1979. Freeze-fracture study of alveolar lining layer in adult rat lungs. *J. Ultrastruct. Res.* 69:86–97

51. Mason RJ, Williams MC, Greenleaf RD, Clements JA. 1977. Isolation and properties of type II alveolar cells from rat lung. *Am. Rev. Resp. Dis.* 115:1015–26

52. Mead J, Whittenberger JL, Radford EP. 1957. Surface tension as a factor in pulmonary volume-pressure hysteresis. *J. Appl. Physiol.* 10:191–96

53. Nicholas TE, Power J, Barr HA. 1982. Surfactant homeostasis in the rat lung during swimming exercise. *J. Appl. Physiol.* 53:1521–28

54. Nogee LM, de Mello DE, Dehner LP, Colten HR. 1993. Brief report: deficiency of pulmonary surfactant protein B in congenital alveolar proteinosis. *N. Engl. J. Med.* 328:406–10

55. Oyarzun MJ, Clements JA. 1978. Control of lung surfactant by ventilation, adrenergic mediators, and prostaglandins in the rabbit. *Am. Rev. Respir. Dis.* 117:879–91

56. Pattle RE. 1955. Properties, function and origin of the alveolar lining layer. *Nature* 175:1125–26

57. Pattle RE, Thomas LC. 1961. Lipoprotein composition of the film lining of the lung. *Nature* 189:844

58. Persson A, Chang D, Rust K, Moxley M, Longmore W, Crouch E. 1989. Purification and biochemical characterization of CP4 (SP-D), a collagenous

surfactant-associated protein. *Biochemistry* 28:6361–67

59. Phibbs RH, Ballard RA, Clements JA, Heilbron DC, Phibbs CS, et al. 1991. Initial clinical trial of EXOSURF, a protein-free synthetic surfactant, for the prophylaxis and early treatment of hyaline membrane disease. *Pediatrics* 88:1–9

60. Phizackerley P, Town MH, Newman GE. 1979. Hydrophobic proteins of lamellated osmiophilic bodies isolated from pig lung. *Biochem. J.* 183:731–36

61. Post M, Smith BT. 1992. Hormonal control of surfactant metabolism. See Reference 63a, pp. 379–424

62. Poulain FR, Clements JA. 1995. Pulmonary surfactant therapy. *West. J. Med.* 162:43–50

63. Radford EJ. 1954. Method for estimating respiratory surface area of mammalian lungs from their physical characteristics. *Proc. Soc. Exp. Biol. Med.* 87:58–61

63a. Robertson B, van Golde LMG, Batenburg JJ. 1992. *Pulmonary Surfactant.* Amsterdam: Elsevier

64. Scarpelli EM, Mautone AJ. 1995. The surface monolayer theory does not explain surfactant function in vivo [letter]. *Pediatr. Pulmonol.* 19:198–202

65. Schürch S, Goerke J, Clements JA. 1976. Direct determination of surface tension in the lung. *Proc. Natl. Acad. Sci. USA* 73:4698–702

66. Schürch S, Possmayer F, Cheng S, Cockshutt AM. 1992. Pulmonary SP-A enhances adsorption and appears to induce surface sorting of lipid extract surfactant. *Am. J. Physiol.* 263:L210–18

67. Suzuki Y, Fujita Y, Kogishi K. 1989. Reconstitution of tubular myelin from synthetic lipids and proteins associated with pig pulmonary surfactant. *Am. Rev. Respir. Dis.* 140:75–81

68. Thet LA, Clerch L, Massaro GD, Massaro D. 1979. Changes in sedimentation of surfactant in ventilated excised rat lungs. Physical alterations in surfactant associated with the development and reversal of atelectasis. *J. Clin. Invest.* 64:600–8

69. Tooley WH, Clements JA, Muramatsu K,

Brown CL, Schlueter MA. 1987. Lung function in prematurely delivered rabbits treated with a synthetic surfactant. *Am. Rev. Respir. Dis.* 136:651–56

70. van Iwaarden JF, van Strijp JA, Ebskamp MJ, Welmers AC, Verhoef J, van Golde LM. 1991. Surfactant protein A is opsonin in phagocytosis of herpes simplex virus type 1 by rat alveolar macrophages. *Am. J. Physiol.* 261:L204–9

71. von Neergaard K. 1929. Neue Auffasungen über einen Grundbegriff der Atemmechanik. *Z. Gesamte. Exp. Med.* 66:373–94

72. Weaver TE. 1992. Biosynthesis and intracellular processing of surfactant proteins. See Reference 63a, pp. 283–93

73. Weibel ER, Kistler GS, Töndury G. 1966. A stereologic electron microscope study of "tubular myelin figures" in alveolar fluids of rat lungs. *Z. Zellforschung.* 69:418–27

74. Whitsett JA, Ohning BL, Ross G, Meuth J, Weaver T, et al. 1986. Hydrophobic surfactant-associated protein in whole lung surfactant and its importance for biophysical activity in lung surfactant extracts used for replacement therapy. *Pediatr. Res.* 20:460–67

75. Williams MC. 1982. Ultrastructure of tubular myelin and lamellar bodies in fast-frozen adult rat lung. *Exp. Lung Res.* 4:37–46

76. Williams MC, Hawgood S, Hamilton RL. 1991. Changes in lipid structure produced by surfactant proteins SP-A, SP-B, and SP-C. *Am. J. Respir. Cell. Mol. Biol.* 5:41–50

77. Wirtz HR, Dobbs LG. 1990. Calcium mobilization and exocytosis after one mechanical stretch of lung epithelial cells. *Science* 250:1266–69

78. Wright JR, Wager RE, Hawgood S, Dobbs L, Clements JA. 1987. Surfactant apoprotein $M_r$ = 26,000–36,000 enhances uptake of liposomes by type II cells. *J. Biol. Chem.* 262:2888–94

79. Wright JR, Youmans DC. 1993. Pulmonary surfactant protein A stimulates chemotaxis of alveolar macrophage. *Am. J. Physiol.* 264:L338–44

*Annu. Rev. Physiol. 1997. 59:23–43*

# O$_2$-SENSING MECHANISMS IN EXCITABLE CELLS: Role of Plasma Membrane K$^+$ Channels

*Gabriel G. Haddad*[1,2] *and Chun Jiang*[1]

[1] Department of Pediatrics, Section of Respiratory Medicine and [2] Cellular and Molecular Physiology, Yale University School of Medicine, New Haven, Connecticut 06520

KEY WORDS:  membrane proteins, ion channels, K$^+$ flux, central neurons, carotid bodies, muscle cells, hypoxia

---

## ABSTRACT

Although carotid chemosensitive glomus cells have been the most extensively studied from the vantage point of how cells sense the lack of O$_2$, it is clear that all tissues sense O$_2$ deprivation. In addition, all mammalian cells can trigger a cascade of events that, depending on the severity and duration of hypoxia-induced stress, can lead to permanent injury and death or to adaptation and survival. Crucial in this cascade, we believe, how the cascade is initiated, how O$_2$ lack is detected by cells, and how these initial steps can activate further processes. In this chapter, we focus on the initial steps of O$_2$ sensing in tissues most commonly studied, i.e. carotid glomus cells, central neurons, smooth muscle cells, and neuro-epithelial bodies of the airways.

Recently it has become clear that plasma membranes of various tissues can sense the lack of O$_2$, not only indirectly via alterations in the intracellular milieu (such as pH, Ca, ATP, etc), but also directly through an unknown mechanism that involves plasma-membrane K channels and possibly other membrane proteins. This latter mechanism is suspected to be totally independent of cytosolic changes because excised patches from plasma membranes were used in these experiments from carotid cells and neurons.

There are a number of questions in this exciting area of research that pertain to the role of this plasma-membrane O$_2$-sensing mechanism in the overall cell response, identification of all the important steps in O$_2$ sensing, differences

0066-4278/97/0315-0023$08.00

between $O_2$-tolerant and $O_2$-susceptible cells, and differences between acute and chronic cell responses to lack of $O_2$.

---

## INTRODUCTION

With the evolution from single prokaryotic cells to more complex multicellular organisms, $O_2$ became a basic nutritive element without which aerobic cellular life could not be sustained. Higher organisms became "addicted" to it, very much like the newly born mammal becomes more addicted to $O_2$ in postnatal than in intrauterine life. In higher vertebrates and mammals, $O_2$ regulatory systems involve negative feedback loops and special organs such as the carotid bodies that play an important role in detecting or sensing alterations in arterial $PO_2$. A drop in $PO_2$, for example, is sensed by the carotid body, which increases its nerve discharge and induces an increase in respiratory motoneuronal output. Furthermore, the response to hypoxia includes important alterations in blood flow. Consider, for example, the constriction of pulmonary arteries and shunting of blood from hypoxic alveolar regions to less hypoxic ones. This shunting has the beneficial effect of decreasing ventilation/perfusion mismatch and sustaining a higher $O_2$. Of major importance, however, if the hypoxia is too severe, is that the increase in cardio-respiratory output hardly compensates for the drop in blood $PO_2$. This is true for a number of reasons, including the fact that with the stimulation, body $O_2$ requirements and consumption increase. Therefore, the cardiovascular-respiratory system, which in most instances is the culprit in producing defects in oxygenation, cannot adjust and protect other organs from lack of oxygenation. Hence various tissues and cells in the body developed separate inherent mechanisms to adjust their functions during periods of $O_2$ lack. This is clearly the case because we know, for instance, that renal, liver, muscle, and nerve cells have mechanisms for sensing and responding to $O_2$ deprivation. A number of these mechanisms are not cell specific, but others are highly individual and not shared among cells.

Major questions in this area include (*a*) What are some of the $O_2$-sensing mechanisms in various cell types and how ubiquitous are they? (*b*) How do they work? (*c*) Are they dependent on mitochondrial energy mechanisms or are there other mechanisms in the cytosol, nucleus, or on the plasma membrane that can sense microenvironmental $O_2$ changes? In this chapter, we focus mainly on some of the newer data showing that the plasma membrane is itself capable of sensing changes in $O_2$ levels. We limit the review to excitable cells because most of the work in this area has been done on either carotid bodies, neurons, or muscle cells. Potential molecular models are proposed for how such mechanisms could operate.

# CAROTID BODIES, NEURO-EPITHELIAL BODIES, AND VASCULAR SMOOTH MUSCLES: O$_2$-SENSITIVE PLASMA AND MEMBRANE SENSORS

## Carotid Bodies

The carotid bodies have long been the subject of extensive investigation (33) for at least two reasons. First, we would like to know how a decrease in blood $PO_2$, which affects all organs, is sensed or transduced by the carotid body, recalling that this organ is the body's primary sensor for detecting a lack of O$_2$ and for stimulating the cardio-respiratory system to respond. It is well known from studies in animals and humans that the ventilatory and cardiovascular responses to hypoxia are greatly attenuated (or even depressed) when the carotid bodies are removed (6, 7, 33, 54, 70). Second, the carotid bodies are an example of a sensory organ, and knowledge of the mechanism(s) of chemotransduction could be helpful to understanding other sensory organs such as a taste and olfaction. Although some progress was made in the 1960s and 1970s, especially from ultrastructural studies and from studies on the overall and systemic role of the carotid bodies in response to hypoxia (35), information about the cellular and subcellular basis of transduction has been available only with the development of newer technologies, including patch clamping and confocal imaging. Intracellular dyes have made possible the study of ionic fluxes and activities and a better evaluation of cellular protein expression and distribution. Indeed, in the last seven to eight years, we have seen a number of theories emerge and expand (3, 4, 23, 29, 31, 32, 47, 56, 57). Although it is not the aim of this chapter to review in detail the pros and cons of each of these theories, one that appears to have gained momentum is discussed below.

The ion channel-based mechanisms of carotid body transduction of $PO_2$ center on the role played by a plasmalemmal K$^+$ channel in carotid glomus cells. Simply stated, the plasma membrane itself is responsive to a lowering in microenvironmental $PO_2$ (29, 32, 47). Low $PO_2$ inhibits a voltage-dependent, delayed-rectifier type of K$^+$ channel (Figure 1) that is not inhibitable by cellular levels of ATP. This decreased channel activity is primarily dependent on a decrease in open probability ($P_o$) of the channel and not on its single-channel conductance (29). Of functional relevance is that this decrease in K$^+$ channel activity is presumed to depolarize the glomus cells; this depolarization is manifested by an increase in glomus cell and organ excitability and an increase in action potentials traveling along the carotid sinus nerve to the medulla oblongata. Parallel to these experiments, additional studies show that intracellular Ca$^{2+}$ (Ca$_i^{2+}$) increases with hypoxia in glomus cells (5, 65, 67). This increase in Ca$_i^{2+}$ is derived almost totally from outside the cell, and blockade of

A                                      B

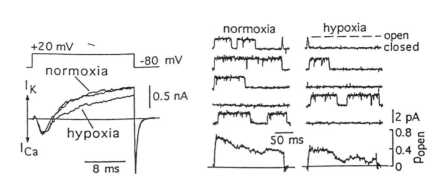

*Figure 1*  (*A*) Inward and outward current of glomus cells. Na conductance blocked with TTX. Note that the whole-cell outward current is inhibited reversibly when $PO_2$ is dropped from $PO_2 =$ 150 to 20 torr and back. (*B*) Single-channel recordings from excised patches of carotid glomus cell membranes. Depolarizing pulses performed from $-80$ mV to $+20$ mV. Ensemble averages given at the bottom of the traces. Note the drop in $P_0$ with low $O_2$ (47).

voltage-dependent Ca channels eliminates the increase in $Ca_i^{2+}$. With this increase in $Ca_i^{2+}$, neurotransmitters such as dopamine are released from the carotid glomus cells that, in turn, increase in nerve discharge (31, 32, 66). From these data, it appears that the glomus cells in the carotid bodies play the role of a presynaptic terminal in which $Ca^{2+}$ entry is critical for the release of transmitters and action potential generation in the sinus nerve terminal abutting glomus cells.

Clearly, this model is intriguing and intuitively appealing because it relies on proteins in the plasma membrane, a component of the cell that is first exposed to low $PO_2$. The culmination of this process ends in activating nerve discharge and stimulating cardio-respiratory centers. However, this model is based on a number of assumptions that may not be consistent with experimental observations to date.

First, the model assumes that low $PO_2$ interacts somehow with $K^+$ channels to close them with the consequence of depolarizing glomus cells. These channels are of the delayed-rectifier type; and for them to open, which is clearly required for hypoxia to have its effect, glomus cells need to assume a membrane potential more positive than about $-30$ or $-20$ mV. Therefore, two issues are relevant: (*a*) What is the membrane potential of these glomus cells at rest during normoxia and during hypoxia? Such measurements have been attempted but suffer from problems that are related either to cell injury secondary to use of sharp electrodes used in very small cells or to cell run-down secondary to dialysis of intracellular glomus components with patch electrodes (19, 27). (*b*) If these $K^+$ channels do not cause depolarization, then what are the mechanism(s) that initiate depolarization and activate these channels in order for hypoxia to act upon the channels and deactivate them?

Second, this model is based somewhat on the fact that dopamine is released, presumably from glomus cells, when $Ca_i^{2+}$ increases with depolarization. However, many investigations have cast doubt on the role of dopamine as a major neurotransmitter responsible for the increase in carotid sinus discharge during hypoxia (19, 20–22, 35).

Third, the relation between $K^+$ channel closure and $PO_2$ level is not parallel to the observed modulation of carotid sinus activity by $PO_2$: Channel closure takes place at a much higher $PO_2$ (70–150 torr) than that required for increased nerve discharge (<60 torr) (29). This finding is intriguing, and recently the contradiction was linked to the increase in $Ca_i^{2+}$ and the $Ca_i^{2+}$ level needed in glomus cells for transmitter release (35). In other words, although there is an increase in $Ca_i^{2+}$, release of neurotransmitter does not take place before a certain $Ca_i^{2+}$ threshold is reached. In addition, $Ca^{2+}$ channels may first be separately modulated by $PO_2$ and not open before the membrane is further depolarized, which would account for the inconsistency of the phase lag between closure of $K^+$ channels and nerve discharge activity. It should be noted that $PO_2$ inhibition of $Ca^{2+}$ channels (50) is not based on single-channel measurements; therefore the modulation may be indirect, which complicates the picture even further. Moreover, the $Ca^{2+}$ channel inhibition occurs at fairly positive membrane potentials such as $-10$ mV; the increase in $Ca_i^{2+}$ is assumed to occur with a release of this inhibition only at more depolarized potentials (50).

Fourth, newer data have shown that tetraethylammonium (TEA), which blocks $K^+$ channels including the delayed-rectifier type, does not prevent an increase in nerve discharge with hypoxia (8, 24). This observation does not seem to support an important role for these channels during hypoxia in the carotid bodies.

Although there are numerous questions regarding the central role $K^+$ channels might play in the chemotransduction process, these questions can be experimentally addressed. If the $K^+$ channels in the glomus cell plasma membrane have a role in hypoxic transduction, then the nature of these transduction mechanisms also needs to be examined. For example, are the $K^+$ channels themselves sensors? Alternatively, do they interact with primary sensors in the plasma membrane and does this interaction result in a decrease in $K^+$ open channel $P_o$ probability? This question is discussed below when neurons and their $PO_2$-sensing mechanisms are considered.

The ion channel model for transduction of $PO_2$ signals by the carotid bodies is challenging, with a number of questions still unanswered.

## What About Neuro-Epithelial Bodies?

Neuro-epithelial bodies (NEB) are conglomerations of cells found mostly at large airway bifurcations (14, 15, 16). These neuro-endocrine cells belong to the amine precursor uptake and decarboxylation cell system (APUD) with paracrine function (14–16). Because these cells lose amine fluorescence with hypoxia (14–16), they have been considered previously as chemosensitive cells in the airways.

Neuro-epithelial cells have been the subject of many studies, but it was not until recently that, with the use of patch-clamp techniques, a relation between whole-cell $K^+$ channels and $PO_2$ was obtained (73). In NEB culture preparations, whole-cell $K^+$ currents were inhibited by hypoxia (Figure 2), and there was an increase in the depolarizing pacemaker potential leading to an increase in firing frequency of these cells (73) (Figure 2). Aside from data suggesting that these channels probably do not belong to a BK-type of channel, no information is available on their nature (73). Also, whereas there is ample evidence that the carotid glomus single $K^+$ channels are altered by a change in $PO_2$ (33), there is no NEB data on single-channel conductance or open channel $P_o$ probability (73). Therefore, it is not clear whether NEB $K^+$ channels are themselves affected by a drop in $PO_2$ or whether $PO_2$ affects cellular processes that, in turn, modulate the activity of these channels (see below). In addition, there are no data on the functional importance of these neuro-epithelial bodies in the overall organismal response of hypoxia. These issues await additional experimentation.

## The Effect of Hypoxia on Pulmonary Vascular Smooth Muscles

Hypoxia dilates systemic vascular beds but causes constriction of small pulmonary arteries. This is expressed clinically as pulmonary hypertension in the presence of hypoxia/ischemia (68). The constriction of the pulmonary arterial smooth muscles is the result of a cascade of events triggered by the inhibition of $K^+$ channels during hypoxia (10, 58, 71). This inhibition of $K^+$ channels depolarizes smooth muscle cells and activates voltage-dependent $Ca^{2+}$ channels. Thus the increased $Ca^{2+}$ concentration in the cytosol leads to muscle constriction (37, 49).

The underlying mechanisms for the hypoxia-induced inhibition of $K^+$ channels in pulmonary arteries have been studied over the past few years. It is now

$\longrightarrow$

*Figure 2*    (A) Whole-cell outward $K^+$ currents from NEB cells in culture. Note the decrease in $K^+$ currents with hypoxia (from normoxic gas to about 25–30 torr) with step depolarization from −60 mV to +50 mV. Two exposures to hypoxia performed. (B) IV relation from cell in panel A (73).

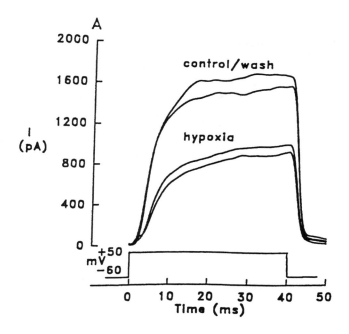

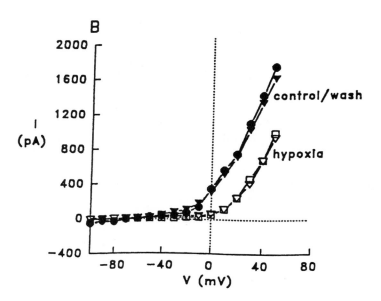

known that more than one type of $K^+$ channel may be involved, such as those that are sensitive to 4-aminopyridine, TEA, and charybdotoxin (10, 58, 71). Modulation of these $K^+$ channels appears to be mediated by a redox-sensing mechanism. Reducing agents such as glutathione (GSH) and NADH inhibit these $K^+$ channels in pulmonary arterial smooth muscles (1, 46, 59, 72). Also as in carotid glomus cells, a diphenyliodonium (DPI)-sensitive NADPH oxidase seems to play a role in the pulmonary vasomotor smooth muscle cells (65, 69). ATP-sensitive $K^+$ ($K_{ATP}$) channels may also be involved in the later stage of hypoxia, i.e. after alterations in ATP, pH, and other substrates. Activation of these $K_{ATP}$ channels appears to counteract the vasoconstriction effect of hypoxia.

Although it is clear that $K^+$ channels are involved in the hypoxic response of smooth muscle cells, it is not known whether these $K^+$ channels are also sensitive to lack of $O_2$ directly rather than through intracellular $O_2$ that, in turn, influences the activity of these channels. More work needs to be done to understand how these channels interact with $O_2$.

## CENTRAL NEURONS AND $O_2$ SENSITIVITY: PLASMA MEMBRANE SENSORS

There is little doubt from our work and the work of others that a number of ion channels, including $Na^+$ and $K^+$ channels, are responsive to $O_2$ deprivation (12, 13, 34, 45, 51, 52, 62). In these studies, the investigators did not focus on the direct effect of $O_2$ on channel activity but rather on how changes in certain cytosolic components during $O_2$ deprivation alter the activity of $Na^+$ and certain species of $K^+$ channels. For example, the activity of the voltage-sensitive $Na^+$ channel ($I_{Na}$) is markedly reduced when neurons are exposed to low $O_2$ (Figure 3). In addition, the steady-state inactivation ($h\,\infty$) curve is markedly shifted to the left, indicating that at physiologically relevant membrane potentials (e.g. about $-100$ to $-40$ mV), whole-cell $I_{Na}$ is smaller (12, 13). With these results (12, 13), we have argued that hypoxia or metabolic inhibitors (e.g. cyanide) increase the probability of these channels to be in an inactivated state. This would have the benefit of decreasing the $Na^+$ load on the cell, thus minimizing energy cost needed to maintain ionic homeostasis. What controls this decrease in $I_{Na}$, and how it occurs is not yet known; also, it is not clear if alterations in cytosolic $Ca^{2+}$, pH, ATP, or protein kinases play a role in modulating this current during hypoxia. However, recent preliminary evidence from our laboratory suggests that ATP is important in modulating $I_{Na}$ magnitude and the shift of the $h\,\infty$ curve during $O_2$ deprivation (13). In addition, we have more recently demonstrated that protein kinase activation during hypoxia is greatly responsible for the reduction of $I_{Na}$ (J O'Reilly & GG Haddad, unpublished data) (Figure 4).

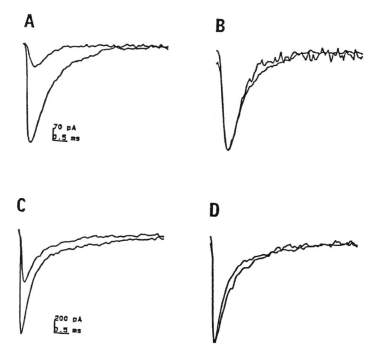

*Figure 3*  Representative traces of Na current during normoxia and cyanide (*A,B*) and during anoxia (*C,D*). Note that the effect is to decrease $I_{Na}$ in both conditions. *B* and *D* show that there was no change in the shape of the trajectory of $I_{Na}$ when scaled back to the amplitude of the control trace (13).

Although the involvement of $Na^+$ channels in the response to hypoxia would seem to be important in decreasing $Na^+$ influx, newer data are emerging to suggest that other modes of $Na^+$ entry into cells involving additional membrane proteins are important. Na-H and Na-Ca exchangers, for example, can be activated early during hypoxia (9), and their increased activity may have a negative effect on cell survival. A detailed understanding of the activity of membrane proteins, whether they are involved in the influx or efflux of various ionic species, would seem to be critical at this stage for elucidating the overall behavior of cells undergoing hypoxic stress.

Another example, the subject of many recent investigations, is a $K^+$ conductance that is sensitive to a number of cytosolic factors (e.g. ATP, ADP, $Ca^{2+}$, and pH) and membrane potential (42). $K^+$ conductances that are sensitive to ATP are present in pancreatic, myocardial, and smooth muscle cells and in neurons

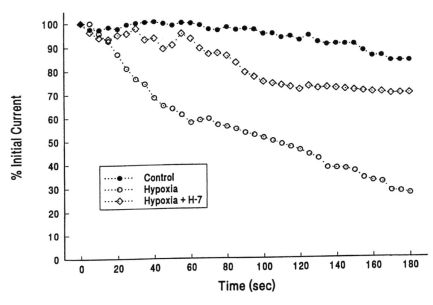

*Figure 4*    The hypoxic inhibition of whole-cell Na$^+$ current in hippocampal CA1 neurons is greatly attenuated by the kinase inhibitor H-7 (100 $\mu$M). Whole-cell Na$^+$ current was recorded every 5 s with a step depolarization to $-10$ mV from a holding potential of $-70$ mV. Shown are representative traces from three neurons.

(34, 42, 55). In relation to hypoxia in the CNS, we have recently presented the first direct evidence that this type of channel responds to low O$_2$ levels in the cellular microenvironment (42). Because these channels are sensitive to ATP and Ca$^{2+}$ in nerve cells (42), it is possible that channel activity is modulated during low O$_2$ conditions by alterations in ATP and Ca$^{2+}$ (42), alterations known to occur during hypoxia (18, 25, 28, 44, 55, 64). Of relevance is the fact that these ATP-inhibitable K$^+$ channels are found not only in rats, in which most experiments have been undertaken, but also in human cortical neurons, as we have recently shown (43). In addition to these modulators, other factors such as pH (17, 36) could affect this conductance in neurons during metabolic stress, similar to that which occurs in muscle cells (42).

The new development in this area is related to recent findings from our laboratory showing that ion channels of neuronal plasma membranes respond to changes in molecular O$_2$, not indirectly through cytosolic changes, but directly in a cytosol-independent and membrane-delimited manner. Qualitatively, this is not dissimilar to $PO_2$ modulation of K$^+$ channel carotid glomus cells (see below) (40, 41, 42). We have shown experimentally that certain species of K$^+$ channels in neocortical neurons or neurons in the substantia nigra decrease their activity when O$_2$ is depleted around the cell-free excised patch in an inside-out or outside-out configuration (40, 41) (Figure 5). This decrease in overall channel activity is mostly due to a decrease in open channel probability ($P_o$) and, to a lesser extent, to a reduction in unitary conductance (40). The $PO_2$-$P_o$ dose-response curve of these neuronal channels is relevant to the physiology of oxygen delivery and transport to the brain because the channel response is consistent with the $PO_2$ that normally exists in the interstitium at rest and during conditions of O$_2$ depletion. These K$^+$ channels begin responding to $PO_2$ at about 20 torr, with 50% reduction of activity at about 10 torr (Figure 5). It is also of interest that O$_2$ sensitivity in these K$^+$ channels is not shared by all K$^+$ channels but is highly specific to a channel with well-identified properties (40, 42). Although the exact molecular mechanism underlying the change in activity as a function of $PO_2$ is not completely understood, these K$^+$ channels appear to be directly sensitive to O$_2$ and thus are called O$_2$-sensing K$^+$ channels or OK channels.

## How Direct Is the Direct Modulation of Neuronal K$^+$ Channels by Molecular O$_2$?

Recent experiments performed on neurons, NEB, and carotid cells (29, 30, 73) indicate the mechanisms of O$_2$ modulation may not be the same in various tissues. In neurons, for example, we favor one of two possibilities.

First, some data suggest a change in the redox state of the OK channel itself during O$_2$ deprivation alters the activity of the channel. Indeed, when we exposed inside-out excised patches to reducing agents such as reduced GSH or dithiothreitol, K$^+$ channel $P_o$ decreased markedly, with a pattern of ion channel flickering that is similar to that seen during O$_2$ deprivation alone (41). Oxidized GSH did not significantly affect ion channel activity in neuronal excised patches (41). It is interesting that this type of channel modulation has been previously described in yeast (2), as well as in pulmonary artery myocytes (72), and hence may not be limited to neurons. The basis for such modulation could be similar to the reduction of thiol groups of cysteine residues on the N-terminal portion of a shaker-type channel molecule, found to be critical in fast inactivation kinetics (63). Indeed, K$^+$ channels with fast inactivation kinetics, such as the A current, are modulated by intracellular substances that can reduce or oxidize cysteine residues (63). The reduced form of glutathione induces an inactivation that occurs in a tenth of a second (63). Mutant channels that have serine instead of cysteine in specific sites (N-terminal portion) are not modulated by oxidizing or reducing agents (63). Although the exact biochemical nature of the reaction leading to fast inactivation is not well understood, it is likely that this

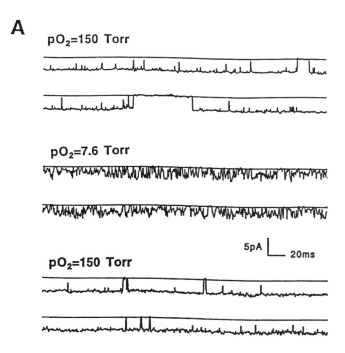

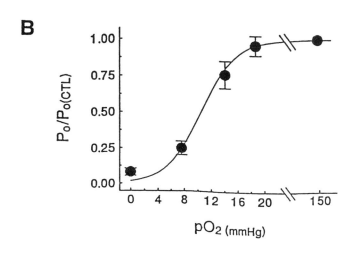

modulation of activation and inactivation involving cysteine residues is based on the formation of disulfide bridges between the inactivation gate or "ball domain" and a part of the K$^+$ channel protein that has not been identified. With respect to the ATP-inhibited K$^+$ channel that is responsive to lack of O$_2$ in neurons, it is difficult to make an analogy with the fast-inactivating K$^+$ channel, because the molecular structure of the K$^+$ channel that we characterized electrophysiologically is not known. It should be remembered that the $\beta$-subunit may itself have oxireductase enzymatic activity, as has been recently suggested (48).

Second, it is possible that molecules such as plasma membrane metal-containing proteins are associated with specific K$^+$ channels and that, by an unknown mechanism, they affect channel activity when O$_2$ is depleted. This idea of a link between a membrane protein and the OK channel is based on recent data from our laboratory showing that metal-center blockers or chelators (agents that bind to proteins with metal centers) such as 1, 10 phenanthroline, deferoxamine, or cyanide suppress K$^+$ channel activity in a fashion similar to that of hypoxia (41) (Figure 6), suggesting that iron-containing nonheme proteins are likely to be part of the O$_2$-sensing apparatus in neuronal membranes. Oxidant species and radicals such as H$_2$O$_2$ and nitric oxide (NO) are probably not important modulators of this K$^+$ channel in neurons because superoxide dismutase and hemoglobin were not effective in altering channel activity (41) (Figure 6). Clearly, this does not totally eliminate their role in vivo or in whole-cell preparations because enzyme systems (e.g. oxidases) that are not membrane bound can generate oxidant species and affect K$^+$ channel activity. This type of experiment on whole cells was done in NEBs, and whole-cell K$^+$ channel activity was inhibited when the generation of H$_2$O$_2$ was decreased by DPI, an inhibitor of NADPH oxidase (73). In summary, although the mechanism(s) of modulating channel activity by lack of O$_2$ can be inherent to the channel molecule itself (e.g. change in channel redox state), mechanisms based on other membrane proteins (e.g. metal-containing centers) that affect channel activity may also be plausible.

---

*Figure 5*   A large conductance K$^+$ current is inhibited during O$_2$ deprivation. (*A*) Continuous recordings of a single K$^+$ current from an inside-out patch with the same solution (150 mM K$^+$) on both internal and external sides, with the membrane potential at 20 mV. During baseline (*top two traces*), this channel had a P$_o$ of 0.92 and a unitary conductance of 188 pS. Straight lines indicate the channel closed level. Hypoxia (*PO$_2$* $\approx$ 8 torr) induced a decrease in P$_o$ to 0.24 (*middle two traces*). Recovery of P$_o$ (0.96) is seen after washout (*lower two traces*). (*B*) A dose-dependent inhibition of P$_o$ by graded hypoxia. Note that P$_o$ was normalized to its control level. Data presented as means $\pm$ SE ($n = 3$) are fitted with an equation of $y = 1/(1 + \exp(K_d - x/h))$, where $y = P_o/P_o$ (CTL), $x = PO_2$, $K_d = 10.5$, a $PO_2$ level for 50% inhibition of $y$, and $h = 2.8$ (40).

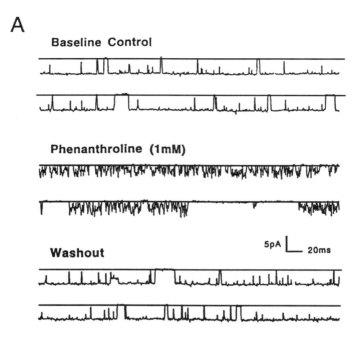

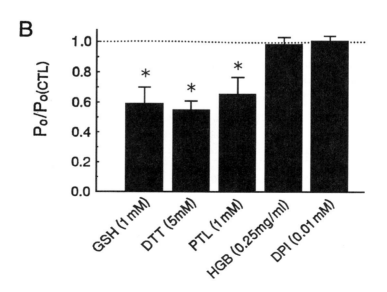

## What Role Does This Membrane-Sensing Mechanism Play in the Overall Neuronal Response to O$_2$ Deprivation?

One important observation with respect to neurons is that the same channel sensitive to ATP, Ca$^{2+}$, and voltage is also sensitive to O$_2$ (40–42). This K$^+$ channel responds to ATP and O$_2$ in an intriguing way. It is blocked by ATP, indicating that in the absence of metabolic stress this channel is not activated. However, it is also inhibited by lack of O$_2$, which would seem at first to be in conflict with the effect of ATP. Indeed, what is the net K$^+$ channel activity when O$_2$ is being depleted around nerve cells while intracellular ATP and other cytosolic factors are changing in concentration? We believe the answer resides in the temporal profile of the various alterations that take place during hypoxia and in the time constants of channel response to molecular O$_2$ and cytosolic components such as ATP. Keeping in mind that (*a*) neuronal whole-cell K$^+$ current (as well as specific single K$^+$ channel activity) response to O$_2$ deprivation is biphasic, i.e. it increases in the first few minutes and then decreases to well below baseline level in the continued absence of O$_2$ (40–42), and that (*b*) the response of the channel to ATP, Ca$^{2+}$, and membrane potential change is much faster than to O$_2$, we believe the following scenario is conceivable. At the outset of deprivation, the increase in K$^+$ channel activity is based on changes in intracellular ATP, Ca$^{2+}$, and membrane potential (42). As O$_2$ level is reduced further around nerve cells and as channel activity changes relatively slowly in response to low O$_2$, the effect of continuing O$_2$ lack on channel activity (which has a higher P$_o$ at that time) becomes observable and contributes to the decline in whole-cell K$^+$ current seen several minutes after the initiation of hypoxia. We note, parenthetically, that the carotid body OK channel does not respond to changes in intracellular ATP and Ca$^{2+}$ and has a smaller conductance and a different $PO_2$-P$_o$ profile than does the neuronal channel. Hence, we suggest the carotid O$_2$-sensing K$^+$ channel and the neuronal O$_2$-sensing K$^+$ channel are different members of this OK channel family.

---

*Figure 6*  (*A*) Channel activity is reversibly inhibited by 1,10 phenanthroline. Currents were recorded in the same condition as in Figure 2. During baseline (*top two traces*), the K$^+$ channel had a P$_o$ of 0.92. P$_o$ was reduced to 0.48 when the internal side of the patch was exposed to 1 mM 1,10 phenanthroline (*middle two traces*). This was followed by a recovery (P$_o$ = 0.89) after washout (*lower two traces*). (*B*) Effects of different agents on P$_o$. Abbreviations: GSH, reduced glutathione ($n = 6$); DTT, reduced dithiothreitol ($n = 5$); PTL, 1,10 phenanthroline ($n = 7$); HGB, hemoglobin ($n = 5$); DPI, diphenyliodonium ($n = 7$). Stars indicate that changes are significantly different from baseline levels ($P > 0.05$) (41).

Is this biphasic response of the neuronal $K^+$ channels beneficial for cell survival under stressful conditions? We believe so, although this is speculative at present. An initial hyperpolarization, resulting from an initial $K^+$ channel activation, would decrease excitability and reduce cell energy expenditure (34). A subsequent closure of these channels would prevent further efflux of $K^+$ into the interstitium (39), thus potentially preventing excessive subsequent depolarization, glutamate release, and excitotoxicity (34).

## OTHER SMALL MOLECULES AND ION CHANNEL MODULATION

If $O_2$ modulates ion channels directly, this poses two questions: (*a*) Are there other gaseous small molecules, similar to $O_2$, that can modulate ion channels; and if so, under what conditions? (*b*) Do such small molecules (gaseous or non-gaseous) have their own receptors? Recent experiments (some involved with hypoxia) answer these questions in the affirmative.

Examples of these small molecules include NO and CO. NO, which is a reactive species, gaseous, quickly diffusible, and highly labile, can inhibit an electrically induced relaxation of guinea pig trachea in a manner similar to that of charybdotoxin and iberiotoxin (26). This supports the idea that $Ca^{2+}$-activated $K^+$ channels mediate the action of NO. Similar studies have been done in carotid arteries, and the possibility that NO's action is mediated by these same BK-type channels is also raised in smooth muscle cells (11, 53). Whether NO acts directly on these K channels or acts indirectly, for example, via cGMP or other second messenger systems is not resolved. CO is a small gaseous molecule that may affect ion channels. In freshly dissociated corneal epithelial cells, CO exposure produces a hyperpolarization that is blocked by $K^+$ channel blockers (61).

Small molecules such as inorganic ions recently have been shown to have their own receptors on the surface of specific cells; an excellent example of this type of interaction between an ion and its outside receptor is $Ca^{2+}$ (38). Injection of poly-A enriched mRNA extracted from bovine parathyroid cells into *Xenopus* oocytes has resulted in the expression of an extracellular $Ca^{2+}$ receptor with high affinity to $Ca^{2+}$ (60).

Small ions or small gaseous molecules besides $O_2$ can either interact with specific ion channels such as $K^+$ and $Ca^{2+}$ or bind to their own receptors to bring about specific effects. It is likely that other small molecules that interact with surface molecules will be discovered that will yield environmental clues to cytosolic or nuclear events that many have short- or long-term efects on cell physiology and biology.

## SUMMARY

Although considerable work has been performed on carotid bodies, O$_2$ sensing and its importance extend beyond this organ. It is clear that mechanisms of O$_2$ sensing are present in many types of tissues, in excitable and non-excitable cells. However, these mechanisms are varied. Consider for example, the renal or hepatic response to hypoxia and the genetic up-regulation of erythropoietin. We have not focused on this type of long-term response to hypoxia, but it certainly reflects one consequence of O$_2$ sensing.

Studying O$_2$-sensing mechanisms is essential for a number of reasons. We believe that a detailed knowledge of the initial cascade of events that occur with the onset of hypoxia, including mechanisms of O$_2$ sensing, could be of paramount importance not only for appreciating cellular physiology and biology, but also for understanding the pathophysiology of cellular injury or survival during O$_2$ deprivation. For example, understanding of how neurons sense the lack of O$_2$ and how the initial mechanisms are triggered might be helpful in designing strategies that can alleviate or even prevent injury. Indeed, such studies have already proven helpful (9).

The plasma membrane OK channel/protein apparatus can be thought of as an O$_2$ sensor or a membrane receptor for O$_2$. Important considerations now have to be given to the interaction among environmental O$_2$, membrane proteins, and intracellular signaling. Although mitochondrial ATP and energy processes must be included when considering the cascade of events during O$_2$ deprivation, energetics have to be factored in within the context of the rest of the cellular changes that occur during short- or long-term hypoxia; i.e. they are not necessarily the main trigger during this stress.

An important challenge for future investigation is the comprehensive assessment of the functional importance and the structural properties of this sensor/receptor complex in various conditions. We doubt that the importance of this channel is restricted to situations of metabolic stress, and we believe that it may have additional roles in a variety of redox reactions, neurotransmission, and pathologic states.

Another important challenge for the future is to understand the differences in O$_2$-sensing mechanisms between hypoxia-sensitive and hypoxia-tolerant organisms. Do anoxia-tolerant organisms lack the mechanisms to sense the lack of O$_2$? Do they have mechanisms that protect their cells from injury, or do they have quick repair mechanisms? Why are lower vertebrates (e.g. turtles) or invertebrates (e.g. insects) so resistant to lack of O$_2$? Can we learn from their cellular blueprints in order to understand the addiction of mammalian cells to molecular O$_2$? Are these mechanisms constitutive or mostly inducible with stress? How important are the genetic components versus changes in fast regulatory alterations? This is an exciting area of research with many answers yet to be found.

*Literature Cited*

1. Archer SL, Huang J, Henry TD, Peterson DA, Weir EK. 1993. A redox-based O$_2$ sensor in rat pulmonary vasculature. *Circ. Res.* 73:1100–12
2. Bertl A, Slayman CL. 1990. Cation-selective channels in the vacuolar membrane of *Saccharomyces*: dependence on calcium, redox state, and voltage. *Proc. Natl. Acad. Sci. USA* 87(20):7824–28
3. Biscoe TJ, Duchen MR. 1989. Electrophysiological responses of disassociated type I cells of the rabbit carotid body to cyanide. *J. Physiol.* 413:447–68
4. Biscoe TJ, Duchen MR. 1990. Responses of type I cells dissociated from the rabbit carotid body to hypoxia. *J. Physiol.* 428:39–59
5. Buckler KJ, Vaughan-Jones RD. 1994. Effects of hypoxia on membrane potential and intracellular calcium in rat neonatal carotid body type I cells. *J. Physiol.* 476:423–28
6. Bureau MA, Lamarche J, Foulon P, Dalle D. 1985. Postnatal maturation of respiration in intact and carotid body chemodenervated lambs. *J. Appl. Physiol.* 59:869–74
7. Bureau MA, Lamarche J, Foulon P, Dalle D. 1985. The ventilatory response to hypoxia in the newborn lamb after carotid body denervation. *Respir. Physiol.* 60:109–19
8. Cheng P, Donnelly DF. 1995. Relationship between changes of glomus cells current and neural response of rat carotid body. *J. Neurophysiol.* 74:2077–86
9. Chidekel AS, Friedman JE, Haddad GG. 1995. The role of extracellular sodium in anoxia-induced injury in rat neocortical neuronal culture. *Soc. Neurosci.* 21:218 (Abstr.)
10. Clapp L, Gurney A. 1991. Outward currents in rabbit pulmonary artery cells dissociated with a new technique. *Exp. Physiol.* 76:677–93
11. Cowan CL, Palacino JJ, Najibi S, Cohen RA. 1993. Potassium channel-mediated relaxation to acetylcholine in rabbit artery. *J. Pharmacol. Exp. Ther.* 266:1482–89
12. Cummins TR, Donnelly DF, Haddad GG. 1991. Effect of metabolic inhibition on the excitability of isolated hippocampal CA1 neurons: developmental aspects. *J. Neurophysiol.* 66:1471–82
13. Cummins TR, Jiang C, Haddad GG.

1993. Human neocortical excitability is decreased during anoxia via sodium channel modulation. *J. Clin. Invest.* 91:608–15
14. Cutz E. 1982. Neuroendocrine cells of the lung: an overview of morphologic characteristics and development. *Exp. Lung Res.* 3:185–208
15. Cutz E. 1984. Neuro-endocrine (APUD-type) cells of the lung. In *Ultrastructure of Endocrine Cells and Tissues,* ed. PM Motta, pp. 148–58. Boston: Nijhoff
16. Cutz E, Gillan J, Track N. 1984. Pulmonary endocrine cells in the developing human lung and during neonatal adaptation. In *The Endocrine Lung in Health and Disease,* ed. KL Becker, AF Gazdar, pp. 210–31. Philadelphia: Saunders
17. Davies NW, Standen NB, Stanfield PR. 1992. The effect of intracellular pH on ATP-dependent potassium channels of frog skeletal muscle. *J. Physiol.* 445:549–68
18. de La Torre JC, Saunders J, Fortin T, Butler K, Richard M. 1991. Return of ATP, PCr and EEF after 75 min of global brain ischemia. *Brain Res.* 542(1):71–76
19. Donnelly DF. 1995. Modulation of glomus cell membrane currents of intact rat carotid body. *J. Physiol.* 489:677–88
20. Donnelly DF. 1995. Does catecholamine secretion mediate the hypoxia-induced increase in nerve activity? *Biol. Sig.* 4:304–9
21. Donnelly DF. 1996. Peripheral and central oxygen sensors. In *Tissue Oxygen Deprivation: From Molecular to Integrated Function,* ed. GG Haddad, G Lister, pp. 701–22. New York: Dekker
22. Donnelly DF, Doyle TP. 1994. Hypoxia-induced catecholamine release from rat carotid body, in vitro, during maturation and following chronic hypoxia. *Adv. Exp. Med. Biol.* 360:197–99
23. Donnelly DF, Kholwadwala D. 1992. Hypoxia decreases intracellular calcium in adult rat carotid body glomus cells. *J. Neurophysiol.* 67:1543–51
24. Doyle TP, Donnelly DF. 1994. Effect of Na$^+$ and K$^+$ channel blockade on baseline and anoxia-induced catecholamine release from rat carotid body. *J. Appl. Physiol.* 77:2606–11
25. Ekholm A, Asplund B, Siesjo BK. 1992. Perturbation of cellular energy state in complete ischemia: relationship

to dissipative ion fluxes. *Exp. Brain Res.* 90(1):47–53

26. Ellis JL, Conanan ND. 1994. Effect of potassium channel blockers on relaxations to a nitric oxide donor and to nonadrenergic nerve stimulation in guinea pig trachea. *J. Pharmacol. Exp. Ther.* 271:782–86

27. Eyzaguirre C, Monti-Bloch L, Baron M. Hayashida Y, Woodbury JW. 1989. Changes in glomus cell membrane properties in response to stimulants and depressants of carotid nerve discharge. *Brain Res.* 477:265–79

28. Friedman JE, Haddad GG. 1993. Major differences in Ca$_i^{2+}$ between neonatal and adult rat CA1 neurons in response to anoxia: role of Ca$_o^{2+}$ and Na$_o^+$. *J. Neurosci.* 13(1):63–72

29. Ganfornina MD, Lopez-Barneo J. 1991. Single K$^+$ channels in membrane patches of arterial chemoreceptor cells are modulated by O$_2$ tension. *Proc. Natl. Acad. Sci USA* 88:2927–30

30. Ganfornina MD, Lopez-Barneo J. 1992. Potassium channel types in arterial chemoreceptor cells and their selective modulation by oxygen. *J. Gen. Physiol.* 100(3):401–26

31. Gonzalez C, Almaraz L, Fidone S. 1977. Increased release of $^3$H-dopamine during low O$_2$ stimulation of rabbit carotid body in vitro. *Neurosci. Lett.* 6:95–99

32. Gonzalez C, Almaraz L, Obeso A, Rigual R. 1992. Oxygen and acid chemoreception in the carotid body chemoreceptors. *Trends Neurosci.* 15:146–53

33. Gonzalez C, Almaraz L, Obeso A, Rigual R. 1994. Carotid body chemoreceptors: from natural stimuli to sensory discharges. *Physiol. Rev.* 74(4):829–98

34. Haddad GG, Jiang C. 1993. O$_2$ deprivation in the central nervous system: on mechanisms of neuronal response, differential sensitivity and injury. *Prog. Neurobiol.* 40:277–318

35. Haddad GG, Donnelly DF, Bazzy-Asaad AR. 1995. Developmental control of respiration: neurobiological basis. In *Lung Biology in Health and Disease,* ed. JA Dempsey, AI Pack, 79:743–96. New York: Dekker. 1134 pp.

36. Haimann C, Magistretti J, Pozzi B. 1992. Sodium-activated potassium current in sensory neurons: a comparison of cell-attached and cell-free single-channel activities. *Pflügers Arch.* 422:(3):287–94

37. Harder D, Madden J, Dawson C. 1985. Hypoxic induction of Ca$^{2+}$-dependent action potentials in small pulmonary arteries of the cat. *J. Appl. Physiol.* 59:1389–93

38. Hebert SC, Brown EM. 1995. The extracellular calcium receptor. *Curr. Opin. Cell. Biol.* 7:484–92

39. Jiang C, Haddad GG. 1991. The effect of anoxia on intracellular and extracellular potassium activity in hypoglossal neurons in vitro. *J. Neurophysiol.* 66:103–11

40. Jiang C, Haddad GG. 1994. Oxygen deprivation inhibits a K$^+$ channel independently of cytosolic factors in central neurons. *J. Physiol.* 481.1:15–26

41. Jiang C, Haddad GG. 1994. A direct mechanism for sensing low oxygen levels by central neurons. *Proc. Natl. Acad. Sci. USA* 91:7198–201

42. Jiang C, Sigworth FJ, Haddad GG. 1994. O$_2$ deprivation activates an ATP-inhibitable K$^+$ channel in substantia nigra neurons. *J. Neurosci.* 14:5590–602

43. Jiang C, Haddad GG. 1995. Characterization of three distinct K$^+$ currents modulated by ATP in human neocortical neurons. *Soc. Neurosci.* 21:1825 (Abstr.)

44. Kass IS, Lipton P. 1989. Protection of hippocampal slices from young rats against anoxic transmission damage is due to better maintenance of ATP. *J. Physiol.* 413:1–11

45. Leblond J, Krnjevic K. 1989. Hypoxic changes in hippocampal neurons. *J. Neurophysiol.* 62(1):1–14

46. Lee S, Park M, So I, Earm Y. 1994. NADH and NAD modulates Ca$^{2+}$-activated K$^+$ channels in small pulmonary arterial smooth muscle cells of the rabbit. *Pflügers Arch.* 427:378–80

47. Lopez-Barneo J, Lopez-Lopez JR, Urena J. Gonzalez C. 1988. Chemotransduction in the carotid body: K$^+$ current modulated by *PO$_2$* in type I chemoreceptor cells. *Science* 241:580–82

48. McCormack T, McCormack K. 1994. Shaker K$^+$ channel $\beta$ subunits belong to an NAS(P)H-dependent oxidoreductase superfamily. *Cell* 79:1133–35

49. McMurtry I, Davidson B, Reeves J, Grover R. 1976. Inhibition of hypoxic pulmonary vasoconstriction by calcium antagonists in isolated rat lungs. *Circ. Res.* 38:99–104

50. Montoro RJ, Urena J. Fernandez-Chacon R, Alvarez de Toledo G, Lopez-Barneo J. 1996. Oxygen sensing by ion channels and chemotransduction in single glomus cells. *J. Gen. Physiol.* 107(1):133–43

51. Mourre C, Ben-Ari Y, Bernardi H, Fosset H, Lazdunski M. 1989. Antidiabetic sulfonylureas: localization of binding sites in the brain and effects on the hyperpolarization induced by anoxia in hippocampal slices. *Brain Res.* 486(1):159–64

52. Murphy KPS, Greenfield SA. 1992.

Neuronal selectivity of ATP-sensitive potassium channels in guinea-pig substantia nigra revealed by responses to anoxia. *J. Physiol.* 453:167–83

53. Najibi S, Cowan CL, Palacino JJ, Cohen RA. 1994. Enhanced role of potassium channels in relaxations to acetylcholine in hypercholesterolemic rabbit carotid artery. *Am. J. Physiol.* 266:H2061–67

54. Nakayama K. 1961. Surgical removal of the carotid body for bronchial asthma. *Dis. Chest* 40:595–604

55. Nichols CG, Lederer WJ. 1991. Adenosine triphosphate-sensitive potassium channels in the cardiovascular system. *Am. J. Physiol.* 261:H1675–86

56. Peers C. 1990. Effect of lowered extracellular pH on $Ca^{2+}$-dependent $K^+$ currents in type I cells from the neonatal rat carotid body. *J. Physiol.* 422:381–95

57. Peers C. 1990. Hypoxic suppression of $K^+$ currents in type I carotid body cells: selective effect on the $Ca^{2+}$ activated $K^+$ current. *Neurosci. Lett.* 119:253–56

58. Post J, Hume J, Weir E. 1992. Direct role of potassium channel inhibition in hypoxic pulmonary vasoconstriction. *Am. J. Physiol.* 262:C882–90

59. Post J, Weir EK, Archer SL, Hume J. 1993. Redox regulation of $K^+$ channels and hypoxic pulmonary vasoconstriction. In *Ion Flux in Pulmonary Vascular Control,* ed. EK Weir, J Hume, J Reeves, pp. 189–204. New York: Plenum

60. Racker FK, Hammerland JG, Dubyak GR, Nemeth EF. 1993. Functional expression of the parathyroid cell calcium receptor in *Xenopus* oocytes. *FEBS Lett.* 333:132–36

61. Rich A, Farrugia G, Rae JL. 1994. Carbon monoxide stimulates a potassium-selective current in rabbit corneal epithelial cells. *Am. J. Physiol.* 267:C435–42

62. Riepe M, Hori N, Ludolph AC, Carpenter DO, Spencer PS, Allen CN. 1992. Inhibition of energy metabolism by 3-nitropropionic acid activates ATP-sensitive potassium channels. *Brain Res.* 586(1):61–66

63. Ruppersberg JP, Stocker M, Pongs O,

64. Silver IA, Erecinska M. 1990. Intracellular and extracellular changes of $Ca^{2+}$ in hypoxia and ischemia in rat brain in vivo. *J. Gen. Physiol.* 95(5):837–66

65. Thomas HCR, Fried E, Novitch R. 1991. Inhibition of hypoxic pulmonary vasoconstriction by diphenyleneiodonium. *Biochem. Pharmacol.* 42:R9–12

66. Urena J, Lopez-Lopez J, Gonzalez C, Lopez-Barneo J. 1989. Ionic currents in dispersed chemoreceptor cells of the mammalian carotid body. *J. Gen. Physiol.* 93:979–99

67. Urena J, Benot AR, Fernandez-Chacon R, Alvarez de Toledo G, Lopez-Barneo J. 1994. Hypoxia induces voltage-dependent $Ca^{2+}$ entry and quantal dopamine secretion in carotid body glomus cells. *Proc. Natl. Acad. Sci. USA* 91:10208–11

68. Weir EK, Archer SL. 1995. The mechanisms of acute hypoxic pulmonary vasoconstriction: the tale of two channels. *FASEB J.* 9:183–89

69. Weir EK, Wyatt C, Reeve HL, Huang J, Archer SL, Peers C. 1994. Diphenyleneiodonium inhibits both potassium and calcium currents in isolated pulmonary artery smooth muscle cells. *J. Appl. Physiol.* 76:2611–15

70. Winter BJ. 1991. Carotid body resection in chronic obstructive pulmonary disease. *Chest* 100:883

71. Yuan XJ, Goldman WF, Tod ML, Rubin LJ, Blaustein MP. 1993. Hypoxia reduces potassium currents in cultured rat pulmonary but not mesenteric arterial myocytes. *Am. J. Physiol.* 264:L116–23

72. Yuan XJ, Tod M, Rubin L, Blaustein M. 1994. Deoxyglucose and reduced glutathione mimic effects of hypoxia on $K^+$ and $Ca^{2+}$ conductances in pulmonary artery cells. *Am. J. Physiol.* 267:L52–63

73. Youngson C, Nurse CA, Yeger H, Cutz E. 1993. Oxygen sensing in airway chemoreceptors. *Nature* 365:153–55

64. Heinemann SH, Frank R, Koenen M. 1991. Regulation of fast inactivation of cloned mammalian IK(A) channels by cysteine oxidation. *Nature* 352(6337):711–14

*Annu. Rev. Physiol. 1997. 59:43–62*

# THE PULMONARY LIPOFIBROBLAST (LIPID INTERSTITIAL CELL) AND ITS CONTRIBUTIONS TO ALVEOLAR DEVELOPMENT[1]

## Stephen E. McGowan and John S. Torday

Department of Veterans Affairs Research Service and the University of Iowa College of Medicine and the Department of Pediatrics at the University of Maryland

KEY WORDS:  adipocyte, surfactant, retinoids, extracellular matrix, prostaglandin

### ABSTRACT

The pulmonary lipofibroblast is located in the alveolar interstitium and is recognizable by its characteristic lipid droplets. During alveolar development it participates in the synthesis of extracellular matrix structural proteins, such as collagen and elastin, and as an accessory cell to the type II pneumocyte, in the synthesis of surfactant. The lipofibroblast contains cortical contractile filaments and is thereby related to the contractile interstitial cells that are normally found at the alveolar septal tips and after lung injury. The morphologic, immunologic, and biochemical characteristics of the lipofibroblast and its probable physiologic functions are reviewed. The retinoid and lipid metabolism of the lipofibroblast is compared with that of the hepatic lipocyte and the adipocyte. Although the functions of the lipofibroblast remain incompletely characterized, this cell type is emerging as an important contributor to pulmonary alveolar septal development.

## INTRODUCTION

### History and Terminology

Lung development has been most extensively studied in rodents and in particular in the rat. Qualitatively, the development of the rat lung holds many similarities to that of the human lung. However, in humans the time course is much more

---

[1] The US Government has the right to retain a nonexclusive, royalty-free license in and to any copyright covering this paper.

protracted, and a larger portion of the alveolar development occurs in utero. Both rat and human lungs develop most of their alveoli postnatally (8).

As early as 1970, a morphologically distinct, lipid-laden interstitial cell was observed in the lungs of fetal and neonatal rats (30). The distinguishing structural and biochemical characteristics of this cell were detailed in the late 1970s and early 1980s, and the cell was named the lipid interstitial cell. Based on their lipid content, pulmonary interstitial cells were divided into two populations: the lipid droplet–laden, lipid interstitial cell and the nonlipid interstitial cell (NLIC), which lacks the characteristic lipid droplets and is located more peripherally in the alveolar septum. With more detailed characterization of the lipid interstitial cell during the last 15 years, it has become clear that it is a mesenchymal cell with fibroblastic characteristics. Therefore, for purposes of this review, the pulmonary lipid interstitial cell will be referred to as the pulmonary lipofibroblast, or simply the lipofibroblast. However, as discussed below, this nomenclature has some shortcomings: The lipofibroblast has characteristics that overlap with other mesenchymal cells, namely adipocytes, smooth muscle cells, and pericytes. The pulmonary lipofibroblast has been most extensively characterized in the rat but has also been observed in mice, hamsters, and humans (8, 35, 43). This review focuses primarily on data gathered from studying rats, which appear to be representative of most mammals.

## An Overview of the Morphology of Lung Development

Embryonic lung development can be divided into four stages: The earliest pseudoglandular stage is characterized by repetitive branching that produces nearly all of the airway divisions comprising the conducting airway zone. During the same period, the pulmonary vasculature also undergoes progressive branching. The arborization of the vascular system parallels that of the airways, but the two units are separated by abundant mesenchymal tissue. The second stage, the canalicular, marks three processes: (a) the advent of the acinus, (b) the differentiation of the pulmonary epithelium and formation of the air-blood barrier, and (c) the onset of surfactant synthesis. By the end of the canalicular stage, airway division is completed to the level of the future alveolar ducts. The subsequent, terminal saccular stage of lung development is characterized by further widening of the air spaces and rearrangement of the capillaries to form a more intimate air-blood interface. At parturition, a physiologically functional gas exchange unit has been formed by the alveolar ducts and saccules in close apposition to the capillary network (8).

Shortly after birth, the surface area of the air-blood interface begins to increase markedly as the terminal saccules give rise to the alveolar ducts and alveolar sacs. This septation of the terminal sacs is initiated by protrusion of the secondary crests from the primary septae. The primary septae are comprised of three layers: a central fibroblastic and connective tissue core surrounded on each side by capillaries (8). On postnatal days 2 to 4 in the rat, there is abundant fibroblast proliferation at the origin of the secondary crest to cause the septum to lengthen and project perpendicularly into the alveolar sac. After day 4, fibroblast proliferation decreases in the proximal septum but persists at a higher level at the distal septal tips. The proximal portion of septum then contains primarily fibroblasts that are not rapidly dividing but instead are producing abundant elastin (7). The increase in the length of the septae is accompanied by an increase in the mass of lamellar bodies in type II epithelial cells and a corresponding increase in surfactant secretion. The final stage of septal formation is marked by further lengthening and thinning of the septae and by extensive capillary remodeling (44a). During alveolarization, the surface area of the lung increases to the 1.6th power of lung volume consistent with septation.

## FIBROBLAST HETEROGENEITY

The pulmonary mesenchymal cells, including smooth muscle, pericytes, endothelial cells, and fibroblasts, have some overlapping characteristics. However, their location and ultrastructural morphology generally provide unique distinguishing characteristics. As more detailed electron micrographic and immunochemical studies have been performed, it is now clear that there are different populations of fibroblasts. The relative proportion of these various populations varies during lung development and in pulmonary diseases. However, these populations have some overlapping biochemical and, presumably, functional characteristics. The populations have been classified based on characteristics of their cytoskeletal proteins and more recently on the presence of a particular cell surface glycoprotein, Thy-1. The details of these two classification systems have recently been reviewed and are only briefly summarized here as they pertain to the lipofibroblast (17, 39).

### Classification of Lung Fibroblast Phenotype by the Thy-1 Antigen

Prompted by data obtained using dermal fibroblasts, Phipps and associates examined the expression of the T-lymphocyte surface glycoprotein Thy-1 by adult mouse lung fibroblasts (63). Thy-1 is a glycosylphosphatidylinositol-linked protein that acts as an accessory molecule in T lymphocytes and is involved in transmembrane signal transduction. The studies of Phipps and others have recently been reviewed (17). Using fluorescence-activated flow cytometry, Phipps and coworkers separated suspensions of cells, obtained after digestion of adult mouse lungs with proteases, into Thy-1+ and Thy-1− cells (63). The two cell populations were separately cultured on tissue culture plastic and cloned (62).

After two weeks, all the cells in both types of culture had morphologic characteristics of fibroblasts at both light and electron microscopic levels. This enabled
the identification of a variety of characteristics that differentiate between the two
fibroblast populations. Cultured Thy-1+ lung fibroblasts are more elongated,
are spindle-shaped, and have filopodia, whereas the Thy-1− cells are more
rounded and spread and lack filopodia. Of particular relevance to this review is
the observation that some Thy-1+ cells contain lipid droplets immediately after
isolation and that all Thy-1+ cells acquire lipid droplets after 7 days in culture medium containing 10% fetal bovine serum (62). Thy-1− cells lack lipid
droplets and do not acquire them during culture. Thy-1+ fibroblasts produce
approximately threefold more collagen but less fibronectin than do Thy-1− cells
in vitro. Thy-1+ cells appear to be more abundant in mouse lungs that are undergoing repair following injury (17). Both the Thy-1+ and Thy-1− fibroblast
phenotypes exhibit similar growth kinetics in culture and express interleukin-6
mRNA and its translated protein, which appears to be an autocrine growth stimulant of both types of cells (18). Comparative characterization of Thy-1+ and
Thy-1− cells has focused on immunomodulatory cytokines. After exposure
to interferon-$\gamma$, Thy-1− fibroblasts, but not Thy-1+ fibroblasts, express Class
II MHC molecules, present antigen to T lymphocytes, and promote antigen-
specific T-cell proliferation (63). Both Thy-1+ and Thy-1− fibroblasts secrete
TGF-$\beta$ in culture. In Thy-1+ fibroblasts, TGF-$\beta$1 decreases interleukin-1 receptor expression and in turn decreases interleukin-1-stimulated interleukin-6
secretion by these cells (73). The secretion of interleukin-1 receptor antagonist
and the laminin-receptor, and interleukin-4 receptor expression, are similar in
Thy-1+ and Thy-1− fibroblasts. Cultured Thy-1+ cells are more proliferative
and produce more collagen in response to exogenous interleukin-4 (70).

## CHARACTERISTICS OF THE LIPOFIBROBLAST

### Initial Descriptions and Morphologic Characterization

The presence of lipid droplets in pulmonary interstitial cells had been described
earlier, but in 1978 Vaccaro & Brody were the first to assign the name lipid interstitial cell (86). Their initial morphologic description emphasized the strikingly
abundant lipid droplets, the high glycogen content, and the localization of lipofibroblasts to the central region of the alveolar septum (86). The droplets stained
with Sudan black and lacked a distinct membrane bilayer at their perimeter,
although Spit described a circumferential linear boundary (76, 86). Some of
the droplets were surrounded by glycogen deposits (76). Subsequent studies
established that lipofibroblasts contain intermediate contractile filaments similar to those observed in contractile myofibroblasts (35, 76). These filaments
are generally more dense than in the NLIC, are oriented with their long axis
perpendicular or oblique to the plasma membrane, and appear to intersect with

the basement membrane (7). Elastic fibers are found adjacent to both NLIC and lipofibroblasts, and the density of the contractile filaments is greatest where fibroblasts contact elastic and collagen fibers (1). Both lipofibroblasts and NLIC independently undergo cell division during alveolarization, and neither type appears to be a precursor for the other cell (7).

Lipofibroblasts are evident in rat lungs at gestational day 16, and the triglyceride content of whole lung tissue increases threefold between gestational days 17 and 19 (84). The lung triglyceride content then increases another 2.5-fold between gestational day 21 and postnatal day 1 and peaks during the second postnatal week (84). The abundance of lipofibroblasts in the lung follows the same time course, as evidenced by the yield of lipofibroblasts isolated by density sedimentation techniques at various postnatal ages (43). The volume of lipid per cell appears to remain constant from postnatal days 4 through 8. The lipid droplets contain primarily neutral lipids—65% triglycerides, 14% cholesterol esters—and an additional 7% are free fatty acids and cholesterol (43). Phospholipids comprise the remaining 14% of the cellular lipids. When neonatal rat lipofibroblasts are cultured in fetal bovine serum, the size and density of their lipid droplets decrease, but they retain their ability to acquire exogenous triglycerides and enlarge when cultured in the presence of neonatal rat serum (42). These data indicate that despite losing their lipid droplets, the lipofibroblasts retain some phenotypic characteristics that promote the acquisition of triglycerides (42). Lipofibroblasts contain lipoprotein lipase and are able to accumulate neutral lipids when purified triglycerides are added to the culture medium (42). The number of lipofibroblasts decreases prior to weaning and appears to result in part from a decrease in cellular proliferation (7). The labeling index decreases approximately ninefold in lipofibroblasts and approximately fourfold in NLIC from postnatal days 4 to 11, and NLICs continue to proliferate longer than the lipofibroblasts (7). Lipofibroblasts are present in the lungs of mice and hamsters at postnatal day 8, although the volume density of lipid droplets is lower than in neonatal rats (35). When identified by their characteristic location in the alveolar wall and their cytoplasmic filaments, lipofibroblasts are observed in adult rats, mice, and hamsters, although in adults they contain much less lipid than in the neonate (35). The volume density of the lipid droplets among adult fibroblasts is higher in the adult mouse than in the adult rat or hamster (35). These early studies by Maksvytis and associates clearly demonstrate that the neonatal pulmonary interstitium contains two populations of fibroblasts that differ in location, lipid contents, and growth kinetics. However, the functional properties of the two populations with respect to protein synthesis and their contributions to alveolar growth have remained incompletely understood. Subsequently, more extensive biochemical studies have been performed to elucidate some of the functional properties of these cells.

It is clear that the volume density of lipofibroblasts in the alveoli decreases markedly after the second postnatal week (7, 43). However, lipofibroblasts are present at the base of the alveolar septae in adult rats, and their number can be increased by the administration of retinyl palmitate (59, 76). Kaplan and associates related contractile microfilaments in neonatal lipofibroblasts to those found in the contractile interstitial cell (CIC) in the adult lung (35). Based on the ultrastructure of the contractile microfibrils, several investigators have speculated that the lipofibroblasts may be a neonatal equivalent of the CIC (1). The relationship between the two cells is discussed in more detail below.

## Biochemical Characterization

Biochemical studies of the lipofibroblast primarily have been performed immediately after isolating the cells from neonatal rat lungs or after culturing them on a standard plastic tissue culture surface. Density sedimentation techniques have exploited the low density of the lipid droplets to isolate the lipofibroblasts from other pulmonary cells. Maksyvitis and coworkers used metrizimide and, in a more recent adaptation of the initial technique, Berk and coworkers used Percoll (3, 43). In both isopycnic centrifugation systems, the lipofibroblasts sediment at approximately 1.04 g/ml. Without further purification, approximately 85% of the cells that sediment at a density of 1.04 stain with lipophilic oil red-O, which is characteristic of lipofibroblasts; the remaining 15% of the cells are primarily macrophages (47). Further purification is achieved by allowing the cells to adhere to tissue culture plastic. Virtually 100% of the adherent cells stain with oil red-O (3, 47). The cytoskeletal proteins in uncultured lipofibroblasts have been partially elucidated. The cells contain both vimentin and desmin in their intermediate filaments and alpha-smooth muscle actin ($\alpha$-SMA) (SE McGowan, unpublished data). After culturing for 48 h in fetal bovine serum, nearly all the lipofibroblasts show a marked decrease in the volume density of their lipid droplets and proliferate until they reach confluence. The cells can be subcultured two or three times, but they grow poorly after additional passages.

Studies of gene expression by cultured lipofibroblasts primarily have focused on extracellular matrix (ECM) and cytoskeletal proteins. The cells abundantly express mRNAs for elastin, the $\alpha$-1(I) chain of procollagen 1, entactin, and $\alpha$-SMA (64). Insoluble elastin has been demonstrated ultrastructurally and its amino acid composition is similar to that of purified rat lung elastin (3, 40). Entactin and $\alpha$-SMA proteins have been identified and localized using specific antibodies for immunohistochemistry (64). Isolated lipofibroblasts and NLIC demonstrate similar patterns of ECM protein expression in culture. In general, the patterns of ECM gene expression by purified lipofibroblasts do not differ from those of a heterogeneous population of lung fibroblasts that have been isolated by proteolytic enzyme dispersion and early (within 3 h) adherence to tissue culture plastic. The abundant expression of $\alpha$-SMA may relate to the culture conditions (52). $\alpha$-SMA mRNA and protein expression is higher in confluent cells and in the presence of 0.5% serum (52). TGF-$\beta$ increases $\alpha$-SMA protein levels but does not alter the steady-state level of its mRNA (52).

The effects of various peptide mediators on elastin and collagen production by lipofibroblasts have been characterized. Berk and associates demonstrated that interleukin-1-$\beta$ (IL-1$\beta$) decreases both $\alpha$-1(I) procollagen and tropoelastin mRNA and that the required concentration (50 pg/ml) is fivefold lower for tropoelastin relative to that for $\alpha$-1(I) procollagen. In contrast to lipofibroblasts, IL-1$\beta$ increases tropoelastin mRNA in dermal fibroblasts (3). McGowan and associates have shown that TGF-$\beta$1 increases the steady-state level of tropoelastin mRNA by approximately twofold in cultured lipofibroblasts by increasing the stability of the message rather than by increasing elastin gene transcription (48, 49). Pierce and associates have shown that dexamethasone also increases tropoelastin mRNA in cultured lipofibroblasts, as it does in fetal lung explants (64, 65). In contrast, fibroblast growth factor-2 (FGF-2, basic fibroblast growth factor) decreases tropoelastin mRNA and protein by reducing transcription (5, 45). Elastin gene expression is regulated differently in lipofibroblasts compared with vascular smooth muscle cells. Although IGF-1 and insulin increase elastin mRNA in cultured rat aortic smooth muscle cells, they have no demonstrable effect on lipofibroblasts (3, 66). The differential responsiveness of the two types of mesenchymal cells in culture is also evident at the organ level in neonatal rats. Whereas IGF-1 increases elastin mRNA in the aorta, it does not alter the steady-state level in the lung (15).

## FUNCTIONS OF THE LIPOFIBROBLAST

### Surfactant Synthesis

During lung development, mesenchymal cells lie in close apposition to epithelium (see Figure 1) and play a central role in its growth (36) and differentiation (26) into the alveolar type II cells that are the site of pulmonary surfactant synthesis. Lipofibroblasts are first evident during the canalicular phase of fetal rat lung development, and triglyceride content is maximal just prior to the appearance of surfactant-containing lamellar bodies in neighboring type II cells (75). Despite such circumstantial evidence for a precursor-product relationship between fibroblast triglycerides and type II cell surfactant phospholipids, there had been no empiric evidence for the existence of such a mechanism until Torday and associates demonstrated that triglycerides of fibroblast origin are used for surfactant phospholipid synthesis by type II cells in culture (80). Initially Torday and coworkers demonstrated the accumulation of triglyceride by the developing fetal rat lung fibroblast, increasing four- to fivefold between

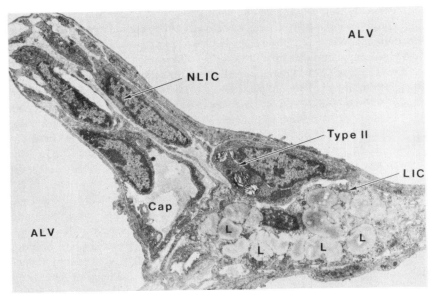

*Figure 1*    The pulmonary lipofibroblast (lipid interstitial cell; LIC) is located in the thick portion of the pulmonary interstitium and is sometimes adjacent to an alveolar type II cell (Type II). The lipofibroblast is distinguished by its lipid droplets (L). Also shown are a nonlipid interstitial cell (NLIC), the alveolar space (ALV), and a capillary (Cap). [Contributed by J Brody, with permission (6).]

days 18 and 22 of gestation (day 22 = term), with little or no increase in type II cell triglyceride content. Study of triglyceride uptake by isolated fetal rat lung fibroblasts and type II cells revealed that fibroblasts actively take up triglyceride but type II cells cannot, thus providing a mechanistic explanation for the observed accumulation of triglycerides by fibroblasts but not by type II cells in vivo. In subsequent studies, the fibroblasts were loaded with radiolabeled and nonlabeled triglyceride and recombined in organotypic culture to evaluate transit and metabolism of fibroblast triglyceride by type II cells. There was quantitative transfer of the triglyceride from fibroblasts to type II cells, resulting in as much as a threefold increase in the saturated phosphatidylcholine content of the type II cells. In subsequent work, the rate of fibroblast $^3$H-triglyceride incorporation into type II cell phospholipids was compared with the rate of incorporation of extracellular $^{14}$C-glucose. Both triacylglycerol and glucose were incorporated into type II cell phospholipids, particularly disaturated phosphatidylcholine and phosphatidylglycerol, which are the principal surfactant phospholipids. The rate of triglyceride incorporation into disaturated phosphatidylcholine and phosphatidylglycerol was 10- to 24-fold higher, respectively, than that of glucose. It was inferred from these data that there must be a specific mechanism(s) for the shuttling of triglyceride from the fibroblast to the type II cell. Because of the well-recognized hormonal regulation of surfactant production, studies were undertaken to determine whether such a putative mechanism for transit of triglyceride from fibroblasts to type II cells was stimulated by glucocorticoids. Using the same organotypic model system in which fibroblasts are preloaded with triglyceride and then recombined with type II cells, dexamethasone was shown to stimulate triglyceride incorporation into disaturated phosphatidylcholine by 40% (80), indicating that the mechanism of triglyceride mobilization from the fibroblast to the type II cell is hormonally regulated (see Figure 2).

In companion experiments, it was found that alveolar type II cells produce prostaglandin $E_2$ (PGE$_2$), which stimulates the release of triglyceride from

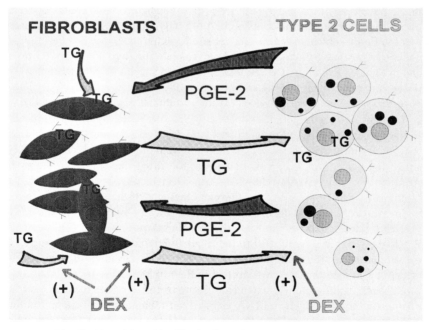

*Figure 2*   Lipofibroblast triglyceride utilization for surfactant synthesis. Triglyceride (TG) is taken up by lipofibroblasts and stored; type 2 alveolar epithelial cells produce prostaglandin $E_2$ (PGE-$_2$), which stimulates the release of triglyceride by lipofibroblasts. Triglyceride is incorporated into disaturated phophatidylcholine and phosphatidylglycerol by type 2 cells. The uptake, prostaglandin $E_2$-stimulated release, and incorporation of triglyceride into disaturated phosphatidylcholine and phosphatidylglycerol are all stimulated by dexamethasone.

fibroblasts. The effect of $PGE_2$ on triglyceride release is potentiated by dexamethasone exposure, as is the synthesis of $PGE_2$ by type II cells (83). This mechanism may provide the basis for the observed effect of dexamethasone on triglyceride mobilization (see Figure 2) (58).

## Retinoid Storage and Metabolism

The retinoid content (primarily retinyl palmitate) of the fetal rat lung increases markedly after gestational day 15, peaks at day 18, and then decreases fourfold by gestational day 21 (72). Premature delivery can hasten the decline in retinyl ester content (11). At its peak, the pulmonary concentration of retinyl palmitate is comparable to that in the liver, which is the major storage site for retinoids postnatally and in the adult. A pre-hatch decline in retinoids has also been observed in chicks, although retinol, rather than retinyl palmitate, appears to be the major retinoid in the avian lung (77). Okabe and associates and Spit found that retinyl esters are stored in fibroblastic cells of the adult rat and hamster lung that contain lipid droplets (59, 76). These data, coupled with the knowledge that lipofibroblasts contain abundant amounts of lipids at birth, led to the hypothesis that the lipofibroblast may be a storage site for retinoids in the late gestational and early postnatal lung (10, 47). To investigate this hypothesis, McGowan and associates examined the retinoid contents of rat lipofibroblasts that were isolated at gestational day 19 and postnatal days 2, 4, 8, and 12 (47). They observed a decline in retinyl esters from gestational day 19 to postnatal day 2. Concurrently, retinol and retinoic acid (RA) increased by postnatal day 2. Retinol remained elevated through postnatal day 8 and then declined, whereas RA fell abruptly after day 2 (47). The rise in retinol and RA, the biologically active form of retinoids outside the retina, following the decline in the ester storage form, suggests that the esters can be metabolized to yield the more biologically active retinoids. The timing of these events has led several groups of investigators to hypothesize that retinoids may be important in the early postnatal development of the lung (the alveolar phase) (10, 44, 47). Because RA is the retinoid directly tied to the regulation of gene expression, most of the attention has focused on RA. Ong & Chytil have shown that the levels of cellular retinoic acid binding protein (CRABP) increase after postnatal day 2 and peak at postnatal day 10 in the rat lung (61). More recently, it was demonstrated that CRABP mRNA expression in whole lung tissue and in the isolated lipofibroblasts follows the same temporal sequence as CRABP protein in whole lung tissue (47). The perinatal ontogeny of retinoic acid receptor (RAR) gene expression has also been examined in rats (28, 47). Grummer & Zachman examined whole lung tissue using Northern analysis and found that RAR-$\alpha$, RAR-$\beta$, and RAR-$\gamma$ increase significantly at birth (27, 28). McGowan and associates, using a ribonuclease protection assay, also observed a small increase in RAR-$\beta$ and RAR-$\gamma$ in whole lung tissue, but this was not statistically significant in their study (47). In isolated lipofibroblasts, RAR-$\beta$ increases approximately fourfold, whereas RAR-$\gamma$ increases approximately eightfold between gestational day 18 and postnatal day 2 (47). In whole lung tissue and in isolated lipofibroblasts, the steady-state levels of RAR-mRNA appear to be the highest in the early neonatal period (28, 47). The transient increase in the expression of RARs in the whole lung and in lipofibroblasts suggests that they could regulate transiently expressed retinoid-responsive genes during alveolar formation.

## Effects of Exogenous Retinoic Acid on Gene Expression by Cultured Lipofibroblasts

Two biochemical processes found maximal during alveolarization are the production of tropoelastin and deposition of elastic fibers and the production of surfactant. The period of rapid alveolar growth necessitates the formation of a structurally competent interstitial extracellular matrix. Elastin is an essential component of the ECM and is primarily responsible for the elastic forces essential for normal expiratory lung recoil. Surfactant must be produced to cover the alveolar surface, which is increasing exponentially during this time. Examination of the effect of retinoids on ECM production by pulmonary mesenchymal cells has focused on elastin synthesis. Liu and associates examined the effects of exogenous all-*trans* RA on elastin production by cultured lipofibroblasts. These studies demonstrated that all-*trans* RA increases tropoelastin mRNA, tropoelastin protein, and insoluble elastin (40). All-*trans* RA also increases elastin mRNA in cultured NLIC (SE McGowan, unpublished data).

Studies of the effects of RA on collagen gene expression in cultured lipofibroblasts have not been published. Studies using the IMR-90 human fetal lung fibroblast continuous cell line have shown that relatively high concentrations of all-*trans* RA ($1 \times 10^{-5}$ M) selectively decrease $\alpha$-1(I) procollagen mRNA by decreasing transcription rather than by reducing mRNA stability (38). RA decreases surfactant apo-protein A and C mRNAs and increases surfactant apo-protein B in human fetal lung explant cultures (50). Presumably, this represents a primary effect of RA on alveolar type II pneumocytes, although an indirect effect mediated through mesenchymal cells cannot be excluded.

# RELATIONSHIP OF THE LIPOFIBROBLAST TO OTHER MESENCHYMAL CELLS

## Relationship to the Contractile Interstitial Cell

The contractile interstitial cell, originally described by Kapanchi and associates, is located in the thick portion of the alveolar wall (1). It is identified electronmicroscopically by characteristic parallel bundles of cytoplasmic microfilaments beneath the plasmalemma that are oriented obliquely to the basement membrane. The collections of microfilaments are particularly dense and form hemidesmosome-like structures where the cells contact fibers of extracellular collagen and elastin (1). These cells are related to the pulmonary myofibroblast that has been described in inflammatory alveolar diseases associated with interstitial fibrosis and in post-capillary pulmonary hypertension (34). Based on the presence of the characteristic microfilaments, Kaplan and associates and Spit concluded that the lipofibroblast is synonymous with the contractile interstitial cell (CIC) during the alveolar phase of lung development (35, 76). During adult life, when lipid droplets are much less abundant, the CICs maintain their microfilaments and characteristic location in the thick portion of the alveolar interstitium, at the junction between alveoli. During the development of fibrotic lung diseases, the number and volume density of myofibroblasts expands in conjunction with an increase in extracellular collagen (1, 53). Adler and associates have pointed out that the CIC may not be the only progenitor for the myofibroblast (1). Another candidate is the smooth muscle-like cell that resides at the septal tips of alveoli bordering the distal portion of the terminal bronchioles. Although they usually lack abundant microfilaments, the NLIC could also undergo a phenotypic modification to the myofibroblast. The function(s) of the CIC in the normal lung remain(s) undefined but may include the maintenance of matched ventilation and perfusion and/or the regulation of lung compliance. In the adult bovine lung, fibroblasts with characteristics of the CIC have been shown to contain abundant prostaglandin (PG) F synthase, which converts $PGH_2$ or $PGD_2$ to $PGF_2$s (19). The number and volume density of CICs increase during the fibrotic response in animal models and humans (1, 53), and these cells contribute to the accumulation of collagen in fibrotic diseases.

More recently, investigators have used immunocytochemistry to study the cytoskeletal proteins of the CIC and myofibroblast during lung development, in the normal adult lung, and during the genesis of fibrotic diseases of the distal lung parenchyma. The presence and distribution of four proteins have been studied in detail. Vimentin and desmin are intermediate filament proteins, whereas actin and myosin form the contractile filaments. In general, fibroblasts contain vimentin in their intermediate filaments and $\beta$ and $\gamma$ cytoplasmic actin and nonmuscle myosin in their contractile filaments. However, mesenchymal cells that are producing abundant elastin and basement membrane proteins can contain an $\alpha$-smooth muscle isoform of actin ($\alpha$-SMA). The interstitium of the gas-exchange portion of the lung first becomes defined in the late canalicular and early saccular stages. At this time, mesenchymal cells contain $\alpha$-SMA and nonmuscle myosin (51). In the rat, these cells contain both desmin and vimentin intermediate filaments, whereas in humans they only contain vimentin (33). The primary alveolar septal buds are formed during the saccular stage and contain what later becomes the septal tip cells. In the rat, these cells are vimentin positive and contain $\alpha$-SMA and smooth muscle myosin (51). Based on these characteristics, the septal tip cell phenotype is more akin to a smooth muscle cell than a fibroblast. These cells produce abundant elastin that forms part of the contractile apparatus at the junction between the terminal bronchiole and the alveolar sac (39). The prenatal coexpression of $\alpha$-SMA and elastin has also been observed in bovine calves (57). Thus different subpopulations of mesenchymal cells may be responsible for the majority of the elastin expression in the primary as opposed to the secondary septae. During adult life, the CICs comprise approximately 30% of the interstitial fibroblast population in the alveolar wall. However, during the fibrotic phase of the pulmonary response to bleomycin, they give rise to myofibroblasts that can comprise up to approximately 80% of all fibroblasts (53).

## Comparison of the Hepatic Lipocyte and the Pulmonary Lipofibroblast

The hepatic lipocyte has become the central subject in the investigation of the pathogenesis of hepatic cirrhosis. The lipocyte, also called the perisinusoidal fibroblast or Ito cell, is located between hepatocytes and adjacent to the sinusoidal space of Disse (25). The lipocyte is the major storage depot for retinoids during adult life. These cells contain large amounts of retinyl esters (primarily retinyl palmitate) that are acquired as retinol from the blood or as esters from chylomicron remnants in the portal circulation (4). Following hepatic injury, by a variety of mechanisms, the lipocytes lose their lipid droplets and consequently the stored retinyl esters, and begin to proliferate. Proliferation is associated with an increase in the production of extracellular matrix proteins by these cells, which results in increased collagen, entactin, fibronectin, and proteoglycans in their surrounding ECM (16, 25). The isolation of individual types of cells from the liver and the study of their properties when cultured individually or in co-cultures have contributed greatly to an understanding of the pathogenesis of cirrhosis. These studies have been the subject of several recent reviews (25, 67). Lipocyte proliferation results from the withdrawal of growth inhibitory factors that are normally produced by adjacent hepatocytes. The withdrawal results from physical disruption of cell-cell contacts and toxin-induced hepatocyte death. The hepatocyte can also be the source of pro-fibrotic molecules such as acetaldehyde. Hepatocyte injury is accompanied by acute and chronic inflammation, which also contributes to the proliferation and activation of lipocytes. Peptide growth factors such as platelet-derived growth factors, FGF-2, and insulin-like growth factor-1 stimulate proliferation, whereas

TGF-$\beta$ promotes the production of fibronectin, collagen, and proteoglycans (67). The withdrawal of intracellular retinoids also contributes to the increase in collagen and fibronectin production (69). Furthermore, the vimentin- and desmin-containing lipocytes transform to myofibroblasts and express $\alpha$-SMA and sarcomeric myosin. Their production of TGF-$\beta$ also increases, which serves as an autocrine stimulus for the increase in collagen, fibronectin, and proteoglycan synthesis. This sequence of events holds many similarities to the proposed relationship between the pulmonary lipofibroblast and the pulmonary CIC or myofibroblast. The proliferative and transformation sequence can be induced by culturing freshly isolated hepatic lipocytes on uncoated plastic. The cultured hepatic lipocytes lose their lipid droplets and retinoids; acquire more filopodia; produce $\alpha$-SMA; secrete TGF-$\beta$1; and export procollagen, fibronectin, proteoglycans, and entactin. This phenotype of the cultured cells is very similar to that of the cultured lipofibroblast, which also loses its lipid droplets when cultured in fetal bovine serum; proliferates; and produces $\alpha$-SMA, entactin, elastin, and collagen (40, 42, 64). The cultured lipofibroblast expresses the TGF-$\beta$1 and TGF-$\beta$2 genes and secretes both TGF-$\beta$ isotypes into the culture medium (SE McGowan, unpublished data) (46). Studies using isotype-specific neutralizing antibodies and antisense oligonucleotides have shown that TGF-$\beta$1 increases elastin gene expression by cultured lipofibroblasts in an autocrine fashion (48). This autocrine regulation by the lipofibroblast is similar to the autocrine regulation of fibronectin and proteoglycan synthesis by the hepatic lipocyte (25). Despite the numerous similarities between the hepatic lipocyte and the lipofibroblast, there are important differences. The lipofibroblast appears to express the characteristic contractile microfilaments in the normal lung, whereas these filaments are only observed after the lipocyte has converted to a myofibroblast during a fibrotic response. The hepatic lipocyte contains approximately 1000-fold more retinyl ester than the pulmonary lipofibroblast in animals that have not been fed a diet enriched in vitamin A (47). Finally, the lipid storage by the pulmonary lipofibroblast appears to be a transient phenotype, whereas this mechanism is a persistent characteristic of the hepatic lipocyte.

## Comparison of Adipocyte and Lipofibroblast Maturation

Both the adipocyte and lipofibroblast are physically distinguished by having large pools of triglyceride stores in their cytoplasm (24, 30). The metabolism of lipid by these two cell types is also similar with respect to their enzymatic pathways and hormonal regulation. Because of these commonalities and the far more extensive studies of adipocyte biochemistry, particularly with regard to adipocyte differentiation, it is useful to compare the processes of differentiation in these two cell types. Both the preadipocyte and lipofibroblast originate from the mesoderm as fibroblast-like cells (23, 86). Much of our current knowledge of adipocyte maturation comes from studies of various preadipocyte cell types, which mature in cell culture. Green & Kehinde (24) were the first to observe that adipogenesis could occur spontaneously in cell culture using the Swiss 3T3 cell model of pluripotential stem cell differentiation. When these cells differentiate, they accumulate classic lipid pools of triglyceride (24) by a process that can be accelerated by exposing the undifferentiated cells to a combination of glucocorticoid, insulin, and the phosphodiesterase inhibitor methylxanthine (68). This observation has triggered a large body of studies to determine the cellular mechanism(s) that regulate adipogenesis (for a review, see 12).

Glucocorticoids stimulate a number of key steps in adipocyte maturation, including the expression of lipoprotein lipase (2) and fatty acid synthetase (9) under serum-free culture conditions. The regulation of lipoprotein lipase is of particular interest in adipogenesis because it is one of only a few recognized early markers of adipocyte differentiation (41) along with the expression of the $\alpha 2$ chain of collagen VI (31), pObw24 (13), clone 5 (55), and clone 154 (32), and is the only marker with known functional significance. The lipofibroblast is also characterized by lipoprotein lipase activity, which is hormonally regulated (43). As to the mechanism of glucocorticoid action, it has been found that steroids stimulate cAMP (87), in part by inhibiting phosphodiesterase activity (29), which results in the induction of a number of adipogenic genes (20). In the lung, dexamethasone and cAMP augment triglyceride metabolism by lipofibroblasts in cell cultures (58) and in vivo (58), consistent with developmental studies of both the ontogeny of the lipofibroblast (80) and lipoprotein lipase activity in whole lung (54).

On the other hand, androgens inhibit the maturation of the adipocyte by down-regulating the glucocorticoid receptor (79), which results in down-regulation of glucose 6-phosphate dehydrogenase (G6PD) (22). Androgens have the same effect on the glucocorticoid receptor (79) and 11-oxidoreductase (79) (which is regulated by G6PD via NADPH) (82) in lung maturation. Androgen regulation of both adipocytes and lipofibroblasts is of particular interest because it has been linked to the action of TGF-$\beta$, which also inhibits adipogenesis and lipofibroblast differentiation (81, 85). Furthermore, in both cases the loss of the TGF-$\beta$ inhibitory effect during maturation appears to be the result of down-regulation of the TGF-$\beta$ receptor (71, 81) and, in the case of the lipofibroblast, loss of this effect was shown to be regulated by glucocorticoid (down-regulation) and androgen (up-regulation).

Prostaglandins have also been implicated in the regulation of adipocyte differentiation. Arachidonic acid promotes the conversion of preadipocytes to adipocytes through its effects on cAMP (20), IP$_3$ (87), and intracellular calcium (87). Prostaglandin metabolites of arachidonic acid such as PGE$_2$ and PGF$_2\alpha$ are able to stimulate the differentiation of Ob1771 preadipocytes (56). This effect of arachidonic acid may be mediated by these or other prostaglandin metabolites because phospholipase A2, which is the rate-limiting step in eicosanoid synthesis, increases by 20- to 24-fold during the differentiation of the adipocyte (21), a change associated with increased prostaglandin production. Furthermore, indomethacin inhibits the differentiation of adipocytes. More recent studies have shown that 15-deoxy-$\Delta$ 12,14 prostaglandin $J_2$, a metabolite of prostaglandin $D_2$, promotes adipocyte differentiation by binding to its nuclear receptor, peroxisome proliferator-activated receptor-gamma (PPAR-$\gamma$) (37). PPAR-$\gamma$ binds, as a heterodimer with the retinoid-X receptor, to responsive elements in the regulatory regions of target genes (14). Transfection of NIH-3T3 fibroblasts, which are not of the adipocyte lineage, with a DNA construct that expresses PPAR-$\gamma$ receptor induces lipid accumulation and the expression of several genes thought to be adipocyte specific (78). Therefore, signaling through the PPAR-$\gamma$ nuclear receptor appears to be sufficient to execute the adipocyte differentiation program. Prostaglandins are also implicated in lipofibroblast maturation. For example, whereas the phospholipase A2 inhibitor indomethacin inhibits fetal lung maturation, prostaglandins stimulate fetal lung maturation. This may be the result of paracrine regulation of fibroblast differentiation by the alveolar epithelium because type II cells synthesize prostaglandins (60), which stimulate cAMP generation by lung fibroblasts (74), thus leading to increased triglyceride accumulation by lipofibroblasts. The lipofibroblast triglyceride, in turn, provides substrate for epithelial type II cell surfactant synthesis.

## SUMMARY AND FUTURE DIRECTIONS

The pulmonary lipofibroblast was recognized as a morphologically distinct interstitial cell nearly 20 years ago, when its prominence during lung development was first articulated. The presence of cortical microfilaments and the prominent lipid droplets drew attention to its potential function as a contractile cell, a storage depot for retinoids, or an accessory cell to surfactant synthesis by the type II alveolar epithelial cell. During the ensuing two decades, the cell has been better characterized with respect to its lipid metabolism, retinoid content and metabolism, cytoskeleton, and synthesis of ECM proteins. Although these studies have yielded a better understanding of the physiology of the lipofibroblast, the precise functions of this cell during lung development and in normal and diseased adult lungs still await definition. Important topics for future exploration include (*a*) a detailed developmental analysis of the progression of gene expression that marks adipocyte differentiation, with particular attention to various nuclear receptors; (*b*) definition of lipid-binding proteins and metabolic enzymes that are involved in triglyceride assimilation and export; and (c) exploration of the relationship between the adipocyte and contractile interstitial phenotypes and the extent to which these associations are cooperative or mutually exclusive. Continued interest in the lipofibroblast is well deserved, as it likely contributes to several critical processes involved in normal lung development and the response to injury.

*Literature Cited*

1. Adler K, Low RB, Leslie K, Mitchell J, Evans JN. 1989. Contractile cells in normal and fibrotic lung. *Lab. Invest.* 60:473–85
2. Ailhaud G, Dani C, Amri E, Djion P, Vannier C, et al. 1989. Coupling growth arrest and adipocyte differentiation. *Environ. Health. Perspect.* 80:17–23
3. Berk JL, Franzblau C, Goldstein RH. 1991. Recombinant interleukin-1$\beta$ inhibits elastin formation by a neonatal rat lung fibroblast subtype. *J. Biol. Chem.* 266:3192–97
4. Blomhoff R, Green MH, Berg T, Norum KR. 1990. Transport and storage of vitamin A. *Science* 250:399–404
5. Brettell LM, McGowan SE. 1994. Basic fibroblast growth factor decreases elastin production by neonatal rat lung fibroblasts. *Am. J. Respir. Cell. Mol. Biol.* 10:306–15
6. Brody JS. 1985. Cell-to-cell interactions in lung development. *Pediatr. Pulmonol.* 1:S42–48
7. Brody JS, Kaplan NB. 1983. Proliferation of alveolar interstitial cells during postnatal lung growth. Evidence for two distinct populations of pulmonary fibroblasts. *Am. Rev. Respir. Dis.* 127:763–70
8. Burri PH. 1985. Development and growth of the human lung. In *Handbook of Physiology*, ed. AP Fishman, pp. 1–31. Bethesda, MD: Am. Physiol. Soc.
9. Butterwith SC. 1994. Molecular events in adipocyte differentiation. *Pharmacol. Ther.* 61:399–411
10. Chytil F. 1992. The lungs and vitamin A. *Am. J. Physiol.* 262:L517–27
11. Chytil F, Geevarghese SK. 1994. Depletion of retinyl esters in the lungs coincides with lung prenatal morphological maturation. *Biochem. Biophys. Res. Commun.* 200:529–35
12. Cornelius P, MacDougald OA, Lane MD. 1994. Regulation of adipocyte development. *Annu. Rev. Nutr.* 14:99–129
13. Dani C, Doglio A, Amri EZ, Bardon S, Fort P, et al. 1989. Cloning and regulation of a mRNA specifically expressed in the preadipose state. *J. Biol. Chem.* 264:10119–25
14. Forman BM, Tontonoz P, Chen J, Brun RP, Spiegelman BM, Evans RM. 1995. 15-deoxy-delta 12,14-prostaglandin J$_2$ is a ligand for the adipocyte determination factor PPAR-$\gamma$. *Cell* 83:803–12
15. Foster JA, Rich CB, Miller M, Benedict MR, Richman RA, Florini JR. 1990. Effect of age and IGF-1 administration on elastin gene expression of rat aorta. *J. Gerentol. Biol. Sci.* 45:B113–18
16. Friedman SL, Roll FJ, Boyles J, Bissell DM. 1985. Hepatic lipocytes: the principal collagen-producing cells of normal rat liver. *Proc. Natl. Acad. Sci. USA* 82:8681–85
17. Fries KM, Blieden T, Looney RJ, Sempkowski GD, Silvera, MR. et al. 1994. Evidence of fibroblast heterogeneity and the role for fibroblast subpopulations in fibrosis. *Clin. Immunol. Immunopathol.* 72:283–92
18. Fries KM, Felch ME, Phipps RP. 1994. Interleukin-6 is an autocrine growth factor for murine lung fibroblast subsets. *Am. J. Respir. Cell. Mol. Biol.* 11:552–60
19. Fukui M, Fujimoto T, Wantanabe K, Endo K, Kuno K. 1996. Prostaglandin F synthetase is localized to contractile interstitial cells in bovine lung. *J. Histochem. Cytochem.* 44:251–57
20. Gaillard D, Negrel R, Lagarde M, Ailhaud G. 1989. Requirement and role of arachidonic acid in the differentiation of preadipose cells. *Biochem. J.* 257:389–97
21. Gao G, Serrero G. 1990. Phospholipase A2 is a differentiation-dependent enzymatic activity for adipogenic cell line and adipocyte precursors in primary culture. *J. Biol. Chem.* 265:2431–34
22. Gordon GB, Newitt JA, Shantz LM, Weng DE, Talalay P. 1986. Inhibition of the conversion of 3T3 fibroblast clones to adipocytes by dehydroepiandrosterone and related anticarcinogenic steroids. *Cancer Res.* 46:3389–95
23. Green H, Kehinde O. 1974. Sublines of mouse 3T3 cells that accumulate lipid. *Cell* 1:113–16
24. Green H, Kehinde O. 1975. An established preadipose cell line and its differentiation

in culture. II. Factors affecting adipose conversion. *Cell* 5:19–27

25. Gressner AM, Bachem MG. 1994. Cellular communications and cell-matrix interactions in the pathogenesis of fibroproliferative diseases: liver fibrosis as a paradigm. *Ann. Biol. Clin.* 52:205–26

26. Grobstein C. 1967. Mechanisms of organogenic tissue interaction. *Natl. Cancer Inst. Monogr.* 26:279–99

27. Grummer MA, Thet LA, Zachman RD. 1994. Expression of retinoic acid receptor genes in fetal and newborn rat lung. *Pediatr. Pulmonol.* 17:234–38

28. Grummer MA, Zachman RD. 1995. Postnatal rat lung retinoic acid receptor (RAR) mRNA expression and effects of dexamethasone on RAR-$\beta$ mRNA. *Pediatr. Pulmonol.* 20:234–40

29. Hege Thoresen G, Gjone IH, Gladhaud IP, Refsnes M, Ostby E, Christoffersen T. 1989. Studies of glucocorticoid enhancement of the capacity of hepatocytes to accumulate cyclic AMP. *Pharmacol. Toxicol.* 65:175–80

30. Hitchcock O'Hare K, Sheridan MN. 1970. Electron microscopic observations on the morphogenesis of the albino rat lung, with special reference to pulmonary epithelial cells. *Am. J. Anat.* 127:181–206

31. Ibrahimi A, Bertrand B, Bardon S, Amri EZ, Grimaldi P, et al. 1993. Cloning of alpha-2 chain of type VI collagen and expression during mouse development. *Biochem. J.* 289:141–47

32. Jiang HP, Harris SE, Serrero G. 1992. Molecular cloning of a differentiation-related messenger RNA in the adipogenic cell line 1246. *Cell Growth Diff.* 3:21–30

33. Kapanci Y, Ribaux C, Chaponnier C, Gabbiani G. 1992. Cytoskeletal features of alveolar myofibroblasts and pericytes in normal human and rat lung. *J. Histochem. Cytochem.* 40:1955–63

34. Kapanci Y, Burgan S, Pietra GG, Conne B, Gabbiani G. 1990. Modulation of actin isoform expression in alveolar myofibroblasts (contractile interstitial cells) during pulmonary hypertension. *Am. J. Pathol.* 136:881–89

35. Kaplan NB, Grant MM, Brody JS. 1985. The lipid interstitial cell of the pulmonary alveolus. Age and species differences. *Am. Rev. Respir. Dis.* 132:1307–12

36. Kauffman SI. 1980. Cell proliferation in the mammalian lung. *Int. Rev. Exper. Pathol.* 22:131–90

37. Kliewer SA, Lenhard JM, Willison TM, Patel I, Morris DC, Lehmann JM. 1995. A prostaglandin $J_2$ metabolite binds peroxisome proliferator-activated receptor-$\gamma$ and promotes adipocyte differentiation. *Cell* 83:813–19

38. Krupsky M, Fine A, Berk JL, Goldstein RH. 1994. Retinoic acid-induced inhibition of type I collagen gene expression by human lung fibroblasts. *Biochem. Biophys. Acta* 1219:335–41

39. Leslie KO, Mitchell J, Low R. 1992. Lung myofibroblasts. *Cell Motil. Cytoskelet.* 22:92–98

40. Liu R, Harvey CS, McGowan SE. 1993. Retinoic acid increases elastin in neonatal rat lung fibroblast cultures. *Am. J. Physiol.* 265:L430–37

41. MacDougald OA, Lane MD. 1995. Transcriptional regulation of gene expression during adipocyte differentiation. *Annu. Rev. Biochem.* 64:345–73

42. Maksvytis HJ, Niles RM, Simanovsky L, Minassian IA, Richardson LL, et al. 1984. In vitro characteristics of the lipid-filled interstitial cell associated with postnatal lung growth: evidence for fibroblast heterogeneity. *J. Cell. Physiol.* 118:113–23

43. Maksvytis HJ, Vaccaro C, Brody JS. 1981. Isolation and characterization of the lipid-containing interstitial cell from the developing rat lung. *Lab. Invest.* 45:248–59

44. Massaro G, Massaro D. 1996. Postnatal treatment with retinoic acid increases the number of alveoli in rats. *Am. J. Physiol.* 270:L305–10

44a. Massaro GD, Massaro D. 1996. Formation of pulmonary alveoli and gas-exchange surface area: quantitation and regulation. *Annu. Rev. Physiol.* 58:73–92

45. Mauview A, Chen YQ, Kahari VM, Ledo I, Wu M, et al. 1993. Human recombinant interleukin-1$\beta$ up-regulates elastin gene expression in dermal fibroblasts. *J. Biol. Chem.* 268:6520–24

46. McGowan SE. 1992. Influences of endogenous and exogenous TGF-$\beta$ on elastin in rat lung fibroblasts and aortic smooth muscle cells. *Am. J. Physiol.* 263:L257–63

47. McGowan SE, Harvey CS, Jackson SK. 1995. Retinoids, retinoic acid receptors, and cytoplasmic retinoid binding proteins in perinatal rat lung fibroblasts. *Am. J. Physiol.* 269:L463–72

48. McGowan SE, Jackson SJ. 1994. TGF-$\beta$1 increases elastin mRNA half-life in neonatal rat lung fibroblasts. *Mol. Biol. Cell.* 5:175a (Abstr.)

49. McGowan SE, McNamer R. 1990. Transforming growth factor-$\beta$ increases elastin production by neonatal rat lung fibroblasts. *Am. J. Respir. Cell. Mol. Biol.* 3:369–76

50. Metzler MD, Snyder JM. 1993. Retinoic acid differentially regulates expression of

surfactant-associated proteins in human fetal lung. *Endocrinology* 133:1990–98

51. Mitchell JJ, Reynolds SE, Leslie KO, Low RB, Woodcock-Mitchell J. 1990. Smooth muscle cell markers in developing rat lung. *Am. J. Respir. Cell. Mol. Biol.* 3:515–23

52. Mitchell JJ, Woodcock-Mitchell JL, Perry L, Zhao J, Low RB, et al. 1993. In vitro expression of the $\alpha$-smooth muscle actin isoform by rat lung mesenchymal cells: regulation by culture conditions and transforming growth factor-$\beta$. *Am. J. Respir. Cell. Mol. Biol.* 9:10–18

53. Mitchell JJ, Woodcock-Mitchell J, Reynolds S, Low R, Leslie K, et al. 1989. $\alpha$-smooth muscle actin in parenchymal cells of bleomycin-injured rat lung. *Lab. Invest.* 60:643–50

54. Mostello DJ, Hamosh M, Hamosh P. 1981. Effect of dexamethasone on lipoprotein lipase activity of fetal rat lung. *Biol. Neonate* 40:121–28

55. Navre M, Ringold GM. 1986. A growth factor-repressible gene associated with protein kinase C-mediated inhibition of adipocyte differentiation. *J. Cell Biol.* 107:279–86

56. Negrel R, Grimaldi P, Ailbaud G. 1981. Differentiation of Ob17 preadipocytes to adipocytes. Effects of prostaglandin F2$\alpha$ and relationship to prostaglandin synthesis. *Biochem. Biophys. Acta* 666:15–24

57. Noguchi A, Reddy R, Kursar JD, Parks WC, Mecham RP. 1989. Smooth muscle isoactin and elastin in fetal bovine lung. *Exper. Lung Res.* 15:537–52

58. Nunez JS, Torday JS. 1995. The developing rat lung fibroblast and alveolar type II cell actively recruit surfactant phospholipid substrate. *J. Nutr.* 125:1639S–44S

59. Okabe T, Yorifuji H, Yamada E, Takaku F. 1984. Isolation and characterization of vitamin A-storing lung cells. *Exper. Cell Res.* 154:125–35

60. Olson DM, Transwell AK. 1989. Production of prostaglandins by fetal rat lung type II pneumocytes and fibroblasts. *Biochem. Biophys. Acta* 1003:327–30

61. Ong DE, Chytil F. 1976. Changes in levels of cellular retinol and retinoic acid binding proteins of liver and lung during perinatal development of rat. *Proc. Natl. Acad. Sci. USA* 73:3976–78

62. Penny DP, Keng PC, Derdak S, Phipps RP. 1992. Morphologic and functional characteristics of subpopulations of murine lung fibroblasts grown in vitro. *Anat. Rec.* 232:432–43

63. Phipps RP, Penny DP, Keng P, Quill H, Paxhia A, et al. 1989. Characterization of two major populations of lung fibroblasts:

distinguishing morphology and discordant display of Thy 1 and Class II MHC. *Am. J. Respir. Cell. Mol. Biol.* 1:65–74

64. Pierce RA, Griffin GL, Mudd MS, Senior RM. 1994. Production of entactin by rat lung mesenchymal cells: modulation by glucocorticoids and TGF-$\beta$. *Mol. Biol. Cell.* 5:305a (Abstr.)

65. Pierce RA, Mariencheck WI, Sandefur S, Crouch EC, Parks WC. 1995. Glucocorticoids upregulate tropoelastin expression during late stages of fetal lung development. *Am. J. Physiol.* 268:L491–500

66. Rich CB, Ewton DZ, Martin BM, Florini JR, Bashir M, et al. 1992. IGF-1 regulation of elastogenesis: comparison of aortic and lung cells. *Am. J. Physiol.* 263:L276–82

67. Rosenbaum J, Blazejewsik S. 1995. Regulation of Ito cell proliferation by soluble factors. *J. Hepatol.* 22:65–70 (Suppl.)

68. Rubin CS, Hirsch A, Fung C, Rosen OM. 1978. Development of hormone receptors and hormonal responsiveness in vitro. Insulin receptors and insulin sensitivity in the preadipocyte and adipocyte forms of 3T3-L1 cells. *J. Biol. Chem.* 253:7570–78

69. Sato T, Kato R, Tyson CA. 1995. Regulation of differentiated phenotype of rat hepatic lipocytes by retinoids in primary culture. *Exper. Cell Res.* 217:72–83

70. Sempkowski GD, Beckmann MP, Derdak S, Phipps RP. 1994. Subsets of murine lung fibroblasts express membrane-bound and soluble IL-4 receptors. *J. Immunol.* 152:3606–14

71. Serro G, Mills D. 1991. Decrease in transforming growth factor-$\beta$1 binding during differentiation of rat adipocyte precursors in primary culture. *Cell Growth Diff.* 2:173–78

72. Shenai JP, Chytil F. 1990. Vitamin A storage in lungs during perinatal development in the rat. *Biol. Neonate* 57:126–32

73. Silvera MR, Sempkowski GD, Phipps RP. 1994. Expression of TGF-$\beta$ isoforms by Thy-1+ and Thy-1− pulmonary fibroblast subsets: evidence for TGF-$\beta$ as a regulator of IL-1-dependent stimulation of IL-6. *Lymphokine Cytokine Res.* 13:277–85

74. Skinner SJM, Lowe C, Ashby CJ, Liggins GC. 1989. Effects of corticosteroids, prostaglandin E2, and beta-agonists on adenylate cyclase activity in fetal rat lung fibroblats and type II epithelial cells. *Exper. Lung Res.* 15:335–43

75. Sorokin S, Padykula HA, Herman E. 1959. Comparative histochemical patterns in developing mammalian lungs. *Dev. Biol.* 1:125–51

76. Spit BJ. 1983. Induction of lipid droplets

in fibroblasts of the hamster lung by a diet high in vitamin A. *Exper. Lung Res.* 4:247–57

77. Takase S, Goda T. 1990. Developmental changes in vitamin A level and lack of retinyl palmitate in chick lungs. *Comp. Biochem. Physiol.* 96B:415–19

78. Tontonoz P, Hu E, Spiegelman BM. 1994. Stimulation of adipogenesis in fibroblasts by PPAR-$\gamma$, a lipid-activated transcription factor. *Cell* 79:1147–56

79. Torday JS. 1992. Cellular timing of fetal lung development. *Semin. Perinatol.* 16:130–39

80. Torday JS, Hua J, Slavin R. 1995. Metabolism and fate of neutral lipids of fetal lung fibroblast origin. *Biochem. Biophys. Acta* 1254:198–206

81. Torday JS, Kourembanas S. 1990. Fetal lung fibroblasts produce a TGF-$\beta$ homolog that blocks alveolar type II cell maturation. *Dev. Biol.* 139:35–41

82. Torday JS, Olson EB, First NL. 1976. Production of cortisol from cortisone by the isolated, perfused rabbit lung. *Steroids* 27:869–80

83. Torday JS, Sun H, Qin JT. 1996. Type II cell prostaglandin stimulation of triglyceride release from lung fibroblasts. *Am. J. Physiol.* Submitted

84. Tordet C, Marin L, Dameron F. 1981. Pulmonary di- and tri-glycerides during the perinatal development of the rat. *Experientia* 37:333–34

85. Torti FM, Torti SV, Larrick JW, Ringold GM. 1989. Modulation of adipocyte differentiation by tumor necrosis factor and transforming growth factor-$\beta$. *J. Cell Biol.* 108:1105–13

86. Vaccaro C, Brody JS. 1978. Ultrastructure of developing alveoli. I. The role of the interstitial fibroblast. *Anat. Rec.* 192:467–80

87. Vassaux G, Gaillard D, Ailhaud G, Negrel R. 1992. Prostacyclin is a specific effector of adipose cell differentiation. Its dual role as a cAMP- and $Ca^{2+}$-elevating agent. *J. Biol. Chem.* 267:11092–97

*Annu. Rev. Physiol. 1997. 59:63–88*

# EMERGING ROLES FOR CYSTEINE PROTEASES IN HUMAN BIOLOGY

*Harold A. Chapman, Richard J. Riese, and Guo-Ping Shi*

Department of Medicine, Brigham and Women's Hospital, and Harvard Medical School, Boston, Massachusetts 02115

KEY WORDS:   thiol protease, cathepsin, lung, MHC class II, macrophage

---

### ABSTRACT

Cysteine proteases have traditionally been viewed as lysosomal mediators of terminal protein degradation. However, recent findings refute this limited view and suggest a more expanded role for cysteine proteases in human biology. Several newly discovered members of this enzyme class are regulated proteases with limited tissue expression, which implies specific roles in cellular physiology. These roles appear to include apoptosis, MHC class II immune responses, prohormone processing, and extracellular matrix remodeling important to bone development. The ability of macrophages and other cells to mobilize elastolytic cysteine proteases to their surfaces under specialized conditions may also lead to accelerated collagen and elastin degradation at sites of inflammation in diseases such as atherosclerosis and emphysema. The development of inhibitors of specific cysteine proteases promises to provide new drugs for modifying immunity, osteoporosis, and chronic inflammation.

---

## INTRODUCTION

Proteases are enzymes that catalyze hydrolysis of amide bonds. Although proteins may undergo many reversible posttranslational modifications during their lifespan, e.g. phosphorylation and allosteric transitions, proteolysis is irreversible. Once proteins are hydrolyzed, the only means available for rebuilding the intact molecule is to translate more mRNA. Based on the nature of proteolysis, it is not surprising that proteolytic enzymes have evolved to mediate processes that are themselves frequently irreversible: coagulation, digestion, maturation of cytokines and prohormones, apoptosis, and breakdown of intracellular proteins. Proteolysis is a ubiquitous mechanism the cell employs

63

to regulate the function and fate of proteins (1, 2). Accordingly, the number of proteases identified in and around cells is enormous, and many are vital for normal homeostasis. This is also true for the respiratory system. Since the demonstration of emphysema following intratracheal instillation of papain in experimental animals (3), much of what has been reported about proteases and the respiratory system has centered on the potential for proteases to cause damage in the lungs and airways. However, proteases are as vital to normal lung function as anywhere else. Indeed, the lung airways normally contain free proteases and peptidases (urokinase, Factor VII, neutral endopeptidase), and lining cells and stromal cells of the lung depend on regulated protease activity for their "housekeeping" functions, as well as for responses to the frequent injurious insults to which this organ is subjected (4–6). Clearance of organic particulates and microorganisms from the lung is dependent on intracellular proteases and occurs daily without any evident injury. Injury more often takes place when proteases are unable to effect clearance, such as occurs after inhalation of inorganic dusts and cigarette smoke.

All proteases share in common the general mechanism of a nucleophilic attack on the carbonyl-carbon of an amide bond (7). This results in a general acid-base hydrolytic process that disrupts the covalent bond. Different proteases utilize different strategies to generate the nucleophile and to juxtapose the nucleophile with the targeted bond. These distinctions serve as a useful classification scheme, and on this basis proteases can be grouped into four major classes: serine, cysteine, aspartate, and metallo. The latter two groups of enzymes utilize aspartate residues and heavy metals, respectively, to immobilize and polarize a water molecule so that the oxygen atom in water becomes the nucleophile (8). Serine and cysteine proteases utilize their HO- and HS-side chains, respectively, directly as nucleophiles. Although not identical, the catalytic mechanisms of serine and cysteine proteases are remarkably similar. In general, these enzymes are folded into two relatively large globular domains surrounding a cleft containing the active site residues. Substrate entry into the cleft is a prerequisite for cleavage, and efficient entry is dictated by the structural fit between the potential substrate and the topology of the cleft, a major determinant of enzyme specificity. The formation of a spatial fit between a targeted bond of the substrate and the active site nucleophile is obviously also a critical determinant of substrate specificity. Crystallographic analysis of several members of the serine and cysteine class enzymes reveals detailed structure of the active site regions and the importance of additional amino acids to the catalytic mechanism (9, 10). In both serine and cysteine proteases, the formation of an oxyanion or thiolate anion (the nucleophile), respectively, is critical to catalysis, and the formation of these anions appears to be dependent on ion pair formation between the active site amino acid and neighboring basic amino acids (histidine). Several recent reviews detailing the mechanism of catalysis by serine and cysteine proteases are available (2, 11).

This review focuses on the role of cysteine proteases in cellular physiology. These enzymes have been a major interest of this laboratory and many developments have occurred within this class of enzymes in the last several years. Importantly, the elucidation of new members of the cysteine protease class appears to be a preface to delineation of novel roles for these enzymes in human biology, affecting the function of the respiratory systems as well as other organs. A distinguishing feature of the newer proteases is their restricted tissue expression and regulated behavior, which probably accounts for the fact that most were not identified by standard biochemical methods but, instead, required the advent of RNA and DNA screening techniques for characterization. Correspondingly, a view of the biological role of cysteine proteases must take into account the function of these new enzymes. The presence of regulated enzymes with restricted tissue distribution implies specific cellular functions rather than simply cooperative mediation of terminal protein degradation. This is an important change in the conceptual view of the role of cysteine proteases in human biology because, if true, therapeutic targeting of these enzymes could affect specific changes in cell function without broad inhibition of lysosomal function. Where possible, this review will attempt to highlight specific functions for cysteine proteases, even if these putative functions are based on preliminary evidence, in the hope of stimulating further investigation and insight.

## CLASSIFICATION OF CYSTEINE PROTEASES

Cysteine proteases can be grouped into two superfamilies: the family of enzymes related to interleukin $1\beta$ converting enzyme (ICE), and the papain superfamily of cysteine proteases (12). Distinctive features of their structures and functions are summarized in Table 1. Although each superfamily of enzymes employs an active site cysteine for nucleophilic attack, important evolutionary and structural differences distinguish them. The ICE superfamily of enzymes, other than the active site cysteine itself, shares no sequence homology with the papain superfamily (13). They are remarkable in their specificity for aspartate as the SI amino acid, an uncommon cleavage site among proteases. Their emerging role in inflammation and programmed cell death has been recently reviewed and is not discussed further here (14). The calpains are a group of cytoplasmic cysteine proteases within the papain superfamily whose activity is strictly calcium dependent but whose protease domain is nonetheless very much like that of papain. The calcium sensitivity results from the ancestral fusion of a papain-type protease domain with a calmodulin-like domain (15, 16). These enzymes are implicated in limited proteolysis of a number of

**Table 1**    Structural and functional features of human cysteine proteases

| Enzyme family[a] | Interleukin-1β converting enzyme (ICE) | Calpain | Papain |
|---|---|---|---|
| Active site motifs | $^{279}$–V I I IQ A C R G D S— | | –$^{19}$N Q G C G S C W A F S[b]— |
| Members | ICE | m-calpain | cathepsin B, H, L, S, O, |
| | Cpp32, others | μ-calpain | K, others |
| Preferred cleavage sites | –Y/D-V-A–D▼–X- | -X-I/V-L/R▼–X | –R/K–X▼–X (CAT B-like)[c] |
| | | | –L/I—X–X- (CAT L-like) |
| Location | Cytoplasm | Cytoplasm inner membranes | Endosomes/lysosomes |
| Function | IL-1-β release | Regulation of membrane signaling | Digestion Antigen presentation Hormone processing |
| | Apoptosis | | Matrix remodeling ? Tumor invasion |

[a] An additional group of enzymes in the papain superfamily not listed in the table are the bleomycin hydrolases. See text for discussion.
[b] Sequence shown is for cathepsin B. See Figure 1 for sequence homologies among the cathepsins.
[c] Substrate specificity for the papain group of enzymes is determined primarily by amino acid preferences in the S2 subsite rather than the S1 cleavage site (arrowheads). Cathepsin B-like enzymes accomodate basic amino acids into the S2 subsite and efficiently cleave proteins after Arg-Arg or Lys-Arg sequences. By contrast, cathepsin L-like enzymes strongly prefer hydrophobic or branched chain amino acids in the S2 subsite. Only these enzymes are efficient elastases.

intracellular proteins in association with rises in intracellular calcium concentration. Protease activation appears to correlate with membrane binding and is followed quickly by autolysis. Although the exact physiological role of these enzymes is still being elucidated, the demonstration of limited cleavage of several regulatory proteins, such as protein kinase C, actin-binding proteins, and integrin cytoplasmic tails, by calpains, makes a regulatory role for these enzymes in cellular signaling likely (16, 17). The discovery of tissue-specific calpains, e.g. a muscle-specific calpain, has further opened the physiological possibilities (18). Recent linkage of limb-girdle dystrophy with mutations in this calpain underscore this point (19). Additional calpains are almost certain to be forthcoming, along with a better view of their biological role. The structure and function of calpains including the newer enzymes are also the subject of several recent reviews (15, 16).

A second group of enzymes in the papain superfamily, not listed in Table 1, are the bleomycin hydrolases (20). These enzymes were identified originally as an activity in rabbit and bovine lung extracts that mediate bleomycin inactivation and were subsequently reported to protect human tumor cells from bleomycin toxicity (21, 22). Isolation and molecular cloning of the rabbit enzyme demonstrated the activity to be due to a papain-type cysteine protease (20).

The enzyme appears to self-assemble into hexamers of its 50-kDa single chain, reminiscent of proteasome organization and, because there is no signal peptide, to localize to the cytoplasm. Recently, a yeast homologue of the mammalian enzyme was crystallized and found to contain both DNA-binding and papain-type motifs in each of its five chains, implying that DNA-binding and protease functions of the enzyme are intertwined (23). Although identified on the basis of its bleomycin hydrolase activity, this enzyme appears to be the first example of a mammalian protease with DNA-binding and presumably transcriptional regulatory functions. Further characterization of this activity and elucidation of other proteins with similar properties should determine whether this enzyme provides a new paradigm for transcriptional regulation.

The papain family itself (the third enzyme group within the papain super-family) has been extensively studied, with over 80 distinct and complete entries in sequence databases (12). Papain (from *Carica papaya*) and, more recently, cathepsin B have been analyzed by X-ray crystallography and their functional properties have been examined (10, 24). Until recently, information about mammalian members of the papain family has been more limited. The discovery of mammalian papain-type cysteine proteases can now be divided roughly into two eras. Prior to 1990, the known enzymes (cathepsins B, H, L, and S) were entirely characterized by standard protein isolation of enzyme activities and subsequent physical characterization. Although bovine cathepsin S had been isolated as an enzyme activity, complete sequence data were available for only B, L, and H (25–29). These enzymes had been purified from adult solid organs, where they constitute the most abundant lysosomal enzymes. Perhaps, in part, because of their strong homology to papain (common meat tenderizer) and because of the long-standing view of lysosomes as terminal degradative organelles, these enzymes had been viewed largely as collective mediators for terminal digestion of endocytized and endogenous proteins entering lysosomes (30). This was not unreasonable because nonspecific inhibitors of cysteine proteases have been reported to inhibit up to 40% of total cellular protein turnover (31).

Recently, the techniques of molecular biology have been employed to investigate papain-type cysteine proteases. What has emerged is at least five new human enzymes of the papain family and an evolving view of the role of these enzymes in biology. In 1990, our laboratory utilized degenerate nucleotide primers spanning the highly conserved amino acid sequences within the catalytic domains of known human cysteine proteases and reverse-transcribed RNA from human alveolar macrophages to search by polymerase chain amplification for new cysteine protease sequences. With this technique we were able to isolate partial cDNA sequences for all of the known human enzymes (cathepsins H, B, and L), as well as three new sequences. One of these, cathepsin S, had previously been purified and partially sequenced (25), whereas the other two, now designated cathepsins K and F, had not been observed. Full sequences for these enzymes were subsequently obtained by screening appropriate cDNA libraries (32, 33). Wiederanders and colleagues independently obtained a full cDNA for cathepsin S (34). This technique was also applied by other investigators to reveal additional human and rodent members of the papain family (35, 36). Figure 1 summarizes the sequence alignment of the known human enzymes (25–29, 32, 33, 36). There are almost certainly additional sequences forthcoming. Another enzyme not listed in Table 1 (dipeptidyl peptidase I or cathepsin C) has been fully sequenced in rodents and found to be a typical papain-type enzyme, albeit exhibiting only aminodipeptidase activity (37). To date no human sequence for this enzyme has been entered into a database. Dipeptidylpeptidase I is found in various myleoid cells and functions as a processing enzyme for activation of several serine proteases (38).

Inspection of the sequence alignments reveals several interesting points:

1. All enzymes shown contain a signal peptide and a propiece, which is removed at maturation. This propiece is important because enzymes, e.g. cathepsin B, expressed without the propiece are not properly folded and remain inactive (39). Moreover, the isolated propieces themselves inhibit their mature enzymes, suggesting that the propiece functions as a chaperone to permit proper folding and to block the active site cleft until the enzyme is in an activation environment (40, 40a) . Interestingly, one of the newer sequences identified in our laboratory is a typical papain-type protease except that it lacks a characteristic signal peptide (cathepsin F). Where this enzyme localizes and functions within cells will be interesting to explore.

2. Cathepsin B has an additional ≈30-amino acid sequence inserted proximal to the active site histidine. In the crystal structure of cathepsin B, this sequence loops over the active site cleft in the mature enzyme and restricts access of potential substrates (24). This probably accounts in part for the relatively weak endoprotease activity of cathepsin B compared with other members of this family. By contrast, cathepsin B has particularly good carboxypeptidase activity. Three-dimensional modeling of cathepsin H also reveals a closed active site cleft, which may in part account for its predominant function as an aminopeptidase (41).

3. Two regions of marked sequence similarity (denoted by ts) are evident in the Figure 1. The proximal region surrounds the active site cysteine 25 and the

→

*Figure 1* Amino acid sequence alignment of the known human cysteine proteases. Conserved amino acid residues in the human sequences relevative to papain are denoted with an asterisk. The dash indicates a gap relative to the papain sequence. Numbering shown is that for papain.

```
Human  Cat K:  M W G L K - V L L L P V V S F A - L Y P E E I L D T H W E - L W K K T H
Human  Cat S:  * K R * V C - * * * V C S S A V * Q * H K D P T * H * * H - * * * * Y
Human  Cat O:  * D V R A L P W - * * W L L W L L C R G G G D A D S R A P F T P T W P R
Human  Cat L:  * N P T L - I * A A F C L G I A S A T L T F - - * H S L * A Q * T * W K
Human  Cat H:  * * A T L - P * * C A G A W L L G V P V C G A A E L S V N S * E * F - *
Human  Cat B:  * * Q * W A S * C C L L * L A N A R S R P S F H P V S D * - Q V N Y V N
                         SIGNAL PEPTIDE

HCK:  R K Q Y N N K V D - - E I S R R L I W E K N L K Y I S I H N L E A S L - G V H T Y
HCS:  G * * * K E * N E - - * A V * * * * * * * * * * F V M L * * * H * M - * M * S *
HCO:  S R E R E A A A F R - * S L N * H R Y L N S * F P S E N S T A F Y G I N Q F S Y L
HCL:  A M H N R L Y G M N E * G W - * A V - * * * M * M I E L H * Q * Y R E - * K * S F
HCH:  F K S W M S * H R K T Y S T E E Y H H R L Q T F A S N W R K I N H H N N * N * * F
HCB:  K R N T T W Q A G H N F Y N V D M S Y L * R * C G T F L G G P K P P Q R V M F * E
                         PROPIECE

HCK:  E L A M N H L G D M T S E E V V Q K M T G L K V P L S H S R - S N D T L Y I P E W
HCS:  D * G * * * * * * * * * * * M S L T S S * R * - - * Q W Q - R * I * - * K S N P
HCO:  F P - - - - - - - - * F K A I Y L R S - * P S K F P R Y S A E V H M S * * N V
HCL:  T M * * * A F * * * * * F R * V M N * F Q N R K P R K G K V F Q E P L F - - Y
HCH:  K M * L * Q F S * * S F A * I K H * Y L W S E P Q N C S A T K * F Y L R G T G P Y
HCB:  D * K L P A S F * A R - * Q W P * C P * I - * E I - - R D - - - - - - - - - - -
                                                                    t
Papain:     I P E Y V D W R Q K G - A V T P V K N Q G S C G S C W A F S A V V T I E G I  37
HCK:  E G R A * D S * * Y * K * - - Y * * * * * * * * Q * * * * * * S * G A L * * Q
HCS:  N R I L * D S * * * E * - C * * E * Y * * * * A * * * * * * G A L * A Q
HCO:  S - - L * L R F * * * D * Q - V * * Q * R * * Q M * * G * * * * V * G A V * S A
HCL:  * - - A * R S * * * * E * - Y * * * * * * * * Q * * * * * * * T G A L * * Q
HCH:  - - - - * P S * * * * K * * N F * S * * * * * A * * * * * T * * T T G A L * S A
HCB:  - - - - - - - - - - - - - - - - - - - - - * * * * * * * * G * * E A * S D R
                         PROTEASE DOMAIN

PAP:  I K I R T G N L N Q Y S E Q E L L D C D R R S Y - - - - - G C N G G Y P W S A L Q  73
HCK:  L * K K * * K * L N L * P * N * V * * V S E N D - - - - - * G * * M T N * F *
HCS:  L * L K * * K * V T L * A * N * V * * S T * K * G - - N K * * * * F M T T * F *
HCO:  Y A * K G K P * E D L * V * Q V I * * S Y N N * - - - - - * * * S T L N * * N
HCL:  M F R K * * R * I S L * * * N * V * * - S G P Q G - - N E * * * * L M D Y * F *
HCH:  * A * A * * K M L S L A * * Q * V * * A Q D F N - - - N Y * * Q * * L * S Q * F E
HCB:  * C * H * N A H V S V E V - S A E * L L T C C G S M C G D * * * - * * * A E * W N

PAP:  L V A Q Y - G I H Y R N - T P Y Y E G V Q R Y C R S R E K G P Y A A K T D G V R Q  111
HCK:  Y * Q K N R * * D S E D A Y * Y V - * - * E E S C M Y N P T G K * * * C R * Y * E
HCS:  Y I I D N K * * D S D A S Y * * - K A M D Q K * Q Y D S * Y R - * * T C S K Y T E
HCO:  W L N K M Q V K L V K D S E - * P F K A * N G L C H Y F S * S H S G F S I K G Y S
HCL:  Y * Q D N G * L D S E E E S Y * * - E A T E E S * K Y N P * Y S V * N D * G F - V D
HCH:  Y I L Y N K * * M G E D T Y * * - Q * K D G * * K F Q P - * K A I G F V K D * A N
HCB:  F W T R - K * L V S G G L Y E S H V * C R P * S I P P C E H H V N G S R P P C T G

PAP:  V Q P Y N Q G A L L Y S I - A N Q - P V S V V L Q A A G K D F Q L Y R G G I F V G  152
HCK:  I - * E G N E K * * K R A V * R V G * * * A I D * S L T S * * F * S K * V Y Y D
HCS:  L - * * G R E D V * K E A V * K G * * * * G V D * R H P S * F * * * S * V Y Y E
HCO:  A Y D F S D Q E D E M A K A L L T F G P L * * I V D * V S W Q D - * L * * * I Q H
HCL:  I - * K Q - * K * M K A V * T V G * I * * A I Q * G H E S * L F * K E * * Y F E
HCH:  I - T I * D * E * M V E A V * L Y N - * * F A F E V T Q D - * M M * * T * * Y S S
HCB:  E - G D T P - K C S K I C E P G Y S * T Y K Q D K H Y G Y N S Y S V S N S E K - D
                                                                                    t
PAP:  P - C G N K V D - - - - - - - - - - - - - - - - - - - - - - - - - - - - H A  161
HCK:  E S - * S - * N L N - - - - - - - - - - - - - - - - - - - - - - - - * *
HCS:  * S - - * T Q N V N - - - - - - - - - - - - - - - - - - - - - - - - - * G
HCO:  H - * S S G E A N - - - - - - - - - - - - - - - - - - - - - - - - * *
HCL:  * D * S - - S E D M D - - - - - - - - - - - - - - - - - - - - - - - - * G
HCH:  T S * H K T P * K V N - - - - - - - - - - - - - - - - - - - - - - - - * *
HCB:  I M A E I Y K N G P V E G A F S V Y S D F L L Y K S G V Y Q H V T G E M M G G * *

PAP:  V A A V G Y N P - - - - - - - G - - Y I L I K N S W G T G W G E N G Y I R I K R G  191
HCK:  * L * * * * G I Q - - - - - - - K * N K H W I * * * * * E N * * N K * * * L M A * N
HCS:  * L V * * * G D - - - - - L N - * K E * W * V * * * * H N F * * E * * * M A * N
HCO:  * L I T * F D K T G - - - - - S T P * W I V R * * * * S S * * V D * * A H V * M *
HCL:  * L * * * * G F E S T E S D - N N K * W * V * * * * E E * * M G * * V K M A K D
HCH:  * L * * * * G E - - - - - K N * I P * W I V * * * * P Q * M * * * F L * E * *
HCB:  I R I L * W G V E N - - - - - * T P * W * V A * * * N * D * D * * F F K * L * *

PAP:  T G N S Y G V C G L Y T S - S F - - Y P V K N STOP!          CHROMOSOME:
HCK:  K N * A - - - * * I A N L A * * - - * - * STOP!              1Q21
HCS:  K G * - - * H * * I A - - * * P S * * E I STOP!              1Q21
HCO:  S - - - * * * * I A D * V * S I F V STOP!                   ?
HCL:  R R * - - * H * * I A - * A A S - - * T V STOP!             9
HCH:  K N - - - - M * * I A - A C A S - - * I P L V STOP!         15
HCB:  Q D - - - - H * * I E - * E V V A G I P R T D Q Y W E K I STOP!  8
```

distal region surrounds the active site histidine 159, which functions to form an ion pair with the cysteine in the active enzyme. Three-dimensional modeling shows the targeted carbonyl-carbon, and these amino acids are juxtaposed in a plane (24, 41). Of note, the asparagine 175 is also highly conserved and has been considered a possible member of a "catalytic triad" for cysteine proteases analogous to the serine-histidine-aspartate triad of serine proteases. However, recent mutagenesis studies demonstrate that this asparagine is not critical for enzymatic function, although mutation to alanine results in an $\approx$100-fold loss of enzymatic activity (42).

4. There is little sequence homology in the regions between the active site amino acids, with the notable exception of several glycine residues (positions 64, 65) that are markedly conserved among all members of the papain super-family (12). Amino acids in this region must confer functional idiosyncrasies upon the enzymes, which for the most part remain to be defined.

Therefore, members of the papain superfamily of cysteine proteases share the basic building blocks of a signal peptide, a propiece, and a protease domain. In addition, the calpains have one or two other domains conferring calcium sensitivity. Although each of the enzymes is structurally and functionally distinct, in no case has it been shown that any of these enzymes has a single, specific substrate, as is the case for many serine proteases.

## Regulation of Cysteine Protease Activity

For many types of proteases, especially those with only limited proteolytic potential, activity is regulated by the balance between the amount of active enzyme present and the amount of active inhibitors. Dysregulation implies either an overabundance or a deficiency of enzyme relative to inhibitors. However, regulation of cysteine proteases is more complicated. Aside from the determinants of gene expression, numerous factors govern the proteolytic activity of cysteine proteases:

1. pH. Most cysteine proteases are unstable and weakly active at neutral pH and thus are optimized to function in acidic intracellular vesicles.

2. Redox potential. The active site cysteine is readily oxidized, and hence these enzymes are most active in a reducing environment. Endosomes specifically accumulate cysteine to maintain such an environment (43).

3. Synthesis as an inactive precursor. All enzymes require proteolytic activation. Activation generally requires an acidic pH, thus preventing indiscriminate activation following accidental secretion.

4. Targeting of enzymes to endosomes and lysosomes. All of the known enzymes possess N-glycosylation sites that are subsequently mannosylated and targeted on the basis of phosphomannosyl residues, which promote binding to

mannose-6-phosphate receptors, the major receptor for lysosomal targeting of proteins in the secretory pathway.

5. The presence of cysteine protease inhibitors. In the case of the papain-type cysteine proteases all of these factors combine to tightly compartmental-ize protease activity. Protease inhibitors appear to function predominantly to inhibit active enzyme that escapes compartmentalization by the mechanisms listed above. Accordingly, the cytoplasm and extracellular spaces are endowed with cysteine protease inhibitors in high stoichiometric excess over enzyme. Nonetheless, some cells, especially macrophages, appear capable of mobilizing the active enzymes within endosomal and/or lysosomal compartments to the cell surface under special circumstances (44). An important point underscored by this study is that simple expression of a cysteine protease does not mean cells will utilize the protease in matrix remodeling. To do so also requires mobilization of acid, enzymes, and possibly other unknown factors to the cell surface. In this case, the cell surface/substrate interface becomes a compartment from which inhibitors are excluded and can be viewed as a physiological extension of the lysosome. This type of physiology is an innate trait of osteoclasts (45–47), a bone macrophage, and, as discussed below, may also be exploited by other macrophages or cells in the context of inflammation.

## Protease Inhibitors

Numerous inhibitors of cysteine proteases have been described. The most abundant is the superfamily of cystatins: the intracellular type lacking a signal peptide (Type 1, cystatin A and B), commonly termed stefins; the abundant secreted, extracellular inhibitor, cystatin C (Type II); and the circulating kininogens (Type III) (11, 48). These proteins interact with active cysteine proteases through multiple sites on the inhibitor, implying a more complex mechanism of interaction than that of serine protease inhibitors (49) (see below). Nonetheless, they bind tightly and essentially irreversibly. Combined with the other factors listed above, these inhibitors appear to protect cells, tissues, and the circulation from unwarranted cysteine protease activity. The first genetic deficiency of a cystatin was recently reported (50). Loss of cystatin B activity was found to underlie a congenital seizure disorder, raising the question of what cytoplasmic protease is left unprotected. It is hoped that this finding will lead to further elucidation of the role of calpains and other intracytoplasmic cysteine proteases in cellular function.

The recent discovery of two new cysteine protease inhibitors highlights the similarity between serine and cysteine proteases. Two new members of the serpin family (a family of serine protease inhibitors) appear to possess potent inhibitory activity toward cysteine proteases. Crm A is a viral serpin first discovered because of its ability to inhibit ICE and block the apoptotic process (51). This inhibitor has strong amino acid sequence homology with plasminogen activator inhibitor type II and the ovalbumin subfamily of serpins. Similar to all members of the serpin family, the inhibitor employs a reactive site loop that serves as a bait for protease attack, following which the inhibitor changes conformation and forms a tight inhibitory complex with enzyme. The discovery of Crm A has triggered a search for mammalian analogues with ICE inhibitory activity, but to date none has been reported. It is intriguing that several PAI-II type serpins lack signal peptides and are found predominantly in the cytoplasm.

A novel serpin of the PAI-II type was also identified as a tumor cell marker of squamous carcinoma and termed squamous cell carcinoma antigen (SSCA) (52). This serpin was subsequently found to inhibit cathepsin L (53). Recently, Silverman and colleagues reported the localization of two SSCA genes within a serpin cluster on chromosome 18q21.3 (53a). They have also studied their expression and function (G Silverman, unpublished observations). SSCA1 appears to be expressed in a highly restricted fashion limited to squamous cells of the skin and the conducting airways of the lung. Interestingly, in the lung, this inhibitor localizes almost exclusively to ciliated columnar epithelial cells. Functionally, SSCA was found to be a high-affinity inhibitor not only for cathepsin L but also for cathepsins S, K, and papain itself. Why would cells express such an inhibitor, again predominantly intracellularly? It is possible that the inhibitor primarily functions in the setting of injury to protect the upper airway from unrestricted cysteine protease activity. The preliminary evidence that these cells also produce cathepin S would be consistent with this notion (see below). However, its constitutive expression in specific cells also suggests a more fundamental role in the normal function of these cells; this remains an enigma.

## PHYSIOLOGICAL ROLES OF CYSTEINE PROTEASES

Almost all cells express some level of papain-type lysosomal proteases. This appears to be required for the housekeeping function of lysosomes in protein turnover by cells. Cathepsin B is the most abundant and widely expressed of this family and its role appears to be reflected by the housekeeping nature of its promoter. The delineation of novel cathepsin sequences has been paralleled by new information regarding the physiological roles of these enzymes in biology, although several of the newer enzymes are still being characterized, and little mature information is available. For example, cathepsin O is a typical papain-type enzyme first isolated from a breast cancer cDNA library but then found to be widespread in its tissue distribution (36). To date its role is completely obscure. A cathepsin L-like enzyme expressed mainly in human thymus seems particularly interesting in terms of ontological development of immunity, but no functional work has been completed to date (D Bromme, unpublished observations). The same is true for cathepsin F, alluded to above, which has the interesting property of no obvious signal peptide (GP Shi, unpublished observations). The roles of these new enzymes in human biology await detailed functional studies.

We focus on two enzymes, cathepsin S and K, for which new functional information is available. Recent observations regarding these enzymes seem particularly relevant to the respiratory system. General reviews of the biochemistry and function of papain-type cysteine proteases have been published recently (11, 54).

## CATHEPSIN K

Cathepsin K was first discovered as a cDNA prominent in rabbit osteoclasts and referred to as OC-2 (55). One of the papain-type cDNA sequences we had identified by RT-PCR of human lung macrophage mRNA proved to be the human orthologue of this enzyme. In collaboration with Weiss et al, we obtained the full coding sequence of this enzyme and studied its functional properties (33). Independently, Inaoka et al, as well as other investigators, also reported the full coding sequence of the human enzyme (56, 57). The enzyme was given different names by the various groups describing the human orthologue, but we refer to the enzyme as cathepsin K, as suggested by Inaoka et al (56). Cathepsin K is a typical cysteine protease with a signal peptide, short propiece, and a catalytic domain characteristic of the papain family. The protein shares highest DNA and amino acid sequence homology with cathepsins S and L, and these three enzymes can reasonably be considered a subfamily within the human group of papain cysteine proteases. This is borne out by recent studies of the gene structure for this cathepsin, which is quite similar to that of cathepsins S and L. Moreover, cathepsin K maps physically to chromosome 1q21, essentially next to cathepsin S (GP Shi & C Mort, unpublished observations). This is the first pair of cysteine proteases found to be clustered in the genome and highlights the concept of gene duplication as the basic mechanism underlying the appearance of many cathepsins in mammals.

Expression of cathepsin K is both restricted and regulated. Although we identified cathepsin K in human lung macrophages by PCR, Northern blot analysis reveals little mRNA, and immunostaining of lung sections shows only weak immunoreactivity in nonsmokers (33). In contrast, cathepsin K is highly expressed in ovaries and osteoclasts (57). Retinoic acid is reported to induce transcription and protein accumulation in osteoclastic cell lines (58). Moreover, cathepsin K appears to be upregulated at sites of inflammation. Macrophages from cigarette smokers contain approximately twofold increase in mRNA and more protein than nonsmokers (GP Shi, unpublished observations). Normal human vascular smooth muscle cells contain no detectable cathepsin K by immunostaining, but cells within atherosclerotic plaques are clearly positive, as are macrophages (GP Shi & P Libby, unpublished observations). Hence, whereas tissue expression of cathepsin K is normally quite low outside bone, the enzyme has now been observed in several cell types within the context of inflammation.

Recent observations indicate that cathepsin K is the most potent mammalian elastase yet described (57). Table 2 provides a tentative placement of cathepsin K in the ranking of potency of known elastases (57, 59–64). Although cathepsin K is more potent than either cathepsin L or S, cathepsin K is not stable at neutral pH (unlike cathepsin S). Thus in relatively short assays of elastinolytic activity (<3 h), cathepsin K appears more potent than S at neutral pH, whereas in longer assays (18–24 h), cathepsin S is more potent. The pH instability of cathepsin K is consistent with its primary function as a lysosomal enzyme and as an enzyme secreted into an acidic milieu by osteoclasts (or other cells exhibiting osteoclast-like physiology). It should be noted that elastin is a model substrate for an extracellular matrix protein relatively resistant to proteases, and its degradation

**Table 2**  Approximate order of potency of known mammalian elastases[a]

| Enzyme | Rank | Reference |
|---|---|---|
| Cathepsin K | | |
| pH 5.5 | 10 | 57 |
| pH 7.4 | 6 | |
| Pancreatic elastase[b] | 8 | 57, 62, 63 |
| Cathepsin L | | |
| pH 5.5 | 5 | 59 |
| Cathepsin S[b] | | |
| pH 5.5 | 7 | 64 |
| pH 7.4 | 2.5 | |
| Leukocyte elastase | 3 | 62 |
| 72-kDa gelatinase | 2.5 | 60 |
| Matrilysin (PUMP) | 1.5 | 61 |
| Proteinase 3 | 1.5 | 63 |
| Macrophage metalloelastase | 1 | 60, 61 |
| 92-kDa gelatinase | 1 | 60 |

[a]The most potent enzyme, cathepsin K, was assigned a value of 10. Relative potencies of other enzymes were derived from a survey of published studies in which various mammalian elastases had been compared with pancreatic or neutrophil elastase. Studies examined are listed in the right-hand column. Unless otherwise stated, all enzymes were examined at their optimal pH. Potency may not correlate with in vivo potential because expression of potential also depends on enzyme activation, localization to elastin, and the abundance of specific protease inhibitors, among other factors.
[b]Although cathepsin K is a potent elastase even at neutral pH, the enzyme is not stable at neutral pH. Consequently in assays of elastin degradation longer than a few hours, both pancreatic elastase and cathepsin S are more potent enzymes.

identifies these cathepsins as potent endoproteases. As such, cathepsin K, as well as cathepsins S and L, is also a potent collagenase and gelatinase.

Expression of cathepsin K has recently been correlated with a degradative phenotype of macrophages (33, 65). Freshly explanted monocytic cells exhibit almost no cathepsin K mRNA. Within 2 to 3 days of in vitro culture in the presence of human serum, the levels of cathepsins B, L, and S increase in the cells, but the cells nonetheless do not degrade extracellular particulate elastin. However, beginning on days 9–11 of culture, the monocyte-derived macrophages begin to secrete large amounts of acid and acidic hydrolases, including cathepsins L and S, into the extracellular space and degrade large amounts of elastin (44). The process is stimulated rather than inhibited by the presence of serum. At this time, there is a marked induction of cathepsin K mRNA. Because there are several elastases being secreted at once, it is unclear which, if any , is predominantly mediating degradation. Nonetheless, these observations illustrate that under some conditions macrophages are quite capable of using cathepsins to degrade extracellular matrix protein, as had been previously postulated (4, 65), and that under these culture conditions, the appearance of cathepsin K correlates with the expression of this potential.

That cathepsin K (and by inference other cathepsins) is actually important to extracellular matrix remodeling has recently been verified by the identification of mutations in the coding sequence of cathepsin K in individuals with pycnodysostosis (66). Pyknodysostosis is an autosomal recessive disorder characterized by premature closure of long bone growth, facial hypoplasia (especially micrognathia), and brittle, dense long bones with osteosclerosis (67). Patients have fractures and the hallmark skeletal features of the disorder. Obstructive sleep apnea is also a clinical problem (68). Pycnodysostosis maps to chromosome 1q21 in several distinct family pedigrees (69, 70). Screening of cDNA and genomic DNA obtained by PCR from lymphoblastoid cells reveals distinct mutations in affected members of three separate families (66). One of the mutations transcribes a premature stop codon near the active site cysteine. A second large family with 16 affected members carries a mutation in the native stop codon that results in the predicted addition of 18 amino acids to the carboxy-terminal end, but in fact results in misfolded or mistargeted protein that is unstable and undetectable in cells expressing this mutant mRNA. The demonstration of altered bone formation and growth in individuals deficient in cathepsin K is the first direct demonstration of a critical role for cathepsins in extracellular matrix remodeling and provides a rationale for inhibition of cathepsin K in bone disorders such as osteoporosis.

There are several clinical situations in which the mobilization of cathepsin K or its closely related partners could be relevant. Large amounts of elastin are degraded rather quickly in the context of vascular inflammation, especially giant cell arteritis, leading to aneurysm formation. Immunostaining of both atherosclerotic plaques and sites of elastin degradation in giant cell aortitis reveal vivid immunostaining for cathepsins S and K in smooth muscle cells and giant cells, respectively (G Sukhova, unpublished observations). Because large amounts of elastin are degraded in these disorders, these proteases are good candidates for mediators of the process. This also may be true in other disorders associated with extensive elastin degradation such as lymphangiomyomatosis. Histologic studies indicate extensive lung elastin remodeling in the setting of lymphangiomyomatosis (71). In this disorder there is abnormal proliferation of smooth muscle cells and extensive matrix remodeling leading to emphysematous changes and airway obstruction. To date, the presence of cathepsin K or other potent elastases in smooth muscle cells from patients with this disorder has not been tested.

The elastolytic cathepsins (K, L, and S) may also be important to elastin destruction in the more common disorder of smokers' lung. Although the paradigm of protease inhibitor deficiency exemplified by alpha-1-antitrypsin deficiency is still attractive as an etiologic mechanism for emphysema (72), the proteases mainly involved in this process may have little to do with alpha-1-antitrypsin. In spite of thirty years of trying to fit smoking-related injury into a model of functional deficiency of alpha-1-antitrypsin as the sole cause of emphysema, this model remains much in doubt (73, 74). The recent demonstration of a longer time for inhibition of neutrophil elastase by alpha-1-antitrypsin obtained by bronchoalveolar lavage from cigarette smokers over that of nonsmokers (75) is of uncertain significance, as an even longer $t_{1/2}$ would be predicted in individuals with the MZ phenotype, and yet there is little or no increased risk for emphysema in this genotype. Instead, the list of proteases in the lung that could mediate emphysema independently of neutrophil elastase continues to grow (Table 2). The group of metalloenzymes, especially macrophage metalloelastase, along with the elastolytic cathepsins all have the potential to mediate elastin and other matrix protein destruction without impugning a deficiency of protease inhibitors. This is because these enzymes can be compartmentalized by macrophages to degrade matrix proteins with which they are in direct contact. Unfortunately, it remains unclear which if any of the potentially destructive proteases is actually important. This uncertainty may be resolved by molecular genetics. The generation of mice specifically deficient in a single protease would allow the direct test of whether the enzyme is necessary for lung injury in the context of smoking or other inflammatory disorders of the lung. Mice subjected to smoke inhalation for several weeks are reported to develop pathologic features of emphysema (76). Indeed, several protease genes, including both metalloenzymes and cathepsins, have now been disrupted in mice and are being studied in this context.

A second approach is to better delineate the genetics of human emphysema. Surprisingly, this may be made possible by the interest in lung transplantation for chronic obstructive lung disease (COPD). The referral of young people with end-stage emphysema to transplant centers has revealed numerous probands (age less than 50 years) with smoking-related severe emphysema and normal alpha-1-antitrypsin levels (77). The incidence of reduced lung function in their family members is much higher than that of the general population. Although emphysema in this setting is likely a complex trait, identification of genes that underlie early-onset disease may help elucidate the major pathways of destruction in this disorder. It would be surprising if this did not also reveal new information about susceptibility to tissue destruction in chronic inflammatory disorders involving other organs, e.g. arthritis.

The attempts to elucidate the role of cathepsin K and the other elastinolytic cathepsins in human disease is not without therapeutic importance. Several classes of nontoxic specific inhibitors of cysteine proteases are becoming available. What is critically missing is the elucidation of a biological role justifying their use. One example of the use of these types of inhibitors to delineate a specific function for a cathepsin is discussed below.

## *Cathepsin S*

Cathepsin S was originally identified as a distinct enzyme activity in lymph nodes and was found to be prominently expressed in and subsequently purified from spleen (25). The human orthologue of this enzyme was identified by DNA sequence homologies to cathepsins B and L and cloned in a human lung macrophage cDNA library (32). The full coding sequence was also obtained independently by Wiederanders from a cDNA library screen (34). Our original intent on isolating the human enzyme was to identify new elastolytic enzymes and, indeed, cathepsin S proved to be a potent elastase with substantial enzymatic activity and stability at neutral pH (Table 2). Moreover, this enzyme also exhibited restricted and regulated tissue expression and was found to be inducible by cytokines such as interferon-gamma and interleukin $1\beta$. In rats, cathepsin S is expressed in thyroid tissue and is inducible by thyroid-stimulating hormone, which suggests a possible specific role in intracellular thyroglobulin processing for the release of thyroid hormone (35). Cathepsin S is also highly expressed in the spleen and antigen-presenting cells, including B lymphocytes, macrophages, and dendritic cells (32, 78, 79). Because of its high expression in spleen (and lymph nodes) and inducibility by cytokines known to be involved in major histocompatibility complex (MHC) class II antigen expression, we explored the role of this enzyme in class II antigen presentation.

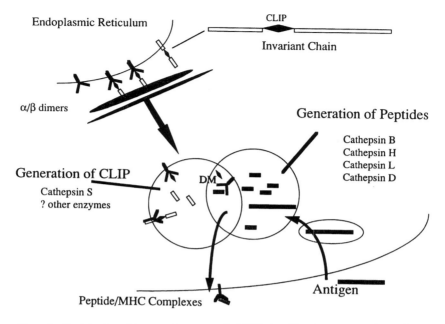

*Figure 2* Participation of lysosomal proteases in MHC class II antigen presentation pathway. Lysosomal proteases are essential for two steps: (*a*) the degradation of Ii to CLIP (residues 81–104 of Ii) to permit dissociation of CLIP from class II molecules and subsequent peptide binding; and (*b*) the generation of antigenic peptide fragments from larger polypeptide/protein moieties.

## MHC Class II Antigen Presentation and Cathepsin S

Lysosomal proteases play an essential role in the MHC class II antigen presentation pathway, as schematically reviewed in Figure 2. Proteases are involved in two critical steps: the degradation of the class II chaperone, the invariant chain (Ii), prior to its removal from the class II peptide binding cleft; and the generation of antigenic peptides (13–26 amino acids in length) capable of replacing the invariant chain in the peptide-binding grove of the class II molecules. Class II $\alpha\beta$ dimers associate with Ii in the endoplasmic reticulum to form nonamer complexes consisting of a scaffold of homotrimers associated with up to three class II $\alpha\beta$ dimers (80, 81). These complexes traverse the Golgi apparatus and are targeted to intracellular compartments where degradation of the Ii occurs, followed by binding of exogenous, antigenic peptides (82–86). Ii associates with class II molecules via direct interaction of residues 81–104 of its lumenal domain (87–90), designated CLIP (class II-associated invariant chain peptides), with the antigen-binding groove of class II (91). Most class II alleles require an additional class II-like molecule, HLA-DM, to liberate the peptide-binding groove of CLIP and to facilitate loading with antigenic peptide (92–94). The

$\alpha\beta$-peptide complexes formed by this pathway are then transported to the cell surface to initiate MHC class II-restricted T cell recognition (95).

Proteolysis of Ii from $\alpha\beta$-Ii complexes and formation of $\alpha\beta$-CLIP is required prior to class II peptide association because mature $\alpha\beta$-Ii heterodimers are unable to load peptides (96). Moreover, Roche & Cresswell (97) have demonstrated that proteolysis of Ii from $\alpha\beta$-Ii complexes promotes peptide binding in vitro. Of the known lysosomal proteases, cysteine proteases have been most clearly implicated in Ii proteolysis. Cysteine protease inhibition with leupeptin impairs Ii breakdown and results in accumulation of Ii fragments in B-lymphoblastoid cells (98–100). Also, lysosomotropic agents such as chloroquine (101) and concanamycin B (102) interrupt Ii proteolysis and cause accumulation of Ii fragments, presumably by neutralizing endosomal pH and disrupting protease activity. Accumulation of the Ii breakdown intermediates has been shown to impair peptide loading onto MHC class II molecules leading to diminished SDS-stable $\alpha\beta$-peptide complexes (103, 104), decreased MHC class II cell surface expression (103) and attenuation of antigen-stimulated T cell proliferation (105, 106).

Cathepsin S has recently been demonstrated to play an essential role in Ii protelolysis and peptide loading (107). Convincing evidence for participation of cathepsin S in Ii processing was provided by using a novel, specific cathepsin S inhibitor (morpholinurea-leucine-homophenylalanine-vinylsulfone-phenyl; LHVS). LHVS has an ≈67-fold increased activity toward cathepsin S over cathepsin L and ≈6000-fold increase over cathepsin B (108). Specific inhibition of cathepsin S with 1 nM and 5 nM LHVS in B lymphoblastoid (HOM2) cells results in accumulation of a class II-associated 13-kDa Ii fragment and a concomitant reduction in peptide loading of class II molecules, as evidenced by a marked decrease in formation of SDS-stable complexes migrating at ≈50 kDa (Figure 3, lanes 2, 3). This 50-kDa band represents class II molecules associated with antigenic peptides. The class II-peptide complex is stable in SDS at room temperature but not when boiled (Figure 3, compare lane 1 with lane 4). Inhibition of all cysteine proteases with the cysteine-class inhibitor 2S, 3S-*trans*-epoxysuccinyl-L-leucylamido-3-methylbutane ethyl ester (E64D) results in a buildup of a class II-associated 23-kDa Ii fragment with a decrease in SDS-stable dimer formation (Figure 3, lane 4). This suggests that cathepsin S acts on a relatively late Ii breakdown intermediate and is required for efficient proteolysis of Ii necessary for subsequent peptide loading. Furthermore, purified cathepsin S, but not cathepsin B, H, or D, specifically digests Ii from $\alpha\beta$-Ii trimers, generating $\alpha\beta$-CLIP complexes capable of binding exogenously added peptide in vitro (107). The finding that a single cysteine protease may be crucial for Ii proteolysis and subsequent class II-peptide binding reinforces the emerging view that lysosomal proteases may play specific roles in biologic systems.

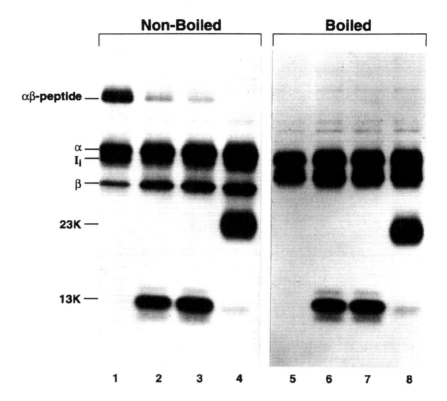

*Figure 3*  Specific inhibition of cathepsin S impairs class II-associated Ii proteolysis and peptide loading. HOM2 (B lymphoblastoid) cells were labeled with $^{35}$S-methionine/cysteine and chased for 5 h without inhibitor (lanes 1, 5), in the presence of 1 nM LHVS (lanes 2, 6); 5 nM LHVS (lanes 3, 7); and 20 $\mu$M E64D (lanes 4, 8). Class II-Ii complexes were immunoprecipitated from cell lysates with monoclonal antibody Tü36 and analyzed by 14% SDS-PAGE under mildly denaturing conditions (non-boiled, non-reduced) (lanes 1–4) and denaturing conditions (lanes 5–8).

Lysosomal proteases are also essential for generation of the antigenic peptides presented to T cells on the class II molecules (Figure 2). Proteins may enter the endocytic pathway by binding to membrane-bound immunoglobulin on B cells, or by pinocytosis primarily in dendritic cells and macrophages (109). Peptide processing of endocytosed antigens has been localized to dense compartments colocalizing with lysosomes (110) and low-density endosomal compartments distinct from the denser lysosomes (111). Once in the endocytic pathway, these proteins are broken down into peptides and loaded onto class II $\alpha\beta$ dimers. It is unclear whether free peptides are generated first followed by class II binding or whether class II molecules bind larger peptide/polypeptide fragments that are then digested to smaller peptide fragments while bound to class II molecules. The carboxypeptidase and aminopeptidase activities of cathepsins B and H, respectively, could be functionally important at this point. In this way the class II binding groove may act as a protective pocket preventing terminal proteolysis of presented peptides.

Both cysteine class and aspartyl class proteases have been implicated in generation of antigenic epitopes. The ability of the cysteine protease inhibitor, leupeptin, to alter ovalbumin and tetanus toxin processing appears to be epitope dependent (112, 113). In vitro digestion of ovalbumin by the aspartyl protease cathepsin D, but not by the cysteine protease cathepsin B, generated peptides capable of stimulating T cells in association with class II molecules (114). Cathepsin D from bovine alveolar macrophages also produces epitopes capable of binding to class II molecules, which suggests a structural relationship between the antigenic motif generated by cathepsin D digestion and the antigenic structure recognized by MHC class II molecules (115). A specific inhibitor of the nonlysosomal aspartyl protease, cathepsin E, inhibited the processing of ovalbumin in a murine antigen-presenting cell line (116). These data suggest that several enzymes from the cysteine and aspartyl protease classes may be important in generating suitable peptide epitopes for presentation by class II molecules, dependent on epitope structure and mode of entry into the secretory pathway.

In summary, lysosomal protease involvement is required for Ii degradation so that efficient class II-Ii dissociation and peptide loading may occur and for generation of the antigenic peptides presented on the class II $\alpha\beta$ dimers. Cysteine proteases, and specifically cathepsin S, appear to mediate Ii processing, whereas several cysteine and aspartyl proteases may participate in antigenic peptide generation.

Antigen presentation is an important function of the lung. Recent studies indicate a network of dendritic cells within the epithelium of lung airways that are repeatedly exposed to antigenic agents (117, 118). The surprising finding that a single cysteine protease is essential in antigen presentation raises the possibility that targeted inhibition of this enzyme may be beneficial in settings in which exaggerated immune responses to exogenous antigens mediate disease: transplantation, asthma, hypersensitivity pneumonitis, and potentially autoimmune disorders.

## Role for Cathepsin S in Cilial Function?

Immunostaining of normal human lung with cathepsin S antibodies also suggests an additional previously unsuspected role for this enzyme in lung biology. As illustrated in Figure 4, monospecific antibodies to cathepsin S vividly stain the cilia of conducting airway cells for cathepsin S antigen (*Panel A*). In contrast

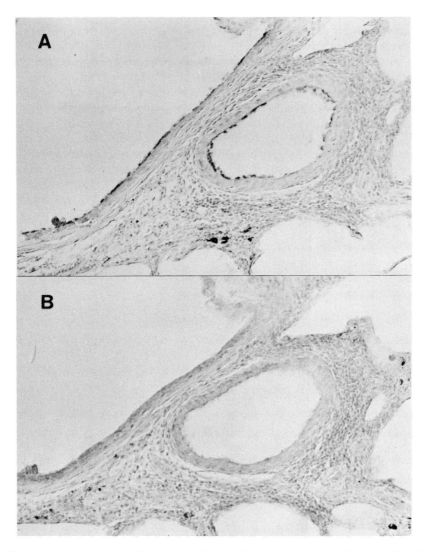

*Figure 4*   Immunostaining of human lung airways with antiserum against cathepsin S (*A*) and cathepsin K (*B*).

neither cathepsin S antibodies adsorbed with antigen (not shown) nor monospecific antibodies to cathepsin K stain these structures (*Panel B*). This result raises the intriguing possibility that because of its stability at neutral pH and potential for broad endoprotease activity, ciliated cells have captured the enzyme onto their surfaces to promote motility of their cilia. Indeed, airway inflammation is known to produce dysfunctional ciliary motion. One could envision that plasma-derived proteins, in the setting of inflammation, could bind and impair cilial motility and that cathepsin S would be protective. If so, this would represent another example of the importance of protease activity, even of nonspecific endoproteases, to normal lung function. Thus far no functional studies have been performed to test this hypothesis.

## FUTURE DIRECTIONS

Remarkable advances in the last twenty years in understanding the catalytic mechanism and fine structural features of proteases and their inhibitors have had important implications for medicine. The detailed view of the active site pockets of numerous proteases now available makes the rational design of protease inhibitors feasible. Indeed, the limiting step in the use of novel protease inhibitors in medicine is not so much the discovery of an effective inhibitor but elucidation of the exact physiological role of the protease in the biology of the cell and the intact organism. Where successfully understood and applied, both proteases and protease inhibitors have proven to be therapeutically useful. Angiotensin-converting-enzyme inhibitors and, more recently, HIV protease inhibitors, as well as the proteases urokinase and tissue plasminogen activator, are good examples of merging molecular and cell biology for therapeutic advance. In this regard, the identification of new cysteine proteases and their inhibitors in the last five years alone poses a big challenge for cell biology. In this review, we have summarized recent advances in understanding the role of cysteine proteases in both the physiology of the lung as well as in other organ systems. The field is energized by these findings; yet much of what is presented is new and the importance too early to judge. Still, there is promise that the continued elucidation of specific physiological functions for cysteine proteases will presage new therapeutic tools.

ACKNOWLEDGMENTS

Work in the investigators' laboratory (HAC) was supported by National Institutes of Health grant HL48261. The authors thank D Bromme, GA Silverman, G Sukhova, and P Libby for communicating results prior to publication.

*Literature Cited*

1. Neurath H, Walsh KA. 1976. Role of proteolytic enzymes in biological regulation. *Proc. Natl. Acad. Sci. USA* 73:3825–32
2. Polgar L. 1989. General aspects of proteases. In *Mechanisms of Protease Action*, ed. L Polar, pp. 43–76. Boca Ratan, FL: CRC Press
3. Gross P, Babyak MA, Tolker E, Kaschak M. 1964. Enzymatically produced pulmonary emphysema: a preliminary report. *J. Occup. Med.* 6:481
4. Chapman HA, Stone OL, Vavrin Z. 1984. Degradation of fibrin and elastin by human alveolar macrophages in vitro. Characterization of a plasminogen activator and its role in matrix degradation. *J. Clin. Invest.* 73:806–15
5. Chapman HA Jr, Stahl M, Fair DS, Allen CL. 1988. Regulation of the procoagulant activity within the alveolar compartment of normal human lung. *Am. Rev. Resp. Dis.* 37:1417–25
6. Nadel JA. 1991. Neutral endopeptidase modulates neurogenic inflammation. *Eur. Resp. J.* 4:745–54
7. Polgar L, ed. 1989. Metalloproteases. In *Mechanisms of Protease Action*, pp. 208–210. Boca Ratan, FL: CRC Press
8. Menard R, Storer A. 1992. Oxyanion hole interactions in serine and cysteine proteases. *Hoppe-Seyler's Z. Biol. Chem.* 373:393–400
9. Matthews BW, Sigler PB, Henderson R, Blow DM. 1967. Three-dimensional structure of tosyl-α-chymotrypsin. *Nature* 214:652–56
10. Varughese KL, Ahmed FR, Careys PR, Hasnain S, Huber CP, Storer AC. 1989. Crystal structure of papain-E-64 complex. *Biochemistry* 28:1330–32
11. Mason RW, Wilcox D. 1993. Chemistry of lysosomal cysteine proteases. *Adv. Cell Mol. Biol. Membr.* 1:81–116
12. Berti PJ, Storer AC. 1995. Alignment/phylogeny of the papain superfamily of cysteine proteases. *J. Mol Biol.* 246:273–83
13. Thornberry N, Bull HG, Calaycay JR, Chapman KT, Howard AD, et al. 1992. A novel heterodimeric cysteine protease is required for inteleukin-1 beta processing in monocytes. *Nature* 356:768–74
14. Henkart PA. 1996. ICE family proteases: mediators of all apoptotic cell death? *Immunity* 4:194–201
15. Saido TC, Sorimachi H, Suzuki K. 1994. Calpain: new perspectives in molecular diversity and physiological-pathological involvement. *FASEB J.* 8:814–22
16. Croall DE, DeMartino GN. 1991. Calcium-activated neutral protease (calpain) system: structure, function, and regulation. *Physiol. Rev.* 71:813–47
17. Du X, Saido TC, Tsubuki S, Indig FE, Wiklliams MJ, Ginsberg MH. 1995. Calpain cleavage of the cytoplasmic domain of the integrin beta 3 subunit. *J. Biol. Chem.* 270:26146–51
18. Sorimachi H, Saido TC, Suzuki K. 1994. New era of calpain research. Discovery of tissue-specific calpains. *FEBS Lett.* 343:1–5
19. Richard I, Broux O, Allamand V, Fougerousse F, Chiannilkulchai N, et al. 1995. Mutations in the proteolytic enzyme calpain 3 cause limb-girdle muscular dystrophy type 2A. *Cell* 81:27–40
20. Sebti SM, Mignano JE, Jani JP, Srimatkandada S, Lazo JS. 1989. Bleomycin hydrolase: molecular cloning, sequencing, and biochemical studies reveal membership in the cysteine proteinase family. *Biochemistry* 28: 6544–48
21. Sebti SM, DeLeon JC, Lazo JS. 1987. Purification, characterization, and amino acid composition of rabbit pulmonary bleomycin hydrolase. *Biochemistry* 26: 4213–19
22. Lazo JS, Boland CJ, Schwartz PE. 1982. Bleomycin hydrolase activity and cytotoxicity in human tumors. *Cancer Res.* 42:4026–31
23. Joshua-Tor L, Xu HE, Johnston SA, Rees DC. 1995. Crystal structure of a conserved protease that binds DNA: the bleomycin hydrolase, Gal6. *Science* 269:945–50
24. Musil D, Zucic D, Turk D, Engh RA, Mayr L, et al. 1991. The refined 2.15 AA X-ray crystal structure of human liver cathepsin B: the structural basis for its specificity. *EMBO J.* 10:2321–30
25. Kirschke H, Weideranders B, Bromme D, Rinne A. 1989. Cathepsin from bovine spleen. Purification, distribution, intracellular localization and action on proteins. *Biochem. J.* 264:467–73
26. Fuchs R, Gassen HG. 1989. Nucleotide sequence of human preprocathepsin H, a lysosomal cysteine proteinase. *Nucleic Acids Res.* 17:9471
27. Joseph LJ, Chang LC, Stemenkovich D, Sukhatme VP. 1988. Complete nucleotide and deduced amino acid sequence of hu-

man and murine preprocathepsin L. *J. Clin. Invest.* 81:1621–29

28. Chan SJ, Segundo BS, McCormick MB, Steiner DF. 1986. Nucleotide and predicted amino acid sequence of cloned human and mouse preprocathepsin B cDNAs. *Proc. Natl. Acad. Sci. USA* 83:7721–28

29. Fong D, Calhoun DH, Hsieh W-T, Lee B, Wells RD. 1986. Isolation of a cDNA clone for the human lysosomal proteinase cathepsin B. *Proc. Natl. Acad. Sci. USA* 83:2909–13

30. Barrett AJ, Kirschke H. 1981. Cathepsins B, H, and L. *Meth. Enzymol.* 80:535–61

31. Shaw E, Dean RT. 1980. The inhibition of macrophage protein turnover by a selective inhibitor of thiol proteases. *Biochem. J.* 186:385–90

32. Shi GP, Munger JS, Meara JP, Rich DH, Chapman HA. 1992. Molecular cloning and expression of human alveolar macrophage cathepsin S, an elastinolytic cysteine protease. *J. Biol. Chem.* 267:7258–62

33. Shi GP, Chapman HA, Bhairi SM, DeLeeuw C, Reddy VY, Weiss SJ. 1995. Molecular cloning of human cathepsin O, a novel endoproteinase and homologue of rabbit OC-2. *FEBS Lett.* 357:129–34

34. Wiederanders B, Bromme D, Kirschke H, Kalkkiner N, Rinne A, et al. 1991. Primary structure of bovine cathepsin S. Comparison to cathepsins L, H, and B. *FEBS Lett.* 286:189–92

35. Petanceska S, Devi L. 1992. Sequence analysis, tissue distribution, and expression of rat cathepsin S. *J. Biol. Chem.* 267:26038–43

36. Velasco G, Ferrando AA, Puente XS, Sanchez LM, Lopez-otin C. 1994. Human cathepsin O. Molecular cloning from a breast carcinoma, production of the active enzyme in *Escherichia coli,* and expression analysis in human tissues. *J. Biol. Chem.* 269:27136–42

37. McGuire MJ, Lipsky PE, Thiele DL. 1992. Purification and characterization of dipeptidyl peptidase I from human spleen. *Arch. Biochem. Biophys.* 295:280–88

38. Dikov MM, Springman EB, Yeola S, Serafin WE. 1994. Processing of procarboxypeptidase A and other zymogens in murine mast cells. *J. Biol. Chem.* 269:25897–904

39. Vernet T, Berti PJ, de Montigny C, Musil R, Tessier DC, et al. 1995. Processing of the papain precursor. The ionization state of a conserved amino acid motif within the pro region participates in the regula-

tion of the intramolecular processing. *J. Biol. Chem.* 270:10838–46

40. Fox T, de Miguel E, Mort JS, Storer AC. 1992. Potent slow-binding inhibition of cathepsin B by its propeptide. *Biochemistry* 31:12571–76

40a. Tao K, Stearns NA, Dong J, Wu QL, Sahagian GG. 1994. The pro region of cathepsin L is required for proper folding, stability, and ER exit. *Arch. Biochem. Biophys.* 311:19–27

41. Baudys M, Meloun T, Gan-Erdene T, Fusek M, Mares M, et al. 1991. S-S bridges of cathepsin B and H from bovine spleen: a basis for cathepsin B model building and possible functional implications for discrimination between exo- and endopeptidase activities among cathepsins B, H and L. *Biomed. Biochim. Acta* 50:569–77

42. Vernet T, Tessier DC, Chatellier J, Plouffe C, Lee TS, et al. 1995. Structural and functional roles of asparagine 175 in the cysteine protease papain. *J. Biol. Chem.* 270:16645–52

43. Pisoni RL, Acker TL, Lisowski KM, Lemons RM, Theone JG. 1990. A cysteine-specific lysosomal transport system provides a major route for the delivery of thiol to human fibroblast lysosomes: possible role in supporting lysosomal proteolysis. *J. Cell Biol.* 110: 327–35

44. Reddy VY, Zhang Q-Y, Weiss SJ. 1995. Pericellular mobilization of the tissue-destructive cysteine proteases, cathepsins B, L, and S, by human macrophages. *Proc. Natl. Acad. Sci. USA* 92:3849–53

45. Baron R, Neff L, Louvard D, Courtoy PJ. 1985. Cell mediated extracellular acidification and bone resorption: evidence to a low pH in resorbing lacunae and localization of a 100 kD lysosomal membrane protein at the osteoclast ruffled border. *J. Cell Biol.* 101:2210–28

46. Baron R. 1989. Molecular mechanisms of bone resorption by the osteoclast. *Anat. Rec.* 224:2317–429

47. Dalaisse JM, Eeckhout Y, Vaes G. 1980. Inhibition of bone resorption in culture by inhibitors of thiol proteinases. *Biochem. J.* 192:365–68

48. Barrett AJ. 1987. The cystatins: a new class of peptidase inhibitors. *Trends Biochem. Sci.* 12:193–96

49. Lindahl P, Ripoll D, Abrahamson M, Mort JS, Storer AC. 1994. Evidence for the interaction of valine-10 in cystatin C with the S₂ subsite of cathepsin B. *Biochemistry* 33:4384–92

50. Penacchio LA, Lehesjoki AE, Stone NE, Willour VL, Virtaneva K, et al. 1996. Mu-

tations in the gene encoding cystatin B in progressive myoclonus epilepsy (EPM1). *Science* 271:1731–34

51. Ray CA, Black RA, Kronheim SR, Greenstreet TA, Sleath PR, et al. 1992. Viral inhibition of inflammation: cowpox virus encodes an inhibitor of the interleukin-1 beta converting enzyme. *Cell* 69:597–604

52. Suminami Y, Kishi F, Sekiguchi K, Kato H. 1991. Squamous cell carcinoma antigen is a new member of the serine protease inhibitors. *Biochem. Biophys. Res. Commun.* 181:51–58

53. Takeda A, Yamamoto T, Nakamura Y, Takahashi T, Hibino T. 1995. Squamous cell carcinoma antigen is a potent inhibitor of cysteine proteinase cathepsin L. *FEBS Lett.* 359:78–80

53a. Schneider SS, Schick C, Fish KE, Miller E, Pena JG, et al. 1995. A serine proteinase inhibitor locus at 18q21.3 contains a tandem duplication of the human squamous cell carcinoma antigen gene. *Proc. Natl. Acad. Sci. USA* 92:3147–51

54. Chapman HA, Munger JS, Shi GP. 1994. Role of thiol proteases in tissue injury. *Am. J. Resp. Crit. Care Med.* 150:S155–59

55. Tezuka K, Tezuka Y, Maejima A, Sato T, Nemoto K, et al. 1994. Molecular cloning of a possible cysteine proteinase predominantly expressed in osteoclasts. *J. Biol. Chem.* 269:1106–9

56. Inaoka T, Bilbe G, Ishibashi O, Tezuka K, Kumegawa M, et al. 1995. Molecular cloning of human cDNA for cathepsin K: novel cysteine proteinase predominantly expressed in bone. *Biochem. Biophys. Res. Commun.* 206:89–96

57. Bromme D, Okamoto K, Wang BB, Biroc S. 1996. Human cathepsin O2, a matrix protein-degrading cysteine protease expressed in osteoclasts. *J. Biol. Chem.* 271:2126–32

58. Saneshige S, Mano H, Tezuka K, Kakudo S, Mori Y, et al. 1995. Retinoic acid directly stimulates osteoclastic bone resorption and gene expression of cathepsin K/OC-2. *Biochem. J.* 309:721–24

59. Mason RW, Johnson D, Barret AJ, Chapman HA Jr. 1986. Elastolytic activity of human cathepsin L. *Biochem. J.* 122:925–27

60. Senior RM, Griffin GL, Fliszar CJ, Shapiro SD, Goldberg GI, Welgus HG. 1991. Human 92 kDA and 72 kDA Type IV collagenases are elastases. *J. Biol. Chem.* 266:7870–75

61. Murphy G, Cockett ML, Ward RV, Docherty AJP. 1991. Matrix metalloproteinase degradation of elastin, type IV collagen, and proteoglycan. *Biochem. J.* 277:277–79

62. Baugh RJ, Travis J. 1976. Human leukocyte granule elastase: rapid isolation and characterization. *Biochemistry* 15:836–41

63. Kao RC, Wehmer NG, Skubitz KM, Gray BH, Hoidal JR. 1988. Proteinase 3. A distinct human polymorphonuclear leukocyte proteinase that produced emphysema in hamsters. *J. Clin. Invest.* 82:1963–73

64. Xin XQ, Gunesekera B, Mason RW. 1992. The specificity and elastinolytic activities of bovine cathepsins S and H. *Arch. Biochem. Biophys.* 299:334–39

65. Chapman HA, Stone OL. 1984. Comparison of live human neutrophil and alveolar macrophage elastolytic activity in vitro: relative resistance of macrophage elastolytic activity to serum and alveolar protease inhibitors. *J. Clin. Invest.* 74:1693–700

66. Gelb B, Shi GP, Chapman HA, Desnick RJ. 1996. Pycnodysostosis is caused by a deficiency of cathepsin K. *Science.* 273:1236–38

67. Edelson JG, Obad S, Geiger R, On A, Artul HJ. 1992. Pycnodysostosis. Orthopedic aspects with a description of 14 new cases. *Clin. Orth.* 280:263–76

68. Aronson DC, Heymans HS, Bijlmer RP. 1984. Cor pulmonale and acute liver necrosis, due to upper airway obstruction as part of pycnodysostosis. *Eur. J. Pediatr.* 141:251–53

69. Gelb BD, Edelson JG, Desnick RJ. 1995. Linkage of pycnodysostosis to chromosome 1q21 by homozygosity mapping. *Nat. Genet.* 10:235–37

70. Polymeropoulos MH, Ortiz De Luna RI, Ide SE, Torres R, et al. 1995. The gene for pycnodysostosis maps to human chromosome 1cen-q21. *Nat. Genet.* 10:238–39

71. Fukuda Y, Kawamoto M, Yamamoto A, Ishizaki M, Basset F, Masugi Y. 1990. Role of elastic fiber degradation in emphysema-like lesions of pulmonary lymphangiomyomatosis. *Hum. Pathol.* 21:1252–61

72. Janoff A. 1985. Elastases and emphysema. Current assessment of the protease-antiprotease hypothesis. *Am. Rev. Resp. Dis.* 132:417–33

73. Tetley TD. 1993. New perspectives on basic mechanisms in lung disease. 6. Proteinase imbalance: its role in lung disease. *Thorax* 48:560–65

74. Snider GL. 1992. Emphysema: the first two centuries—and beyond. A historical overview, with suggestions for future

research: Part 2. *Am. Rev. Resp. Dis.* 146:1615–22

75. Ogushi F, Hubbard RC, Vogelmeier C, Fells GA, Crystal RG. 1991. Risk factors for emphysema. Cigarette smoking is associated with a reduction in the association rate constant of lung alpha-1-antitrypsin for neutrophil elastase. *J. Clin. Invest.* 87:1060–65

76. Belaaouaj A, Shapiro SD. 1996. Identification of differentially expressed genes in lungs of mice following exposure to cigarette smoke. *Resp. Crit. Care Med.* 153:A30 (Abstr.)

77. Silverman P, Chapman H, Drazen J, O'Donnell W, Reilly J, et al. 1996. Early-onset chronic obstructive pulmonary disease (COPD): preliminary evidence for genetic factors other than PI type. *Resp. Crit. Care Med.* 153:A48 (Abstr.)

78. Shi GP, Webb AC, Foster KE, Knoll JHM, Lemere CA, et al. 1994. Human cathepsin S: chromosomal localization, gene structure, and tissue distribution. *J. Biol. Chem.* 269:11530–36

79. Morton PA, Zacheis ML, Giacoletto KS, Manning JA, Schwartz BD. 1995. Delivery of nascent MHC class II-invariant chain complexes to lysosomal compartments and proteolysis of invariant chain by cysteine proteases precedes peptide binding in B-lymphoblastoid cells. *J. Immunol.* 154:137–50

80. Roche PA, Marks MS, Cresswell P. 1991. Formation of a nine-subunit complex by HLA class II glycoproteins and the invariant chain. *Nature* 354:392–394

81. Lamb C, Cresswell P. 1992. Assembly and transport properties of invariant chain trimers and HLA-DR-invariant chain complexes. *J. Immunol.* 148:3478–82

82. Guagliardi LE, Koppelman B, Blum JS, Marks MS, Cresswell P, Brodsky FM. 1990. Co-localization of molecules involved in antigen processing and presentation in an early endocytic compartment. *Nature* 343:133–39

83. Peters PJ, Neefjes JJ, Oorschot V, Ploegh HL, Geuze HJ. 1991. Segregation of MHC class II molecules from MHC class I molecules in the Golgi complex for transport to lysosomal compartments. *Nature* 349:669–75

84. Amigorena S, Drake JR, Webster P, Mellman I. 1994. Transient accumulation of new class II MHC molecules in a novel endocytic compartment in B lymphocytes. *Nature* 349:113–20

85. Tulp A, Verwoerd D, Dobberstein B, Ploegh HL, Peters J. 1994. Isolation and characterization of the intracellular MHC class II compartment. *Nature* 349:120–26

86. West MA, Lucocq JM, Watts C. 1994. Antigen processing and class II MHC peptide-loading compartments in human B-lymphoblastoid cells. *Nature* 369:147–51

87. Bijlmakers M-JE, Benaroch P, Ploegh HL. 1994. Mapping functional regions in the lumenal domain of the class II-associated invariant chain. *J. Exp. Med.* 180:623–29

88. Rudensky AY, Preston-Hurlburt P, Hong SC, Barlow A, Janeway CA Jr. 1991. Sequence analysis of peptides bound to MHC class II molecules. *Nature* 353:622–27

89. Riberdy JM, Newcomb JR, Surman MJ, Barbosa JA, Cresswell P. 1992. HLA-DR molecules from an antigen-processing mutant cell line are associated with invariant chain peptides. *Nature* 360:474–76

90. Chicz RM, Urban RG, Lane WS, Gorga JC, Stern LJ, et al. 1992. Predominant naturally processed peptides bound to HLA-DR1 are derived from MHC-related molecules and are heterogeneous in size. *Nature* 358:764–68

91. Ghosh P, Amaya M, Merlins E, Wiley DC. 1995. The structure of an intermediate in class II maturation: CLIP bound to HLA-DR3. *Nature* 378:457–62

92. Denzin LK, Cresswell P. 1995. HLA-DM induces CLIP dissociation from MHC class II alpha beta dimers. *Cell* 82:155–65

93. Sherman MA, Weber DA, Jenson PE. 1995. DM enhances peptide binding to class II MHC by release of invariant chain-derived peptide. *Immunity* 3:197–205

94. Sloan VS, Cameron P, Porter G, Gammon M, Amaya M, et al. 1995. Mediation by HLA-DM of dissociation of peptides from HLA-DR. *Nature* 375:802–6

95. Cresswell P. 1994. Assembly, transport, and function of MHC class II molecules. *Annu. Rev. Immunol.* 12:259–93

96. Roche PA, Cresswell P. 1990. Invariant chain association with HLA-DR molecules inhibits immunogenic peptide binding. *Nature* 345:615–18

97. Roche PA, Cresswell P. 1991. Proteolysis of the class II-associated invariant chain generates a peptide binding site in intracellular HLA-DR molecules. *Proc. Natl. Acad. Sci. USA* 88:3150–54

98. Blum JS, Cresswell P. 1988. Role for intracellular proteases in the processing and transport of class II HLA antigens. *Proc. Natl. Acad. Sci. USA* 85:3975–79

99. Nguyen QV, Knapp W, Humphreys RE. 1988. Inhibition by leupeptin and antipain of the intracellular proteolysis of Ii. *Hum. Immunol.* 24:153–63

100. Nguyen QV, Humphreys RE. 1989. Time course of intracellular associations, processing, and cleavages of Ii forms and class II major histocompatibility complex molecules. *J. Biol. Chem.* 264:1631–37

101. Humbert M, Bertolino P, Forquet F, Rabourdine-Comb C, Gerlier D, et al. 1993. Major histocompatibility complex class II-restricted presentation of secreted and endoplasmic reticulum resident antigens requires the invariant chains and is sensitive to lysosomotropic agents. *Eur. J. Immunol.* 23:3167–72

102. Benaroch P, Mamadi Y, Raposo G, Ito K, Miwa K, et al. 1995. How MHC class II molecules reach the endocytic pathway. *EMBO J.* 14:37–49

103. Neefjes JJ, Ploegh HL. 1992 Inhibition of endosomal proteolytic activity by leupeptin blocks surface expression of MHC class II molecules and their conversion to SDS resistant $\alpha\beta$ heterodimers in endosomes. *EMBO J.* 11:411–16

104. Demotz S, Danieli C, Wallny H-J, Majdic O. 1994. Inhibition of peptide binding to DR molecules by a leupeptin-induced invariant chain fragment. *Mol. Immunol.* 31:885–93

105. Buus S, Werdelin O. 1986. A group-specific inhibitor of lysosomal cysteine proteinases selectively inhibits both proteolytic degradation and presentation of the antigen dinitrophenyl-poly-L-lysine by guinea pig accessory cells to T cells. *J. Immunol.* 136:452–58

106. Diment S. 1990. Different roles for thiol and aspartyl proteases in antigen presentation of ovalbumin. *J. Immunol.* 145:417–22

107. Riese RJ, Wolf PR, Bromme D, Natkin LR, Villadangos JA, et al. 1996. Essential role for cathepsin S in MHC class II-associated invariant chain processing and peptide loading. *Immunity* 4:357–65

108. Palmer JT, Rasnick D, Klaus JL, Bromme D. 1995. Vinyl sulfones as mechanism-based cysteine protease inhibitors. *J. Med. Chem.* 38:3193–96

109. Lanzavecchia A. 1990. Receptor-mediated antigen uptake and its effect on antigen presentation to class II-restricted T lymphocytes. *Annu. Rev. Immunol.* 8:773–93

110. Qiu Y, Xu X, Wandinger-Ness A, Dalke DP, Pierce SK. 1994. Separation of subcellular compartments containing functional forms of MHC class II. *J. Cell Biol.* 119:531–42

111. Barnes KA, Mitchell RN. 1995. Detection of functional class II-associated antigen: role of a low density endosomal compartment in antigen processing. *J. Exp. Med.* 181:1715–27

112. Vidard L, Rock KL, Benacerraf B. 1991. The generation of immunogenic peptides can be selectively increased or decreased by proteolytic enzyme inhibitors. *J. Immunol.* 147:1786–91

113. Demotz S, Matricardi PM, Irle C, Panina P, Lanzavecchia A, Corradin G. 1989. Processing of tetanus toxin by human antigen-presenting cells. Evidence for donor and epitope-specific processing pathways. *J. Immunol.* 143:3881–86

114. Rodriguez GM, Diment S. 1992. Role of cathepsin D in antigen presentation of ovalbumin. *J. Immunol.* 149:2884–98

115. van Noort JM, Boon J, van der Drift ACM, Wagenaar JPA, Boots AMH, Boog CJP. 1991. Antigen processing by endosomal proteases determines which sites of sperm-whale myoglobin are eventually recognized by T cells. *Eur. J. Immunol.* 21:1989–96

116. Bennett K, Levine T, Ellis JS, Peanasky RJ, Samloff IM, et al. 1992. Antigen processing for presentation by class II major histocompatibility complex requires cleavage by cathepsin E. *Eur. J. Immunol.* 22:1519–24

117. Heft PG, Heining S, Nelson DJ, Sedgwick JD. 1994. Origin and steady-state turnover of class II MHC-bearing dendritic cells in the epithelium of conducting airways. *J. Immunol.* 153:256–61

118. Holt PG. 1993. Regulation of antigen-presenting cell function(s) in lung and airway tissues. *Eur. Res. J.* 6:120–29

*Annu. Rev. Physiol. 1997. 59:89–144*

# CELLULAR AND MOLECULAR MECHANISMS OF PULMONARY VASCULAR REMODELING

## K. R. Stenmark

University of Colorado Health Sciences Center, Developmental Lung Biology
Laboratory, Denver, Colorado 80262

## R. P. Mecham

Department of Cellular Biology, Washington University School of Medicine, St.
Louis, Missouri 63110

KEY WORDS:  pulmonary hypertension, lung development, vascular development, vascular
injury, smooth muscle cells, fibroblasts, endothelial cells

## ABSTRACT

In many organs and tissues, the cellular response to injury is associated with
a reiteration of specific developmental processes. Studies have shown that, in
response to injury, vascular wall cells in adult organisms express genes or gene
products characteristic of earlier developmental states. Other genes, expressed
preferentially in adult cells in vivo, are down-regulated following injurious stimuli. Complicating matters, however, are recent observations demonstrating that
the vascular wall is comprised of phenotypically heterogeneous subpopulations of
endothelial cells, smooth muscle cells, and fibroblasts. It is unclear how specific
subsets of cells respond to injury and thus contribute to the vascular remodeling
that characterizes chronic pulmonary hypertension. This review discusses vascular development in the lung and the cellular responses occurring in pulmonary
hypertension; special attention is given to heterogeneity of responses within cell
populations and reiteration of developmental processes.

## INTRODUCTION

In several adult tissues (e.g. liver and heart), the cellular response to injury is
associated with a reiteration of specific developmental processes. This seems to
be true for the vasculature as well. Studies have shown that adult smooth muscle cells (SMCs) responding to injury express genes or gene products (such as

89

0066-4278/97/0315-0089$08.00

tropoelastin, fibronectin, tenascin, F31/H19, cytokeratin 8, and extra domain-A fibronectin) characteristic of earlier developmental states (76, 90, 101, 113, 134, 141). In addition, genes such as smooth muscle-specific $\alpha$-actin, tropomyosin, desmin, and myosin, which are expressed preferentially in adult cells in vivo, are down-regulated when adult cells are stimulated to migrate and divide following injurious stimuli (116, 117). Similar though less extensive reports exist regarding re-expression of developmentally regulated genes by endothelial cells and fibroblasts in response to injury. Complicating matters, however, are recent observations demonstrating that the vascular media is comprised of phenotypically heterogeneous subpopulations of SMCs. It is unclear if all adult medial SMC subpopulations are capable of responding to injury with changes in gene expression and replicative potential, or if the post-injury response is limited to specific subsets of cells within the vessel wall (222). The goal of this review is thus twofold: (a) to discuss vascular development in the lung, especially the mechanisms that control growth and differentiation (in an effort to lay the groundwork for understanding the cellular responses and the mechanisms that control them in the setting of pulmonary vascular injury) and (b) to discuss the cellular changes that occur in various forms of pulmonary hypertension, with special attention to heterogeneity of responses within cell populations and reiteration of developmental processes (Figure 1).

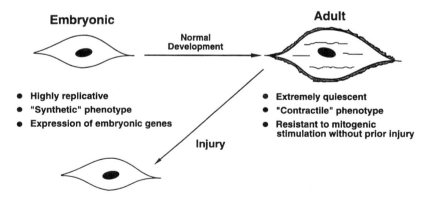

*Figure 1*  Conceptual figure demonstrating the dramatic changes that occur in SMC phenotype during development. In response to injury, a reiteration of specific developmental processes is observed. SMCs responding to injury express genes or gene products characteristic of earlier developmental states.

# DEVELOPMENT OF THE PULMONARY VASCULATURE

The lung is a highly complex organ comprised of more than 40 different cell types (38) that are involved in both respiratory and nonrespiratory functions. Despite its eventual complexity of structure and function, the lung has ostensibly simple beginnings. The lung epithelium originates as paired outpocketings from the floor of the pharyngeal endoderm that expand into mesenchyme derived from splanchnic mesoderm. The epithelial rudiments subsequently undergo a series of repetitive branchings to give rise to the pulmonary tree. Much effort has been directed at defining the mechanisms that regulate normal epithelial pattern formation (termed branching morphogenesis), but much less is known about how the pulmonary vasculature is formed. The development and maintenance of normal vascular structure clearly plays a critical role in lung function, yet several major questions about the regulation of this process in the normal and diseased lung remain unanswered.

## Endothelial Cell Replication and Vasculogenesis in the Developing Lung

In the embryonic lung, endothelial precursor cells (angioblasts) initially form a primary vascular plexus within the tissue, which eventually links up to the main circulation, of sixth branchial arch origin, coming from the heart. Studies using intracoelomic chimeric recombinations between quail and chick embryonic lungs have demonstrated that the endoderm seems to control lung vasculogenesis by inducing the emergence of endothelial cells in its associated mesoderm (184). Furthermore, tissue mixing experiments also suggest that vessel formation in the lung, like branching morphogenesis, may depend on the interaction between epithelium and mesenchyme (129, 143, 212). Thus a true reciprocity would exist in which epithelial proliferation and differentiation are induced by an as-yet-unidentified mesenchymal cell population. The induced epithelium (or a subpopulation of cells thereof) in turn produces factors that stimulate endothelial cell proliferation and organization. The endothelium itself may then produce factors to recruit other mesenchymal cells (e.g. SMC precursors) necessary for the completion of vessel structure.

Specific growth factors found in the developing lung, including acidic fibroblast growth factor (aFGF), basic fibroblast growth factor (bFGF), and platelet-derived endothelial cell growth factor (PD-ECGF), regulate endothelial cell proliferation in vivo and in vitro (81, 84, 99, 216). Another candidate molecule likely to play a major role in lung vascular development is vascular endothelial growth factor (VEGF), a member of the PDGF family that is identical to vascular permeability factor (157) and vasculotropin (190). It is abundant in highly vascularized tissues such as kidney, placenta, and lung. Unlike the FGFs,

VEGF appears to be an endothelial-specific mitogen and is involved in both vasculogenesis and angiogenesis (57). VEGF is detected by antibody staining only in epithelial cells in the glandular stage human fetal lung (232). In situ hybridization studies in the adult rat (157) and guinea pig (19) lung suggest that VEGF expression is localized primarily to the epithelium, although mesenchymal cells may also express VEGF (58).

Two closely related receptor tyrosine kinases are receptors for VEGF: One is the fms-like tyrosine kinase [flt-1 (231)]; the other is the fetal liver kinase [flk-1, the murine homologue of the human KDR gene (197)]. Flk-1 is expressed exclusively in the vascular endothelium in mouse embryos and is the earliest known marker for endothelium and endothelial cell precursors (58, 154, 261). Flk-1 has been detected in the mouse lung as early as day 12.5 (glandular stage) of gestation (279). Beyond the description of the presence of VEGF in the lung and flk-1 in the pulmonary endothelium, however, little is known about the role of VEGF (or other growth factors) in the developing pulmonary vasculature.

## Smooth Muscle Cell Replication During Development

The blood vessel initially consists of a single layer of endothelial cells embedded in mesoderm and a scaffolding of extracellular matrix. Development of larger blood vessels (i.e. arteries and veins) from these initial vessels involves recruitment of SMC precursor cells into the region followed by proliferation and then differentiation into mature SMCs. Previous studies in rats have documented the daily replication rates of aortic SMCs throughout development (36). Briefly, SMCs replicate at a high rate (>80% per day) throughout embryonic life (Figure 2). At the embryonic-to-fetal transition (between days e17 and e19), the SMC replication rate declines dramatically to approximately 40% per day. During postnatal life, SMCs gradually acquire a quiescent phenotype, reaching a replication rate of <0.06% per day in the adult. A nearly identical pattern has been seen in large pulmonary vessels during development (JK Belknap, MCM Weiser, SS Grieshaber, KR Stenmark, RA Majack, submitted for publication). Vascular SMCs therefore undergo a greater than 2000-fold decrease in replication rate from embryonic to adult life.

Available data indicate that rat SMC replication during early development (up to day e17) is autonomous (self-driven) and is not related to secretion of a mitogen. Further, these early embryonic SMCs exhibit poor mitogenic responses to serum and growth factors (36). The dramatic decline in in vivo proliferation observed between days e17 and e19 corresponds with a loss of autonomous growth capacity in SMCs cultured from the great vessels of animals at these time points (36). The switch from autonomous to serum- and growth-factor-dependent growth appears to be caused by the developmental acquisition of a *trans*-acting adult factor capable of suppressing autonomous

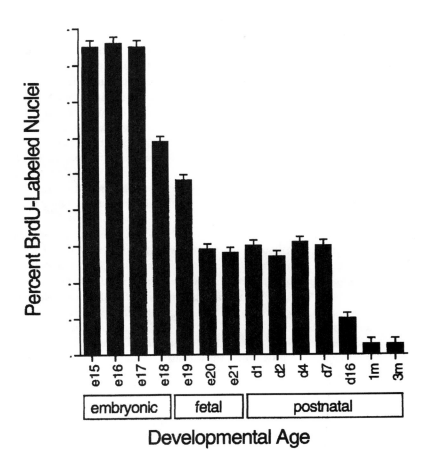

*Figure 2*  Vascular SMC replication in vivo decreases dramatically during rat pulmonary artery development. Timed pregnant rats were injected with bromodeoxyuridine (BrdU) at the indicated developmental stages, and embryos or fetuses were removed and fixed in 10% formalin. Lung tissue from postpartum rats was processed similarly. Replicating intraparenchymal pulmonary arterial SMCs were identified by BrdU histochemistry. Note that SMC replication rates decrease markedly at the embryonic-fetal transition, remain high until postnatal day 7, and then gradually decline to adult levels (JK Belknap, MCM Weiser, SS Grieshaber, KR Stenmark, RA Majack, submitted for publication).

DNA replication (138). Thus SMC replication during early embryonic vascular development seems to be genetically predetermined and independent of the secretion of mitogens by other cells or tissues.

In the fetal and neonatal periods, in contrast, mechanisms involving growth factors are probably involved in the regulation of vascular cell growth. Recent studies have tested this hypothesis directly (44). SMCs cultured from neonatal calves were compared with cells cultured from adult animals and tested for size differences, serum-stimulated proliferation, susceptibility to senescence, resistance to serum withdrawal, autocrine growth capacity, and responsiveness to growth factors. Neonatal SMCs were significantly smaller in size, grew faster and reached higher plateau density, and were less susceptible to senescence under serum-stimulated conditions than were adult cells. They were also more resistant to induction of a quiescent state, had spontaneous autocrine growth capacity, and were more responsive to mitogens, including IGF-1, phorbol myristate acetate (PMA), or a combination of both.  The enhanced growth capacity depended on age at time of harvest.

Neonatal cells also showed an increase in activated PKC activity under basal conditions that may contribute to enhanced responsiveness to IGF-I. The increase was equal to that stimulated by a low concentration (1 nM) of PMA in adult SMCs, a pretreatment that allowed adult cells to be as responsive to IGF-I as untreated neonatal ones. Thus this increased growth of isolated neonatal pulmonary artery SMCs depended on cell size, age at time of cell harvest, IGF-1, and autoactivation of PKC (44).

The factors that drive SMC proliferation during development are largely unknown. Studies have confirmed roles for various growth factors in influencing SMC proliferation in vitro, although the in vivo roles of these factors during development have not been firmly established. Because some of these growth factors play a role in vascular repair and disease, they are likely to play a role in the developing vessel as well. Table 1 lists many of the growth factors, cytokines, and lipids that are produced by vascular wall cells and are known to influence SMC growth and matrix protein synthesis (for review, see 158).

Several vasoactive mediators produced by the vascular endothelium may also play roles in vascular development. Blood flow to the lung is limited during fetal life, and regulation by locally produced vasoconstrictors is important (158).  These same vasoconstrictors may exert growth-promoting effects on vascular SMCs, as has been described for thromboxane A2 (100), angiotensin II (ATII) (110), endothelin (24), leukotrienes (183), substance P (168), and 5-hydroxytryptamine (166). Recent studies have suggested potential roles for ATII and endothelin-1 in vascular development.

ATII is a powerful vasoconstrictor in the pulmonary circulation. In addition, angiotensin can stimulate specific intracellular growth events in vascular SMCs

**Table 1**   Factors regulating SMC growth and matrix protein synthesis

| Factors | SMC growth | Elastin | Type I collagen |
|---|---|---|---|
| IGF-I | ↑ | ↑ | ↑ |
| IGF-II | ↑ | ↑ | ↑ |
| TGF $\beta$ | ↑/↓ | ↑ | ↑ |
| PDGF | ↑ | ↑ | ↑/↔ |
| Leukotriene C$_4$(LTC$_4$) | ↑ | ND | ↑ |
| PAF | ↑ | ↑ | ND |
| IL-1 | ↑/↓ | ↓ | ↑/↓[a] |
| EGF | ↑ | ↓ | ↔ |
| Prostaglandins (PGE$_2$,PGI$_2$) | ↓ | ↔/↓ | ↓ |
| Interferons | ↓ | ↓ | ↓ |
| Protein kinase C activation (PKC) | ↑ | ↓ | ↓ |
| bFGF | ↑ | ND | ND |
| aFGF | ↑ | ND | ND |
| Insulin | ↑ | | |
| TGF$\alpha$ | ND | ND | ND |
| HB-EGF | ↑ | ND | ND |
| PD-ECGF | ↔ | ND | ND |
| VEGF (VPF) | ↔ | ND | ND |
| Serotonin | ↑ | ND | ND |
| Histamine | ↑ | ND | ND |
| TNF$\alpha$ | ↓ | ND | ND |
| Heparin sulfates | ↓ | ND | ND |

[a]Effects depend on cell type studied; ND, not determined.

(224). It stimulates protein and DNA synthesis, up-regulates c-fos and c-myc expression, and stimulates PDGF-A chain gene expression in vascular SMCs (18, 224, 225). Moreover, ATII selectively increases the expression of $\alpha$-SM-actin and myosin heavy chain by rat aortic SMCs in culture (269), and it affects the synthesis of extracellular matrix proteins by SMCs (226).

The angiotensin receptor subtypes (AT1a, AT1b, and AT2) are highly regulated during fetal development (82, 268). However, the tissue distribution of angiotensin receptors in the fetus varies considerably, and the fetal lung expresses only the AT1a receptor subtype (228). The expression of angiotensin receptors in undifferentiated fetal mesenchyme also supports a possible role for ATII as a growth and differentiation factor during development (82, 228, 268). The developmental patterns of angiotensin-converting enzyme (ACE) and angiotension I (ATI) expression in the developing lung vasculature were examined recently. Morrell et al (160) demonstrated that ACE expression in developing pulmonary arteries of the rat occurred in a regulated fashion starting with larger proximal vessels as early as day 15 of gestation and spread distally to involve progressively smaller vessels, so that by term all vessels accompanying airways down to the level of terminal bronchioles expressed ACE. In addition, the distal extension of ACE expression into progressively smaller arteries during lung development was correlated closely with the appearance of markers specific for SMCs in the walls of these vessels.

Moreover, in situ hybridization studies demonstrated expression of ATI mRNA by undifferentiated lung mesenchyme surrounding endothelial structures, beginning one day before the appearance of vascular ACE and $\alpha$-SM actin in the peripheral lung. ATI mRNA expression was reduced greatly in the differentiated smooth muscle of the histologically apparent tunica media. These results suggest that local production of ATII by ACE, and the expression of the ATI receptor by undifferentiated lung mesenchyme, could play a role in the muscularization of developing pulmonary arteries.

Endothelin (ET) is the most potent vasoconstrictor known (30). Three isopeptides (ET-1, ET-2, and ET-3), encoded by different gene loci, act on two distinct G-protein-coupled receptors (ETA and ETB) with different affinities. Endothelin mRNAs and binding sites are present in the developing rat lung vasculature as early as fetal day 19 (137). In addition to vasoconstrictive effects on vascular SMCs, endothelin stimulates proliferation of vascular SMCs (121, 259). However, its potency as a smooth muscle mitogen is poor in the absence of other growth factors. Endothelin also stimulates pulmonary artery adventitial fibroblast proliferation and chemotaxis (187) and up-regulates fibroblast collagen synthesis (106). SMCs can also produce endothelin, suggesting an autocrine function, and exposure to ATII, arginine vasopressin, or PDGF-AA increases vascular SMC production of endothelin (205). These effects of ET-1 suggest endothelin may participate in the regulation of cardiovascular development and/or homeostasis. Recent studies evaluating homozygous ET-1 null mutation mice confirm that ET-1 is essential to normal development of the heart and great vessels. Edn1 −/− homozygotes displayed cardiovascular malformations, including interrupted aortic arch, tubular hypoplasia of the aortic arch, aberrant right subclavian artery, and ventricular septal defect with abnormalities of the outflow tract (126).

## Extracellular Matrix Protein Changes During Development

ECM protein production by all cells in the vascular wall also changes significantly during the course of normal development. ECM not only provides structural integrity to the developing vessel and a lattice to which cells can anchor themselves, but it also provides informational clues that affect a variety of cell processes, including proliferation, migration, differentiation, and the synthesis of other types of matrix molecules. Information encoded in or received by the ECM can be transmitted to the internal domain of the cell (31, 209). The connective tissue elements of the vascular wall are complex and include molecules from virtually every class of extracellular matrix: elastin, collagens, proteoglycans, and structural and adhesive glycoproteins. The relative proportions of each matrix component appear to reflect either the physical and functional properties expected of a particular vascular segment or the forces to which that vascular segment is exposed. Thus pulmonary vascular protein composition changes significantly with development and with type and location of the vessel studied (155).

For example, elastin is the most abundant protein in major arteries subjected to large pulsatile pressures generated by cardiac contraction (132). Elastogenic progenitor cells, giving rise to at least some of the SMCs that constitute the aorta and other elastic vessels, arise from mesenchyme adjacent to the myocardium (226). Elastogenic activity in these cells, at least in developing chick aorta, appears in an orderly, sequential, proximal-to-distal deployment, beginning nearest the heart and advancing downstream into all nascent elastic vessels. In the developing rat aorta, peak elastin synthesis occurs during late fetal and early postnatal life and remains high through the first postnatal month (147, 163). By two months, tropoelastin expression is virtually undetectable, and no significant tropoelastin is produced by the normal adult vascular smooth muscle cells (147, 192, 245). The developmentally confined period of elastin production suggests that tropoelastin expression is controlled accurately by tissue- and temporal-specific mechanisms, but the precise mechanisms that govern elastogenesis are unknown.

As distance from the heart increases, a progressive decrease in the amount of vascular elastin and a progressive increase in the amount of collagen is observed (41). Mature cross-linked collagen is much stiffer than elastin and thus confers different structural properties to the vessel wall. Collagens are an important family of structural proteins localized in the basement membrane and interstitial spaces of the vascular wall. Many excellent studies have evaluated accumulation of collagen in both systemic and pulmonary vessels during normal development (112, 277). The amount of collagen in a vessel wall depends on both age and site of the vessel studied. Furthermore, the amount of this fibrous protein, like elastin, can be correlated with differences in vascular wall tension that normally occur in different arteries during growth.

Immunohistochemical studies have evaluated the appearance and distribution of various collagen types in the developing pulmonary artery. During embryonic development, the interstitial collagens are deposited in the order of types V, III, and I (155). The amount of types I and V collagen in pulmonary arterial media increases with age. Particularly striking is the relative paucity of type I collagen in resistance-sized pulmonary arteries of the newborn compared with the adult lung (53, 155). Interesting functional implications can be drawn from these studies. Type I collagen is characterized by a high tensile strength; large quantities of this protein are prominent in tissues that are relatively indistensible. In contrast, type III collagen is present in distensible connective tissues (e.g. the uterus). The relative lack of type I collagen in developing pulmonary vessels may help explain the plasticity observed in the pulmonary arteries in fetal and early neonatal life. Cells composing the vessel wall change rapidly in shape and position during the first hours of life. The vessel walls themselves are remodeled continually with growth. These events may be facilitated by a paucity of type I collagen. However, although present in small amounts, type I collagen appears crucial for the maintenance of vascular integrity during normal development: Mutant mice, deficient in type I collagen, die at about 15 days of gestation with ruptured major blood vessels (124).

Components of the ECM, such as collagen, laminin, fibronectin, and perlecan, are capable of influencing the proliferation, migration, and differentiation of cultured endothelial and smooth muscle cells (59, 89, 91). The distribution of these proteins and the sequence of their appearance have been studied in various tissues during development in attempts to determine whether ECM components play a role in regulating the growth and patterning of blood vessels in vivo. Information on the timing of basement membrane formation during vascular development is crucially important to our understanding of the role the ECM may play in the control of SMC replication, migration, gene expression, and growth responsiveness during development and in response to injury.

Studies of blood vessel formation in the chick chorioallantoic membrane (CAM) have demonstrated that fibronectin is one of the earliest components to be deposited in the vascular basal laminae. The appearance of fibronectin in the perivascular ECM precedes by at least two days the appearance of ultrastructurally identifiable basal laminae, which are not evident until day 6 (9). The location of fibronection relative to the developing blood vessels is consistent with it playing a role in certain critical stages in the formation of capillaries and larger vessels. The presence of fibronectin in the allantois, where the primitive blood vessels are first formed, suggests this molecule participates in the early aggregation of mesenchymal cells to form capillary tubes. As in other embryonic tissues, fibronectin could promote the migration of capillary endothelial cells because it stimulates the migration of vascular endothelial cells in vitro (270).

As fibronectin levels peak in developing arterioles and venules of the CAM, glycosaminoglycans (8) and type IV collagen are detected. The ability of fibronectin to bind to cell surfaces as well as to matrix components such as collagen and proteoglycans (97, 213) suggests fibronectin plays a role in the progressive accumulation and organization of the basal lamina of endothelial and smooth muscle cells. Fibronectin content then diminishes in the basal laminae with time and is usually a minor component of adult vascular basal laminae. The mRNA for fibronectin undergoes extensive alternative splicing that results in at least ten different fibronectin variants (121). At least two of these peptides appear to be developmentally regulated in vascular SMCs. For example, the aortic media of the 10- to 12-week old human fetus expresses fibronectin protein that binds to monoclonal antibodies recognizing both extradomain A (ED-A) and extradomain B (ED-B) fibronectin sequences. With continued development to 20–25 weeks, the proportion of ED-A antibody-recognizing fibronectin decreases fivefold and that for ED-B decreases twofold. By adulthood, no ED-A- or ED-B-recognizing fibronectin sequences can be found in the vessel media; however, ED-A is seen in SMCs in the normal adult arterial intima (76).

Laminin also appears early in vessel walls although later than fibronectin. It promotes the morphological differentiation of human capillary and venous endothelial cells, cultured in vitro, into capillary-like structures (125) and promotes the maintenance of the contractile phenotype and other differentiated properties of cultured arterial SMCs, which in the absence of laminin tend to lose their microfilaments and assume a less differentiated and more synthetically active phenotype (89). The appearance of laminin in vivo does not seem to inhibit endothelial cell proliferation as it does in vitro.

Type IV collagen is the last basement membrane collagen to appear in the matrix surrounding CAM vessels. It is not present during the earliest stages of vessel development, when endothelial cells are proliferating rapidly, but appears only as endothelial cell division starts to slow (9). Type IV collagen appears in the vascular basal laminae at approximately the same time as sulfated proteoglycans (8). Type IV collagen enables cultured SMCs to maintain a contractile phenotype (90) and thus could be involved in the progressive differentiation that occurs later in vascular development.

Endogenous heparin-like molecules are believed to play critical roles in the control of vascular SMC replication (17, 32, 65, 262), migration (139), and differentiated functions (134, 263). The pattern of expression of perlecan, the predominant basement membrane heparan sulfate proteoglycan (HSPG), during pulmonary and aortic development has been described in studies of the rat (JK Belknap, MCM Weiser, SS Grieshaber, KR Stenmark, RA Majack, submitted for publication; 275). Expression of perlecan mRNA and protein in aortic SMCs was first observed at day e19, a time that marks a dramatic decline in SMC replication rate and a change in growth phenotype (Figure 3) (275). Expression of perlecan message and protein was high throughout fetal and early neonatal life and remained readily detectable in the adult aorta. Several studies suggest the expression of perlecan by vascular SMCs is regulated by apparent developmental age as well as by cellular growth state. The developmental timing of perlecan expression suggests this HSPG may play a determining role in the cessation of SMC replication during vascular morphogenesis and participate in maintaining SMCs in a quiescent state in the adult blood vessel

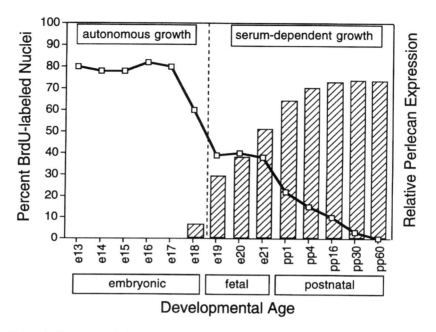

*Figure 3*  Inverse correlation between perlecan expression and SMC replication during aortic development. During development, aortic SMCs demonstrate very high in vivo replication indices (analyzed as the percent of BrdU-positive cells) throughout embryonic life (to e18) and demonstrate the potential for autonomous (serum-independent) growth in culture. At the embryonic-to-fetal transition, the SMC replication rate decreases dramatically and then more gradually until the adult level of less than 0.1% is reached. This transition point appears to mark a major change in SMCs to a nonautonomous (serum-dependent) growth phenotype (36). Concurrent with the decline in replication during development is a marked increase in the expression of perlecan by nonreplicating aortic SMCs, suggesting that the gradual deposition of a perlecan-rich, growth-inhibitory ECM may prevent SMC replication in the adult, uninjured blood vessel. The line represents percent of BrdU-positive aortic SMCs. Bars indicate perlecan expression by aortic medial SMCs (275).

wall. Alternatively or in addition, perlecan expression by quiescent SMC may reflect the deposition of a protective growth-suppressive and differentiation-promoting basement membrane. Removal of such growth-inhibitory influences may be a major determinant of the extent of SMC replication following injury.

## Changes in Contractile Protein Expression During Development

Significant changes also occur in expression of contractile and cytoskeletal proteins during normal development. Morphological studies have demonstrated that the volume percentage of myofilaments in the aorta increases from 5% at birth to a maximum of 20% at 8 weeks of age. The noncollagenous, alkaline-soluble protein fraction of the vessel wall, which in part represents the contractile proteins, does not change after 10 weeks of age. Thus the net production of contractile protein increases during the first 10 weeks after birth and then remains constant. Concomitant with the increase in actin (a major SMC contractile protein) content accompanying SMC maturation is a switch from predominant expression of non-muscle $\beta$-actin by neonatal aortic SMC to predominant expression of smooth muscle (SM)-specific $\alpha$-actin isoforms by adult SMC (116).

In addition to this shift from non-muscle $\beta$-actin to the SM-specific form of $\alpha$-actin during maturation, the cellular content of tropomyosin, vimentin, and desmin in SMCs increases with age (162, 181). Recently the SM2 isoform of SM-myosin heavy chain (SM-MHC) was found to be expressed only in adult blood vessels, while the SM1 isoform was found to be expressed earlier in development (127, 218). Newborn rat aortic SMCs underexpressing $\alpha$-actin isoforms exhibit a higher replication rate than do $\alpha$-actin positive cells, suggesting an inverse correlation between acquisition of the adult phenotype and cell replication. However, during development, contractile and synthetic function of SMCs are not mutually exclusive. SMCs in developing vessels simultaneously express multiple SM contractile proteins, a variety of ECM proteins, and they proliferate (181, 227).

Studies in the developing human aorta have evaluated expression of the regulatory contractile proteins h-caldesmon and calponin, in conjunction with expression of $\alpha$-SM-actin and SM-MHC (62, 75, 78). Actin and myosin are expressed far earlier in development than caldesmon and calponin, suggesting these latter proteins, because they are involved in the regulation of contraction, may serve as markers of more highly differentiated SMCs. In addition, expression of meta-vinculin, a marker of microfilament-membrane association sites, also occurs later in development in more differentiated SMCs (77).

Substantial differences clearly exist among the proliferative, secretory, and contractile phenotypes of fetal and adult vascular wall cells. Additional differences may exist at the gene and protein level, and these differences may play pivotal roles in the control of SMC replication and differentiation during vascular development. Furthermore, these differences in gene expression could contribute to significant variations in the response of cells to injurious stimuli during vascular development.

## Factors Possibly Contributing to Growth Suppression in Adult SMCs

In vivo, adult SMCs are replicatively quiescent and relatively unresponsive to mitogens that stimulate cultured SMCs. Exposure of SMCs to exogenous mitogens alone, either in vivo or in cultured tissue explants, does not appear sufficient to initiate DNA synthesis, suggesting the presence of potent growth-suppressive mechanisms in the adult vessel wall (222). Intracellular and extracellular factors probably contribute to SMC quiescence in the adult blood vessel wall. Intracellular factors that exist in SMCs include tumor suppressor genes, whose loss-of-function mutations or inactivation (e.g. by binding to viral gene products) can lead to a loss of normal growth control (133). Similarly, the existence of an adult factor capable of suppressing the autonomous growth phenotype of embryonic SMCs has been inferred from heterokaryon studies (138). This factor is probably functionally related to tissue-specific extinguishers such as fibroblast TSE-1 (102), which suppresses liver-specific gene expression in fibroblast:hepatoma fusion cells. Other tissue-specific extinguishers appear to play important roles in regulating the expression of differentiation-specific genes (229). Finally, Blau and colleagues have shown that the 3' untranslated regions of several muscle-specific mRNAs exert growth-inhibitory, tumor suppressive, and differentiation-promoting activity (203). Their data suggest that the expression of differentiation-specific mRNAs may in turn contribute to the maintenance of the quiescent, differentiated state. A similar situation may exist for vascular SMCs.

Extracellular factors that may contribute to developmental growth suppression in vascular SMCs include growth factors whose disappearance during development might lead to passive growth arrest and growth inhibitors such as those of the transforming growth factor beta (TGF-$\beta$) superfamily (114). Components of the ECM also appear to contribute substantially to the control of SMC growth and differentiation. For example, when actively replicating synthetic SMCs are cultured on basement membrane components isolated from the Engelbreth-Holm-Swarm (EHS) mouse tumor (commercially available as Matrigel), they become growth inhibited, activate MAP kinases less efficiently in response to mitogens, and exhibit more differentiated functions (134, 274). Fibronectin appears to facilitate the expression of a synthetic SMC phenotype, while other matrix components may induce the expression of a contractile phenotype and inhibit SMC proliferation (262, 263). Components of the basement membrane or ECM that have been reported to inhibit SMC replication or to promote SMC differentiation include heparan sulfates, laminin, and collagen type IV (263, 282). Other studies have indicated that the developmentally timed expression of perlecan, the predominant basement membrane HSPG, may contribute substantially to the establishment and/or maintenance of SMC quiescence in the mature blood vessel wall and may regulate the expression of certain growth-essential transcription factors (274, 275) (see Figure 3). The mechanism(s) by which perlecan or heparin-like molecules regulate SMC replication and gene expression is not yet clear, but it may include a number of parallel growth-inhibitory pathways (7).

**Table 2**   In vivo characterization of four SMC populations within the mature bovine pulmonary artery media

|                          | L1-cells        | L2-SMCs         | L3-i-cells      | L3-C-SMCs[a]    |
|--------------------------|-----------------|-----------------|-----------------|-----------------|
| Location                 | Preluminal      | Inner-middle    | Outer           |                 |
| Morphology               | Small, irregular| Spindle         | Thin, spindle   | Outer           |
| Cell orientation         | Irregular       | Circumferential | Circumferential | Thick, spindle  |
| Pattern of elastic       | Fragmented      | Well-developed  | Well-developed  | Longitudinal    |
| Lamellae                 | Particles       | Continuous      | Continuous      | None            |
| Immunobiochemical characteristics | | | | |
| Immunostaining:          |                 |                 |                 |                 |
| $\alpha$-SM-actin        | −               | +               | −               | +               |
| SM-myosin                | −               | +               | −               | +               |
| Calponin                 | −               | +               | −               | +               |
| Desmin                   | −               | +               | −               | +               |
| Meta-vinculin            | −               | −               | −               | +               |
| Western blotting:        |                 |                 |                 |                 |
| 150-kDa caldesmon        | −               | −               | −               | +               |
| SM-MHCs:                 |                 |                 |                 |                 |
| SM-1                     | −               | +               | −               | +               |
| SM-2                     | −               | −               | ND              | +               |

[a] i indicates cells in interstitial areas; C indicates cells in compact clusters. SM, smooth muscle; MHC, myosin heavychain; and ND, not determined.

## Heterogeneity of SMC Phenotype in the Vascular Wall

A growing body of literature is based on both in vivo and in vitro studies documenting the existence of phenotypic heterogeneity within the resident SMC population of a given tissue at a specified developmental stage.

IN VIVO STUDIES   The hypothesis that multiple distinct SMC subpopulations comprise the normal mammalian arterial media is supported by previous observations in the systemic circulation. Several laboratories have reported the existence of SMCs of different size, shape, and differentiation state in the mature systemic vessel wall (180, 239, 281). Recent studies have demonstrated that the pulmonary artery is also composed of multiple phenotypically distinct (as defined by cytoskeletal and matrix protein expression) SMC subpopulations (61, 194, 245, 252) (Figure 4 and Table 2). Further, the data demonstrate that these cells progress along different developmental pathways, thus suggesting the existence of distinct vascular SMC lineages (61) (Figure 5).

The observation of multiple SMC subpopulations comprising the arterial media raises an important question as to why this cellular diversity exists. Numerous functions are required of vascular SMCs under both normal and pathologic conditions including contraction, proliferation, and synthesis of matrix proteins. Different SMC functions may require different phenotypes. Accordingly, in

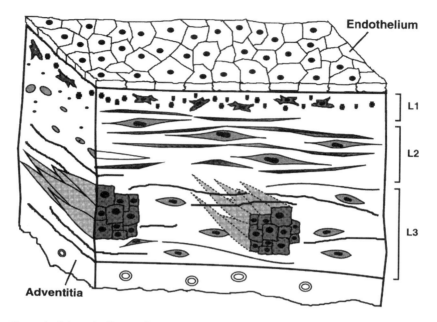

*Figure 4*   Schematic diagram demonstrating the structural and cellular heterogeneity within the bovine main pulmonary artery. L1, subendothelial media; L2, middle media; L3, outer media. Table 2 describes characteristics of cells located in each layer.

response to pathologic stimuli, some medial SMCs are likely to maintain their normal, mainly contractile functions, whereas others are likely to exhibit elevated proliferation and/or matrix protein synthesis. This diversity in cellular responses would lend itself to a better maintenance of vascular homeostasis after hypoxic injury. Most functions could continue without the severe or fatal compromise that would occur if all (or most) cells shifted simultaneously from one phenotype (contractile) to another (proliferative and/or synthetic).

IN VITRO STUDIES   Recent in vitro studies also support the hypothesis that phenotypically distinct SMC subpopulations exist within normal arterial media and exhibit unique and selective responses to the same stimuli. Vascular SMCs of multiple phenotypes have been isolated and maintained in culture over many passages. SMCs distinct in morphology; growth factor requirements; saturation density; and expression of cytoskeletal/contractile proteins, growth factors, and ECM molecules have been derived from systemic vessels from normal rats of different ages and from injured vessels. For example, subpopulations of SMCs have been isolated from the normal arterial media of neonatal rats, which can

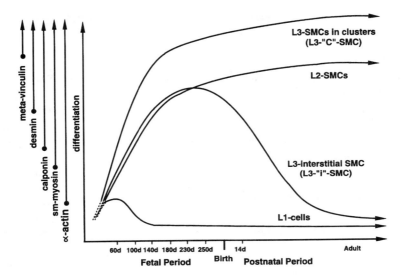

*Figure 5*  Schematic representation of the pattern of SMC contractile and cytoskeletal protein expression in different cell populations during development. Time is represented along the x axis, and expression of various smooth muscle proteins is represented by the arrows along the y axis. Four distinct developmental patterns are observed. L1-cells are those observed in the preluminal media. L2-SMCs are those identified within the inner-middle media. L3-C-SMCs and L3-i-cells are those observed in the outer media (L3-C-SMCs, in the cell clusters; L3-i-cells, in interstitial areas between the clusters).

grow in PDGF-depleted media, whereas other, simultaneously isolated SMC subpopulations require exogenous PDGF for proliferation (130, 223).

Other studies have shown that a subpopulation of SMCs less sensitive to the growth-inhibitory effects of heparin can be isolated selectively from the adult rat aortic media (13). Most recently, two morphologically distinct SMC populations, isolated from the mature rat aortic media, were shown to differ dramatically in their ionic responses to vasoactive agonists (167). Two stable SMC subpopulations were isolated from human systemic arteries with markedly different growth properties (66). In vitro data from our laboratory (63, 64) demonstrate that multiple morphologically and phenotypically distinct SMC subpopulations can be isolated selectively from the normal mature bovine main pulmonary artery. These SMC subpopulations exhibit dramatically different responses to growth-promoting and growth-inhibiting stimuli. Stable clones of SMCs retaining unique characteristics have been obtained from the systemic circulation as well as from pulmonary arteries (211, 223).

## PHENOTYPIC CHANGES IN VASCULAR WALL CELLS DURING THE DEVELOPMENT OF PULMONARY HYPERTENSION

Marked changes in the structure and function of endothelial cells, SMCs, and adventitial fibroblasts take place during the development of chronic pulmonary hypertension. Collectively, these cellular changes determine the alterations in tone, reactivity, and vascular resistance that characterize the chronic pulmonary hypertensive state. Injury-induced changes in cell phenotype are complex and depend on many factors. For example, the age and thus possibly the differentiation state of the cell at the time of injury significantly influence the response observed (199, 245, 251). Further, cellular responses differ remarkably at various locations within the pulmonary circulation. The observed difference may result from the variations in stimuli imparted by pulmonary hypertension at different locations within the vascular bed. Alternatively, cells of a similar type (e.g. SMCs) may exhibit unique characteristics at different locations and thus respond in unique ways to the pulmonary hypertensive stimulus. Finally, even within the endothelial, smooth muscle, and fibroblast populations at a specific location within the pulmonary vascular bed, there is a marked heterogeneity in the cells comprising these general populations. Hidden in this heterogeneity and in the heterogeneity of responses are clues that will help us better define the mechanisms contributing to the structural and functional changes that occur in response to chronic hypoxic pulmonary hypertension. In the following sections, we discuss the response of each cell population in the vessel wall to hypertensive stimuli.

### Endothelial Changes Occurring During the Development of Chronic Pulmonary Hypertension

The endothelium creates a nonthrombogenic, semipermeable barrier between the blood stream and all extravascular tissues and fluid compartments in the body. It also influences vascular tone, hemostasis, growth, differentiation, chemotaxis, and the vascular response to injury. Given this important role in such a wide array of vascular functions, it is not surprising that significant adaptations in the structure and function of the endothelial cell take place during the development of hypoxic pulmonary hypertension.

HISTOLOGY/MORPHOLOGY    Several studies have characterized the histological changes occurring in the endothelial cells of both large and small vessels in response to chronic pulmonary hypertension (96, 149, 151, 198, 200). In chronic hypoxic pulmonary hypertension, increases in intimal thickness secondary to hypertrophy and hyperplasia is observed in both the endothelial and subendothelial layers. Focal disruption and lysis of the endothelial cell basement membrane often occur, creating a patchy appearance of microfibrillar material in the thickened subendothelial layer much like that reported in the aorta of hypertensive rats. In addition, the presence of collagen fibers, elastin, and microfibrils in the subendothelial space, internal to the endothelial cell basement membrane, suggests an increase in the production of these proteins by the endothelial cell. In support of this possibility are recent in situ hybridization studies demonstrating that during normal growth and development, endothelial cells contribute to formation of the basement membrane and internal elastic laminae via production and secretion of elastin (248). Under normal conditions, endothelial cell production of elastin appears to be suppressed sometime in late fetal or early neonatal life. In response to injury, the endothelial cell re-expresses tropoelastin mRNA (248). In addition, recruitment of SMCs into this enlarging subendothelial space has also been observed. These cells could also contribute to the protein accumulation that occurs in the subendothelial space in chronic hypoxic pulmonary hypertension.

ENDOTHELIAL CELL MEMBRANE PROPERTIES    The structural changes in pulmonary endothelial cells and their plasma membranes observed in pulmonary hypertension are accompanied by alterations in the physiological and metabolic function of the cell. For instance, hypoxic exposure decreases the antithrombotic potential, increases the permeability, impairs normal regulation of vascular tone, promotes release of cytokines and growth factors, and interferes with a variety of plasma membrane–dependent receptor, metabolic, and transport functions of the endothelial cell (20, 171–173).

Hypoxia exerts profound effects on the physical state and composition of pulmonary artery endothelial cell plasma membrane lipids (20, 22). Alterations in the properties of membrane lipids interfere with a number of fundamental cellular membrane functions, including cell cycling, differentiation, proliferation, and transmembrane signal transduction (256, 257). In addition, the activity and kinetics of membrane-bound enzymes and carriers can be affected markedly by membrane lipid composition and fluidity (256, 257). The alterations in endothelial structure and membrane properties observed in pulmonary hypertensive conditions also appear to alter permeability. Stelzner et al (242) have demonstrated increased pulmonary transvascular protein and water leak in rats exposed to chronic hypoxia. Further, hypoxia also increases endothelial cell permeability in vitro (172, 173). These permeability changes in endothelial cultures correlate with the formation of intracellular gaps.

Significant changes in surface coagulant properties and proinflammatory cytokine production by endothelial cells are noted in pulmonary hypertension. For instance, hypoxia suppresses normal thrombomodulin production and induces procoagulant activity (172). Hypoxia also increases interleukin-1 (IL-1) mRNA levels and IL-1$\alpha$ production in cultured endothelial cells (234). The IL-1 thus produced induces endothelial-leukocyte adhesion molecule-1 (ELAM-1) and increases the expression of intracellular adhesion molecule-1 (ICAM-1) on endothelial cells. Increased expression of ICAM-1 has also been reported in the lungs of hypoxic mice (234). Voelkel et al (272) demonstrated the presence of IL-1$\alpha$ and low-level expression of IL-1$\alpha$ mRNA in lungs from monocrotaline-treated rats, and that treatment of the rats with the interleukin-1 receptor antagonist IL-1r$\alpha$ inhibited the development of chronic pulmonary hypertension. IL-1 could participate indirectly in the vascular remodeling by stimulating platelet-activating factor (PAF) production, c-fos protooncogene expression, and activation of the transcription factor NF-$\kappa$B (272). These observations suggest that hypoxia induces changes in the endothelial cell, which may lead to prothrombotic or altered interactions with circulating cells that could participate in the pulmonary hypertensive response. Indeed, increased adherence of leukocytes and platelets to the endothelium has been observed in vivo in experimental rats with chronic pulmonary hypertension (96).

PRODUCTION AND RELEASE OF VASOACTIVE MEDIATORS BY THE ENDOTHELIUM
Chronic pulmonary hypertension is associated with changes in the production and release of potent vasoactive substances by the endothelium. Several vasoactive agents possess growth-regulatory properties, and pulmonary vascular remodeling could result from an imbalance of growth-inhibitory vasodilators and growth-promoting vasoconstrictors (246).

Changes in the local production of vasodilatory substances in chronic pulmonary hypertensive states are well described. Decreases in prostacyclin and increases in thromboxane production occur in human primary pulmonary hypertension (PPH) (33). Chronic hypoxia decreases biosynthesis of the potent vasodilator prostacyclin ($PGI_2$) in freshly excised pulmonary artery rings from neonatal calves (10). A similar reduction in $PGI_2$ production occurs in endothelial cells cultured from these calves, most likely resulting from inhibition of enzyme activity (cyclooxygenase or prostacyclin synthase) (271). Decreased $PGI_2$ synthesis by cells in the vessel wall could permit coagulation to occur at the endothelial surface, promote SMC proliferation, and impair local vasodilation, all of which contribute to the chronic pulmonary hypertensive state.

Production of endothelial-derived relaxing factor/nitric oxide (EDRF/NO) by endothelial cells both mediates vasodilation and moderates vasoconstriction in the normal pulmonary circulation (79, 85). However, contradictory reports exist concerning EDRF/NO activity in pulmonary hypertension. Whether NO production is altered is of some importance because a decrease in the production of this potent vasodilator would contribute to the vasoconstriction augmenting the hypertensive state. Studies of hypertensive human and animal conduit pulmonary arteries have demonstrated impaired endothelial-dependent relaxation to acetylcholine and ADP (5, 49, 208). Recent studies have demonstrated little or no expression of nitric oxide (NO) synthase in the pulmonary vascular endothelium of patients with pulmonary hypertension (70). Similarly, some researchers have demonstrated attenuation of agonist-induced vasodilation in hypertensive lung tissue isolated from chronically hypoxic animals (1). In contrast, others have shown augmented vasodilatory responses to acetylcholine, bradykinin, and platelet-activating factor in hypoxic pulmonary hypertensive calf and rat lungs, suggesting that EDRF/NO activity might be increased in hypertensive pulmonary arteries (12, 179).

Several studies have demonstrated that the competitive NO synthase inhibitor L-NNA causes a marked precapillary vasoconstriction in lungs isolated from rats with pulmonary hypertension, whereas no effect is seen on normoxic vascular tone in normotensive lungs (175). Although other investigators have found no change in baseline vascular tone in response to EDRF inhibitors, chronically hypertensive lungs, at least in some species, exhibit increased levels of both basal and stimulated EDRF/NO activity. Further, based on a study of acetylcholine-induced vasodilation in pulmonary hypertensive calves and on results with ADP in fawn-hooded rats with spontaneous pulmonary hypertension, impaired endothelium-dependent relaxation of isolated conduit pulmonary arteries does not necessarily reflect the vasodilator responsiveness of intact pulmonary vascular beds (5, 179). Additional work is needed to precisely identify the role of EDRF/NO in chronic pulmonary hypertensive states.

Of related interest and particular importance in chronic pulmonary hypertension are the effects of NO and $PGI_2$ on the proliferative state of the underlying SMCs. Researchers have suggested that the normal low rate of proliferation in SMCs of the tunica media may result partly from the inhibitory action of endogenous vasodilator agents from the endothelium that act by increasing cAMP concentration ($PGI_2$, $PGE_1$, and adenosine) or cGMP concentration (NO) (166, 197, 219). For instance, NO-containing drugs are capable of inhibiting stimulated SMC proliferation, although they may do so only at much higher concentrations than might be expected from the basal endogenous release of NO (6, 164, 170). Recent studies have suggested that, depending on the developmental age of the SMC and the dose of NO given, stimulation of growth by NO donors is possible (240). cAMP-stimulating agents may exert greater inhibitory effects on cell proliferation than do cGMP-stimulating agents, while the opposite is true for their effects on vascular tone (166). Further work is needed to define the role of EDRF/NO and PGI$_2$ in the control of SMC proliferation under both normal and hypertensive conditions.

The endothelial cell is also capable of producing and releasing potent vaso-constrictors, such as endothelin-1 (ET-1) and thromboxane (54, 186). Recent studies have demonstrated increased circulating levels of ET-1 in the pulmonary circulation of adults with both primary and secondary forms of pulmonary hypertension as well as in infants with severe pulmonary hypertension, sug-gesting a possible role for ET-1 in these conditions (210, 254). Increased tissue expression of ET-1 has also been reported in PPH (72). Recent experi-mental studies also support the involvement of ET-1 and the ETA receptor in the development of chronic hypoxic and idiopathic pulmonary hyperten-sion (25, 243). ET-1 has been shown to be a mitogen for pulmonary vascular SMCs and fibroblasts, although species differences do exist (93, 187). Thus changes in endothelial ET-1 production occur in chronic pulmonary hyper-tension and could contribute significantly to vasoconstriction and possibly to remodeling.

In the systemic circulation, ATII formed by the action of ACE on ATI is an important mediator of vascular SMC growth (72) and thus could modulate some of the structural changes associated with pulmonary hypertension. However, substantive evidence of a role for ACE in pulmonary hypertension was lacking until recently. Although inhibitors of ACE attenuate the medial thickening and right ventricular hypertrophy (35), most workers have reported a decrease in whole lung ACE activity during the development of pulmonary hypertension induced by chronic hypoxia (176) or ingestion of monocrotaline (111). These disparate findings have led others to conclude that the beneficial effects of ACE inhibitors on pulmonary hypertension are either independent of inhibition of lung ACE or that down-regulation of lung ACE may be a protective mechanism.

An explanation for this paradox, however, is that whole lung ACE activity does not reflect local pulmonary vascular ACE expression. This result was shown by combining in vivo hemodynamic studies in control and chronically hypoxic rats with measurement of whole lung ACE activity and determination of local pulmonary vascular ACE expression by in situ hybridization and immuno-histo chemistry. Morrell et al found that total lung ACE activity was reduced to 50% of control activity by five days of hypoxia and remained low for the dura-tion of the study (159). Immunohistochemistry showed a marked reduction of ACE staining in alveolar capillary endothelium. However, an increase in ACE staining was observed in the walls of small, newly muscularized pulmonary arteries at the level of alveolar ducts and walls. In situ hybridization studies showed increased signal for ACE mRNA in the same vessels (159; Figure 6a). Inhibition of ACE by captopril during chronic hypoxic exposure–attenuated pulmonary hypertension and markedly reduced distal muscularization of small

(a)

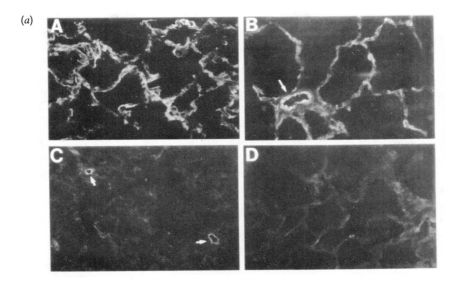

(b)

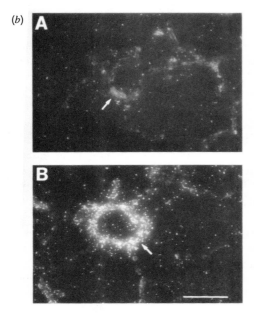

*Figure 6* (*a*) ACE immunofluorescence staining in alveolar capillaries in normoxic rat lung and in lungs of rats exposed to chronic hypoxia. Lung sections were incubated with a monoclonal antibody to human ACE (A-C) or control mouse IgG (D). Normoxic lung demonstrated intense staining of the alveolar capillary endothelium (A), which was reduced markedly by day 8 of hypoxia (B and C). ACE staining of the endothelium of small pulmonary arteries was prominent in the hypoxic rats (arrows) (B and C). The staining was specific since virtually no signal was seen in the normoxic lung incubated with control mouse IgG (D). A, B, and D original magnification is 400×; C is 100×. (*b*) In situ hybridization studies of ACE mRNA expression in normoxic (A) and chronically hypoxic (B) rat lung. Virtually no specific signal (white dots) was seen over alveolar capillaries and small pulmonary arteries (arrow) in normal lung (A). An increased signal for ACE mRNA was observed in the walls of small pulmonary arteries at the level of alveolar ducts and walls in chronically hypoxic rats (B). In hypoxic rats, a signal was detected both in endothelial cells and in cells in deeper layers of the vessel wall (B). Bar = ~50 mm.

pulmonary arteries. In addition, marked longitudinal variation in ACE expression along the normal pulmonary vasculature was demonstrated, and the highest levels were found in small muscular arteries associated with terminal and respiratory bronchioles. Thus local ACE expression is increased in the walls of small pulmonary arteries during the development of hypoxic pulmonary hypertension, despite a generalized reduction in alveolar capillary ACE expression.

In normoxic rats, immunohistochemistry demonstrated that ACE expression was confined to pulmonary vascular endothelium. In the neomuscularized arterioles associated with alveolar ducts and walls in hypoxic rats, the proximity of endothelial and smooth muscle layers (often an incomplete single cell layer) made it difficult to determine whether nonendothelial cells also expressed ACE (159). In situ hybridization studies showed an increased signal for ACE mRNA in these vessels, which often appeared to involve the entire vessel wall rather than the endothelium alone, indicating ACE expression in SMCs or pericytes (Figure 6b). Somatic ACE expression has been demonstrated by immunohistochemistry in many nonendothelial cell types, including macrophages, renal tubular epithelium, jejunal epithelium, and neointimal SMCs of the balloon-injured aorta (201, 237). In addition, ACE activity can be detected in fibroblasts and SMCs of the normal rat aorta, albeit at a much lower level than in endothelial cells, and aortic SMC ACE expression is increased in animals with systemic hypertension (4). Increased ACE activity in proliferating vascular SMCs might stimulate their growth in an autocrine and/or paracrine fashion. Study of microvascular SMCs and pericytes isolated from the pulmonary vessels will be necessary to determine whether ACE expression is increased in these cells in chronic pulmonary hypertension.

CYTOKINES AND MITOGENS RELEASED BY ENDOTHELIAL CELLS UNDER CONDITIONS KNOWN TO CAUSE PULMONARY HYPERTENSION    The production of several other vasoactive and growth-promoting agents changes in vascular endothelial cells under conditions that cause pulmonary hypertension. Increased PDGF-B chain mRNA levels in lungs of chronically hypoxic rats have been reported (109). In vivo PDGF-B mRNA levels reached a maximum after 1 day of hypoxia, were sustained through day 3, and then decreased gradually over the next 11 days. In addition, PDGF-A mRNA levels were increased but followed a different time course. Hypoxic exposure has also been shown to increase the transcriptional rate of the PDGF-B chain in human umbilical vein endothelial cells (122, 123). Increased shear stress is associated with pulmonary hypertension, and shear stresses are capable of inducing PDGF-A and PDGF-B chain gene expression in cultured vascular endothelial cells (95). Further, stretch of the isolated pulmonary arterial wall, a condition present in larger upstream pulmonary arteries when downstream resistance is increased, induces PDGF-B chain expression (266). Thus PDGF-A and PDGF-B chain products appear to be involved coordinately and sequentially in the hypoxic pulmonary vascular remodeling process. In a hyperoxic model of pulmonary hypertension, increases in PDGF-B and its receptor ligand have also been found and may be involved in the early stimulation and proliferation of precursor muscle cells (192).

VEGF and its receptors may also play an important role in lung vascular remodeling by functioning as an hypoxia-inducible angiogenic factor (236). VEGF mRNA levels increase dramatically within a few hours of hypoxic exposure and return to background levels when normal oxygen supply is resumed. Tuder et al (267) assessed the distribution of VEGF and of VEGF mRNA in lung tissue of chronically hypoxic rats. The VEGF mRNA and protein were increased in the hypertensive compared with normal lung. Transcripts for the VEGF receptors KDR/Flk and Flt were also increased in chronically hypoxic lungs, and the increase of VEGF receptor expression coincided with the first histologic evidence of vascular remodeling. Increases in bFGF production have also been demonstrated in hypoxic endothelial cells (3).

These observations suggest a remarkable capacity for the endothelial cell to influence local vascular structure and function through the production and release of potent mitogens. As indicated by differences in ET-1 and PDGF production by pulmonary artery versus systemic endothelial cells, however, caution must be taken in extrapolating information from experiments done with systemic cells to the pulmonary circulation.

INJURY-INDUCED CHANGES IN PROTEIN PRODUCTION BY ENDOTHELIAL CELLS
Endothelial cells, in response to hypoxia, are also capable of increased synthesis of several classes of ECM proteins. For example, human umbilical vein endothelial cells have increased mRNA levels for thrombospondin, plasminogen activator inhibitor-1, laminin, and fibronectin in response to hypoxia, while production of actin and von Willebrand factor mRNAs are unchanged (136). These responses appear to be distinct to hypoxia and not the result of either a common stress or a nonspecific response to stress because heat shock produces a much different protein synthetic response than hypoxia.

Of particular importance in chronic pulmonary hypertension may be changes in endothelial cell proteoglycan production. Chronically hypoxic endothelial cells produce and secrete less HSPGs than do normoxic cells (16). Further, experiments in which endothelial cells were exposed to high shear conditions again demonstrated decreased production of the growth-inhibiting HSPGs (16). Thus certain conditions associated with chronic pulmonary hypertension may impair the ability of the endothelium to produce important growth-restrictive matrix molecules. These observations are consistent with the inverse correlation between perlecan expression and SMC proliferation described during development (see Figure 3).

## Changes in Smooth Muscle Cell Phenotype During the Development of Chronic Pulmonary Hypertension

The severity of chronic hypoxic pulmonary hypertension is determined, at least in part, by the extent of structural changes in the medial compartment of the pulmonary arterial wall. These changes include SMC proliferation, hypertrophy, and matrix protein deposition. Blood-borne and locally produced mitogens, hypoxia, and mechanical stress are the stimuli that collectively drive these cellular responses by activating a cascade of intracellular signaling mechanisms, including tyrosine kinases, calcium ($Ca^{2+}$), and protein kinase C (PKC), that promote SMC growth and/or matrix protein synthesis. Synergy among these stimuli and the resulting cross-talk among signal transduction pathways augments the extent of vascular changes. Susceptibility to these stimuli is enhanced when inhibiting mechanisms such as endothelial barrier function, local production of heparan sulfates, and prostacyclin- and NO-induced increases in cyclic nucleotides are impaired. Intrinsic (i.e. developmental, genetic, and acquired) differences in growth and matrix synthetic capacity and local and regional phenotypic heterogeneity of pulmonary artery SMCs also regulate the pattern of remodeling in the tunica media in response to chronic hypoxia.

HISTOLOGY/MORPHOLOGY    Common to all forms of human pulmonary arteriolar hypertension are increases in the thickness of the medial layer of normally muscular arteries and an extension of muscle into smaller and more peripheral vessels (153). These features are found in a variety of clinical conditions but especially in those associated with chronic hypoxia such as chronic obstructive pulmonary disease, pulmonary interstitial fibrosis, kyphoscoliosis, central hypoventilation, cystic fibrosis, and residence at high altitude. Detailed characterization of the changes in SMCs induced by chronic hypoxia, hyperoxia, and monocrotaline have been examined in numerous animal studies (for review, see 153).

Meyrick & Reid (149, 152, 204) described the SMC changes of both the proximal and distal pulmonary vasculature and reported that both the timing and the nature of the responses differ. In the proximal pulmonary arteries of adult rats, the media thickens due to hypertrophy and hyperplasia of the individual muscle cells and an increase in the synthesis and deposition of ECM proteins, including elastin and collagen. In the distal vasculature, the muscularization of previously nonmuscular arteries (so-called extension) is probably brought about by a differentiation and hypertrophy of intermediate cells and pericytes already in the wall (153, 204). Both types of cells proliferate and acquire a more SM-like appearance.

Using hyperoxia as a stimulus to induce pulmonary hypertension, Jones et al have shown that interstitial fibroblasts are recruited to the vessel wall and undergo a phenotypic switch to the synthesis of proteins producing contractile components (104). These cells produce a network of elastin, which appears to induce the formation of a new elastic lamina between the muscle layer and the endothelium. This internal lamina is not as complete as in normal muscular arteries, so that now the endothelial cell and new muscle cells form frequent contacts. These contacts are different from those observed in normal muscular pulmonary arteries, suggesting that a close and perhaps different communication system may exist between these cells in the newly muscularized vessels.

If the injurious stimulus occurs at or around the time of birth, different cellular responses are noted than if pulmonary vascular injury occurs later in life (87, 245, 251). In newborns dying in the first 36 h after an hypoxic event, the peripheral pulmonary arteries show an extremely thick-walled fetal-like structure (87). Similarly, in pigs exposed to hypoxia from the moment of birth, and calves exposed to hypoxia within 24 h of birth, endothelial and smooth muscle cells retain their fetal appearance at 3 days of age (2, 52, 83). In the case of the calves, this observation correlates with the maintenance of high pulmonary artery pressure, similar to that in fetal life. SMCs of all animals exposed to hypoxia during the first week of life demonstrate an increase in the concentration of myofilaments. In the large arteries the abluminal SMCs show a greater increase in myofilaments than do the abluminal cells. This response is rapid and dramatic in neonates but requires a much longer period of exposure to elicit in older animals. In addition, a marked increase in connective tissue is noted in the neonatal SMCs and vascular wall, and it has been postulated that this increase in connective tissue synthesis and accumulation helps the vessel remain in a contracted or restrictive state.

CHANGES IN SMC PROLIFERATION DURING THE DEVELOPMENT OF PULMONARY HYPERTENSION    As described above, rapid SMC proliferation characterizes normal vascular development. Once morphogenesis is complete, however, the medial SMC replicative index decreases to very low levels and remains so under normal conditions. This tight control over SMC proliferation appears to be perturbed in hypertension. For example, significant increases are seen in the $[^3H]$-thymidine labeling index of pulmonary artery cells in adult rats exposed to hypoxia or hyperoxia (103, 150). Concominant morphometric studies of these vessels, however, suggested that hypertrophy, in addition to hyperplasia, of the SMCs was present. Thus the medial thickening of the hilar pulmonary artery from hypoxia-exposed adult rats may be caused in part by polypoid hypertrophy rather than pure hyperplasia. This theory is consistent with studies in systemic arteries in rats, indicating that SMCs are capable of two in vivo growth responses: hypertrophy or hyperplasia (182).

To determine whether the dramatic increase in medial thickening observed in neonatal hypoxia-induced pulmonary hypertension was the result of hypertrophy or hyperplasia, Orton and colleagues (14, 177) showed that the bromodeoxyuridine (BrdU)-labeling index of pulmonary artery medial cells in hypoxic calves was much higher than that found in control calves. Even in control calves the labeling index was at least tenfold higher than the thymidine-labeling index reported for the medial cells from normal adult rats, a difference probably due to normal smooth muscle growth that is still occurring in the newborn period.

Medial cells from the pulmonary artery of control calves had a high fraction of tetraploid (4N) cells and a low fraction of BrdU-positive cells compared with medial cells from hypoxia-exposed calves. This observation suggested that at least a portion of the 4N cells were stable tetraploid cells rather than cells simply traversing G2 in the cell cycle and that polyploid hypertrophy existed or was developing in the media of control calves. This conclusion is consistent with previous findings showing that medial thickening during normal development in the aorta is associated with an increase in the fraction of large polyploid cells (182). This normal developmental pattern is interrupted by hypoxic exposure and/or hemodynamic stress in the immediate neonatal period, and the subsequent acquisition of large polyploid cells is not observed. The hyperplasia of the newborn in response to stress stands in contrast to the hypertrophy observed in the adult.

An interesting observation in the neonatal calf model shed some light on these findings. Botney et al demonstrated a steady increase in TGF-$\beta$ mRNA in the pulmonary artery following a normal birth. In those animals with hypoxia-induced pulmonary hypertension, no increase in TGF-$\beta$ was seen (29). TGF-$\beta$ inhibits SMC growth (under all conditions tested) in neonatal vascular SMC and induces hypertrophy (RA Majack, personal communication). Thus increases in TGF-$\beta$ in the normal neonatal pulmonary artery could participate in the cessation of proliferation and the increase in ploidy normally occurring after birth. An absence of TGF-$\beta$ could contribute to the excessive or continued proliferation observed in large neonatal pulmonary arteries.

CONTROL OF SMC PROLIFERATION IN PULMONARY HYPERTENSION    Many factors contribute to the suppression of SMC growth in vivo. Access to blood-borne mitogens, coagulant proteins with proliferative effects, platelet products (including PDGF, serotonin, TXB-A2, and ATP), and inflammatory mediators is normally restricted. Under basal conditions, vasodilatory substances such as prostacyclin and NO are produced that exert antiproliferative effects on adjacent pulmonary artery SMCs. Endothelial-derived heparan sulfates also exert an inhibitory effect on SMC growth mediated, at least in part, by inhibiting the PKC pathway (195).

Collectively, these inhibitory mechanisms counterbalance an elaborate cascade of pro-mitogenic signaling pathways present in pulmonary artery SMCs. Activation of cell surface receptors and their associated tyrosine kinases and phospholipases (C-gamma, A2, or D) leads to the generation of lipid second messengers [e.g. inositol triphosphate (IP$_3$), diacylglycerol (DAG), and free fatty acids (FFA)] (118, 169). IP$_3$ promotes mobilization of intracellular Ca$^{2+}$ stores (79). DAG is an endogenous activator of PKC (169).

An array of other lipids can also stimulate PKC (131, 230). Intracellular Ca$^{2+}$ concentration can also be increased by direct or indirect activation of Ca$^{2+}$ channels that span the plasma membrane. There is almost certainly important cross-talk (and resulting synergy) between the Ca$^{2+}$ and PKC signaling pathways. Ca$^{2+}$ is a cofactor for the classical family of PKC isozymes (169). Increases in intracellular Ca$^{2+}$ can directly activate PKC (94), and PKC-mediated phosphorylation regulates Ca$^{2+}$ ion channel activity (67). Activators of the PKC pathway promote many of the same cellular responses (e.g. contraction, hypertrophy, and proliferation) observed in response to pulmonary hypertensive stimuli (46, 178, 241).

Ca$^{2+}$ and PKC-induced protein phosphorylation initiates a cascade of events resulting in increased DNA synthesis and cell proliferation (169, 233). Identified phosphorylation targets include MAP kinases, K and Ca$^{2+}$ channels, Na/H antiporter, heat shock proteins, and mitogen receptors (98, 156, 238). By activating gene regulatory proteins, these signaling mechanisms can also up-regulate the synthesis of proteins (including polyamine transport proteins, mitogens, receptors, mitogen-binding proteins, and transcription factors) that lead to additional SMC growth (23, 86, 235).

Chronic hypoxia and mechanical stress are two stimuli important to the development of pulmonary hypertension. Both stimulate ion channels (seconds) and key signaling mechanisms early (minutes) and increase growth factor expression later (hours). These effects may stimulate growth directly or they could promote cell proliferation indirectly by enhancing responsiveness to other mitogens (so-called permissive effects). Salvaterra (215) and Cornfield (37) have found that hypoxia causes Ca$^{2+}$ influx in pulmonary artery SMCs. Whether this increase in Ca$^{2+}$ contributes to SMC growth is not yet known. Dempsey has reported that hypoxia stimulates PKC to a small extent in pulmonary artery SMCs, which does not by itself lead to cell proliferation but may increase proliferation of growth factors, such as IGF-1, which synergize with even slight activation of PKC (45–47). Gillespie and coworkers (86) have found that hypoxia increases polyamine transport in pulmonary artery SMCs. Increased intracellular polyamine levels are important in cell growth, and this hypoxia-induced effect could alter SMC response to other mitogens. In other cell systems, $O^2$ radicals (perhaps produced in the settings of increased or reduced $O^2$ tension) increase intracellular $Ca^{2+}$ and activate and then inactivate PKC (80, 202). Finally, Langelben et al (128) have detected increased ET-1 expression by pulmonary artery SMCs upon exposure to hypoxia.

Emerging evidence suggests PKC and $Ca^{2+}$ may be important in the transduction of signals associated with mechanical stress (214). Komuro et al (119) have identified a potential role for PKC in the myocyte hypertrophic response to mechanical loading. Others have described early stretch-induced calcium influx (21) and a later increase in PDGF expression (276) in pulmonary artery SMCs. These mechanical stress-induced effects will likely be found to activate PKC, augment responsiveness to other growth-promoting stimuli, and stimulate proliferation of pulmonary artery SMCs. Therefore, PKC and $Ca^{2+}$ signaling pathways appear to be uniquely important in the regulation of pulmonary artery SMC proliferative responses to hypoxia and mechanical stress. How activation of these pathways leads to gene expression is still unclear, but hypoxia-inducible factor-1 and the shear-stress response element are likely important (145, 206).

Local vascular injury (secondary to hypoxia, mechanical stress, and inflammation) also induces the local expression and release of autocrine and paracrine factors that can change the responsiveness of local SMCs to hypoxic stimuli. Using in situ hybridization and immunohistochemical techniques, researchers have demonstrated many growth factors, including IGF-I, IGF-II, TGF-$\beta$, EGF, and bFGF, to be locally synthesized in the media or adjacent compartments of the pulmonary arterial wall during the development of pulmonary hypertension (3, 26, 29, 73, 109, 188, 189, 259, 265). As noted above, cultured vascular cells, including endothelial and smooth muscle cells, release PDGF and/or ET-1 in response to hypoxia. Inflammatory mediators (e.g. IL-1) released in response to hypoxia by endothelial cells enhance the expression of bFGF in nearby SMCs (69). Once present, growth factors such as PDGF-B can also initiate the autocrine production of complementary mitogens such as IGF-I, with which they interact synergistically (42). Similarily, Majack et al (140) have demonstrated that TGF-$\beta$ stimulates increased PDGF-A expression in vascular SMCs. Many of these up-regulated growth factors (e.g. PDGF, bFGF, and ET-1) stimulate PKC activation and can augment responsiveness to other growth factors (e.g. IGFs) and allow proliferation to occur in response to local environmental changes such as hypoxia (45, 46). These findings also emphasize the potential impact that synergistic interactions between different growth stimuli can have in pulmonary vascular remodeling (43–45).

CHANGES IN MATRIX PROTEIN SYNTHESIS BY SMOOTH MUSCLE CELLS DURING THE DEVELOPMENT OF PULMONARY HYPERTENSION    Marked increases in ECM protein synthesis by SMCs in vivo in pulmonary hypertension have been well described (112, 147). Studies in chronically hypoxic adult and neonatal animals from several species uniformly demonstrate increases in the production and accumulation of collagen and elastin in the media of conducting pulmonary arteries. In the adult rat, substantial and rapid increases in the relative rates of connective tissue protein synthesis in the explants of main pulmonary arteries have been demonstrated (191, 207). Within the first few days after blood pressure elevation, relative protein synthesis by vascular medial cells is modestly increased (1.7-fold), yet marked increases in the relative synthetic rates per vessel of collagen (8-fold) and insoluble elastin (9-fold) have been observed. These results have demonstrated a shift toward a greater percent of total protein synthesis devoted to collagen and elastin synthesis in hypertensive SMCs.

Similar findings have been reported in neonatal animals with severe hypoxic pulmonary hypertension (39, 51, 53, 148, 244, 252). Lobar pulmonary artery tissue from hypertensive calves demonstrated an approximately fourfold increase in elastin synthesis and steady-state elastin mRNA levels compared with control vessels. Further studies showed an increase in collagen content, a two- to threefold increase in collagen synthesis, and a twofold increase in the steady-state collagen type I and IV mRNA levels in hypertensive lobar pulmonary arteries. As was observed in the adult rat, no changes in elastin or collagen synthesis were observed over the same time period in the thoracic aorta of the animals. In contrast, SMCs in pulmonary veins demonstrated a marked decrease in elastin and collagen production, demonstrating a regional heterogeneity of the SMC response to chronic hypoxia (185). SMCs cultured from the pulmonary artery of hypertensive animals continued to synthesize increased amounts of elastin and collagen and had increased mRNA levels for elastin and collagen (147). These increases in matrix protein production and mRNA levels persisted through several cell passages. Thus significant changes in the synthetic capability of both adult and neonatal pulmonary artery SMCs appear to occur in response to pulmonary hypertension.

Additional studies were performed with in situ hybridization techniques to determine the spatial distribution and relative concentrations of tropoelastin mRNA production by SMC in intralobar pulmonary arteries during the development of neonatal pulmonary hypertension. Initial studies demonstrated marked differences in the distribution of cells producing elastin in the pulmonary arteries of neonatal calves with pulmonary hypertension compared with controls (194). In 15-day-old control animals, the in situ hybridization signal for tropoelastin mRNA was localized in the inner third of the media. In hypertensive vessels, hybridization signal was observed throughout the entire media of the vessel, and the strongest signal was seen in the outer media. Based on these findings, it was initially hypothesized that SMCs in the outer vessel wall were rapidly recruited into an elastin-producing phenotype during the development of pulmonary hypertension. This could have been due to an increase in the responsiveness of these cells to local humoral or mechanical stimuli. Alternatively, the pattern of tropoelastin gene expression could have been due to a persistence of a fetal pattern of gene expression that was maintained in the face of continued high pressures in the pulmonary circulation.

We found that in the late-gestation fetus, tropoelastin mRNA was expressed by cells throughout the media of the lobar pulmonary artery, but the relative signal strength varied within the vessel wall (252). The strongest signals were detected in the outer medial SMCs, which were separated by dense foci of tropoelastin mRNA negative cells. In normal animals after birth, all of the lobar pulmonary artery gradually thinned, and the pattern of tropoelastin expression was altered markedly. Serial examination of the arteries demonstrated a gradual decrease in signal intensity for tropoelastin mRNA beginning at the outer medial wall and then progressing toward the lumen. At maturity, no consistent hybridization signal was observed in medial SMCs of the lobar pulmonary artery. In the hypoxic calf, however, these age-dependent changes in pulmonary vessel morphology and tropoelastin expression did not occur. Instead, the fetal and early neonatal pattern of tropoelastin expression and wall thickness persisted after 1, 3, 7, and 14 days of hypoxic exposure (252).

Studies in human PPH suggest that this pattern of response is unique to the neonate and is not observed in adult forms of pulmonary hypertension (27). However, the activation or re-expression of tropoelastin by at least some SMCs in the adult vessel wall may represent, at least in part, a reversion to a more fetal or neonatal phenotype of the SMC.

Changes in ECM production, including increased vascular tropoelastin and type I procollagen synthesis and deposition (107, 264), have also been noted in monocrotaline-induced pulmonary hypertension. Re-expression of tropoelastin by endothelial cells has been observed in adult animals as an early and reliable marker for vascular injury. As discussed above, endothelial cells produce elastin early in vascular development although the elastin gene is suppressed in late fetal or early neonatal life.

Using in situ hybridization to identify the vascular compartments responding to monocrotaline injury, Tanaka et al (259) found that active remodeling was induced in two separate and discrete vascular compartments–along the vascular lumen where injury occurred and at the medial-adventitial border distant from the site of injury. The nature of the response differed by location: Tropoelastin expression was found near the lumen, and procollagen expression was found in the medial-adventitial area. Total TGF-$\beta$ protein was fourfold higher in remodeling lungs compared with controls, and gene expression for all three isoforms of TGF-$\beta$ co-localized with regions of active tropoelastin synthesis along the vascular lumen but not with procollagen gene expression (259).

The above studies suggest that increased local production of autocrine or paracrine factors contributes to changes in smooth muscle ECM production (50). Mecham et al (149) have described a soluble factor called smooth muscle elastogenic factor (SMEF) that appears to be produced by hypertensive but not control pulmonary artery SMCs and is capable of exerting significant effects on SMCs as well as neighboring fibroblast and endothelial cells. This factor does not demonstrate any mitogenic properties yet is capable of significantly up-regulating both the elastin- and collagen-producing capabilities of both SMCs and fibroblasts. Further, this factor is capable of inducing the elastogenic phenotype in cells not previously expressing this phenotype. Although this factor has not been identified definitively, its characteristics appear to differ from those of other mitogenic or differentiating factors produced by SMCs. Local changes in factors such as TGF-$\beta$, IGF-I, and IGF-II, agents known to stimulate elastin and collagen synthesis, may occur in response to pulmonary hypertension and act to modify SMC phenotype within the vascular wall (26, 29, 188, 189, 260, 265).

ROLE OF ENDOGENOUS VASCULAR ELASTASES AND PROTEASES IN PULMONARY HYPERTENSION    Several studies have shown that activation of vascular elastase may have a primary causative role in the development of hypertension, particularly in the pulmonary artery. As described above, breaks in the internal elastic membrane are one of the first morphological events observed in pulmonary hypertension (264). Fragmentation of this elastin-rich structure implies the activation of elastases in the vessel wall.

Further, several studies have demonstrated that increases in elastase activity precede other morphological and biochemical responses, including intimal thickening, extension of smooth muscle into peripheral vessels, and increased production of elastin and collagen (142, 264, 280). Inhibition of elastase activity with the serine elastase inhibitors (SC-37698, SC-39026, and $\alpha$-1-antitrypsin), during early stages of both monocrotaline- and hypoxia-induced hypertension prevents or attenuates these structural responses (142, 280), establishing that elastase activity is not only present but may in fact cause the development of pulmonary hypertension. This endogenous vascular elastase is immunologically related to, and may be a derivative of, adipsin, a serine protease first identified in adipocytes (115).

Signals for the early up-regulation of elastase activity have not been delineated fully, but recent data suggest involvement of serum factors and the cell-surface elastin-binding protein linked to tyrosine kinase activation (115).

Moreover, recent studies suggest an increase in activity of a similar elastase in accelerated neointimal formation in coronary arteries following heart transplantation (174).

As mentioned above, endothelial perturbation leads to loss of barrier function. Leak of a serum factor into the subendothelial space and vascular media could thus induce SMC elastase production or activation. The consequences of increased SMC elastase activity include breakdown of growth-inhibitory basement membranes (e.g. perlecan), subsequent activation of transcription factors (e.g. Oct-1; 274), proteolytic release and activation of growth factors stored in the matrix in an inactive form [e.g. bFGF, TGF-$\beta$], stimulation of elastin synthesis by released elastin peptides, and elastin peptide–stimulated chemotaxis (60). SMC thus activated in the vascular media would be prone to excessive proliferation when stimulated by other growth factors released by the endothelial cell or the SMC itself (Figure 7). The net effect of these processes is intimal and/or medial thickening and altered metabolism of SMCs, ultimately leading to luminal narrowing and pulmonary hypertension. Thus early increases in elastase activity, at least in smaller vessels, may have a causative role in the initiation of structural changes associated with pulmonary hypertension, and as a corollary, very early treatment with elastase inhibitors may be useful in repressing the development of hypertension.

HETEROGENEITY OF SMC RESPONSES IN PULMONARY HYPERTENSION    As discussed above, there is increasing evidence that the pulmonary artery is composed of several phenotypically distinct SMC subpopulations. The possibility that these cell populations exhibit unique responses to stress was established by evaluating proliferation and matrix protein production in vivo in response to chronic hypoxia (51, 252, 278). The clusters of highly differentiated SMCs (meta-vinculin-positive cells) in the outer pulmonary arterial media of neonatal calves never expressed collagen or elastin mRNA under either normotensive or hypertensive conditions. Meta-vinculin-negative cells (in the areas between these clusters) (see Figure 4) expressed increased levels of collagen and elastin mRNA in the hypertensive state. Further, marked increases in cell proliferation occurred only in the meta-vinculin negative cells (278).

These observations suggest that not all cells in the vascular wall respond to a hypertensive stimulus in the same way. Each SMC subpopulation identified may respond differently to important stimuli (e.g. hypoxia, mechanical stress, and blood-borne or locally produced growth factors). This heterogeneity in response to various trigger factors could reflect variable responses of SMCs in various states of differentiation. Alternatively, it could provide further evidence for the existence of distinct cell populations, with different lineages, each capable of exhibiting unique responses to stress. Some SMCs may be

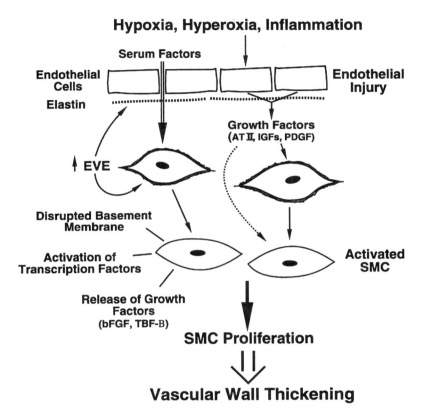

*Figure 7*   Schematic drawing illustrating that injurious stimuli can cause endothelial injury, leading to increased permeation of serum factors into the subendothelial space or vascular media. Concomitantly, growth-promoting factors may be released by the perturbed endothelial cell. Serum factors appear to activate endogenous vascular elastase (EVE), which may not only degrade elastin (producing elastin peptides that can stimulate SMC migration) but may also disrupt the growth-restrictive basement membrane of the mature, quiescent SMCs. This disruption leads to activation of transcription factors (e.g. Oct-1) and release of growth factors from the basement membrane. These activated SMCs may exhibit heightened growth potential to locally present growth factors. Excessive SMC proliferation occurs, leading to vascular wall thickening.

responsible for initiating early responses to trigger factors, while others may participate in the amplification of these signals. Thus it will be important to know which cells are secreting which cytokines, and which cells are expressing receptors that recognize the cytokines. Understanding how these phenotypes are modulated by environmental and developmental triggers will be important in understanding vascular remodeling in disease.

## Adventitial Fibroblast Changes in Pulmonary Hypertension

The earliest and most dramatic structural changes in experimental models of pulmonary hypertension are found in the adventitial compartment. The resident fibroblasts proliferate, hypertrophy, and increase production of matrix proteins in response to locally expressed mitogens, hypoxia, and mechanical stress. What sets these cells apart from neighboring SMCs is their ability to grow directly in response to hypoxia in the absence of exogenous priming factors as well as their augmented responsiveness to mitogens and mechanical stress. Differences in signal transduction pathways and autocrine growth factor expression probably contribute to this enhanced growth and synthetic capacity as well. The existence of fewer local inhibitory mechanisms (i.e. heparan sulfates, prostacyclin, nitric oxide) in the adventitia also may be important. Finally, similar to SMCs in the medial layer, heterogeneity of the pulmonary arterial fibroblast phenotype appears to exist and likely influences susceptibility and pattern of response to chronic hypoxia.

CHANGES IN FIBROBLAST PHENOTYPE DURING THE DEVELOPMENT OF PULMONARY HYPERTENSION    The response of the pulmonary vascular bed to stimuli that lead to the development of pulmonary hypertension (e.g. hypoxia and hyperoxia) differs along its longitudinal axis. While the structural remodeling process that occurs in the large conducting pulmonary arteries appears predominately in the vascular media, and the pericyte and intermediate cells play a major role in the remodeling of the pulmonary microcirculation, the structural changes in the resistance-sized muscular pulmonary arteries are most prominent in the adventitia (207, 250). Indeed, dramatic thickening of the adventitia in small muscular pulmonary arteries, including both increased cellularity and matrix protein deposition, has been observed in newborns dying from persistent pulmonary hypertension (161).

Animal models of pulmonary hypertension support findings in human pathologic specimens. In a neonatal calf model of chronic hypoxic pulmonary hypertension, for instance, the most dramatic structural changes are in the adventitial layer of small pulmonary arteries (53, 250). The structural changes observed result from rapid and dramatic changes in the proliferative and matrix protein–synthesizing phenotypes of the adventitial fibroblast. Increases in proliferation have been demonstrated by increased BrdU uptake and by morphometric studies demonstrating that the increase in DNA synthesis results in an increase in adventitial fibroblast number (14, 53, 177).

In the rat model of hypoxic pulmonary hypertension, the adventitial fibroblast has an earlier and greater proliferative response than either the endothelial cell or SMCs (150). In hyperoxic models of pulmonary hypertension, again the adventitial fibroblast demonstrates the earliest and most dramatic increase in proliferation as measured by $^3[H]^-$ thymidine uptake (103, 104). The increase in proliferation in the hyperoxic model occurs prior to any increase in pulmonary artery pressure, suggesting that in vivo the adventitial fibroblast may be responding directly to oxygen concentration and not to later changes in flow and pressure.

In addition to an increase in the number of fibroblasts observed in the adventitia of hypoxic pulmonary arteries, marked increases in matrix protein deposition have been noted. Particularly striking have been the increases in collagen and elastin described in human and animal studies of pulmonary hypertension. Although the principal matrix component secreted by the adult fibroblast is collagen, in the normal neonatal period, very little type I collagen is produced or accumulates in the vascular wall and little to no type I collagen is produced by the fetal adventitial fibroblast (53, 155). Recent studies have demonstrated a dramatic increase in mRNA expression for type I collagen in neonatal adventitial fibroblasts during the development of hypoxic pulmonary hypertension (53). The appearance of type I collagen in the neonatal fibroblast is particularly interesting because it appears to be the result of the premature induction of type I collagen synthesis. Therefore, hypoxia-induced pulmonary hypertension seems to significantly change the ability of the neonatal adventitial fibroblast to produce type I collagen.

Significant increases in tropoelastin mRNA levels and elastin protein deposition have also been documented in the adventitia of small pulmonary arteries from chronically hypoxic calves (53, 148). This is particularly important because in the mature pulmonary artery, elastin production is normally limited to the SMCs. However, the adventitial fibroblast expresses tropoelastin mRNA during prenatal lung vascular growth and development, which then disappears during normal postnatal development. Perinatal lung injury may interfere with this normal developmental process and cause the fibroblast to re-express fetal-like proteins and genes. Indeed, both immunohistochemical and in situ hybridization studies demonstrate that the adventitial fibroblast produces elastin under chronic hypoxia (53).

During normal pulmonary vascular development, fibronectin mRNA is expressed in high levels in the fetal adventitia of small resistance-sized vessels. Expression of fibronectin mRNA by the fibroblast gradually decreases postnatally. However, in the setting of severe neonatal pulmonary hypertension induced by hypoxia, high fetal-like levels of fibronectin mRNA continue to be expressed in the adventitia. Thus hypoxia induces various but specific changes in matrix protein expression by the fibroblast. There is a fetal-like persistence of fibronectin mRNA expression, a re-expression of tropoelastin mRNA expression, and an induction of type I collagen mRNA expression (53).

In addition to changes in the proliferative and structural protein-producing phenotypes, the pulmonary vascular fibroblast appears to undergo changes in cytoskeletal and contractile protein expression, which may significantly alter fibroblast function (217). Sappino et al (217) suggested that during normal vascular growth and development many mesenchymal cells are capable of expressing SMC markers. They speculated that the population of mesenchymal cells destined to become SMCs persist in their expression of SM contractile proteins (in particular $\alpha$-SM actin), whereas this protein expression is lost in the adventitial fibroblast. There is increased expression (or perhaps re-expression) of $\alpha$-SM actin by fibroblasts (myofibroblasts) in the alveolar walls and vessels in humans with pulmonary hypertension (107). In addition, cells in the adventitia of calves with severe pulmonary hypertension also express $\alpha$-SM actin, suggesting conversion to a myofibrolast-like phenotype or simply re-expression of fetal protein (248). This conversion to a contractile-like cell could have dramatic functional effects on the ability of the pulmonary vasculature to respond to vasoconstrictor and dilator stimuli.

POTENTIAL MECHANISMS CONTRIBUTING TO UNIQUE CHANGES IN FIBROBLAST PHENOTYPE IN PULMONARY HYPERTENSION    Fibroblasts exist as a heterogeneous cell population with functions and activity that change during development and with location within the body (105, 220). They even exist as different subsets within the same specific tissue (105). Fibroblasts also have an inherent phenotypic instability and are able to rapidly change their proliferative and secretory capabilities in response to physiologic or pathophysiologic stimuli. For instance, fibroblasts isolated from human lungs with interstitial fibrotic disease can be separated into several subpopulations that grow at different rates and react differently to mitogenic stimuli (105).

Fetal fibroblasts are especially notable for their phenotypic instability and almost malignant growth characteristics. These cells produce a PDGF-like competence factor and have a proliferative response to TGF-$\beta$ that differs from adult cells (34, 92). They also synthesize different isoforms of matrix molecules from their adult counterparts and form colonies on semi-soft media, a characteristic often associated with neoplastic cells (144). In addition, fibroblasts are able to transform into myofibroblast-like cells with contractile capabilities (68). This inherent phenotypic flexibility allows them to respond quickly and

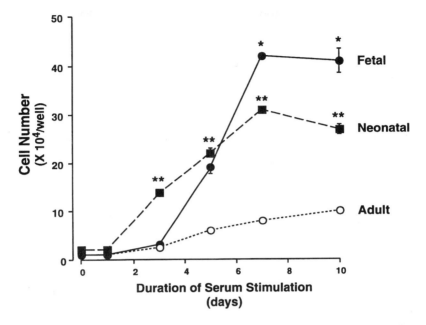

*Figure 8*  Serum-stimulated fetal and neonatal pulmonary artery adventitial fibroblasts grow faster and reach higher plateau densities than do adult cells. Values are means $\pm$ SE. Cells were seeded at low density ($0.5 \times 10^4$ cells/cm$^2$) and grown in MEM/10% serum.

exuberantly to changes in surrounding conditions. However, this same inherent instability and population heterogeneity makes it difficult to study the unique responses of the fibroblast under cell culture conditions.

Proliferation of fibroblasts is enhanced in neonatal compared with adult forms of pulmonary hypertension. Recent studies have demonstrated striking developmental differences in the growth of pulmonary artery adventitial fibroblasts that appears at least partially dependent on developmental differences in the PKC signaling pathway (40). First, under serum-stimulated conditions, fetal and neonatal fibroblasts had increased DNA synthesis, grew faster, and reached higher plateau densities than did adult cells (Figure 8). The earlier during gestation that fetal fibroblasts were harvested, the more rapid the observed growth (Figure 9*a*). Serum-deprived fetal fibroblasts had increased DNA synthesis in response to a panel of potentially relevant mitogens (PMA, IGF-I, PDGF, and PMA plus IGF-I) compared with adult cells. Neonatal fibroblasts had a greater response to the PKC agonist PMA, alone and in combination with IGF-I, than did adult cells.

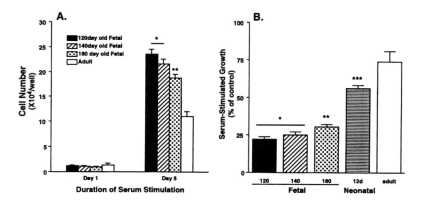

*Figure 9* (A) Growth of fetal pulmonary artery adventitial fibroblasts depends on time of harvest during the fetal period. Fetal (120-, 140-, and 180-day-old) and adult pulmonary artery adventitial fibroblasts were seeded at $0.5 \times 10^4$ cells/cm$^2$ and grown in MEM-10% serum. Medium was supplemented but not replaced on day 4. *: $P < 0.05$ compared with 180-day-old fetal and adult values. **: $P < 0.05$ compared with adult. (B) Fetal and neonatal pulmonary artery adventitial fibroblasts are more sensitive than adult cells to the antiproliferative effects of the protein kinase C (PKC) inhibitor dihydrosphingosine (DS). On day 1, DS (3 mM) or vehicle (EtOH and 2.5 mM bovine serum albumin) was added. Cells were counted on day 1 and day 5. Similar results were obtained if DS was re-added on day 3. *: $P < 0.05$ compared with 180-day-old fetal, neonatal, and adult. **: $P < 0.05$ compared with adult and neonatal. ***: $P < 0.05$ compared with adult. Similar results were obtained with different cell populations in a second independent experiment.

Finally, using three different antagonist strategies and direct measurements of PKC catalytic activity, we demonstrated that the observed developmental differences in serum-stimulated growth were dependent on the PKC signal transduction pathway (Figure 9b). Thus enhanced growth of fetal and neonatal cells may contribute to the dramatic adventitial thickening observed in fetal and neonatal forms of pulmonary hypertension.

Few studies have investigated potential mechanisms contributing to the changes noted in pulmonary artery adventitial fibroblasts that occur during the development of hypoxic pulmonary hypertension. Recent studies, however, show that fibroblasts respond to lowered oxygen tension by increasing thymidine incorporation and accomplishing cell division in the absence of exogenous primiting as is required in SMCs, and that this hypoxia-induced cell proliferation depends on PKC (48, 55, 255). In addition, fibroblasts grown under conditions of hypoxia demonstrate an augmented response to mitogens, including IGF-I, IGF-II, and PDGF, in comparison with fibroblasts grown under 21% oxygen. In terms of matrix protein synthesis, fibroblasts cultured under hypoxic conditions do not demonstrate the decrease in tropoelastin synthesis seen with pulmonary artery SMCs, and collagen synthesis increases in response to hypoxia (56). These experiments indicate a unique ability of the fibroblast to respond directly to hypoxia.

Hypoxia-induced changes in proliferation and matrix synthesis may result from local changes in growth factor production by the fibroblast. Significant increases in IGF-I and IGF-II mRNA expression are observed in vivo in the adventitial fibroblasts of neonatal calves with hypoxic pulmonary hypertension (265). IGF mRNA expression correlates directly with the observed increases in fibroblast proliferation and collagen synthesis. In vitro studies demonstrated that IGF-I and IGF-II stimulate both proliferation and matrix protein synthesis in neonatal pulmonary artery SMCs and fibroblasts. In addition, TGF-$\beta$, an established stimulus for collagen synthesis, increases under hypoxic conditions in dermal fibroblasts (58). Further, the stimulatory effect of hypoxia on procollagen mRNA levels was diminished by antibodies to TGF-$\beta$. Thus at least some hypoxia-mediated changes in fibroblast phenotype are the result of changes in growth factor production by the fibroblast.

## CELLULAR MECHANISMS OF VASCULAR REMODELING IN PRIMARY PULMONARY HYPERTENSION

Studies of PPH in humans have shown two fundamental structural changes in the pulmonary vasculature: the abnormal presence of SM-like cells in normally nonmuscular compartments of the vessel and the abnormal synthesis and deposition of connective tissue proteins within different layers of the vessel wall. The muscular arteries and arterioles are the primary sites of these structural changes in patients with pulmonary hypertension. Medial SMCs extend peripherally into partially muscularized or nonmuscularized arterioles; and medial connective tissue, in particular elastin and collagen, increases (88, 273). A hyperplastic neointima develops, composed of SMCs and ECM proteins, which may partially or completely occlude the vascular lumen. Complex histologic abnormalities, such as plexiform lesions, may be observed. Interestingly, studies demonstrate marked heterogeneity in the vascular changes with some normal vessels decreased even in patients with severe and long-standing PPH. Large vessels in the adult develop a thick, fibrous neointima composed of SM-like cells, macrophages, and ECM (27). In many ways, the neointimal changes in large vessels of the hypertensive lung resemble typical atherosclerotic changes of the systemic vasculature.

Little is known about the regulation of vascular remodeling in humans with PPH. Unfortunately, animal models of pulmonary hypertension have been of limited benefit in elucidating underlying disease mechanisms in the human with PPH because remodeling in animals, in response to hypoxia, hyperoxia, or monocrotaline, is confined largely to the media and adventitia and a neointima does not form in the elastic pulmonary arteries.. Furthermore, models involving neonatal or young animals may not apply to the disease process in adults because remodeling in younger animals must be interpreted against a context of normal vascular growth and development.

Significant advances in elucidating the etiology of the pulmonary vascular remodeling observed in PPH have been made possible because of the availability of freshly harvested human lung tissues removed from patients with PPH at the time of lung transplantation. Molecular biological techniques similar to those used to study animal models of pulmonary hypertension (see above) can be used on this tissue to determine cell phenotypes and to catalog active gene expression within different cell populations of the pulmonary vessels at the time the lung was removed from the patient.

Evidence for active remodeling in vascular tissue associated with late-stage PPH was obtained recently by Botney et al (27). Using immunohistochemistry and in situ hybridization, they found increased expression of elastin, collagen, fibronectin, and thrombospondin (all gene products characteristic of early vascular development) within the thickened intima of hypertensive vessels. Cellular changes as defined by expression of these ECM marker proteins were confined to the neointima in elastic pulmonary arteries but were observed in the media as well as intima of small muscular arteries (26, 27). Vessels in normal adult lungs demonstrated no evidence of cellular activation, at least as measured by the expression of these ECM genes.

The absence of a good animal model of human PPH has made it difficult to identify mediators of vascular remodeling. Several factors described earlier in this review as playing important roles in vascular development and in the vascular response to injury in animal models of pulmonary hypertension, including ACE (221), VEGF (267), endothelin (71), and NO (70), have been observed to change in PPH and undoubtedly play a role, although in most cases, a direct effect of these agents on the remodeling process has been difficult to demonstrate. Recent studies have focused on a possible role for TGF-$\beta$ in the vascular remodeling of PPH because of its known stimulatory effect on collagen and elastin production (146) and its presence in various animal models of pulmonary hypertension.

Immunohistochemistry performed on lung tissue from patients with PPH with isoform-specific TGF-$\beta$ antibodies demonstrated TGF-$\beta$2 and TGF-$\beta$3 in nearly all small muscular pulmonary arteries, in close proximity to areas of activated cells expressing procollagen (26). In large vessels, however, the findings were more complex. Immunohistochemistry revealed two populations of macrophages in the neointima of hypertensive lobar pulmonary arteries. Many macrophages resembled foam cells and tended to be found in clusters deeper within the neointima. A second population of small nonfoamy macrophages, with a small rim of cytoplasm surrounding the nucleus, were observed more frequently within the luminal inner-third of the neointima. These nonfoamy macrophages were in proximity to neointimal cells expressing fibronectin and procollagen (135), as shown by immunohistochemistry combined with in situ hybridization. Immunohistochemistry with isoform-specific TGF-$\beta$ antibodies identified all three isoforms of TGF-$\beta$ associated with nonfoamy macrophages, but no immunoreactivity was associated with foamy macrophages (11). As might be predicted, large, foamy macrophages with extensive cytoplasmic vacuoles were not associated with matrix-expressing intimal cells.

Why neointimal formation occurs in human PPH but not in monocrotaline hypoxia or hyperoxic models of pulmonary hypertension injury is unknown, although recent studies suggest that the combination of vascular injury and changes in hemodynamics may direct the neointimal response. In contrast to systemic arteries, normotensive elastic pulmonary arteries rarely show neointimal or atherosclerotic changes, even in the presence of risk factors for systemic vascular atherosclerosis (11). One explanation for the absence of atherosclerosis-like lesions in pulmonary vessels is the low blood pressure in normal pulmonary arteries, rather than an intrinsic difference between pulmonary and systemic vessels (74).

The differences in hemodynamics between the pulmonary and systemic circulations raise the possibility that neointimal formation may occur in injured pulmonary arteries subjected to systemic hemodynamics. To investigate this possibility, Tanaka et al (260) created subclavian-pulmonary artery anastomoses in rats treated with monocrotaline or subjected to balloon endarterectomy injury. No remodeling, as assessed by increased ECM gene expression, was found in pulmonary vessels subjected to subclavian-pulmonary anastomosis alone. However, a non-neointimal pattern of remodeling following mild monocrotaline-induced injury was converted into a neointimal pattern in the presence of the anastomosis. Tropoelastin, type I procollagen and TGF-$\beta$ gene expression was confined to the neointima and resembled the pattern of gene expression and immunoreactivity in human PPH. In the case of balloon endarterectomy, neointima was also observed even in the absence of anastomosis.

These results confirm previous observations that injury may be required to induce neointimal change in the pulmonary artery and suggest that elevated pressure alone is not perceived by the uninjured elastic pulmonary artery as a sufficient stimulus for neointimal formation. Hemodynamic conditions, however, can modulate the response to injury since neointimal formation is seen following monocrotaline-induced injury in the presence of systemic hemodynamics although no neointima is observed with monocrotaline-treatment in the presence of normal pulmonary hemodynamics. If the injury is severe enough, such as after balloon endarterectomy, neointima will form even in the presence of normal pulmonary hemodynamics.

These findings raise the interesting possibility that injuries initiating pulmonary vascular remodeling in humans may be subtle and that the neointimal formation associated with severe pulmonary hypertension develops secondary to previous or concomitant hemodynamic changes.

*Literature Cited*

1. Adnot S, Raffestin B, Eddahibi S, Braquet P, Chabrier PE. 1991. Loss of endothelium-dependent relaxant activity in the pulmonary circulation of rats exposed to chronic hypoxia. *J. Clin. Invest.* 87:155–62
2. Allen KM, Haworth SG. 1989. Cytoskeletal features of immature pulmonary vascular smooth muscle cells: the influence of pulmonary hypertension on normal development. *J. Pathol.* 158:311–17
3. Arcot SS, Lipke DW, Gillespie MN, Olson JW. 1993. Alterations of growth-factor transcripts in rat lungs during development of monocrotaline-induced pulmonary hypertension. *Biochem. Pharmacol.* 46:1086–91
4. Arnal JF, Battle T, Rasetti C, Challah M, Costerousse O, et al. 1994. ACE in three tunicae of rat aorta: expression in smooth muscle and effect of renovascular hypertension. *Am. J. Physiol.* 267:H1777–84
5. Ashmore RC, Rodman DM, Sato K, Webb SA, O'Brien RF, et al. 1991. Paradoxical constriction of platelets by arteries from rats with pulmonary hypertension. *Am. J. Physiol.* 260:H1929–34
6. Assender JW, Southgate KM, Newby AC. 1992. Does nitric oxide inhibit smooth muscle proliferation? *J. Cardiovasc. Pharmacol.* 17(3):S104–7
7. Au YP, Kenagy RD, Clowes MM, Clowes AW. 1993. Mechanisms of inhibition by heparin of vascular smooth muscle cell proliferation and migration. *Haemostasis* 23:177–82
8. Ausprunk DH. 1986. Distribution of hyaluronic acid and sulfated glycosaminoglycans during blood vessel development in the chick chorioallantoic membrane. *Am. J. Anat.* 177:313–31
9. Ausprunk DH, Dethlefsen SM, Higgins ER. 1991. Distribution of fibronectin, laminin and type IV collagen during development of blood vessels in the chick chorioallantoic membrane. In *The Development of the Vascular System*, ed. RN Feinberg, GK Sherer, R Auerbach, 14:93–108. Basel: Karger Issues Biomed. 192 pp.
10. Badesch DB, Orton EC, Zapp LM, Westcott JY, Hester J, et al. 1989. Decreased arterial wall prostaglandin production in neonatal calves with severe chronic pulmonary hypertension. *Am. J. Respir. Cell Mol. Biol.* 1:489–98
11. Bahadori L, Milder J, Gold LI, Botney MD. 1995. Active macrophage-associated TGF-β colocalizes with type I procollagen gene expression in atherosclerotic human hypertensive pulmonary arteries. *Am. J. Pathol.* 146:1140–49
12. Barer GR, Cai Y, Russell PC, Emery CJ. 1989. Reactivity and site of vasomotion in pulmonary vessels of chronically hypoxic rats: relation to structural changes. *Am. Rev. Respir. Dis.* 140:1483–85
13. Barzu T, Herbert J-M, Desmouliere A, Carayon P, Pascal M. 1994. Characterization of rat aortic smooth muscle cells resistant to the antiproliferative activity of heparin following long-term heparin treatment. *J. Cell. Physiol.* 160:239–48
14. Belknap JK, Orton EC, Ensley B, Tucker A, Stenmark KR. 1996. Hypoxia increases bromodeoxyuridine labeling indices in bovine neonatal pulmonary arteries. *Am. J. Resp. Cell Mol. Biol.* In press
15. Deleted in proof
16. Benitz WE, Bernfield M. 1990. Endothelial cell proteoglycans: possible mediators of vascular response to injury. *Am. J. Respir. Cell Mol. Biol.* 2:407–8
17. Benitz WE, Kelley RT, Anderson CM, Lorant DE, Bernfield M. 1990. Endothelial heparan sulfate proteoglycan. I. Inhibitory effects on smooth muscle cell proliferation. *Am. J. Respir. Cell. Mol. Biol.* 2:13–24
18. Berk BC, Vekshtein V, Gordon HM, Tsuda T. 1989. Angiotensin-II-stimulated protein-synthesis in cultured vascular

smooth-muscle cells. *Hypertension* 13:305–14

19. Berse B, Brown LF, Van De Water L, Dvorak HF, Senger DR. 1992. Vascular permeability factor (vascular endothelial growth factor) gene is expressed differentially in normal tissues, macrophages, and tumors. *Mol. Biol. Cell* 3:211–20

20. Bhat GB, Block ER. 1992. Effect of hypoxia on phospholipid metabolism in porcine pulmonary artery endothelial cells. *Am. J. Physiol.* 262:L606–13

21. Bialecki RA, Kulik TJ, Colucci WS. 1992. Stretching increases calcium influx and efflux in cultured pulmonary arterial smooth muscle cells. *Am. J. Physiol.* 263:L602–6

21a. Bishop JE, Reeves JT, Laurent GJ, eds. 1995. *Pulmonary Vascular Remodeling.* London: Portland. 278 pp.

22. Block ER, Patel JM, Edwards D. 1989. Mechanism of hypoxic injury to pulmonary artery endothelial cell plasma membranes. *Am. J. Physiol.* 257:C223–31

23. Bobik A, Grinpukel S, Little PJ, Grooms A, Jackson G. 1990. Angiotensin II and noradrenaline increase PDGF-BB receptors and potentiate PDGF-BB stimulated DNA synthesis in vascular smooth muscle. *Biochem. Biophys. Res. Commun.* 166:580–88

24. Bobik A, Grooms A, Millar JA, Mitchell A, Grinpukel S. 1990. Growth-factor activity of endothelin on vascular smooth-muscle. *Am. J. Physiol.* 258:C408–15

25. Bonvallet ST, Zamora MR, Hasunuma K, Sato K, Hanasato N, et al. 1994. BQ 123 an ETA receptor antagonist attenuates hypoxic pulmonary hypertension in rats. *Am. J. Physiol.* 266:H1327–31

26. Botney MD, Bahadori L, Gold LI. 1994. Vascular remodeling in primary pulmonary hypertension. Potential role for transforming growth factor-$\beta$. *Am. J. Pathol.* 144:286–95

27. Botney MD, Kaiser LR, Cooper JD, Mecham RP, Parghi D, et al. 1992. Extracellular matrix protein gene expression in atherosclerotic hypertensive pulmonary arteries. *Am. J. Pathol.* 140:357–64

28. Botney MD, Liptay MJ, Kaiser LR, Cooper JD, Parks WC, Mecham RP. 1993. Active collagen synthesis by pulmonary vascular cells in human primary pulmonary hypertension. *Am. J. Pathol.* 143:121–29

29. Botney MD, Parks WC, Crouch EC, Stenmark KR, Mecham RP. 1992. TGF-$\beta$-1 is decreased in remodeling hypertensive bovine pulmonary arteries. *J. Clin. Invest.* 89:1629–35

30. Brain SD, Crossman DC, Buckley TL, Williams TJ. 1989. Endothelin-1 demonstration of potent effects of the microcirculation of human and other species. *J. Cardiovasc. Pharmacol.* 13:S147–50

31. Carey DJ. 1991. Control of growth and differentiation of vascular cells by extracellular matrix proteins. *Annu. Rev. Physiol.* 53:161–77

32. Castelott JJ, Addonzio ML, Rosenberg RD, Karnovsky MJ. 1981. Cultured endothelial cells produce a heparin-like inhibitor of smooth muscle cell growth. *J. Cell. Biol.* 90:372–79

33. Christman BW, McPherson CD, Newman JH, King GA, Bernard GR, et al. 1992. An imbalance between the excretion of thromboxane and prostacyclin metabolites in pulmonary hypertension. *N. Engl. J. Med.* 327:70–75

34. Clemens DR. 1983. Age-dependent production of a competence factor by human fibroblasts. *J. Cell. Physiol.* 114:61–67

35. Clozel J-P, Saunier C, Hartemann D, Fischli W. 1991. Effects of cilazapril, a novel angiotensin converting enzyme inhibitor, on the structure of pulmonary arteries of rats exposed to chronic hypoxia. *J. Cardiovasc. Pharmacol.* 17:36–40

36. Cook CL, Weiser MCM, Schwartz PE, Jones CL, Majack RA. 1993. Developmentally timed expression of an embryonic growth phenotype in vascular smooth muscle cells. *Circ. Res.* 74:189–96

37. Cornfield DN, Stevens T, McMurtry IF, Abman SH, Rodman DM. 1993. Acute hypoxia increases cytosolic calcium in fetal pulmonary artery smooth muscle cells. *Am. J. Physiol.* 265:L53–56

38. Crapo JD, Barry BE, Gehr P, Bachofen M, Weibel ER. 1982. Cell number and cell characteristics of the normal human lung. *Am. Rev. Respir. Dis.* 125:332

39. Crouch EC, Parks WC, Rosenbaum JL, Chang D, Whitehouse L, et al. 1989. Regulation of collagen production by medial smooth muscle cells in hypoxic pulmonary hypertension. *Am. Rev. Respir. Dis.* 140:1045–51

40. Das M, Stenmark KR, Dempsey EC. 1995. Enhanced growth of fetal and neonatal pulmonary artery adventitial fibroblasts is dependent on protein kinase C. *Am. J. Physiol.* 269:L660–67

41. Davidson JM, Hill KE, Mason ML, Giro MG. 1985. Longitudinal gradient of collagen and elastin gene expression in the

porcine aorta. *J. Biol. Chem.* 260:1901–08

42. Delafontaine P, Lou H, Alexander RW. 1991. Regulation of insulin-like growth factor I messenger RNA levels in vascular smooth muscle cells. *Hypertension* 18:742–47

43. Dempsey EC. 1992. Hypoxia alone stimulates translocation of PKC and when combined with PMA can augment phorbol-ester-induced activation of the same pathway in bovine PA SMC. *Am. Rev. Respir. Dis.* 146:A568

44. Dempsey EC, Badesch DB, Dobyns E, Stenmark KR. 1994. Enhanced growth capacity of neonatal pulmonary artery smooth muscle cells in vitro: dependence on cell size, time of harvest, insulin-like growth factor-1, and auto-activation of protein kinase C. *J. Cell Physiol.* 160:469–81

45. Dempsey EC, Das M, Frid MG, Stenmark KR. 1996. Unique growth properties of neonatal pulmonary vascular cells: importance of time- and site-specific responses, cell-cell interaction, and synergy. *J. Perinatol.* 16:S2–11

46. Dempsey EC, McMurtry IF, O'Brien RF. 1991. Protein kinase C activation allows pulmonary artery smooth muscle cells to proliferate to hypoxia. *Am. J. Physiol.* 260:L136–45

47. Dempsey EC, Stenmark KR, McMurtry IF, O'Brien RF, Voelkel NF, Badesch DB. 1990. Insulin-like growth factor I and protein kinase C activation stimulate pulmonary artery smooth muscle cell proliferation through separate but synergistic pathways. *J. Cell. Physiol.* 144:159–65

48. Dempsey EC, Walchak SJ, Peach JL, Stenmark KR. 1992. Adult bovine PA adventitial fibroblasts, but not matched SMC, have a potential PKC-dependent autocrine growth loop. *Am. Rev. Respir. Dis.* 145:A481

49. Dinh-Xuan AT, Higenbottam TW, Clelland CA, Pepke-Zaba J, Cremona G, et al. 1991. Impairment of endothelium-dependent pulmonary-artery relaxation in chronic obstructive lung disease. *N. Engl. J. Med.* 324:1539–47

50. Durmowicz AG, Badesch DB, Stenmark KR. 1990. Elastin production under hypoxic conditions is influenced by vascular wall cell-cell interaction. *Am. Rev. Respir. Dis.* 141:A187

51. Durmowicz AG, Frid MG, Wohrley JD, Stenmark KR. 1996. Expression and localization of tropoelastin mRNA in the developing bovine pulmonary artery is dependent on vascular cell phenotype.

*Am. J. Respir. Cell Mol. Biol.* 14:569–76

52. Durmowicz AG, Orton EC, Stenmark KR. 1993. Progressive loss of vasodilator responsive component of pulmonary hypertension in neonatal calves exposed to 4,570m. *Am. J. Physiol.* 265:H2175–83

53. Durmowicz AG, Parks WC, Hyde DM, Mecham RP, Stenmark KR. 1994. Persistence, re-expression, and induction of pulmonary arterial fibronectin, tropoelastin, and type I procollagen mRNA expression in neonatal hypoxic pulmonary hypertension. *Am. J. Pathol.* 145:1411–20

54. Dzau VJ, Gibbons GH. 1993. Vascular remodeling: mechanisms and implications. *J. Cardiovasc. Pharmacol.* 21(1):S1–S5

55. Falanga V, Kirsner RS. 1993. Low oxygen stimulates proliferation of fibroblasts seeded as single cells. *J. Cell. Physiol.* 154:506–10

56. Falanga V, Martin TA, Takagi H, Kirsner RS, Helfman T, et al. 1993. Low oxygen tension increases mRNA levels of alpha-1 (I) procollagen in human dermal fibroblasts. *J. Cell. Physiol.* 157:408–12

57. Ferrara N, Houck K, Jakeman L, Leung DW. 1992. Molecular and biological properties of the vascular endothelial growth factor family of proteins. *Endocrinol. Rev.* 13:18–32

58. Flamme I, Breier G, Risau W. 1995. Vascular endothelial growth factor (VEGF) and VEGF receptor 2 (flk-1) are expressed during vasculogenesis and vascular differentiation in the quail embryo. *Dev. Biol.* 169:699–712

59. Form DM, Pratt BM, Madri JA. 1986. Endothelial cell proliferation during angiogenesis. In vitro modulation by basement membrane components. *Lab. Invest.* 55:521–30

60. Foster JA, Rich CB, Miller MF. 1990. Pulmonary fibroblasts, an in vitro model of emphysema. Regulation of elastin gene expression. *J. Biol. Chem.* 265:14444–49

61. Frid MG, Moiseeva EP, Stenmark KR. 1994. Multiple phenotypically distinct smooth muscle cell populations exist in the adult and developing bovine pulmonary arterial media in vivo. *Circ. Res.* 75:669–81

62. Frid MG, Shekhonin BV, Koteliansky VE, Glukhova MA. 1992. Phenotypic changes of human smooth muscle cells during development: late expression of heavy caldesmon and calponin. *Dev. Biol.* 153:185–93

63. Frid MG, Stenmark KR. 1994. An immature smooth muscle cell subpopulation exists in the normal adult bovine pul-

monary arterial media. *Am. J. Respir. Crit. Care Med.* 149:A823

64. Frid MG, Stenmark KR. 1995. Distinct adult bovine arterial smooth muscle cell subpopulations exhibit unique growth characteristics in vitro. *Am. J. Respir. Crit. Care Med.* 151:A526

65. Fritze LM, Reilly CF, Rosenberg RD. 1985. An antiproliferative heparan sulfate species produced by postconfluent smooth muscle cells. *J. Cell. Biol.* 100:1041–49

66. Fujita H, Shimokado K, Yutani C, Takaichi S, Masuda J, Ogata J. 1993. Human neonatal and adult vascular smooth muscle cells in culture. *Exp. Mol. Pathol.* 58:25–39

67. Furukawa K-I, Tansada Y, Shigekawa M. 1989. Protein kinase C activation stimulates plasma membrane $Ca^{2+}$ pump in cultured vascular smooth muscle cells. *J. Biol. Chem.* 264:4844–49

68. Gabbiani G, Hirschel BJ, Ryan GB, Statkov PR, Majno G. 1972. Granulation tissue as a contractile organ. A study of structure and function. *J. Exp. Med.* 135:719

69. Gay CG, Winkles JA. 1991. Interleukin 1 regulates heparin-binding growth factor 2 gene expression in vascular smooth muscle cells. *Proc. Natl. Acad. Sci. USA* 88:296–300

70. Giaid A, Saleh D. 1995. Reduced expression of endothelial nitric oxide synthase in the lungs of patients with pulmonary hypertension. *N. Engl. J. Med.* 333:214–21

71. Giaid A, Yanagisawa M, Langleben D, Michel RP, Levy R, et al. 1993. Expression of endothelin-1 in the lungs of patients with pulmonary hypertension. *N. Engl. J. Med.* 328:1732–39

72. Gibbons GH, Pratt RE, Dzau VJ. 1992. Vascular smooth muscle cell hypertrophy versus hyperplasia. Autocrine transforming growth factor-$\beta$-1 expression determines growth response to angiotensin II. *J. Clin. Invest.* 90:456–61

73. Gillespie MN, Rippetoe PE, Haven CA, Shiao R-T, Orlinska U, et al. 1989. Polyamines and epidermal growth-factor in monocrotaline-induced pulmonary-hypertension. *Am. Rev. Respir. Dis.* 140:1463–66

74. Glagov S, Ozoa AK. 1968. Significance of the relatively low incidence of atherosclerosis in the pulmonary, renal, and mesenteric arteries. *Ann. NY Acad. Sci.* 149:940–55

75. Glukhova MA, Frid MG, Koteliansky VE. 1990. Developmental changes in expression of contractile and cytoskeletal proteins in human aortic smooth muscle. *J. Biol. Chem.* 265:13042–46

76. Glukhova MA, Frid MG, Shekhonin BV, Balabanov YV, Koteliansky VE. 1990. Expression of fibronectin variants in vascular and visceral smooth muscle cells in development. *Dev. Biol.* 141:1930–02

77. Glukhova MA, Kabakov AE, Belkin AM, Frid MG, Ornatsky OI, et al. 1986. Metavinculin distribution in adult human tissues and cultured cells. *FEBS Lett.* 207:139–41

78. Glukhova MA, Kabakov AE, Frid MG, Ornatsky OL, Belkin AM, et al. 1988. Modulation of human aorta smooth muscle cell phenotype: a study of muscle-specific variants of vinculin, caldesmon, and actin expression. *Proc. Natl. Acad. Sci. USA* 85:9542–46

79. Gold ME, Wood KS, Byrns RE, Fukato J, Ignaro LJ. 1990. NG-methyl-L-arginine causes endothelium-dependent contraction and inhibition of cyclic GMP formation in artery and vein. *Proc. Natl. Acad. Sci. USA* 87:4430–34

80. Gopalakrishna R, Anderson WB. 1989. $Ca^{2+}$-and phospholipid-independent activation of protein kinase C by selective oxidative modification of the regulatory domain. *Proc. Natl. Acad. Sci. USA* 86:6758–62

81. Gospodarowicz D, Ferrara N, Schweigerer L, Neufeld G. 1987. Structural characterization and biological functions of fibroblast growth factor. *Endocrinol. Rev.* 8:95–114

82. Grady EF, Sechi LA, Griffin CA, Schambelan M, Kalinyak JE. 1991. Expression of AT2 receptors in the developing rat fetus. *J. Clin. Invest.* 88:921–33

83. Hall SM, Haworth SG. 1986. Conducting pulmonary arteries: structural adaptation to extra-uterine life. *Cardiovasc. Res.* 21:208–16

84. Han RNN, Mawdsley C, Souza P, Tanswell AK, Post M. 1992. Platelet-derived growth factors and growth-related genes in rat lung. III. Immunolocalization during fetal development. *Pediatr. Res.* 31:323–29

85. Hasunuma K, Yamaguchi T, Rodman DM, O'Brien FR, McMurtry IF. 1991. Effects of inhibitors of EDRF and EDHF on vasoreactivity of perfused rat lungs. *Am. J. Physiol.* 260(4):L97–104

86. Haven CA, Olson JW, Arcot SS, Gillespie MN. 1992. Polyamine transport and ornithine decarboxylase activity in hypoxic pulmonary artery smooth muscle

cells. *Am. J. Respir. Cell Mol. Biol.* 7:286–92

87. Haworth SG. 1993. Pulmonary hypertension in childhood. *Eur. Respir. J.* 6:1037–43

88. Heath D, Wood E, Dushane J, Edwards J. 1959. The structure of the pulmonary trunk at different ages and in cases of pulmonary hypertension and pulmonary stenosis. *J. Pathol. Bacteriol.* 77:443–50

89. Hedin U, Bottger BA, Forsberg E, Johansson S, Thyberg J. 1988. Diverse effects of fibronectin and laminin on phenotypic properties of cultured arterial smooth muscle cells. *J. Cell Biol.* 107:307–19

90. Hedin U, Holm J, Hansson GK. 1991. Induction of tenascin in rat arterial injury. Relationship to altered smooth muscle cell phenotype. *Am. J. Pathol.* 139:649–56

91. Herbst TJ, McCarthy JB, Tsilibary EC, Furcht LT. 1988. Differential effects of laminin, intact type IV collagen, and specific domains of type IV collagen on endothelial cell adhesion and migration. *J. Cell Biol.* 106:1365–73

92. Hill DJ, Strain SF, Elstow SF, Swenne I, Milner RDG. 1986. Bifunctional action of transforming growth factor-$\beta$ on DNA synthesis in early passage human fetal fibroblasts. *J. Cell Physiol.* 128:322–28

93. Hirata Y, Takagi Y, Fukunda Y, Marumo F. 1989. Endothelin is a potent mitogen for rat vascular smooth muscle cells. *Atherosclerosis* 78:225–28

94. Ho AK, Thomas TP, Chik CL, Anderson WB, Klein DC. 1988. Protein kinase C: subcellular redistribution by increased $Ca^{2+}$ influx. *J. Biol. Chem.* 263:9292–97

95. Hsieh H-J, Li N-Q, Frangos JA. 1991. Shear stress increases endothelial platelet-derived growth factor mRNA levels. *Am. J. Physiol.* 260:H642–46

96. Hung K-S, McKenzie JC, Mattioli L, Klein RM, Menon CD, Poulose AK. 1986. Scanning electron microscopy of pulmonary vascular endothelium in rats with hypoxia-induced hypertension. *Acta Anat.* 126:13–20

97. Hynes RO, Yamada KM. 1982. Fibronectins: multifunctional modular glycoproteins. *J. Cell Biol.* 95:369–77

98. Ido M, Sekiguchi K, Kikkawa U, Nishizuka Y. 1987. Phosphorylation of the EGF receptor from A431 epidermoid carcinoma cells by three distinct types of PKC. *FEBS Lett.* 219:215–18

99. Ishikawa F, Miyazono K, Hellman U, Drexler H, Wernstedt C, et al. 1989. Identification of angiogenic activity and the cloning and expression of platelet-derived endothelial cell growth factor. *Nature* 338:557–62

100. Ishimitsu T, Uehara Y, Ishii M, Ikeda T, Matsuoka H, Sugimoto T. 1988. Thromboxane and vascular smooth-muscle cell growth in genetically hypertensive rats. *Hypertension* 12:46–51

101. Jahn L, Kreuzer J, von Hodenberg E, Kubler W, Franke WW, et al. 1993. Cytokeratins 8 and 18 in smooth muscle cells. Detection in human coronary artery, peripheral vascular, and vein graft disease and in transplantation-associated arteriosclerosis. *Arterioscler. Thromb.* 13:1631–39

102. Jones KW, Shapero MH, Chevrettm M, Fournier REK. 1991. Subtractive hybridization cloning of tissue-specific extinguisher: TSE1 encodes a regulatory subunit of protein kinase A. *Cell* 66:861–72

103. Jones R, Adler C, Farber F. 1989. Lung vascular cell proliferation in hyperoxic pulmonary hypertension and return to air: [$^3$H]-thymidine pulse-labeling of intimal, medial, and adventitial cells in microvessels and at the hilum. *Am. Rev. Respir. Dis.* 140:1471–77

104. Jones R, Reid L. 1995. Vascular remodeling in clinical and experimental pulmonary hypertensions. See Ref. 21a, 3:47–115

105. Jordana M, Schulman J, McSharky C, Irving LB, Newhouse MT, et al. 1988. Heterogeneous proliferative characteristics of human adult lung fibroblast lines and clinically derived fibroblasts from control and fibrotic tissue. *Am. Rev. Respir. Dis.* 137:579–84

106. Kahaleh MB. 1991. Endothelin, an endothelial dependent vasoconstrictor in scleroderma enhanced production and profibrotic action. *Arthritis Rheum.* 34:978–83

107. Kameji R, Otsuka H, Hayashi Y. 1980. Increase of collagen synthesis in pulmonary arteries of monocrotaline-treated rats. *Experientia* 36:441–42

108. Kapanci Y, Burgan S, Pietra GG, Conne B, Gabbiani G. 1990. Modulation of actin isoform expression in alveolar myofibroblasts (contractile interstitial cells) during pulmonary hypertension. *Am. J. Pathol.* 136:881–90

109. Katayose D, Ohe M, Yamauchi K, Ogata M, Shirato K, et al. 1993. Increased expression of PDGF A- and B-chain genes in rat lungs with hypoxic pulmonary hypertension. *Am. J. Physiol.* 264:L100–6

110. Kawahara Y, Sunako M, Tsuda T, Fukuzaki H, Fukumoto Y, Takai Y. 1988. Angiotensin-II induces expression of the c-fos gene through protein kinase-c activation and calcium mobilization in cultured vascular smooth-muscle cells. *Biochem. Biophys. Res. Commun.* 150:52–59

111. Kay JM, Keane PM, Suyama KL, Gauthier D. 1982. Angiotensin converting enzyme activity and evolution of pulmonary vascular disease in rats with monocrotaline pulmonary hypertension. *Thorax* 37:88–96

112. Keeley FW, Rabinovitch M. 1995. Vascular matrix metabolism in hypertension. See Ref. 21a, 5:149–69

113. Kim DK, Zhang L, Dzau VJ, Pratt RE. 1994. H19, a developmentally regulated gene, is reexpressed in rat vascular smooth muscle cells after injury. *J. Clin. Invest.* 93:355–60

114. Kingsley DM. 1994. The TGF-$\beta$ superfamily: new members, new receptors, and new genetic tests of function in different organisms. *Genes Dev.* 8:133–46

115. Kobayashi J, Wigle D, Childs T, Zhu L, Keeley FW, Rabinovitch M. 1994. Serum-induced vascular smooth muscle cell elastolytic activity through tyrosine kinase intracellular signalling. *J. Cell. Physiol.* 160:121–31

116. Kocher O, Gabbiani G. 1986. Expression of actin mRNA in rat aortic smooth muscle cells during development, experimental intimal thickening, and culture. *Differentiation* 32:245–51

117. Kocher O, Skalli O, Bloom WS, Gabbiani G. 1984. Cytoskeleton of rat aortic smooth muscle cells. Normal conditions and experimental intimal thickening. *Lab. Invest.* 50:645–52

118. Kohno M, Chatani Y, Tanaka E, Hattori A, Nishizawa N. 1992. Mitogen-induced tyrosine phosphorylation of 41 kDa and 43 kDa proteins. *Biochem. J.* 287:917–24

119. Komuro I, Katoh Y, Kaida T, Shibazaki Y, Kurabayashi M, et al. 1991. Mechanical loading stimulates cell hypertrophy and specific gene expression in cultured rat myocytes–possible role of protein kinase C activation. *J. Biol. Chem.* 266:1265–68

120. Komuro I, Kurihara H, Sugiyama T, Takaku F, Yazaki Y. 1988. Endothelin stimulates c-fos and c-myc expression and proliferation of vascular smooth-muscle cells. *FEBS Lett.* 238:249–52

121. Kornblihtt AR, Umezawa K, Vige-Pedersen K, Baralle F. 1985. Primary structure of human fibronectin: Differential splicing may generate at least 10 polypeptides from a single gene. *EMBO J.* 4:1755–59

122. Kourembanas S, Hannan RL, Faller DV. 1990. Oxygen tension regulates the expression of the platelet-derived growth factor-$\beta$ chain gene in human endothelial cells. *J. Clin. Invest.* 86:670–74

123. Kourembanas S, McQuillan LP, Leung GK, Faller DV. 1993. Nitric oxide regulates the expression of vasoconstrictors and growth factors by vascular endothelium under both normoxia and hypoxia. *J. Clin. Invest.* 92:99–104

124. Kratochwil K, Dziadek M, Lohler J, Harbers K, Jaenisch R. 1986. Normal epithelial branching morphogenesis in the absence of collagen. *Dev. Biol.* 117:596–606

125. Kubota Y, Kleinman HK, Martin GR, Lawley TJ. 1988. Role of laminin and basement membrane in the morphological differentiation of human endothelial cells in capillary-like structures. *J. Cell Biol.* 107:1589–98

126. Kurihara Y, Kurihara H, Oda H, Maemura K, Nagai R, et al. 1995. Aortic arch malformations and ventricular septal defect in mice deficient in endothelin-1. *J. Clin. Invest.* 96:293–300

127. Kuro-O M, Nagai R, Tsuchimochi H, Katoh H, Yazaki Y, et al. 1989. Developmentally regulated expression of vascular smooth muscle myosin heavy chain isoforms. *J. Biol. Chem.* 264:18272–75

128. Langleben D, Serban L, Blais D, Mohamed F, Stewart DJ. 1991. Hypoxia stimulates endothelin-1 release from PA SMC in vitro. *Circulation* 84(II):A92

129. Lawson KA. 1983. Stage specificity in the mesenchyme requirement of rodent lung epithelium in vitro: a matter of growth control? *J. Embryol. Exp. Morphol.* 74:183–206

130. Lemire JM, Covin CW, White S, Giachelli CM, Schwartz SM. 1994. Characterization of cloned aortic smooth muscle cells from young rats. *Am. J. Pathol.* 144:1068–81

131. Lester DS, Collin C, Etcheberrigaray R, Alkon DL. 1991. Arachidonic acid and diacylglycerol act synergistically to activate protein kinase C in vitro and in vivo. *Biochem. Biophys. Res. Commun.* 179:1522–28

132. Leung DYM, Glagov S, Mathews MB. 1977. Elastin and collagen accumulation in rabbit ascending aorta and pulmonary trunk during postnatal growth. *Circ. Res.* 41:316–23

133. Levine AJ. 1993. The tumor suppressor genes. *Annu. Rev. Biochem.* 62:623–51

134. Li X, Tsai P, Wieder ED, Kribben A, Van

Putten V, et al. 1994. Vascular smooth muscle cells grown on Matrigel. A model of the contractile phenotype with decreased activation of mitogen-activated protein kinase. *J. Biol. Chem.* 269:19653–58

135. Liptay MJ, Parks WC, Mecham RP, Roby J, Kaiser LR, et al. 1993. Neointimal macrophages co-localize with extracellular matrix gene expression in human atherosclerotic pulmonary arteries. *J. Clin. Invest.* 91:588–94

136. Lynch DC, Ansel PL, Levine RB. 1988. Effects of anoxia on gene expression in human endothelial cells. *J. Cell Biol.* 107(6):A581

137. MacCumber MW, Ross CA, Glaser BM, Snyder SH. 1989. Endothelin: visualization of mRNAs by in situ hybridization provides evidence for local action. *Proc. Natl. Acad. Sci. USA* 86:7285–89

138. Majack RA. 1995. Extinction of autonomous growth potential in embryonic:adult vascular smooth muscle cell heterokaryons. *J. Clin. Invest.* 95:464–68

139. Majack RA, Clowes AW. 1984. Inhibition of vascular smooth muscle cell migration by heparin-like glycosaminoglycans. *J. Cell. Physiol.* 118:253–56

140. Majack RA, Majesky MW, Goodman LV. 1990. Role of PDGF-A expression in the control of vascular smooth muscle cell growth by transforming growth factor-$\beta$. *J. Cell Biol.* 111:139–47

141. Majesky MW, Giachelli CM, Reidy MA, Schwartz SM. 1992. Rat carotid neointimal smooth muscle cells reexpress a developmentally regulated mRNA phenotype during repair of arterial injury. *Circ. Res.* 71:759–68

142. Maruyama K, Ye C, Woo M, Venkatacharya H, Lines LD, et al. 1991. Chronic hypoxic pulmonary hypertension in rats and increased elastolytic activity. *Am. J. Physiol.* 261:H1716–26

143. Masters JRW. 1976. Epithelial-mesenchymal interaction during lung development: the effect of mesenchymal mass. *Dev. Biol.* 51:98–108

144. Matsura H, Hakomori SI. 1985. The oncofetal domain of fibronectin defined by a monoclonal antibody FDC-6: it's presence in fetal and tumor tissues and its absence in those from normal tissue and plasma. *Proc. Natl. Acad. Sci. USA* 83:6517–21

145. Maxwell PH, Pugh CW, Ratcliffe PJ. 1993. Inducible operation of the erythropoietin 3' enhancer in multiple cell lines: evidence for a widespread oxygen-sensing mechanism. *Proc. Natl. Acad. Sci. USA* 90:2423–27

146. McGowan SE. 1992. Extracellular matrix and the regulation of lung development and repair. *FASEB J.* 6:2895–904

147. Mecham RP, Stenmark KR, Parks WC. 1991. Connective tissue production by vascular smooth muscle in development and disease. *Chest* 99:43S–47S

148. Mecham RP, Whitehouse LA, Wrenn DS, Parks WC, Griffin GL, et al. 1987. Smooth muscle–mediated connective tissue remodeling in pulmonary hypertension. *Science* 237:423–26

149. Meyrick B, Reid L. 1978. The effect of continued hypoxia on rat pulmonary arterial circulation. An ultrastructural study. *Lab. Invest.* 38:188–200

150. Meyrick B, Reid L. 1979. Hypoxia and incorporation of $^3$H-thymidine by cells of the rat pulmonary arteries and alveolar wall. *Am. J. Pathol.* 96:51–70

151. Meyrick B, Reid L. 1980. Endothelial and subintimal changes in rat hilar pulmonary artery during recovery from hypoxia. *Lab. Invest.* 42:603–15

152. Meyrick B, Reid L. 1980. Hypoxia-induced structural changes in the media and adventitia of the rat hilar pulmonary artery and their regression. *Am. J. Pathol.* 100:151–78

153. Meyrick BO, Perkett EA. 1989. The sequence of cellular and hemodynamic changes of chronic pulmonary hypertension induced by hypoxia and other stimuli. *Am. Rev. Respir. Dis.* 140:1486–89

154. Millauer B, Wizigmann-Voos S, Schnrch H, Martinez R, Moller NPH, et al. 1993. High affinity VEGF binding and developmental expression suggest Flk-1 as a major regulator of vasculogenesis and angiogenesis. *Cell* 72:835–46

155. Mills AN, Haworth SG. 1987. Pattern of connective tissue development in swine pulmonary vasculature by immunolocalization. *J. Pathol.* 153:171–76

156. Mitsuka M, Berk BC. 1991. Long-term regulation of $Na^+$-$H^+$ exchange in vascular smooth muscle cells: role of protein kinase C. *Am. J. Physiol.* 260:C562–69

157. Monacci WT, Merrill MJ, Oldfield EH. 1993. Expression of vascular permeability factor/vascular endothelial growth factor in normal rat tissues. *Am. J. Physiol.* 264:C995–1002

158. Morin FC, Stenmark KR. 1995. Persistent pulmonary hypertension of the newborn. State-of-the-Art. *Am. J. Respir. Crit. Care Med.* 151:2010–32

159. Morrell NW, Atochina EN, Morris KG,

Danilov SM, Stenmark KR. 1995. Angiotensin converting enzyme expression is increased in small pulmonary arteries of rats with hypoxia-induced pulmonary hypertension. *J. Clin. Invest.* 96:1823–33

160. Morrell NW, Grieshaber SS, Danilov SM, Majack RA, Stenmark KR. 1996. Developmental regulation of angiotensin converting enzyme and angiotensin type I receptor in the rat pulmonary circulation. *Am. J. Respir. Cell. Mol. Biol.* 14:569-76

161. Murphy JD, Rabinovitch M, Goldstein JD, Reid LM. 1981. The structural basis of persistent pulmonary hypertension of the newborn infant. *J. Pediatr.* 98(6):962–67

162. Muthuchamy M, Pajak L, Howles P, Doetschman T, Wieczorek DF. 1993. Developmental analysis of trypomyosin gene expression in embryonic stem cells and mouse embryos. *Mol. Cell. Biol.* 13:3311–23

163. Myers B, Dubich M, Last JA, Ruche RB. 1983. Elastin synthesis during perinatal lung development in the rat. *Biochem. Biophys. Acta* 761:17–22

164. Nakaki T, Nakayama M, Kato R. 1990. Inhibition by nitric oxide and nitric oxide-producing vasodilators of DNA synthesis in vascular smooth muscle cells. *Eur. J. Pharmacol.* 189:347–53

165. Nemecek GM, Coughlin SR, Handley DA, Moskowitz MA. 1986. Stimulation of aortic smooth-muscle cell mitogenesis by serotonin. *Proc. Natl. Acad. Sci. USA* 83:674–78

166. Newby AC, Southgate KM, Assender JW. 1992. Inhibition of vascular smooth muscle cell proliferation by endothelium-dependent vasodilators. *Herz* 17(5):291–99

167. Neylon CB, Avdonin PV, Dilley RJ, Larsen MA, Tkachuk VA, Bobik A. 1994. Different electrical responses to vasoactive agonists in morphologically distinct smooth muscle cell types. *Circ. Res.* 75:733–41

168. Nilsson J, Von Euler AM, Dalsgaard CJ. 1985. Stimulation of connective-tissue cell-growth by substance-P and substance-K. *Nature* 315:61–63

169. Nishizuka Y. 1992. Intracellular signaling by hydrolysis of phospholipids and activation of protein kinase C. *Science* 258:607–14

170. O'Connor KJ, Knowles RG, Patel KD. 1991. Nitrovasodilators have proliferative as well as antiproliferative effects. *J. Cardiovasc. Pharmacol.* 17(3):S100–3

171. Ogawa S, Clauss M, Kuwabara K, Shreeniwas R, Butura C, et al. 1991. Hypoxia induces endothelial cell synthesis of membrane-associated proteins. *Proc. Natl. Acad. Sci. USA* 88(21):9897–901

172. Ogawa S, Gerlach H, Esposito C, Pasagian-Macaulay A, Brett J, Stern D. 1990. Hypoxia modulates the barrier and coagulant function of cultured bovine endothelium. Increased monolayer permeability and induction of procoagulant properties. *J. Clin. Invest.* 85(4):1090–98

173. Ogawa S, Koga S, Kuwabara K, Brett J, Morrow B, et al. 1992. Hypoxia-induced increased permeability of endothelial monolayers occurs through lowering of cellular cAMP levels. *Am. J. Physiol.* 262:C546–54

174. Oho S, Rabinovitch M. 1994. Postcardiac transplant arteriopathy in piglets is associated with fragmentation of elastin and increased activity of a serine elastase. *Am. J. Pathol.* 145:202–10

175. Oka M, Hasunuma K, Webb SA, Stelzner TJ, Rodman DM, McMurtry IF. 1993. EDRF suppresses an unidentified vasoconstrictor mechanism in hypertensive rat lungs. *Am. J. Physiol.* 264(8):L587–97

176. Oparil S, Narkates AJ, Jackson RM, Ann HS. 1988. Altered angiotensin converting enzyme in lung and extrapulmonary tissues of hypoxia adapted rats. *J. Appl. Physiol.* 65:218–27

177. Orton EC, LaRue SM, Ensley B, Stenmark KR. 1992. Bromodeoxyuridine labeling and DNA content of pulmonary arterial medial cells from hypoxia-exposed and non-exposed healthy calves. *Am. J. Vet. Res.* 53:1925–30

178. Orton EC, Raffestin B, McMurtry IF. 1990. Protein kinase C is a determinant of rat pulmonary vascular reactivity. *Am. Rev. Respir. Dis.* 141:654–58

179. Orton EC, Reeves JT, Stenmark KR. 1988. Pulmonary vasodilation with structurally altered pulmonary vessels and pulmonary hypertension. *J. Appl. Physiol.* 65:2459–67

180. Osborn M, Caselitz J, Weber K. 1981. Heterogeneity of intermediate filament expression in vascular smooth muscle: a gradient in desmin positive cells from the rat aortic arch to the level of the arteria iliaca communis. *Differentiation* 20:196–202

181. Owens GK. 1995. Regulation of differentiation of vascular smooth muscle cells. *Physiol. Rev.* 75:487–17

182. Owens GK. 1989. Control of hypertrophic versus hyperplastic growth of vascular smooth muscle cells. *Am. J. Physiol.* 257:H1755–65

183. Palmberg L, Claesson HE, Thyberg J. 1987. Leukotrienes stimulate initiation

of DNA-synthesis in cultured arterial smooth-muscle cells. *J. Cell Sci.* 88:151–59

184. Pardanaud L, Yassine F, Dieterlen-Lievre F. 1989. Relationship between vasculogenesis, angiogenesis and haemopoiesis during avian ontogeny. *Development* 105:473–85

185. Parks WC, Mecham RP, Crouch EC, Orton EC, Stenmark KR. 1989. Response of lobar vessels to hypoxic pulmonary hypertension. *Am. Rev. Respir. Dis.* 140:1455–57

186. Patrignani P, Daffonchio L, Hernandez A, De Caterina R, Pelosi G, Patrono C. 1992. Release of contracting autocoids by aortae of normal and atherosclerotic rabbits. *J. Cardiovasc. Pharmacol.* 20(12):S208–10

187. Peacock AJ, Dawes KE, Shock A, Gray AJ, Reeves JT, Laurent GJ. 1992. Endothelin-1 and endothelin-3 induce chemotaxis and replication of pulmonary artery fibroblasts. *Am. J. Respir. Cell Mol Biol.* 7:492–99

188. Perkett EA, Badesch DB, Roessler MK, Stenmark KR, Meyrick B. 1992. Insulin-like growth factor-1 and pulmonary hypertension induced by continuous air embolization in sheep. *Am. Rev. Respir. Cell Mol. Biol.* 6:82–87

189. Perkett EA, Lyons RM, Moses HL, Brigham KL, Meyrick B. 1990. Transforming growth-factor-$\beta$ activity in sheep lung lymph during the development of pulmonary-hypertension. *J. Clin. Invest.* 86:1459–64

190. Ploüet J, Schilling J, Gospodarowicz D. 1989. Isolation and characterization of a newly identified endothelial cell mitogen produced by AtT-20 cells. *EMBO J.* 8:3801–6

191. Poiani GJ, Tozzi CA, Yohn SA, Pierce RA, Belsky SA, et al. 1990. Collagen and elastin metabolism in hypertensive pulmonary arteries of rats. *Circ. Res.* 66:968–78

192. Powel JT, Whitney PL. 1980. Postnatal development of rat lung. *Biochem J.* 188:1–8

193. Powell PP, Wang CC, Jones R. 1992. Differential regulation of the genes endoding platelet: derived growth-factor receptor and its ligand in rat lung during microvascular and alveolar wall remodeling in hyperoxia. *Am. J. Respir. Cell. Mol. Biol.* 7:278–85

194. Prosser IW, Stenmark KR, Suthar M, Mecham RP, Crouch EC, Parks WC. 1989. Regional heterogeneity of elastin and collagen gene expression in intralobar

arteries in response to hypoxic pulmonary hypertension as demonstrated by in situ hybridization. *Am. J. Pathol.* 135:1073–88

195. Pukac LA, Ottlinger ME, Karnovsky MJ. 1992. Heparin suppresses specific second messenger pathways for protooncogene expression in rat vascular smooth muscle cells. *J. Biol. Chem.* 267:3707–11

196. Quinn TP, Peters KG, De Vries C, Ferrara N, Williams LT. 1993. Fetal liver kinase 1 is a receptor for vascular endothelial growth factor and is selectively expressed in vascular endothelium. *Proc. Natl. Acad. Sci. USA* 90:7533–37

197. Rabinovitch M. 1987. Prostaglandins and structural changes in pulmonary arteries. *Am. Rev. Respir. Dis.* 136:777–79

198. Rabinovitch M, Bothwell T, Hayakawa B, Williams WG, Trusler GA, et al. 1986. Pulmonary artery endothelial abnormalities in patients with congenital heart defects and pulmonary hypertension. *Lab. Invest.* 55(6):632–53

199. Rabinovitch M, Gamble WJ, Miettinen OS, Reid L. 1981. Age and sex influence on pulmonary hypertension of chronic hypoxia and recovery. *Am. J. Physiol.* 240:H62–72

200. Rabinovitch M, Gamble W, Nada AS, Miettinen OS, Reid L. 1979. Rat pulmonary circulation after chronic hypoxia: hemodynamic and structural features. *Am. J. Physiol.* 236:H818–27

201. Rakugi H, Kim DK, Krieger JE, Wang DS, Dzau VJ, Pratt RE. 1994. Induction of angiotensin converting enzyme in the neointima after vascular injury: possible role in restenosis. *J. Clin. Invest.* 93:339–46

202. Rao GN, Berk BC. 1992. Active oxygen species stimulate vascular smooth muscle cell growth and proto-oncogene expression. *Circ. Res.* 70:593–99

203. Rastinejad F, Blau HM. 1993. Genetic complementation reveals a novel regulatory role for 3' untranslated regions in growth and differentiation. *Cell* 72:903–17

204. Reid LM, Davies P. 1989. Control of cell proliferation in pulmonary hypertension. In *Lung Biology in Health and Disease*, exec. ed. C Lenfant, *Pulmonary Vascular Physiology and Pathophysiology*, ed. EK Weir, JT Reeves, 38:541–611. New York: Dekker

205. Resink TJ, Hahn AWA, Scott-Burden T, Powell J, Weber E, Buhler FR. 1990. Inducible endothelin messenger-RNA expression and peptide secretion in cul-

tured human vascular smooth-muscle cells. *Biochem. Biophys. Res. Commun.* 168:1303–10

206. Resnick N, Collins T, Atkinson W, Bonthron DT, Dewey CF Jr, Gimbrone MA Jr. 1993. Platelet-derived growth factor β chain promoter contains a cis-acting fluid shear-stress-responsive element. *Proc. Natl. Acad. Sci. USA* 90:4591–95

207. Riley DJ, Poiani GJ, Tozzi CA, Rosenbloom J, Pierce RA, Deak SB. 1986. Collagen and elastin gene expression in the hypertensive pulmonary artery of the rat. *Trans. Assoc. Am. Phys.* 99:180–88

208. Rodman DM. 1992. Chronic hypoxia selectively augments rat pulmonary artery $Ca^{2+}$ and $K^+$ channel-mediated relaxation. *Am. J. Physiol.* 263:L88–94

209. Roman J, Little CW, McDonald JA. 1991. Potential role of RGD-binding integrins in mammalian lung branching morphogenesis. *Development* 112:551–58

210. Rosenberg AA, Kennaugh J, Koppenhafer SL, Loomis M, Chatfield BA, Abman SH. 1993. Elevated immunoreactive endothelin-1 levels in newborn infants with persistent pulmonary hypertension. *J. Pediatr.* 123:109–14

211. Rothman A, Kulik TJ, Taubman MB, Berk BC, Smith CWJ, Nadal-Ginard B. 1992. Development and characterization of a cloned rat pulmonary arterial smooth muscle cell line that maintains differentiated properties through multiple subcultures. *Circulation* 86:1977–86

212. Rudnick D. 1933. Developmental capacities of the chick lung in chorioallantoic grafts. *J. Exp. Zool.* 66:125

213. Ruoslahti E, Engvall E, Hayman EG. 1981. Fibronectin: current concepts of its structure and function. *Collagen Res.* 1:95–128

214. Sadoshima J-I, Takahashi T, Jahn L, Izumo S. 1992. Roles of mechanosensitive ion channels, cytoskeleton, and contractile activity in stretch-induced immediate-early gene expression and hypertrophy of cardiac myocytes. *Proc. Natl. Acad. Sci. USA* 89:9905–9

215. Salvaterra CG, Goldman WF. 1993. Acute hypoxia increases cytosolic calcium in cultured pulmonary arterial myocytes. *Am. J. Physiol.* 264:L323–28

216. Sannes PL, Burch KK, Khosla J. 1992. Immunohistochemical localization of epidermal growth factor and acidic and basic fibroblast growth factors in postnatal developing and adult rat lungs. *Am. J. Respir. Cell Mol. Biol.* 7:230–37

217. Sappino AP, Schurch W, Gabbiani G.

1990. Biology of disease. Differentiation repertoire of fibroblastic cells: expression of cytoskeletal proteins as markers of phenotypic modulation. *Lab. Invest.* 63:144–61

218. Sartore S, Scatena M, Chiavegato A, Faggin E, Giuriato L, Pauletto P. 1994. Myosin isoform expression in smooth muscle cells during physiological and pathological vascular remodeling. *J. Vasc. Res.* 31:61–81

219. Schiffers PMH, Janssen GMJ, Fazzi GE, Struijker-Boudier HAJ, De Mey JGR. 1992. Endothelial modulation of DNA synthesis in isolated arteries of the rat. *J. Cardiovasc. Pharmacol.* 20(12):S124–27

220. Schor SL, Schor AM. 1987. Clonal heterogeneity in fibroblast phenotype: implications for the control of epithelial-mesenchymal interactions. *BioEssays* 7:200–4

221. Schuster DP, Crouch EC, Parks WC, Johnson T, Botney MD. 1996. Angiotensin converting enzyme expression in primary pulmonary hypertension. *Am. Rev. Respir. Crit. Care Med.* In press

222. Schwartz SM. 1994. Biology of the neointima. *Exp. Nephrol.* 2:63–67

223. Schwartz SM, Foy L, Bowen-Pope DF, Ross R. 1990. Derivation and properties of platelet-derived growth factor-independent rat smooth muscle cells. *Am. J. Pathol.* 136:1417–28

224. Scott-Burden T, Resink TJ, Baur U, Burgin M, Buhler FR. 1988. Amiloride sensitive activation of S-6 kinase by angiotensin-II in cultured vascular smooth-muscle cells. *Biochem. Biophys. Res. Commun.* 151:583–89

225. Scott-Burden T, Resink TJ, Hahn AWA, Buhler FR. 1991. Angiotensin-induced growth related metabolism is activated in cultured smooth muscle cells from spontaneously hypertensive rats and Wistar-Kyoto rats. *Am. J. Hypertens.* 4:183–88

226. Selmin O, Volpin D, Bressan GM. 1991. Changes of cellular expression of mRNA for tropoelastin in the intraembryonic arterial vessels of developing chick revealed by in situ hybridization. *Matrix* 11:347–58

227. Shanahan CM, Weissberg PL, Metcalfe JC. 1993. Isolation of gene markers of differentiated and proliferating vascular smooth muscle cells. *Circ. Res.* 73:193–204

228. Shanmugan S, Corvol P, Gasc J-M. 1994. Ontogeny of the two angiotensin II type I receptor subtypes in rats. *Am J. Physiol.* 267:E828–36

229. Shapero MH, Langston AA, Fournier RE.

1994. Tissue-specific extinguisher loci in the human genome: a screening study based on random marking and transfer of human chromosomes. *Somat. Cell Mol. Genet.* 20:215–31

230. Shearman MS, Naor Z, Sekiguchi K, Kishimoto A, Nishizuka Y. 1989. Selective action of the gamma-subspecies of protein kinase C from bovine cerebellum by arachidonic acid and its lipoxygenase metabolites. *FEBS Lett.* 243:177–82

231. Shibuya M, Yamaguchi S, Yamane A, Ikeda T, Tojo A, et al. 1990. Nucleotide sequence and expression of a novel human receptor-type tyrosine kinase gene (flt) closely related to the fms family. *Oncogene* 5:519–24

232. Shifren JL, Doldi N, Ferrara N, Mesiano S, Jaffe RB. 1994. In the human fetus, vascular endothelial growth factor is expressed in epithelial cells and myocytes, but not vascular endothelium: implications for mode of action. *J. Clin. Endocrinol. Metab.* 79:316–22

233. Short AD, Bian J, Ghosh TK, Waldron RT, Rybak SL, Gill DL. 1993. Intracellular $Ca^{2+}$ pool content is linked to control of cell growth. *Proc. Natl. Acad. Sci. USA* 90:4986–90

234. Shreeniwas R, Koga S, Karakurum M, Pinsky D, Kaiser E, et al. 1992. Hypoxia-mediated induction of endothelial cell interleukin-1-$\alpha$. *J. Clin. Invest.* 90:2333–39

235. Shubeita HE, Martinson EA, Vanbilsen M, Chien KR, Heller-Brown CJ. 1992. Transcriptional activation of the cardiac myosin light chain 2 and atrial natriuretic factor genes by protein kinase C in neonatal rat ventricular myocytes. *Proc. Natl. Acad. Sci. USA* 89:1305–9

236. Shweiki D, Itin A, Soffer D, Keshet E. 1992. Vascular endothelial growth factor induced by hypoxia may mediate hypoxia-initiated angiogenesis. *Nature* 359:843–48

237. Sibony M, Gasc J-M, Soubrier F, Alhenc-Galas F, Corvol P. 1993. Gene expression and tissue localization of the two isoforms of angiotensin I converting enzyme. *Hypertension* 21:827–35

238. Simonson MS, Wang Y, Jones JM, Dunn MJ. 1992. Protein kinase C regulates activation of mitogen-activated protein kinase and induction of proto-oncogene c-fos by endothelin-1. *J. Cardiovasc. Pharmacol.* 20:529–32

239. Skalli O, Ropraz P, Trzeciak A, Benzonana G, Gillessen D, Gabbiani G. 1986. A monoclonal antibody against a-smooth muscle actin: a new probe for smooth muscle differentiation. *J. Cell. Biol.* 103:2787–96

240. Smith LE, Durmowicz AG, Stenmark KR. 1995. Target cell related differences in the anti-proliferative effects of nitric oxide (NO) on cultured vascular smooth muscle cells (VSMC). *Am. J. Respir. Crit. Care Med.* 151:A517

241. Starksen NF, Simpson PC, Bishopric N, Coughlin SR, Lee WMF, et al. 1986. Cardiac myocyte hypertrophy is associated with c-myc protooncogene expression. *Proc. Natl. Acad. Sci. USA* 83:8348–50

242. Stelzner TF, O'Brien RF, Sato K, Weil JV. 1988. Hypoxia-induced increases in pulmonary transvascular protein escape in rats. *J. Clin. Invest.* 82:1840–47

243. Stelzner TJ, O'Brien RF, Yanagisawa M, Sakurai T, Sato K, et al. 1992. Increased lung endothelin-1 production in rats with idiopathic pulmonary hypertension. *Am. J. Physiol.* 262:L614–20

244. Stenmark KR, Aldashev A, Orton EC, Durmowicz AG, Badesch DB, et al. 1991. Cellular adaptation during chronic neonatal hypoxic pulmonary hypertension. *Am. J. Physiol. Suppl.* 261:97–104

245. Stenmark KR, Badesch DB, Dempsey EC, Frid M, Mecham RP, Parks WC. 1993. Regulation of pulmonary vascular wall cell growth: developmental and site-specific heterogeneity. *Eur. Respir. Rev.* 3:629–37

246. Stenmark KR, Badesch DB, Durmowicz AG, Voelkel NF. 1991. Control of vascular tone and cell proliferation in the pulmonary circulation. In *Basic Mechanisms of Pediatric Respiratory Disease Cellular and Integrative*, ed. V Chernick, RB Mellins, pp. 169–87. Philadelphia: Decker

247. Deleted in proof

248. Stenmark KR, Durmowicz AG, Dempsey EC. 1995. Modulation of vascular wall cell phenotype in pulmonary hypertension. See Ref. 21a, 6:171–212

249. Deleted in proof

250. Stenmark KR, Fasules J, Hyde DM, Voelkel NF, Henson J, et al. 1987. Severe pulmonary hypertension and arterial adventitial changes in newborn calves at 4,300m. *J. Appl. Physiol.* 62:821–30

251. Stenmark KR, Majack RA. 1991. Response of the developing pulmonary circulation to injury. In *Developmental Mechanisms of Disease in the Newborn. Rep. 101st Ross Conf. Pediatric Res.*, pp. 102–10

252. Stenmark KR, Mecham RP, Durmowicz

AG, Roby JB, Parks WC. 1994. Persistence of the fetal pattern of tropoelastin gene expression in severe neonatal pulmonary hypertension. *J. Clin. Invest.* 93:1234–42

253. Stenmark KR, Orton EC, Crouch EC, Parks WC, Voelkel NF, et al. 1988. Vascular remodeling in neonatal pulmonary hypertension: role of the smooth muscle cell. *Chest* 92:S127–32

254. Stewart DJ, Levy RP, Cernacek P, Langleben D. 1991. Increased plasma endothelin-1 in pulmonary hypertension: marker or mediator of disease? *Ann. Intern. Med.* 114:464–69

255. Storch TG, Talle GD. 1988. Oxygen concentration regulates the proliferative response of human fibroblasts to serum and growth factors. *Exp. Cell Res.* 175:317–25

256. Stubbs CD. 1983. Membrane fluidity: structure and dynamics of membrane lipids. *Essays Biochem.* 19:1–39

257. Stubbs CD, Smith AD. 1984. The modification of mammalian membrane polyunsaturated fatty acid composition in relation to membrane fluidity and function. *Biochim. Biophys. Acta* 779:89–137

258. Takuwa N, Takuwa Y, Yanagisawa M, Yamashita K, Masaki T. 1989. A novel vasoactive peptide endothelin stimulates mitogenesis through insitol lipid turnover in Swiss 3T3 fibroblasts. *J. Biol. Chem.* 264:7856–61

259. Tanaka Y, Bernstein ML, Mecham RP, Patterson GA, Cooper JD, Botney MD. 1996. Site-specific responses to monocrotaline-induced vascular injury: evidence for two distinct mechanisms of remodeling. *Am. J. Res. Cell Mol. Biol.* In press

260. Tanaka Y, Schuster DP, Davis EC, Patterson GA, Botney MD. 1996. The role of vascular injury and hemodynamics in rat pulmonary artery remodeling. *J. Clin. Invest.* 98:434–42

261. Terman BI, Dougher-Vermazen M, Carrion ME, Dimitrov D, Armellino DC, et al. 1992. Identification of the KDR tyrosine kinase as a receptor for vascular endothelial cell growth factor. *Biochem. Biophys. Res. Commun.* 187:1579–86

262. Thyberg J, Hedin U, Sjolund M, Palmberg L, Bottger BA. 1990. Regulation of differentiated properties and proliferation of arterial smooth muscle cells. *Atherosclerosis* 10:966–90

263. Thyberg J, Hultgardh-Nilsson A. 1994. Fibronectin and the basement membrane components laminin and collagen type IV influence the phenotypic properties of subcultured rat aortic smooth muscle cells differently. *Cell Tissue Res.* 276:263–71

264. Todorovich-Hunter L, Dodo H, Ye C, McCready L, Keeley FW, Rabinovitch M. 1992. Increased pulmonary artery elastolytic activity in adult rats with monocrotaline-induced progressive hypertensive pulmonary vascular disease compared with infant rats with nonprogressive disease. *Am. Rev. Respir. Dis.* 146:213–23

265. Townsend SF, Han VKM, Stenmark KR. 1994. Persistence of the fetal pattern of IGF-II expression in the adventitia of small pulmonary arteries in neonatal hypoxic pulmonary hypertension. *Growth Regul.* 4(1):S12

266. Tozzi CA, Poiani GJ, Harangozo AM, Boyd CD, Riley DJ. 1989. Pressure-induced connective tissue synthesis in pulmonary artery segments is dependent on intact endothelium. *J. Clin. Invest.* 84:1005–12

267. Tuder RM, Flook BE, Voelkel NF. 1995. Increased gene expression for VEGF and the VEGF receptors KDR/Flk and Flt in lungs exposed to acute or to chronic hypoxia. Modulation of gene expression by nitric oxide. *J. Clin. Invest.* 95:1798–807

268. Tufro-McReddie A, Harrison JK, Everett AD, Gomez RA. 1993. Ontogeny of type I angiotensin II receptor gene expression in the rat. *J. Clin. Invest.* 91:530–37

269. Turla MB, Thompson MM, Corjay MH, Owens GK. 1991. Mechanisms of angiotensin II- and arginine vasopressin-induced increases in protein synthesis and content in cultured rat aortic smooth muscle cells. *Circ. Res.* 68:288–99

270. Ungari S, Katari RS, Alessandri G, Gullino PM. 1985. Cooperation between fibronectin and heparin in the mobilization of capillary endothelium. *Invasion Metastasis* 5:193–205

271. Voelkel NF, Badesch DB, Zapp LM, Stenmark KR. 1990. Impaired prostacyclin synthesis of endothelial cells derived from hypertensive calf pulmonary arteries. *Prog. Respir. Res.* 26:63–69

272. Voelkel NF, Tuder RM, Bridges J, Arend WP. 1994. Interleukin-1 receptor antagonist treatment reduces pulmonary hypertension generated in rats by monocrotaline. *Am. J. Respir. Cell Mol. Biol.* 11:664–75

273. Wagenvoort CA, Wagenvoort N. 1977. *Pathology of Pulmonary Hypertension.* New York: Wiley & Sons

274. Weiser MCM, Grieshaber NA, Schwartz

PE, Majack RA. 1996. Perlecan heparan sulfates regulate Oct-1 gene expression in vascular smooth muscle cells. *Mol. Biol. Cell.* In press

275. Weiser MCM, Grieshaber SS, Belknap JK, Kinsella MG, Majack RA. 1996. Developmental regulation of perlecan gene expression in aortic smooth muscle cells. *Matrix Biol.* In press

276. Wilson E, Mai Q, Sudhir K, Weiss RH, Ives HE. 1993. Mechanical strain induces growth of vascular smooth muscle cells via autocrine action of PDGF. *J. Cell Biol.* 123:741–47

277. Winlove CP, Bishop JE, Chambers RC, Laurent GJ. 1995. The structure and function of extracellular matrix in the pulmonary vasculature. See Ref. 21a, 2:21–46

278. Wohrley JD, Frid MG, Orton EC, Belknap JK, Stenmark KR. 1995. Hypoxia selectively induces proliferation in a specific subpopulation of smooth muscle cells in the bovine neonatal pulmonary arterial media. *J. Clin. Invest.* 96:273–81

279. Yamaguchi TP, Dumont DJ, Conlon RA, Breitman ML, Rossant J. 1993. flk-1, an flt-related receptor tyrosine kinase is an early marker for endothelial cell precursors. *Development* 118:489–98

280. Ye C, Rabinovitch M. 1991. Inhibition of elastolysis by SC37698 (Searle) reduces development and progression of monocrotaline pulmonary hypertension. *Am. J. Physiol.* 261:H1255–67

281. Zanellato AM, Borrione AC, Giuriato L, Tonello M, Scannapieco G, et al. 1990. Myosin isoforms and cell heterogeneity in vascular smooth muscle. I. Developing and adult bovine aorta. *Dev. Biol.* 141:431–46

282. Zhou J, Mochizuki T, Smeets H, Antignac C, Laurila P, et al. 1993. Deletion of the paired alpha-5(IV) and alpha-6(IV) collagen genes in inherited smooth muscle tumors. *Science* 261:1167–69

*Annu. Rev. Physiol. 1997. 59:145–70*

# ION CHANNELS IN VASCULAR ENDOTHELIUM

*Bernd Nilius, Félix Viana, and Guy Droogmans*
Laboratorium voor Fysiologie, Campus Gasthuisberg, KU Leuven, B-3000 LEUVEN, Belgium

KEY WORDS:    endothelium, patch clamp, electrophysiology, membrane potential, calcium signaling, mechanosensitivity, store-operated channels

## ABSTRACT

The functional impact of ion channels in vascular endothelial cells (ECs) is still a matter of controversy. This review describes different types of ion channels in ECs and their role in electrogenesis, $Ca^{2+}$ signaling, vessel permeability, cell-cell communication, mechano-sensor functions, and pH and volume regulation. One major function of ion channels in ECs is the control of $Ca^{2+}$ influx either by a direct modulation of the $Ca^{2+}$ influx pathway or by indirect modulation of $K^+$ and $Cl^-$ channels, thereby clamping the membrane at a sufficiently negative potential to provide the necessary driving force for a sustained $Ca^{2+}$ influx. We discuss various mechanisms of $Ca^{2+}$ influx stimulation: those that activate nonselective, $Ca^{2+}$-permeable cation channels or those that activate $Ca^{2+}$-selective channels, exclusively or partially operated by the filling state of intracellular $Ca^{2+}$ stores. We also describe the role of various $Ca^{2+}$- and shear stress-activated $K^+$ channels and different types of $Cl^-$ channels for the regulation of the membrane potential.

## ION CHANNELS IN ENDOTHELIUM: WHAT FOR?

Endothelial cells (ECs) are an interesting example of a multifunctional cell type. They form an ideal surface for blood flow; they prevent blood clotting but can also trigger it in response to various signals, and they can exert thrombolytic as well as thrombogenic activity. As antigen-presenting cells, they are involved in immune responses. Changes in their contractile state and their ability to modulate cell-cell contacts control the permeability of the blood-tissue interface. Furthermore, ECs initiate angiogenesis and vessel repair. They help adjust the vessel diameter to hemodynamic needs. These multiple functions are mediated

0066-4278/97/0315-0145$08.00

by the production and release of a variety of vasoactive agents that affect the cells in the vessel wall or in its immediate vicinity, including the endothelial cells themselves. These substances include nitric oxide (NO or endothelium-derived relaxing factor, EDRF), endothelium-derived hyperpolarizing factor (EDHF), various prostaglandins, endothelins (ET), natriuretic peptide, small signaling molecules such as substance P, ATP, growth factors, steroids, and even large proteins such as receptors and proteins involved in the blood clotting cascade (69, 108). ECs respond not only to humoral substances, which bind to receptors on their luminal and abluminal cell surfaces, but also to mechanical forces such as changes in flow rate (shear stress) or blood pressure (biaxial tensile stress) (31, 32, 34, 87, 114, 142). Secretory signals also arise from cell-cell contacts with other cells such as blood cells and extracellular matrix proteins (33, 108). Our current knowledge of the mechanisms that regulate the production and release of these substances is very limited. It is well documented that production and release of most of these agents is initiated by $Ca^{2+}$-dependent mechanisms. Ion channels activated by agonists and/or mechanical forces provide influx routes for $Ca^{2+}$ (107). The membrane potential, which is mainly controlled by $K^+$, $Cl^-$, and possibly nonselective cation channels, is an important regulator of intra- and intercellular signal transduction in various vascular functions, especially by modulating the driving force for transmembrane $Ca^{2+}$ fluxes. Ion channels also may be responsible for the mechano-sensor properties of endothelial cells that control cell responses to hemodynamic forces and to volume-regulatory steps during cell division, angiogenesis, and wound healing. Our understanding of the biophysical properties of ion channels in ECs and their functional impact is hampered by the extreme degree of multifunctionality of these cells and also by the large phenotypic variability among EC types. Due to space limitations, this review focuses mainly on ion channels in vascular endothelial cells and excludes a large body of literature on endocardium, lens, etc.

## ELECTROGENESIS IN ENDOTHELIAL CELLS

ECs are generally regarded as non-excitable, although a number of reports have provided evidence for the existence of voltage-gated tetrodotoxin (TTX)-sensitive $Na^+$ channels and $Ca^{2+}$ channels (see below).

### Membrane Potential at Rest

Values of resting membrane potential, cell capacitance, and input resistance range between $-10$ and $-70$ mV, 40 and 60 pF, and 1 and 5 G$\Omega$ in isolated, nonconfluent macrovascular ECs. Confluent cells have a higher membrane capacitance (up to 160 pF) and a lower input resistance 0.01–0.4 G$\Omega$ (182), which is consistent with the presence of intercellular electrical couplings, presumably via gap junction channels (see below). The membrane potential also depends on the cell type and is generally more negative in macrovascular than in microvascular ECs (30, 182, 196). The membrane potential in electrically coupled confluent ECs is more negative than in nonconfluent cells (182, 196), suggesting that electrogenesis depends on the degree of confluence.

The expression of $K^+$ channels varies greatly between different EC types and even within the same strain of cultured ECs. For example, inwardly rectifying $K^+$ channels, which determine the resting potential in most cell types (26, 49), are mainly expressed in macrovascular ECs. This variability may be linked to progression through different stages of the cell cycle (109). The heterogeneous expression contributes to the large variability in resting potential of ECs within the same cell type as illustrated in Figure 1. Some studies describe a bimodal distribution of resting membrane potential. The N-shaped current-voltage relationship observed in some ECs (see Figure 1A) may underlie this bistability (30, 98). ECs can be subdivided into two extremes, i.e. cells in which the resting potential is mainly controlled by the $K^+$ conductance ($K^+$-type EC) and those in which the $Cl^-$ conductance is dominating ($Cl^-$-type EC). The resting potential of $K^+$-type cells ranges between $-70$ and $-60$ mV, and is mainly determined by an inwardly rectifying $K^+$ channel. $Cl^-$-type cells have a resting potential

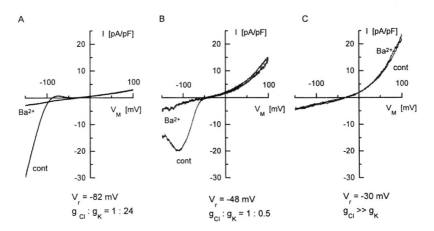

$V_r = -82$ mV
$g_{Cl} : g_K = 1 : 24$

$V_r = -48$ mV
$g_{Cl} : g_K = 1 : 0.5$

$V_r = -30$ mV
$g_{Cl} \gg g_K$

*Figure 1* Examples of resting I-V relationships in three cultured bovine pulmonary artery ECs. Panels *A–C* show I-V curves, normalized to cell size, from nonstimulated cells with a variable contribution of the inwardly rectifying $K^+$ and the outwardly rectifying $Cl^-$ currents. Control traces are labeled cont and, after application of 200 $\mu$M $Ba^{2+}$ to block IRK, are labeled $Ba^{2+}$. The contribution of the $K^+$ and $Cl^-$ conductances to the reversal potential ($V_r$) has been estimated from $V_r = (g_K V_K + g_{Cl} V_{Cl})/(g_K + g_{Cl})$.

between $-40$ and $-10$ mV, which is close to $E_{Cl}$, suggesting that a $Cl^-$ current is activated under resting conditions. This current, which disappears under conditions of cell shrinking, represents basal activity of swelling-induced $Cl^-$ channels (see below for more detail). In addition, hyperpolarization induced by decreasing $[Na^+]_e$ is consistent with a contribution of either a $Na^+$-selective or a nonselective cation conductance to the resting permeability. The relative contributions of the conductance for $Na^+$, $K^+$, and $Cl^-$, which determine the resting potential, range from 3 to 30%, 27 to 95%, and 9 to 35%, respectively (61, 90, 100, 182).

## Membrane Potential During Cell Stimulation

Any stimulation, receptor-mediated or mechanical, may affect the membrane potential of ECs. Vasoactive stimuli such as acetylcholine, bradykinin, and histamine, hyperpolarize those cells in which the resting potential is not dominated by a large inwardly rectifying $K^+$ current. This initial hyperpolarization, which is mediated by activation of $Ca^{2+}$-dependent $K^+$ currents, is often followed by a sustained depolarization of the membrane by activation of nonselective cation channels (30, 85, 90, 98, 174).

## Membrane Potential and Electrogenic Pumps

The electrogenic $Na^+/K^+$ ATPase contributes $\approx -8$ mV to the resting potential of ECs (30, 103, 120). Pump activity may also modulate oscillations in intracellular free $Ca^{2+}$ because blockade of the pump facilitates agonist-induced, synchronized $Ca^{2+}$ oscillations in confluent ECs (81). Small changes in electrogenic pump current induce pronounced changes in membrane potential in ECs, which are characterized by a high membrane resistance (30, 160). Evidence for $Na^+/Ca^{2+}$ exchanger activity has been presented in pulmonary artery cells, but its electrogenicity has not been studied (150).

# ENDOTHELIAL ION CHANNELS

In the last decade, a plethora of channels has been described in ECs, but a clear picture of their characteristics, distribution, modulation, and molecular identity is not available yet.

## Potassium Channels

INWARD RECTIFIER CHANNELS    The predominant ion channel in $K^+$-type endothelial cells is an inwardly rectifying $K^+$ channel (IRK) (60). Its single channel conductance ranges from 23 to 30 pS in symmetrical $K^+$ solutions (42, 72, 115, 126, 131, 163, 164) but is smaller at lower extracellular $K^+$ concentrations (114, 131, 164, 196). Its permeation profile is $P_K > P_{Rb} > P_{Cs}$

(131, 164). Extracellular $Ba^{2+}$, tetraethylammonium (TEA), tetrabutylammonium (TBA), $Cs^+$ and the NO-releaser LP-805 block this channel (72, 110, 129, 143, 185). The channel shows time-dependent inactivation, which depends on extracellular $Na^+$ and $Mg^{2+}$ (42). Internal $Mg^{2+}$ concentrations near the physiological level and below 20 mM have only marginal effects. This contrasts with other cell types where inward rectification is attributed to a time- and voltage-dependent block by intracellular $Mg^{2+}$. Rectification may therefore represent an intrinsic gating property of IRK channels in ECs (182). However, outward currents activated in excised patches in the absence of $Mg^{2+}$ are blocked by reapplication of $Mg^{2+}$ (42). Agonists such as angiotensin II, arginine-vasopressin, VIP, endothelin 1 (ET-1), and histamine inhibit the inward rectifier in capillary and macrovascular ECs (67, 115, 129, 194). Inhibition of IRK by GTP$\gamma$S suggests that this effect is mediated via G proteins (67). The mechanism of modulation of IRK channels in these ECs, as well as their molecular-biological identification, is still to be resolved. They probably belong to the Kir2 or Kir4 family (40).

Other IRK channels in ECs are functional only in the presence of intracellular ATP. In inside out patches, ATP withdrawal induces channel closure and ATP$\gamma$S reactivates the channel (126). The similar conductance, ATP dependence, and activation pattern suggest that these inwardly rectifying channels belong to the Kir1 subfamily (ROMK, 31, 62). Importantly, IRK channels can also be activated by shear stress (see below, and 74, 187).

An IRK channel with a conductance of 170 pS has been described in aorta ECs. This channel is activated by isoprenaline, adenosine, forskolin, and membrane-permeant analogues of cAMP and is inhibited by PKA inhibitors (50). Obviously this channel does not belong to any of the cloned subfamilies of $K^+$ channels.

CALCIUM-ACTIVATED $K^+$ CHANNELS    The presence of $Ca^{2+}$-activated $K^+$ currents in ECs has been extensively documented (28, 37, 53, 72). Based on their single channel conductance, three classes of $Ca^{2+}$-dependent $K^+$ channels ($K_{Ca}$ channels) have been described in ECs.

High-conductance "maxi" or big $K_{Ca}$ channels ($BK_{Ca}$ channels) have a conductance between 165 and 220 pS (8, 66, 83, 114, 146, 148). They show $Ca^{2+}$- and voltage-dependent activation and are blocked by TEA, charybdotoxin, $d$-tubocurarine (8, 30, 147), and by extracellular alkalinization (170). The NO-releaser LP-805 (72) potentiates outward $Ca^{2+}$-dependent $K^+$ currents in bovine pulmonary artery ECs, but it is not clear whether this effect is direct or mediated by changes in $[Ca^{2+}]_i$. $Ca^{2+}$ release from either Ins(1,4,5)$P_3$ or caffeine-sensitive pools activates $BK_{Ca}$ channels and induces spontaneous transient outward currents (STOCs) (148).

Medium-conductance $K_{Ca}$ channels ($MK_{Ca}$ channels) have a conductance between 30 and 80 pS in symmetrical $K^+$ and are inwardly rectifying. Their conductance at physiological extracellular $K^+$ concentrations is about 15 pS (83, 152, 153, 179, 181). The 30 pS channels are clearly $Ca^{2+}$ dependent, but it is uncertain whether they belong to the class of Kir1 (ROMK) channels or to the class of $Ca^{2+}$- and voltage-activated $K^+$ channels (*slo*-like channels, after the channel whose mutation causes *slowpoke* behavior in *Drosophila*). A G protein-dependent mechanism modulates these channels, probably by increasing their $Ca^{2+}$ sensitivity (179). GTP, together with $Mg^{2+}$, as well as $GTP\gamma S$, stimulates these channels, whereas $GDP\beta S$ reverses the stimulatory effects. The $MK_{Ca}$ channels with a conductance between 40 and 80 pS are activated by $Ins(1,4,5)P_3$-sensitive $Ca^{2+}$ release induced by agonists such as bradykinin, acetylcholine, and ATP (152; for a review, see 61, 110, 143, 167). In brain micro-vasculature, endothelium ET-1 and ET-3 activate $MK_{Ca}$ channels via endothelin-A receptors (181) but are without effect on the IRK channels. Charybdotoxin, as well as quinine and TBA, are efficient blockers of $MK_{Ca}$ channels (30, 181). These channels are also inhibited by noxiustoxin, a toxin purified from *Centuroides* scorpion toxin (27, 175).

Small-conductance $K_{Ca}$ channels ($SK_{Ca}$ channels), with a conductance of about 10 pS in asymmetrical conditions, have also been observed in ECs (52, 151). These channels lack voltage dependence and are blocked by extracellular TBA and apamin (52). Recently, two types of $SK_{Ca}$ channels were identified in excised patches of rat aorta endothelium, with conductances of 18 and 9 pS in symmetrical 150 mM $K^+$, and 6.7 pS and 2.8 pS at physiological extracellular $K^+$ concentrations (92). The smaller conductance was completely blocked by 10 nM apamin or 100 $\mu$M $d$-tubocurarine; the larger conductance was insensitive to apamin but was inhibited by charybdotoxin at concentrations >50 nM.

The abundance of $K_{Ca}$ channels, as well as their $Ca^{2+}$ sensitivity and voltage dependence, varies enormously between various EC classes. For example, freshly isolated rabbit aortic ECs express $BK_{Ca}$ channels (147). In contrast, in situ recordings from rat aortic ECs reveal two types of $SK_{Ca}$ channels (92), whereas cultured bovine aortic ECs express primarily $MK_{Ca}$ channels in some studies (179) and both $MK_{Ca}$ and $BK_{Ca}$ channels in others (83). It is unclear whether this variability is related to the expression of different proteins, different metabolic control mechanisms, or different signaling mechanisms during agonist stimulation.

$K^+$ CHANNELS MODULATED BY INTRACELLULAR ATP ($K_{ATP}$)    These channels have also been described in ECs. They are activated by micromolar concentrations of the $K^+$ channel opener levcromakalim, a $K^+$ channel metabolic inhibitor, and also by shear stress. They are blocked by an increase in intracellular

ATP; glibenclamide and tolbutamide (sulphonylurea drugs); extracellular $Ca^{2+}$ and TEA; and by an elevation of intracellular pH (68, 75, 77, 79).

## Nonselective Cation Channels

These channels are of special interest because they may represent $Ca^{2+}$ entry pathways. Agonists such as histamine, bradykinin, ATP, serotonin, thrombin, substance P, and ET1 activate nonselective cation currents (NSC channels) in microvascular and macrovascular ECs (1, 18, 53, 71, 116, 128, 136, 137, 167, 194). The single channel conductance for monovalent cations in physiological solutions ranges between 20 and 30 pS, whereas that for $Ca^{2+}$ or $Ba^{2+}$ is between 4 and 12 pS (1, 19, 106, 111, 136, 167, 193). Cell swelling also activates a NSC channel with a conductance of 28 pS for monovalent cations and 13 pS for $Ca^{2+}$ (83). In general, these channels do not discriminate between monovalent cations, and the permeability ratio for $Ca^{2+}$ over monovalent cations ($P_{Ca}:P_{K,Na}$) is 0.2–0.6 (83, 106, 111, 114; for endocardial cells, see 89). Others report these channels to be impermeable for $Ca^{2+}$ (137). An amiloride-sensitive, poorly selective cation channel (23 pS for $Na^+$, $K^+$) has been observed in brain microvessels (183), which may control cation fluxes across the blood-brain barrier. It is interesting to note that amiloride inhibits angiogenesis (4), which may be related to modulation of this channel. The mechanism of activation of NSC channels in endothelial cells is unclear. A nonselective, agonist-induced current, which is activated by $[Ca^{2+}]_i$ and suppressed by inhibitors of the cyclo-oxygenase pathway, has been described in aortic ECs (60). Activation of the 44 pS NSC channel in ECs of pig coronary artery is also $Ca^{2+}$ dependent (8). This channel, with a permeability ratio $P_{Ca}:P_{Na}$ of 0.7, is half-maximally activated at 0.7 $\mu$M $[Ca^{2+}]_i$. This gating by $[Ca^{2+}]_i$ represents an interesting positive feedback mechanism for a sustained $Ca^{2+}$ influx. Activation by agonists may be mediated via G proteins, but it is not clear whether this activation is direct or caused by an increase in $[Ca^{2+}]_i$ (83, 137). Application of sarco (endoplasmic) reticulum calcium ATPase (SERCA) $Ca^{2+}$ pump inhibitors thapsigargin, dibenzohydroquinone (BHQ), and cyclopiazonic acid (CPA), and also intracellular application of $Ins(1,4,5)P_3$, which releases $Ca^{2+}$ from intracellular stores, activate NSC channels. Activation of these channels has been correlated with store depletion (46, 71, 128). The antihypertensive drug LP-805 also activates $Ca^{2+}$ influx via a nonselective channel. This activation does not depend on $[Ca^{2+}]_i$ or on depletion of intracellular $Ca^{2+}$ stores (70, 71). Oxidant stress activates a 30 pS NSC, which is equally permeable for $Na^+$ and $K^+$ and also permeable for $Ca^{2+}$. This channel opens in two gating modes that do not depend on intracellular $Ca^{2+}$ stores or $[Ca^{2+}]_i$. Activation of these channels and the concomitant membrane depolarization may limit $Ca^{2+}$ influx (78). The $Ca^{2+}$ entry blocker SK& F 96365 inhibits nonselective channels in

ECs, but only in a narrow concentration range (70, 159). $Ni^{2+}$, $Gd^{3+}$, $La^{3+}$, niflumic acid, flufemic acid, and carboxylate derivatives (DPC, DCDPC) also inhibit these channels (53, 71, 83, 136, 137).

## Voltage-Dependent Channels

Although several reports have provided evidence for the existence of voltage-gated ion channels in ECs, it is generally accepted that they are nonexcitable and that voltage-gated channels are functionally not important (61, 110, 167). Voltage-activated $Na^+$ channels with a low TTX sensitivity have been observed in ECs from human umbilical vein and from rat interlobar artery (48). A 4-aminopyridine-sensitive, voltage-dependent, transient outward current (A-type $K^+$ channel, 168) has also been described in some cultured ECs. Voltage-gated $Ca^{2+}$ channels, which share some similarities with the classical L- and T-type $Ca^{2+}$ channels, have been described in capillary endothelial cells disso-ciated from bovine adrenal glands (15–17). These T-type $Ca^{2+}$ channels have a conductance of approximately 8 pS. $Ca^{2+}$ transients, evoked by applying short pulses of high $K^+$, were sensitive to the T-type $Ca^{2+}$ channel blockers $Cd^{2+}$ and amiloride, which suggests a role of T-type $Ca^{2+}$ channels in the control of $[Ca^{2+}]_i$. L-type $Ca^{2+}$ channels in these ECs have a single channel conductance of approximately 20 pS and are sensitive to dihydropyridines (DHPs). An-other $Ca^{2+}$ channel with a tiny conductance of 2.8 pS in 110 mM $Ba^{2+}$, which is sensitive to the $Ca^{2+}$ agonist BayK 8644, but not to the $Ca^{2+}$ antagonist nicardipine, has been observed in capillary ECs (SB, small conductance, sensi-tive to BayK 8644) $Ca^{2+}$ channel; 16). This channel shows very long openings in hyperpolarized cells and may be involved in a low-threshold $Ca^{2+}$ entry. A novel type of voltage-dependent $Ca^{2+}$ channel, the R-type $Ca^{2+}$ channel, may be important during activation of ECs by platelet-activating factor (14). These channels, which are activated by a long-lasting depolarization, are insensitive to DHP derivatives such as nifedipine, but are blocked by the $Ca^{2+}$ channel blockers (-) isradipine and PN 200-110 (13). Because they do not inactivate at depolarized potentials, they might be candidates for a sustained $Ca^{2+}$ influx. A hyperpolarization-activated current carried by $K^+$ and $Na^+$ and modulated by NO has been described in vascular brain ECs (76).

## $Ca^{2+}$-Permeable Channels

Changes in $[Ca^{2+}]_i$ induced by agonists such as acetylcholine, ATP, bradykinin, substance P, histamine, the hypotensive peptide adrenomedullin, and ET-1 (2, 53, 73, 116, 161, 162, 177) consist of an initial fast peak due to release of $Ca^{2+}$ from $Ins(1,4,5)P_3$-sensitive intracellular stores followed by a sustained rise due to $Ca^{2+}$ entry. Figure 2 illustrates these two components for an EC stimulated with ATP. The increase in $[Ca^{2+}]_i$ activates a $BK_{Ca}$ current, which

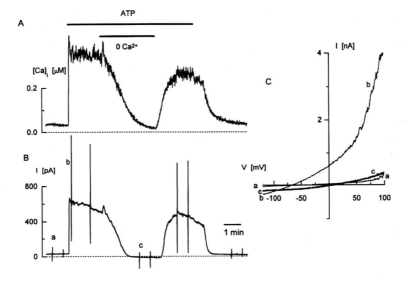

*Figure 2* Ca$^{2+}$ responses and ionic currents in EAhy 926 cell, a permanent cell line derived from human umbilical vein (41). *A*, Maximal agonist stimulation with 10 $\mu$M ATP produces an early peak and a sustained Ca$^{2+}$ plateau. Removal of extracellular Ca$^{2+}$ and addition of 1.5 mM EGTA leads to a rapid and reversible decline in Ca$^{2+}$ below resting levels. *B*, Simultaneous recording of whole-cell membrane current at a holding potential of 0 mV. Elevation of intracellular Ca$^{2+}$ activates an outward current, which is abolished in Ca$^{2+}$-free solution where a much smaller inward current is activated. The brief spikes represent currents evoked by voltage ramps from −120 to +100 mV. *C*, I-V relationships in the same cell: (a) at rest; note the absence of inward rectifier; (b) during the elevated Ca$^{2+}$ plateau; note the strong outward rectification characteristic of BKCa; and (c) in the absence of external Ca$^{2+}$; note the nonselective cation current. Same experimental conditions as in Figure 1.

modulates the driving force for Ca$^{2+}$ influx. The long-lasting plateau, as well as the BK$_{Ca}$ current, disappears in Ca$^{2+}$-free extracellular solution (Figure 2*A*, *B*). Under these conditions, activation of an agonist-dependent cationic current becomes apparent (Figure 2*C*).

The biophysical characterization and molecular identity of the Ca$^{2+}$ influx pathways is still confusing; also the relation between store depletion and activation of these pathways is not always clear. Activation of Ca$^{2+}$ influx pathways by Ca$^{2+}$ mobilizing agonists and SERCA pump inhibitors is not unequivocal evidence for a link between Ca$^{2+}$ influx activation and store depletion, unless other mechanisms such as activation by changes in intracellular calcium or by other mediators not directly linked to store depletion have been excluded. The interpretation of Ca$^{2+}$ influx data from nonvoltage-clamped cells is even more questionable because of the possible concomitant changes in membrane potential and driving force for $Ca^{2+}$.

Compounds such as BHQ and thapsigargin, which deplete intracellular $Ca^{2+}$ stores without affecting $Ins(1,4,5)P_3$ production, activate a $Ca^{2+}$ influx in ECs (23, 39, 123, 154), but the link with store depletion has not been unequivocally demonstrated. This is also true for the small, bradykinin-activated whole cell current ($\approx 10$ pA/cell at a potential of $-60$ mV) in bovine aortic ECs (99), which inactivates if $Ca^{2+}$ is the main charge carrier, but not if it is carried by $Na^+$ and is blocked by $La^{3+}$. This link is also missing for the bradykinin-stimulated calcium influx pathway that is permeable to divalent cations ($Ca^{2+}$, $Ba^{2+}$, $Sr^{2+}$), depends on the membrane potential, and deactivates in the presence of elevated $[Ca^{2+}]_i$ (155). Bradykinin, ATP, and BHQ activate a $Ca^{2+}$-selective channel in cell-attached patches of bovine aortic ECs, but it cannot be excluded that this channel is activated secondarily to changes in $[Ca^{2+}]_i$ rather than by store depletion (177).

Several intracellular messengers, such as a low-molecular weight, nonpeptide $Ca^{2+}$ influx factor (140) and cGMP (6), have been proposed to be responsible for signaling the degree of store filling to the plasma membrane. In ECs, this signaling may be mediated by 5,6-epoxyeicosatrienoic acid (5,6-EET), an arachidonic acid metabolite synthesized by a P450 mono-oxygenase located in the ER membrane and activated by a decrease of intraluminal $Ca^{2+}$ (51; for a review, see 9, 12).

Two low-molecular weight tyrosine kinases (42 and 44 K MAP-kinases) (43) and another tyrosine kinase (MAP-kinase, integrin-associated $Ca^{2+}$ entry) (156), as well as PKA (50) and PKC (102), have been reported to modulate $Ca^{2+}$ influx. $Ni^{2+}$, $La^{3+}$, heparin, SK & F 96365, the tyrosine kinase inhibitor genistein, P450-inhibitors, and surprisingly, also the $Cl^-$ channel blocker 5-nitro-2-(3-phenylpropylamino) benzoic acid (NPPB) inhibit this influx (23, 39, 43, 47, 51, 73, 154, 177).

This $Ca^{2+}$ influx pathway may be extremely important for several EC functions such as the synthesis and release of vasoactive substances, e.g. NO, $PGI_2$, the synthesis of various proteins, and gene expression (69, 108, 142). The contribution of $Ca^{2+}$ influx to the whole-cell membrane current has been estimated from the $Ca^{2+}$ signals induced by reapplication of 10 mM extracellular $Ca^{2+}$ to store-depleted cells in which ER $Ca^{2+}$ uptake was blocked with thapsigargin. Its amplitude is about 1 pA/cell at a potential of $-100$ mV (123). The putative channels gated by store depletion have been called CRAC (calcium release-activated $Ca^{2+}$ channels) or more general SOC (store-operated $Ca^{2+}$ channels) (25; for a review, see 12).

A cation channel activated by agonists such as ATP and bradykinin that is selective for $Ca^{2+}$ and $Mn^{2+}$ has been identified at both the whole-cell and single-channel level in bovine aorta ECs (86). $Ins(1,3,4,5)P_4$, but not $Ins(1,4,5)P_3$, increases the open probability of this channel, which has a conductance of 2.5 pS for $Mn^{2+}$. Its open probability is about 50% lower at 1 $\mu M$ $[Ca^{2+}]_i$ than that at 1 mM $[Ca^{2+}]_i$.

A $Ca^{2+}$-permeable channel activated by agonists such as ATP and bradykinin, but also by store depletion induced by BHQ and thapsigargin, has been described recently in ECs (177). It has a conductance of 5 pS in symmetrical $Na^+$, of 11 pS with 10 mM $[Ca^{2+}]_e$, and is about 10 times more permeable for $Ca^{2+}$ than for $Na^+$. This channel shows strong inward rectification and can be activated in excised patches by $Ins(1,4,5)P_3$ but not by $Ins(1,3,4,5)P_4$. It is blocked by $La^{3+}$ and heparin, and high extracellular $Ca^{2+}$ concentrations decrease its open probability (177, 178). It is obvious that store depletion is not the only trigger for $Ca^{2+}$ influx through this channel. Interestingly, $Ins(1,4,5)P_3$ receptor-like proteins have been identified in the plasma membrane of endothelial cells and in endothelial caveolae (45, 178).

Another nonspecific cation channel activated by depletion of stores with CPA has been described in umbilical vein ECs (193). It has a conductance of 6 pS for $Ca^{2+}$ and 28 pS for $Na^+$ or $K^+$. Histamine, when applied inside the pipette, transiently activates a cation channel in patches of ECs of rat intrapulmonary artery (191). This channel ($\approx 25$ pS) is about 16 times more permeable for $Ca^{2+}$ than for monovalent cations and is blocked by $Mg^{2+}$ from either side of the membrane. Neither acetylcholine nor $GTP\gamma S$ could mimic the histamine effect. This channel is not $Ca^{2+}$ dependent.

The properties of these channels clearly differ from those of the CRAC channels originally described in mast cells and other nonexcitable cells that are also highly $Ca^{2+}$ selective but have a conductance of $\approx 20$ fS (65, 197; for a review, see 9). Interestingly, similar differences have also been reported for CRAC-like channels and $Ca^{2+}$-permeable channels related to the *Drosophila* photoreceptor protein, encoded by the *trp* and *trpl* genes (trp and trpl stand for transient receptor potential and trp-like; 9). The gene products, TRP and TRPL, are $Ca^{2+}$-and $Na^+$-permeable channels. TRP is activated by all known procedures that release intracellular $Ca^{2+}$, whereas TRPL is insensitive to store depletion by thapsigargin. TRPL is much less $Ca^{2+}$ selective than TRP and shares functional properties with the $Ins(1,4,5)P_3$-activated channels described in ECs (177, 178). Recently, two human homologues of *trp*, i.e. TRPC1 (Htrp1; 195) and TRPC3 (188) have been described. TRPC1 but not TRPC3 is present in human umbilical vein ECs (L Raeymaekers & B Nilius, personal communication). The striking differences in ion selectivity and conductance between CRAC channels (highly $Ca^{2+}$-selective, $\approx 20$ fS) and TRP or TRPL channels ($Na^+$ and $Ca^{2+}$ permeable, $\approx 3$ pS) point to a family of store-operated channels (SOCs) rather than to a single class of highly selective CRAC channels.

## Chloride Channels

Electrophysiological interest in endothelial cells has long focused on cation permeable channels. However, anion channels are also ubiquitously expressed in these cells. Three classes of $Cl^-$ channels have been described in ECs: $Ca^{2+}$-activated $Cl^-$ channels ($Cl_{Ca}$ channels), volume-activated $Cl^-$ channels ($Cl_{vol}$ channels), and high-conductance $Cl^-$ channels, which may not be regulated by $Ca^{2+}$ nor by cell volume, but by voltage and cAMP (BCl channels). Small-conductance, cAMP-regulated CFTR channels are not expressed in ECs, although abnormal vessel permeability has been described in patients with cystic fibrosis (38, 95, 96).

Agonists such as histamine, ATP, and thrombin activate $[Ca^{2+}]_i$-dependent $Cl^-$ fluxes and $Cl^-$ currents with slow activation at positive potentials (53, 60, 186, 189, 192). They show outward rectification and are blocked by N-phenylanthranilic acid (NPA), 4,4'-diisothiocyanostilbene-2,2'-disulfonate (DIDS), $Zn^{2+}$, and by calmodulin antagonists (53, 186). Activation of these currents requires intracellular ATP (186). PKC activation inhibits them, suggesting that the production of diacylglycerol (DAG) during agonist stimulation may exert a negative feedback on these $Cl^-$ currents (189). Typical densities of these $Ca^{2+}$-activated $Cl^-$ currents range from 10 to 30 pA/pF of membrane capacitance at $+100$ mV and are much smaller than those of the volume-activated $Cl^-$ currents.

Adenosine has been shown to activate a $Cl^-$ channel in a $Ca^{2+}$-independent way via a PTX-sensitive G protein (5).

Changes in cell volume activate large whole-cell currents with densities up to 120 pA/pF at $+100$ mV (44, 112, 165, 166). This current is $Ca^{2+}$ independent, but its activation requires a very low permissive intracellular $Ca^{2+}$ concentration (166) and intracellular ATP (122). In contrast to voltage-gated ClC channels, activation of this current is voltage independent, and it slowly inactivates at very positive potentials (165). This volume-activated $Cl^-$ current probably occurs through small-conductance channels (1–5 pS; 113, 117), it shows outward rectification, and the channel is more permeable for iodide than for chloride. The physiological stimulus for its activation may be an increase in cell volume, but also other mechanical stimuli and changes in cell shape (112, 121, 173). $Cl_{vol}$ is partially activated in resting cells since it is inhibited by cell shrinkage and contributes to the chloride conductance and resting potential in nonstimulated cells (see Figure 1). Micromolar concentrations of the anti-estrogen tamoxifen, niflumic acid, NPPB, and extracellular nucleotides and nucleosides (112, 165) block the current, but it is less sensitive to DIDS. Four molecular candidates have been proposed for this current: the voltage and volume-dependent ClC-2 channel (55, 169); a member of the ABC-cassette transporter family, P-glycoprotein (Pgp; 180); the putative channel-forming,

ATP-sensitive protein pICln (22, 130); and phospholemman (101). The bio-physical properties of ClC-2 do not match those of Clvol. Pgp and pICln might play a role as channel regulators rather than as volume-activated Cl$^-$ channels. The role of phospholemman is also questionable (112).

High-conductance Cl$^-$ channels, BCl, which are virtually silent in intact cells or in cell-attached patches, become active after excision of the patch. Their single-channel conductance ranges from 113 to 400 pS (54, 125, 139, 176), and their open probability is higher at more positive potentials. Isoproterenol and cAMP shift their voltage dependence toward more negative potentials (176). A prolonged increase in intracellular Ca$^{2+}$, as well as inhibition of PKC, appears to increase the incidence of the channel in cell-attached patches. Zn$^{2+}$ from either side of the membrane blocks the channel (54).

## Mechano-Sensitive Channels

Endothelial cells are constantly exposed to mechanical forces: shear forces resulting from blood flow and mechanical strain (biaxial tensile stress) depend-ing on changes in the transmural pressure (87). These forces induce a variety of biological responses, among which is activation of mechano-sensitive ion channels (31, 32, 34, 87; see 149 for a review). These channels may be the pri-mary target of mechanical stimuli, and their activation may trigger other cellular responses. It is not clear how force is transmitted to these ion channels. Cy-toskeletal structures, possibly the microfilament or the microtubule network, might transmit force to focal adhesion contacts (31, 34, 87), which is then processed via modulation of focal adhesion contact-associated proteins (talin, vinculin, paxillin, pp125[fak]). Cytoskeletal tyrosine kinases (87) and also the 42 and 44 kDa MAP-kinases (172) are activated by shear stress. Other mech-anisms, such as activation of tyrosine kinases, which are similar to the yeast protein kinase HOG1 (145), cannot be excluded. It is not clear whether this mechanically activated phosphorylation modulates ion channels, but findings on mechanically modulated Cl$^-$ channels have been negative thus far (166).

CHANNELS ACTIVATED BY TENSILE STRESS    Tensile stress, applied as negative pressure to the patch pipette, activates a channel in ECs from pig aorta, which is permeable for monovalent cations (40–56 pS) and Ca$^{2+}$ (19 pS) and has a per-meability ratio $P_{Ca}$:$P_{Na}$ of around 6 (80). Stretch-activated nonselective cation channels with a conductance of 20–30 pS for monovalent cations and 10–20 pS for Ca$^{2+}$ and Ba$^{2+}$ have been described in microvascular endocardium ECs (66, 138). The increase in [Ca$^{2+}$]$_i$ from Ca$^{2+}$ influx through these stretch-sensitive channels is sufficient to activate BK$_{Ca}$ channels and to hyperpolarize the membrane. This interplay of mechano-sensitive and BK$_{Ca}$ channels estab-lishes a positive feedback on Ca$^{2+}$ entry by increasing the driving force (66).

Stretch-activated $Ca^{2+}$-permeable cation channels are blocked by amiloride and $Gd^{3+}$ (94, 105). This could be of interest because amiloride-sensitive $Na^+$ channels, which are linked to the cytoskeleton via ankyrin, and proteins with a high homology to these channels, have been identified as mechano-sensitive ion channels in *C. elegans* (7). Direct activation of $Ca^{2+}$-permeable ion channels by positive pressure (not stretch) has been suggested by several groups (J Hoyer, personal communication; 7, 93). Volume-sensitive $Cl^-$ channels in ECs, as described above, also respond to mechanical forces (112). Cell swelling mediated tensile stress also activates $K^+$ channels which, if co-activated with $Cl^-$ channels, may be involved in volume regulation (35, 133).

CHANNELS ACTIVATED BY SHEAR STRESS    Functionally, shear stress is regarded as a more important mechanical signal than stretch in ECs (31). Pharmacological studies suggest that the population of $K^+$ channels sensitive to mechanical stimulation is heterogeneous. It has been proposed that changes in shear stress resulting from changes in the frequency of pulsatile flow activate $SK_{Ca}$ ($MK_{Ca}$) and $BK_{Ca}$ but not $K_{ATP}$ channels, whereas changes in the shear rate from a variation of the viscosity do not affect $SK_{Ca}$ channels ($MK_{Ca}$) but do affect KATP and $BK_{Ca}$ channels (68). Opening of these $K^+$ channels induces hyperpolarization in native (104) and in cultured (74) ECs, which may modulate the membrane potential in cells that are electrically coupled to the ECs. An inwardly rectifying, 30 pS $K^+$ channel has been described as a possible mechano-sensor of shear stress (74, 127). Its single-channel conductance, degree of rectification, and $Ca^{2+}$ sensitivity in excised patches suggest that this channel belongs to the class of $MK_{Ca}$ or $BK_{Ca}$ channels, but not to the $SK_{Ca}$ channels (29; see above). It also shares some properties with the ROMK-like channels (31) and the previously described $Ca^{2+}$- and GTP-modulated inwardly rectifying $K^+$ channels (119, 126, 179). However, it clearly differs from the classical IRK channel (164). PTX-sensitive mechanisms, cGMP, and NO seem to be involved in the activation of shear stress-dependent $K^+$ channels (56, 119).

Shear stress also activates cation channels, which are about 12 times more permeable for $Ca^{2+}$ than for $Na^+$ (158). This pathway is permeable for $Ni^{2+}$, $Ba^{2+}$, and $Ca^{2+}$. It is insensitive to activators of PKC and is reversibly blocked by $La^{3+}$ and nonsteroid inflammation inhibitors such as mefenamic acid. Modulators of the cytoskeleton such as cytochalasin B increase the sensitivity of ECs to shear stress (110, 157, 158). Shear stress activated $Ca^{2+}$ influx is completely abolished after removal of sialic acid in the glycocalyx of ECs (59).

## Gap Junction Channels

Gap junction connections between neighboring endothelial cells, as well as between endothelial cells and lymphocytes and smooth muscle cells, have been intensively investigated (33). ECs form club-like protrusions that contact neighboring smooth muscle cells through the basement membrane (144). The formation of functional low-resistance cell-cell connections depends on which isoform of connexin is expressed; this may explain the great variability of these connections. At least three isoforms of connexins (Cx37, 40, 43) are expressed in ECs. Macrovascular ECs express more Cx43 than microvascular cells; some ECs co-express Cx37 and Cx43; some express only Cx40 (36, 84). They form functional channels between ECs, which can be disrupted by uncoupling agents such as heptanol (36, 141). Functional channels can be formed between the same isoforms. Interaction does not occur between the Cx40 and Cx43 isoforms, but possibly between Cx40 or Cx43 and Cx37 (20). Expression of connexins depends on the functional state of ECs and is modulated by growth factors such as bFGF (132) and by mechanical forces. Low shear induces expression of gap junction channels, whereas high shear and aging reduce cell-cell contacts (36, 124, 190).

The electrical coupling between ECs (100) may be responsible for the electrotonic spread of electrical signals along the vessel wall. This is consistent with the large electrical length constant of about 0.1 cm in capillaries of small arterioles (30). Electrical coupling via high-conductance gap junction channels between ECs and smooth muscle cells (10, 33) could be functionally important in ECs of small terminal arterioles where a large total EC surface contacts a much smaller smooth muscle surface, which would allow an efficient modulation of the smooth muscle membrane potential by the EC (myo-endothelial regulatory unit; 30). In contrast, other results show that agonist-induced hyperpolarization of ECs does not spread electrotonically to the smooth muscle cells (10), whereas the inverse process, i.e. electrotonic spread from smooth muscle to the lining EC, does occur (11, 91).

# FUNCTIONAL ROLE OF ENDOTHELIAL ION CHANNELS

Our current knowledge about the physiological function of the various channels examined in this review is preliminary, and often rather speculative. We briefly discuss some possible functions.

## $Ca^{2+}$ Signaling

Agonist- or shear stress-mediated $Ca^{2+}$ influx in ECs is controlled by the membrane potential. Depolarizing endothelial cells by increasing the extracellular $K^+$ concentration or by preincubation with $K^+$ channel blockers decreases the plateau phase of the $Ca^{2+}$ signal upon stimulation with ATP or bradykinin. This in turn reduces the production and release of NO and $PGI_2$. The interplay

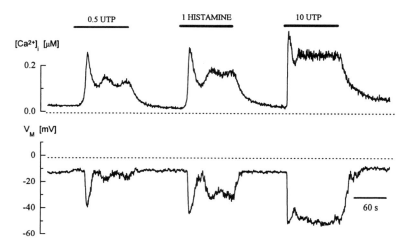

*Figure 3*    Example of the complex pattern of $[Ca^{2+}]_i$ and membrane potential response in a cultured EC (EAhy 926) to different agonists (0.5 and 10 $\mu$M UTP, 1 $\mu$M histamine). Note the oscillatory $Ca^{2+}$ and membrane potential response at low agonist concentrations and the biphasic response, an early $Ca^{2+}$ peak followed by a plateau, and a mirrored hyperpolarization of the membrane during the elevated $Ca^{2+}$ phase. Whole-cell current-clamp recording. The cell was pre-incubated in 2 $\mu$M fura-2 AM for 30 min and the K-aspartate internal solution contained 50 $\mu$M fura-2.

between ion channels, membrane potential, and $Ca^{2+}$ influx might also be important for the generation of $Ca^{2+}$ oscillations in endothelial cells. Figure 3 illustrates this interaction. Stimulation with ATP or histamine induces $Ca^{2+}$ release, which is seen as the early peak, followed by $Ca^{2+}$ oscillations or a $Ca^{2+}$ plateau. Simultaneously, the cell hyperpolarizes. This hyperpolarization by activation of a $Ca^{2+}$- and voltage-dependent high conductance $K^+$ channel ($BK_{Ca}$; see also Figure 2), increases the driving force for $Ca^{2+}$ entry.

As a rule, shear stress or $Ca^{2+}$ mobilizing agonists activate $K^+$ channels ($BK_{Ca}$, $SK_{Ca}$, $K_{ATP}$) and hyperpolarize endothelial cells and thereby support $Ca^{2+}$ influx (21, 23, 29, 59, 85, 118, 119). A similar mechanism may operate in endocardial ECs (88). In many cases, the initial hyperpolarization is followed by depolarization through activation of nonselective cation channels, which would limit the extent of $Ca^{2+}$ influx (30, 90, 97, 98, 174). Interestingly, a similar mechanism for modulation of the driving force has also been proposed for $Cl^-$ channels (63, 64, 192). ATP- and histamine-induced $Ca^{2+}$ entry, and also store-depletion-activated $Ca^{2+}$ entry, can be inhibited by $Cl^-$ channel blockers (NPA) or by a shift of the $Cl^-$ equilibrium potential toward more positive values.

## Vessel Permeability

One of the most prominent functional activities of ECs is the regulation of exchange between blood and tissue. Some agonists (thrombin, histamine) induce a short-lived increase in vascular permeability, whereas others (cytokines, growth factors) induce a more sustained change. This increase in permeability is due to changes in the cytoskeleton and in cell-cell coupling (36). The hydraulic permeability of many EC types, especially in the microvascular bed, is regulated by $Ca^{2+}$ entry, which in turn depends on the membrane potential (57, 58). Modulation of $Ca^{2+}$ entry, activated via SOC-dependent or -independent mechanisms, and the control of $Ca^{2+}$ influx by the electrochemical driving force, might be responsible for this regulation of permeability (58).

## Cell-Cell Contacts

ECs undergo dramatic changes in phenotype and function in response to various stimuli triggered by cell adhesion (3). Their contact with blood cells (lymphocytes, T-helper cell to antigen-presenting EC), extracellular matrix proteins, other ECs during angiogenesis, and circulating tumor cells are modulated by $[Ca^{2+}]_i$ (134). Elevation of $[Ca^{2+}]_i$ increases the potency of ECs to adhere to other cells (82, 135). Binding of ECs to matrix proteins, fibronectin, and vitronectin, and stimulation with integrin monoclonal antibodies also activate $Ca^{2+}$ influx (156). This $Ca^{2+}$ entry depends critically on $\beta 1$ and $\beta 3$ integrins and the $\beta 2$ integrin cellular adhesion molecule ICAM-1 (134). The influx pathway appears to be different from the agonist-mediated $Ca^{2+}$ entry. An integrin-associated protein (IAP-50) physically bound at $\beta 3$ has been proposed to function as a $Ca^{2+}$ entry channel (156). This signaling pathway is obviously linked to the generation of inositol phosphate and the production of $Ins(1,4,5)P_3$ (134) and might be related to the mechanisms proposed for TRP and TRPL.

## Mechano-Sensor Functions and Volume Regulation

Volume-activated $Cl^-$ channels contribute to regulatory volume decrease. Cell swelling initiates a cascade of events, including the activation of $Cl^-$ channels, but it is uncertain whether this activation of $Cl^-$ channels is involved in regulatory volume changes in ECs that occur during metabolic activity, during the cell cycle in proliferating cells, during secretory events, and under pathophysiological conditions. Coactivation of $K^+$ and $Cl^-$ channels shifts the membrane potential to a value between the two reversal potentials and modulates $Ca^{2+}$ entry by affecting the driving force for $Ca^{2+}$ ions (63, 64, 123). Volume-activated $Cl^-$ channels in ECs also transport small organic molecules such as taurine, aspartate, and gluconate, but not arginine, and might thus be important for nonsaturable $Na^+$-independent endothelial transport (112).

## pH Regulation

Agonist stimulation and changes in cell shape activate substantial $Cl^-$ currents ($\approx$100 pA/pF cell membrane capacitance) in ECs (123, 165, 166, 173), which may produce pronounced changes in the intracellular or intercellular $Cl^-$ concentrations. These changes could affect other $Cl^-$-dependent transport mechanism such as the $Cl^-$ exchanger and the $Na^+$-$K^+$-$2Cl^-$ cotransporter, which are involved in intracellular pH regulation. They may also affect a $Cl^-$- and GTP-dependent plasma membrane protein kinase discovered recently (171). Modulation of these $Cl^-$-dependent protein kinases could provide a completely new signaling pathway.

## Cell Proliferation and Differentiation

Most blockers of volume-sensitive $Cl^-$ channels, e.g. tamoxifen, NPPB, and quinine, also suppress the growth of ECs (184). This current may therefore play an important modulatory role in cell proliferation through a mechanism that is linked to its role in volume and/or pH regulation. The functional expression of volume-activated $Cl^-$ channels appears to change if the cells switch from proliferation to differentiation (184). It is intriguing to speculate that processes involving these channels may inhibit angiogenesis and impair neovascularization of tumoral tissue (24, 112, 184)

We have summarized electrophysiological and functional aspects of endothelial ion channels. Their main function appears to be the regulation of $Ca^{2+}$ influx, either directly by modulation of $Ca^{2+}$ channels or indirectly by modulating $K^+$ and $Cl^-$ channels, thereby clamping the membrane potential at a more negative value to provide the necessary driving force for a sustained $Ca^{2+}$ influx.

*Literature Cited*

1. Adams DJ, Barakeh J, Laskey R, Van Breemen C. 1989. Ion channels and regulation of intracellular calcium in vascular endothelial cells. *FASEB J.* 3:2389–400
2. Adams DJ, Rusko J, van Slooten G . 1993. Calcium signalling in vascular endothelial cells: $Ca^{2+}$ entry and release. In *Ion Flux in Pulmonary Vascular Control*, ed. EK Weir, JR Hume, JT Reeves, 251:259–75. New York: Plenum
3. Albelda SM, Buck CA. 1990. Integrins and other cell adhesion molecules. *FASEB J.* 4:2868–80
4. Alliegro MC, Alliegro MA, Cragoe EJ Jr, Glaser BM. 1993. Amiloride inhibition of angiogenesis in vitro. *J. Exp. Zool.* 267:245–52
5. Arima M, Ueda S, Matsushita S, Ozawa T, Yamaguchi H. 1994. Adenosine in-

duces $Cl^-$ efflux in endothelial cells via a pertussis toxin-sensitive G protein. *Biochem. Biophys. Res. Commun.* 204:1143–49
6. Bahnson TD, Pandol SJ, Dionne VE. 1993. Cyclic GMP modulates depletion-activated $Ca^{2+}$ entry in pancreatic acinar cells. *J. Biol. Chem.* 268:10808–12
7. Bargmann CI. 1994. Molecular mechanisms of mechanosensation? *Cell* 78:729–31
8. Baron A, Frieden M, Chabaud F, Bény J-L. 1996. $Ca^{2+}$-dependent nonselective cation and potassium channels activated by bradykinin in pig coronary artery endothelial cell. *J. Physiol.* 49:699–706
9. Bennett DL, Petersen CCH, Cheek TR. 1995. Cracking $I_{CRAC}$ in the eye. *Curr. Biol.* 5:1225–28

10. Beny JL. 1990. Endothelial and smooth muscle cells hyperpolarized by bradykinin are not dye coupled. *Am. J. Physiol.* 258:H836–41

11. Beny JL, Pacicca C. 1994. Bidirectional electrical communication between smooth muscle and endothelial cells in the pig coronary artery. *Am. J. Physiol.* 266:H1465–72

12. Berridge MJ. 1995. Capacitative calcium entry. *Biochem. J.* 312:1–11

13. Bkaily G. 1991. Receptor and second messenger modulation of $Ca^{2+}$ and $K^+$ channels activity in vascular smooth muscle cells. In *Ion Channels of Vascular Smooth Muscle Cells and Endothelial Cells*, ed. N Sperelakis, H Kuriyama, pp. 185–98. Amsterdam/Lausanne/New York: Elsevier

14. Bkaily G, Dorleansjuste P, Naik R, Perodin J, Stankova J, et al. 1993. PAF Activation of a voltage-gated R-type $Ca^{2+}$ channel in human and canine aortic endothelial cells. *Br. J. Pharmacol.* 110:519–20

15. Bossu JL, Elhamdani A, Feltz A. 1992. Voltage-dependent calcium entry in confluent bovine capillary endothelial cells. *FEBS Lett.* 299:239–42

16. Bossu JL, Elhamdani A, Feltz A, Tanzi F, Aunis D, Thierse D. 1992. Voltage-gated Ca entry in isolated bovine capillary endothelial cells—evidence of a new type of BAY-K 8644-sensitive channel. *Pflügers Arch.* 420:200–7

17. Bossu JL, Feltz A, Rodeau JL, Tanzi F. 1989. Voltage-dependent transient calcium currents in freshly dissociated capillary endothelial cells. *FEBS Lett.* 255:377–80

18. Brauneis U, Gatmaitan Z, Arias IM. 1992. Serotonin stimulates a $Ca^{2+}$ permeant nonspecific cation channel in hepatic endothelial cells. *Biochem. Biophys. Res. Commun.* 186:1560–66

19. Bregestovski P, Bakhramov A, Danilov S, Moldobaeva A, Takeda K. 1988. Histamine-induced inward currents in cultured endothelial cells from human umbilical vein. *Br. J. Pharmacol.* 95:429–36

20. Bruzzone R, Haefliger JA, Gimlich RL, Paul DL. 1993. Connexin40, a component of gap junctions in vascular endothelium, is restricted in its ability to interact with other connexins. *Mol. Biol. Cell* 4:7–20

21. Busse R, Mulsch A, Fleming I, Hecker M. 1993. Mechanisms of nitric oxide release from the vascular endothelium. *Circulation* 87:18–25

22. Buyse G, DeGreef C, Raeymaekers L, Droogmans G, Nilius B, Eggermont J. 1996. The ubiquitously expressed pI$_{Cln}$ protein forms homomeric complexes in vitro. *Biochem. Biophys. Res. Commun.* 218:822–27

23. Cabello OA, Schilling WP. 1993. Vectorial $Ca^{2+}$ flux from the extracellular space to the endoplasmic reticulum via a restricted cytoplasmic compartment regulates inositol 1,4,5-trisphosphate-stimulated $Ca^{2+}$ release from internal stores in vascular endothelial cells. *Biochem. J.* 295:357–66

24. Chou C-Y, Shen M-R, Wu S-N. 1995. Volume-sensitive chloride channels associated with human cervical carcinogenesis. *Cancer Res.* 55:6077–83

25. Clapham DE. 1995. Calcium signaling. *Cell* 80:259–68

26. Colden Stanfield M, Cramer EB, Gallin EK. 1992. Comparison of apical and basal surfaces of confluent endothelial cells—patch-clamp and viral studies. *Am. J. Physiol.* 263:C573–83

27. Colden Stanfield M, Schilling WP, Possani LD, Kunze DL. 1990. Bradykinin-induced potassium current in cultured bovine aortic endothelial cells. *J. Membr. Biol.* 116:227–38

28. Colden Stanfield M, Schilling WP, Ritchie AK, Eskin SG, Navarro LT, Kunze DL. 1987. Bradykinin-induced increases in cytosolic calcium and ionic currents in cultured bovine aortic endothelial cells. *Circ. Res.* 61:632–40

29. Cooke JP, Rossitch E Jr, Andon NA, Loscalzo J, Dzau VJ. 1991. Flow activates an endothelial potassium channel to release an endogenous nitrovasodilator. *J. Clin. Invest.* 88:1663–71

30. Daut J, Standen NB, Nelson MT. 1994. The role of the membrane potential of endothelial and smooth muscle cells in the regulation of coronary blood flow. *J. Cardiovasc. Electrophysiol.* 5:154–81

31. Davies PF. 1995. Flow-mediated endothelial mechanotransduction. *Physiol. Rev.* 75:519–60

32. Davies PF, Barbee KA. 1994. Endothelial cell surface imaging: insights into hemodynamic force transduction. *News Physiol. Sci.* 9:153–57

33. Davies PF, Olesen SP, Clapham DE, Morrel EM, Schoen FJ. 1988. Endothelial communication. State of the art lecture. *Hypertension* 11:563–72

34. Davies PF, Tripathi SC. 1993. Mechanical stress mechanisms and the cell—an

endothelial paradigm. *Circ. Res.* 72:239–45

35. De Smet P, Oike M, Droogmans G, van Driessche W, Nilius B. 1994. Responses of endothelial cells to hypotonic solutions: lack of regulatory volume decrease. *Pflügers Arch.* 428:94–96

36. Dejana E, Corada M, Lampugnani MG. 1995. Endothelial cell-to-cell junctions. *FASEB J.* 9:910–18

37. Demirel E, Rusko J, Laskey RE, Adams DJ, van Breemen AC. 1994. TEA inhibits ACh-induced EDRF release: endothelial $Ca^{2+}$-dependent $K^+$ channels contribute to vascular tone. *Am. J. Physiol.* 267:H1135–41

38. Denning GM, Ostedgaard LS, Cheng SH, Smith AE, Welsh MJ. 1992. Localization of cystic fibrosis transmembrane conductance regulator in chloride secretory epithelia. *J. Clin. Invest.* 89:339–49

39. Dolor RJ, Hurwitz LM, Mirza Z, Strauss HC, Whorton AR. 1992. Regulation of extracellular calcium entry in endothelial cells. Role of intracellular calcium pool. *Am. J. Physiol.* 262:C171–81

40. Doupnik CA, Davidson N, Lester HA. 1995. The inward rectifier potassium channel family. *Curr. Opin. Neurobiol.* 5:268–77

41. Edgell CJ, McDonald CC, Graham JB. 1983. Permanent cell line expressing human factor VIII-related antigen established by hybridization. *Proc. Natl. Acad. Sci. USA* 80:3734–37

42. Elam TR, Lansman JB. 1995. The role of $Mg^{2+}$ in the inactivation of inwardly rectifying $K^+$ channels in aortic endothelial cells. *J. Gen. Physiol.* 105:463–84

43. Fleming I, Fisslthaler B, Busse R. 1995. Calcium signaling in endothelial cells involves activation of tyrosine kinases and leads to activation of mitogen-activated protein kinases. *Circ. Res.* 76:522–29

44. Fransen PF, Demolder MJ, Brutsaert DL. 1995. Whole cell membrane currents in cultured pig endocardial endothelial cells. *Am. J. Physiol.* 268:H2036–47

45. Fujimoto T, Nakade S, Miyawaki A, Mikoshiba K, Ogawa K. 1992. Localization of inositol 1,4,5-trisphosphate receptor-like protein in plasmalemmal caveolae. *J. Cell Biol.* 119:1507–13

46. Gericke M, Droogmans G, Nilius B. 1993. Thapsigargin discharges intracellular calcium stores and induces transmembrane currents in human endothelial cells. *Pflügers Arch.* 422:552–57

47. Gericke M, Oike M, Droogmans G, Nilius B. 1994. Inhibition of capacitative $Ca^{2+}$

entry by a $Cl^-$ channel blocker in human endothelial cells. *Eur. J. Pharmacol.* 269:381–84

48. Gordienko DV, Tsukahara H. 1994. Tetrodotoxin-blockable depolarization-activated $Na^+$ currents in a cultured endothelial cell line derived from rat interlobar artery and human umbilical vein. *Pflügers Arch.* 428:91–93

49. Graier WF, Groschner K, Schmidt K, Kukovetz WR. 1992. SK & F 96365 inhibits histamine-induced formation of endothelium-derived relaxing factor in human endothelial cells. *Biochem. Biophys. Res. Commun.* 186:1539–45

50. Graier WF, Kukovetz WR, Groschner K. 1993. Cyclic AMP enhances agonist-induced $Ca^{2+}$ entry into endothelial cells by activation of potassium channels and membrane hyperpolarization. *Biochem. J.* 291:263–67

51. Graier WF, Simecek S, Sturek M. 1995. Cytochrome P450 mono-oxygenase-regulated signalling of $Ca^{2+}$ entry in human and bovine endothelial cells. *J. Physiol.* 482:259–74

52. Groschner K, Graier WF, Kukovetz WR. 1992. Activation of a small-conductance $Ca^{2+}$-dependent $K^+$ channel contributes to bradykinin-induced stimulation of nitric oxide synthesis in pig aortic endothelial cells. *Biochim. Biophys. Acta* 1137:162–70

53. Groschner K, Graier WF, Kukovetz WR. 1994. Histamine induces $K^+$, $Ca^{2+}$, and $Cl^-$ currents in human vascular endothelial cells. Role of ionic currents in stimulation of nitric oxide biosynthesis. *Circ. Res.* 75:304–14

54. Groschner K, Kukovetz WR. 1992. Voltage-sensitive chloride channels of large conductance in the membrane of pig aortic endothelial cells. *Pflügers Arch.* 421:209–17

55. Grunder S, Thiemann A, Pusch M, Jentsch TJ. 1992. Regions involved in the opening of ClC-2 chloride channel by voltage and cell volume. *Nature* 360:759–62

56. Hassessian H, Bodin P, Burnstock G. 1993. Blockade by glibenclamide of the flow-evoked endothelial release of ATP that contributes to vasodilatation in the pulmonary vascular bed of the rat. *Br. J. Pharmacol.* 109:466–72

57. He P, Curry FE. 1991. Depolarization modulates endothelial cell calcium influx and microvessel permeability. *Am. J. Physiol.* 261:H1246–54

58. He P, Curry FE. 1994. Endothelial cell hyperpolarization increases $[Ca^{2+}]_i$ and venular microvessel permeability. *J. Appl. Physiol.* 76:2288–97

59. Hecker M, Mulsch A, Bassenge E, Busse R. 1993. Vasoconstriction and increased flow. Two principal mechanisms of shear stress-dependent endothelial autacoid release. *Am. J. Physiol.* 265:H828–33

60. Himmel HM, Rasmusson RL, Strauss HC. 1994. Agonist-induced changes of $[Ca^{2+}]_i$ and membrane currents in single bovine aortic endothelial cells. *Am. J. Physiol.* 267:C1338–50

61. Himmel HM, Whorton AR, Strauss HC. 1993. Intracellular calcium, currents, and stimulus response coupling in endothelial cells. *Hypertension* 21:112–27

62. Ho K, Nichols CG, Lederer WJ, Lytton J, Vassilev PM, et al. 1993. Cloning and expression of an inwardly rectifying ATP-regulated potassium channel. *Nature* 362:31–38

63. Hosoki E, Iijima T. 1994. Chloride-sensitive $Ca^{2+}$ entry by histamine and ATP in human aortic endothelial cells. *Eur. J. Pharmacol.* 266:213–18

64. Hosoki E, Iijima T. 1995. Modulation of cytosolic $Ca^{2+}$ concentration by thapsigargin and cyclopiazonic acid in human aortic endothelial cells. *Eur. J. Pharmacol.* 288:131–37

65. Hoth M, Penner R. 1993. Calcium release-activated calcium current in rat mast cells. *J. Physiol.* 465:359–86

66. Hoyer J, Distler A, Haase W, Gogelein H. 1994. $Ca^{2+}$ influx through stretch-activated cation channels activates maxi $K^+$ channels in porcine endocardial endothelium. *Proc. Natl. Acad. Sci. USA* 91:2367–71

67. Hoyer J, Popp R, Meyer J, Galla HJ, Gogelein H. 1991. Angiotensin II, vasopressin and GTPgammaS inhibit inward-rectifying $K^+$ channels in porcine cerebral capillary endothelial cells. *J. Membr. Biol.* 123:55–62

68. Hutcheson IR, Griffith TM. 1994. Heterogeneous populations of $K^+$ channels mediate EDRF release to flow but not agonists in rabbit aorta. *Am. J. Physiol.* 266:H590–96

69. Inagami T, Naruse M, Hoover R. 1995. Endothelium as an endocrine organ. *Annu. Rev. Physiol.* 57:171–89

70. Inazu M, Zhang H, Daniel EE. 1993. LP-805, a releaser of endothelium-derived nitric oxide, activates an endothelial cal-cium permeable non-specific cation channel. *Life Sci.* 53:315–20

71. Inazu M, Zhang H, Daniel EE. 1994. Different mechanisms can activate $Ca^{2+}$ entrance via cation currents in endothelial cells. *Life Sci.* 56:11–17

72. Inazu M, Zhang H, Daniel EE. 1994. Properties of the Lp-805-induced potassium currents in cultured bovine pulmonary artery endothelial cells. *J. Pharmacol. Exp. Ther.* 268:403–8

73. Jacob R. 1990. Agonist-stimulated divalent cation entry into single cultured human umbilical vein endothelial cells. *J. Physiol.* 421:55–77

74. Jacobs ER, Cheliakine C, Gebremedhin D, Birks EK, Davies PF, Harder DR. 1995. Shear activated channels in cell-attached patches of cultured bovine aortic endothelial cells. *Pflügers Arch.* 431:129–31

75. Janigro D, West GA, Gordon EL, Winn HR. 1993. ATP-sensitive $K^+$ channels in rat aorta and brain microvascular endothelial cells. *Am. J. Physiol.* 265:C812–21

76. Janigro D, West GA, Nguyen TS, Winn HR. 1994. Regulation of blood-brain barrier endothelial cells by nitric oxide. *Circ. Res.* 75:528–38

77. Katnik C, Adams DJ. 1995. An ATP-sensitive potassium conductance in rabbit arterial endothelial cells. *J. Physiol.* 485:595–606

78. Koliwad SK, Kunze DL, Elliott SJ. 1996. Oxidant stress activates a non-selective cation channel responsible for membrane depolarization in calf vascular endothelial cells. *J. Physiol.* 491:1–12

79. Kuo L, Chancellor JD. 1995. Adenosine potentiates flow-induced dilation of coronary arterioles by activating $K_{ATP}$ channels in endothelium. *Am. J. Physiol.* 269:H541–49

80. Lansman JB, Hallam TJ, Rink TJ. 1987. Single stretch-activated ion channels in vascular endothelial cells as mechano-transducers? *Nature* 325:811–13

81. Laskey RE, Adams DJ, Johns A, Rubanyi GM, van Breemen C. 1990. Membrane potential and $Na^+$-$K^+$ pump activity modulate resting and bradykinin-stimulated changes in cytosolic free calcium in cultured endothelial cells from bovine atria. *J. Biol. Chem.* 265:2613–19

82. Leavesley DI, Schwartz MA, Rosenfeld M, Cheresh DA. 1993. Integrin beta 1- and beta 3-mediated endothelial cell migration is triggered through distinct signaling mechanisms. *J. Cell Biol.* 121:163–70

83. Ling BN, O'Neill WC. 1992. $Ca^{2+}$-dependent and $Ca^{2+}$-permeable ion chan-

nels in aortic endothelial cells. *Am. J. Physiol.* 263:H1827–38

84. Little TL, Beyer EC, Duling BR. 1995. Connexin 43 and connexin 40 gap junctional proteins are present in arteriolar smooth muscle and endothelium in vivo. *Am. J. Physiol.* 268:H729–39

85. Luckhoff A, Busse R. 1990. Activators of potassium channels enhance calcium influx into endothelial cells as a consequence of potassium currents. *Naunyn Schmiedebergs Arch. Pharmacol.* 342:94–99

86. Luckhoff A, Clapham DE. 1992. Inositol 1,3,4,5-tetrakisphosphate activates an endothelial $Ca^{2+}$-permeable channel. *Nature* 355:356–58

87. Malek AM, Izumo S. 1994. Molecular aspects of signal transduction of shear stress in the endothelial cell. *J. Hypertens.* 12:989–99

88. Manabe K, Ito H, Matsuda H, Noma A. 1995. Hyperpolarization induced by vasoactive substances in intact guinea-pig endocardial endothelial cells. *J. Physiol.* 484:25–40

89. Manabe K, Takano M, Noma A. 1995. Non-selective cation current of guinea-pig endocardial endothelial cells. *J. Physiol.* 487:407–19

90. Marchenko SM, Sage SO. 1993. Electrical properties of resting and acetylcholine-stimulated endothelium in intact rat aorta. *J. Physiol.* 462:735–51

91. Marchenko SM, Sage SO. 1994. Smooth muscle cells affect endothelial membrane potential in rat aorta. *Am. J. Physiol.* 267:H804–11

92. Marchenko SM, Sage SO. 1996. Calcium-activated potassium channels in the endothelium of intact rat aorta. *J. Physiol.* 492:53–60

93. Marchenko SM, Sage SO. 1996. Mechanosensitive cation channels from endothelium of excised intact rat aorta. *Biophys. J.* 70:A365 (Abst.)

94. Mazzoni MC, Intaglietta M, Cragoe EJ Jr, Arfors KE. 1992. Amiloride-sensitive $Na^+$ pathways in capillary endothelial cell swelling during hemorrhagic shock. *J. Appl. Physiol.* 73:1467–73

95. McCannel CA, Scanlon PD, Thibodeau S, Brubaker RF. 1992. A study of aqueous humor formation in patients with cystic fibrosis. *Invest. Ophthalmol. Vis. Sci.* 33:160–64

96. McCormack D. 1990. Endothelium-derived relaxing factors and the human pulmonary circulation. *Lung* 168:35–42

97. Mehrke G, Daut J. 1990. The electrical response of cultured guinea-pig coronary endothelial cells to endothelium-dependent vasodilators. *J. Physiol.* 430:251–72

98. Mehrke G, Pohl U, Daut J. 1991. Effects of vasoactive agonists on the membrane potential of cultured bovine aortic and guinea-pig coronary endothelium. *J. Physiol.* 439:277–99

99. Mendelowitz D, Bacal K, Kunze DL. 1992. Bradykinin-activated calcium influx pathway in bovine aortic endothelial cells. *Am. J. Physiol.* 262:H942–48

100. Miao K, Wondergem R, Hossler FE, Joyner WL. 1993. Contributions of $K^+$, $Na^+$, and $Cl^-$ to the membrane potential of intact hamster vascular endothelial cells. *J. Cell. Physiol.* 156:550–59

101. Moorman JR, Ackerman SJ, Kowdley GC, Griffin MP, Mounsey JP, et al. 1995. Unitary anion currents through phospholemman channel molecules. *Nature* 377:737–40

102. Murphy HS, Maroughi M, Till GO, Ward PA. 1994. Phorbol-stimulated influx of extracellular calcium in rat pulmonary artery endothelial cells. *Am. J. Physiol.* 267:L145–51

103. Nag S. 1990. Ultracytochemical localisation of $Na^+$, $K^+$-ATPase in cerebral endothelium in acute hypertension. *Acta Neuropathol.* 80:7–11

104. Nakache M, Gaub HE. 1988. Hydrodynamic hyperpolarization of endothelial cells. *Proc. Natl. Acad. Sci. USA* 85:1841–43

105. Naruse K, Sokabe M. 1993. Involvement of stretch-activated ion channels in $Ca^{2+}$ mobilization to mechanical stretch in endothelial cells. *Am. J. Physiol.* 264:C1037–44

106. Nilius B. 1990. Permeation properties of a non-selective cation channel in human vascular endothelial cells. *Pflügers Arch.* 416:609–11

107. Nilius B. 1991. Regulation of transmembrane calcium fluxes in endothelium. *News Physiol. Sci.* 6:110–14

108. Nilius B, Casteels R. 1996. Biology of the vascular wall and its interaction with migratory and blood cells. In *Comprehensive Human Physiology,* ed. R Gerger, U Windhorts, 2:1981–94. Berlin/Heidelberg: Springer-Verlag

109. Nilius B, Droogmans G. 1994. A role for $K^+$ channels in cell proliferation. *News Physiol. Sci.* 9:105–10

110. Nilius B, Droogmans G. 1995. Ion channels of endothelial cells. In *Physiology and Pathophysiology of the Heart,* ed.

N Sperelakis, pp. 961–73. Dordrecht: Kluwer

111. Nilius B, Droogmans G, Gericke M, Schwartz G. 1993. Non-selective ion pathways in human endothelial cells. In *Nonselective Cation Channels, Physiology and Biophysics,* ed. D Siemen, J Hescheler, pp. 269–80, Basel: Birkhäuser Verlag

112. Nilius B, Eggermont J, Voets T, Droogmans G. 1996. Volume-activated $Cl^-$-channels. *Gen. Pharmacol.* In press

113. Nilius B, Oike M, Zahradnik I, Droogmans G. 1994. Activation of a $Cl^-$ current by hypotonic volume increase in human endothelial cells. *J. Gen. Physiol.* 103:787–805

114. Nilius B, Riemann D. 1990. Ion channels in human endothelial cells. *Gen. Physiol. Biophys.* 9:89–112

115. Nilius B, Schwarz G, Droogmans G. 1993. Modulation by histamine of an inwardly rectifying potassium channel in human endothelial cells. *J. Physiol.* 472:359–71

116. Nilius B, Schwarz G, Oike M, Droogmans G. 1993. Histamine-activated, nonselective cation currents and $Ca^{2+}$ transients in endothelial cells from human umbilical vein. *Pflügers Arch.* 424:285–93

117. Nilius B, Sehrer J, Viana F, Degreef C, Raeymaekers L, et al. 1994. Volume-activated $Cl^-$ currents in different mammalian non-excitable cell types. *Pflügers Arch.* 428:364–71

118. Ohno M, Cooke JP, Dzau VJ, Gibbons GH. 1995. Fluid shear stress induces endothelial transforming growth factor beta-1 transcription and production. Modulation by potassium channel blockade. *J. Clin. Invest.* 95:1363–69

119. Ohno M, Gibbons GH, Dzau VJ, Cooke JP. 1993. Shear stress elevates endothelial cGMP. Role of a potassium channel and G protein coupling. *Circulation* 88:193–97

120. Oike M, Droogmans G, Casteels R, Nilius B. 1993. Electrogenic $Na^+/K^+$-transport in human endothelial cells. *Pflügers Arch.* 424:301–7

121. Oike M, Droogmans G, Nilius B. 1994. Mechanosensitive $Ca^{2+}$ transients in endothelial cells from human umbilical vein. *Proc. Natl. Acad. Sci. USA* 91:2940–44

122. Oike M, Droogmans G, Nilius B. 1994. The volume-activated chloride current in human endothelial cells depends on intracellular ATP. *Pflügers Arch.* 427:184–86

123. Oike M, Gericke M, Droogmans G, Nilius B. 1994. Calcium entry activated by store depletion in human umbilical vein endothelial cells. *Cell Calcium* 16:367–76

124. Okano M, Yoshida Y. 1993. Influences of shear stress on endothelial cell shapes and junction complexes at flow dividers of aortic bifurcations in cholesterol-fed rabbits. *Front. Med. Biol. Eng.* 5:95–120

125. Olesen SP, Bundgaard M. 1992. Chloride-selective channels of large conductance in bovine aortic endothelial cells. *Acta Physiol. Scand.* 144:191–98

126. Olesen SP, Bundgaard M. 1993. ATP-dependent closure and reactivation of inward rectifier $K^+$ channels in endothelial cells. *Circ. Res.* 73:492–95

127. Olesen SP, Clapham DE, Davies PF. 1988. Haemodynamic shear stress activates a $K^+$ current in vascular endothelial cells. *Nature* 331:168–70

128. Pasyk E, Inazu M, Daniel EE. 1995. CPA enhances $Ca^{2+}$ entry in cultured bovine pulmonary arterial endothelial cells in an $IP_3$-independent manner. *Am. J. Physiol.* 37:H138–46

129. Pasyk E, Mao YK, Ahmad S, Shen SH, Daniel EE. 1992. An endothelial cell-line contains functional vasoactive intestinal polypeptide receptors: they control inwardly rectifying $K^+$ channels. *Eur. J. Pharmacol.* 212:209–14

130. Paulmichl M, Li Y, Wickman K, Ackerman M, Peralta E, Clapham D. 1992. New mammalian chloride channel identified by expression cloning. *Nature* 356:238–41

131. Pennefather PS, Decoursey TE. 1994. A scheme to account for the effects of $Rb^+$ and $K^+$ on inward rectifier K channels of bovine artery endothelial cells. *J. Gen. Physiol.* 103:549–81

132. Pepper MS, Meda P. 1992. Basic fibroblast growth factor increases junctional communication and connexin 43 expression in microvascular endothelial cells. *J. Cell Physiol.* 153:196–205

133. Perry PB, Oneill WC. 1993. Swelling-activated K-fluxes in vascular endothelial cells. Volume regulation via K-Cl cotransport and K-channels. *Am. J. Physiol.* 265:C763–69

134. Pfau S, Leitenberg D, Rinder H, Smith BR, Pardi R, Bender JR. 1995. Lymphocyte adhesion-dependent calcium signaling in human endothelial cells. *J. Cell Biol.* 128:969–78

135. Pili R, Corda S, Passaniti A, Ziegelstein RC, Heldman AW, Capogrossi MC. 1993.

Endothelial cell $Ca^{2+}$ increases upon tumor cell contact and modulates cell-cell adhesion. *J. Clin. Invest.* 92:3017–22

136. Popp R, Englert HC, Lang HJ, Gogelein H. 1993. Inhibitors of nonselective cation channels in cells of the blood-brain barrier. *Exp. Suppl.* 66:213–18

137. Popp R, Gogelein H. 1992. A calcium and ATP sensitive nonselective cation channel in the antiluminal membrane of rat cerebral capillary endothelial cells. *Biochim. Biophys. Acta* 1108:59–66

138. Popp R, Hoyer J, Meyer J, Galla HJ, Gogelein H. 1992. Stretch-activated nonselective cation channels in the antiluminal membrane of porcine cerebral capillaries. *J. Physiol.* 454:435–49

139. Queyroy A, Verdetti J. 1992. Cooperative gating of chloride channel subunits in endothelial cells. *Biochim. Biophys. Acta* 1108:159–68

140. Randriamampita C, Tsien RY. 1993. Emptying of intracellular $Ca^{2+}$ stores releases a novel small messenger that stimulates $Ca^{2+}$ influx. *Nature* 364:809–14

141. Reed KE, Westphale EM, Larson DM, Wang HZ, Veenstra RD, Beyer EC. 1993. Molecular cloning and functional expression of human connexin37, an endothelial cell gap junction protein. *J. Clin. Invest.* 91:997–1004

142. Resnick N, Gimbrone MA. 1995. Hemodynamic forces are complex regulators of endothelial gene expression. *FASEB J.* 9:874–82

143. Revest PA, Abbott NJ. 1992. Membrane ion channels of endothelial cells. *Trends Pharmacol. Sci.* 13:404–7

144. Rhodin JAG. 1980. Architecture of the vessel wall. In *Handbook of Physiology. Sec. 2. The Cardiovascular System,* ed. DF Bohr, AP Somlyo, HV Sparks, II:1–31. Bethesda, MD: Am. Physiol. Soc.

145. Rouse J, Cohen P, Trigon S, Morange M, Alonso Llamazares A, et al. 1994. A novel kinase cascade triggered by stress and heat shock that stimulates MAPKAP kinase-2 and phosphorylation of the small heat shock proteins. *Cell* 78:1027–37

146. Rusko J, Li L, van Breemen C. 1995. 17-beta-estradiol stimulation of endothelial $K^+$ channels. *Biochem. Biophys. Res. Commun.* 214:367–72

147. Rusko J, Tanzi F, van Breemen C, Adams DJ. 1992. Calcium-activated potassium channels in native endothelial cells from rabbit aorta. Conductance, $Ca^{2+}$ sensitivity and block. *J. Physiol.* 455:601–21

148. Rusko J, Vanslooten G, Adams DJ. 1995. Caffeine-evoked, calcium-sensitive membrane currents in rabbit aortic endothelial cells. *Br. J. Pharmacol.* 115:133–41

149. Sackin H. 1995. Mechanosensitive channels. *Annu. Rev. Physiol.* 57:333–53

150. Sage SO, van Breemen C, Cannell MB. 1991. Sodium-Calcium exchange in cultured bovine pulmonary artery endothelial cells. *J. Physiol.* 440:569–80

151. Sakai T. 1990. Acetylcholine induces Ca-dependent K currents in rabbit endothelial cells. *Jpn. J. Pharmacol.* 53:235–46

152. Sauve R, Chahine M, Tremblay J, Hamet P. 1990. Single-channel analysis of the electrical response of bovine aortic endothelial cells to bradykinin stimulation: contribution of a $Ca^{2+}$-dependent $K^+$ channel. *J. Hypertens.* 8:S193–201

153. Sauve R, Parent L, Simoneau C, Roy G. 1988. External ATP triggers a biphasic activation process of a calcium-dependent $K^+$ channel in cultured bovine aortic endothelial cells. *Pflügers Arch.* 412:469–81

154. Schilling WP, Cabello OA, Rajan L. 1992. Depletion of the inositol 1,4,5-trisphosphate-sensitive intracellular $Ca^{2+}$ store in vascular endothelial cells activates the agonist-sensitive $Ca^{2+}$-influx pathway. *Biochem. J.* 284:521–30

155. Schilling WP, Rajan L, Strobl Jager E. 1989. Characterization of the bradykinin-stimulated calcium influx pathway of cultured vascular endothelial cells. Saturability, selectivity, and kinetics. *J. Biol. Chem.* 264:12838–48

156. Schwartz MA, Brown EJ, Fazeli B. 1993. A 50-kDa integrin-associated protein is required for integrin-regulated calcium entry in endothelial cells. *J. Biol. Chem.* 268:19931–34

157. Schwarz G, Callewaert G, Droogmans G, Nilius B. 1992. Shear stress-induced calcium transients in endothelial cells from human umbilical cord veins. *J. Physiol.* 458:527–38

158. Schwarz G, Droogmans G, Nilius B. 1992. Shear stress induced membrane currents and calcium transients in human vascular endothelial cells. *Pflügers Arch.* 421:394–96

159. Schwarz G, Droogmans G, Nilius B. 1994. Multiple effects of SK& F 96365 on ionic currents and intracellular calcium in human endothelial cells. *Cell Calcium* 15:45–54

160. Seiss-Geuder M, Mehrke G, Daut J. 1992. Sustained hyperpolarization of cultured guinea-pig endothelial cells induced by adenosine. *J. Cardiovasc. Pharmacol.* 20:S97-100

161. Sharma NR, Davis MJ. 1995. Substance P-induced calcium entry in endothelial cells is secondary to depletion of intracellular stores. *Am. J. Physiol.* 268:H962–73

162. Shimekake Y, Nagata K, Ohta S, Kambayashi Y, Teraoka H, et al. 1995. Adrenomedullin stimulates two signal transduction pathways, cAMP accumulation and $Ca^{2+}$ mobilization, in bovine aortic endothelial cells. *J. Biol. Chem.* 270:4412–17

163. Silver MR, Decoursey TE. 1990. Intrinsic gating of inward rectifier in bovine pulmonary artery endothelial cells in the presence or absence of internal $Mg^{2+}$. *J. Gen. Physiol.* 96:109–33

164. Silver MR, Shapiro MS, Decoursey TE. 1994. Effects of external $Rb^+$ on inward rectifier $K^+$ channels of bovine pulmonary artery endothelial cells. *J. Gen. Physiol.* 103:519–48

165. Szücs G, Buyse G, Eggermont J, Droogmans G, Nilius B. 1996. Characterisation of volume-activated chloride currents in endothelial cells from bovine pulmonary artery. *J. Membr. Biol.* 179:189–97

166. Szücs G, Heinke S, De Greef C, Raeymaekers L, Eggermont J, et al. 1996. The volume-activated $Cl^-$ current in endothelial cells from bovine pulmonary artery is not modulated by phosphorylation. *Pflügers Arch.* 431:540–48

167. Takeda K, Klepper M. 1990. Voltage-dependent and agonist-activated ionic currents in vascular endothelial cells: a review. *Blood Vessels* 27:169–83

168. Takeda K, Schini V, Stoeckel H. 1987. Voltage-activated potassium, but not calcium currents in cultured bovine aortic endothelial cells. *Pflügers Arch.* 410:385–93

169. Thiemann A, Grunder S, Pusch M, Jentsch TJ. 1992. A chloride channel widely expressed in epithelial and nonepithelial cells. *Nature* 356:57–60

170. Thuringer D, Diarra A, Sauve R. 1991. Modulation by extracellular pH of bradykinin-evoked activation of $Ca^{2+}$-activated $K^+$ channels in endothelial cells. *Am. J. Physiol.* 261:H656–66

171. Treharne KJ, Marshall LJ, Mehta A. 1994. A novel chloride-dependent GTP-utilizing protein kinase in plasma membranes from human respiratory epithelium. *Am. J. Physiol.* 267:L592–601

172. Tseng H, Peterson TE, Berk BC. 1995. Fluid shear stress stimulates mitogen-activated protein kinase in endothelial cells. *Circ. Res.* 77:869–78

173. Ueda S, Lee SL, Fanburg BL. 1990. Chloride efflux in cyclic AMP-induced configurational change of bovine pulmonary artery endothelial cells. *Circ. Res.* 66:957–67

174. Usachev YM, Marchenko SM, Sage SO. 1995. Cytosolic calcium concentration in resting and stimulated endothelium of excised intact rat aorta. *J. Physiol.* 489:309–17

175. Vaca L, Gurrola GB, Possani LD, Kunze DL. 1993. Blockade of a $K_{Ca}$ channel with synthetic peptides from noxiustoxin, a $K^+$ channel blocker. *J. Membr. Biol.* 134:123–29

176. Vaca L, Kunze DL. 1993. cAMP-dependent phosphorylation modulates voltage gating in an endothelial $Cl^-$ channel. *Am. J. Physiol.* 264:C370–75

177. Vaca L, Kunze DL. 1994. Depletion of intracellular $Ca^{2+}$ stores activates a $Ca^{2+}$-selective channel in vascular endothelium. *Am. J. Physiol.* 36:C920–25

178. Vaca L, Kunze DL. 1995. $IP_3$-activated $Ca^{2+}$ channels in the plasma membrane of cultured vascular endothelial cells. *Am. J. Physiol.* 269:C733–38

179. Vaca L, Schilling WP, Kunze DL. 1992. G-protein-mediated regulation of a $Ca^{2+}$-dependent $K^+$ channel in cultured vascular endothelial cells. *Pflügers Arch.* 422:66–74

180. Valverde MA, Diaz M, Sepulveda FV, Gill DR, Hyde SC, Higgins CF. 1992. Volume-regulated chloride channels associated with the human multidrug-resistance P-glycoprotein. *Nature* 355:830–33

181. van Renterghem C, Vigne P, Frelin C. 1995. A charybdotoxin-sensitive, $Ca^{2+}$-activated $K^+$ channel with inward rectifying properties in brain microvascular endothelial cells: properties and activation by endothelins. *J. Neurochem.* 65:1274–81

182. Vargas FF, Caviedes PF, Grant DS. 1994. Electrophysiological characteristics of cultured human umbilical vein endothelial cells. *Microvasc. Res.* 47:153–65

183. Vigne P, Champigny G, Marsault R, Barbry P, Frelin C, Lazdunski M. 1989. A new type of amiloride-sensitive cationic channel in endothelial cells of brain microvessels. *J. Biol. Chem.* 264:7663–68

184. Voets T, Szücs G, Droogmans G, Nilius B. 1995. Blockers of volume-activated $Cl^-$ currents inhibit endothelial cell proliferation. *Pflügers Arch.* 431:132–34

185. von Beckerath M, Dittrich M, Klieber H-G, Daut J. 1996. Inwardly rectifying $K^+$

channels in freshly dissociated coronary endothelial cells from guinea-pig heart. *J. Physiol.* 491:357–65

186. Watanabe M, Yumoto K, Ochi R. 1994. Indirect activation by internal calcium of chloride channels in endothelial cells. *Jpn. J. Physiol.* 44:S233-36

187. Wellman GC, Bevan JA. 1995. Barium inhibits the endothelium-dependent component of flow but not acetylcholine-induced relaxation in isolated rabbit cerebral arteries. *J. Pharmacol. Exp. Ther.* 274:47–53

188. Wes PD, Chevesich J, Jeromin A, Rosenberg C, Stetten G, Montell C. 1995. TRPC1, a human homolog of a *Drosophila* store-operated channel. *Proc. Natl. Acad. Sci. USA* 92:9652–56

189. White CR, Brock TA. 1994. Calcium-mobilizing agonists stimulate anion fluxes in cultured endothelial cells from human umbilical vein. *J. Membr. Biol.* 142:171–79

190. Xie HQ, Hu VW. 1994. Modulation of gap junctions in senescent endothelial cells. *Exp. Cell Res.* 214:172–76

191. Yamamoto Y, Chen G, Miwa K, Suzuki H. 1992. Permeability and $Mg^{2+}$ blockade of histamine-operated cation channel in endothelial cells of rat intrapulmonary artery. *J. Physiol.* 450:395–408

192. Yumoto K, Watanabe M, Yamaguchi H, Ochi R. 1994. ATP-induced chloride current and tonic increase of internal $Ca^{2+}$ concentration in vascular endothelial cells. *Jpn. J. Physiol.* 44:S241–43

193. Zhang H, Inazu M, Weir B, Buchanan M, Daniel E. 1994. Cyclopiazonic acid stimulates $Ca^{2+}$ influx through non-specific cation channels in endothelial cells. *Eur. J. Pharmacol.* 251:119–25

194. Zhang H, Inazu M, Weir B, Daniel E. 1994. Endothelin-1 inhibits inward rectifier potassium channels and activates nonspecific cation channels in cultured endothelial cells. *J. Pharmacol.* 49:11–22

195. Zhu X, Chu PB, Peyton M, Birnbaumer L. 1995. Molecular cloning of a widely expressed human homologue for the *Drosophila trp* gene. *FEBS Lett.* 373:193–98

196. Zunkler BJ, Henning B, Grafe M, Hildebrandt AG, Fleck E. 1995. Electrophysiological properties of human coronary endothelial cells. *Basic Res. Cardiol.* 90:435–42

197. Zweifach A, Lewis RS. 1995. Rapid inactivation of depletion-activated calcium current ($I_{CRAC}$) due to local calcium feedback. *J. Gen. Physiol.* 105:209–26

*Annu. Rev. Physiol. 1997. 59:171–91*

# INWARD RECTIFIER POTASSIUM CHANNELS

## C. G. Nichols and A. N. Lopatin

Department of Cell Biology and Physiology, Washington University School of Medicine, 660 South Euclid Avenue, St. Louis, Missouri 63110

KEY WORDS: cloning, mutation, polyamines, currents, expression

---

### ABSTRACT

The past three years have seen remarkable progress in research on the molecular basis of inward rectification, with significant implications for basic understanding and pharmacological manipulation of cellular excitability. Expression cloning of the first inward rectifier K channel (Kir) genes provided the necessary breakthrough that has led to isolation of a family of related clones encoding channels with the essential functional properties of classical inward rectifiers, ATP-sensitive K channels, and muscarinic receptor-activated K channels. High-level expression of cloned channels led to the discovery that classical inward so-called anomalous rectification is caused by voltage-dependent block of the channel by polyamines and $Mg^{2+}$ ions, and it is now clear that a similar mechanism results in inward rectification of $\alpha$-amino-3-hydroxy-5-methyl-4-isoxazolepropionate (AMPA)-kainate receptor channels. Knowledge of the primary structures of Kir channels and the ability to mutate them also has led to the determination of many of the structural requirements of inward rectification.

---

## INTRODUCTION: THE PHYSIOLOGY OF INWARD RECTIFIER POTASSIUM CHANNELS

As an empirical description of membrane ionic currents, rectification means change of conductance with voltage. The term is used to refer to a voltage dependence of macroscopic current, resulting from voltage-dependent channel gating, as well as to a genuine voltage dependence of the open channel current, resulting from asymmetry of the conductance pathway. Most, if not all, ion channels show some degree of rectification. For K channels, inward rectification means that at any given driving force (voltage), the inward flow of $K^+$ ions is

171

greater than the outward flow for the opposite driving force. Inward rectification was originally termed anomalous rectification (69) because it is opposite to the normal outward rectification that is seen in delayed rectifier K channels. The functional role of inward rectifier channels depends critically on their degree of rectification. Classical, strong inward rectification was first described in skeletal muscle (69), but it is also present in glial cells and neurons in the central nervous system (15, 47, 108, 109), and a very prominent inward rectifier current ($i_{K1}$) is essential for the stable resting potential and long plateau that is a feature of the cardiac action potential. In physiological conditions, rectification of these channels is sufficiently strong that very little current flows through them at potentials positive to about $-40$ mV (115, 160). A high conductance at negative voltages allows cells to maintain a stable resting potential, but the greatly reduced conductance at positive potentials avoids short-circuiting the action potential.

ATP-sensitive K ($K_{ATP}$) channels are present in all muscle cell types, in the brain, and in pancreatic $\beta$ cells (7). In the pancreas, they are centrally involved in the regulation of insulin secretion. In contrast to classical inward rectifiers, $K_{ATP}$ channels display only weak rectification and allow substantial outward current to flow at positive potentials (112, 116). Between these extremes, the brain is particularly well endowed with K channels that have intermediate rectification properties. Many of these channels are strongly dependent on ligand activation, often through G proteins or other second messenger systems (15, 24, 47, 60, 108, 109, 164).

In 1993, Ho et al (50) and Kubo et al (80) reported the cloning, by expression, of the first inwardly rectifying K channel genes. These initial breakthroughs have led to the elucidation of the structural components of each of the major types of inward rectifier channels, as well as of the mechanistic basis of inward rectification. The purpose of our article is to review this recent work. For additional reviews of inwardly rectifying K channels, the reader is referred to References 14, 17, 29, 41, 79, 84, 101, 110, 112, 113, 160.

## THE INWARD RECTIFIER FAMILY: TWO TRANSMEMBRANE DOMAIN POTASSIUM CHANNELS

Since the cloning of the *Drosophila Shaker* locus (118, 155), a large family of voltage-gated potassium (Kv) channel genes have been isolated and expressed. Kv channel subunits consist of cytoplasmic N- and C-termini, six transmembrane domains, and a hydrophobic P- or H5-loop between the fifth and sixth transmembrane domains (48). Homology screening with Kv subunits did not reveal any inwardly rectifying K channels, and cloning of the first members of the new Kir channel family [Kir1.1a (ROMK1), Kir2.1 (IRK1), and Kir3.1

(GIRK1)] had to wait until 1993 after expression in *Xenopus* oocytes (26, 50, 80). Kir channel subunits have only two transmembrane domains within each subunit (20, 50, 80, 110), but they retain the H5-loop that is responsible for $K^+$ selectivity in Kv channels (43) (Figure 1*B*). Evidence from mutants that express channels with altered rectification properties indicates that Kir channels, like Kv channels (96), form as tetramers (39, 170). There are now at least six Kir channel subfamilies, sharing ≈40% amino acid identity; individual members within each subfamily sharing ≈60% identity. Doupnik et al (29) have reviewed the cloned Kir channels by subfamily. At the risk of duplicating their efforts, we reconsider cloned Kir channels by subfamily and update the classification to include recent findings (Figure 1*A*).

## Kir1 Subfamily

Kir1.1 (50) encodes a weak inward rectifier and is expressed predominantly in the kidney, but also in various brain tissues (11, 50, 71). Alternate splicing at the 5′ end generates multiple variants (137, 172, 177). Unlike members of the other Kir subfamilies, Kir1.1 contains a putative phosphate-binding loop in the C-terminal region (50). McNicholas et al (105) have presented evidence that one isoform (ROMK2) is inhibited by cytoplasmic ATP, acting through this site, and a detailed analysis by Xu et al (167) has demonstrated the role of three consensus protein kinase A phosphorylation sites in constitutive maintenance of activity.

## Kir2 Subfamily

Three distinct Kir2 subfamily members have been cloned to date (Figure 1), and all encode strong inward rectifiers. The expressed channels differ in single channel conductance (Kir2.1 ≈20 pS, Kir2.2 ≈35pS, Kir2.3 ≈10pS, all in 140 mM external $[K^+]$) and in sensitivity to phosphorylation and other second messengers (19, 33, 46). Kir2 subfamily members appear to be ubiquitously expressed in the heart and nervous system (64, 80, 121, 124, 162), and the time- and voltage-dependent rectification of the expressed channels is virtually indistinguishable from native $i_{K1}$ channels in the heart (62, 63, 83, 117, 144), or the inward rectifier K current in glial cells (109).

## Kir3 Subfamily

Members of the Kir3 family all express G protein–activated strongly rectifying K channels (26, 80, 86), and there is now substantial evidence that they express G protein–coupled receptor-activated currents in heart, brain, and endocrine tissues (34, 68, 81). Ashford et al (8) cloned a cDNA (rcKATP) from cardiac tissue that reportedly encodes a $K_{ATP}$ channel. rcKATP is a member of the Kir3 family (Kir3.4). Krapivinsky et al (77) have provided compelling evidence that Kir3.4 subunits co-assemble with Kir3.1 (GIRK1) to form the

*(A)*

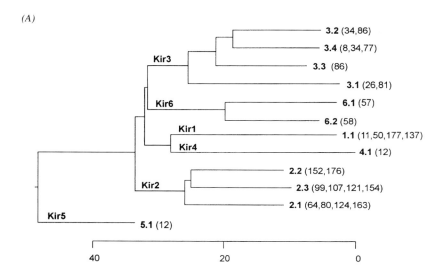

*(B)*

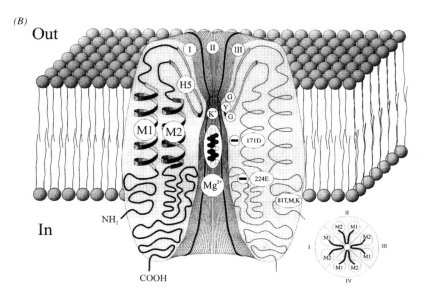

cardiac muscarinic receptor activated $iK_{ACh}$ and that they do not form $K_{ATP}$ channels in monomeric expression. Additional studies have provided evidence for a promiscuous coupling between the various members of the Kir3 subfamily (30, 34, 65, 73, 143). Although not the central aim of this review, it is important to mention that considerable effort has gone into defining the interactions between G proteins and Kir3 channels. There is now substantial evidence for a direct activation of the channel by $G\beta\gamma$ subunits binding to either the N- or C-terminal regions of the channel (56, 59, 73, 78, 126). There is also evidence for direct binding of $G\alpha$ subunits to the channel (56), and a recent report suggests that some specificity of G protein action might be conferred by differential binding of inhibitory $G\alpha$ subunits to the channel (132).

## Kir4 and 5 Subfamilies

Two more subfamilies of Kir channels have been discovered in brain (Kir4 and Kir5) (12, 153). Kir4.1 forms weakly rectifying K channels when expressed alone, but Kir5.1 does not form channels in homomeric expression in oocytes (12). Recent work has demonstrated that these two subunits can co-express to form novel channels, and tandem dimers and tetramers in a specific 4-5-4-5 arrangement reproduce the characteristics of these channels (123). Intriguingly, a 4-4-5-5 tetrameric arrangement produces channels with the properties of homomeric Kir4.1 channels, which provides evidence for the importance of subunit position in the properties of heterotetrameric Kir channels.

## Kir6 Subfamily

Kir1.1, the first Kir channel to be cloned (50), contains a putative ATP-binding domain, and rectification properties of expressed channels are similar to those of endogenous kidney $K_{ATP}$ channels (94, 111). For these reasons, it seemed that Kir1.1 might form a constituent of $K_{ATP}$ channels, but the evidence for ATP inhibition is inconclusive (50, 104). Based on homology to Kir1.1 and other Kir family members, Inagaki et al (58) isolated a novel ubiquitously expressed

<------------------------------------------------

*Figure 1*    (*A*) Phylogenetic tree of the Kir channel family. Unbalanced branch cladogram generated using Megalign software (DNAStar Inc.). The scale indicates residue substitutions from a hypothetical ancestral channel. Members of the same subfamily (e.g. Kir3.1 to 3.4) are typically 50–70% identical, members of different subfamilies (e.g. Kir2.1 and Kir1.1) are ≈40% identical. References to original cloning papers are indicated beside clone names. The nomenclature is based on that originally proposed by Doupnik et al (29) after Chandy & Gutman (18). (*B*) Cartoon representation of the proposed topology of Kir channels, with the approximate positions of residues that have been shown to be critically involved in high-affinity $Mg^{2+}$ and polyamine block and in determining $K^{+}$ selectivity. The inset shows the tetrameric structure of the channel viewed from above the membrane at the outside.

gene, which they named uKATP1 (Kir6.1 in the unified nomenclature). A pancreas-specific isoform (Kir6.2) was subsequently found to encode a $K_{ATP}$ channel subunit (57), but expression of active channels required co-expression of Kir6.2 or Kir6.1 (4), with the high-affinity sulfonylurea receptor (SUR) (2). Mutation of homologous pore-lining residues in Kir1.1 (94) and Kir6.2 (138) clearly demonstrates that Kir6.2 forms the channel pore in a way analogous to formation in other Kir subunits, and the SUR subunit provides at least some of the nucleotide sensitivity (114). There is no evidence for SUR-independent activity of Kir6.2 channels, and sulfonylurea binding studies show that although SUR can be photolabeled with azidoglibenclamide (a cross-linkable sulfony-lurea) (134) in the absence of Kir6.2, Kir6.2 itself can only be cross-linked when co-expressed with SUR (J Bryan, unpublished observation), which suggests that there is a very close physical association between Kir6.2 and SUR and opens up the possibility of novel regulation of other Kir channels by association with regulatory proteins (104).

## KirD: A New Family of Double-Pored Inward Rectifier Channels?

Ketchum et al (72) recently described a novel yeast K channel subunit (TOK1), which was structurally equivalent to a Kir subunit in tandem with a six-trans-membrane domain Kv subunit and expressed outwardly rectifying K currents in *Xenopus* oocytes. Recently, Lesage et al (87) reported the cloning and expression of a mammalian channel (which they call TWIK-1), consisting of two Kir subunits in tandem. Although only limited expression data are available, the expressed currents through TWIK-1 channels appear to be weakly inwardly rectifying, similar to those expressed by Kir1.1 channels. It seems likely that this TWIK-1 cDNA was formed from a gene duplication and provides a whole new series of possibilities for the generation of novel Kir channels.

## Inward Rectification in Other $K^+$ Channels

Many, if not all, Kv channels also show weak inward rectification under physi-ological conditions (37, 38, 91, 125). Like the rectification of weak inward rec-tifiers, rectification of Kv channels involves a weakly voltage-dependent block by internal $Na^+$ and $Mg^{2+}$ (see below). One recently cloned Kv channel shows quite strong inward rectification, superimposed on steep voltage-dependent ac-tivation typical of Kv channels (132, 156). This channel (HERG) underlies the delayed rectifier current in human cardiac ventricular muscle (iKr), and mutations in this gene are responsible for certain inherited forms of long QT syndrome (25, 131). Smith et al (142) have examined the rectification prop-erties of expressed HERG and conclude that rectification results from C-type voltage-dependent inactivation, an incompletely understood intrinsic process that is present in other Kv channels (55) but is distinguishable from strong inward rectification in Kir channels (see below).

## MECHANISMS OF INWARD RECTIFICATION

### A Unifying Hypothesis to Explain Ion Channel Gating

Since the work of Hodgkin & Huxley (51), a common nomenclature for the voltage-dependent transitions of the depolarization-activated Kv, Na, and Ca channels has been utilized to describe the opening upon depolarization (activation), subsequent closing of the channels at such voltages (inactivation), reversal of the activation process at negative voltages (deactivation), and subsequent recovery of availability of channels at negative voltages (recovery from inactivation). At the molecular level, a picture has emerged of the physically distinct processes that underlie these events. Accumulated evidence supports the hypothesis that activation and deactivation are dependent on the movement of the highly charged S4 segment within the membrane in response to depolarization (outward) and hyperpolarization (inward), respectively, coupled to a physical gate within the membrane (88, 119, 157, 158). Fast inactivation has been shown to involve the blocking of the pore from the inside by a cytoplasmic "ball" after the channel has opened. In some Kv channels, this ball may consist of the amino terminus (54, 176) of the channel protein, or in the case of sodium channels, the inter-III-IV domain linker region (148). In some cases, the C-terminus and specific residues within the S6 domain are also shown to be involved in Kv inactivation (55, 147).

In Kir channels, the increase of current that follows hyperpolarization has been referred to as activation, so that the reduction of channel current at positive potentials has generally been described as deactivation or rectification. However, recent experiments with cloned Kir channels (discussed below) show that the reduction of channel current at positive potentials results from a block of the open channel (either by $Mg^{2+}$ or by polyamines). This phenomenon is then analogous to inactivation of voltage-gated channels, and at least some Kv channels also show voltage-dependent block by $Mg^{2+}$, i.e. mild inward rectification (37, 91, 125). Although less attention has been paid to this phenomenon than to inward rectification, most, if not all, inwardly rectifying channels also show some tendency to close at negative voltages, although the mid-point voltage for such closure is typically around $-80$ to $-100$ mV, and the steepness is much less than that for deactivation of Kv channels (75, 90, 111). These parallels between the voltage-dependent behavior of Kv and Kir channels lead us to hypothesize that the voltage-dependent behavior of both, although quantitatively differing, might arise from similar processes in channels that have essentially similar structures, i.e. both Kir and Kv channels share the inner core of the Kir channel (110). Hence, closure of both Kv and Kir channels at positive potentials results from pore block by internal cations or inactivating particles. Both Kv and Kir channels deactivate at negative potentials. Although Kir channels do not contain an S4 region that is predicted to span the membrane, there is a region, denoted M0 by Ho et al (50), with some homology and containing repeated charged residues. Several mutations in S4 were shown to cause negative shifts in the voltage dependence of activation of Kv channels. In confirmation of the above unifying hypothesis, Miller & Aldrich (106) have recently demonstrated that, by making three such mutations within one Kv1 subunit, activation is shifted from $V_{1/2} = -42.5$ mV to $-221.9$ mV, such that minimal deactivation in the physiological voltage range is similar to that observed with inwardly rectifying channels. Interestingly, these mutations, by shifting activation so far in the negative direction, also uncouple N-type inactivation from activation, demonstrating the intrinsic voltage dependence of inactivation. Under these conditions, inactivation is relatively steeply voltage dependent, and the overall behavior of this Kv channel is then indistinguishable from that of a strong inward rectifier.

## Pore Block by Internal Cations

Armstrong (5) originally suggested that inward rectification might result from a positively charged substance blocking the channel in a voltage-dependent manner from the internal side of the membrane. $Mg^{2+}$ and $Na^+$ ions were subsequently shown to cause inward rectification of weakly inwardly rectifying $K_{ATP}$ channels (22, 53). Internal $Mg^{2+}$ ions were also shown to be capable of causing inward rectification of cardiac $i_{K1}$ channels, but a seemingly intrinsic voltage dependence of the open probability was a dominant cause of strong inward rectification in these and other strongly rectifying channels (70, 101–103, 117, 140, 159). For both $Mg^{2+}$-dependent and intrinsic rectification, a strong dependence on external $[K^+]$ ($K_o$) has been demonstrated. Increasing $K_o$ relieves the rectification, and this effect is explained by $K^+$-ion binding at external sites and knocking-off $Mg^{2+}$ from sites deeper inside a multi-ion pore (6, 49, 53, 173). Earlier studies modeled intrinsic rectification as an activation gate with opening and closing rates that are also dependent on $K_o$ (21, 23, 63, 117, 144).

## Channel Block by Polyamines as the Cause of Intrinsic Rectification

The availability of cloned Kir channels has permitted high-level expression, facilitating study of the mechanism of intrinsic rectification. In macro-patch experiments on Kir2.3 channels expressed in *Xenopus* oocytes, rectification of Kir2.3 channels gradually disappeared after patch excision (89), as had been reported to occur in cardiac $i_{K1}$ channels by Matsuda (100). Rectification of Kir2.3 channels was restored by placing excised membrane patches close to the surface of the oocyte or other cells, thereby suggesting that rectification was caused by soluble intrinsic factors. Subsequent biochemical characterization (89) suggested that these factors are polyamines, metabolites of amino acids found in almost all cells (149). HPLC analysis of active fractions confirmed that the naturally occurring polyamines (spermine, spermidine, putrescine) were indeed present, and application of these polyamines to inside-out patches containing Kir2 channels restores all the essential features of intrinsic rectification (31, 36, 89, 90). Steeply voltage-dependent rectification of Kir2 channels is caused by micromolar concentrations of spermine and spermidine at the cytoplasmic surface. Although less effective, putrescine and cadaverine also cause rectification and with efficacy similar to that of $Mg^{2+}$. The voltage dependences of spermine and spermidine block are steeper than that of $Mg^{2+}$ block (31, 36, 89, 90), which explains why in situ inward rectification is steeper than predicted by $Mg^{2+}$ block alone (48). The voltage dependences of spermine and spermidine unblock match the time constants of channel activation in cell-attached patches (90). Kir1.1 (ROMK1) and Kir4.1 channels, $K_{ATP}$ channels and delayed rectifier DRK1 (Kv2.1) channels all show only weak inward rectification. In contrast to Kir2 channels, these channels have only shallowly voltage-dependent, millimolar sensitivity to block by $Mg^{2+}$ and polyamines (31, 89, 94, 111, 138). It is apparent that high polyamine and $Mg^{2+}$ sensitivity is seen only with strongly rectifying channels. Mutational analyses (see below) further suggest that $Mg^{2+}$ and polyamines may in fact share the same binding sites within Kir channels. Interestingly, however, the relative blocking efficacy of $Mg^{2+}$ and polyamines differs between the strong and weak rectifiers. In the weakly rectifying $K_{ATP}$ channel, $Mg^{2+}$ causes steeper rectification than spermine (138). However, a point mutation that converts the channel to a strongly rectifying channel (see below), while increasing sensitivity to block by both $Mg^{2+}$ and spermine, now renders the block by spermine much steeper than the block by $Mg^{2+}$ (138).

Since the initial discovery of polyamine-induced rectification, polyamines have also been demonstrated to cause strong inward rectification in cardiac $iK_{ACh}$ channels (168) and in AMPA-kainate receptors (13, 28, 61, 66, 74). Block of these channels does not seem to be as potent as the block of Kir channels and is relieved at strong depolarizations (13), consistent with polyamines permeating the channels at strong depolarizations. However, there is little or no relief of polyamine block of Kir channels with depolarization (89), and polyamines do not permeate Kir2.1 channels (136).

Polyamines have been the subject of interest as cellular metabolites since they were first discovered by van Leeuwenhoek (161). They are essential for normal and neoplastic cell growth and may have a role as stabilizing moieties for DNA

(149), but other cellular functions remain undefined. Nanomolar to micromolar concentrations of free polyamines would be required to reproduce the degree of rectification seen in intact cells (13, 32, 36), and induction of inward rectification may be the most potent physiological property of polyamines. Although cellular polyamines are strongly buffered, total cellular polyamine concentrations (10–10,000 $\mu$M, 135) are sufficient to cause very strong rectification of Kir channels. Given the steep voltage dependence of polyamine block, it is likely that cytoplasmic concentrations will always be within the range necessary to dynamically affect rectification over the physiological voltage range, such that alterations of polyamine levels will change rectification. Accordingly, Fakler et al (32) demonstrated that inclusion of ATP in the whole-cell patch-clamp pipette could relieve inward rectification of Kir2.1 channels, consistent with a partial chelation of free polyamines. Recently, Bianchi et al (10) demonstrated relief of inward rectification of endogenous currents in RBL-1 cells after treatment with an inhibitor of the polyamine synthetic enzyme S-adenosylmethionine decarboxylase (SAMDC). Such treatment resulted in an increase in cellular putrescine and a decrease in spermidine and spermine levels, with a shallowing of the I-V relationship and significant increase in outward currents. Shyng et al (139) reported similar results in *Xenopus* oocytes expressing Kir2.1 channels and also utilized a Chinese hamster ovary cell line, deficient in ornithine decarboxylase activity (146) and requiring putrescine in the medium for normal cell growth, to demonstrate the effects of polyamine depletion on the rectification of expressed Kir2.3 channels without pharmacological intervention. In these cells, removal of putrescine leads to gradual decline in intracellular levels of putrescine, then spermidine, and finally spermine, and these changes correlate with alterations in Kir2.3 kinetics predicted by excised-patch experiments. The effects of altered polyamine levels on inward rectification and excitability in intact tissues is currently unexplored, but it is possible that physiological regulation of excitability occurs through polyamine levels and that pharmacological manipulation of polyamine levels in specific tissues becomes an approach to treatment of disorders of excitability (113).

## Long-Pore Plugging Mechanism of Polyamine Action

There is now substantial evidence that polyamines are responsible for strong inward rectification (31, 36, 89, 168, 169) by blocking the channel pore. The steepness of the voltage dependence of channel block by polyamines increases as the charge on the polyamine increases (36, 89), and mutations that alter $Mg^{2+}$ block sensitivity also affect polyamine blocking affinity (31, 169). External potassium ions substantially relieve rectification by increasing polyamine off-rate (92), as expected for a channel blocker that interacts with permeant ions within the pore. Much evidence has accumulated to suggest that K channels are actually long pores, with binding sites for several $K^+$ ions within them (49, 52). $Mg^{2+}$ ions are spherical charges, with diameters similar to those of $K^+$ ions, and it is reasonable to suggest that these ions block the channel occupying $K^+$ ion binding sites within the pore. Spermine is a long (almost 20 Å) and thin ion (diameter $\approx$3 Å). It is a tantalizing possibility that in blocking Kir channels, spermine lies in the long pore, binding at multiple sites that would otherwise be occupied by $K^+$ ions (90). Yang et al (169) have examined steady-state polyamine block of Kir2.1 channels over a wide concentration range, and their data suggest that at least two polyamines bind within the channel, with different affinities. We have proposed that two concentration-dependent binding reactions (i.e. two polyamines independently entering the channel pore) and a voltage-dependent transition deep within the voltage field (that may reflect repulsion between the two polyamines) account for the voltage and concentration dependence of spermine-induced rectification (90). Such models, based on the original pore-blocking model of Woodhull (166), ignore interactions of the blocking particle with permeant ions, and hence may underestimate the voltage dependence of block (129). One reason for proposing that two polyamine molecules could reside in the Kir pore is that the apparent charge movement in steady-state spermine block of Kir2.3 ($\approx$5.3) (90) is greater than that which would result from movement of one spermine molecule through the whole voltage field. However, if the channel was blocked by only one spermine molecule, but the entering spermine molecule had to sweep out permeant ions in order to reach its binding site, excess charge movement could result (129).

## TOWARD A STRUCTURAL MODEL OF INWARD RECTIFIER K CHANNELS

Over the last few years, a picture has emerged of the major structural features of both voltage-gated and inwardly rectifying $K^+$ channels. All such channels contain an invariant G-Y/F-G sequence within the H5- or P-loop (Figure 1*B*) that probably forms the $K^+$ selectivity filter (40, 98, 175). This P-loop also contains residues that determine external and internal tetraethylammonium (TEA) blocking potency in Kv channels (27, 43, 44, 97, 150, 174) and was originally envisioned as looping deeply into the membrane and lining the channel pore (Figure 1*B*). Most mutations of the H5 region of Kir channels either result in inactive channels or are without effect (82), although by constructing tandem tetramers containing only one or two mutant subunits, Yang et al (171) have shown that mutations in this region do alter pore properties in a manner consistent with H5 forming the outer entrance to the Kir channel pore.

The S6 region and the presumed cytoplasmic region beyond S6 also have been implicated in determining internal TEA and $Mg^{2+}$ sensitivity of Kv channels

(3, 93). Stanfield et al (145) demonstrated that a glutamate residue in the second transmembrane domain M2 (analogous to S6 in Kv channels) of Kir2.1 (IRK1) is at least partially responsible for $Mg^{2+}$ block. Neutralization of this residue reduces $Mg^{2+}$ block and rectification (163), as well as reducing external $Cs^+$ and $Ba^{2+}$ blocking affinity (1, 45), consistent with this glutamate lining the channel pore. Subsequent mutational analyses showed that this residue also partially determines polyamine blocking affinity (31, 89, 163, 169). Neutralization of glutamate in the strong inward rectifier Kir4.1 (BIR10) causes a reduction of $Mg^{2+}$ and spermine affinity by five orders of magnitude (31). In Kir1.1, the equivalent residue is neutral, and expressed Kir1.1 currents exhibit much shallower rectification and $Mg^{2+}$ blocking affinity (94, 111). Lu & MacKinnon (94) have shown that by replacing this residue with a positively charged lysine, channels rectify permanently, and rectification is shallow and polyamine insensitive. A histidine residue at this site also leads to permanent rectification at low internal pH (95). The rectification is titrated at higher pH, as the histidine residue is neutralized, but is insensitive to external pH. These results indicate that internal, but not external, protons have free access to this site, consistent with the idea (Figure 1B) that a tight selectivity filter, formed by the H5 region, exists at the outer mouth of Kir channels and blocks access of ions other than $K^+$ to the long inner vestibule. Studies with chimeras between weakly rectifying Kir1.1 (ROMK1) and strongly rectifying Kir2.1 (IRK1) indicate that the C-terminal region, beyond M2, might contain necessary structural elements for strong inward rectification and high-affinity $Mg^{2+}$ block (122, 151). Yang et al (169) subsequently demonstrated that E224 (in the C-terminal of Kir2.1) is a major determinant of both high $Mg^{2+}$ and polyamine sensitivity and that dual neutralization of the negative charges in M2 (D172N) and in the C-terminal (E224G) reduced polyamine and $Mg^{2+}$ sensitivity almost to that of Kir1.1 (ROMK1). In the original reports of polyamine-induced rectification, Lopatin et al (89, 90) and Ficker et al (36) reported much slower unbinding of spermine and spermidine than of $Mg^{2+}$ from Kir2.1 and Kir2.3 channels. Using a nearly identical Kir2.1 clone, Fakler et al (32) reported the opposite result, unbinding of $Mg^{2+}$ ions was much slower than spermidine or spermine. The clone used by Fakler et al (32) contained a threonine residue at position 84 immediately preceding the M1 transmembrane domain. Ruppersberg et al (128) have now demonstrated that the absolute and relative off-rates of different polyamines and $Mg^{2+}$ from the channel depend critically on the residue at this position (Figure 1B). It is suggested that this region also contributes to the structure of the inner entrance to the channel, analogous to the demonstration of a role for the corresponding S4-S5 linker region in internal $Mg^{2+}$ block of *Shaker* channels (141).

Glutamate receptor channels have complex responses to polyamines. Externally, polyamines have an agonistic effect that enhances the stimulatory action of glutamate and glycine (127). External polyamines also cause a voltage-dependent block of these channels, and this phenomenon led Fakler et al (31) to the realization that internal polyamines could cause inward rectification of K channels. Subsequent to the discovery that K channel inward rectification resulted from block by internal polyamines, it was demonstrated that inward rectification of AMPA and kainate types of glutamate receptors also show strong inward rectification resulting from internal polyamine block (13, 28, 66, 74). Importantly, this rectification is only observed for receptor channels assembled from subunits containing glutamine (Q) at a site that can contain arginine as a consequence of alternative splicing (13). This site is in a region originally designated as the second transmembrane domain. However, there is now considerable evidence to support the notion that glutamate receptor channels are inserted in the membrane like an inverted Kir channel and that this region corresponds to H5 in Kir channels (165). In Kir channels, H5 faces the outside of the cell, and the site equivalent to this glutamine would be close to the $K^+$ selectivity filter (G144-G146 in Kir2.1), which we propose is the final barrier to outward movement of polyamines. Although there is no evidence for polyamine block of Kir channels from the outside, an outwardly rectifying channel might conceivably be generated by engineering a site similar to that formed by this glutamine in the glutamate receptor channels.

   Thus the Kir channel structural features are being delineated. Rather than H5 looping deeply into the membrane, the weight of evidence, supported by physical data (133), suggests that the H5 regions of the channel form more of a shallow disk at the outer surface of the channel (Figure 1*B*). The inner vestibule is formed at least by residues at the cytoplasmic end of M1, residues in M2, and residues in the C-terminal region and must be physically large enough to contain one, and possibly two, molecules of spermine simultaneously.

## PERSPECTIVE AND PROSPECTS

The structural components of inwardly rectifying K channels are homologous to those that make up Kv channels, but not closely enough to have been isolated by homology. Expression cloning of the first inward rectifiers (26, 50, 80, 120) was groundbreaking work that quickly led to elucidation of the structural basis of classical anomalous rectifiers, G protein–activated K channels, and ATP-sensitive K channels. High-level expression of these cloned channels has permitted the molecular basis of inward rectification and the interactions of G proteins with Kir3 channels to be substantially defined. Several avenues are now ripe for exploration. From a biophysical perspective, the availability of high-affinity ligands (polyamines) for the inner vestibule, with a very large number of structural variants (9), will permit a detailed probing of the inner vestibule of the Kir channel and analysis of the residues involved in lining the channel pore. Polyamines are easily labeled for radioactive or fluorescent (130) analyses, which could be used to look at Kir channel localization or for biochemical dissection of Kir channels. From a biochemical perspective, further effort is likely to be expended to understand the nature of the protein-protein interactions involved in G protein regulation of Kir3 channels and in SUR regulation of Kir6 channel activities, as well as the determinants of tetramer formation within and between Kir channel subfamilies. From a physiological and clinical perspective, the possibility that alterations in polyamine levels during altered physiological or pathophysiological conditions (9, 16, 35, 42, 85) might affect cellular excitability by altering Kir channel rectification is unexplored. Preliminary experiments (10, 139) clearly demonstrate that modulation of polyamine levels, and consequent alteration of rectification, is possible.

ACKNOWLEDGMENTS

Our experimental work has been supported by the National Institutes of Health (grants HL45742 and HL54171 to CGN), American Heart Association (Missouri Affiliate Fellowship to ANL, Established Investigatorship to CGN), and the Juvenile Diabetes Foundation (Grant-In-Aid to CGN).

*Literature Cited*

1. Abrams CJ, Davies NW, Stanfield PR. 1996. An aspartate residue outside the H5 domain determines the selectivity of the inwardly rectifying potassium channel IRK1 for $Rb^+$ and $Cs^+$. *J. Physiol.* (Abstr.) In press
2. Aguilar-Bryan L, Nichols CG, Wechsler SW, Clement JP IV, Boyd AE III, et al. 1995. Cloning of the $\beta$-cell high affinity sulfonylurea receptor: a regulator of insulin secretion. *Science* 268:423–26
3. Aiyar J, Nguyen AN, Chandy KG, Grissmer S. 1994. The P-region and S6 of Kv3.1 contribute to the formation of the ion conduction pathway. *Biophys. J.* 67:2261–64
4. Ammala C, Moorhouse A, Gribble F, Ashfield R, Proks P, et al. 1996. Promiscuous coupling between the sulphonylurea receptor and inwardly rectifying potassium channels. *Nature* 379:545–48
5. Armstrong CM. 1969. Inactivation of the potassium conductance and related phenomena caused by quaternary ammonium ion injected in squid axons. *J. Gen. Physiol.* 54:553–75
6. Armstrong CM. 1971. Interaction of tetraethylammonium ion derivatives with the potassium channel of giant axons. *J. Gen. Physiol.* 58:413–37
7. Ashcroft FM. 1988. Adenosine 5'-triphosphate-sensitive potassium channels. *Annu. Rev. Neurosci.* 11:97–118
8. Ashford ML, Bond CT, Blair TA, Adelman JP. 1994. Cloning and functional expression of a rat heart $K_{ATP}$ channel. *Nature* 370:456–59
9. Basu HS, Pellarin M, Feuerstein BG, Shirahata A, Samejima K, et al. 1993. Interaction of a polyamine analogue, 1,19-bis-(ethylamino) -5,10,15-triazanonadecane, BE-4-4-4-4), with DNA and effect on growth, survival, and polyamine levels in seven human brain tumor cell lines. *Cancer Res.* 53:3948–55
10. Bianchi L, Roy ML, Taglialatela M, Lundgren DW, Brown AM, Ficker E. 1996. Regulation by spermine of native inward rectifier $K^+$ channels in RBL-1 cells. *J. Biol. Chem.* 271:6114–21
11. Boim MA, Ho K, Shuck ME, Bienkowski MJ, Block JH, et al. 1995. ROMK inwardly rectifying ATP-sensitive $K^+$ channel. II. Cloning and distribution of alternative forms. *Am. J. Physiol.* 268:F1132–40

12. Bond CT, Pessia M, Xia XM, Lagrutta A, Kavanaugh MP, Adelman JP. 1994. Cloning and expression of a family of inward rectifier potassium channels. *Recept. Channels* 2:183–91

13. Bowie D, Mayer ML. 1995. Inward rectification of both AMPA and kainate subtype glutamate receptors generated by polyamine-mediated ion channel block. *Neuron* 15:453–62

14. Breitwieser GE. 1991. G protein-mediated ion channel activation. *Hypertension* 17:684–92

15. Brismar T, Collins VP. 1989. Inwardly rectifying potassium channels in human malignant glioma cells. *Brain Res.* 480:249–58

16. Caldarera CM, Orlandini G, Casti A, Moruzzi GJ. 1974. Polyamine and nucleic acid metabolism in myocardial hypertrophy of the overloaded heart. *Mol. Cell. Cardiol.* 6:95–104

17. Carmeliet E. 1993. $K^+$ channels and control of ventricular repolarization in the heart. *Fundam. Clin. Pharmacol.* 7:19–28

18. Chandy KG, Gutman GA. 1993. Nomenclature for mammalian potassium channel genes. *Trends Pharmacol. Sci.* 14:434

19. Chang H, Jan YN, Jan LY. 1996. A strongly inwardly rectifying K channel modulated by M1 acetylcholine receptor. *Biophys. J.* 70:A73

20. Choe S, Stevens CF, Sullivan JM. 1995. Three distinct structural environments of a transmembrane domain in the inwardly rectifying potassium channel ROMK1 defined by perturbation. *Proc. Natl. Acad. Sci. USA* 92:12046–49

21. Ciani S, Krasne S, Miyazaki S, Hagiwara S. 1988. A model for anomalous rectification: electrochemical-potential-dependent gating of membrane channels. *J. Membr. Biol.* 44:103–34

22. Ciani S, Ribalet B. 1988. Ion permeation and rectification in ATP-sensitive channels from insulin-secreting cells (RINm5F): effects of $K^+$, $Na^+$ and $Mg^{2+}$. *J. Membr. Biol.* 103:171–80

23. Cleemann L, Morad M. 1979. Potassium currents in frog ventricular muscle: evidence from voltage clamp currents and extracellular K accumulation. *J. Physiol.* 286:113–43

24. Constanti A, Galvan M, 1983. Fast inward-rectifying current accounts for anomalous rectification in olfactory cortex neurones. *J. Physiol.* 335:153–78

25. Curran ME, Splawski I, Timothy KW, Vincent GM, Green ED, Keating MT. 1995. A molecular basis for cardiac arrhythmia: HERG mutations cause long QT syndrome. *Cell* 80:795–804

26. Dascal N, Schreibmayer W, Lim NF, Wang W, Chavkin C, et al. 1993. Atrial G protein-activated $K^+$ channel: expression cloning and molecular properties. *Proc. Natl. Acad. Sci. USA* 90:10235–39

27. De Biasi M, Drewe JA, Kirsch GE, Brown AM. 1993. Histidine substitution identifies a surface position and confers $Cs^+$ selectivity on a $K^+$ pore. *Biophys. J.* 65:1235–42

28. Donevan SD, Rogawski MA. 1995. Intracellular polyamines mediate inward rectification of Ca(2+)-permeable alpha-amino-3-hydroxy-5-methyl-4-isoxazolepropionic acid receptors. *Proc. Natl. Acad. Sci. USA* 92:9298–302

29. Doupnik CA, Davidson N, Lester HA. 1995. The inward rectifier potassium channel family. *Curr. Opin. Neurobiol.* 5:268–77

30. Duprat F, Lesage F, Guillemare E, Fink M, Hugnot JP, et al. 1995. Heterologous multimeric assembly is essential for $K^+$ channel activity of neuronal and cardiac G-protein-activated inward rectifiers. *Biochem. Biophys. Res. Commun.* 212:657–63

31. Fakler B, Brandle U, Bond C, Glowatzki E, Konig C, et al. 1994. A structural determinant of differential sensitivity of cloned inward rectifier $K^+$ channels to intracellular spermine. *FEBS Lett.* 356:199–203

32. Fakler B, Brandle U, Glowatzki E, Weidemann S, Zenner HP, Ruppersberg JP. 1995. Strong voltage-dependent inward rectification of inward rectifier $K^+$ channels is caused by intracellular spermine. *Cell* 80:149–54

33. Fakler B, Brandle U, Glowatzki E, Zenner HP, Ruppersberg JP. 1994. Kir2.1 inward rectifier $K^+$ channels are regulated independently by protein kinases and ATP hydrolysis. *Neuron* 13:1413–20

34. Ferrer J, Nichols CG, Makhina EN, Salkoff L, Bernstein J, et al. 1995. Pancreatic islet cells express a family of inwardly rectifying $K^+$ channel subunits which interact to form G-protein-activated channels. *J. Biol. Chem.* 270:26086–91

35. Feuerstein BG, Szollozi J, Basu HS, Marton LJ. 1992. alpha-Difluoromethylornithine alters calcium signaling in platelet-derived growth factor-stimulated A172 brain tumor cells in culture. *Cancer Res.* 52:6782–89

36. Ficker E, Taglialatela M, Wible BA, Henley CM, Brown AM. 1994. Sper-

mine and spermidine as gating molecules for inward rectifier K channels. *Science* 266:1068–72

37. Forsythe ID, Linsdell P, Stanfield PR. 1992. Unitary A-currents of rat locus coeruleus neurones grown in cell culture: rectification caused by internal $Mg^{2+}$ and $Na^+$. *J. Physiol.* 451:553–83

38. French RJ, Wells JB. 1977. Sodium ions as blocking agents and charge carriers in the potassium channel of the squid giant axon. *J. Gen. Physiol.* 70:707–24

39. Glowatzki E, Fakler G, Brandle U, Rexhausen U, Zenner HP, et al. 1995. Subunit-dependent assembly of inward-rectifier $K^+$ channels. *Proc. R. Soc. London Ser. B* 261:251–61

40. Hartmann HA, Kirsch GE, Drewe JA, Taglialatela M, Joho RH, Brown AM. 1991. Exchange of conduction pathways between two related $K^+$ channels. *Science* 251:942–44

41. Hartzell HC. 1988 Regulation of cardiac ion channels by catecholamines, acetylcholine and second messenger systems. *Prog. Biophys. Mol. Biol.* 52:165–247

42. Hayashi Y, Hattori Y, Moriwaki A, Lu YF, Hori Y. 1993. Increases in brain polyamine concentrations in chemical kindling and single convulsion induced by pentylenetetrazol in rats. *Neurosci. Lett.* 149:63–66

43. Heginbotham L. Abramson T, MacKinnon R. 1992. A functional connection between the pores of distantly related ion channels as revealed by mutant $K^+$ channels. *Science* 258:1152–55

44. Heginbotham L, MacKinnon R. 1992. The aromatic binding site for tetraethylammonium ion on potassium channel. *Neuron* 8:483–91

45. Henry P, Lopatin AN, Makhina EN, Nichols CG. 1995. A negative charge in M2 regulates sensitivity of inward rectifier K channel to external cation block. *Biophys. J.* 68:A264

46. Henry P, Pearson WL, Nichols CG. 1996. Protein kinase C inhibition of cloned inward (HRK1/Kir2.3) $K^+$ channels. *J. Physiol.* In press

47. Hestrin S. 1987. The properties and function of inward rectification in rod photoreceptors of the tiger salamander. *J. Physiol.* 390:319–33

48. Hille B. 1992. *Ionic Channels of Excitable Membranes.* Sunderland, MA: Sinauer

49. Hille B, Schwarz W. 1978. Potassium channels as multi-ion single-file pores. *J. Gen. Physiol.* 72:409–42

50. Ho K, Nichols CG, Lederer WJ, Lytton J, Vassilev PM, et al. 1993. Cloning and expression of an inwardly rectifying ATP-regulated potassium channel. *Nature* 362:31–38

51. Hodgkin AL, Huxley AM. 1952. Currents carried by sodium and potassium ions through the membrane of the giant axon of *Loligo. J. Physiol.* 116: 449–72

52. Hodgkin AL, Keynes RD. 1955. The potassium permeability of a giant nerve fibre. *J. Physiol.* 128:28–60

53. Horie M. Irisawa H, Noma A. 1987. Voltage-dependent magnesium block of adenosine-triphosphate-sensitive potassium channel in guinea-pig ventricular cells. *J. Physiol.* 387:251–72

54. Hoshi T, Zagotta WN, Aldrich RW. 1990. Biophysical and molecular mechanisms of Shaker potassium channel inactivation. *Science* 250:533–38

55. Hoshi T, Zagotta WN, Aldrich RW. 1991. Two types of inactivation in Shaker $K^+$ channels: effects of alterations in the carboxy-terminal region. *Neuron* 7:547–56

56. Huang CL, Slesinger PA, Casey PJ, Jan YN, Jan LY. 1995. Evidence that direct binding of G beta gamma to the GIRK1 G protein-gated inwardly rectifying $K^+$ channel is important for channel activation. *Neuron* 15:1133–43

57. Inagaki N, Gonoi T, Clement JP, Namba N, Inazawa J, et al. 1995. Reconstitution of $I_{KATP}$: an inward rectifier subunit plus the sulfonylurea receptor. *Science* 270:1166–70

58. Inagaki N, Tsuura Y, Namba N, Masuda K, Gonoi T, et al. 1995. Cloning and functional characterization of a novel ATP-sensitive potassium channel ubiquitously expressed in rat tissues, including pancreatic islets, pituitary, skeletal muscle, and heart. *J. Biol. Chem.* 270:5691–94

59. Inanobe A, Morishige KI, Takahashi N, Ito H, Yamada M, et al. 1995. G beta gamma directly binds to the carboxyl terminus of the G protein-gated muscarinic $K^+$ channel, GIRK1. *Biochem. Biophys. Res. Commun.* 212:1022–28

60. Inoue M, Nakajima S, Nakajima Y. 1988. Somatostatin induces an inward rectification in rat locus coeruleus neurones through a pertussis toxin-sensitive mechanism. *J. Physiol.* 407:177–98

61. Isa T, Iino M, Itazawa S, Ozawa S. 1995. Spermine mediates inward rectification of Ca(2+)-permeable AMPA receptor channels. *NeuroReport* 6:2045–48

62. Ishihara K, Hiraoka M. 1994. Gating mechanisms of the cloned inward recti-

fier potassium channel from mouse heart. *J. Membr. Biol.* 142:55–64

63. Ishihara K, Mitsuiye A, Noma A, Takano M. 1989. The $Mg^{2+}$ block and intrinsic gating underlying inward rectification of the $K^+$ current in guinea-pig cardiac myocytes. *J. Physiol.* 419:297–320

64. Ishii K, Yamagashi T, Taira N. 1994. Cloning and functional expression of a cardiac inward rectifier $K^+$ channel. *FEBS Lett.* 338:107–11

65. Isomoto S, Kondo C, Takahashi N, Matsumoto S, Yamada M, et al. 1996. A novel ubiquitously distributed isoform of GIRK2 (GIRK2B) enhances GIRK1 expression of the G-protein-gated $K^+$ current in *Xenopus* oocytes. *Biochem. Biophys. Res. Commun.* 218:286–91

66. Kamboj SK, Swanson GT, Cull-Candy SG. 1995. Intracellular spermine confers rectification on rat calcium-permeable AMPA and kainate receptors. *J. Physiol.* 486:297–303

67. Kandel E, Tauc L. 1966. Anomalous rectification in the metacerebral giant cells and its consequences for synaptic transmission. *J. Physiol.* 183:287–304

68. Karschin C, Schreibmayer W, Dascal N, Lester H, Davidson N, Karschin A. 1994. Distribution and localization of a G protein-coupled inwardly rectifying $K^+$ channel in the rat. *FEBS Lett.* 348:139–44

69. Katz B. 1949. Les constantes électriques de la membrane du muscle. *Arch. Sci. Physiol.* 2:285–99

70. Kelly ME, Dixon SJ, Sims SM. 1992. Inwardly rectifying potassium current in rabbit osteoclasts: a whole-cell and single-channel study. *J. Membr. Biol.* 126:171–81

71. Kenna S, Roper J, Ho K, Hebert S, Ashcroft SJ, Ashcroft FM. 1994. Differential expression of the inwardly-rectifying K-channel ROMK1 in rat brain. *Mol. Brain Res.* 24:353–56

72. Ketchum KA, Joiner WJ, Sellers AJ, Kaczmarek LK, Goldstein SA. 1995. A new family of outwardly rectifying potassium channel proteins with two pore domains in tandem. *Nature* 376:690–95

73. Kofuji P, Davidson N, Lester HA. 1995. Evidence that neuronal G-protein-gated inwardly rectifying $K^+$ channels are activated by G beta gamma subunits and function as heteromultimers. *Proc. Natl. Acad. Sci. USA* 92:6542–46

74. Koh DS, Burnashev N, Jonas P. 1995. Block of native Ca(2+)-permeable AMPA receptors in rat brain by intracellular polyamines generates double rectification. *J. Physiol.* 486:305–12

75. Koumi S, Sato R, Hayakawa H. 1994. Modulation of voltage-dependent inactivation of the inwardly rectifying $K^+$ channel by chloramine-T. *Eur. J. Pharmacol.* 258(3):281–84

76. Koyama H, Morishige K, Takahashi N, Zanelli JS, Fass DN, Kurachi Y. 1994. Molecular cloning, functional expression and localization of a novel inward rectifier potassium channel in the rat brain. *FEBS Lett.* 341:303–7

77. Krapivinsky G, Gordon EA, Wickman K, Velimirovic B, Krapivinsky L, Clapham DE. 1995. The G-protein-gated atrial $K^+$ channel IKACh is a heteromultimer of two inwardly rectifying $K(^+)$-channel proteins. *Nature* 374:135–41

78. Krapivinsky G, Krapivinsky L, Wickman K, Clapham DE. 1995. G beta gamma binds directly to the G protein-gated $K^+$ channel, IKACh. *J. Biol. Chem.* 270:29059–62

79. Kubo Y. 1994. Towards the elucidation of the structural-functional relationship of the inward rectifying $K^+$ channel family. *Neurosci. Res.* 21:109–17

80. Kubo Y, Baldwin TJ, Jan YN, Jan LY. 1993. Primary structure and functional expression of a mouse inward rectifier potassium channel. *Nature* 362:127–33

81. Kubo Y, Reuveny E, Slesinger PA, Jan YN, Jan LY. 1993. Primary structure and functional expression of a rat G-protein coupled muscarinic potassium channel. *Nature* 364:802–6

82. Kugler JL, Nelson DJ. 1995. Mutational analysis of a cloned inwardly rectifying $K^+$ channel. *Biophys. J.* 68:A30

83. Kurachi Y. 1985. Voltage-dependent activation of the inward rectifier potassium channel in the ventricular cell membrane of guinea-pig heart. *J. Physiol.* 366:365–85

84. Kurachi Y, Tung RT, Ito H, Nakajima T. 1992. G protein activation of cardiac muscarinic $K^+$ channels. *Prog. Neurobiol.* 39:229–46

85. Laschet J, Trottier S, Grisar T, Leviel V. 1992. Polyamine metabolism in epileptic cortex. *Epilepsy Res.* 12:151–56

86. Lesage F, Duprat F, Fink M, Guillemare E, Coppola T, et al. 1994. Cloning provides evidence for a family of inward rectifier and G-protein coupled $K^+$ channels in the brain. *FEBS Lett.* 353:37–42

87. Lesage F, Guillemare E, Fink M, Duprat F, Lazdunski M, et al. 1996. TWIK-1, a

ubiquitous human weakly inward rectifying $K^+$ channel with a novel structure. *EMBO J.* 15:1004–11

88. Liman ER, Hess P, Weaver F, Koren G. 1991. Voltage-sensing residues in the S4 region of a mammalian K channel. *Nature* 353:752–56

89. Lopatin AN, Makhina EN, Nichols CG. 1994. Potassium channel block by cytoplasmic polyamines as the mechanism of intrinsic rectification. *Nature* 372:366–69

90. Lopatin AN, Makhina EN, Nichols CG. 1995. The mechanism of inward rectification of potassium channels. *J. Gen. Physiol.* 106:923–55

91. Lopatin AN, Nichols CG. 1994. Inward rectification of outward rectifying DRK1 (Kv2.1) potassium channels. *J. Gen. Physiol.* 103:203–16

92. Lopatin AN, Nichols CG. 1996. [$K^+$] dependence of polyamine-induced rectification in inward rectifier potassium channels. *J. Gen. Physiol.* 108:105–13

93. Lopez GA, Jan YN, Jan LY. 1993. Evidence that the S6 segment of the Shaker voltage-gated $K^+$ channel comprises part of the pore. *Nature* 367:179–82

94. Lu Z, MacKinnon R. 1994. Electrostatic tuning of $Mg^{2+}$ affinity in an inward rectifier $K^+$ channel. *Nature* 371:243–46

95. Lu Z, MacKinnon R. 1995. Probing a potassium channel pore with an engineered protonatable site. *Biochemistry* 34:13133–38

96. MacKinnon R. 1991. Determination of the subunit stoichiometry of a voltage-activated potassium channel. *Nature* 350:232–35

97. MacKinnon R. 1995. Pore loops: an emerging theme in ion channel structure. *Neuron* 14:889–92

98. MacKinnon R, Yellen G. 1990. Mutations affecting TEA blockade and ion permeation in voltage-activated $K^+$ channels. *Science* 250:276–79

99. Makhina EN, Kelly AJ, Lopatin AN, Mercer RW, Nichols CG. 1994. Cloning and expression of a novel inward rectifier potassium channel from human brain. *J. Biol. Chem.* 269:20468–74

100. Matsuda H. 1988. Open-state substructure of inwardly rectifying potassium channels revealed by magnesium block in guinea-pig heart cells. *J. Physiol.* 397:237–58

101. Matsuda H. 1991. Magnesium gating of the inwardly rectifying $K^+$ channel. *Annu. Rev. Physiol.* 53:289–98

102. Matsuda H, Matsuura H, Noma A. 1989. Triple-barrel structure of inwardly rectifying $K^+$ channels revealed by $Cs^+$ and $Rb^+$ block in guinea-pig heart cells. *J. Physiol.* 413:139–57

103. Matsuda H, Saigusa A, Irisawa H. 1987. Ohmic conductance through the inwardly rectifying $K^+$ channel and blocking by internal $Mg^{2+}$. *Nature* 325:156–59

104. McNicholas CM, Guggino WB, Schwiebert EM, Hebert SC, Giebisch G, Egan ME. 1996. Sensitivity of a renal $K^+$ channel (ROMK2) to the inhibitory sulfonylurea compound, glibenclamide, is enhanced by co-expression with the ATP-binding cassette transporter CFTR. *Proc. Natl. Acad. Sci. USA.* In press

105. McNicholas CM, Wang W, Ho K, Hebert SC, Giebisch G. 1994. Regulation of ROMK1 $K^+$ channel activity involves phosphorylation processes. *Proc. Natl. Acad. Sci. USA* 91:8077–81

106. Miller AG, Aldrich RW. 1996. Conversion of a delayed rectifier $K^+$ channel to a voltage-gated inward rectifier $K^+$ channel by three amino acid substitutions. *Neuron* 16:853–58

107. Morishige K, Takahashi N, Jahangir A, Yamada M, Koyama H, et al. 1994. Molecular cloning and functional expression of a novel brain-specific inward rectifier potassium channel. *FEBS Lett.* 346:251–56

108. Nakajima Y, Nakajima S, Inoue M. 1988. Pertussis toxin-insensitive G protein mediates substance P-induced inhibition of potassium channels in brain neurons. *Proc. Natl. Acad. Sci. USA* 85:3643–47

109. Newman EA. 1993. Inward-rectifying potassium channels in retinal glial (Muller) cells. *J. Neurosci.* 13:3333–45

110. Nichols CG. 1993. The 'inner core' of inward rectifier potassium channels. *Trends Pharmacol. Sci.* 14:320–23

111. Nichols CG, Ho K, Hebert S. 1994. $Mg^{2+}$-dependent inward rectification of ROMK1 potassium channels expressed in *Xenopus* oocytes. *J. Physiol.* 476:399–409

112. Nichols CG, Lederer WJ. 1991. ATP-sensitive potassium channels in the cardiovascular system. *Am. J. Physiol.* 261:H1675–86

113. Nichols CG, Lopatin AN, Makhina EN, Pearson WL, Sha Q. 1996. Inward rectification and implications for cardiac excitability. *Circ. Res.* 78:1–7

114. Nichols CG, Shyng SL, Nestorowicz A, Glaser A, Clement JP IV, et al. 1996. ADP as the intracellular regulator of insulin secretion. *Science* 272:1785–87

115. Noble D. 1965. Electrical properties of cardiac muscle attributable to inward going (anomalous) rectification. *J. Cell. Comp. Physiol.* 66:127–36

116. Noma A. 1983. ATP-regulated $K^+$ channels in cardiac muscle. *Nature* 305:147–48

117. Oliva C, Cohen IS, Pennefather P. 1990. The mechanism of rectification of $I_{K1}$ in canine Purkinje myocytes. *J. Gen. Physiol.* 96:299–318

118. Papazian DM, Schwarz TL, Tempel BL, Jan YN, Jan LY. 1987. Cloning of genomic and complementary DNA from Shaker, a putative potassium channel gene from *Drosophila*. *Science* 237:749–53

119. Papazian DM, Timpe LC, Jan YN, Jan L. 1991. Alteration of voltage-dependence of Shaker potassium channel by mutations in the S4 sequence. *Nature* 349:305–10

120. Perier F, Coulter KL, Radeke CM, Vandenberg CA. 1992. Expression of an inwardly rectifying potassium channel in *Xenopus* oocytes. *J. Neurochem.* 59:1971–74

121. Perier F, Radeke CM, Vandenberg CA. 1994. Primary structure and characterization of a small-conductance inwardly rectifying potassium channel from human hippocampus. *Proc. Natl. Acad. Sci. USA* 91:6240–44

122. Pessia M, Bond CT, Kavanaugh MP, Adelman JP. 1995. Contributions of the C-terminal domain to gating properties of inward rectifier potassium channels. *Neuron* 14:1039–45

123. Pessia M, Tucker SJ, Lee K, Bond CT, Adelman JP. 1996. Subunit positional effects revealed by novel heteromeric inwardly rectifying $K^+$ channels. *EMBO J.* 15:2980–87

124. Raab-Graham KF, Radeke CM, Vandenberg CA. 1994. Molecular cloning and expression of a human heart inward rectifier potassium channel. *NeuroReport* 5:2501–5

125. Rettig J, Wunder F, Stocker M, Lichtinghagen R, Mastiaux F, et al. 1992. Characterization of a Shaw-related potassium channel family in rat brain. *EMBO J.* 11:2473–86

126. Reuveny E, Slesinger PA, Inglese J, Morales JM, Iniguez-Lluhi JA, et al. 1994. Activation of the cloned muscarinic potassium channel by G protein beta gamma subunits. *Nature* 370:143–46

127. Rock DM, Macdonald RL. 1995. Polyamine regulation of *N*-methyl-D-aspartate receptor channels. *Annu. Rev. Pharmacol. Toxicol.* 35:463–82

128. Ruppersberg JP, Fakler B, Brandle U, Zenner H-P, Schultz JH. 1996. An N-terminal site controls blocker-release in Kir2.1 channels. *Biophys. J.* 70:A361

129. Ruppersberg JP, van Kitzing E, Schoepfer R. 1994. The mechanism of magnesium block of NMDA receptors. *Sem. Neurosci.* 6:87–96

130. Sabri MI, Soiefer AI, Kisby GE, Spencer PS. 1989. Determination of polyamines by precolumn derivatization with 9-fluorenylmethyl chloroformate and reverse-phase high-performance liquid chromatography. *J. Neurosci. Meth.* 29:27–31

131. Sanguinetti CM, Jiang C, Curran ME, Keating MT. 1995. A mechanistic link between an inherited and an acquired cardiac arrhythmia: HERG encodes the IKr potassium channel. *Cell* 81:299–307

132. Schreibmayer W, Dessauer CW, Vorobiov D, Gilman AG, Lester HA, et al. 1996. Inhibition of an inwardly rectifying $K^+$ channel by G-protein a subunits. *Nature* 380:624–27

133. Schwalbe RA, Wang Z, Brown AM. 1996. N-glycosylation studies of ROMK1 reveal unexpected extracellular regions in the pore-forming segment. *Biophys. J.* 70:A309

134. Schwanstecher M, Loser S, Chudziak F, Bachmann C, Panten U. 1994. Photoaffinity labeling of the cerebral sulfonylurea receptor using a novel radioiodinated azidoglibenclamide analogue. *J. Neurochem.* 63:698–708

135. Seiler N. 1994. Formation, catabolism and properties of the natural polyamines. In *The Neuropharmacology of Polyamines*, ed. C Carter, pp. 1-36. New York/London: Academic; Harcourt Brace

136. Sha Q, Romano C, Lopatin AN, Nichols CG. 1996. Spermidine release from *Xenopus* oocytes: electrodiffusion through a membrane channel. *J. Biol. Chem.* 271:3392–97

137. Shuck ME, Bock JH, Benjamin CW, Tsai TD, Lee KS, et al. 1994. Cloning and characterization of multiple forms of the human kidney ROM-K potassium channel. *J. Biol. Chem.* 269:24261–70

138. Shyng SL, Clement JP IV, Bryan J, Nichols CG. 1996. Cloned $K_{ATP}$ channels show mild inward rectification resulting from voltage-dependent block by $Mg^{2+}$ and polyamines. *J. Physiol.* (Abstr.) 494:p51–52

139. Shyng SL, Sha Q, Ferrigni T, Lopatin AN, Nichols CG. 1996. Depletion of intracellular polyamines relieves inward rectification of potassium channels. *Proc. Natl. Acad. Sci. USA.* In press

140. Silver MR, DeCoursey TE. 1990. Intrinsic gating of inward rectifier in bovine pulmonary artery endothelial cells in the presence or absence of internal magnesium. *J. Gen. Physiol.* 96:109–33

141. Slesinger PA, Jan YN, Jan LY. 1993. The S4-S5 loop contributes to the ion-selective pore of potassium channels. *Neuron* 11:739–49

142. Smith PL, Baukrowitz T, Yellen G. 1996. The inward rectification mechanism of the HERG cardiac potassium channel. *Nature* 379:833–36

143. Spauschus A, Lentes KU, Wischmeyer E, Dissmann E, Karschin C, Karschin A. 1996. A G-protein-activated inwardly rectifying $K^+$ channel (GIRK4) from human hippocampus associates with other GIRK channels. *J. Neurosci.* 16:930–38

144. Stanfield PR, Davies NW, Shelton PA, Khan IA, Brammar WJ, et al. 1994. The intrinsic gating of inward rectifier K channels expressed from the murine IRK1 gene depends on voltage, $K^+$ and $Mg^{2+}$. *J. Physiol.* 475:1–4

145. Stanfield PR, Davies NW, Shelton PA, Sutcliffe MJ, Khan IA, et al. 1994. A single aspartate residue is involved in both intrinsic gating and blockage by $Mg^{2+}$ of the inward rectifier, IRK1. *J. Physiol.* 478:1–6

146. Steglich C, Scheffler IE. 1982. An ornithine decarboxylase-deficient mutant of Chinese hamster ovary cells. *J. Biol. Chem.* 257:4603–9

147. Stocker M, Pongs O, Hoth M, Heinemann SH, Stuhmer W, et al. 1991. Swapping of functional domains in voltage-gated $K^+$ channels. *Proc. R. Soc. London Ser. B* 245:101–7

148. Stuhmer W, Conti F, Suzuki H, Wang XD, Noda M, et al. 1989. Structural parts involved in activation and inactivation of the sodium channel. *Nature* 339:597–603

149. Tabor CW, Tabor H. 1984. Polyamines. *Annu. Rev. Biochem.* 53:749–90

150. Taglialatela M, Drewe JA, Kirsch GE, De Biasi M, Hartmann HA, Brown AM. 1993. Regulation of $K^+/Rb^+$ selectivity and internal TEA blockade by mutations at a single site in $K^+$ pores. *Pflügers Arch.* 423:104–12

151. Taglialatela M, Wible BA, Caporoso R, Brown AM. 1994. Specification of the pore properties by the carboxyl terminus

of inwardly rectifying $K^+$ channels. *Science* 264:844–47

152. Takahashi N, Morishige K, Jahangir A, Yamada M, Findlay I, et al. 1994. Molecular cloning and functional expression of cDNA encoding a second class of inward rectifier potassium channels in the mouse brain. *J. Biol. Chem.* 269:23274–79

153. Takumi T, Ishii T, Horio Y, Morishige K, Takahashi N, et al. 1995. A novel ATP-dependent inward rectifier potassium channel expressed predominantly in glial cells. *J. Biol. Chem.* 270:16339–46

154. Tang W, Yang XC. 1994. Cloning a novel human brain inward rectifier potassium channel and its functional expression in *Xenopus* oocytes. *FEBS Lett.* 348:239–43

155. Tempel BL, Jan YN, Jan LY. 1988. Cloning of a probable potassium channel gene from mouse brain. *Nature* 332:837–39

156. Trudeau MC, Warmke JW, Ganetzky B, Robertson GA. 1995. HERG, a human inward rectifier in the voltage-gated potassium channel family. *Science* 269:92–95

157. Tytgat J, Hess P. 1992. Evidence for cooperative interactions in potassium channel gating. *Nature* 359:420–23

158. Tytgat J, Nakazawa K, Gross A, Hess P. 1993. Pursuing the voltage sensor of a voltage-gated mammalian potassium channel. *J. Biol. Chem.* 268:23777–79

159. Vandenberg CA. 1987. Inward rectification of a potassium channel in cardiac ventricular cells depends on internal magnesium ions. *Proc. Natl. Acad. Sci. USA* 84:2560–66

160. Vandenberg CA. 1994. Cardiac inward rectifier potassium channel. In *Ion Channels in the Cardiovascular System*, ed. PM Spooner, AM Brown, pp. 145–67. New York: Futura

161. van Leeuwenhoek A. 1678. Observationes D. Anthonii Leeuwenhoek, de natis e semine genitali animalculis. *Philos. Trans. R. Soc.* 12:1040–43

162. Wible BA, De Biasi M, Majumder K, Taglialatela M, Brown AM. 1995. Cloning and functional expression of an inwardly rectifying $K^+$ channel from human atrium. *Circ. Res.* 76:343–50

163. Wible BA, Taglialatela M, Ficker E, Brown AM. 1994. Gating of inwardly rectifying $K^+$ channels localized to a single negatively charged residue. *Nature* 371:246–49

164. Williams JT, Colmers WF, Pan ZZ. 1988. Voltage- and ligand-activated inwardly

rectifying currents in dorsal raphe neurons in vitro. *J. Neurosci.* 8:3499–506

165. Wo ZG, Oswald RE. 1995. Unraveling the modular design of glutamate-gated ion channels. *Trends Neurosci.* 18:161–68

166. Woodhull AM. 1973. Ionic blockage of sodium channels in nerve. *J. Gen. Physiol.* 61:687–708

167. Xu ZC, Yang Y, Hebert SC. 1996. Phosphorylation of the ATP-sensitive, inwardly rectifying $K^+$ channel, ROMK, by cyclic AMP-dependent protein kinase. *J. Biol. Chem.* 271:9313–19

168. Yamada M, Kurachi Y. 1995. Spermine gates inward-rectifying muscarinic but not ATP-sensitive $K^+$ channels in rabbit atrial myocytes. Intracellular substance-mediated mechanism of inward rectification. *J. Biol. Chem.* 270:9289–94

169. Yang J, Jan YN, Jan LY. 1995. Control of rectification and permeation by residues in two distinct domains in an inward rectifier $K^+$ channel. *Neuron* 14:1047–54

170. Yang J, Jan YN, Jan LY. 1995. Determination of the subunit stoichiometry of an inwardly rectifying potassium channel. *Neuron* 15:1441–47

171. Yang JN, Jan YN, Jan LY. 1996. Role of the H5 region in ion selectivity and permeation in an inward rectifier $K^+$ channel. *Biophys. J.* 70:A78

172. Yano H, Philipson LH, Kugler JL, Tokuyama Y, Davis EM, et al. 1994. Alternative splicing of human inwardly rectifying $K^+$ channel ROMK1 mRNA. *Mol. Pharmacol.* 45:854–60

173. Yellen G. 1984. Relief of $Na^+$ block of $Ca^{2+}$-activated $K^+$ channels by external cations. *J. Gen. Physiol.* 84:187–99

174. Yellen G, Jurman ME, Abramson T, MacKinnon R. 1991. Mutations affecting internal TEA blockade identify the probable pore-forming region of a $K^+$ channel. *Science* 251:939–42

175. Yool AJ, Schwartz TL. 1991. Alteration of ionic selectivity of a $K^+$ channel by mutation in the H5 region. *Nature* 349:700–4

176. Zagotta WN, Hoshi T, Aldrich RW. 1990. Restoration of inactivation in mutants of Shaker potassium channels by a peptide derived from ShB. *Science* 250:568–71

177. Zhou H, Tate SS, Palmer LG. 1994. Primary structure and functional properties of an epithelial K channel. *Am. J. Physiol.* 266:C809–24

*Annu. Rev. Physiol. 1997. 59:193–220*

# CYTOPLASMIC ATP-DEPENDENT REGULATION OF ION TRANSPORTERS AND CHANNELS: Mechanisms and Messengers

## Donald W. Hilgemann

University of Texas Southwestern, Medical Center at Dallas, Dallas, Texas 75235-9040

KEY WORDS:   ion channels, ATP, phosphorylation, cytoskeleton, phosphatidylinositol phosphates

### ABSTRACT

Many ion transporters and channels appear to be regulated by ATP-dependent mechanisms when studied in planar bilayers, excised membrane patches, or with whole-cell patch clamp. Protein kinases are obvious candidates to mediate ATP effects, but other mechanisms are also implicated. They include lipid kinases with the generation of phosphatidylinositol phosphates as second messengers, allosteric effects of ATP binding, changes of actin cytoskeleton, and ATP-dependent phospholipases. Phosphatidylinositol-4,5-bisphosphate ($PIP_2$) is a possible membrane-delimited messenger that activates cardiac sodium-calcium exchange, $K_{ATP}$ potassium channels, and other inward rectifier potassium channels. Regulation of $PIP_2$ by phospholipase C, lipid phosphatases, and lipid kinases would thus tie surface membrane transport to phosphatidylinositol signaling. Sodium-hydrogen exchange is activated by ATP through a phosphorylation-independent mechanism, whereas ion cotransporters are activated by several protein kinase mechanisms. Ion transport in epithelium may be particularly sensitive to changes of cytoskeleton that are regulated by ATP-dependent cell signaling mechanisms.

## INTRODUCTION

Investigations of how GTP modifies the function of receptors, enzymes, and ion channels allowed profound advances in the field of cell regulation (1). It

193

0066-4278/97/0315-0193$08.00

is hardly surprising that ATP, as well as GTP, modulates the function of many ion transporters and channels. After all, ATP is the energy stuff of life, and regulation by protein kinases (2–4) requires ATP. The surprise, then, is the multiplicity of ATP-dependent modulation mechanisms identified that do not involve protein kinases. Some require ATP hydrolysis whereas others do not. Some clearly involve membrane proteins that have not been identified. Some involve well-known regulatory molecules and proteins, such as phosphatidylinositol bisphosphate (PIP$_2$) (5) and actin (6, 7) whose roles in modulating ion channels and transporters are only now emerging. At the same time, the functional significance of protein kinase-mediated phosphorylation of some transporters has remained enigmatic. Our premise is that the ATP-dependent modulation mechanisms not involving protein kinases may provide important new insights into (a) multiple cell signaling pathways, (b) regulatory mechanisms that respond to physiological changes of cytoplasmic ATP, and (c) constitutive processes that are a prerequisite for ion transport function in intact cells and tissues.

A common finding in whole-cell studies is that activity of a transporter or channel decreases when ATP is depleted (8, 9). Such ATP responses may be protective or degenerative. In calcium homeostasis, for example, sarcoplasmic reticulum calcium pumps (10, 11), calcium release channels (12, 13), calcium channels (14, 15), plasmalemmal calcium pumps (16, 17), and Na,Ca exchange (18) are all inhibited by regulatory mechanisms that do not involve protein kinases when ATP drops to the range of hundreds of micromolar. These mechanisms appear to shut down transmembrane calcium signaling, thereby protecting cells from excitatory calcium signals and the energy consumption required to maintain calcium movements and calcium-dependent processes.

Another possibility for protection is that certain mechanisms sense physiologically important changes of ATP concentrations, respond to them, and initiate appropriate cell signaling cascades. ATP-inhibited (K$_{ATP}$) potassium channels (19–21; CG Nichols & AN Lopatin, this volume) are the best example. It is well documented that potassium channels of this type exist in many tissues and open in response to metabolic stress. Outward transmembrane current is generated, thereby shortening action potentials, reducing calcium influx, and eventually modifying cell functions such as insulin release and cardiac contraction. That cytoplasmic ATP concentrations oscillate locally in cells, and that such oscillations may constitute important cell signals, contradicts the conventional notion that ATP concentrations are tightly regulated in cells. Although multiple stress-activated protein kinases exist in all cells (23, 24) and respond to stress-related factors such as a rise of AMP (25, 26), ion channels and transporters are not known to be modulated by such protein kinases, at least not directly. How then does one determine whether an effect of ATP depletion

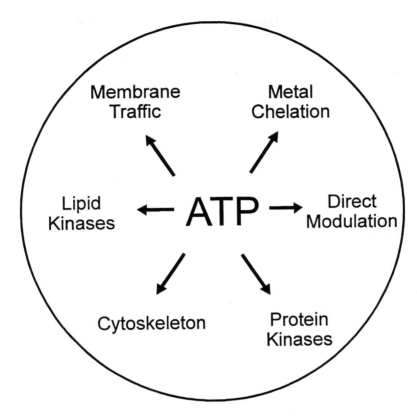

*Figure 1*    Mechanisms by which cytoplasmic ATP modulates ion transporter and channel function.

reflects a physiologically important ATP-sensing mechanism, a genuinely dele-terious effect of compromising energy reserves, or an ATP-dependent reaction coupled to an important cell regulatory pathway? When ATP acts on channels or transporters with no requirement for its hydrolysis, ATP-sensing per se can be suggested, and examples of such are numerous. When ATP-specific ef-fects require millimolar ATP concentrations, as occur in the cytoplasm of cells, ATP-sensing can also be suggested as an attractive interpretation.

This review emphasizes those ATP-dependent mechanisms that are poorly understood and/or have received little attention (see Figure 1). First, we in-troduce examples of ATP effects and the mechanisms involved, then the ATP dependence of individual ion transporters and channels are considered in more detail. Subjects not reviewed include (*a*) extracellular effects of ATP (27, 28), (*b*) transmembrane movements of ATP (29), (*c*) ATP hydrolysis by ion pumps, and (d) the function of CFTR chloride channels (30) and MDR transporters (31). Recent references are given whenever possible.

## Protein Kinase-Independent ATP Effects and Mechanisms

Figure 2 shows typical effects of cytoplasmic ATP that are observed in recordings of transporter and channel currents in giant excised membrane patches (32). In each case, the recording conditions reliably isolate the individual ion transport current from other current-generating mechanisms in the patch. Although the time courses and concentration dependencies of the different responses to ATP shown are similar, multiple mechanisms are certainly involved.

PROTEIN KINASES    Protein kinases are the obvious candidates to explain an ATP effect that requires ATP hydrolysis. However, a wide range of tests for the involvement of protein kinases in the responses described in Figure 2 were negative. Pretreatment of patches with several specific and nonspecific protein kinase inhibitors had no evident effect on the results, and several phosphatases did not reverse or diminish the effects of ATP. The half-maximal ATP concentration for each stimulatory effect was in the range of hundreds of micromolar to several millimolar, whereas no example can be cited of a protein kinase requiring more than a few tens of micromolar ATP.

LIPID KINASES    Panel $A$ shows the typical response of outward cardiac Na,Ca exchange current to application of 2 mM ATP on the cytoplasmic side of a cardiac membrane patch (18, 33). The outward exchange current (calcium influx mode) was first activated by cytoplasmic sodium. Thereafter, the current inactivated (decreased) as usual over several seconds to a steady-state level about 20% of the initial peak level. ATP (2 mM) stimulated the current by about fivefold over 1 min, and the current remained stimulated for minutes after removal of ATP. This effect of ATP requires magnesium; GTP and nonhydrolyzable analogues of ATP do not stimulate the current, and a wide range of protein kinase inhibitors do not block the effect. The rate of onset of the effect has a $K_d$ for ATP in the range of 5 mM, a much lower affinity than expected for protein kinases. As outlined below, this stimulatory effect of ATP probably involves the generation of phosphatidylinositol 4,5-bisphosphate ($PIP_2$) by lipid kinases (34), which phosphorylate phosphatidylinositol (PI) and phosphatidylinositol 1-phosphate (PIP) (35).

REGULATORY ATP-BINDING PROTEINS    Panel $B$ of Figure 2 describes an equivalent experiment in which sodium pump current was monitored in a giant cardiac patch. In this case, ATP is required for pump activity, but it also appears to act on the pump via a secondary activation process (36). The pump current is turned on by applying ATP in the presence of potassium on the extracellular

**A.  Na,Ca Exchange Current**

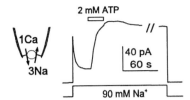

**C.  K-ATP  Channel Current**

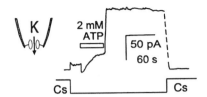

**B.     Na,K Pump Current**

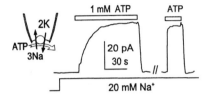

**D.  Ca²⁺-Activated Cl Channel Current**

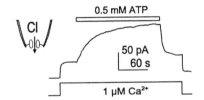

*Figure 2*   Stimulation of ion transporter and channel activities by cytoplasmic ATP in giant membrane patches. (*A*) Outward Na,Ca exchange current in a cardiac membrane patch with 2 mM (pipette) extracellular calcium and 90 mM cytoplasmic sodium. Cytoplasmic Mg-ATP (2 mM) stimulates the steady state current >fivefold in 40 s, and the stimulatory effect is nearly stable over >60 s after removal of ATP. (*B*) Na,K pump current in a cardiac membrane patch with 5 mM extracellular potassium and 20 mM cytoplasmic ATP. On first application of cytoplasmic ATP (1mM), the current turns on in a biphasic manner. Thereafter, ATP can be removed for up to 30 min, and the pump current turns on immediately on application of ATP. (*C*) Inward potassium current in a giant cardiac membrane patch with 140-mM extracellular and 20-mM cytoplasmic potassium. The potassium current is blocked and unblocked by application and removal of 120 mM cytoplasmic cesium. Cytoplasmic ATP (2 mM) at first inhibits the potassium current and then activates it over 1 min. Removal of ATP unblocks current, thereby revealing that potassium current was stimulated >tenfold by ATP. (*D*) Calcium-activated chloride current in a *Xenopus* oocyte patch in the presence of 50-mM extracellular chloride and 5-μM cytoplasmic chloride. Current is activated by applying 1 micromolar free cytoplasmic calcium (10 mM EGTA). Cytoplasmic ATP (0.5 mM) stimulates the current by about fourfold over 90 s, and the effect reverses within 20 s upon removal of ATP.

(pipette) side and sodium on the cytoplasmic side. The first time the pump current is activated by cytoplasmic ATP, it typically turns on with a slow time course, very similar to that of the stimulation of Na,Ca exchange current by ATP. During this time course, the pump current can be turned off and on rapidly by the removal or reapplication of ATP, which indicates that the slow rise of pump current on first application of ATP reflects a slow activation process. However, regardless of how long the pump is left inactive by removing ATP, and regardless of whether pump ligands such as potassium, ADP and phosphate are applied for up to 20 min, the pump reactivates immediately when ATP is reapplied. Thus the slow activation by ATP occurs as a one-shot effect after removing the patch from a cell. This is very different from the ATP effect on Na,Ca exchange current. With the Na,K pump, application of the nonhydolyzable ATP analogue 5′ adenylimidodiphosphate (AMP-PNP) before application of ATP can fully preactivate the pump while not activating any pump current; the current then turns on immediately when ATP is applied the first time. Evidently, ATP binding to a low-affinity site shifts the pump from an inactive to an active state; GTP, ADP, phosphate, or pyrophosphate cannot substitute for ATP. Because pump currents in giant patches are two- to fourfold larger than expected from whole-cell measurements (37), one possible explanation is that an endogenous pump inhibitor is being lost from the patches during the first application of ATP. As discussed below, glucose (GLUT4) transporters are a precedent for a transporter that probably binds and releases an ATP-binding protein in an ATP-dependent manner (38).

Panel $C$ of Figure 2 illustrates the typical dual effects of ATP on potassium channel currents in giant cardiac membrane patches—an immediate inhibitory effect and a long-term stimulatory effect—both of which appear to be protein kinase independent. Potassium current was recorded as inward current at 0 mV with 150 mM extracellular and 20 mM cytoplasmic potassium concentrations. It reversed as expected at +40 mV (not shown), and a cytoplasmic solution with 120 mM cesium blocked all current assumed to be potassium current. When 2 mM ATP was applied, the small baseline potassium current was blocked at first, and then current rebounded over a minute to a level higher than the original level without ATP. Upon removal of ATP, the current increased by about threefold, indicating that the stimulatory effect of ATP on the ATP-inhibited potassium current was very large. This stimulatory effect of ATP had characteristics similar to the effect of ATP on Na,Ca exchange current. As discussed below, the generation of $PIP_2$ appears to underlie (34) the stimulatory effect, but the effect may also involve actin cytoskeleton (133).

POLYVALENT CATION CHELATION BY ATP    Panel $D$ of Figure 2 shows the typical effect of cytoplasmic ATP (0.5 mM) on the calcium-activated chloride current in excised *Xenopus* oocyte patches (39). Chloride current was recorded as an outward current with an inwardly directed 10:1 ion gradient at 0 mV. It was activated by applying a cytoplasmic solution with 1 $\mu$M free calcium, buffered with 10 mM EGTA. As with Na,Ca exchange current, the chloride current was stimulated about fourfold over 1 min by ATP. As opposed to the other ATP effects described, the stimulation typically reversed in a few seconds after removal of ATP. In contrast to the ATP actions on Na,Ca exchange and potassium current, the current enhancement did not require magnesium, and nonhydrolyzable ATP analogues (e.g. ANP-PNP) were effective. In addition, GTP and GTPγS duplicated the effects with equal or higher affinity ($K_d$, 0.1–0.3 mM) and pyrophosphate, fluoride, and EDTA had stimulatory effects with similar kinetics.

Common to all stimulatory anions is their ability to bind polyvalent cations. Magnesium chelation cannot explain the effect, however, because the anions were effective as magnesium salts. The effect of ATP on calcium-activated chloride current was substantially reduced when solutions were treated overnight with Chelex (40) to remove polyvalent metals, before calcium and magnesium were added. All these anions stopped reversal of the ATP effect on Na,Ca exchange current as well as the ability of a few micromolar aluminum to induce a fast reversal of the ATP effect. Given the potency of trace metals to act on these mechanisms, it may be significant for cell function that ATP depletion releases not only physiological polyvalent cations such as magnesium, but also pathological trace metals such as aluminum.

Other mechanisms that may be important in understanding effects of ATP on ion transporters and channels include the following.

ATP-DEPENDENT CHANGES OF CYTOSKELETON    Many transporters and channels are anchored in the membrane by direct or indirect linkages to cytoskeleton, and important functional consequences of such interactions have been suggested (41–43). The localization and anchoring of channels and transporters in epithelial cells is a prerequisite for vectorial ion transport (reviewed in 44), and ATP depletion can disrupt cell polarity (45) with an internalization and redistribution of individual transporters (e.g. 46). Depletion of ATP in many cells is associated with pronounced changes of cytoskeletal organization that often appear as a thinning (depolymerization) of F-actin associated with membranes (e.g. cortical regions of epithelial cells) (47). Cytoskeletal elements, in particular actin, bind ATP and can hydrolyze it (6, 7). Thus effects of ATP requiring ATP hydrolysis, as well as those that do not, can conceivably involve actin and/or actin cytoskeleton. Furthermore, because cytoskeletal elements, including actin in certain organisms (48), can be phosphorylated and because multiple cytoskeletal elements interact with lipids involved in cell signaling such as $PIP_2$ (49, 50), there are strong but unproved grounds for possible cytoskeleton involvement in ATP-dependent modulation of transporter and channel function.

In giant membrane patches, we have extensively tested chemical and enzymatic cytoskeletal reagents on the four phenomena described in Figure 2. No clear evidence for a role of actin cytoskeleton in any effect of ATP was obtained. A possible explanation is that cytoskeleton is disrupted in giant patches.

ATP-DEPENDENT MEMBRANE TRAFFIC    The insertion and removal of a number of transporters and channels from surface membranes are ATP-dependent processes. Examples in which ATP depletion favors either insertion or retrieval of membrane are described below. Ionic mechanisms that are probably regulated by membrane insertion and removal include water channels (aquaporins) and proton pumps in the kidney; H,K pumps of the gastric mucosa; Na,K pumps in certain cell types; and glucose transporters (44). In giant membrane patches, we have tried unsuccessfully to establish conditions under which the insertion or retrieval of membrane could be monitored, either as a change of membrane capacitance, or as a change of membrane current.

MEMBRANE-COMPARTMENTALIZED ATP    It is proposed that ATP can move from one protein to another along cell membranes without mixing with free ATP in solution in the cytoplasm. If correct, such a mechanism could have many implications for ATP-dependent membrane processes. The primary experimental evidence for this idea is that membrane-bound enzymes of glycolysis can generate ATP that fuels sodium pumps (51–53) and calcium pumps (52–55) and shuts off $K_{ATP}$ potassium channels (20). The physical basis of such an ATP shuttle would presumably be either direct interactions of neighboring ATP-binding sites and or effective restriction of ATP movements from its binding sites to free solution.

With regard to giant membrane patches, the ATP depletion occurring at the cytoplasmic membrane surface as a result of Na,K pump activity has been estimated and could be reasonably accounted for by free diffusion of ATP through the pipette orifice up to the membrane surface (56). Similarly, calcium depletion and accumulation next to the membrane of giant patches during the activation of Na,Ca exchange current were estimated, and no evidence for diffusion barriers at the membrane was obtained (57). Possibly, accumulation and depletion phenomena under the surface membrane in heart cells occur at couplings between the surface and subplasmalemmal membranes (52) that do not exist in the excised cardiac membrane patches. In red blood cell membranes, about 500 ATP molecules are estimated to be bound per Na,K pump molecule (53). Actin microfilaments (6, 7) would easily account for these sites.

## Ion Exchangers

NA,CA EXCHANGE    Phospholipids interact physically with all ion channels and transporters. Ion transporters may be more sensitive to the membrane phospholipid composition because they undergo conformational changes with each transport cycle. The idea that individual lipids may be second messengers is attractive because they would have preferential access to membrane-associated proteins. The cardiac Na,Ca exchanger is strongly activated by most anionic lipids (33, 162). In giant cardiac membrane patches, phospholipids on the cytoplasmic side appear to exchange well with most phospholipids applied in the form of sonicated liposomes (32), and the stimulatory effects of anionic lipids are strikingly similar to those of ATP (33). It was a question, therefore, whether the effects of ATP and anionic lipids represent the end point of cell regulation pathways.

To test for changes of anionic lipids during application of ATP, changes of membrane surface potential were monitored by examining currents generated by the ionophore nonactin, whose transport activity depends in predictable ways on surface potential (33). During onset of the ATP effect, the negative surface potential of the cytoplasmic membrane face appeared to increase, and the increase could be "screened" by polyvalent cations. It was suggested that the effect might involve ATP-dependent transport of phosphatidylserine from the extracellular side to the cytoplasmic side, or the generation of negatively charged lipids on the cytoplasmic side by lipid kinases. The former mechanism was favored by results suggesting a decrease of negative charges on the extracellular side and by the fact that phosphatidylserine is the major anionic lipid of the membrane. However, the apparent decrease of extracellular surface charges was not confirmed by other probes, and further tests for phosphatidylserine transport were negative. Thus the flippase hypothesis is not viable. Tests for generation of phosphatidic acid from diacylglycerol were also negative.

Several tests for generation of $PIP_2$ from PI were positive (34): The action of ATP was abolished by pretreatment of patches with a PI-specific phospholipase C, and it could be recovered by incorporation of PI from sonicated PI liposomes. The effect of ATP could be reversed by a $PIP_2$-specific PLC, and was mimicked by exogenous $PIP_2$. High concentrations (5–20 $\mu$M) of free $Ca^{2+}$ accelerated reversal of the ATP effect, and PLC activity in myocyte membranes was activated with a similar calcium dependence. Finally, aluminum (in micromolar and submicromolar concentrations) was found to reverse the ATP effect, even in the presence of 10 mM EGTA, and the action of aluminum was traced to its binding with extremely high affinity to $PIP_2$. ATP-sensitive potassium channels also were highly sensitive to all the interventions affecting $PIP_2$ and were stimulated with a similar ATP dependence and time course. In addition, ATP and $PIP_2$ activated a potassium current that was not blocked by ATP; it is probable that the second current is generated by inward rectifier potassium channels. That $PIP_2$ might be a second messenger that activates specific transporters and channels is consistent with a complete insensitivity of $Na^+,K^+$ pumps, $Na^+$ channels and GAT1 (GABA) neurotransmitter transporters in giant patches to $PIP_2$ and other negatively charged lipids.

How can the generation of $PIP_2$, a trace phospholipid in most membranes, be an effective activation signal when most, if not all, negatively charged lipids are capable of stimulating Na,Ca exchange and $K_{ATP}$ channels? The best explanation at present is that anionic lipid effectivity increases at least one order of magnitude with each additional negative charge. With three negative charges,

$PIP_2$ is much more potent than PS, and $PIP_3$ is known to be more potent than $PIP_2$. A major involvement of $PIP_3$ seems unlikely, however, because it is a minor phosphatidylinositol phosphate and because the ATP effect is reversed by a $PIP_2$-specific phospholipase.

A role of $PIP_2$ as a second messenger in the regulation of cardiac Na,Ca exchange and background potassium channels is attractive for several reasons. First, the general role of phosphatidylinositol signaling in cardiac muscle has been enigmatic. The ubiquitous enzymes of PI-dependent signaling pathways are present in heart, but $IP_3$ does not seem to play a major role in the regulation of calcium movements (e.g. 58). Possibly, $PIP_2$ is the more important messenger. Second, there has been a decades-long search for mechanisms and drugs that modulate primarily cardiac contraction strength, similar to heart glycosides, without modifying the frequency of contraction or the rate of relaxation, as do mechanisms that act via cyclic adenosine monophosphate (cAMP). The $PIP_2$ signaling pathway could play that role: Activation of phospholipase C would generally tend to deplete $PIP_2$ from the membrane, thereby inhibiting Na,Ca exchange and decreasing calcium extrusion. An increase of the average cytoplasmic free calcium concentration, for example with increase of cardiac frequency, could lead to a positive feedback in calcium homeostasis. $PIP_2$ would be hydrolyzed, resulting in inhibition of Na,Ca exchange and ultimately an increase in contraction strength. Such a potentiation mechanism could equally occur in nervous tissue where Na,Ca exchange plays a strong role in calcium homeostasis. Third, phospholipase C activity in heart appears to be stretch sensitive (59). Thus a fall of $PIP_2$ could be a mechanism by which an increase in cardiac filling enhances the contractile state, the so-called Frank-Starling mechanism. Obviously, much experimental work lies ahead to test such speculations, as well as to understand the hormonal regulation of $PIP_2$ in heart via lipid kinases, phosphatases, and phospholipases.

In perfused squid giant nerve axons, as well as in cardiac cells (61), Na,Ca exchange is inhibited by depletion of cytoplasmic ATP (62–64). Recently, ATP-dependent stimulation of Na,Ca exchange has also been reported in cardiac vesicles (164), although it was not noted previously (165). Most results from the axon system suggest that a protein kinase is involved: Activation by ATP requires magnesium, and ATP$\gamma$S can substitute for ATP, whereas non-hydrolyzable ATP analogues cannot. Activation at suboptimal ATP concentrations is enhanced by nonspecific phosphatase inhibitors such as vanadate and paranitrophenylphosphate. However, the protein kinase involved would be novel in two respects. First, the dependence of exchange activity on cytoplasmic ATP is half-maximal at about 0.3 mM (62), which is a lower affinity than for activation of calcium pumps in squid axons. It is also a substantially lower affinity than that for ATP-dependent modulation of Na,K,Cl cotransport and delayed potassium channels in squid axons (see below). Second, the activation by ATP is not inhibited by several nonspecific and specific protein kinase inhibitors. An alternative explanation accounting for differences between squid axons and cardiac membrane patches could be that lipid kinases in squid axons utilize the ATP$\gamma$S derivative of ATP more effectively than do cardiac membrane lipid kinases, and the lipid phosphatases in the axon might be inhibited by the nonspecific phosphatase inhibitors employed.

Although we have detected no functional effects of protein kinases on Na,Ca exchange in the excised patch model, phosphorylation of the cardiac Na,Ca exchanger by protein kinase C (PKC) has been demonstrated by immunoprecipitation techniques in cardiac vesicles and in intact myocytes (65). Stimulation of exchanger activity was correlated with the phosphorylation.

Na,H EXCHANGE    Na,H exchange is one of the best-studied membrane transporters, which is regulated by multiple cell signaling mechanisms. They include calcium/calmodulin, protein kinases and G proteins (e.g. 66–68). Na,H exchange is also strongly inhibited by hypoxia and ATP depletion (68, 69). Initially, the identification of consensus phosphorylation sites in the cloned exchanger suggested a common molecular target for many regulatory processes, namely those involvling phosphorylation. Surprisingly, however, deletion of phosphorylation sites from the Na,H exchanger did not disrupt, or only partially disrupted, agonist-dependent activation of the exchanger (70). Thus either auxiliary proteins are phosphorylated and mediate growth factor regulation of the transporter, or additional messengers (e.g. lipid messengers) modulate the transporter without phosphorylation. In addition, it is now known that the Na,H exchanger dependence on cytoplasmic ATP involves a mechanism that does not require ATP hydrolysis. In CHO fibroblasts, AMP-PNP and ANP-PCP can substantially replace ATP in the activation of Na,H exchange, and ATP$\gamma$S and ATP are fully effective in activating exchange activity in the absence of magnesium (69). Furthermore, the ATP-dependent regulation takes place over a millimolar concentration range, which also makes protein kinase involvement unlikely. Because the Na,H exchanger contains no consensus binding sites for ATP, additional proteins are almost certainly involved.

What is the biological sense of metabolic regulation of Na,H exchange? The role of Na,H exchange in most cells is to extrude protons, and a considerable energetic cost is incurred by pumping sodium to maintain proton extrusion. Perhaps, critical energy reserves are conserved by sacrificing fast proton extrusion during ATP depletion.

ANION EXCHANGE (BAND 3)    There is no clear evidence to suggest that the anion exchanger is regulated by any cell signaling pathway or by changes of ATP in cells. Nevertheless, the anion exchanger, a major protein in red blood cell membranes, is highly phosphorylated at both serine and tyrosine residues (71). Phosphorylation can be induced by protein phosphatase inhibitors, and in Skate red blood cells, the exchanger is phosphorylated in response to swelling (72). What is the role of phosphorylation? One suggestion is that phosphorylation modifies the activity of glycolytic enzymes, which are physically coupled to the anion exchanger (73, 74). A clear elucidation of the role of phosphorylation could provide an important model for other systems where the role of phosphorylation is enigmatic.

## Cotransporters and Carrier Mechanisms

The Na,K,Cl and K,Cl cotransporters mediate electroneutral ion movements across many cell membranes (44, 74–76). The Na,K,Cl cotransporter (77) generally mediates electrolyte influx, whereas the K,Cl cotransporter mediates efflux. Both cotransporters are regulated hormonally and by cell volume changes. Much of what is known about ATP-dependencies and transporter regulation comes from transport studies with nonmammalian cells and tissues or nonhuman red blood cells that display volume regulation. In contrast to findings for ion exchangers, the current data support the notion of protein kinase-mediated phosphorylation as the major ATP-dependent mechanisms.

Na,K,Cl COTRANSPORT   Regulation studies are more advanced for the Na,K,Cl transporter because cloning was achieved earlier and because phosphorylation could be studied in the shark rectal gland (78, 79). The shark transporter is activated and phosphorylated in response to a rise of cAMP, and it is activated and phosphorylated in response to hypertonicity without a rise in cAMP. Clearly, two phosphorylation mechanisms are involved. Further evidence for dual mechanisms comes from work in HeLa cells (80). Stimulation of transport activity by ATP is acccompanied by an increased affinity for extracellular rubidium (or potassium), which does not occur when the transporter is stimulated by cAMP. The fact that nonspecific phosphatase inhibitors vanadate and fluoride slow inhibition of transport activity observed on depletion of ATP in squid axons (81) supports a role for protein kinases in the effects of ATP. Also in avian red cells, the inhibition of transport activity, which occurs during ATP depletion, is decreased or blocked by phosphatase inhibitors (82). In ATP-limited squid axons, the phosphatase inhibitor okadaic acid stimulates transport activity (83). In chick cardiac cells, cytoplasmic calcium and ATP synergistically stimulate potassium uptake by the cotransporter to rates nearly as high as those of the Na,K pump; calcium/calmodulin-dependent protein kinase involvement is suggested (84).

Nevertheless, some results suggest that the ATP-dependent regulation of Na,K,Cl cotransporters is more complex: First, the concentration dependence is unusual for a phosphorylation mechanism. In HeLa cells, transport is stimulated by ATP with a high $K_d$ of 0.95 mM (80), and the curve is rather steep, suggesting a cooperativity. Similar ATP dependencies are reported in turkey erythrocytes (82), although higher affinities are suggested from studies of ferret red cells (85). A second complication is that the Na,K,Cl cotransporter may be sensitive to changes of actin cytoskeleton (43). Because cytoskeletal agents such as phalloidin can attenuate the stimulatory effects of cAMP in some cells (86, 87), it is possible that ATP-dependent cytoskeletal changes are prerequisite to the stimulation of cotransport by some agonists.

K,Cl COTRANSPORT    The K,Cl cotransport activity of red blood cells is inhibited by an ATP-dependent mechanism (88–90) and stimulated or maintained in an activated state by another ATP/magnesium-dependent mechanism (91, 92). The regulatory activation of K,Cl cotransport by cell swelling has been interpreted as a dephosphorylation mechanism, because activation by swelling is inhibited by nonspecific phosphatase inhibitors (93). In resealed dog red cell ghosts, the incorporation of ATP alone does not permit cell swelling responses; creatine phosphate is also required, and one interpretation is that creatine kinase supplies ATP to a site that is inaccessible to cytoplasmic ATP (91). Alternatively, creatine phosphate itself might modulate transport activity. Interestingly, a stimulatory effect of ATP is observed in inside-out erythrocyte vesicles that does not require creatine phosphate (94). Furthermore, reversible swelling-induced stimulation of KCl transport has been demonstrated in the absence of ATP in resealed human red cell ghosts (95). Probably, multiple mechanisms of volume sensing are at play. A role for tyrosine protein kinases is suggested by inhibition of both basal and stimulated cotransport activity by the tyrosine kinase inhibitors tyrophostin B46 and genistein; the nonspecific tyrosine phosphatase inhibitor vanadate activates transport activity (89, 96). On the other hand, the protein kinase inhibitor staurosporin activates transport activity (88). No effects of nonhydrolyzable ATP analogues are reported for K,Cl cotransport. Metabolic studies may be complicated by the fact that reactive thio groups strongly modulate transport activity (91). In summary, the regulation of KCl cotransport appears to involve multiple protein kinases, as well as ATP-independent mechanisms. There is no clear evidence for ATP-dependent mechanisms that do not involve protein kinases.

GLUCOSE TRANSPORTERS    Glucose uptake in many cell types is stimulated by hypoxia (97), ischemia (98), chemically induced ATP depletion (99), and metabolic stress (100). The enhancement of glucose uptake can be very large and is of obvious protective value to the cells involved. Three different protein kinase-independent mechanisms appear to be involved. A direct mechanism is proposed for a red cell glucose transporter whereby ATP binds to a site on the transporter and allosterically inhibits transport activity (101); this mechanism was not confirmed in reconstituted transporters (102, 103). In heart cells and other cells, glucose carriers associated with the surface membrane increase by a factor of about 2 during ischemia (102). As with the anion exchanger, other membrane-associated proteins are known to interact with glucose transporters. When glyceraldehyde-3-phosphate dehydrogenase binds to glucose transporters, the enzyme is evidently inhibited, whereas the glucose transporter is not inhibited (104). Glucose transporters are associated with clathrin lattices, and in rat adipocytes, which translocate carriers to the surface membrane (105), a 70-kDa cytoplasmic protein associated with the clathrin coat appears to bind specifically to a (GLUT4) glucose transporter (38). Its binding is inhibited by ATP in millimolar concentrations, and it might be an activator of the transporter. Consistent with the idea that membrane insertion is not the major effect of ATP depletion, GLUT1 activity in a rat liver (clone 9) cell line is stimulated 12-fold by inhibition of oxidative phosphorylation without a significant change in cell-associated transporters (99).

## Ion Pumps

Na,K PUMP    In epithelial cells, ATP depletion generally leads to a disruption of cytoskeleton and an internalization of the Na,K ATPase from the disrupted cortical actin cytoskeleton (43, 46, 106, 107). The pump redistributes throughout the epithelial cell, and it can reinsert into apical membrane, where it is functional (108). Thus cytoskeletal association of the pump determines location but not activity. In *Xenopus* oocytes, internalization of the Na,K pump is a physiological process that is part of egg maturation and can also be induced by PKC activation (109, 110). In skeletal muscle, insertion of pumps into the sarcolemma is stimulated by insulin (111, 112), but it is not known whether insulin-induced insertion is particularly sensitive to changes of cytoplasmic ATP.

CALCIUM PUMPS    As inferred above, calcium pump activities of both the sarcoplasmic reticulum and the surface membrane decrease as ATP falls to a few hundred micromolar. Although the details are uncertain, the low affinity regulatory effect of ATP probably does not involve an extra ATP-binding site. In certain states of the pump, ATP appears to bind to the pump when the pump is still phosphorylated, and this binding occurs with relatively low affinity (10, 11). The fact that the plasmalemmal calcium pump can be shifted by calmodulin between states with and without low affinity ATP dependence (16, 17) strongly supports the idea that this effect as a regulatory mechanism.

# ION CHANNELS

An extensive review of ATP effects on ion channels and channel current run down is outside the scope of this article. The following examples illustrate how ATP-dependence has been used to analyze phosphorylation mechanisms. Also, they illustrate the range of ATP-dependent mechanisms implicated in the modulation of channel activity.

## Potassium Channels

DELAYED POTASSIUM CHANNELS    In perfused squid giant axons, the delayed potassium current is strongly affected by depletion of cytoplasmic ATP (113). The major effect of ATP depletion is not simply to turn off a fraction of the channels. Rather, the gating parameters become shifted to more negative potentials, as expected for the loss of a negative charge on the cytoplasmic side of the channel (114, 115). In addition, a slow inactivation process is enhanced, thereby tending to turn off channels (115). As expected for a protein kinase involvement, the effect of replenishing cytoplasmic ATP was half-maximal with only 10 $\mu$M ATP, and the effects of ATP could be reversed by exogenous protein phosphatases (115, 116). Thus all evidence argues strongly that phosphorylation is involved. When outside-out patches were excised from axons, the effects of ATP observed in dialyzed axons were mimicked at the single-channel level by photolysis of "caged" ATP in the presence of a cAMP-dependent protein kinase catalytic subunit on the cytoplasmic (pipette) side (117). Evidently, the protein kinase underlying the ATP effects is not tightly associated with the membrane and is lost during patch formation and excision.

Ca-ACTIVATED POTASSIUM CHANNELS    Studies of the ATP-dependent modulation of other potassium channels suggest a close physical relationship between protein kinases, phosphatases, and ion channels (reviewed in 118). Studies of large-conductance calcium-activated (B-K) potassium channels are particularly instructive because whole-cell configurations, excised patches and planar bilayers were employed. When reconstituted into planar bilayers, the type-2 KCa channels from brain are stimulated by ATP, and the effect reverses upon removal of ATP. Pharmacological studies suggest that the modulation involves PKC and a phosphoprotein phosphatase that is inhibited by microcystin (119). One cloned calcium-dependent potassium channel, the *Drosophila Slo*-KCa, is reported to be modulated by a cAMP-dependent protein kinase activity associated with excised membrane patches from *Xenopus* ooctyes (120).

Specific interactions occurring between ion channels and protein kinases have been directly demonstrated by immunoprecipitation techniques for the hKv1.5 potassium channnel, i.e. this channel binds stably the Src3 tyrosine protein kinase (121). Renal ATP-sensitive K channels provide another example: Excised membrane patches contain various protein kinases and phosphatases necessary to modulate channel activity (122; W Wang, SC Hebert & G Giebisch, this volume). In the case of CFTR chloride channels, excised cardiac membrane patches contain functionally active phosphatases, but activation by ATP has not been observed without first applying an exogenous protein kinase (30). Thus physical associations of channels and protein kinases are certainly not a rule. Transient physical interactions were hypothesized to explain how calcium channel phosphorylation by the catalytic subunit of cAMP protein kinase could be voltage dependent (124). In the case of skeletal muscle, catalytic subunit binding to an anchor protein at the membrane is required for voltage-dependent calcium channel facilitation (125).

Another example of ATP-dependent modulation in excised patches is the calcium-activated large-conductance potassium channels of rat cortical neurons (126). Here a strong stimulatory effect of ATP is observed that reverses within 20 to 120 s on removal of ATP. The effects of ATP were inhibited by the cAMP protein kinase inhibitor protein (PKI), and the reversal was accelerated by application of alkaline phosphatase. If the inhibitor is acting specifically, it is striking that the ATP effects did not require cAMP. The results suggest that the catalytic subunits of cAMP-dependent protein kinase are tethered to the membrane and are functionally important for channel modulation. It is notable that millimolar ATP concentrations were required to obtain strong activation of the channels. High concentrations of ADP could mimic ATP, but the effects of ADP were reduced by application of hexokinase and glucose or of an adenylate kinase inhibitor, thus indicating that ATP had been generated locally from ADP. These results suggest substantial diffusion restriction for ATP and ADPs, perhaps related to the configuration of the patch in the electrode tip, or conceivably involving a membrane-delimited ATP compartment. In summary, all ATP effects described to date on large-conductance potassium channels appear to involve protein kinases, but tests for additional mechanisms remain to be carried out.

$K_{ATP}$ CHANNELS    The role of $K_{ATP}$ potassium channels (CG Nichols & AN Lopatin, this volume) as metabolism sensors (128, 129) would not have been inferred from studies of isolated channel currents because the inhibition of potassium current in excised membrane patches usually occurs over the range of 5 to 100 $\mu$M (19), which is not much different from ATP-hydrolyzing mechanisms such as protein kinases and ion pumps. A major clue to their function was their inhibition by drugs that modify insulin release. In addition, whole-cell work demonstrated that $K_{ATP}$ channel activity was generally more sensitive to changes of metabolic state than other conductances (e.g. 130). How is it that channels with micromolar ATP affinity sense ATP changes during rather mild metabolic stress? One recently proven mechanism is that ADP binds to at least one of the nucleotide sites of the sulfonylurea receptor involved in channel regulation by ATP, but with an activating effect (131). Other cell constituents may also reduce the ATP affinity. In giant patches, the block of cardiac $K_{ATP}$

channels by ATP occurs with a lower affinity ($K_d$ 0.5–2 mM) than usually observed in conventional cardiac patches (34). Perhaps, a factor that decreases the ATP affinity is lost from small patches. Polycations can increase the ATP affinity by >50-fold, and negatively charged amphophilic substances reduce the cytoplasmic affinity for ATP (132). Anionic lipids may be extracted from patches, especially from small patches, by their binding to the glass pipette wall (32).

As described in Figure 2, $K_{ATP}$ channels are both inhibited and stimulated by ATP, and the generation of $PIP_2$ is associated with the stimulatory effect. In conventional patches, the channel current runs down and can usually be recovered by applying ATP (133). The run down may reflect disassembly of the actin cytoskeleton on the basis of the following results (134): Run down rate was greatly accelerated by high cytoplasmic free calcium and roughly doubled by micromolar concentrations of cytochalasin B. Channel activity was inhibited by micromolar concentrations of the actin-binding enzyme DNase I, and activity was stabilized by phalloidin, which blocks depolymerization of actin. Channels that had run down severely and could not be recovered by ATP alone could be recovered by application of actin together with ATP. Although the high concentrations of reagents employed raise a question of specificity, the results make a good case for microfilament involvement. Interestingly, a role for microfilaments is also indicated for Na,Ca exchange (165), which is also a candidate for regulation by $PIP_2$.

CALCIUM CHANNELS    In addition to activation by protein kinases, surface membrane calcium channels and calcium release channels are activated by ATP by mechanisms that do not involve ATP hydrolysis. For neuronal high-voltage channels (i.e. L-type), hundreds of micromolar ATP appear to be required (135). In cardiac myocytes, L-type calcium channels were discovered to be ATP-sensitive in experiments in which ATP was generated from caged ATP (136). Although ATP is expected to fuel protein kinases, the release of ATP stimulated L-type calcium current even when phosphorylation was blocked. In vascular smooth muscle cells, high ATP concentrations are required to maintain activity, and ATP$\gamma$S substitutes only partially (137). That ATP may play a direct role for some types of surface calcium channels is suggested by results with N-type calcium channels. This calcium channel is inhibited by catecholamines via an alpha-receptor mechanism. ATP is required for signal transduction, and nonhydrolyzable ATP (p[NH]ppA) can substitute (138). Surface membrane capacitive calcium channels, which are activated in association with the depletion of internal calcium stores, are inhibited by ATP depletion by a mechanism that has not been studied in detail (139). The ryanodine-sensitive (140, 141) and $IP_3$-sensitive (12, 13, 142) calcium channels of cellular calcium stores are both activated by a direct action of ATP on the channels; the ryanodine-sensitive channel requires hundreds of micromolar ATP for complete activation.

Are these ATP dependencies of calcium channels physiologically or pathologically relevant to changes of cellular ATP? Kinetic studies of the effects of ATP depletion in cardiac cells (130) suggest relevancy: $K_{ATP}$ potassium channels are quickly activated during ATP depletion (143, 144), thereby shortening the action potential and reducing calcium influx. However, the role of $K_{ATP}$ channels can fade within a minute due to their renewed closure (130), which is presumably equivalent to the reversal of the stimulatory effect of ATP shown in Figure 2C. The direct inhibition of surface calcium channels and calcium store channels by ATP depletion may then be very important to inhibit calcium movements and avoid a resurgence of calcium transients.

The run down of calcium channels, like that of $K_{ATP}$ channels, is slowed by ATP, and a similar cytoskeletal mechanism has been proposed. The typical run down of calcium current, observed in excised giant membrane patches from snail (*Lymnaea*) neurons, is slowed and can be partially reversed by addition of ATP, but not by other nucleotides (145). Tests for the involvement of protein kinases in these effects were negative. Phalloidin and taxol, which stabilize microfilaments and microtubules, slowed the run down, whereas cytochalasin B and colchicine, which disrupt cytoskeleton, accelerated it. The results are suggestive of a cytoskeleton role, but the specificity of the drugs at the high concentrations employed ($> 1 \ \mu M$) is a concern. Effects of cytochalasin and other cytoskeletal reagents have not been reported in whole-cell recordings of calcium currents.

ANION CHANNELS    Several anion channels are activated by cytoplasmic ATP, and CFTR chloride channels (30) are the best-studied example. Calcium-activated chloride channels of *Xenopus* oocytes are noted in Figure 2. Volume-sensitive chloride channels (VSOC), another example of anion channels (146–149), are nonspecific in that small neutral solutes such as taurine and inositol can transverse them, which is the basis of their role in volume regulation. In addition to the volume-sensitive channels, some microsomal chloride channels are reported to be ATP sensitive (150). Nonhydrolyzable ATP analogues are effective in each of these channels, although additional effects dependent on ATP hydrolysis are suggested (149). For surface membrane chloride channels, the inhibitory effect of ATP depletion could hyperpolarize cells by allowing $K_{ATP}$ and other potassium channels to bring membrane potential closer to the potassium equilibrium potential. In the case of the VSOC channels, the effect would slow efflux of small organic solutes when ATP falls, thereby preserving cell constituents. Obviously, much remains to be learned, starting with the question of whether the various anion channels bind ATP directly.

EPITHELIAL Na CHANNELS    An important experimental model for studying transcellular ion movements is the toad urinary bladder. Here, sodium transport is regulated via the regulation of amiloride-sensitive sodium channels, and aldosterone is the major agonist known to stimulate sodium transport (151). Relatively mild metabolic inhibition markedly decreases the sodium permeability in aldosterone-stimulated bladders (152). The basis of these effects remains unknown.

A possibly important role of cytoskeleton in the regulation of cloned epithelial sodium channels has recently been suggested from both whole-cell and excised patch studies of epithelial sodium current (153, 154). In contrast to the studies with Ca and $K_{ATP}$ channels, cytochalasin D treatment induces and/or increases channel activity. In excised patches, addition of short actin filaments enhances sodium currents (154–156). The effect of actin is enhanced by ATP, as well as by cytochalasin D. The effects of actin are reversed by the actin-binding protein DNase I, and cytochalasin D treatment prevents channel activation by protein kinase A (PKA). It is suggested that PKA, and thereby ATP, promotes actin phosphorylation, which in turn favors the generation of actin fragments of an appropriate length to activate the sodium channels (152). CFTR chloride channels (157) and Na,K pumps (158) may also be regulated by actin, but much further experimentation is required to rigorously test these hypotheses.

# SUMMARY AND PERSPECTIVES

The modulation mechanisms discussed in this article are united only by a cell regulatory principle: They respond to changes of ATP of a magnitude that may occur in metabolic cell stress, albeit extreme stress in many cases. It is then an open question whether these mechanisms are connected to other forms of cell regulation. For ATP-dependent potassium channels and GTP-dependent enzymes, similar hypotheses proved to be productive.

## Protein Kinases

In contrast to regulation studies to date for cotransporters and several potassium channels, the role of protein kinases in regulating ion exchangers remains enigmatic. The case of Na,H exchange promises to deliver important new insights because unidentified proteins clearly must be involved in well-documented regulatory effects. What signaling mechanisms are regulating Na,H exchange after mutation of its phosphorylation sites? Does phosphorylation have consequences besides the modification of transport function? How is the transporter modulated by ATP without ATP hydrolysis? Phosphorylation of the anion exchanger, for which no functional consequence has been proposed, may be an important experimental model if, for example, further evidence supports the idea that phosphorylation serves as a regulatory signal to other proteins with which the exchanger interacts (73, 74). For Na,Ca exchange as well, further work is essential to elucidate the functional role of phosphorylation.

## Regulatory ATP-Binding Sites

Among those ion transport mechanisms that are modulated allosterically by ATP binding, the ATP-binding sites are identified for CFTR chloride channels, probably for $K_{ATP}$ channels, and for ryanodine- and $IP_3$-sensitive calcium channels. The idea that the ATP affinity of allosteric regulation might change as a result of regulatory influences was noted in connection with the $K_{ATP}$ channels. In the case of CFTR chloride channels, the ATP sensitivity of channel activity must be determined in a complex manner by ATP binding and hydrolysis at two binding sites of each channel. It seems inevitable that ATP sensitivity is modified in different functional states of the channel. $K_{ATP}$ channels can be inhibited by nonhydrolyzable ATP analogues, but there is no reason to think that the ATP receptors do not hydrolyze ATP. Because the probable ATP receptors—sulfonylurea receptors (159)—are related to CFTR chloride channels, similar mechanisms of ATP binding and hydrolysis may be expected. There is no evidence that calcium release channels hydrolyze ATP or that their ATP dependence is modulated, but these points have not been investigated thoroughly. The physical basis of allosteric modulation by ATP of L-type calcium channels, calcium-activated chloride channels, and VSOC chloride channels is unknown. In the case of calcium-activated chloride channels, described in Figure 2, the ATP effects are not specific, and actin is one possible nonspecific polyanion receptor.

## ATP-Dependent Regulation via Cytoskeleton

The mechanisms by which actin cytoskeleton might mediate effects of ATP include allosteric effects of ATP binding, effects on actin polymerization, and effects on membrane traffic. At present, a role of short actin filaments as modulators of channels and transporters is the most easily studied mechanism. For the stabilizing effect of ATP on run down of cardiac $K_{ATP}$ channels and snail neuronal calcium channels, implicated to involve cytoskeletal changes, there is a striking possible overlap with the role of lipid kinases. The ATP-dependent generation of $PIP_2$ would be expected to stabilize actin cytoskeleton (35, 49, 50), and it may therefore be difficult to dissociate the interrelated ATP mechanisms.

## ATP-Dependent Regulation via Lipid Signaling

It will be interesting to determine what transporters and channels, besides Na,Ca exchange and $K_{ATP}$ channels, are modulated by $PIP_2$ in membranes. It will be much more difficult to test definitively the role of $PIP_2$ as a second messenger in ion transporter and channel regulation. Among the inadequately understood issues is the regulation of $PIP_2$ levels in cell membranes. It cannot be assumed, for example, that activation of phospholipase C by hormones will lead to a sustained depletion of $PIP_2$ in heart or other tissues; mechanisms such as product inhibition evidently can maintain its abundance nearly constant (58). Thus the regulation of lipid kinases and phosphatases may prove to be more important for $PIP_2$-sensitive mechanisms than the regulation of phospholipase C activities. The regulation of other negatively charged lipids by ATP-dependent processes also deserves more attention. Potentially important mechanisms include the generation of phosphatidic acid by diacylglycerol kinase and the generation of free fatty acids by an ATP-dependent phospholipase A2, activated allosterically by ATP in the millimolar concentration range (160). Multiple anionic lipids may act together by forming domains in membranes that include proteins with cationic residues at their protein-lipid interfaces (reviewed in 161). The formation of such domains may be regulated by protein kinase phosphorylation. The best example is the positively charged MARKS protein (166), whose phosphorylation by PKC may lead to the break up of anionic lipid domains. Thus one type of lipid-dependent signaling might involve the formation or break up of domains of lipids that modify transporter or channel function.

## Transporter versus Channel Regulation

There is an impression in cell physiology that ion channels are more exquisitely regulated, and therefore more exciting to study, than are ion transporters and pumps. This impression may have been valid when the study of millisecond events of membrane excitability was novel, but it certainly is not valid now in the context of cell regulation. Protein kinases and G proteins are the established currencies of ion channel regulation, but other mechanisms and messengers now also deserve critical attention. They include membrane-associated ATP-binding proteins, lipid-dependent signaling mechanisms, in particular those involving phosphatidylinositol phosphates, and cytoskeletal mechanisms.

*Literature Cited*

1. Linder ME, Gilman AG. 1992. G proteins. *Sci. Am.* 267:56–61
2. Cohen P. 1988. Protein phosphorylation and hormone action. *Proc. R. Soc. London Ser. B* 234:115–44
3. Krebs EG. 1983. Historical perspectives on protein phosphorylation and a classification system for protein kinases. *Philos. Trans. R. Soc. London Ser. A.* 302:3–11
4. Krebs EG, Beavo JA. 1979. Phosphorylation-dephosphorylation of enzymes. *Annu. Rev. Biochem.* 48:923–59

5. Berridge MJ. 1988. Inositol lipids and calcium signalling. *Proc. R. Soc. London Ser. B* 234:359–78
6. Carlier M-F. 1993. Dynamic actin. *Curr. Biol.* 3:321–23
7. Pollard TD. 1990. Actin. *Curr. Opin. Cell Biol.* 2:33–40
8. Nasmith PE, Benos DJ. 1992. Nucleotides and ion channel regulation. *Am. J. Resp. Cell Mol. Biol.* 6:567–68
9. O'Rourke B. 1993. Ion channels as sensors of cellular energy. Mechanisms for modulation by magnesium

and nucleotides. *Biochem. Pharmacol.* 46:1103–12

10. Bishop JE, Al-Shawi MK, Inesi G. 1987. Relationship of the regulatory nucleotide site to the catalytic site of the sarcoplasmic reticulum $Ca^{2+}$-ATPase. *J. Biol. Chem.* 262:4658–63

11. Fernandez-Belda F, Garcia-Carmona F, Inesi G. 1988. Accelerating effect of ATP on calcium binding to sarcoplasmic reticulum ATPase. *Arch. Biochem. Biophys.* 260:118–24

12. Bezprozvanny I, Ehrlich BE. 1993. ATP modulates the function of inositol 1,4,5-trisphosphate-gated channels at two sites. *Neuron* 10:1175–84

13. Ehrlich BE, Bezprozvanny I. 1994. Intracellular calcium release channels. *Chin. J. Physiol.* 37:1–7

14. Backx PH, O'Rourke B, Marban E. 1991. Flash photolysis of magnesium-DM-nitrophen in heart cells. *Am. J. Hypertens.* 4:416–21S

15. O'Rourke B, Backx PH, Marban E. 1992. Phosphorylation-independent modulation of L-type calcium channels by magnesium-nucleotide complexes. *Science* 257:245–48

16. Muallem S, Karlish SJ. 1983. Catalytic and regulatory ATP-binding sites of the red cell $Ca^{2+}$ pump studied by irreversible modification with fluorescein isothiocyanate. *J. Biol. Chem.* 258:169–75

17. Muallem S, Karlish SJ. 1980. Regulatory interaction between calmodulin and ATP on the red cell $Ca^{2+}$ pump. *Biochim. Biophys. Acta* 597:631–36

18. Collins A, Somlyo A, Hilgemann DW. 1992. The giant cardiac membrane patch method: stimulation of outward Na/Ca exchange current by MgATP. *J. Physiol.* 454:37–57

19. Ashcroft SJ, Ashcroft FM. 1990. Properties and functions of ATP-sensitive K-channels. *Cell Signal* 2:197–214

20. Weiss JN, Lamp ST. 1989. Cardiac ATP-sensitive $K^+$ channels. Evidence for preferential regulation by glycolysis. *J. Gen. Physiol.* 94:911–35

21. Terzic A, Tung RT, Kurachi Y. 1994. Nucleotide regulation of ATP sensitive potassium channels. *Cardiovasc. Res.* 28:746–53

22. Deleted in proof

23. Bogoyevitch MA, Ketterman AJ, Sugden PH. 1995. Cellular stresses differentially activate c-Jun N-terminal protein kinases and extracellular signal-regulated protein kinases in cultured ventricular myocytes. *J. Biol. Chem.* 270:29710–17

24. Pombo CM, Bonventre JV, Avruch J, Woodgett JR, Kyriakis JM, Force T. 1994. The stress-activated protein kinases are major c-Jun amino terminal kinases activated by ischemia and reperfusion. *J. Biol. Chem.* 269:26546–51

25. Corton JM, Gillespie JG, Hardie DG. 1994. Role of the AMP-activated protein kinase in the cellular stress response. *J. Cell Biol.* 4:315–24

26. Stapleton D, Mitchelhill KI, Gao G, Widmer J, Michell BJ, et al. 1996. Mammalian AMP-activated protein kinase subfamily. *J. Biol. Chem.* 271:611–14

27. Dalziel HH, Westfall DP. 1995. Receptors for adenine nucleotides and nucleosides: subclassification, distribution, and molecular characterization. *Pharmacol. Rev.* 46:449–66

28. Edwards FA. 1994. ATP receptors. *Curr. Opin. Neurobiol.* 4:347–52

29. Al-Awqati Q. 1995. Regulation of ion channels by ABC transporters that secrete ATP. *Science* 269:805–6

30. Gadsby DC, Nagel G, Hwang T-C. 1995. The CFTR chloride channel of mammalian heart. *Annu. Rev. Physiol.* 57:387–416

31. Doige CA, Ames GF. 1993. ATP-dependent transport systems in bacteria and humans: relevance to cystic fibrosis and multidrug resistance. *Annu. Rev. Microbiol.* 47:291–319

32. Hilgemann DW. 1995. The giant membrane patch. In *Single Channel Recording*, ed. B Sakmann, E Neher, pp. 307–27. New York: Plenum

33. Hilgemann DW, Collins A. 1992. The mechanism of sodium-calcium exchange stimulation by ATP in giant cardiac membrane patches: possible role of aminophospholipid translocase. *J. Physiol.* 454:59–82

34. Hilgemann DW, Ball R. 1996. Regulation of cardiac Na,Ca exchange and $K_{ATP}$ channels by $PIP_2$. *Science* 273:956–59

35. Lee SB, Rhee SG. 1995. Significance of $PIP_2$ hydrolysis and regulation of phospholipase C isozymes. *Curr. Opin. Cell Biol.* 7:183–89

36. Hilgemann DW. 1995. Slow activation of Na,K pump on first application of ATP in giant cardiac patches: comparison to Na/Ca exchange. *Biophys. J.* 68:A307

37. Nakao M, Gadsby DC. 1989. [Na] and [K] dependence of the Na/K pump current-voltage relationship in guinea pig ventricular myocytes. *J. Gen. Physiol.* 94:539–65

38. Liu H, Xiong S, Shi Y, Samuel SJ, Lachaal M, Jung CY. 1995. ATP-sensitive binding of a 70-kDa cytosolic protein to the glucose transporter in rat adipocytes. *J. Biol. Chem.* 270:7869–75
39. Golubev VL, Foley JP, Hilgemann DW. 1994. ATP-, GTP- and phospholipid-dependent modulation of Ca-activated chloride current in giant membrane patch from *Xenopus* oocytes. *Biophys. J.* 66:133
40. van Reyk DM, Brown AJ, Jessup W, Dean RT. 1995. Batch-to-batch variation of Chelex-100 compounds metal-catalyzed oxidation. Leaching of inhibitory compounds from a batch of Chelex-100 and their removal by a pre-washing procedure. *Free Radical Res.* 23:533–35
41. Mills JW, Mandel LJ. 1994. Cytoskeletal regulation of membrane transport events. *FASEB J.* 8:1161–65
42. Mills JW, Schweibert EM, Stanton BA. 1994. The cytoskeleton and membrane transport. *Curr. Opin. Nephrol. Hypertens.* 3:529–34
43. Verrey F, Groscurth P, Bolliger U. 1995. Cytoskeletal disruption in A6 kidney cells: impact on endo/exocytosis and NaCl transport regulation by antidiuretic hormone. *J. Membr. Biol.* 145:193–204
44. Reuss L, ed. 1996. Epithelial Transport. In *Handbook of Physiology: Cell Physiology.* Vol. 2, chpt. 8. New York: Oxford Univ. Press. In press
45. Drubin DG, Nelson WJ. 1996. Origins of cell polarity. *Cell* 84:335–44
46. Molitoris BA, Dahl R, Geerdes A. 1992. Cytoskeleton disruption and apical redistribution of proximal tubule $Na^+$-$K^+$-ATPase during ischemia. *Am. J. Physiol.* 263:F488–95
47. Golenhofen N, Doctro RB, Bacallao R, Mandell LJ. 1996. Actin and villin compartmentation during ATP depletion and recovery in renal cultured cells. *Kidney Int.* 48:1837–45
48. Gettemans J, DeVille Y, Vandekerckhove J, Waelkens E. 1992. Physarum actin is phosphorylated as the actin-fragmin complex at residues Thr203 and Thr202 by a specific 80 kDa kinase. *EMBO J.* 11:3185–91
49. Camilli PD, Emr SD, McPherson PS, Novick P. 1996. Phosphoinositides as regulators in membrane traffic. *Science* 271:1533–38
50. Janmey PA. 1994. Phosphoinositides and calcium as regulators of cellular actin assembly and disassembly. *Annu. Rev. Physiol.* 56:169–91
51. Mercer RW, Dunham PB. 1981. Membrane-bound ATP fuels the Na/K pump. Studies on membrane-bound glycolytic enzymes on inside-out vesicles from human red cell membranes. *J. Gen. Physiol.* 78:547–68
52. Han JW, Thieleczek R, Varsanyi M, Heilmeyer LM Jr. 1992. Compartmentalized ATP synthesis in skeletal muscle triads. *Biochemistry* 31:377–84
53. Hoffman JF, Proverbio F, Geibel JP. 1995. Membrane compartmentalized ATP drives the red cell $Na^+$ and $Ca^{2+}$ pumps. *J. Physiol.* 489:10S
54. Hardin CD, Raeymaekers L, Paul RJ. 1992. Comparison of endogenous and exogenous sources of ATP in fueling $Ca^{2+}$ uptake in smooth muscle plasma membrane vesicles. *J. Gen. Physiol.* 99:21–40
55. Xu KY, Zweier JL, Becker LC. 1995. Functional coupling between glycolysis and sarcoplasmic reticulum $Ca^{2+}$ transport. *Circ. Res.* 77:88–97
56. Kabakov AY, Hilgemann DW. 1996. Modulation of $K_{ATP}$ potassium channel current by Na,K pump depletion of cytoplasmic ATP in guinea pig cardiac myocytes and giant excised patches. *Pflügers Arch.* Submitted
57. Kabakov AY, Hilgemann DW. 1995. Modulation of Na,Ca exchange current by EGTA calcium buffering in giant cardiac membrane patches. *Biochim. Biophys. Acta* 1240:142–48
58. Lamers JM, DeJonge HW, Panagia V, van Heugten HA. 1993. Receptor-mediated signalling pathways acting through hydrolysis of membrane phospholipids in cardiomyocytes. *Cardioscience* 4:121–31
59. von Harsdorf R, Lang RE, Fullerton M, Woodcock EA. 1989. Myocardial stretch stimulates phosphatidylinositol turnover. *Circ. Res.* 65(2):494–501
60. Deleted in proof
61. Haworth RA, Goknur AB. 1992. ATP dependence of calcium uptake by the Na-Ca exchanger of adult heart cells. *Circ. Res.* 71:210–17
62. DiPolo R, Beauge L. 1991. Regulation of Na-Ca exchange: an overview. *Ann. NY Acad. Sci.* 639:100–11
63. DiPolo R, Beauge L. 1994. Effects of vanadate on MgATP stimulation of Na-Ca exchange support kinase-phosphatase modulation in squid axons. *Am. J. Physiol.* 266:C1382–91
64. DiPolo R, Beauge L. 1993. Effects of some metal-ATP complexes on Na(+)-$Ca^{2+}$ exchange in internally dialyzed squid axons. *J. Physiol.* 462:71–86

65. Iwamoto T, Pan Y, Wakabayashi S, Imagawa T, Yamanaka HI, Shigekawa M. 1996. Phosphorylation-dependent regulation of cardiac Na$^+$/Ca$^{2+}$ exchanger via protein kinase C. *J. Biol. Chem.* 271:13609–15

66. Noel J, Pouysségur J. 1995. Hormonal regulation, pharmacology, and membrane sorting of vertebrate Na$^+$/H$^+$ exchanger isoforms. *Am. J. Physiol.* 268:C283–96

67. Bertrand B, Wakabayashi S, Ikeda T, Pouysségur J, Shigekawa M. 1994. The Na$^+$/H$^+$ exchanger isoform 1 (NHE1) is a novel member of the calmodulin-binding proteins. Identification and characterization of calmodulin-binding sites. *J. Biol. Chem.* 269:13703–9

68. Burns KD, Homma T, Harris RC. 1991. Regulation of Na(+)-H$^+$ exchange by ATP depletion and calmodulin antagonism in renal epithelial cells. *Am. J. Physiol.* 261:F607–16

69. Demaurex N, Romanek RR, Orlowski J, Grinstein S. 1996. ATP dependence of Na$^+$/H$^+$ exchange: nucleotide specificity and assessment of the role of phospholipids. *J. Gen. Physiol.* In press

70. Wakabayashi S, Bertrand B, Shigekawa M, Fafournoux P, Pouysségur J. 1994. Growth factor activation and "H$^+$-sensing" of the Na$^+$/H$^+$ exchanger isoform 1 (NHE1). Evidence for an additional mechanism not requiring direct phosphorylation. *J. Biol. Chem.* 269:5583–88

71. Yannoukakos D, Vasseur C, Piau JP, Wajcman H, Bursaux E. 1991. Phosphorylation sites in human erythrocyte band 3 protein. *Biochim. Biophys. Acta* 1061:253–66

72. Musch MW, Leffingwell TR, Goldstein L. 1994. Band 3 modulation and hypotonic-stimulated taurine efflux in skate erythrocytes. *Am. J. Physiol.* 266:R65–74

73. Harrison ML, Rathinavelu P, Arese P, Geahlen RL, Low PS. 1991. Role of band 3 tyrosine phosphorylation in the regulation of erythrocyte glycolysis. *J. Biol. Chem.* 266:4106–11

74. Schneider ML, Post CB. 1995. Solution structure of a band 3 peptide inhibitor bound to aldolase: a proposed mechanism for regulating binding by tyrosine phosphorylation. *Biochemistry* 34:16574–84

75. Hoffmann EK, Dunham PB. 1995. Membrane mechanisms and intracellular signalling in cell volume regulation. *Int. Rev. Cytol.* 161:173–262

76. Katz U. 1995. Cellular water content and volume regulation in animal cells. *Cell Biochem. Funct.* 13(3):189–93

77. Haas M. 1994. The Na-K-Cl cotransporters. *Am. J. Physiol.* 267:C869–85

78. Lytle C, Forbush B III. 1992. The Na-K-Cl cotransport protein of shark rectal gland. II. Regulation by direct phosphorylation. *J. Biol. Chem.* 267:25438–43

79. Torchia J, Lytle C, Pon DJ, Forbush B III, Sen AK. 1992. The Na-K-Cl cotransporter of avian salt gland. Phosphorylation in response to cAMP-dependent and calcium-dependent secretagogues. *J. Biol. Chem.* 267:25444–50

80. Ikehara T, Yamaguchi H, Hosokawa K, Miyamoto H. 1990. Kinetic mechanism of ATP action in Na$^+$,K$^+$,Cl$^-$ cotransport of HeLa cells determined by Rb+ influx studies. *Am. J. Physiol.* 258:C5999–6009

81. Altamirano AA, Breitwieser GE, Russell JM. 1988. Vanadate and fluoride effects on Na$^+$,K$^+$,Cl$^-$ cotransport in squid giant axon. *Am. J. Physiol.* 254:C582–86

82. Ueberschar S, Bakker-Grunwald T. 1985. Effects of ATP and cyclic AMP on the Na$^+$+K$^+$+2Cl$^-$ cotransport system in turkey erythrocytes. *Biochim. Biophys. Acta* 818:260–66

83. Altamirano AA, Breitwieser GE, Russell JM. 1995. Effects of okadaic acid and intracellular Cl$^-$ on Na$^+$,K$^+$,Cl$^-$ cotransport. *Am. J. Phyiol.* 269:C878–83

84. Kohmoto O, Krueger JA, Barry WH. 1990. Activation of furosemide-sensitive K$^+$ fluxes in myocytes by ouabain and recovery from metabolic inhibition. *Am. J. Physiol.* 259:H962–72

85. Flatman PW. 1991. The effects of metabolism on Na$^+$-K$^+$-Cl$^-$ co-transport in ferret red cells. *J. Physiol.* 437:495–510

86. Wu MS, Bens M, Cluzeaud F, van Dewalle A. 1994. Role of F-actin in the activation of Na$^+$,K$^+$,Cl$^-$ cotransport by forskolin and vasopressin in mouse kidney cultured thick ascending limb cells. *J. Membr. Biol.* 142:323–26

87. Mattews JB, Smith JA, Tally KJ, Awtrey CS, Mguyen H, et al. 1994. Na,K,Cl cotranposrt in intestinal epithelial cells. Influence of chloride efflux and F-actin on regulation of cotransport activity and bumetanide binding. *J. Biol. Chem.* 269:15703–9

88. Flatman PW, Adragna NC, Lauf PK. 1996. Role of protein kinases in regulating sheep erythrocyte KCl cotransport. *Am. J. Physiol.* 271:In press

89. Ortiz-Carranza O, Adragna NC, Lauf PK. 1996. Modulation of K-Cl cotransport in volume clamped LK sheep erythrocytes by pH, magnesium and ATP. *Am. J. Physiol.* In press

90. Palfrey HC, Pewitt EB. 1993. The ATP and $Mg^{2+}$ dependence of $Na^+$-$K^+$-$2Cl^-$ cotransport reflects a requirement for protein phosphorylation: studies using calyculin A. *Pflügers Arch.* 425:321–28

91. Colclasure GC, Parker JC, Dunham PB. 1995. Creatine kinase is required for swelling-activated KCl cotransport in dog red blood cells. *Am. J. Physiol.* 268:C660–68

92. Colclasure GC, Parker JC. 1993. ATP dependence of K-Cl cotransport in dog red blood cells. *Am. J. Physiol.* 265:C1648–52

93. Jennings ML, Al-Rohil N. 1990. Kinetics of activation and inactivation of swelling-stimulated $K^+/Cl^-$ transport. *J. Gen. Physiol.* 95:1021–40

94. Kracke GR, Dunham PG. 1990. Volume-sensitive K,Cl cotransport in inside-out vesicles made from erythrocyte membranes from sheep of low-K phenotype. *Proc. Natl. Acad. Sci. USA* 87:8575–79

95. Sachs JR, Martin DW. 1993. The role of ATP in swelling-stimulated KCl cotransport in human red cell ghosts. Phosphorylation-dephosphorylation events are not in the signal transduction pathway. *J. Gen. Physiol.* 102:551–73

96. Lauf PK. 1983. Thiol-dependent passive $K^+$-$Cl^-$ transport in sheep red blood cells. V. Dependence on metabolism. *Am. J. Physiol.* 245:C445–48

97. Cartee GD, Douen AG, Ramial T, Klip A, Holloszy JO. 1991. Stimulation of glucose transport in skeletal muscle by hypoxia. *J. Appl. Physiol.* 70:1593–600

98. Sun D, Nguyen N, DeGrado TR, Schwaiger M, Brosium FC III. 1994. Ischemia induces translocation of the insulin-responsive glucose transporter GLUT4 to the plasma membrane of cardiac myocytes. *Circulation* 89:793–98

99. Shetty M, Loeb JN, Ismail-Beigi F. 1992. Enhancement of glucose transport in response to inhibition of oxidative metabolism: pre- and posttranslational mechanisms. *Am. J. Physiol.* 262:C527–32

100. May JM. 1988. Effects of ATP depletion on the mechanism of hexose transport in intact human erythrocytes. *FEBS Lett.* 241:188–90

101. Carruthers A, Helgerson AL. 1989. The human erythrocyte sugar transporter is also a nucleotide binding protein. *Biochemistry* 28:8337–46

102. Wheeler TJ. 1986. Reconstitution of glucose transport activity from erythrocyte membranes without detergent and its use in studying effects of ATP depletion. *Biochim. Biophys. Acta* 859:180–188

103. Wheeler TJ. 1989. ATP does not regulate the reconstituted glucose transporter. *Biochemistry* 28:3413–20

104. Lachaal M, Berenski CJ, Kim J, Jung CY. 1990. An ATP-modulated specific association of glyceraldehyde-3-phosphate dehydrogenase with human erythrocyte glucose transporter. *J. Biol. Chem.* 265:15449–54

105. Robinson LJ, Pang S, Harris DS, Heuser J, James DE. 1992. Translocation of the glucose transporter (GLUT4) to the cell surface in permeabilized 3T3-L1 adipocytes: effects of ATP, insulin, and $GTP\gamma S$ and localization of GLUT4 to clathrin lattices. *J. Cell Biol.* 117:1181–96

106. Hammerton RW, Krzeminski KA, Mays RW, Ryan TA, Wollner DA, Nelson WJ. 1991. Mechanism for regulating cell surface distribution of $Na^+$, $K^+$-ATPase in polarized epithelial cells. *Science* 254:847–50

107. Hinshaw DB, Burger JM, Miller MT, Adams JA, Beals TF, Omann GM. 1993. ATP depletion induces an increase in the assembly of a labile pool of polymerized actin in endothelial cells. *Am. J. Physiol.* 264:C1171–79

108. Molitoris BA. 1993. $Na^+$-$K^+$-ATPase that redistributes to apical membrane during ATP depletion remains functional. *Am. J. Physiol.* 265:F693–97

109. Vasilets LA, Schmalzing G, Madefessel K, Haase W, Schwarz W. 1990. Activation of protein kinase C by phorbol ester induces downregulation of the $Na^+/K(+)$-ATPase in oocytes of *Xenopus laevis.* *J. Membr. Biol.* 118:131–42

110. Schmalzing G, Eckard P, Kroner S, Passow H. 1990. Downregulation of surface sodium pumps by endocytosis during meiotic maturation of *Xenopus laevis* oocytes. *Am. J. Physiol.* 258:C179–84

111. Lavoie L, He L, Ramlal T, Ackerley C, Marette A, Klip A. 1995. The GLUT4 glucose transporter and the alpha 2-subunit of the $Na^+$,$K(+)$-ATPase do not localize to the same intracellular vesicles in rat skeletal muscle. *FEBS Lett.* 366:109–14

112. Marette A, Krischer J, Lavoie L, Ackerley C, Carpentier JL, Klip A. 1993. Insulin increases the $Na(+)$-$K(+)$-ATPase alpha 2-subunit in the surface of rat skeletal muscle: morphological evidence. *Am. J. Physiol.* 265:C1716–22

113. Bezanilla F, Caputo C, DiPolo R, Rojas H. 1986. Potassium conductance of the squid giant axon is modulated by ATP. *Proc. Natl. Acad. Sci. USA* 83:2743–45

114. Perozo E, Bezanilla F. 1990. Phosphorylation affects voltage gating of the delayed rectifier $K^+$ channel by electrostatic interactions. *Neuron* 5:685–90

115. Perozo E, Vandenberg CA, Jong DS, Bezanilla F. 1990. Phosphorylation modulates potassium conductance and gating current of perfused giant axons of squid. *J. Gen. Physiol.* 95:245–71

116. Perozo E, Bezanilla F, Dipolo R. 1989. Modulation of K channels in dialyzed squid axons. ATP-mediated phosphorylation. *J. Gen. Physiol.* 93:1195–218

117. Perozo E, Jong DS, Bezanilla F. 1991. Single channel studies of the phosphorylation of $K^+$ channels in the squid giant axon. II. Nonstationary conditions. *J. Gen. Physiol.* 98:19–34

118. Levitan IB. 1994. Modulation of ion channels by protein phosphorylation and dephosphorylation. *Annu. Rev. Physiol.* 56:193–212

119. Reinhart PH, Levitan IB. 1995. Kinase and phosphatase activities intimately associated with a reconstituted calcium-dependent potassium channel. *J. Neurosci.* 15:4572–79

120. Esguerra M, Wang J, Foster CD, Adelman JP, North RA, Levitan IB. 1994. Cloned $Ca^{2+}$-dependent $K^+$ channel modulated by a functionally associated protein kinase. *Nature* 369:563–65

121. Holmes TC, Fadool DA, Ren R, Levitan IB. 1996. Direct association of SRC tyrosine kinase with human Kv1.5 potassium channel mediated by an SH3 domain interaction. *Neuroscience* 22:In press (Abstr.)

122. Kubokawa M, McNicholas CM, Higgins MA, Wang W, Giebisch G. 1995. Regulation of ATP-sensitive $K^+$ channel by membrane-bound protein phosphatases in rat principal tubule cell. *Am. J. Physiol.* 269:F355–62

123. Deleted in proof

124. Mensing HJ, Hilgemann DW. 1981. Inotropic effects of activation and pharmacological mechanisms in cardiac muscle. *Trends Pharmacol. Sci.* 2:303–7

125. Johnson BD, Scheuer T, Catterall WA. 1994. Voltage-dependent potentiation of L-type $Ca^{2+}$ channels in skeletal muscle cells requires anchored cAMP-dependent protein kinase. *Proc. Natl. Acad. Sci. USA* 91:11492–96

126. Lee K, Rowe IC, Ashford ML. 1995. Characterization of an ATP-modulated large conductance $Ca^{2+}$-activated $K^+$ channel present in rat cortical neurones. *J. Physiol.* 488:319–37

127. Deleted in proof

128. Misler S, Giebisch G. 1992. ATP-sensitive potassium channels in physiology, pathophysiology, and pharmacology. *Curr. Opin. Nephrol. Hypertens.* 1:21–33

129. Deutsch N, Klitzner TS, Lamp ST, Weiss JN. 1991. Activation of cardiac ATP-sensitive $K^+$ current during hypoxia: correlation with tissue ATP levels. *Am. J. Physiol.* 261:H671–76

130. Thierfelder S, Doepner B, Gebhardt C, Hirche H, Benndorf K. 1994. ATP-sensitive $K^+$ channels in heart muscle cells first open and subsequently close at maintained anoxia. *FEBS Lett.* 351:365–69

131. Nichols CG, Shyng SL, Nestorowicz A, Glaser B, Clement JP, et al. 1996. Adenosine diphosphate as an intracellular regulator of insulin secretion. *Science* 272:1785–87

132. Deutsch N, Matsuoka S, Weiss JN. 1994. Surface charge and properties of cardiac ATP-sensitive $K^+$ channels. *J. Gen. Physiol.* 104:773–800

133. Furukawa T, Virag L, Furukawa N, Sawanobori T, Hiraoka M. 1994. Mechanism for reactivation of the ATP-sensitive $K^+$ channel by MgATP complexes in guinea-pig ventricular myocytes. *J. Physiol.* 479:95–107

134. Furukawa T, Yamane T, Terai T, Katayama Y, Hiraoka M. 1996. Functional linkage of the cardiac ATP-sensitive $K^+$ channel to the actin. *Pflügers Arch.* 431:504–12

135. Stapleton SR, Bell BA, Wootton JF, Scott RH. 1995. Modulation of $Ca^{2+}$-dependent currents in metabolically stressed cultured sensory neurones by intracellular photorelease of ATP. *Br. J. Pharmacol.* 114:544–50

136. Deleted in proof

137. Ohya Y, Sperelakis N. 1989. Modulation of single slow (L-type) calcium channels by intracellular ATP in vascular smooth muscle cells. *Pflügers Arch.* 414:257–64

138. Elmslie KS, Werz MA, Overholt JL, Jones SW. 1993. Intracellular ATP and GTP are both required to preserve modulation of N-type calcium channel current by norepinephrine. *Pflügers Arch.* 423:472–79

139. Marriott I, Mason MJ. 1995. ATP depletion inhibits capacitative $Ca^{2+}$ entry in

rat thymic lymphocytes. *Am. J. Physiol.* 269:C766–74

140. Ashley RH. 1989. Activation and conductance properties of ryanodine-sensitive calcium channels from brain microsomal membranes incorporated into planar lipid bilayers. *J. Membr. Biol.* 111:179–89

141. Smith JS, Coronado R, Meissner G. 1986. Single channel measurements of the calcium release channel from skeletal muscle sarcoplasmic reticulum. Activation by $Ca^{2+}$ and ATP and modulation by $Mg^{2+}$. *J. Gen. Physiol.* 88:573–88

142. Bezprozvanny I, Ehrlich BE. 1995. The inositol 1,4,5-trisphosphate (InsP$_3$) receptor. *J. Membr. Biol.* 145:205–16

143. Benndorf K, Friedrich M, Hirche H. 1991. Alterations of ionic currents after reoxygenation in isolated cardiocytes of guinea-pigs. *Pflügers Arch.* 418:238–47

144. Friedrich M, Benndorf K, Schwalb M, Hirche H. 1990. Effects of anoxia on K and Ca currents in isolated guinea pig cardiocytes. *Pflügers Arch.* 416:207–9

145. Johnson BD, Byerly L. 1993. A cytoskeletal mechanism for $Ca^{2+}$ channel metabolic dependence and inactivation by intracellular $Ca^{2+}$. *Neuron* 10:797–804

146. Ballatori N, Truong AT, Jackson PS, Strange K, Boyer JL. 1995. ATP depletion and inactivation of an ATP-sensitive taurine channel by classic ion channel blockers. *Mol. Pharmacol.* 48:472–76

147. Jackson PS, Morrison R, Strange K. 1994. The volume-sensitive organic osmolyte-anion channel VSOAC is regulated by nonhydrolytic ATP binding. *Am. J. Physiol.* 267:C1203–9

148. Okada Y, Kubo M, Oiki S, Petersen CC, Tominaga M, et al. 1994. Properties of volume-sensitive $Cl^-$ channels in a human epithelial cell line. *Jpn. J. Physiol.* 44:S31–35

149. Meyer K, Korbmacher C. 1996. Cell swelling activates ATP-dependent voltage-gated chloride channels in M-1 mouse cortical collecting duct cells. *J. Gen. Physiol.* In press

150. Begault B, Anagnostopoulos T, Edelman A. 1993. ATP-regulated chloride conductance in endoplasmic reticulum (ER)-enriched pig pancreas microsomes. *Biochim. Biophys. Acta* 1152:319–27

151. Garty H, Edelman IS, Lindemann B. 1983. Metabolic regulation of apical sodium permeability in toad urinary bladder in the presence and absence of aldosterone. *J. Membr. Biol.* 74:15–24

152. Palmer LG, Edelman IS, Lindemann B. 1980. Current-voltage analysis of apical sodium transport in toad urinary bladder: effects of inhibitors of transport and metabolism. *J. Membr. Biol.* 57:59–71

153. Cantiello HF. 1995. Role of actin cytoskeleton on epithelial $Na^+$ channel regulation. *Kidney Int.* 48:970–84

154. Cantiello HF, Stow JL, Prat AG, Ausiello DA. 1991. Actin filaments regulate epithelial $Na^+$ channel activity. *Am. J. Physiol.* 261:C882–88

155. Prat AG, Bertorello AM, Ausiello DA, Cantiello HF. 1993. Activation of epithelial $Na^+$ channels by protein kinase A requires actin filaments. *Am. J. Physiol.* 265:C224–33

156. Bakhram KB, Prat AG, Cantiello HF, Ausiello DA, Fuller CM, et al. 1996. Regulation of epithelial sodium channels by short actin filaments. *J. Biol. Chem.* 271:17704–10

157. Prat AG, Xiao Y-F, Ausiello DA, Cantiello HF. 1995. cAMP-independent regulation of CFTR by the actin cytoskeleton. *Am. J. Physiol.* 268:C1552–61

158. Cantiello HF. 1995. Actin filaments stimulate the $Na^+$-$K^+$-ATPase. *Am. J. Physiol.* 269:F637–43

159. Aguilar-Bryan L, Nichols CG, Wechsler SW, Clement JP IV, Boyd AE III, et al. 1995. Cloning of the beta cell high-affinity sulfonylurea receptor: a regulator of insulin secretion. *Science* 268:372–73

160. Ramanadham S, Wolf MJ, Jett PA, Gross RW, Turk J. 1994. Characterization of an ATP-stimulatable Ca(2+)-independent phospholipase A2 from clonal insulin-secreting HIT cells and rat pancreatic islets: a possible molecular component of the beta-cell fuel sensor. *Biochemistry* 33:7442–52

161. Buser CA, Kim J, McLaughlin S, Peitzsch RM. 1995. Does the binding of clusters of basic residues to acidic lipids induce domain formation in membranes? *Mol. Membr. Biol.* 12:69–75

162. Vermuri R, Philipson KD. 1988. Phospholipid composition modulates the Na-Ca exchange activity of cardiac sarcolemma in reconstituted vesicles. *Biochim. Biophys. Acta* 939:503–8

163. Berberian G, Beaugé L. 1996. ATP stimulation of Na gradient-dependent Ca uptake in cardiac sarcolemma vesicles. *NY Acad. Sci.* 779:282–83

164. Reeves JP, Philipson KD. 1989. Sodium-calcium exchange activity in plasma membrane vesicles. In *Sodium-Calcium Exchange,* ed. TJA Allen, D Noble, H Reuter, pp. 27–53. New York: Oxford Univ. Press

165. Condrescu M, Gardner JP, Chernaya G, Aceto JF, Kroupis C, Reeves JP. 1995. ATP-dependent regulation of sodium-calcium exchange in Chinese hamster ovary cells transfected with the bovine cardiac sodium-calcium exchanger. *J. Biol. Chem.* 270:9137–46

166. Aderem A. 1995. The MARCKS family of protein kinase C substrates. *Biochem. Soc. Trans.* 23:587–91

*Annu. Rev. Physiol. 1997. 59:221–42*

# CHOLECYSTOKININ CELLS

*Rodger A. Liddle*
Department of Medicine, Duke University Medical Center and Durham VA Medical
Center, Durham, North Carolina 27710

KEY WORDS:    gastrointestinal hormone, radioimmunoassay, bioassay, cell culture

### ABSTRACT

Cholecystokinin (CCK) is an important hormonal regulator of the digestive process. CCK cells are concentrated in the proximal small intestine, and hormone is secreted into the blood upon the ingestion of food. The physiological actions of CCK include stimulation of pancreatic secretion and gallbladder contraction, regulation of gastric emptying, and induction of satiety. Therefore, in a highly coordinated manner, CCK regulates the ingestion, digestion, and absorption of nutrients. CCK is produced by two separate cell types: endocrine cells of the small intestine and various neurons in the gastrointestinal tract and central nervous system. Accordingly, CCK can function as either a hormone or a neuropeptide. This review focuses on the physiology of the CCK cell in the intestine and, in particular, on how the CCK cell is regulated to secrete its hormone product. The effects of ingested nutrients on the CCK cell and the intracellular messenger systems involved in controlling secretion are reviewed. A summary is provided of recent studies examining the electrophysiological properties of CCK cells and newly discovered proteins that act as releasing factors for CCK, which mediate feedback pathways critical for regulated secretion in the intact organism.

## Introduction

Cholecystokinin (CCK) was discovered in 1928 by Ivy & Oldberg based on the ability of intestinal extracts to stimulate gallbladder contraction when infused into dogs (1). In 1943, Harper & Raper recognized that similar intestinal extracts also stimulated pancreatic enzyme secretion and proposed the name pancreozymin (2). It was not until the active substance was purified and the amino acid sequence determined that CCK and pancreozymin were proven to be the same hormone that now goes by the name cholecystokinin (3).

In addition to the two biological actions described above, CCK has several other important activities. Among the most notable is its ability to induce

221

0066-4278/97/0315-0221$08.00

satiety and reduce food intake in experimental animals and humans (4–6). It also inhibits gastric emptying and gastric acid secretion and stimulates intestinal peristalsis. Defining the physiological actions of CCK has been greatly facilitated by the development of specific and potent antagonists of the CCK-A (A for alimentary origin) receptor. Each of the above actions ascribed to CCK arises from endogenous CCK, as shown in studies by which the response to a normal meal can be reversed by specific CCK-A receptor antagonists.

CCK release is stimulated by ingestion of food, with fats and protein the most potent secretagogues. CCK secretion is initiated when food leaves the stomach and enters the small intestine, and secretion continues until proteins, fats, and their metabolites have passed the upper small intestine.

CCK receptors have been identified on the gallbladder, pancreas, and stomach (7). Recent evidence indicates that specific CCK-A receptors are also present on peripheral autonomic afferent nerves that enable CCK to initiate certain neural reflexes. The specific site on which CCK acts to affect organ responses is still somewhat unclear. The best evidence for a purely endocrine role for CCK is regulation of gallbladder contraction, whereas other effects may be either neural or a combination of endocrine and neural actions. Nevertheless, the importance of CCK in regulating a variety of digestive processes must not be underestimated. CCK secreted locally or into the blood binds to specific receptors on the gallbladder, pancreas, stomach, or various nerves to stimulate gallbladder contraction, pancreatic enzyme secretion, delay gastric emptying, and regulate satiety (7). Therefore, in a highly regulated fashion, CCK coordinates the ingestion, digestion, and disposal of nutrients (8, 9).

## Peptide Structure

CCK was originally purified from porcine intestine as a 33-amino acid peptide (3). The hormone possesses an amidated carboxy-terminal pentapeptide, Gly-Trp-Asp-Met-Phe-NH$_2$, that is identical to that of gastrin. The carboxyl terminus of CCK is the biologically active portion of the hormone, and because of sequence similarity between CCK and gastrin, each hormone can interact with the receptor of the other (see receptor characterization below). Therefore, gastrin has slight CCK-like bioactivity and CCK possesses some, albeit weak, gastrin-like activity. The homology shared by the two peptides explains why antibodies raised against CCK often cross-react with gastrin. This overlapping cross-reactivity has been a considerable problem in developing radioimmunoassays for CCK, particularly because gastrin circulates in the blood at concentrations 10–100 times greater than those of CCK (10).

Since the discovery of CCK, multiple molecular forms have been identified in intestine, brain, and the circulation of multiple species (11–20). The octapeptide of CCK (CCK-8), consisting of the carboxy-terminal 8 amino acids of CCK,

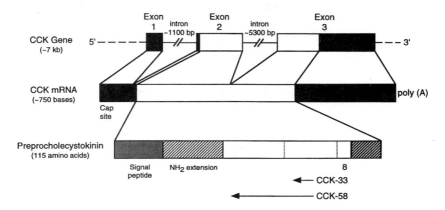

*Figure 1*   Structure of the CCK gene, complementary DNA and preprohormone. (Modified from Reference 8.)

is the most biologically potent small peptide of CCK that has been isolated. However, amino-terminal extended forms have been extracted from brain and intestine of the pig, dog, rat, and human. Using techniques to minimize protein degradation, recent studies have demonstrated that the most abundant molecular form of CCK in these species is CCK-58. Intermediate-sized peptides of 39, 33, 25, 22, 18, 8, 7, 5, and 4 amino acids have been isolated from several species.

## CCK Gene Structure and Expression

The complementary DNA structures have been determined for rat, mouse, pig, and human CCK (21–24). The structure of the rat cDNA is shown schematically in Figure 1. The 345-nucleotide mRNA encodes a 115-amino acid precursor consisting of a 20-amino acid signal peptide, a 25-amino acid spacer peptide, CCK-58, and a 12-amino acid extension at the carboxyl terminus.

The genes for CCK isolated for mouse, rat, and human reveal remarkable conservation (22–25). Each consists of ~7 kilobases containing three exons, the second and third of which encode the prepropeptide. In all species, only a single gene encodes CCK. The human CCK gene is located on chromosome 3 in the 3q12-3pter region (26, 27).

The mature CCK mRNA is ~750 bases. It is expressed in brain and intestine in mature animals in nearly equivalent amounts. CCK mRNA is most abundant in the cerebral cortex and duodenum. In the mouse, at birth, CCK mRNA levels are relatively high in the intestine but very low in brain. Over the first two weeks of life, levels decrease in the gut and increase in brain. These changes correlate with levels of immunoreactive CCK protein in the respective tissues. Intestinal expression of CCK mRNA is modified by diet. CCK mRNA levels decline in either fasting rats or rats fed a diet that does not stimulate CCK secretion (28). CCK mRNA expression increases with feeding under conditions that also stimulate CCK secretion. However, it is possible to stimulate CCK secretion without affecting CCK gene expression by administration of exogenous bombesin (29). Somatostatin has been shown to inhibit CCK gene expression (30).

## Structure-Activity Relationships

To function as a CCK molecule, a peptide must have the sequence Trp-Asp-Met-Phe-NH$_2$. However, because this sequence is identical to the the carboxyl terminus of gastrin, this peptide does not confer CCK-like specificity. In order to bind specifically to CCK receptors, CCK peptides must be extended to 7 amino acids. Full potency is not achieved unless the tyrosine residue at position 7 from the carboxyl terminus is sulfated (31). Although sulfation is unusual for hormones, it is critical for biological potency of CCKs. The unsulfated form of CCK is ~1000-fold less active than its sulfated counterpart. In contrast, sulfation occurs only 50% of the time in gastrin biosynthesis and is not important for its biological activity.

Molecular forms ranging in size from CCK-8 to CCK-33 appear to be of similar biological potency on pancreatic acinar cells (32). However, CCK-58 is somewhat less potent on a molar basis than CCK-8 and is less immunoreactive with CCK antibodies (33). This diminished activity is likely due to the structure of CCK-58, whereby the amino-terminal end shields the biologically active carboxy-terminal end of CCK from interacting with CCK receptors or C-terminal directed antibodies. Cleavage of CCK-58 with trypsin restores both the full biological potency and immunoreactivity to that of CCK-8 (34). Although CCK-58 is the major molecular form in intestine, brain, and the circulation of many species, identification of multiple smaller forms of CCK in circulation, even under conditions that preserve CCK-58, suggests that intracellular processing of CCK occurs to produce small forms of CCK that are secreted into the blood.

## CCK Receptors

CCK exerts its biological effects by binding to specific receptors on its target tissues. Originally receptors were characterized on pancreatic acinar cells, islets, gallbladder, and brain by radioligand binding and autoradiography (31). In the pancreas and gallbladder, CCK bound with an affinity that was ~1,000-fold greater than that of either unsulfated CCK or gastrin. These receptors were termed CCK-A. In the brain, however, CCK and gastrin bound with similar affinities.   These receptors became known as CCK-B (B for brain origin). Along with these two types of CCK receptors, a third related type, "gastrin receptor," which exhibited binding properties similar to those of the brain CCK receptor, was believed to transmit the biological actions of gastrin in the stomach.  However, with recent cloning and expression of the CCK receptor cDNAs, it has become clear that there are only two CCK receptors, A and B, and that the gastrin receptor is identical to the CCK-B receptor.

The CCK-A receptor complementary DNA was cloned following purification of the receptor protein from rat pancreatic acinar cells (35).  The cDNA encodes a seven transmembrane protein typical of G protein-coupled receptors.  It consists of 444 amino acids, which when expressed in transfected cells, demonstrates high affinity for sulfated CCK and much lower affinity for unsulfated CCK or gastrin.

The CCK-B receptor cDNA was identified by expression cloning from canine gastric parietal cells (36).  When expressed in transfected cells, the CCK-B receptor binds CCK and gastrin with similar affinities and demonstrates a ligand-induced increase in intracellular calcium.  When the cDNAs for the rat and human receptors were cloned, it was demonstrated that CCK receptor cloned from brain was identical to the gastrin receptor in the stomach (37).  The deduced amino acid sequences of the rat CCK-A and canine CCK-B receptors are $\sim$50% homologous.

## CCK Cells

As is typical of many gastrointestinal hormones, CCK is produced by endocrine cells of the intestinal mucosa, which are concentrated in the duodenum and proximal jejunum. A gradient of cell density exists such that CCK cell abundance is greatest in the proximal small intestine and less in the distal intestine. Endocrine cells containing CCK are flask-shaped, with their apical surfaces oriented toward the lumen of the gut (38, 39) (Figure 2).  In this position, microvillus-like processes come in contact with lumenal contents.  Secretory granules, which are $\sim$250 nm in size and contain CCK, are concentrated around the basolateral surface of the cell. It is this orientation that allows food or other factors within the intestinal lumen to interact with the apical surface of the CCK cell and initiate a series of as yet unknown intracellular signaling events that ultimately result in secretion of CCK from the basal surface of the cell into the blood. According to the Wiesbaden classification, CCK cells, by their ultrastructural characteristics, have been officially named I cells (40).  Where examined in experimental animals or humans, I cells have not been shown to contain other gut hormones. Outside of the intestinal tract, CCK is synthesized by a subpopulation of pituitary and adrenal meduallary cells (41, 42).  The function of CCK in these locations is unknown.

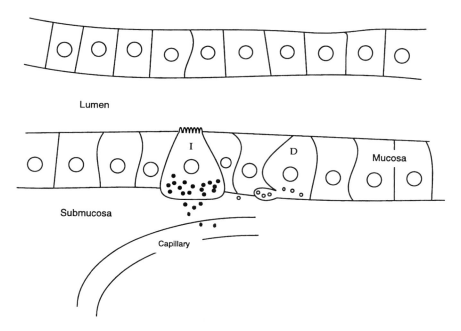

*Figure 2* Schematic diagram of a CCK (I) cell in the upper small intestine. Note that its apical surface is exposed to the lumen of the gut where it may sample lumenal contents (9). Somatostatin-containing (D) cells may influence CCK release.

CCK is expressed in neurons of the brain and gut and as such is a member of the growing family of "brain-gut peptides." In the central nervous system, CCK is distributed in neurons throughout the brain. It is found in highest concentrations in the cerebral cortex (43, 44). CCK cell bodies are localized in layers II–VI and concentrated in layers II and III. In the brain, CCK is colocalized with dopamine in neurons that arise in the mesencephalon and project to the limbic forebrain. CCK neurons also project to the ventromedial hypothalamus, which may be important for central effects of CCK in the regulation of satiety.

In the peripheral autonomic nervous system, CCK-containing neurons are found in the myenteric plexus, submucous plexus, circular muscle layers of the distal small intestine and colon, in the pancreas surrounding the islets of Langerhans, and in the celiac plexus and vagus nerve (45). In the intestine, CCK stimulates release of acetylcholine in postganglionic neurons of Auerbach's and Meissner's plexi and causes smooth muscle contraction. Because CCK stimulates glucagon and insulin release, it is likely that postganglionic cells terminating around islets of Langerhans play a role in modifying $\alpha$ and $\beta$ cell function (46).

## CCK Release

With the development of sensitive and specific radioimmunoassays and bioassays for measuring blood levels of CCK, there is now general agreement that fasting levels of CCK in most mammals are ~1 pM and increase to ~5–10 pM following strong endogenous stimulation (12, 47–50).

CCK release is stimulated by ingestion of food. Before the development of specific in vitro assays for measuring blood levels of CCK, estimates of CCK release were made by inference from examination of target tissue responses such as pancreatic secretion or gallbladder contraction. Although it was not possible to distinguish between hormonal and neural influences, substantial insights were gained about the food components that stimulate pancreactic secretion. Digestion products of fat and protein were found to be the most potent stimulants of secretion (51). Effective stimulation required that triglycerides were hydrolyzed to fatty acids, with chain lengths of 9 or more carbons (52, 53). However, it is important to recognize that not all effects on pancreatic secretion are attributable to circulating CCK because other hormones or neural CCK also may be involved (54).

In most species, for protein to be an effective stimulant of CCK release, its digestion is required to effectively stimulate pancreatic secretion or gallbladder contraction (55–57). Of the amino acids, tryptophan and phenylalanine are the most potent stimulants of canine or human pancreatic secretion. Secretion is most vigorous when the proximal (relative to the distal) half of the small intestine is perfused with nutrients. This finding is consistent with the abundance of CCK cells in the proximal intestine.

In the rat, intact protein is an effective stimulant of CCK release. This is likely due to the ability of protein to preserve the activity of an endogenously produced CCK-releasing factor that is active in the intestinal lumen to modulate CCK secretion (58). Although this regulatory system has been best studied in the rat, it is also present in other species. Regulation of CCK secretion by releasing factors is discussed in more detail below.

The effects of neural factors on CCK secretion have been a matter of controversy but clarified somewhat by the application of specific CCK radioimmunoassays. Although the neuropeptide bombesin is known to affect pancreatic secretion through bombesin receptors on pancreatic acini, only recently has it been shown to directly stimulate CCK release (59).

Vagotomy alters pancreatic and gallbladder responses to dietary stimulation. Therefore, indirect estimates of CCK secretion in vagotomized animals have been limited because the responsiveness of the pancreas or gallbladder could be the result of either changes in CCK release or the effects of vagotomy. Studies using radioimmunoassay measurements have shown that circulating CCK levels were unaltered in dogs administered oleate, despite impaired pancreatic and gallbladder responses (60). In vagotomized subjects, plasma CCK responses were greater following a liquid meal, perhaps because of a more rapid delivery of nutrients to the small intestine following vagotomy (61). In sum, these experiments suggest that vagal innervation does not affect CCK directly, but may alter the target tissue responses to stimulation by CCK.

## Regulation of CCK Secretion by Releasing Factors

The exact mechanisms by which foods cause CCK secretion have yet to be elucidated, but it is likely that multiple factors are involved. The location of the CCK cell in the intestinal mucosa, with its apical surface exposed to the lumen of the gut, provides an opportunity for foods or other factors to interact directly with the CCK cell to stimulate hormone secretion. However, it is not known if food directly interacts with CCK cells to stimulate secretion. Substantial evidence has indicated that at least one mechanism causing CCK release involves endogenously produced releasing factors that are secreted into the lumen of the intestine and under the proper conditions stimulate CCK secretion (62, 63). The rationale for their existence and description of at least two types of CCK-releasing factors are summarized below.

Experiments in rats in the 1970s demonstrated that inactivation or removal of proteolytic activity from the proximal small intestine by either instillation of trypsin inhibitors or diversion of bile-pancreatic juice from the intestine produced a large increase in pancreatic exocrine secretion (64). In addition, intraduodenal infusion of trypsin in the absence of bile-pancreatic juice in the intestine suppressed pancreatic enzyme secretion (65). These observations suggested that a negative feedback mechanism existed whereby pancreatic secretion was controlled by the presence or absence of protease activity within the lumen of the small intestine.

This concept has been used to explain how dietary proteins stimulate pancreatic secretion. In rats, intact proteins are more potent stimulants of CCK release than hydrolyzed proteins or amino acids, suggesting that the ability of dietary protein to stimulate the pancreas is related to its ability to serve as a proteolytic substrate (66). In this regard, dietary proteins are similar to trypsin inhibitors when instilled into the gut because they both bind trypsin and cause pancreatic secretion.

It was proposed that a trypsin-sensitive releasing factor is secreted into the lumen of the intestine and stimulates CCK release (67). In the presence of active proteases such as trypsin, this releasing factor would be degraded. However, when other proteins or potential substrates for trypsin are present in the gut (such as after eating a meal), the putative releasing factor would be protected and able to interact with CCK-secreting cells of the intestine (Figure 3).

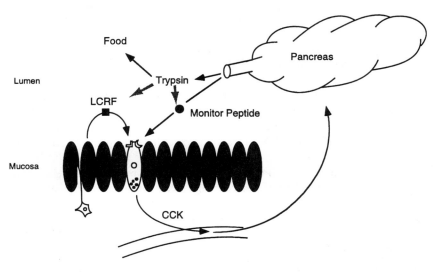

*Figure 3*  CCK release from enteric endocrine cells is regulated by lumenal intestinal CCK-releasing factors. It is proposed that both the pancreatic and intestinal peptides are secreted into the intestinal lumen and interact directly with the CCK cell through specific cell surface receptors to initiate a cascade of intracellular signaling events resulting in CCK release. Under basal conditions, trypsin has the potential to degrade the releasing factors. However, food (or trypsin inhibitor), which also serves as a substrate for trypsin, may temporarily bind trypsin and prevent the degradation of the intestinal-releasing factor or monitor peptide, thus allowing them to stimulate the CCK cell. (Modified from Reference 58.)

There is now strong evidence that a feedback mechanism exists in the chicken, pig, rat, and human, and probably is present in the dog (64, 68–76). In humans, intraduodenal perfusion of phenylalanine not only stimulates pancreatic secretion, but also CCK release; these effects are blocked by simultaneous infusion of trypsin, indicating that negative feedback regulation of CCK is important in this species (77).

The mechanisms regulating the production and secretion of an intestinal CCK-releasing factor are largely unknown. It is controversial whether cholinergic innervation is important for secretion of the releasing peptide. In anesthetized rats, atropine prevents the spontaneous increase in pancreatic secretion caused by diversion of bile-pancreatic juice (78); however, in other studies in conscious rats, atropine has no effect on the increase in pancreatic secretion stimulated by intraduodenal infusion of either dietary protein or trypsin inhibitors (79, 80) or on plasma CCK levels that are appropriately elevated in atropine-treated, conscious rats following bile-pancreatic juice diversion (81).

Therefore, a precise role for cholinergic regulation of CCK-releasing factor secretion remains to be established. It has been demonstrated recently that somatostatin inhibits the elevation in plasma CCK levels normally seen in bile-pancreatic juice-diverted rats by inhibiting the release of a CCK-releasing factor (82).

Regulation of a CCK-releasing factor may also differ among species. In humans, it is postulated that lumenal stimulation by nutrients such as amino acids or fatty acids is necessary to stimulate secretion of the putative CCK-releasing factor (69, 83, 84). This situation differs from the rat, in which spontaneous secretion of CCK-releasing factor occurs and maximal CCK and pancreatic secretion result from removing proteases from the proximal intestine.

Very recently, two putative CCK-releasing factors have been chemically characterized. A novel 8169-kDa protein called lumenal cholecystokinin-releasing factor (LCRF) was purified from rat pancreatic juice (85). LCRF stimulates pancreatic secretion and CCK release when instilled into the intestine. Moreover, this increase in CCK release is blocked by immunoneutralization with LCRF-specific antisera. It is possible that diazepam-binding inhibitor (DBI), which when extracted from porcine intestine was found to possess CCK-releasing activity, is a second CCK-releasing peptide (86). The relative contributions of LCRF and DBI to regulation of CCK secretion following ingestion of a meal remain to be determined.

## Characterization of a CCK-Releasing Factor from Pancreatic Juice: Monitor Peptide

In 1986, a 61-amino acid protein purified from pancreatic juice was found to stimulate CCK secretion when introduced into the lumen of rat intestine (87). This protein was named monitor peptide for its ability to monitor the intraduodenal environment for protein digestion (88, 89). Because of its similarity to other pancreatic trypsin inhibitors, monitor peptide is also known as pancreatic secretory trypsin inhibitor-I (PSTI-61); it is distinct from a 56-amino acid pancreatic trypsin inhibitor known as PSTI-II (PSTI-56) that shares 66% sequence homology with monitor peptide but does not stimulate intestinal CCK release and pancreatic secretion (90).

Monitor peptide is produced by pancreatic acinar cells and is secreted into pancreatic juice where, upon reaching the intestine, it stimulates CCK release. This mechanism for stimulating the CCK cell requires some level of pancreatic secretion to be effective. Therefore, once pancreatic secretion has been initiated, monitor peptide in pancreatic juice would tend to reinforce or perpetuate further secretion via release of CCK. In contrast, intestinal CCK-releasing factors differ from monitor peptide because they are of intestinal rather than pancreatic origin and are present in the gut under basal conditions (91). Lumenal-releasing factors are believed to mediate much of the CCK secretion that results from nutrient ingestion, although it is clear that multiple mechanisms exist to ensure proper regulation of CCK release.

In isolated rat intestinal mucosal cells, monitor peptide stimulates CCK release in a concentration- and calcium-dependent manner, suggesting that monitor peptide has a direct effect on CCK cells and that calcium may serve as an intracellular messenger in monitor peptide-mediated CCK secretion (92). The ability of monitor peptide to elevate $[Ca^{2+}]_i$ and stimulate CCK secretion has been used to enrich CCK cells from the intestine by fluorescence-activated cell sorting (93). Enriched CCK cells respond to stimulation by monitor peptide, dibutyryl cAMP, membrane depolarizing concentrations of potassium chloride, and calcium ionophore.

A putative cell surface receptor that binds monitor peptide has been partially characterized in intestinal mucosal cells of the rat jejunum (94). Autoradiography of an affinity cross-linked complex of [125]I-labeled monitor peptide and its binding site identified a potential receptor with a molecular mass of 33 or 53 kDa in its reduced or nonreduced form, respectively, providing evidence that monitor peptide binds directly to receptors on enteric cells of the small intestine. A proposed scheme for the regulation of CCK by the two classes of lumenal-releasing factors is shown in Figure 4.

## Cellular Regulation of CCK Secretion

The precise signaling pathways involved with CCK secretion are unknown. Studies in isolated canine intestinal mucosal cells enriched in CCK demonstrated that forskolin and cAMP analogues stimulate CCK release (95, 96). Moreover, forskolin-activated secretion was blocked by somatostatin. Stimulation of protein kinase C (PKC) by the phorbol ester, $\beta$-phorbol-12-myristate-13-acetate (PMA), also caused significant CCK secretion, as did exposure to L-phenylalanine.

Recent investigations using the intestinal CCK-containing cell line STC-1 have been useful for examining the receptors on CCK cells and the potential second messenger pathways involved in regulating secretion. The bombesin family of neuropeptides, including gastrin-releasing peptide (GRP), have potent CCK stimulatory effects in animals (29, 97–99) and in organ preparations (100). Although presumed to be a direct effect, the identification of GRP receptors in CCK-secreting cells (by radioligand binding and mRNA analysis) established that CCK cells possess bombesin-like receptors (101). As a G protein-coupled receptor that couples to and signals through the phosphoinositide cascade, generating inositol trisphosphate ($IP_3$), bombesin causes an increase in intracellular calcium concentration ($[Ca^{2+}]_i$) (101). It is believed that this $[Ca^{2+}]_i$ increase is important for evoking CCK secretion because hormone release is reduced

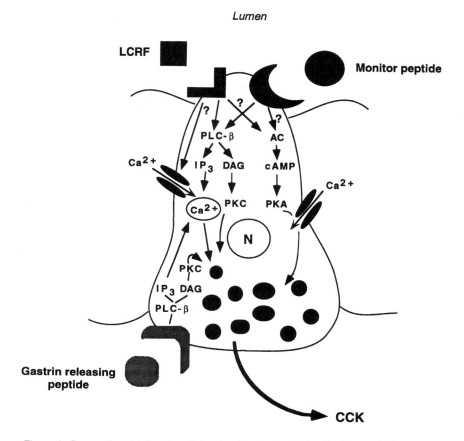

*Figure 4* Proposed model for intracellular signaling in the CCK cell. Because both adenylyl cyclase and phosphoinositide cascades exist in CCK cells, it is possible that potential secretagogues such as bombesin and intralumenal-releasing factors bind to cell surface receptors and initiate a series of signaling events to ultimately cause CCK secretion. Secretion may result through (*a*) activation of phospholipase C-$\beta$ with subsequent generation of IP$_3$ and diacylglycerol (DAG) and subsequent increases in [Ca$^{2+}$]$_i$ and activation of PKC, respectively; (*b*) activation of adenylyl cyclase with subsequent elevation in cAMP concentrations and activation of protein kinase A (PKA); or (*c*) some yet unknown pathway, perhaps involving the activation of calcium channels, that appears to be critical for sustained CCK secretion. The locations of the putative receptors for LCRF, monitor peptide, and GRP are portrayed on the lumenal and basolateral surfaces of the CCK cell, respectively, solely because the corresponding ligands are located in either the intestinal lumen or enteric nerves. A calcium influx pathway can be affected by multiple second messengers. (Modified from Reference 58.)

by exposure to calcium-free media or treatment with L-type calcium channel blockers (59).

Although maneuvers that increase intracellular cAMP have been shown to stimulate CCK release, little is known about the mechanisms for increasing cAMP levels in CCK cells. It was recently demonstrated, using STC-1 cells, that $\beta$-adrenergic receptors on CCK cells effectively coupled to the production of cAMP, resulting in CCK release (102). Interestingly, the $\beta$-adrenergic agonist isoproterenol increased $[Ca^{2+}]_i$, coincident with stimulating hormone secretion. Both CCK secretion and the elevation in $[Ca^{2+}]_i$ were reduced by treatment with the L-type calcium channel blocker diltiazem, indicating that $\beta$ receptors on CCK cells are coupled to the production of cAMP, which may stimulate CCK release through a calcium-dependent process.

The manner by which dietary stimulants affect CCK secretion are largely unknown.  A study of isolated intestinal cells in vitro indicates that dietary proteins which cause CCK release in animals do not have stimulatory effects in perfusion models (103). These findings are consistent with the proposal that effects of protein on CCK release are mediated by an intestinal-releasing factor. However, in native CCK cells and STC-1 cells, L-phenylalanine stimulated CCK release and increased cytosolic calcium levels (in a dose-dependent manner) (104). Both effects were blocked by diltiazem, indicating that phenylalanine stimulates release of CCK by a calcium-dependent process involving a calcium influx pathway in the cell.

The results of these experiments emphasize that influx of extracellular calcium from outside to inside the cell is a common feature of CCK secretion initiated by a variety of mechanisms. The critical role of $[Ca^{2+}]_i$ seems to apply whether the inciting event is due to monitor peptide, bombesin, isoproterenol, or phenylalanine stimulation.  The relationship between intracellular cAMP and calcium signaling pathways becomes more apparent when it is observed that phosphodiesterase inhibitor IBMX not only stimulates CCK release in STC-1 cells, but also increases cytosolic calcium (105). Moreover, the calcium-calmodulin kinase II inhibitor KN-62 markedly reduces IBMX-stimulated secretion and $[Ca^{2+}]_i$, suggesting that cAMP may activate diltiazem-sensitive calcium channels by a calmodulin-dependent process. This conclusion is supported by the finding that the stimulatory effects of forskolin on CCK release are similarly blocked by KN-62 (106). These studies provide evidence that both the adenylyl cyclase and phosphoinositide signaling cascades are active in CCK cells and may be coupled to ligand occupation of cell surface receptors to initiate intracellular events leading to CCK secretion (Figure 4). The two signaling cascades are linked by calcium-calmodulin kinase II activity and regulation of intracellular calcium concentration.

## Role of Ion Channels in CCK Secretion

In many endocrine cells, hormone secretion is coupled to changes in ion channel activity. One of the most apparent relationships is the dependence upon plasma membrane potential. Secretion of insulin, thyrotropin, growth hormone, prolactin, calcitonin, secretin, somatostatin, and cholecystokinin are all induced by solutions containing high potassium concentrations, indicating that the resting potential of these secretory cells is at least partially determined by the activity of potassium channels (107–111).

Models for studying ion channel activity and endocrine secretion have included tissue preparations, dispersed cells, and clonal populations of cells. CCK cells are found scattered in the intestinal mucosa, making it difficult to obtain a uniform population of purified or enriched endocrine cells. Recently, an intestinal CCK-producing cell line (STC-1) was developed that secretes several gastrointestinal hormones, of which CCK is the most abundant (112, 113). STC-1 cells have been used as a model for intestinal CCK secretion because identical stimuli release CCK from dispersed native intestinal cells and STC-1 cells (105, 111, 114–116). Electrophysiological studies have been performed using STC-1 cells, which provide insight into the signal transduction pathways that are linked to ion channel activity and CCK secretion.

Initial patch-clamp recordings from STC-1 cells revealed an outwardly rectifying, calcium-independent, basal whole-cell current that was largely attributable to potassium channel activity (111). The current reversal potential was $-27 \pm 3$ mV in studies where the only ionic species with a negative reversal potential was potassium. The potassium channel blocker $BaCl_2$ rapidly depolarized the reversal potential toward 0 mV and decreased the magnitude of whole-cell current, which was consistent with potassium channel activity playing a predominant role in regulating membrane potential.

At least three types of potassium currents have been identified in STC-1 cells (111, 114–116). One potassium channel is calcium dependent and is activated by secretagogues such as bombesin or thapsigargin that increase intracellular calcium (59, 111). A second potassium current is inwardly rectifying and is inhibited by elevation of cytoplasmic ATP levels. Exposure of the cytoplasmic surface of inside-out membrane patches to ATP has been shown to close this $K_{ATP}$ channel. In addition, the open probability of the $K_{ATP}$ channel was found to be voltage independent. These studies raise the possibility that metabolic processes that significantly alter intracellular ATP concentrations may affect total potassium permeability and membrane potential. Interestingly, glucose has been shown to stimulate CCK release both in vivo and in isolated cell preparations and has significant inhibitory effects on $K_{ATP}$ channel activity (115, 117). In STC-1 cells, glucose and the $K_{ATP}$ channel inhibitor disopyramide inhibit basal $K^+$ channel activity as measured by $^{86}$Rb efflux experiments (115). These studies demonstrate that $K_{ATP}$ channels are open under basal conditions and contribute to the resting membrane potential. Exposure to increased extracellular glucose concentrations closes $K_{ATP}$ channels and causes membrane depolarization. In both native mouse intestinal CCK cells and STC-1 cells, glucose and disopyramide stimulate CCK release, effects that are blocked by the L-type calcium channel blocker diltiazem. Therefore, it appears that $K_{ATP}$ channels are important contributors to the basal membrane potential in CCK-secreting cells and that inhibition of $K_{ATP}$ channels depolarizes the plasma membrane, causing activation of L-type calcium channels that leads to an increase in $[Ca^{2+}]_i$, ultimately producing CCK secretion.

In some species, amino acids are potent stimulants of CCK secretion (12). In particular, tryptophan and phenylalanine produce marked elevation in circulating CCK levels when they are administered into the stomach or duodenum. However, it is not known how amino acids actually affect the CCK cell to stimulate secretion. In vitro, phenylalanine exposure to STC-1 cells causes hormone release (104, 105). This effect is concentration dependent and the secretory response is associated with a concomitant increase in cytoplasmic calcium concentration. The pattern of calcium fluorescence following phenylalanine exposure is a gradual increase over 20 min, similar to the pattern observed with other secretagogues that open calcium channels (102, 105). The observation that diltiazem blocks both the phenylalanine-stimulated increase in $[Ca^{2+}]_i$ and CCK secretion indicates that the changes in $[Ca^{2+}]_i$ are the result of opening of L-type calcium channels. In contrast to glucose, which inhibits $^{86}$Rb efflux, phenylalanine has no effect on $^{86}$Rb efflux, indicating that its activation of calcium channels is not secondary to inhibition of potassium channel activity and depolarization of the plasma membrane. Patch-clamp recordings from cell-attached membrane patches confirm that phenylalanine activates calcium channel activity; however, the exact manner by which phenylalanine causes calcium channel activation and CCK release is unknown (104). Whether an extracellular site is involved or cotransport of phenylalanine into the cell is required for calcium channel activation will be important areas of future investigation.

Considerable evidence indicates the importance of $[Ca^{2+}]_i$ in signaling CCK secretion. First, the calcium channel opener Bay K 8644 was observed to activate calcium channels in STC-1 cells (118). Second, agents that inhibit $K_{ATP}$ channels (e.g. glucose, disopyramide, phenylalanine), or secretagogues that act through cell surface receptors (e.g. bombesin), all increased $[Ca^{2+}]_i$. Moreover, CCK secretion was induced by these agents and was blocked by the L-type calcium channel blockers diltiazem or nifedipine.

The importance of calcium signaling in CCK secretion led to studies designed to determine its relationship with other second messengers such as cAMP. It had been well documented that CCK release can be stimulated either by agents that elevate intracellular cAMP levels or by treatment with cAMP analogues (95). However, recently it has become evident in STC-1 cells that CCK secretion induced by cAMP can be blocked by diltiazem. Other evidence invoking an important role for calcium in the cAMP pathway was the observation that elevation of cAMP was associated with an elevation in $[Ca^{2+}]_i$. To examine the mechanism for this effect, the catalytic subunit of PKA was added to the cytoplasmic surface of inside-out membrane patches. Under these conditions, PKA activated calcium channels, suggesting that the effect of cAMP on calcium channel activity was likely through PKA (105). Therefore, it was extremely interesting when it was found that a selective calcium-calmodulin kinase II (Cam KII) inhibitor blocked the cAMP-mediated increase in $[Ca^{2+}]_i$ and inhibited CCK secretion. Together these observations indicate that phosphorylation events mediated by PKA and Cam KII are involved in calcium channel activation by the cAMP second messenger pathway.

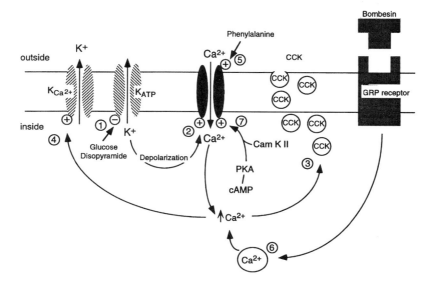

*Figure 5*  Interrelationship between ion channel activity and CCK secretion. See text for detailed description. A portion of the cell membrane is illustrated showing the extracellular (outside) and cytoplasmic (inside) surfaces. Ion channels for potassium ($K_{ATP}$ or $KCa^{2+}$) or calcium are shown with the directional gradient for ion flow. Whether phenylalanine affects calcium channel activity from an extracellular or cytoplasmic location is unknown.

To date, the electrophysiological events described for CCK secretion can be summarized by the diagram in Figure 5. Pharmacological, secretory, and electrophysiological studies have shown that potassium channel activity is important for the generation and maintenance of resting membrane potential in CCK-secreting cells. A decrease in potassium conductance, such as that which occurs by closure of $K_{ATP}$ channels (1), causes depolarization of the plasma membrane, which activates voltage-sensitive (L-type) calcium channels (2). The corresponding increase in $[Ca^{2+}]_i$ serves to trigger CCK release (3) and activate a second family of potassium channels (4). Stimulation of calcium-activated potassium channels serves to hyperpolarize the plasma membrane, thus restoring the basal membrane potential. As shown in the diagram, calcium channels may also be opened by amino acids (e.g. phenylalanine) (5) or through ligand-receptor interactions that couple to the phosphoinositide cascade (e.g. GRP or bombesin) (6). Increases in cAMP levels, which may occur by other receptor-initiated events, activate calcium channels through interaction of PKA with a channel or a closely associated membrane protein (7). Cyclic AMP-mediated activation of calcium channels is dependent upon Cam KII, which indicates that at least two phosphorylation events are necessary for cAMP-stimulated activity.

ACKNOWLEDGMENTS

This work was supported by United States Public Health Service grant DK 38626, the Department of Veterans Affairs, and the Stedman Nutrition Center.

*Literature Cited*

1. Ivy AC, Oldberg E. 1928. A hormone mechanism for gallbladder contraction and evacuation. *Am. J. Physiol.* 65:599–613
2. Harper AA, Raper HS. 1943. Pancreozymin, a stimulant of secretion of pancreatic enzymes in extracts of the small intestine. *J. Physiol.* 102:115–25
3. Mutt V, Jorpes JE. 1968. Structure of porcine cholecystokinin-pancreozymin. Cleavage with thrombin and with trypsin. *Eur. J. Biochem.* 6:156–62
4. Gibbs J, Young RC, Smith GP. 1973. Cholecystokinin decreases food intake in rats. *J. Comp. Physiol. Psychol.* 84:488–95
5. Smith GP, Gibbs J. 1985. The satiety effect of cholecystokinin: recent progress and current problems. *Ann. NY Acad. Sci.* 448:417–23
6. Smith GP, Gibbs J. 1994. Satiating effect

of cholecystokinin. *Ann. NY Acad. Sci.* 713:236–41
7. Mutt V. 1988. Secretin and cholecystokinin. In *Gastrointestinal Hormones,* ed. V Mutt, pp. 251–320. San Diego: Academic
8. Liddle RA. 1994. Cholecystokinin. In *Gut Peptides: Biochemistry and Physiology,* eds. JH Walsh, GJ Dockray, pp. 175–216. New York: Raven
9. Rehfeld JF. 1989. Cholecystokinin. In *Handbook of Physiology: The Gastrointestinal System. Volume II. Neural and Endocrine Biology,* ed. GM Makhlouf, pp. 337–358. New York: Oxford Univ. Press
10. Andersen BN, de Magistris L, Rehfeld JF. 1983. Radioimmunochemical quantitation of sulphated and non-sulphated gastrins in biological fluids. *Clin. Chim. Acta* 127:29–39
11. Liddle RA, Goldfine ID, Williams JA.

1984. Bioassay of plasma cholecystokinin in rats: effects of food, trypsin inhibitor, and alcohol. *Gastroenterology* 87:542–49

12. Liddle RA, Goldfine ID, Rosen MS, Taplitz RA, Williams JA. 1985. Cholecystokinin bioactivity in human plasma: molecular forms, responses to feeding, and relationship to gallbladder contraction. *J. Clin. Invest.* 75:1144–52

13. Rehfeld JF, Holst JJ, Jensen SL. 1982. The molecular nature of vascularly released cholecystokinin from the isolated perfused porcine duodenum. *Regul. Pept.* 3:15–28

14. Cantor P, Rehfeld JF. 1987. The molecular nature of cholecystokinin in human plasma. *Clin. Chim. Acta* 168:153–58

15. Jansen JBMJ, Lamers CBHW. 1983. Molecular forms of cholecystokinin in human plasma during infusion of bombesin. *Life Sci.* 33:2197–205

16. Kothary PC, Vinik AI, Owyang C, Fiddian-Green RG. 1983. Immunochemical studies of molecular heterogeneity of cholecystokinin in duodenal perfusates and plasma in humans. *J. Biol. Chem.* 258:2856–63

17. Eberlein GA, Eysselein VE, Hesse WH, Goebell H, Schaefer M, Reeve JR Jr. 1987. Detection of cholecystokinin-58 in human blood by inhibition of degradation. *Am. J. Physiol.* 253:G477–82

18. Zhou ZZ, Eng J, Pan YCE, Chang M, Hulmes JD, et al. 1985. Unique cholecystokinin peptides isolated from guinea pig intestine. *Peptides* 6:337–41

19. Eng J, Li H-R, Yalow RS. 1990. Purification of bovine cholecystokinin-58 and sequencing of its N-terminus. *Regul. Pept.* 30:15–19

20. Muller JE, Straus E, Yalow RS. 1977. Cholecystokinin and its COOH-terminal octapeptide in the pig brain. *Proc. Natl. Acad. Sci. USA* 74:3035–37

21. Deschenes RJ, Lorenz LJ, Haun RS, Roos BA, Collier KJ, Dixon JE. 1984. Cloning and sequence analysis of a cDNA encoding rat preprocholecystokinin. *Proc. Natl. Acad. Sci. USA* 81:726–30

22. Gubler U, Chua AO, Hoffman BJ, Collier KJ, Eng J. 1984. Cloned cDNA to cholecystokinin mRNA predicts an identical preprocholecystokinin in pig brain and gut. *Proc. Natl. Acad. Sci. USA* 81:4307–10

23. Friedman J, Schneider BS, Powell D. 1985. Differential expression of the mouse cholecystokinin gene during brain and gut development. *Proc. Natl. Acad. Sci. USA* 82:5593–97

24. Takahashi Y, Kato K, Hayashizaki Y, Wakabayashi T, Ohtsuka E, et al. 1985. Molecular cloning of the human cholecystokinin gene by use of a synthetic probe containing deoxyinosine. *Proc. Natl. Acad. Sci. USA* 82:1931–35

25. Deschenes RJ, Haun RS, Funckes CL, Dixon JE. 1985. A gene encoding rat cholecystokinin. *J. Biol. Chem.* 260: 1280–86

26. Lund T, GeurtsvanKessel AHM, Haun S, Dixon JE. 1986. The genes for human gastrin and cholecystokinin are located on different chromosomes. *Hum. Genet.* 73:77–80

27. Takahashi Y, Fukushige S, Murotsu T, Matsubara K. 1986. Structure of human cholecystokinin gene and its chromosomal location. *Gene* 50:353–60

28. Kanayama S, Liddle RA. 1991. Influence of food deprivation on intestinal cholecystokinin and somatostatin. *Gastroenterology* 100:909–15

29. Kanayama S, Liddle RA. 1991. Regulation of intestinal cholecystokinin and somatostatin mRNA by bombesin in rats. *Am. J. Physiol.* 261:G71–77

30. Kanayama S, Liddle RA. 1990. Somatostatin regulates duodenal cholecystokinin and somatostatin messenger RNA. *Am. J. Physiol.* 258:G358–64

31. Williams JA. 1982. Cholecystokinin: a hormone and a neurotransmitter. *Biomed. Res.* 3:107–21

32. Liddle RA, Elashoff J, Reeve JR Jr. 1986. Relative bioactivities of cholecystokinins-8 and -33 on rat pancreas acini. *Peptides* 7:723–27

33. Turkelson CM, Reeve JR Jr, Solomon TE. 1990. Low immunoreactivity of canine cholecystokinin-58. *Gastroenterology* 99:646–51

34. Reeve JR Jr, Eysselein VE, Rosenquist G, Zeeh J, Regner U, et al. 1996. Evidence that CCK-58 has structure that influences its biological activity. *Am. J. Physiol.* 270:G860–68

35. Wank SA, Harkins R, Jensen RT, Shapira H, De Weerth A, Slattery T. 1992. Purification, molecular cloning, and functional expression of the cholecystokinin receptor from rat pancreas. *Proc. Natl. Acad. Sci. USA* 89:3125–29

36. Kopin AS, Lee Y-M, McBride EW, Miller LJ, Lu M, et al. 1992. Expression cloning and characterization of the canine parietal cell gastrin receptor. *Proc. Natl. Acad. Sci. USA* 89:3605–9

37. Pisegna JR, De Weerth A, Huppi K, Wank SA. 1992. Molecular cloning of the human brain and gastric cholecystokinin re-

ceptor: structure, functional expression and chromosomal localization. *Biochem. Biophys. Res. Commun.* 189:296–303

38. Polak J, Pearse A, Bloom S, Buchan A, Rayford P, Thompson J. 1975. Identification of cholecystokinin-secreting cells. *Lancet* 2:1016–21

39. Buchan A, Polak J, Solcia E, Capella C, Hudson D, Pearse A. 1978. Electron immunohistochemical evidence for the human intestinal I cell as the source of CCK. *Gut* 19:403–7

40. Solcia E, Pearse AGE, Grube D, Kobayashi S, Bussolati G, et al. 1973. Revised Wiesbaden classification of gut endocrine cells. *Rend. Gastroenterol.* 5:13–16

41. Rehfeld JF, Hansen HF, Larsson L-I, Stengaard-Pedersen K, Thorn NA. 1984. Gastrin and cholecystokinin in pituitary neurons. *Proc. Natl. Acad. Sci. USA* 81:1902–5

42. Bardram L, Hilsted L, Rehfeld JF. 1989. Cholecystokinin, gastrin and their precursors in pheochromocytomas. *Acta Endocrinol.* 120:479–84

43. Rehfeld JF. 1978. Immunochemical studies on cholecystokinin II. Distribution and molecular heterogeneity in the central nervous system and small intestine of man and hog. *J. Biol. Chem.* 253:4022–30

44. Crawley JN. 1985. Comparative distribution of cholecystokinin and other neuropeptides: why is this peptide different from all other peptides? *Ann. NY Acad. Sci.* 448:1–8

45. Larsson L-I, Rehfeld JF. 1979. Localization and molecular heterogeneity of cholecystokinin in the central and peripheral nervous system. *Brain Res.* 165:201–18

46. Rehfeld JF. 1971. Effect of gastrin and its C-terminal tetrapeptide amide on insulin secretion in man. *Acta Endocrinol.* 66:169–76

47. Byrnes DJ, Henderson L, Borody T, Rehfeld JF. 1981. Radioimmunoassay of cholecystokinin in human plasma. *Clin. Chim. Acta* 111:81–89

48. Himeno S, Tarui S, Kanayama S, Kuroshima T, Shinomura Y, et al. 1983. Plasma cholecystokinin responses after ingestion of liquid meal and intraduodenal infusion of fat, amino acids, or hydrochloric acid in man: analysis with region specific radioimmunoassay. *Am. J. Gastroenterol.* 78:703–7

49. Becker HD, Werner M, Schafmayer A. 1984. Release of radioimmunologic cholecystokinin in human subjects. *Am. J. Surg.* 147:124–29

50. Jansen JBMJ, Lamers CBHW. 1983. Radioimmunoassay of cholecystokinin in human tissue and plasma. *Clin. Chim. Acta* 131:305–16

51. Brodish RJ, Kuvshinoff BW, Fink AS, Turkelson J, McFadden DW, Solomon TE. 1994. Intraduodenal acid augments oleic acid (C18)-induced cholecystokinin release. *Ann. NY Acad. Sci.* 713:388–90

52. Sun G, Chang T-M, Xue W, Wey JFY, Lee KY, Chey WY. 1992. Release of cholecystokinin and secretin by sodium oleate in dogs: molecular form and bioactivity. *Am. J. Physiol.* 262:G35–43

53. Meyer JH, Jones RS. 1974. Canine pancreatic responses to intestinally perfused fat and products of fat digestion. *Am. J. Physiol.* 226:1178–87

54. Brodish RJ, Kuvshinoff BW, Fink AS, McFadden DW, Turkelson J, Solomon TE. 1994. Potentiation of acid-induced pancreatic bicarbonate output by amino acid is mediated by neural elements, but not by circulating cholecystokinin. *Ann. NY Acad. Sci.* 713:391–92

55. Go VLW, Hofmann AF, Summerskill WHJ. 1970. Pancreozymin bioassay in man based on pancreatic enzyme secretion: potency of specific amino acids and other digestive products. *J. Clin. Invest.* 49:1558–64

56. Konturek SJ, Radecki T, Thor P, Dembinski A. 1973. Release of cholecystokinin by amino acids. *Proc. Soc. Exp. Biol. Med.* 143:305–9

57. Meyer JH, Kelley GA, Spingola LJ, Jones RS. 1976. Canine gut receptors mediating pancreatic responses to luminal L-amino acids. *Am. J. Physiol.* 231:669–77

58. Liddle RA. 1995. Regulation of cholecystokinin secretion by intraluminal releasing factors. *Am. J. Physiol.* 269:G319–27

59. Snow ND, Prpic V, Mangel AW, Sharara AI, McVey DC, et al. 1994. Regulation of cholecystokinin secretion by bombesin in STC-1 cells. *Am. J. Physiol.* 267:G859–65

60. Fried GM, Ogden WD, Greeley G, Thompson JC. 1983. Correlation of release and actions of cholecystokinin in dogs before and after vagotomy. *Surgery* 93:786–91

61. Hopman WPM, Jansen JBMJ, Lamers CBHW. 1984. Plasma cholecystokinin response to oral fat in patients with billroth I and billroth II gastrectomy. *Ann. Surg.* 199:276–80

62. Lu L, Louie D, Owyang C. 1989. A cholecystokinin releasing peptide mediates feedback regulation of pancreatic secretion. *Am. J. Physiol.* 256:G430–35

63. Miyasaka K, Guan D, Liddle RA, Green GM. 1989. Feedback regulation by trypsin: evidence for intraluminal CCK-releasing peptide. *Am. J. Physiol.* 257:G175–81
64. Green GM, Lyman RL. 1972. Feedback regulation of pancreatic enzyme secretion as a mechanism for trypsin inhibitor-induced hypersecretion in rats. *Proc. Soc. Exp. Biol. Med.* 140:6–12
65. Green G, Nasset ES. 1977. Effect of bile duct obstruction on pancreatic enzyme secretion and intestinal proteolytic enzyme activity in the rat. *Dig. Dis.* 22:437–44
66. Green GM, Miyasaka K. 1983. Rat pancreatic response to intestinal infusion of intact and hydrolyzed protein. *Am. J. Physiol.* 245:G394–98
67. Miyasaka K, Green GM. 1983. Effect of rapid washout of proximal small intestine on pancreatic secretion in conscious rat. *Gastroenterology* 84:1251
68. Slaff J, Jacobson D, Tillman CR, Currington C, Toskes P. 1984. Protease-specific suppression of pancreatic exocrine secretion. *Gastroenterology* 87:44–52
69. Owyang C, Louie DS, Tatum D. 1986. Feedback regulation of pancreatic enzyme secretion—suppression of cholecystokinin release by trypsin. *J. Clin. Invest.* 77:2042–47
70. Folsch UR, Cantor P, Wilms HM, Schafmayer A, Becker HD, Creutzfeldt W. 1987. Role of cholecystokinin in the negative feedback control of pancreatic enzyme secretion in conscious rats. *Gastroenterology* 92:449–58
71. Schmidt WE, Creutzfeldt W, Höcker M, Nustede R, Choudhury AR, et al. 1991. Cholecystokinin receptor antagonist loxiglumide modulates plasma levels of gastro-entero-pancreatic hormones in man: feedback control of cholecystokinin and gastrin secretion. *Eur. J. Clin. Invest.* 21:501–11
72. Chernick SS, Lepkovsky S, Chaikoff IL. 1948. A dietary factor regulating the enzyme content of the pancreas: changes induced in size and proteolytic activity of the chick pancreas by ingestion of raw soybean meal. *Am. J. Physiol.* 155:33–41
73. Alumot E, Nitsan Z. 1948. The influence of soybean antitrypsin on the intestinal proteolysis of the chick. *J. Nutr.* 73:71–77
74. Ihse I, Lilja P. 1977. Effect of intestinal amylase and trypsin on pancreatic secretion in the pig. *Scand. J. Gastroenterol.* 14:1009–13
75. Shiratori K, Jo YH, Lee KY, Chang TM, Chey WY. 1989. Effect of pancreatic juice

and trypsin on oleic acid-stimulated pancreatic secretion and plasma secretin in dogs. *Gastroenterology* 96:1330–36
76. Jin HO, Song CW, Chang TM, Chey WY. 1994. Roles of gut hormones in negative-feedback regulation of pancreatic exocrine secretion in humans. *Gastroenterology* 107:1828–34
77. Owyang C, May D, Louie DS. 1986. Trypsin suppression of pancreatic enzyme secretion. *Gastroenterology* 91:637–43
78. Owyang C. 1994. Negative feedback control of exocrine pancreatic secretion: role of cholecystokinin and cholinergic pathway. *J. Nutr.* 124:1321S–26
79. Fushiki T, Fukuoka S, Kajiura H, Iwai K. 1987. Atropine-nonsensitive feedback regulatory mechanism of rat pancreatic enzyme secretion in response to food protein intake. *J. Nutr.* 117:948–54
80. Levan VH, Green GM. 1986. Effect of atropine on rat pancreatic secretory response to trypsin inhibitors and protein. *Am. J. Physiol.* 251:G64–69
81. Guan D, Ohta H, Tawil T, Spannagel AW, Liddle RA, Green GM. 1990. Lack of cholinergic control in feedback regulation of pancreatic secretion in the rat. *Gastroenterology* 98:437–43
82. Herzig K-H, Louie DS, Owyang C. 1994. Somatostatin inhibits CCK release by inhibiting secretion and action of CCK-releasing peptide. *Am. J. Physiol.* 266:G1156–61
83. Adler G, Mullenhoff A, Koop I, Bozkurt T, Goke B, et al. 1988. Stimulation of pancreatic secretion in man by a protease inhibitor (camostate). *Eur. J. Clin. Invest.* 18:98–104
84. Layer P, Jansen JBMJ, Cherian L, Lamers CBHW, Goebell H. 1990. Feedback regulation of human pancreatic secretion. *Gastroenterology* 98:1311–19
85. Spannagel AW, Green GM, Guan D, Liddle RA, Faull K, Reeve JR Jr. 1996. Purification and characterization of a luminal cholecystokinin-releasing factor from rat intestinal secretion. *Proc. Natl. Acad. Sci. USA* 93:4415–20
86. Herzig KH, Schon I, Tatemoto K, Ohe Y, Li Y, et al. 1996. Diazepam binding inhibitor is a CCK releasing peptide in the intestine. *Gastroenterology* 110:A1079
87. Iwai K, Fukuoka S-I, Fushiki T, Kodaira T, Ikei N. 1986. Elevation of plasma CCK concentration after intestinal administration of a pancreatic enzyme secretion-stimulating peptide purified from rat bile-pancreatic juice: analysis with N-terminal region specific radioimmunoas-

say. *Biochem. Biophys. Res. Commun.* 136:701–6

88. Iwai K, Fukuoka SI, Fushiki T, Tsujikawa M, Hirose M, Tsunasawa S, et al. 1987. Purification and sequencing of a trypsin-sensitive cholecystokinin-releasing peptide from rat pancreatic juice. *J. Biol. Chem.* 262:8956–59

89. Lin Y-Z, Isaac DD, Tam JP. 1990. Synthesis and properties of cholecystokinin-releasing peptide (monitor peptide), a 61-residue trypsin inhibitor. *Int. J. Pept. Protein Res.* 36:433–39

90. Miyasaka K, Funakoshi A, Nakamura R, Kitani K, Uda K, et al. 1989. Differences in stimulatory effects between rat pancreatic secretory trypsin inhibitor-61 and -56 on rat pancreas. *Jpn. J. Physiol.* 39:891–99

91. Fushiki T, Iwai K. 1989. Two hypotheses on the feedback regulation of pancreatic enzyme secretion. *FASEB J.* 3:121–26

92. Bouras EP, Misukonis MA, Liddle RA. 1992. Role of calcium in monitor peptide-stimulated cholecystokinin release from perfused intestinal cells. *Am. J. Physiol.* 262:G791–96

93. Liddle RA, Misukonis MA, Pacy L, Balber AE. 1992. Cholecystokinin cells purified by fluorescence-activated cell sorting respond to monitor peptide with an increase in intracellular calcium. *Proc. Natl. Acad. Sci. USA* 89:5147–51

94. Yamanishi R, Kotera J, Fushiki T, Soneda T, Saitoh T, et al. 1993. A specific binding of the cholecystokinin-releasing peptide (monitor peptide) to isolated rat small-intestinal cells. *Biochem. J.* 291:57–63

95. Barber DL, Walsh JH, Soll AH. 1986. Release and characterization of cholecystokinin from isolated canine jejunal cells. *Gastroenterology* 91:627–36

96. Koop I, Buchan AMJ. 1992. Cholecystokinin release from isolated canine epithelial cells in short-term culture. *Gastroenterology* 102:28–34

97. Wood SM, Jung RT, Webster JD, Ghatei MA, Adrian TE, et al. 1983. The effect of the mammalian neuropeptide, gastrin releasing peptide (GRP), on gastrointestinal and pancreatic hormone secretion in man. *Clin. Sci.* 65:365–71

98. Nakano I, Miyazaki K, Funakoshi A, Tateishi K, Hamaoka T, Yajima H. 1988. Gastrin-releasing peptide stimulates cholecystokinin secretion in perfused rat duodenum. *Regul. Pept.* 23:153–59

99. Cuber JC, Vilas F, Charles N, Bernard C, Chayvialle JA. 1989. Bombesin and nutrients stimulate release of CCK through

distinct pathways in the rat. *Am. J. Physiol.* 256:G989–96

100. Cantor P, Holst JJ, Knuhtsen S. 1987. Effect of neuroactive agents on cholecystokinin release from the isolated, perfused porcine duodenum. *Acta. Physiol. Scand.* 130:627–32

101. Snow ND, Prpic V, Mangel AW, Sharara AI, McVey DC, et al. 1994. Regulation of cholecystokinin secretion by bombesin in STC-1 cells. *Am. J. Physiol.* 267:G859–65

102. Scott L, Prpic V, Capel WD, Basavappa S, Mangel AW, et al. 1996. β-adrenergic regulation of cholecystokinin secretion in STC-1 cells. *Am. J. Physiol.* 270:G291–97

103. Sharara AI, Bouras EP, Misukonis MA, Liddle RA. 1993. Evidence for indirect dietary regulation of cholecystokinin release in rats. *Am. J. Physiol.* 265:G107–12

104. Mangel AW, Prpic V, Wong H, Basavappa S, Hurst LJ, et al. 1995. Phenylalanine-stimulated secretion of cholecystokinin is calcium dependent. *Am. J. Physiol.* 268:G90–94

105. Prpic V, Basavappa S, Liddle RA, Mangel AW. 1994. Regulation of cholecystokinin secretion by calcium-dependent calmodulin kinase II: differential effects of phenylalanine and cAMP. *Biochem. Biophys. Res. Commun.* 201:1483–89

106. Aucouturier S, Bernard C, Roche C, Philippe J, Chayvialle J-A, Cuber J-C. 1994. Functional coupling between the cyclic adenosine monophosphate pathway and cholecystokinin secretion in RIN cells. *Biochem. Biophys. Res. Commun.* 200:1382–90

107. Petersen OH, Findlay I. 1987. Electrophysiology of the pancreas. *Physiol. Rev.* 67:1054–116

108. Lingle CJ, Sombati S, Freeman ME. 1986. Membrane currents in identified lactotrophs of rat anterior pituitary. *J. Neurosci.* 6:2995–3005

109. Biagi BA, Milnar B, Enyeart JJ. 1992. Membrane currents in calcitonin-secreting human C cell line. *Am. J. Physiol.* 263:C986–94

110. Xue W, Chey WY, Sun Q, Chang T-M. 1993. Characterization of secretin release in secretin cell-enriched preparation isolated from canine duodenal mucosa. *Dig. Dis. Sci.* 38:344–52

111. Mangel AW, Snow ND, Misukonis MA, Basavappa S, Middleton JP, et al. 1993. Calcium-dependent regulation of cholecystokinin secretion and potassium currents in STC-1 cells. *Am. J. Physiol.* 264:G1031–36

112. Rindi G, Grant SGN, Yiangou Y, Ghatei MA, Bloom SR, et al. 1990. Development of neuroendocrine tumors in the gastrointestinal tract of transgenic mice: heterogeneity of hormone expression. *Am. J. Physiol.* 136:1349–63

113. Chang CH, Chey WY, Sun Q, Leiter A, Chang T. 1994. Characterization of the release of cholecystokinin from a murine neuroendocrine tumor cell line, STC-1. *Biochim. Biophys. Acta* 1221:339–47

114. Snow ND, Mangel AW, Sharara AI, Liddle RA. 1993. Potassium channels regulate cholecystokinin secretion in STC-1 cells. *Biochem. Biophys. Res. Commun.* 195:1379–85

115. Mangel AW, Prpic V, Snow ND, Basavappa S, Hurst LJ, et al. 1994. Regulation of cholecystokinin secretion by ATP-sensitive potassium channels. *Am. J. Physiol.* 267:G595–600

116. Basavappa S, Liddle RA, Mangel AW. 1994. Characterization of ATP-sensitive potassium channels in intestinal cholecystokinin-secreting cells. *Biochem. Biophys. Res. Commun.* 204:855–60

117. Mangel AW, Prpic V, Scott L, Liddle RA. 1994. Inhibitors of ATP-sensitive potassium channels stimulate intestinal cholecystokinin secretion. *Peptides* 15:1565–66

118. Mangel AW, Scott L, Liddle RA. 1996. Depolarization-stimulated cholecystokinin secretion is mediated by L-type calcium channels in STC-1 cells. *Am. J. Physiol.* 270:G287–90

*Annu. Rev. Physiol. 1997. 59:243–56*

# PHYSIOLOGY OF ISOLATED GASTRIC ENDOCRINE CELLS

*George Sachs, Ningxin Zeng, and Christian Prinz∗*

Departments of Medicine and Physiology, University of California, Los Angeles, California 90073; ∗Department of Medicine, Technical University of Munich, Munich, Germany

KEY WORDS:   acid secretion, ECL cell, gastrin, CCK, somatostatin, histamine

### ABSTRACT

The regulation of gastric acid secretion is achieved in the periphery by interplay between three major gastric endocrine cells: the enterochromaffin-like (ECL) cell, the gastrin or G cell, and the somatostatin or D cell. Regulation of these cells is via stimulatory or inhibitory paracrine, endocrine, and neural pathways. Upregulation of ECL function is determined by activation of CCK-B receptors, by gastrin, and by activation of $\beta$-adrenergic receptors, as well as by acetylcholine in some (10–29%) of the cells. Gastrin and acetylcholine produce typical biphasic calcium signals. Inhibition of ECL cell histamine release and calcium signaling is produced by somatostatin acting at a type 2 receptor, histamine acting at a histamine-3 receptor, and by peptide PYY. Stimulation of ECL cells results in activation of chloride channels, and there is evidence that voltage-dependent calcium channels, along with the receptor-operated calcium channels, also are responsible for elevation of $[Ca]_i$. Depolarization-activated $K^+$ channels presumably restore the potential after depolarization by activation of the chloride channel. The D cell is activated by either gastrin or CCK and appears to be inhibited by acetylcholine and somatostatin. The G cell is activated by acetylcholine and gastrin-releasing peptide (GRP) and is inhibited by somatostatin. The functional integration of these three cell types is the primary determinant of the degree of stimulation of the parietal cell.

## GASTRIC ENDOCRINE CELLS

Gastric acid secretion is a highly regulated process dependent on neural, endocrine, and paracrine events that either upregulate or downregulate acid secretion by the parietal cell (1, 27, 30, 49, 50, 51, 55). Remarkably, few of these

243

0066-4278/97/0315-0243$08.00

events impinge directly on the parietal cell; most involve influences on the earlier steps in the cascade of events that determines the rate of acid secretion. The effect of this neural and endocrine cascade is to activate one of three stimulatory receptors on the parietal cell: histamine (H2 receptor subtype), acetylcholine (a muscarinic-3 receptor subtype), and gastrin (a CCK-B receptor subtype). Whereas histamine or acetylcholine is able to activate parietal cell acid secretion directly, it appears that prior histamine stimulation of the parietal cell is necessary for any observable response to gastrin, thus histamine stimulation is permissive for gastrin effects on the parietal cell (21).

Early studies on stimulation of acid secretion were carried out on intact animals and humans, notably by Beaumont, Pavlov, Edkins, and others (7, 17, 27, 50). The dog flap preparation and the chambered frog gastric mucosa were models that held sway in the middle of this century. These studies delineated, albeit with considerable controversy, particularly with reference to the role of histamine, many of the major endocrine, neural, and paracrine stimulants of parietal cell function, namely gastrin, acetylcholine, and histamine (4, 8,19, 27, 35, 50, 52, 51). As peptide methodologies improved, additional factors able to affect secretion such as somatostatin or bombesin (gastrin-releasing polypeptide) were discovered (1, 2, 14, 16, 22). Application of molecular biological techniques made possible the identification of receptor proteins and, in part, their localization (33, 41, 590, 64, 66, 68). This methodology also permitted analysis of gene expression and its control (15, 20).

The development of isolated mammalian in vitro preparations from gastric mucosa such as the rabbit gastric gland (6, 12, 13) (in which acid secretion could be monitored) simplified studies by enabling the determination of which agonists or antagonists could directly affect parietal cell function (37, 54, 55). In this in vitro model, the acid secretory response or changes in parietal cell calcium following addition of gastrin were inhibited completely by histamine-2 receptor antagonists or destruction of histamine in the medium (21), similar to data obtained in rat or in humans.

Mixed endocrine cells in culture allowed additional access to investigations of release of stimulants or inhibitors (55–59), but the advent of purified gastric endocrine cell preparations (44) or single-cell methodology (69) was required to explicitly define the cellular site of action of ligands that were acting upstream of the parietal cell, as well as their site of action and second messenger pathways. Single-cell methods also allowed insights into stimulus secretion coupling in the individual cell types (69). In interpretation of data derived from such in vitro preparations, it is important to relate them to the physiology of the intact organ or animal and thus provide an integrated portrayal of acid secretory regulation.

The major endocrine cells known to play an important role in acid secretion are the ECL cell of the fundus, the gastrin (G) cell of the antrum, and the

**Table 1**   Relative percentage of endocrine cells and their products in the rat and human stomach[a]

|  | Antrum (%) | Funds Rat (%) | Funds Human (%) | Amine | Peptide |
|---|---|---|---|---|---|
| ECL | Not present | 60–70 | 30 | Histamine | Unknown |
| EC | 10 | 0–2 | 7 | Serotonin | Unknown |
| D | 20 | 2–5 | 22 | Unknown | Somatostatin |
| G | 60 | 0 | 0 | GABA | Gastrin |
| D$_1$, A/X | Unknown | 20 | 20 | Unknown | Unknown |

[a]References 23, 53.

somatostatin (D) cells of fundus and antrum (14, 19, 27, 49, 50, 51, 54). This is not a complete list of the endocrine cells of the mucosa, but these are the cells of known function. Nerve fibers are known to contain, in addition to acetylcholine, several possible peptide regulators of acid secretion, but they are less well-defined than the ligands released from endocrine cells. The nature of gastric endocrine cells and their distribution are given in Table 1.

These endocrine cells are scattered throughout the fundus and the antrum. However, their location is not random. For example, the histamine released by the ECL cell mostly in the lower one third of the gastric fundic epithelium must have privileged access to the parietal cell, whereas the somatostatin released by fundic or antral D cells should have equivalent access to the ECL and G cells of these regions of the gastric mucosa. The antral D and G cells are also probably affected by either lumenal acidity or the presence of aromatic amino acids.

In this short review, the main aspects of endocrine cell regulation in the process of gastric acid secretion are discussed, with major emphasis on what has been learned from purified or single-cell preparations. Due to space limitations, only a selected bibliography is given.

## ECL CELLS

ECL cells are histamine-containing endocrine cells in the gastric mucosa. They play a central role in the peripheral regulation of mammalian acid secretion because activation of the H2 receptor of the parietal cell appears to be the only means of raising intracellular cAMP (21). It is fortunate that the H2 receptor plays a minor role elsewhere in the periphery so that H2 receptor antagonists can be used liberally to treat peptic ulcer disease (4, 8, 35, 43).

The ECL cell, the first gastric endocrine cell to be purified sufficiently, allowed for studies free of possible contamination from ligands released from other cell types (44). The degree of purification is about 65% in the freshly isolated cells and about 85% or even greater after 48 h culture. Studies using isolated, highly enriched ECL cells have shown that these cells display some of the characteristic features of neuroendocrine cells and other chromaffin cells. However, stimulus secretion coupling is more like that of non-excitable cells such as the mast cell. Activation of histamine secretion requires specific signaling, which is dependent on a distinct receptor distribution on ECL cells (42, 41, 69). ECL cells react to the antral hormone gastrin by histamine secretion, activation of the histamine synthesizing enzyme, histidine decarboxylase (HDC), and also by cellular proliferation (42). Binding of this hormone first induces exocytosis, which is followed by upregulation of selective gene expression evident after 60 min of incubation. Other stimulatory receptors such as muscarinic, adrenergic, peptidergic, and cytokine receptors have been found, as well as inhibitory receptors such somatostatin receptors and PYY (41, 45, 68, 69).

## Importance of Histamine and ECL Cells in the Peripheral Regulation of Acid Secretion

Histamine, a biogenic amine, is produced in several mammalian cells and is one of the most important transmitters, mediating inflammation, neuronal stimulation, and immune responses, as well as controlling gastric acid secretion (8, 35). Treatment with histamine receptor antagonists has been a very successful strategy not only for allergic problems (H1-antagonists), but also for peptic ulcer disease (H2 antagonists) (8, 35).

The importance of gastric ECL cells as the major histamine pool in the stomach was not fully recognized until the development of proton pump inhibitors as anti-ulcer drugs (43, 49, 50). Treatment of rats with these drugs resulted in an increase of gastric ECL cells that resulted from elevation of the antral hormone gastrin (9, 10, 32, 48). This finding focused attention on the ECL cell, in particular its growth regulation. In vitro studies using isolated ECL cells from rat tissue then demonstrated that the cells secreting histamine during regulation of acid secretion originate from the ECL cells (44).

The term enterochromaffin-like was first used in 1971. These cells were identified in the stomach by microscopic techniques. In vivo studies, or those using impure cell preparations, could not provide direct evidence for the function of ECL cells (23, 24). Studies of a purified preparation of rat ECL cells showed that these neuroendocrine cells secrete histamine (44). They also demonstrated that ECL cells decarboxylate histidine and store the product histamine in vesicles. ECL cells in these preparations were identified by electron microscopy, antibody staining for histamine or HDC, as well as by the presence of characteristic acidic vacuoles in the cytoplasm (42, 44, 69).

## The ECL Cell as a Member of the Chromaffin Cell Family

Chromaffin and chromaffin-like cells are endocrine cells that can be identified by chromium or silver staining methods, or with antibodies against chromogranin A or pancreastatin (a degraded product of chromogranin). These cells appear morphologically similar (38, 39, 53). The diameter of the chromaffin cells is about 10 $\mu$m. The nucleus occupies more than 50% of the cellular space, contains few organelles such as the ER, mitochondria, or lysosomes, but has many amine storage granules (19, 23, 28, 39, 43). Amide accumulation is driven by proton/amine counter transport and is dependent on the establishment of a proton gradient across the vesicular membrane (44, 65). Secretion is by exocytosis, and the cells have an endocrine or paracrine function.

All amine-producing cells can be characterized by the uptake of acridine orange into the histamine-, catecholamine-, or serotonin-containing granules. Acridine orange, a weak base, is concentrated in acidic spaces and undergoes a metachromatic shift of fluorescence emission resulting from stacking of the dye. It is bright red in the acidic space and green in the cytoplasm. The granule acidity in ECL cells depends on a V-type ATPase because 1 nM of bafilomycin abolishes this acidification (44). V-type pumps are electrogenic, with $Cl^-$ usually accompanying $H^+$. The intravesicular $H^+$ acts as a counterion in the $H^+$/amine exchange, which is responsible for amine accumulation inside the vacuoles (18, 44).

The chromaffin cells of the adrenal gland have a neuroectodermal origin, show characteristics of a neuronal cell because they are electrically excitable, and have voltage-gated L-type calcium channels. Neonatal chromaffin cells are able to divide and can differentiate into a endocrine tumor (PC12 cell line).

Serotonin-containing enterochromaffin cells are located in the epithelium of the stomach and the small bowel. These cells store and secrete serotonin, and the presence of the GTP-hydrolyzing enzyme GTP-1 cyclohydroxylase has only been shown in enterochromaffin cells. Active proliferation is not known under normal conditions, but malignant transformation is frequent.

The ECL cells produce and store histamine, about 2.8–4.3 pg/cell, which is relatively low compared with that found in mast cells (12–20 pg/cell). The cytoplasm of ECL cells contains numerous electron-translucent vesicles with a characteristic electron-dense core thought to represent the storage of a peptide hormone (23, 24). ECL cells produce a hormone that lowers blood calcium concentrations (40). Exocytosis of histamine involves members of protein families such as SNAP or syntaxins, some of which have been identified in protein homogenates from an enriched ECL cell preparation (C Prinz & G Gratzl, unpublished observations).

ECL cells have a resting potential of $-50$ mV, with depolarization-activated potassium channels and cAMP-activated chloride currents (34). Studies of these cells using patch-clamp electrodes, which provided evidence for depolarization-activated potassium channels and stimulus-dependent chloride currents indicate the presence of chloride channels in the vacuole membrane rather than in the plasma membrane (34). Thus the appearance of active chloride channels in the apical membrane is a reflection of exocytosis, which results in cell depolarization because of insertion of these chloride channels. This, in turn, is followed by potassium channel activation in order to restore the resting membrane potential. The activation of potassium channels is most likely due to calcium entry via receptor-operated and even voltage-dependent calcium channels (42, 67, 69).

Recently, it has been shown that depolarization of the ECL cell by the addition of 40 mM $K^+$ or 20 mM TEA results in a calcium signal (67). The signal is inhibited by calcium channel blockers at appropriately low concentrations (67). This would argue for the presence of not only receptor-operated calcium channels, but also depolarization-activated or voltage-dependent calcium channels in the ECL cell.

## Stimulation of the ECL Cells: Gastrin, Acetylcholine, PACAP, and Epinephrine Receptors

Gastrin has multiple actions on the ECL cell, involving changes in $[Ca]_i$, up-regulation of HDC and stimulation of ECL cell growth in the rat; these effects can be classified as acute, intermediate, or chronic (42). Gastrin is the major physiological ligand that stimulates histamine secretion. This effect is mediated by binding of gastrin to CCK-B receptors located on the surface of the ECL cell, and secretion can be detected within 5 min. The effect of binding the ligand is displayed as a typical G7 receptor-mediated change in $[Ca]_i$, namely a transient followed by a steady-state elevation. Freshly isolated cells have a relatively high basal histamine release, which is also accompanied by a relatively high $[Ca]_i$. Following 48 h culture, the basal histamine release declines, as does $[Ca]_i$. This results in a higher stimulation of histamine release and greater changes in $[Ca]_i$ in cultured as compared with freshly isolated cells. The $EC_{50}$ for gastrin-mediated release of histamine is $4.10^{-11}$ M, a value characteristic for this receptor. The CCK-B antagonist, L 365,260, inhibits this response with an $IC_{50}$ of $10^{-8}$M, whereas the CCK-A antagonist has no effect until a concentration of $10^{-6}$ M is reached. CCK-8 is equipotent to gastrin. These results establish that histamine release and calcium signaling depend on activation of a CCK-B receptor subtype. The stimulation of histamine release is evident within 5 min; the $Ca^{2+}$ signal is virtually instantaneous. Hence the action of gastrin is an acute effect. Presumably, coupling of the CCK-B receptor to regulation of $[Ca]_i$ is mediated via a Gq subtype of the G protein family (42).

Stimulation of ECL cells by acetylcholine also results in the release of histamine and is accompanied by a characteristic change in $[Ca]_i$. However, whereas all ECL cells respond to gastrin, only about 10 to 30% of the cells respond to acetylcholine (69). This may reflect a group of ECL cells that are vagally innervated, as compared with the majority of cells that respond to systemic factors rather than local transmitters (69).

Pituitary adenylate cyclase-activating peptide (PACAP) is also able to stimulate ECL cell histamine release. PACAP-27 and PACAP-36 are equipotent in stimulating histamine release with an $EC_{50}$ of $1.10^{-9}$ M. VIP had no effect when given at dosage below 100 nM, which indicates that this cell possessess a functional PACAP I receptor subtype (66).

Epinephrine also stimulates histamine release from ECL cells, as does forskolin, an activator of adenylate cyclase (44). In vivo data suggest that epinephrine stimulation may be mediated by activation of a $\beta_3$-adrenergic receptor, but the physiological significance of this pathway is unclear.

## Inhibition of ECL Cells: Somatostatin, Histamine-3, and PYY Receptors

Somatostatin is known to be a major peptide inhibitor of gastric acid secretion with several distinct cellular targets, such as the G cell of the antrum, the ECL cell of the fundus, and even the parietal cell itself (14, 30, 33, 37, 41). In the case of the ECL cell, somatostatin binds at a somatostatin-2 receptor subtype, inhibiting both histamine release and calcium signaling. The effect of somatostatin is blocked by pre-incubation with pertussis toxin, indicating that coupling of the receptor is via a $G_i$-like protein (41). Somatostatin is present in both the fundus and the antrum in D cells, which are differentially activated. In the antrum, antral lumenal acidity is thought to stimulate somatostatin release in order to inhibit gastrin release from the G cell (51). In the fundus, the D cell is stimulated by gastrin or CCK-A and by acetylcholine, as well as by other neural peptides (69). This somatostatin pool is probably responsible for inhibition of ECL cell function.

There is growing evidence that gastric acid secretion is sensitive to downregulation by histamine acting at a histamine-3 type receptor. Again, although it is likely that there is more than one location for this inhibitory receptor, only the ECL cell has been shown to respond appropriately to histamine-3 agonists and antagonists (44). Therefore, feedback regulation of histamine release by histamine, presumably at high histamine concentrations, must occur.

PYY is a peptide that also inhibits gastric acid secretion by acting at numerous locations. Pharmacological evidence and RT-PCR in the rat suggest that its site of action on the ECL cell is at a $Y_1$ receptor. Interestingly, this peptide blocks the plateau phase of calcium signaling, but is much less active against the transient elevation of $[Ca]_i$, in contrast to somatostatin, which inhibits both phases of calcium elevation. The PYY effect may account for much of the inhibitory effect of nutrient presentation to the intestine, classified as an enterogastrone effect (66).

## Histamine Production in ECL Cells

ECL cells produce histamine by decarboxylation of histidine and store the product, histamine, in cytoplasmic vesicles. This synthesis is performed by a specific enzyme, HDC, which can be identified by specific antibody staining. In a preparation of isolated ECL cells, there was sufficient concentration to allow measurement of HDC by $^{14}CO_2$ production from histidine-$^{14}COOH$. HDC activation can be stimulated effectively by gastrin (44). Gene activation follows after 30–60 min of gastrin or acetylcholine stimulation. Histidine decarboxylase is present at high concentrations in ECL cells (11, 23). This enzyme contains a PEST (Pro-Glu-Ser-Thr) sequence and therefore has a relatively short half-life (46). It has been known for many years that the level of HDC is elevated by gastrin stimulation and that the effect occurs relatively rapidly in vivo. Associated with activation of the enzyme is an increase in the level of mRNA, which indicates activation of gene transcription (11). Activity of this enzyme is essential for histamine biosynthesis. Inhibition of HDC by alpha-fluoromethyl histidine abolishes gastrin stimulation of acid secretion in the rat, thus pointing to the essential role of ECL cell histamine release in gastrin-stimulated acid secretion (3).

In cultured ECL cell preparations, gastrin stimulates the level of HDC two- to threefold within 60 min (42). This results, in part, from activation of gene transcription as described in vivo and may also involve deinhibition of previously synthesized enzyme because there appears to be a very rapid component of HSC upregulation.

It is not known whether increase of HDC transcription depends in part on histamine release, or whether this increase is entirely the direct effect of gastrin's binding to the CCK-B receptor and consequent signaling via elevation of intracellular calcium. The HDC gene contains $Ca^{2+}$ response elements, hence it is possible that this increased transcription is an effect of $[Ca]_i$ elevation. The G protein coupled to the CCK-B receptor is probably of the Gq subtype, and many of these proteins are coupled via changes in $[Ca]_i$ to alterations in gene transcription (42).

## Growth of ECL Cells

Major clinical interest in the ECL cell was stimulated by the finding that chronic administration of high doses of omeprazole resulted in ECL cell hyperplasia and carcinoid development in the rat stomach (9). Subsequent studies showed that this effect was due entirely to the hypergastrinemia resulting from inhibition of acid secretion in the face of normal food stimulation of gastrin release from the G cell (9, 10, 25, 26, 29, 31, 32, 36, 47, 48, 60, 61–63). Whereas the ECL cell in the rat is clearly capable of growth and division, it has been claimed that the human ECL cell is a terminally differentiated cell, incapable of further growth (5).

The rat ECL cell in culture is able to divide and to be stimulated by gastrin (42). Surprisingly, the effect on growth is the result of binding to a CCK-B-like receptor, with about 50-fold higher affinity than for histamine release. Also some characteristics appear to differ; for example, growth stimulation is sensitive to the tyrosine kinase inhibitor genistein and insensitive to stimulation by CCK-8, in contrast to calcium signaling response and histamine release, which are sensitive to CCK-8 and insensitive to genistein. The molecular basis for this distinction is not understood, but the presence of a shorter form of the CCK-B receptor does not appear to be a factor (C Prinz & N Lambrecht, unpublished observations). Growth responses to changes in $[Ca]_i$ are often found, but it would appear that the gastrin growth response of the rat ECL cell can occur in the absence of measurable changes in intracellular calcium, given the 50-fold or lower affinity of the calcium signal.

The ECL cell of the South African rodent mastomys varies in control of replication from that of the ECL cell in the rat. Not only are ECL carcinoids formed by treatment with either H2 receptor antagonists or proton pump inhibitors, but the carcinoids progress to a malignant form (36). Hence, as in rat, and perhaps in contrast to humans, the mastomys' ECL cell is not a terminally differentiated cell type and provides an interesting model for ECL cell transformation.

## D CELLS

The somatostatin-containing D cell is located in both the fundus and the antrum. Although there have been studies on cultured D cells at about 60% purity, these studies have been largely confined to measurements of somatostatin release. These studies must be interpreted with caution because ligands released from contaminating cells can confound the results. Recently, however, it has been possible to define D cells in a mixed endocrine cell population by immuno-staining with anti-somatostatin antibody and by video microscopic analysis of specific ligand effects on calcium signaling (69). In contrast to the ECL cell, the D cell responds to both CCK-A and CCK-B stimulation, indicating that cholecystokinin may play a significant role in inhibition of fundic ECL cell histamine release, whereas gastrin exerts a feedback control on the antral D cell (66). PACAP and VIP both stimulate somatostatin release from cultured D cells. The response, however, does not correspond to distinct PACAP I or PACAP II (VIP) receptors, which may explained by the fact that D cells

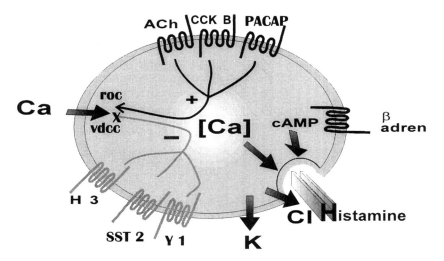

*Figure 1*   A model summarizing observations made on isolated rat ECL cells, showing a number of G7 receptors that stimulate or inhibit histamine release. In addition, the presence of both receptor-operated and voltage-dependent Ca channels are shown, as well as depolarization-activated $K^+$ channels and stimulation-activated $Cl^-$ channels.

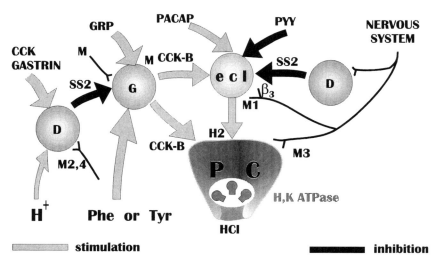

*Figure 2*   A scheme showing some of the integrative pathways involved in regulating parietal cell acid secretion by actions on the three major gastric endocrine cells: the ECL cell, the G cell, and the D cell. This scheme illustrates the complexity of peripheral stimulation and inhibition of gastric acid secretion.

have both receptor subtypes (66). Acetylcholine, in this cell type, appears to downregulate the release of somatostatin and calcium signaling, which suggests that a M2 or M4 receptor is present on the D cells, in contrast to the M1, 3, or 5 receptor present on other gastric cells (69). The D cells also respond to somatostatin, indicating that this peptide exerts feedback control of its release.

## G CELL

This cell is present exclusively in the antrum. Studies have reported gastrin release generated from G cell-enriched populations but, as above, endogenous ligand release may confound physiological interpretation of the data. The isolated G cell, defined by immunostaining with anti-gastrin antibody and by calcium signaling in video imaging, shows characteristic responses. It appears to be the only cell to respond with a calcium signal to gastrin-releasing peptide (GRP) and to demonstrate the absence of a CCK receptor while retaining an activating muscarinic receptor (69). It also responds to aromatic amino acids with a calcium signal (70), but it is not clear whether this is a primary response to binding of the amino acid to a receptor or to a secondary effect due, for example, to $Na^+$ entry.

### Working Model of Endocrine Regulation of Gastric Acid Secretion

The above data allow the construction of an explicit model of not only ECL cell function, but also of peripheral regulation of gastric acid secretion based entirely on in vitro data, either from purified ECL cell cultures or from single cell video imaging in a mixed gastric endocrine cell population.

As shown in Figure 1, the ECL cell has a variety of electrically active transporters in its cell membrane and a variety of receptors able to activate or inhibit histamine release. The model is also consistent with data obtained in in vivo studies, but differs somewhat from data obtained in isolated organ studies, perhaps owing to selective moribund pressures in the latter preparations (51).

In Figure 2, the general pathways involving the major endocrine cells of the stomach are illustrated, showing the complicated interactions between them and between the endocrine and parietal cells. As knowledge accumulates using isolated cell preparations, additional pathways will likely be defined, in particular those involving peptidergic neurones in the stomach.

ACKNOWLEDGMENTS

This work was supported by National Institutes of Health grants DK40615, 41301, and 17294, United States Veterans Administration SMI grant, and by a grant from the Deutsche Forschungsgemeinschaft Pr 411/2-1 to Christian Prinz.

*Literature Cited*

1. Allen JM, Bishop AE, Daly MJ, Larsson H, Carlsson E, et al. 1986. Effect of inhibition of acid secretion on the regulatory peptides in the rat stomach. *Gastroenterology* 90:309–24
2. Anastasi A, Esparmer V, Bucci M. 1971. Isolation and structure of bombesin and alytesin, two analogous peptides from the skin of European amphibians Bombina and Alytes. *Experientia* 27:166–67
3. Andersson K, Chen D, Hakanson R, Mattson H, Sundler F.1992. Enterochromaffin-like cells in the rat stomach: effect of alpha-fluoromethylhistidine evoked histamine depletion. *Cell Tissue Res.* 270:7–13
4. Andersson K, Mattson H, Larsson H. 1990. The role of gastric mucosal histamine in acid secretion and experimentally induced lesions in the rat. *Digestion* 46:1–9
5. Barrett P, Hobbs RC, Coates PJ, Risdon RA, Wright NA, et al. 1995. Endocrine cells of the human gastrointestinal tract have no proliferative capacity. *Histochem. J.* 27:482–86
6. Berglindh T, Helander HF, Obrink KJ. 1976. Effects of secretagogues on oxygen consumption, aminopyrins accumulation and morphology in isolated gastric glands. *Acta Physiol. Scand.* 97: 401–414
7. Beaumont W. 1833. *Experiments and Observations on the Gastric Juice and the Physiology of Digestion,* ed. FP Allen, Plattsburg, NY
8. Black JW, Duncan WAM, Durant CJ, Ganellin CR, Parsons ME. 1972. Definition and antagonism of histamine H2 receptors. *Nature* 236:385–90
9. Boettcher G, Hakanson R, Nilsson G, Seensalu R, Sundler F. 1989. Effects of long-term hypergastrinaemia on the ultrastructure of enterochromaffin-like cells in the stomach of the rat, hamster and guinea pig. *Cell Tissue Res.* 256:247–57
10. Borch K, Renvall H, Liedberg G, Andersen BN. 1986. Relations between circulating gastrin and endocrine cell proliferation in the atrophic fundic mucosa. *J. Gastroenterol.* 21:357–63
11. Chen D, Monstein H-J, Nylander A-G, Zhao C-M, Hakanson R. 1994. Acute responses of rat stomach ECL cells to gastrin: secretory activation and adaptation. *Gastroenterology* 107:18–27
12. Chew CS. 1986. Cholecystokinin, carbachol, gastrin, histamine and forskolin increase $[Ca^{2+}]_i$ in gastric glands. *Am. J. Physiol.* 250:G814–23
13. Chew C, Hersey S. 1982. Gastrin stimulation of isolated gastric glands. *Am. J. Physiol.* 242:G504–12
14. Chiba T, Kadowaki S, Taminato T, Chihara K, Seino Y, et al. 1981. Effect of antisomatostatin gamma-globulin on gastrin release in rats. *Gastroenterology* 81:321–26
15. Dimaline R, Sandvik AK. 1991. Histidine decarboxylase gene expression in rat fundus is regulated by gastrin. *FEBS Lett.* 281:20–22
16. DuVal JW, Saffouri B, Weir GC, Walsh JH, Arimura A, et al. 1981. Stimulation of gastrin and somatostin secretion from the isolated rat stomach by bombesin. *Am. J. Physiol.* 241:G242–47
17. Edkins JS. 1906. The chemical mechanism of gastric secretion. *J. Physiol.* 34:133–44
18. Forgac M. 1989. Structure and function of vacuolar class of ATP-driven proton pumps. *Physiol. Rev.* 69:765–96
19. Forssmann WG, Orci L, Pictet R, Renold AE, Rouiller C. 1969. The endocrine cells in the epithelium of the gastrointestinal mucosa of the rat. An electron microscopic study. *J. Cell. Biol.* 40:692–715
20. Gantz I, Schaeffer M, DelValle J, Logsdon C, Campbell V, et al. 1991. Molecular cloning of a gene encoding the histamine H2-receptor. *Proc. Natl. Acad. Sci. USA* 488:429–33
21. Geibel J, Abraham R, Modlin I, Sachs G. 1995. Gastrin stimulation of changes in $[Ca]_i$ in parietal cells depends on cAMP. *Gastroenterology* 109:1060–67
22. Giraud AS, Soll AH, Cuttitta F, Walsh JH. 1987. Bombesin stimulation of gastrin release from canine gastrin cells in primary culture. *Am. J. Physiol.* 252:G413–20
23. Hakanson R, Boettcher G, Ekblad F, Panula P, Simonsson M, et al. 1986. Histamine in endocrine cells in the stomach. *Histochemistry* 86:5–17
24. Hakanson R, Owman CH, Sporong B, Sundler F. 1971. Electron microscopic identification of the histamine-storing agyrophil (enterochromaffin-like) cells in the rat stomach. *Z. Zellforsch.* 122:460
25. Hakanson R, Sundler F. 1991. Trophic effects of gastrin. *Scand. J. Gastroenterol.* 26(Suppl. 180):130–36
26. Hakanson R, Tielemanns Y, Chen D, Andersson K, Mattson H, et al. 1993. Time-dependent changes in enterochromaffin-like cell kinetics in stomach of hypergastrinemic rats. *Gastroenterology* 105:15–21

27. Hersey SJ, Sachs G. 1995. Gastric acid secretion *Physiol. Rev.* 75:155–89
28. Larsson LI. 1984. Evidence for anterograde transport of secretory granules in processes of gastric paracrine (somatostatin) cells. *Histochemistry* 80:323–26
29. Larsson H, Carlsson E, Mattsson H, Lundell L, Sundler F, et al. 1986. Plasma gastrin and gastric enterochromaffinlike cell activation and proliferation. *Gastroenterology* 90:391–99
30. Larsson H, Golterman N, DeMagistris L, Rehfeld JF, Schwartz TW. 1979. Somatostatin cell processes as pathways for paracrine secretion. *Science* 205:1393–95
31. Deleted in proof
32. Lee H, Hakanson R, Karlsson A, Mattsson H. 1992. Lansoprazole and omeprazole have similar effects on plasma gastrin levels, enterochromaffinlike cells, gastrin cells and somatostatin cells in the rat stomach. *Digestion* 51:125–32
33. Lewin MJM. 1992. The somatostatin receptor in the GI tract. *Annu. Rev. Physiol.* 54:454–68
34. Loo D, Sachs G, Prinz C. 1996. Potassium and chloride currents on rat gastric enterochromaffinlike cells. *Am. J. Physiol.* 270:G739–45
35. MacIntosh FC. 1938. Histamine as a normal stimulant of gastic secretion. *Q. J. Exp. Physiol.* 28:87–98
36. Modlin IM, Tang LH. 1996. The gastric enterochromaffin-like cell: an enigmatic cellular link. *Gastroenterology.* In press
37. Park J, Chiba T, Yamada T. 1987. Mechanisms for direct inhibition of canine gastric parietal cells by somatostatin. *J. Biol. Chem.* 262:14190–96
38. Pearse AGE. 1969. The cytochemistry and ultrastructure of polypeptide hormone-producing cells of the APUD-series and the embryologic, physiologic and pathophysiologic implication of the concept. *J. Histochem. Chem.* 17:303–13
39. Pearse AGE, Polak JM. 1978. The difffuse neuroendocrine system and the APUD-concept. In *Gut Hormones,* ed. SR Bloom, pp. 514–610, Edinburgh: Churchill-Livingstone
40. Persson P, Hakanson R, Axelson J, Sundler F. 1989. Gastrin releases a blood calcium-lowering peptide from the acid-producing part of the stomach. *Proc. Natl. Acad. Sci. USA* 86:2834–38
41. Prinz C, Sachs G, Walsh J, Coy DH, Wu V. 1994. The somatostatin receptor subtype on rat enterochromaffinlike cells. *Gastroenterology* 107:1067–74
42. Prinz C, Scott DR, Hurwitz D, Helander HF, Sachs G. 1994. Gastrin effects on isolated rat enterochromaffinlike cells in primary culture. *Am. J. Physiol.* 267:G663–75
43. Prinz C, Kajimura M, Scott DR, Helander HF, Shin JM, et al. 1992. Acid secretion and the H, K ATPase of stomach. *Yale J. Biol. Med.* 65:577–95
44. Prinz C, Kajimura M, Scott D, Mercier F, Helander H, Sachs G. 1993. Histamine secretion from rat enterochromaffinlike cells. *Gastroenterology* 105:449–61
45. Prinz C, Neumayer N, Classen M, Schepp W. 1996. Interleukin-1 beta effects on isolated rat enterochromaffinlike cells. *Gastroenterology.* Submitted
46. Rogers S, Wells R, Rechsteiner M. 1986. Amino acid sequences common to rapidly degraded proteins: the PEST hypothesis. *Science* 234:364–68
47. Ryberg B, Axelson J, Hakanson R, Sundler F, Mattson H. 1990. Trophic effects of continuous infusion of [Leu15]-gastrin-17 in the rat. *Gastroenterology* 98:33–38
48. Ryberg B, Tielemanns Y, Axelson J, Carlsson E, Hakanson R, et al. 1990. Gastrin stimulates the self-replication rate of enterochromaffinlike cells in the rat stomach. Effects of omeprazole, ranitidine, and gastrin-17 in antrectomized rats. *Gastroenterology* 99:935–42
49. Sachs G. 1994. The gastric proton pump: the H+, K+-ATPase. In *Physiology of the Gastrointestinal Tract,* ed. LR Johnson, pp. 1119–37. New York: Raven
50. Sachs G, Hersey SJ, Prinz C. 1995. *Gastric Acid Secretion: Mystery to Mechanism, Mechanism to Management.* Germany: Shugar
51. Schubert ML, Makhlouf GM. 1987. Neural regulation of gastrin and somatostatin secretion in rat gastric antral mucosa. *Am. J. Physiol.* 253:G721–25
52. Scott DR, Hersey SJ, Prinz C, Sachs G. 1993. Actions of anti-ulcer drugs. *Science* 262:1453–54
53. Solcia E, Capella C, Buffa R, Usellini L, Fiocca R, et al. 1987. Endocrine cells of the digestive sytem. *Physiology of the Gastrointestinal Tract,* ed. LR Johnson. pp. 111–30. New York: Raven. 2nd ed.
54. Soll AH. 1978. The actions of secretagogues on oxygen uptake by isolated mammalian parietal cells. *J. Clin. Invest.* 61:370–80
55. Soll AH. 1978. The interaction of histamine with gastrin and carbaminocholine on oxygen uptake by isolated canine parietal cells. *J. Clin. Invest.* 61:381–89
56. Soll AH. 1980. Secretagogue stimulation of ($^{14}$C) aminopyrine accumulation by iso-

lated canine parietal cells. *Am. J. Physiol.* 238:G366–75

57. Soll AH, Lewin KJ, Beaven MA. 1980. Isolation of histamine-containing cells from rat gastric mucosa: biochemical and morphological differences from mast cells. *Gastroenterology* 80:717–27

58. Soll AH, Yamada T, Park J, Thomas LP. 1984. Release of somatostatin-like immunoreactivity from canine fundic mucosal cells in primary culture. *Am. J. Physiol.* 247:G558–66

59. Soumarmon A, Cheret A, Lewin M. 1977. Localization of gastrin receptors in intact isolated and separated rat fundic cells. *Gastroenterology* 73:900–3

60. Sundler F, Willems G. 1990. Gastrin stimulates the self-replication of enterochromaffinlike cells in the rat stomach. *Gastroenterology* 99:935–42

61. Tielemanns Y, Axelson J, Sundler F, Willems G, Hakanson R. 1990. Serum gastrin affects the self-replication rate of enterochromaffinlike cells in the rat stomach. *Gut* 31:274–78

62. Tielemanns Y, Hakanson R, Sundler F, Willems G. 1989. Proliferation of enterochromaffinlike cells in omeprazole treated hypergastrinemic rats. *Gastroenterology* 96:723–29

63. Tielemanns Y, Willems G, Sundler F, Hakanson, R. 1986. Self replication of enterochromaffinlike cells in the mouse stomach. *Digestion* 35:23–41

64. Vigna SR, Giraud A, Soll AH, Walsh JH. 1988. Bombesin receptors on gastrin cells. *Ann. NY Acad. Sci.* 547:131–37

65. Yoshimori T, Yamamoto A, Moriyama Y, Futai M, Tashiro Y. 1991. Bafilomycin-A1, a specific inhibitor of vacuolar type $H^+$-ATPase, inhibits acidification and protein degradation in lysosomes of cultured cells. *J. Biol. Chem.* 266:17707–12

66. Zeng N, Bayle DB, Walsh JH, Kang T, Sachs G. 1996. Localization of PACAP receptor on rat fundic ECL cell and D cells. *Gastroenterology* 110:A1131

67. Zeng N, Kang T, Walsh JH, Sachs G. 1996. Voltage-dependent calcium channels in gastric ECL cells. *Gastroenterology* 110:A1136

68. Zeng N, Kang T, Walsh JH, Sachs G. 1995. PYY and inhibition of gastric acid secretion. *Physiologist* 38(5):256

69. Zeng N, Walsh JH, Kang T, Helander K, Helander HF, et al. 1996. Selective ligand-induced intracellular calcium changes in a population of isolated gastric endocrine cells. *Gastroenterology* 110:1835–46

70. Zeng N, Zeng TK, Walsh JH, Scott D, Sachs G. 1995. Specific amino acids activate calcium signals in isolated G cells of rat antrum. *Gastroenterology* 108: A1020

*Annu. Rev. Physiol. 1997. 59:257–71*

# ENTEROGLUCAGON

## J. J. Holst

Department of Medical Physiology, the Panum Institute, University of Copenhagen, DK 2200 Copenhagen N, Denmark

KEY WORDS:   glucagon-like peptide-1, GLP-1, glicentin, oxyntomodulin, GLP-2

## ABSTRACT

The gene encoding proglucagon, the biosynthetic precursor of glucagon, is expressed not only in the pancreatic islets but also in endocrine cells of the gastrointestinal mucosa. The proglucagon (PG)-derived peptides from the gut include glicentin (corresponding to PG 1–69); smaller amounts of oxyntomodulin (PG 33–69) and glicentin-related pancreatic polypeptide (GRPP, PG 1–30); glucagon-like peptide-1 (GLP-1, PG 78–107 amide); intervening peptide-2 (IP-2, PG 111–122 amide); and glucagon-like peptide-2 (GLP-2, PG 126–158). All are secreted into the blood in response to ingestion of carbohydrates and lipids. Only oxyntomodulin and GLP-1 have proven biological activity; oxyntomodulin possibly because it interacts (but with lower potency) with GLP-1 and glucagon receptors. GLP-1 is the most potent insulinotropic hormone known and functions as an incretin hormone. It also inhibits glucagon secretion and, therefore, lowers blood glucose. This effect is preserved in patients with non-insulin-dependent diabetes mellitus, in whom infusions of GLP-1 may completely normalize blood glucose. However, GLP-1 also potently inhibits gastrointestinal secretion and motility, and its physiological functions include mediation of the "ileal-brake" effect, i.e. the inhibition of upper gastrointestinal functions elicited by the presence of unabsorbed nutrients in the ileum. As such it may serve to regulate food intake.

## INTRODUCTION

### The Proglucagon-Derived Gut Peptides

The enteroglucagon-producing cell, classified by electron microscopy as the L-cell, is one of the most abundant endocrine cell types in the mucosa of the mammalian ileum and colon (16, 104). It is one of the so-called open-type endocrine cells, i.e. pyramid-shaped, with an apical process equipped

257

with microvillli reaching the intestinal lumen, and a base rich in endocrine granules near the basal lamina. The shape, therefore, suggests that the cell can respond to changes in the milieu of the gut lumen with a basal discharge of the granular contents. The enteroglucagon-producing cells were first identified in 1961 (100), when it was demonstrated that certain antisera raised against the pancreatic hormone glucagon react with intestinal endocrine cells. It was soon realized that the intestinal immunodeterminant responsible for the immune reaction differed chemically from pancreatic glucagon (101), but the nature of the enteroglucagon or gut GLI (glucagon-like immmunoreactivity) remained enigmatic until it was demonstrated that the 69-amino acid peptide glicentin, the molecule likely responsible for the immune reaction, contains the entire 29-amino acid glucagon sequence (28, 95). Small amounts of the same peptide may be found in pancreatic extracts (91), and the fragments of glicentin that remain after excision of the glucagon sequence were found to be secreted in parallel with glucagon from the pancreas (61, 113). Thus glicentin was thought to represent at least a fragment of the glucagon precursor, proglucagon (PG) (61, 95). In 1983, the full structure of proglucagon was deduced from the sequence of a hamster cDNA encoding glucagon (5), and it was confirmed that the sequence of the N-terminal 69 amino acids of hamster proglucagon is almost identical to that of glicentin (which is the porcine counterpart). Only one gene encoding the glucagon sequence has been identified in mammals (111), and identical mRNAs are formed in the mammalian intestinal and the pancreatic cells expressing the gene (67) (but not in avian and piscine species) (44). It appears, therefore, that the different peptide products in the two tissues arise as a consequence of differential posttranslational processing of the precursor (30, 31, 59, 72). In the pancreas, glucagon, which occupies amino acid residues 33 to 61 of PG (and glicentin), is formed (see Figure 1), together with the cleavage products glicentin-related pancreatic peptide, GRPP (PG 1–30) and PG 64–69 (34, 96). In the gut, the main product is glicentin (PG), but part of this peptide is cleaved further to PG 33–69 (29), also designated oxyntomodulin (3), and to corresponding amounts of GRPP (PG 1–30) (30, 31).

However, as already indicated from studies of glucagon biosynthesis (81), proglucagon is a much larger molecule than glicentin, with 160 rather than 69 amino acid residues and, furthermore, contains two additional glucagon-like sequences, the so-called glucagon-like peptides 1 and 2 (GLP-1 and GLP-2) (5). GLP-1 and 2 are glucagon-like because of their close to 50% sequence homology with glucagon. They correspond to the sequences 72–108 and 126–158 of proglucagon, in which they are flanked by pairs of basic amino acid residues, typical proteolytic processing sites. It appears that this C-terminal part of proglucagon is also subject to differential processing (59, 72, 74) (Figure 1).

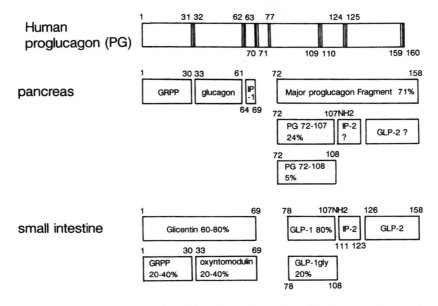

*Figure 1* A schematic representation of the differential processing of proglucagon as it occurs in the pancreatic islets and in the intestinal mucosa in humans. The vertical lines in proglucagon (PG) indicate the positions of the cleavage sites (basic amino acids). GRPP, glicentin-related pancreatic peptide; IP-1, intervening peptide 1; IP-2, intervening peptide-2. Note that in the pancreas, the main products are glucagon itself and GRPP (inactive) and major proglucagon fragment (inactive). Small amounts of N-terminally extended GLP-1 (inactive) may also be formed. In the gut the main products are glicentin, in which the glucagon sequence is buried (whereby glucagon-like bioactivity is lost); GLP-1, the majority of which is amidated; and GLP-2, the function of which is unknown. Thus although the precursor is the same, the differential processing gives rise to two biologically active but completely different products in the two tissues, whereas terminal extensions inactivate the other active product. See text for details.

In the pancreas, the predominant product is a large peptide, the major proglucagon fragment (MPGF) (80), comprising residues 72 to 158 of PG (34). In addition, small amounts of a peptide that correspond to PG 72–107 amide are formed (34). In the gut epithelium, the C-terminal part of the precursor is cleaved to release each of the two glucagon-like peptides (59, 72), which are also secreted from the intestinal mucosa in parallel with glicentin upon appropriate stimulation (72). However, PG is not cleaved at the predicted location of the two basic amino acid residues, Lys[70] and Arg[71], but at a single basic residue, Arg[77] (38). The fully processed GLP-1 is thus truncated by six amino acids, compared with the predicted peptide. Furthermore, at least in humans, the C-terminal Gly[108] serves as a substrate for C-terminal amidation

(70, 77). Thus the structure of natural GLP-1 corresponds to PG 78–107 amide (71, 77), which is frequently designated GLP-1 7–36 amide to indicate the N-terminal truncation.

Among the proglucagon-derived peptides (PGDPs), glucagon, from the pancreas, and GLP-1, from the gut, have attracted the most attention because both are biologically active. In contrast, both MPGF and glicentin, in which the GLP and glucagon sequences, respectively, are buried, are inactive (as is the N-terminally extended GLP-1, PG 72–107 amide from the pancreas). It seems, therefore, that the purpose of the differential processing is to release alternating biologically active sequences from the two tissues, while at the same time ensuring inactivation of the other active sequence. The structure of fully processed human GLP-2 has been found to correspond to PG 126–158 (7, 24, 71). The details of the processing of proglucagon were recently reviewed (37).

The products of the L-cells, all of which are released synchronously in response to appropriate stimulation, are the following: glicentin (PG 1–69); smaller amounts of GRPP (PG 1–30) and oxyntomodulin; GLP-1 (PG 78–107 amide); intervening peptide-2 (PG 111–123); and GLP-2 (126–158). At present, several groups are attempting to identify the enzymes responsible for the differential processing. It seems probable that the subtilisin-like prohormone convertase PC2 is involved in the pancreatic processing of PG, but the intestinal enzymes have not been unambiguously identified (37, 85, 86). Interestingly, it appears that at least a subpopulation of the enteroglucagon cells also produce and secrete the polypeptide PYY (peptide tyrosine, tyrosine) (6) and that a parallel release of this peptide and the proglucagon-derived peptides may occur. This may have important implications for the ileal-brake function of the peptides, as discussed below.

## MEASUREMENT OF THE INTESTINAL PGDPs

Because of the presence of the glucagon sequence in glicentin and oxyntomodulin, these peptides react with antisera against glucagon if they are directed against immunodeterminants that do not include the termini of the peptides (so-called side-viewing antisera). Thus their concentration in plasma can be measured using glucagon radioimmunoassays based on side-viewing antisera, but such assays also cross-react with glucagon from the pancreas. The concentration of pancreatic glucagon, however, may be estimated using assays based on antisera against the C-terminal of glucagon, and glucagon's contribution to the total immunoreactivity measured by the side-viewing antisera may then be subtracted (26). There is extensive literature dealing with secretion of enteroglucagon based on such subtraction assays (for reviews, see 32, 33, 36, 62, 106). Specific determination of glicentin or oxyntomodulin requires a two-site technique, but thus far such assays have not been developed. Determination of the glucagon-like peptides is equally complicated. Most assays for GLP-1 rely on antisera directed against the amidated C-terminus, but such assays also pick up the small amounts of N-terminally extended (inactive) GLP-1 secreted from the pancreas (34). A more serious problem arises as a consequence of extremely rapid and extensive N-terminal degradation of GLP-1 in the circulation, resulting in accumulation of the inactive metabolite, GLP-1 9–36 amide, which is measured quantitatively by the C-terminal assays (12, 13). Therefore, N-terminally directed or two-site assays are required for accurate determination of the concentration of biologically active GLP-1 (14, 83), whereas estimates of the rate of GLP-1 secretion are made with a C-terminal assay. An N-terminal assay is also required for specific determination of GLP-2 (25).

## SECRETION OF THE PGDPs

The secretion of the PGDPs from the gut increases in response to ingestion of ordinary mixed meals (30, 36, 62, 69); i.e. carbohydrates and lipids increase secretion. Stimulatory carbohydrates include actively absorbed and metabolized sugars, whereas other carbohydrates are inactive. If absorption is prevented (by ouabain or phloretin), secretion is abolished (93). However, it is not known if the absorbing enterocytes signal to the L-cells or if the L-cell itself is capable of absorbing and coupling secretion to absorption. The secretory response occurs rapidly after the start of meal ingestion. Indeed, under certain circumstances, increases may be noted within a few minutes of ingestion, i.e. before the nutrients are expected to reach the rather distal regions of the gut mucosa where the bulk of the peptides are found. It has been speculated that neural or endocrine mechanisms also regulate secretion. In rats, the duodenal hormone gastric inhibitory polypeptide (GIP) may function in a stimulatory loop, signaling from the upper to the lower gut (84). In humans and pigs, however, GIP does not increase the secretion of PGDPs (65). Acetylcholine increases the secretion of PGDPs in various experimental settings (27, 82), but in numerous experiments carried out in the author's laboratory, stimulation of the extrinsic nerve supply to the gut revealed exclusively a noradrenergic, inhibitory input to the L-cell. Neither selective parasympathetic stimulation nor stimulation of mixed intestinal nerves after adrenergic blockade resulted in stimulated secretion. However, de-inhibition of tonic noradrenergic inhibition could constitute a stimulatory mechanism.

## ACTIONS OF THE PGDPs

### Glicentin and GRPP

Only extremely small amounts of pure, natural glicentin have been available for research. In rats, the peptide had inconspicuous effects on the pancreas (112), but gastric acid secretion was inhibited (51). Insulin secretion was not affected in mice (1). Synthetic glicentin was recently made available for experimental research and preliminary but contrasting findings have been reported (50, 68). In our laboratory, human glicentin infused into humans had neither endocrine effects nor effects on gastric acid secretion. A hypothesis that glicentin might promote growth and adaptation of the intestinal mucosa has not been confirmed (30, 32, 36, 50). Studies concerning actions of GRPP have not been published, but in studies of Thim and coworkers (96) as well as in the author's laboratory, this peptide had no effects on gastroentero-pancreatic secretion or motility.

## Oxyntomodulin

Oxyntomodulin consists of glucagon plus a small C-terminal extension (3, 29) and, therefore, exhibits glucagon-like bioactivity in most systems (2). Its affinity for the glucagon receptor, however, is only about 2% of that of glucagon. In rats, oxyntomodulin is more potent as an inhibitor of gastric acid secretion than glucagon, and this finding, together with the fact that the 30–37 fragment of oxyntomodulin (not found in glucagon) also inhibits acid secretion, led to the suggestion that oxyntomodulin might act via specific receptors in the rat stomach (45). More recent studies have shown, however, that oxyntomodulin acts as a weaker agonist for the GLP-1 receptors on parietal and other gastric cells (23), and interaction with these receptors could well explain its reported effects. A hydrolysis product of oxyntomodulin exhibiting similar potency as an inhibitor of gastric acid secretion was thought to be a physiological inhibitor (46). In a recent survey of molecules with oxyntomodulin-like immunoreactivity in rats, however, only intact oxyntomodulin was found (9). The naturally occurring proglucagon fragment PG 64–69 (34), which is secreted from the pancreas in parallel with glucagon (113), does not inhibit acid secretion in rats (8).

Oxyntomodulin is an efficient inhibitor of gastric and pancreatic functions in humans (89) and also inhibits gastric motility in a manner similar to that exerted by GLP-1 (see below). This may be because its actions are mediated by GLP-1 receptors. However, rather high infusion rates ($\approx 100$ pmol/kg/h) resulting in supraphysiological plasma levels were required to elicit these effects, and the extent of oxyntomodulin influence on gastrointestinal functions under physiological circumstances is unknown. In conditions with increased rates of secretion of PG-derived gut peptides, it may act as an enterogastrone. Its actions on the liver and on the endocrine pancreas (presumably via interactions with glucagon- and GLP-1 receptors, respectively) are probably too weak to play a physiological role (2).

## GLP-1

PANCREATIC EFFECTS    GLP-1 is the most interesting of the intestinal PGDPs. It is the most potent insulinotropic hormone (38, 60, 69) and is uniquely effective in stimulating insulin secretion and insulin gene expression (18, 19), even in patients with severe type 2 (insulin-independent) diabetes mellitus (65, 66). Because of this, the peptide is presently being evaluated as one of the most promising new therapeutic principles in the treatment of type 2 diabetes (35). It stimulates $\beta$-cell secretion via interaction with the GLP-1 receptor, a specific receptor (97) that belongs to a subfamily of seven-transmembrane spanning, G protein-coupling receptors. These receptors include other members of the glucagon-secretin family of peptides and, interestingly, receptors for calcitonin and PTH. Only a single molecular form of the GLP-1 receptor has been identified thus far. In $\beta$-cells, GLP-1 stimulates adenylate cyclase, and activation of protein kinase A appears essential for transmission of its effects (18). However, a pronounced elevation of intracellular $Ca^{2+}$, apparently representing a $Ca^{2+}$-induced release of intracellular calcium, is probably the mechanism whereby insulin secretion is stimulated (22, 41). The GLP-1 effect on insulin secretion is critically dependent on the presence and concentration of glucose in the medium, and its effect may also be described as a potentiation of glucose-induced insulin secretion. GLP-1 also potentiates amino acid-induced insulin secretion (20). In the rat pancreas, the glucose threshold for potentiation by GLP-1 is 4.5 mmol/l, and at higher glucose concentrations, the effect is amplified (47). It is possible that the opening of voltage-gated $Ca^{2+}$-channels (the result of glucose metabolism-induced closure of ATP-dependent $K^+$-channels) is responsible for the initial $Ca^{2+}$-elevation that is amplified by GLP-1 (22, 40). (In the case of amino acid-induced secretion, depolarization may be caused by entry of positively charged amino acids). Conversely, GLP-1 seems to confer glucose competence on the $\beta$-cells (22, 40). Unlike $\beta$-cells in situ in the islets, single, isolated $\beta$-cells respond poorly to glucose alone, but after exposure to GLP-1, they do respond. Perhaps a certain level of GLP-1-mediated activation of the $\beta$-cell is required for the generation of a sufficient elevation of intracellular calcium to elicit insulin secretion. Under physiological circumstances, this critical level could be provided either by the low circulating concentrations of GLP-1 from the gut (because GLP-1 is very potent), or by glucagon from neighboring $\alpha$-cells interacting with GLP-1 (or glucagon?) receptors on the $\beta$-cells in a paracrine manner (glucagon is a weak agonist for the GLP-1 receptor) (97). This would explain the poor response to glucose in isolated cells compared with $\beta$-cells clustered (together with $\alpha$-cells) in the pancreatic islets. Physiologically, with respect to its insulinotropic actions, GLP-1 functions as an incretin hormone, i.e. one of the intestinal hormones responsible for the enhanced insulin secretion after oral (as compared with parenteral) glucose administration (53, 69). This has been clearly demonstrated in experiments employing exendin 9–39, a specific GLP-1 receptor antagonist; administration of this antagonist almost abolishes the incretin effect of intestinal glucose administration in rats (52, 107). In humans, the insulinotropic effects of GIP and GLP-1 are additive, and together they can fully account for the incretin effect (63).

GLP-1 also potently inhibits glucagon secretion (73), presumably by an indirect mechanism, because the $\alpha$-cells do not possess GLP-1 receptors (58). Thus upon infusion of GLP-1, the portal vein plasma concentration of insulin increases, the glucagon concentration decreases, and as a result, the hepatic glucose production decreases (43). At the same time, $R_d$, the rate of disappearence of glucose, remains constant, and as a consequence, blood glucose decreases. However, because GLP-1's effect on insulin and glucagon secretion wanes with decreasing glucose concentrations, the decrease amounts to only 1 to 1.5 mmol/l. The hypoglycemic effect of GLP-1 is thus self-limiting. This is of particular importance for its potential in the treatment of diabetes where GLP-1, unlike insulin, does not cause dangerous hypoglycemia (35). Based on studies in rodents, where GLP-1 may have direct peripheral actions on adipocytes (15), skeletal muscle (105), and hepatocytes (103), it has been speculated that part of GLP-1's glucose-lowering effect in humans could also be due to direct peripheral effects (10, 11). However, recent studies involving hyperinsulinemic, euglycemic clamp techniques and endocrine clamps, using high doses of somatostatin to eliminate changes in the secretion of the pancreatic glucoregulatory hormones (79, 98), have indicated that the GLP-1-induced effects on glucose disposal are exclusively the result of the effect of GLP-1 on the secretion of these hormones.

GASTROINTESTINAL EFFECTS    GLP-1 has pronounced effects on gastrointestinal secretion and motility in humans (33). In physiological doses, it inhibits pentagastrin- (88) as well as meal-induced gastric acid secretion (110) and powerfully inhibits gastric emptying (110). It also inhibits meal-induced pancreatic exocrine secretion (55), although this may be secondary to its effects on gastric emptying. In physiological doses, GLP- 1 nearly abolished vagally induced acid secretion (induced by sham-feeding) (109) but had no effect on pentagastrin-induced secretion in vagotomized subjects (78). In rats, GLP- 1 increases the secretion of somatostatin from the gastric D-cells (17), which might explain the inhibitory effects in this species. However, at the same time, GLP-1 receptor activation in rat parietal cells stimulates aminopyrin uptake (i.e. acid secretion), and in this species, there is no net effect on acid secretion in vivo (90). In the pig stomach, GLP-1 does not influence somatostatin secretion (73), and the lack of effect on acid secretion in vagotomized subjects (78) also indicates that GLP-1 does not affect gastric secretion directly in humans or pigs. The role of the vagus can be more clearly demonstrated in pigs, in which insulin-induced hypoglycemia stimulates gastric acid secretion, pancreatic secretion, and antral motility (39). These effects can be abolished by vagotomy as well as by infusion

of GLP-1. In human subjects, perfusion of the distal ileum with carbohydrate-
or lipid-containing solutions causes profound inhibition of stimulated as well
as interdigestive gastric and pancreatic secretion (57). During ileal perfusion,
GLP-1 secretion is markedly increased, and it has been speculated that GLP-1
may act as one of the enterogastrone hormones responsible for this ileal-brake
effect (56). Indeed, if GLP-1 is infused into humans in physiological amounts
during the ingestion of a meal, insulin secretion is actually decreased as a consequence of the dramatic inhibitory effects of GLP-1 on gastric emptying (64),
as compared with control experiments with saline infusion. The peptide PYY,
co-stored with GLP-1 in the L-cells, is released in such experiments and also
inhibits gastrointestinal secretion and motility (56, 57, 109). The two hormones
may act together as entergastrones (109).

CEREBRAL ACTIONS    As mentioned above, the gastrointestinal actions of GLP-1
seem to involve an inhibition of efferent, stimulatory vagal pathways. In an attempt to identify the receptors responsible for these effects, radiolabeled GLP-1
was infused intracardially in rats, which were subsequently fixed, sectioned,
and subjected to autoradiography (76). Staining was found in pancreatic islets
(75), stomach, lungs, and kidneys as expected, but specific staining was also
observed in the subfornical organ and the area postrema of the cerebral circumventricular organ, suggesting that peripheral GLP-1 may interact with the
brain via these blood-brain barrier leaks (76). However, many more receptors
than those visualized after peripheral adminstration of labeled GLP-1 can be
demonstrated by incubation of brain sections with labeled GLP-1 (21, 49, 76,
92, 102). With this technique, numerous specific binding sites were revealed in
the hypothalamus and in the periventricular strata of the third ventricle. Most
likely the binding results from the presence of GLP-1 receptors identical to the
pancreatic receptors (108), and it is doubtful whether additional receptors exist.
The occurrence of GLP-1 receptors appears to correspond to the presence of
GLP-1-containing nerve fibers in these areas of the brain (48, 54). These nerve
fibers appear to project from nerve cell bodies in the brain stem, particularly localized in the caudal part of the nucleus of the solitary tract. Interestingly, these
nuclei are known to receive afferent inputs from gastrointestinal organs including the stomach and the intestine. Furthermore, the brain GLP-1 receptors are
mainly localized to hypothalamic nuclei involved in regulation of digestive behavior. Moreover, intraventricular administration of GLP-1 profoundly inhibits
food intake in rats (87, 94, 99). This effect seems to be highly specific. Thus
N-terminally extended GLP-1 (PG 72–107 amide) is inactive, and appropriate
doses of the GLP-1 antagonist exendin 9–39 abolish the effects of GLP-1 (94).
It is possible that neural signals ascending from upper gastrointestinal organs
registering a plentitude of nutritional supplies activate GLP-1-containing brain

stem neurons, which in turn, using GLP-1 as a transmitter, transmit to hypothalamic centers and regulate food intake. Peripheral administration of GLP-1
does not inhibit food intake acutely in rats (94, 99). However, it is possible that
GLP-1 secreted from the intesinal L-cells also acts as a satiety signal, by either
interacting with the receptors in the subfornical organ and the area postrema
or with nerve endings in the periphery, or merely by inhibiting gastric motility,
which is likely to elicit a sensation of satiety.

## Intervening Peptide-2 and GLP-2

The sequences of IP-2 and GLP-2 are highly conserved during evolution (7) but
not to the same degree as GLP-1 and glucagon. The structure of GLP-1 is identical in all mammals investigated thus far. The human IP-2 is an amidated peptide
(7), and porcine IP-2 is secreted in parallel with glicentin and GLP-1 from the
isolated perfused porcine ileum. Nothing is known about the possible biological
effects of IP-2. GLP-2 is also secreted in parallel with glicentin and GLP-1 (72),
and its concentration in peripheral plasma varies in parallel with that of GLP-1,
i.e. with clear responses to the main meals (25). Thus far nothing is known with
certainty about its biological actions. It does not interact with the glucagon or the
GLP-1 receptors or any other known receptors, and a receptor for GLP-2 has not
been cloned. An early report (42) claimed activation of hypothalamic adenylate
cyclase by GLP-2. A C-terminally extended molecular form, the only commercially available product, was employed, but its importance is unknown. GLP-2
does not share any of the effects of glucagon or GLP-1 on the endocrine pancreas
or the liver. A recent report claims induction of intestinal epithelial proliferation
by GLP-2, an observation of particular interest in view of the hypothesis alluded to above that the PGDPs promote growth and adaptation of the intestinal
mucosa (14a, 32).

## CONCLUSION

Essential physiological functions have not been convincingly demonstrated for
the intestinal PGDPs except for GLP-1. GLP-1 appears to have a dual function. One is as an incretin hormone. As demonstrated in experiments with the
potent GLP-1 receptor antagonist exendin 9–39, GLP-1 secretion is likely to be
responsible, together with secretion of the duodenal hormone GIP for most of
the enhanced insulin secretion seen in response meal ingestion in excess of that
caused by increased concentrations of insulinotropic substrates (glucose, amino
acids etc). The glucose-lowering effect of GLP-1, which is a combination of
its insulinotropic and glucagonostatic effects, is preserved in patients with diabetes mellitus, and GLP-1 or analogues of GLP-1 are currently being evaluated
as therapeutic agents for diabetes treatment. A second function of GLP-1 is

to inhibit gastrointestinal secretion and motility, and the hormone is likely to mediate, perhaps together with the ileal hormone PYY, the ileal-brake effect. GLP-1 may also function as a neurotransmitter, transmitting signals from upper gastrointestinal organs to the hypothalamus, where activation of GLP-1 receptors potently inhibits food intake. Because GLP-1 may reach at least some of the brain receptors via the circulation, intestinal GLP-1 conceivably also regulates digestive behavior.

*Literature Cited*

1. Ahrén B, Lundquist I. 1980. Effects of glicentin on insulin secretion. *Horm. Metab. Res.* 12:582–86
2. Baldissera FGA, Holst JJ, Knuhtsen S, Hilsted L, Nielsen OV. 1988. Oxyntomodulin (glicentin 33-69) pharmacokinetics, binding to liver cell membranes, effects on isolated perfused pig pancreas, and secretion from isolated perfused lower small intestine of pigs. *Regul. Pept.* 21:151–66
3. Bataille D, Tatemoto K, Gespach C, Jörnvall H, Rosselin G, Mutt V. 1982. Isolation of glucagon-37 (bioactive enteroglucagon/oxyntomodulin) from porcine jejuno-ileum. Characterization of the peptide. *FEBS Lett.* 146:79–86
4. Bell GI, Sanchez-Pescador R, Laybourn PJ, Najarian RC. 1983. Exon duplication and divergence in the human preproglucagon gene. *Nature* 304:368–71
5. Bell GI, Santerre RF, Mullenbach GT. 1983. Hamster preproglucagon contains the sequence of glucagon and two related peptides. *Nature* 302:716–18
6. Böttcher G. 1991. *Peptide YY in gut and pancreas.* PhD thesis. Univ. Lund, Sweden. 56 pp.
7. Buhl T, Thim L, Kofod H, Ørskov C, Harling H, Holst JJ. 1988. Naturally occurring products of proglucagon 111–160 in the porcine and human small intestine. *J. Biol. Chem.* 263:8621–24
8. Carles-Bonnet C, Jarrousse C, Niel H, Martinez J, Bataille D. 1991. Oxyntomodulin and its (19-37) and (30-37) fragments inhibit histamine-stimulated gastric acid secretion in the conscious rat. *Eur. J. Pharmacol.* 203:245–52
9. Collie NL, Walsh JH, Wong HC, Shively JE, Davis MT, et al. 1994. Purification and sequence of rat oxyntomodulin. *Proc. Natl. Acad. Sci. USA* 91:9362–66
10. D'Alessio DA, Kahn SE, Leusner C, Ensinck JW. 1994. Glucagon-like peptide 1 enhances glucose tolerance both by stimulation of insulin release and by increasing insulin-independent glucose disposal. *J. Clin. Invest.* 93:2263–66
11. D'Alessio DA, Prigeon RL, Ensinck JW. 1995. Enteral enhancement of glucose disposition by both insulin-dependent and insulin-independent processes. A physiological role of glucagon-like peptide-1. *Diabetes* 44:1433–37
12. Deacon CF, Johnsen AH, Holst JJ. 1995. Degradation of glucagon-like peptide-1 by human plasma in vitro yields an N-terminally truncated peptide that is a major endogenous metabolite in vivo. *J. Clin. Endocrinol. Metab.* 80:952–57
13. Deacon CF, Nauck MA, Toft-Nielsen M, Pridal L, Willms B, Holst JJ. 1995. Both subcutaneous and intravenously administered glucagon-like peptide-1 are rapidly degraded from the amino terminus in type II diabetic patients and in healthy subjects. *Diabetes* 44:1126–31
14. Deacon CF, Klarskov L, Olesen M, Pridal L, Holst JJ. 1996. Differential organ specific metabolism of glucagon-like peptide-1 in the anesthetized pig. *Am. J. Physiol.* 271:E458–64
14a. Drucker DJ, Ehrlich P, Asa SL, Brubaker PL. 1996. Induction of intestinal epithelial proliferation by glucagon-like peptide-2. *Proc. Natl. Acad. Sci. USA* 93:7911–16
15. Egan JM, Montrose-Rafizadeh C, Wang Y, Berrnier M, Roth J. 1994. Glucagon-like peptide-1(7–36) amide (GLP-1) enhances insulin-stimulated glucose metabolism in 3t3-L1 adipocytes: one of several potential extrapancreatic sites of GLP-1 action. *Endocrinology* 135:2070–75
16. Eissele R, Göke R, Willemer S, Harthus HP, Vermeer H, et al. 1992. Glucagon-like peptide-1 cells in the gastrointestinal tract and pancreas of rat, pig and man. *Eur. J. Clin. Invest.* 22:283–91
17. Eissele R, Koop H, Arnold R. 1990. Effect of glucagon-like peptide-1 on gastric

somatostatin and gastrin secretion in the rat. *Scand. J. Gastroenterol.* 25:449–54

18. Fehmann H-C, Göke R, Göke B. 1995. Cell and molecular biology of the incretin hormones glucagon-like peptide-I (GLP-1) and glucose-dependent insulin releasing polypeptide (GIP). *Endocr. Rev.* 16:390–410

19. Fehmann H-C, Habener JF. 1992. Insulinotropic hormone glucagon-like peptide-I (7–37) stimulation of proinsulin gene expression and proinsulin biosynthesis in insulinoma βTC-1 cells. *Endocrinology* 130:159–66

20. Fieseler P, Bridenbaugh S, Nustede R, Martell J, Ørskov C, et al. 1995. Physiological augmentation of amino acid-induced insulin secretion by GIP and GLP-1 but not by CCK-8. *Am. J. Physiol.* 268:E949–55

21. Göke R, Larsen PJ, Mikkelsen JD, Sheikh S. 1995. Distribution of GLP-1 binding sites in the rat brain. Evidence that exendin-4 is a ligand of brain GLP-1 binding sites. *Eur. J. Neurosci.* 7:2294–2300

22. Gromada J, Dissing S, Bopkvist K, Renström E, Frøkjär-Jensen J, et al. 1995. Glucagon-like peptide I increases cytoplasmic calcium in insulin-secreting βTC3-cells by enhancement of intracellular calcium mobilization. *Diabetes* 44:767–74

23. Gros L, Thorens B, Bataille D, Kervran A. 1993. Glucagon-like peptide-1-(7–36) amide, oxyntomodulin, and glucagon interact with a common receptor in a somatostatin-secreting cell line. *Endocrinology* 133:631–38

24. Hartmann B, Johnsen AH, Ørskov C, Holst JJ. 1996. Structure, analysis and secretion of human glucagon-like peptide-2 (GLP-2). *Diabetes* 45:300A (Suppl.)

25. Hartmann B, Ørskov C, Wettergren A, Holst JJ. 1995. Diurnal profiles of glucagon-like peptides 1 and 2 (GLP-1 and GLP-2) in normal man. *Diabetologia* 38(Suppl. 1):A167

26. Heding LG. 1971. Radioimmunological determination of pancreatic and gut glucagon in plasma. *Diabetologia* 7:10–19

27. Herrmann-Rinke C, Vöge A, Hess M, Göke B. 1995. Regulation of glucagon-like peptide-1 secretion from rat ileum by neurotransmitters and peptides. *J. Endocrinol.* 147:25–31

28. Holst JJ. 1980. Evidence that glicentin contains the entire glucagon sequence. *Biochem. J.* 187:337–43

29. Holst JJ. 1982. Evidence that enteroglucagon (II) is identical with the C-terminal sequence (residues 33-69) of glicentin. *Biochem. J.* 207:381–88

30. Holst JJ. 1983. Gut glucagon, enteroglucagon, gut GLI, glicentin—current status. *Gastroenterology* 84:1602–13

31. Holst JJ. 1983. Radioreceptorassays for glucagon. In *Glucagon: Handbook of Experimental Pharmacology,* ed. PJ Lefebvre, 60/1:245–61. Berlin: Springer-Verlag

32. Holst JJ. 1988. Enteroglucagon. In *Gastrointestinal Hormones. Advances in Metabolic Disorders,* ed. M Mutt, 11:393–420. San Diego: Academic

33. Holst JJ. 1994. Glucagon-like peptide-1 (GLP-1)—a newly discovered GI hormone. *Gastroenterology* 107:1848–55

34. Holst JJ, Bersani M, Johnsen AH, Kofod H, Hartmann B, Ørskov C. 1994. Proglucagon processing in porcine and human pancreas. *J. Biol. Chem.* 269:18827–33

35. Holst JJ, Nauck MA, Deacon CF, Ørskov C. 1996. Potential of GLP-1 in diabetes management. In *Glucagon III. Handbook of Experimental Pharmacology,* ed. PJ Lefebvre, vol. 123. Berlin: Springer-Verlag. In press

36. Holst JJ, Ørskov C. 1994. Glucagon and other proglucagon-derived peptides. In *Gut Peptides: Biochemistry and Physiology,* ed. JH Walsh, GJ Dockray, pp. 305–40. New York: Raven

37. Holst JJ, Ørskov C, Hartmann B, Deacon CF. 1996. Posttranslational processing of proglucagon and postsecretory fate of proglucagon products. In *The Insulinotropic Gut Hormone Glucagon-like Peptide-1. Frontiers in Diabetes,* ed. HC Fehmann, B Göke. Basel: Karger. In press

38. Holst JJ, Ørskov AC, Schwartz TW, Nielsen OV. 1987. Truncated glucagon-like peptide I, an insulin-releasing hormone from the distal gut. *FEBS Lett.* 211:169–74

39. Holst JJ, Wettergren A, Wøjdemann M, Poulsen SS, Ørskov C. 1995. Glucagon-like peptide-1 (GLP-1): an important enterogastrone acting via the central nervous system. *Hepato-Gastroenterology* 42:1071

40. Holz GG, Kühtreiber WM, Habener JF. 1993. Pancreatic beta-cells are rendered glucose competent by the insulinotropic hormone glucagon-like peptide-1(7–37). *Nature* 361:362–65

41. Holz GG, Leech CA, Habener JF. 1995. Activation of a cAMP-regulated $Ca^{2+}$-signaling pathway in pancreatic β-cells

by the insulinotropic hormone glucagon-like peptide-1. *J. Biol. Chem.* 270:17749–59
42. Hoosein NM, Gurd RS. 1985. Human glucagon-like peptides 1 and 2 activate rat brain adenylate cyclase. *FEBS Lett.* 178:83–86
43. Hvidberg A, Toft Nielsen M, Hilsted J, Orskov C, Holst JJ. 1994. Effect of glucagon-like peptide-1 (proglucagon 78–107 amide) on hepatic glucose production in healthy man. *Metabolism* 43:104–8
44. Irwin DM, Wong J. 1995. Trout and chicken proglucagon: alternative splicing generates mRNA transcripts encoding glucagon-like peptide 2. *Mol. Endocrinol.* 9:267–77
45. Jarrousse C, Audousset-Puech M-P, Dubrasquet M. 1985. Oxyntomodulin (glucagon-37) and its C-terminal octapeptide inhibit gastric acid secretion. *FEBS Lett.* 188:81–84
46. Jarrousse C, Carles-Bonnet C, Niel H, Sabatier R, Audousset-Puech M-P, et al. 1993. Inhibition of gastric acid secretion by oxyntomodulin and its 19–37 fragment in the conscious rat. *Am. J. Physiol.* 264:G816–23
47. Jia X, Brown JC, Pederson RA, McIntosh CHS. 1995. The effects of glucose dependent insulinotropic polypeptide and glucagon-like peptide-1 (7–36) on insulin secretion. *Am. J. Physiol.* 268:E645–51
48. Jin SL, Han VK, Simmons JG, Towle AC, Lauder JM, Lund PK. 1988. Distribution of glucagon-like peptide I (GLP-I), glucagon, and glicentin in the rat brain: and immunocytochemical study. *J. Comp. Neurol.* 271:519–32
49. Kanse SM, Kreymann B, Ghatei MA, Bloom SR. 1988. Identification and characterization of glucagon-like peptide-7–36 amide binding sites in the rat brain and lung. *FEBS Lett.* 241:209–12
50. Kawai K, Sasaki K, Yokota C, Sato T, Yamashita K. 1995. Recombinant DNA glicentin and its biological activity. *Diabetologia* 38(Suppl. 1):A130
51. Kirkegaard P, Loud FB, Moody AJ, Holst JJ, Christiansen J. 1982. Glicentin inhibits gastric acid in the rat. *Nature* 297:156–57
52. Kolligs F, Fehmann HC, Göke R, Göke B. 1995. Reduction of the incretin effect in rats by the glucagon-like peptide-1 receptor antagonist exendin (9–39) amide. *Diabetes* 44:16–19
53. Kreymann B, Ghatei MA, Williams G, Bloom SR. 1987. Glucagon-like peptide-1 7–36: a physiological incretin in man. *Lancet* II:1300–3

54. Larsen PJ, Tang-Christensen M, Holst JJ, Orskov C. 1996. Distribution of glucagon-like peptide-1 (GLP-1) and other preproglucagon derived peptides in the rat hypothalamus and brain stem. *Neuroscience.* In press
55. Layer P, Franke A, Holst JJ, Grandt D, Goebell H. 1996. Glucagon-like peptide-1 (GLP-1) inhibits pancreatic enzyme secretion in humans. *Gastroenterology* 110:F1409
56. Layer P, Holst JJ. 1993. GLP-1: A humoral mediator of the ileal brake in humans? *Digestion* 54:385–86
57. Layer P, Holst JJ, Grandt D, Goebell H. 1995. Ileal release of glucagonlike peptide-1 (GLP-1): association with inhibition of gastric acid in humans. *Dig. Dis. Sci.* 40:1074–82
58. Moens K, Heimberg H, Flamez D, Huypens P, Quartier E, et al. 1996. Expression and functional activity of glucagon- GLP-1 and GIP receptors in rat pancreatic islets cells. *Diabetes* 45:257–61
59. Mojsov S, Heinrich G, Wilson IB, Ravazzola M, Orci L, Habener JF. 1986. Preproglucagon gene expression in pancreas and intestine diversifies at the level of post-translational processing. *J. Biol. Chem.* 261:11880–89
60. Mojsov S, Weir GC, Habener JF. 1987. Insulinotropin: glucagon-like peptide-I (7–37) co-encoded in the glucagon gene is a potent stimulator of insulin release in the perfused pancreas. *J. Clin. Invest.* 79:616–19
61. Moody AJ, Holst JJ, Thim L, Jensen SL. 1981. Relationship of glicentin to proglucagon and glucagon in the porcine pancreas. *Nature* 289:514–16
62. Moody AJ, Thim L. 1983. Glucagon, glicentin and related peptides. In *Glucagon: Handbook of Experimental Pharmacology*, ed. PJ Lefebvre 66/1:139–74. Berlin: Springer-Verlag
63. Nauck MA, Bartels E, Orskov C, Ebert R, Creutzfeldt W. 1993. Additive insulinotropic effects of exogenous synthetic human gastric inhibitory polypeptide and glucagon-like peptide-1 (7–36) amide infused at near-physiological insulinotropic and glucose concentrations. *J. Clin. Endocrinol. Metab.* 76:912–17
64. Nauck MA, Ettler R, Niedereichholz U, Orskov C, Holst JJ, Schmiegel W. 1995. Inhibition of gastric emptying by GLP-1 (7–36 amide) or (7–37): effects on postprandial glycemia and insulin secretion. *Gut* 37(Suppl. 2):A124 (Abstr.)
65. Nauck MA, Heimesaat MM, Orskov C, Holst JJ, Ebert R, Creutzfeldt W. 1993.

Preserved incretin activity of GLP-1 (7–36 amide) but not of synthetic human GIP in patients with type 2-diabetes mellitus. *J. Clin. Invest.* 91:301–7

66. Nauck MA, Kleine N, Orskov C, Holst JJ, Willms B, Creutzfeldt W. 1993. Normalization of fasting hyperglycemia by exogenous GLP-1 in type-2 diabetic patients. *Diabetologia* 36:741–44

67. Novak U, Wilks A, Buell G, McEwen S. 1987. Identical mRNA for preproglucagon in pancreas and gut. *Eur. J. Biochem.* 164:553–58

68. Ohneda A, Ohneda K, Nagasaki T, Sasaki K. 1995. Insulinotropic action of human glicentin in dogs. *Metabolism* 44:47–51

69. Ørskov C. 1992. Glucagon-like peptide-1, a new hormone of the enteroinsular axis. *Diabetologia* 35:701–11

70. Ørskov C, Bersani M, Johnsen AH, Højrup P, Holst JJ. 1989. Complete sequences of glucagon-like peptide-1 (GLP-1) from human and pig small intestine. *J. Biol. Chem.* 264:12826–29

71. Ørskov C, Buhl T, Rabenhøj L, Kofod H, Holst JJ. 1989. Carboxypeptidase-B-like processing of the C-terminus of glucagon-like peptide-2 in pig and human small intestine. *FEBS Lett.* 247:193–206

72. Ørskov C, Holst JJ, Knuhtsen S, Baldissera FGA, Poulsen SS, Nielsen OV. 1986. Glucagon-like peptides GLP-1 and GLP-2, predicted products of the glucagon gene, are secreted separately from the pig small intestine, but not pancreas. *Endocrinology* 119:1467–75

73. Ørskov C, Holst JJ, Nielsen OV. 1988. Effect of truncated glucagon-like peptide-1 (proglucagon 78–107 amide) on endocrine secretion from pig pancreas, antrum and stomach. *Endocrinology* 123:2009–13

74. Ørskov C, Holst JJ, Poulsen SS, Kirkegaard P. 1987. Pancreatic and intestinal processing of proglucagon in man. *Diabetologia* 30:874–81

75. Ørskov C, Poulsen SS. 1991. Glucagon-like peptide-1 receptors in islets of Langerhans. Autoradiographic survey of extracerebral tissues in rats. *Diabetes* 40:1292–96

76. Ørskov C, Poulsen SS, Møller M, Holst JJ. 1996. GLP-1 receptors in the subfornical organ and the area postrema are accessible to circulating glucagon-like peptide-1. *Diabetes* 45:832–35

77. Ørskov C, Rabenhøj L, Kofod H, Wettergren A, Holst JJ. 1994. Production and secretion of amidated and glycine-extended glucagon-like peptide-1 (GLP-1) in man. *Diabetes* 43:535–39

78. Ørskov C, Wettergren A, Poulsen SDS, Holst JJ. 1995. Is the effect of glucagon-like peptide-1 on gastric emptying centrally mediated? *Diabetologia* 38(Suppl. 1):A39 (Abstr.)

79. Ørskov L, Holst JJ, Ørskov C, Møller N, Schmitz O. 1996. Acute GLP-1 administration does not affect insulin sensitivity in healthy man. *Diabetologia* 139:1227–32

80. Patzelt C, Schiltz E. 1984. Conversion of proglucagon in pancreatic alpha cells: the major endproducts are glucagon and a single peptide, the major proglucagon fragment, that contains two glucagon-like sequences. *Proc. Natl. Acad. Sci. USA* 81:5007–12

81. Patzelt C, Tager HS, Carroll RJ, Steiner DF. 1979. Identification and processing of proglucagon in pancreatic islets. *Nature* 282:260–64

82. Plaisance P, Bernhard C, Chayvialle J-A, Cuber J-C. 1994. Regulation of glucagon-like peptide-1-(7-36) amide secretion by intestinal neurotransmitters and hormones in the isolated vascularly perfused rat colon. *Endocrinology* 135:2398–93

83. Pridal L, Ingwersen SH, Larsen FS, Holst JJ, Adelhorst K, Kirk O. 1995. Comparison of sandwich ELISA and RIA for determination of exogenous GLP-1 (7–36 amide) in plasma. *J. Pharmaceut. Biomed. Anal.* 13:841–50

84. Roberge JN, Brubaker PL. 1993. Regulation of proglucagon-derived peptide secretion by glucose-dependent insulinotropic peptide in a novel enteroendocrine loop. *Endocrinology* 133:233–40

85. Rouillé Y, Martin S, Steiner DF. 1995. Differential processing by the subtilisin-like prohormone convertases PC2 and PC3 to generate either glucagon or glucagon-like peptide. *J. Biol. Chem.* 270:26488–96

86. Rouillé Y, Westermark G, Martin SK, Steiner DF. 1994. Proglucagon is processed to glucagon by prohormone convertase PC2 in $\alpha$ TC1–6 cells. *Proc. Natl. Acad. Sci. USA* 91:3242–46

87. Schick RR, vorm Walde T, Zimmermann JP, Schusdziarra V, Classen M. 1994. Glucagon-like peptide 1—a novel brain peptide involved in feeding regulation. In *Obesity in Europe*, ed. H Ditschuneit, FA Gries, H Hauner, V Schusdziarra, JG Wechsler, pp. 363–67. London: Libbey

88. Schjoldager BTG, Mortensen PE, Christiansen J, Orskov C, Holst JJ. 1989. GLP-1 (glucagon-like peptide-1) and truncated GLP-1, fragments of human proglucagon, inhibit gastric acid secretion in man. *Dig.*

*Dis. Sci.* 35:703–8

89. Schjoldager BTG, Mortensen PE, Myhre J, Christiansen J, Holst JJ. 1989. Oxyntomodulin from the distal gut: role in the regulation of gastric and pancreatic functions. *Dig. Dis. Sci.* 34:1411–19

90. Schmidtler J, Schepp W, Janczewska I, Weigert Fürlinger C, Schusdziarra V, Classen M. 1991. GLP-1-(7–36) amide, -(1–37), and -(1–36) amide: potent cAMP-dependent stimuli of rat parietal cell function. *Am. J. Physiol.* 260:G940–50

91. Sheikh SP, Baldissera FGA, Karlsen FØ, Holst JJ. 1985. Glicentin is present in the pig pancreas. *FEBS Lett.* 179:1–6

92. Shimizu I, Hirota M, Obhoshi C, Shima K. 1987. Identification and localization of glucagon-like peptide-1 and its receptor in rat brain. *Endocrinology* 121:1076–82

93. Sugiyama K, Manaka H, Kato T, Yamatani K, Tominaga M, Sasaki H. 1994. Stimulation of truncated glucagon like peptide-1 secretion from isolated perfused canine ileum by glucose absorption. *Digestion* 55:24–28

94. Tang-Christensen M, Larsen PJ, Göke R, Fink-Jensen A, Jessop DS, et al. 1996. Brain GLP-1 (7–36) amide receptors play a major role in regulation of food and water intake. *Am. J. Physiol.* 271:In press

95. Thim L, Moody AJ. 1981. The primary structure of glicentin (proglucagon). *Regul. Pept.* 2:139–51

96. Thim L, Moody AJ. 1982. Purification and chemical characterization of a glicentin-related pancreatic peptide (proglucagon fragment) from porcine pancreas. *Biochim. Biophys. Acta* 703:134–41

97. Thorens B. 1992. Expression cloning of the pancreatic β cell receptor for the gluco-incretin hormone glucagon-like peptide 1. *Proc. Natl. Acad. Sci. USA* 89:8641–45

98. Toft-Nielsen M, Madsbad S, Holst JJ. 1996. The effect of GLP-1 on glucose elimination. *Diabetes* 45:552–56

99. Turton MD, O'Shea D, Gunn I, Beak SA, Edwards CMB, Meeran K, et al. 1996. A role for glucagon-like peptide-1 in the regulation of feeding. *Nature* 379:69–72

100. Unger RH, Eisentraut AM, Sims K, McCall MS, Madison LL. 1961. Sites of origin of glucagon in dogs and humans. *Clin. Res.* 9:53

101. Unger RH, Ohneda A, Valverde I, Eisentraut AM, Exton J. 1968. Characterization of the responses of circulating glucagon-like immunoreactivity to intraduodenal and intravenous administration of glucose. *J. Clin. Invest.* 47:48–65

102. Uttenthal LO, Toledano A, Blazquez E.

1992. Autoradiographic localization of receptors for glucagon-like peptide-1 (7–36) amide in rat brain. *Neuropeptides* 21:143–46

103. Valverde I, Morales M, Clemente F, Lopez-Delgado MI, Delgado E, et al. 1994. Glucagon-like peptide 1: a potent glycogenic hormone. *FEBS Lett.* 349:313–16

104. Varndell IM, Bishop A, Sikri E, Uttenthal LO, Bloom SR, Polak JM. 1985. Localization of glucagon-like peptide GLP immunoreactants in human gut and pancreas using light and electron microscopic immunocytochemistry. *J. Histochem. Cytochem.* 33:1080–90

105. Villanueva-Penacarrillo ML. Alcanatara AI, Clemente F, Delgado E, Valverde I. 1994. Potent glycogenic effect of GLP-1 (7–36) amide in rat skeletal muscle. *Diabetologia* 37:1163–66

106. Walsh JH. 1994. Gastrointestinal hormones. In *Physiology of the Gastrointestinal Tract*, ed. LR Johnson, pp. 1–128. New York: Raven. 3rd ed.

107. Wang Z, Wang RM, Owji AA, Smith DM, Ghatei M, Bloom SR. 1995. Glucagon-like peptide-1 is a physiological incretin in rat. *J. Clin. Invest.* 95:417–21

108. Wei Y, Mojsov S. 1995. Tissue-specific expression of the human receptor for glucagon-like peptide-1: brain, heart and pancreatic forms have the same deduced amino acid sequences. *FEBS Lett.* 358:219–24

109. Wettergren A, Petersen H, Orskov C, Christiansen J, Sheikh SP, Holst JJ. 1994. Glucagon-like peptide-1 (GLP-1) 7–36 amide and peptide YY from the L-cell in the ileal mucosa are potent inhibitors of vagally induced gastric acid in man. *Scand. J. Gastroenterol.* 29:501–5

110. Wettergren A, Schjoldager B, Mortensen PE, Myhre J, Christiansen J, Holst JJ. 1993. Truncated GLP-1 (proglucagon 72–107 amide) inhibits gastric and pancreatic functions in man. *Dig. Dis. Sci.* 38:665–73

111. White JW, Saunders GF. 1986. Structure of the human glucagon gene. *Nucleic Acids Res.* 14:4719–30

112. Yamada T, Solomon TE, Petersen H. 1980. Effects of gastrointestinal polypeptides on hormone content of the endocrine pancreas in the rat. *Am. J. Physiol.* 238:G525–30

113. Yanaihara C, Matsumoto T, Kadowaki M, Iguchi K, Yanaihara N. 1985. Rat pancreas contains the proglucagon (64–69) fragment and arginine stimulates its release. *FEBS Lett.* 187:307–10

*Annu. Rev. Physiol. 1997. 59:273–98*

# THE G CELL

## Mitsutaka Sawada and Chris J. Dickinson

University of Michigan Medical Center, 1500 West Medical Center Drive, Pediatric
Gastroenterology, A510E MSRBI, Ann Arbor, Michigan 48109-0658

KEY WORDS:   gastrin, posttranslational processing, receptors, *Helicobacter pylori,* growth,
signal transduction

### ABSTRACT

The study of gastrin continues to serve as an excellent model for gastrointestinal
regulatory processes. This review highlights some recent advances in the field
by outlining gastrin biosynthesis, summarizing current understanding of gastrin
receptors, describing the regulation of gastrin release, and discussing the clinical
implications of gastrin in the pathogenesis of peptic ulcer disease. Emphasis is on
three emerging areas of gastrin research: the novel finding that one of gastrin's
posttranslational processing intermediates has biological activity distinct from
that of the mature peptide; elucidation of gastrin's signal transduction mechanisms
that mediate the trophic effects of the peptide; and the role of gastrin in peptic
ulcer disease pathogenesis secondary to *Helicobacter pylori* infection.

## HISTORICAL ASPECTS AND OVERVIEW

After their discovery of secretin in 1902, Bayliss & Starling surmised that a
similar hormone might exert control over gastric acid secretion (3). Edkins then
identified a substance found in antral but not fundic mucosal extracts that stimulated gastric acid secretion, and termed it gastrin (32, 33). In 1962, Gregory &
Tracy (47) purified an amidated heptadecapeptide that we now refer to as gastrin.
Shortly thereafter, a gastrin peptide was synthesized that allowed investigators
to examine the physiological actions of gastrin (62). The subsequent development of a gastrin radioimmunoassay (79, 138) helped researchers examine its
secretion in physiologic and pathophysiologic states. As outlined in a chapter
by G Sachs, N Zeng & C Prinz, this volume, it quickly became apparent that
the regulation of gastric acid secretion was quite complex and that to elucidate
molecular mechanisms, it would be necessary to examine all the regulatory cells
in isolation to determine the precise biological actions of gastrin and other gut

273

0066-4278/97/0315-0273$08.00

peptides. Isolation of acid-secreting parietal cells, gastrin-producing G cells, and somatostatin-producing D cells from the stomach in primary culture was an important step in our understanding of gastrin secretion and biological actions (118, 119, 126). To explore the mechanisms of gastrin biosynthesis, investigators initially tried to identify larger molecular forms of gastrin presumed to be precursors of the mature peptide. However, the results were difficult to interpret. Isolation of a complementary DNA encoding gastrin (4, 146) allowed investigators to hypothesize the presence of various precursors and then develop antisera to confirm their existence in tissues and their relationship to the mature peptide. Finally, characterization and isolation of the receptor(s) for gastrin on various cells have allowed researchers to elucidate the mechanisms of gastrin's biological actions on target cells (65, 120).

## GASTRIN POSTTRANSLATIONAL PROCESSING

### Overview

To understand the physiology of gastrin, it is necessary to review gastrin biosynthesis. As is the case with other peptide hormones, gastrin requires extensive posttranslational modification prior to secretion for full biological activity (80). From the earliest studies, multiple molecular forms of gastrin were characterized in the circulation and in the stomach (145). The first two principal forms of gastrin identified were of 17 and 34 amino acids in length (G17 and G34). The presence of little (G17) gastrin within the structure of big gastrin (G34) gave rise to the notion that they shared a common precursor (30). The identification of the cDNA and subsequent biosynthetic studies confirmed this relationship (4, 127, 146). Gastrin has served as an ideal model for the study of prohormone posttranslational processing because progastrin undergoes many of the reactions common to other peptide precursors and because investigators can now link these modifications with distinct changes in the bioactivity of the gastrin product.

Peptide hormones and other secreted proteins are initially synthesized from the amino-terminal end on ribosomes and enter the secretory pathway via translocation into the endoplasmic reticulum (ER) (Figure 1). The prohormone then proceeds to the Golgi stack, where it undergoes further posttranslational modification (88). Finally, prohormones are condensed in the secretory granule and processed to their mature forms. It is now known that gastrin's precursor peptide, preprogastrin, undergoes several important modifications in each of these cellular compartments that are necessary for full biological activity. These are described below and include signal peptide cleavage, tyrosine sulfation, serine $O$-phosphorylation, dibasic cleavage at two or more sites, carboxypeptidase removal of basic residues, and carboxyl-terminal amidation.

## Events in the ER

The first few amino acids of the preprohormone, translated from the leader sequence of the specific mRNA, are called the signal peptide (139). This peptide (designated as the presequence in preprohormones) is not secreted under normal circumstances but serves as a means of translocating the newly synthesized and gradually elongating polypeptide chain into the ER and the secretory pathway. The signal peptide is later cleaved by a specific enzyme (signal peptidase) located on the inner membrane of the ER (36). The 21–amino acid signal peptide of preprogastrin possesses the three general characteristics shared by other signal peptides: (*a*) a positively charged amino-terminal region of 3 amino acids, (*b*) a central hydrophobic region of 15 amino acids, and (*c*) a more polar pattern of amino acids adjacent to the site of cleavage (85).

## Events in the Golgi

Progastrin then proceeds from the ER to the Golgi stack, where it is variably sulfated. Although sulfation of carbohydrate residues on a protein backbone occurs in all eukaryotic cells, sulfation of prohormones at specific tyrosine residues is far less common. Biosynthetic studies using $^{35}S$-sulfate have demonstrated that even large molecular forms of gastrin are sulfated at $Tyr^{87}$ (7). This is consistent with the presumption that sulfation occurs in the Golgi prior to endoproteolytic cleavage, which occurs later in the secretory granule. On the basis of studies using a gastrin peptide fragment as a substrate for the sulfation reaction, it appears that the gastrin sulfation enzyme is similar to the tyrosine sulfotransferase described in other tissues (13). From examination of a large number of sulfated secretory proteins, it has been possible to identify the structural features that promote tyrosine sulfation (57). These include the presence of numerous acidic residues around the sulfation site and an absence of basic residues and glycosylation sites. Gastrin conforms to these criteria, and this has been tested experimentally by expressing mutant progastrins in endocrine cell lines and observing the effects of the mutation on gastrin sulfation (8). Interestingly, these studies suggest that sulfation of $Tyr^{87}$ enhances the subsequent endoproteolytic maturation of progastrin. Although sulfation is essential for the biological action of cholecystokinin (CCK) at $CCK_A$ receptors located in the gall bladder and pancreas, the acid secretagogue effect of gastrin at gastrin/$CCK_B$ receptors is not influenced by tyrosine sulfation (15, 29).

Progastrin is also phosphorylated at $Ser^{96}$ and this modification can be blocked with brefeldin in accordance with the localization of the phosphorylation reaction to the distal Golgi stack (133). Because of the proximity of the $Ser^{96}$ residue to the carboxyl-terminal $Gly^{93}Arg^{94}Arg^{95}$ amidation site, it has been suggested that phosphorylation of this site may influence the formation of the peptide amide. Indeed, fasting in rats leads to a relative decrease in

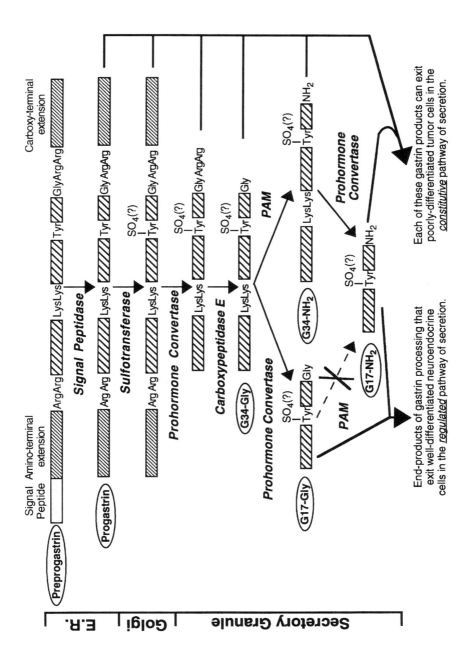

Ser$^{96}$ phosphorylation that coincides with decreased amidated gastrin, but with no effect on endoproteolysis at Arg$^{94}$Arg$^{95}$ (134).

It appears that the movement of progastrin through the Golgi stack is by bulk-flow as opposed to a process mediated by a sorting signal (98, 99). Bulk transport of soluble ER proteins to the Golgi and through the various Golgi compartments (*cis*, stack, and *trans*-Golgi network (TGN)) is accomplished via transport vesicles. Proteins exiting cells via either the constitutive or regulated secretory pathways share a common trail from the endoplasmic reticulum through the Golgi stack, but diverge in the TGN where proteins are sorted according to their final destination (10). Proteins in the constitutive pathway generally do not undergo extensive posttranslational processing (e.g. albumin secretion from hepatocytes) and are transported in secretory vesicles that continuously fuse with the plasma membrane. Conversely, polypeptide hormones in the regulated pathway are stored and processed in secretory granules of neuroendocrine cells for hours or days before secretagogue-induced release. This observation has particular relevance when one examines the processing and secretion of prohormones that are expressed in poorly differentiated endocrine or non-endocrine cells. As an example, progastrin is efficiently processed to mature, amidated gastrin when heterologously expressed in endocrine but not non-endocrine cell lines (27). Thus when investigators looked for gastrin expression in non-endocrine cells such as colon cancers, the results were often inconclusive. Because most gastrin antisera recognize only fully processed gastrins, early studies found significant quantities of gastrin in only a few tumors.

←——————————————————————————————————————

*Figure 1*    Gastrin post-translational processing. Preprogastrin is synthesized on the endoplasmic reticulum (E.R.) and its pre or signal peptide is cleaved just after translocation into the E.R. lumen. Progastrin, gastrin, and other secretory proteins are then transported to the Golgi, wherein gastrin is often sulfated at a tyrosine residue (Tyr). In well-differentiated neuroendocrine cells, progastrin is sorted in the *trans*-Golgi network to the regulated pathway of secretion and into secretory granules that contain the enzymes necessary to complete progastrin processing. In these granules, the amino- and carboxyl-terminal flanking regions are cleaved by a prohormone convertase at dibasic arginine residues (ArgArg) and the carboxyl-terminal arginines removed by carboxypeptidase E revealing G34-Gly. G34-Gly can then be amidated by PAM to form G34-NH$_2$, or cleaved at internal lysine/lysine (LysLys) residues, resulting in the production of G17-Gly. Recent biosynthetic studies suggest that although G34-NH$_2$ can be cleaved at the LysLys site by a prohormone convertase to yield G17-NH$_2$, G17-Gly is not amidated by PAM. Thus G17-Gly may be a distinct end product of progastrin processing in antral G cells. In general, only amidated and glycine-extended forms of gastrin are produced in neuroendocrine cells. Conversely, gastrin in poorly differentiated non-endocrine cells found in colon cancers bypasses the processing machinery found in secretory granules and is secreted in larger, unprocessed forms that exit cells via the constitutive secretory pathway.

Recently, investigators suspected that gastrin processing might not be as efficient in these non-endocrine cells and detected unprocessed gastrins in all tested human colon cancers, whereas fully processed gastrins were detected in far fewer carcinomas. Furthermore, they noted that although these cells often contained significant quantities of progastrins, these products were constitutively secreted from cells and did not accumulate intracellularly to the same degree as gastrin found in endocrine gastrin-producing G cells of the stomach (16, 63, 84, 132).

Because the pre or signal peptide directs sorting to the endoplasmic reticulum, some have hypothesized that there is a particular sequence of amino acids in the pro sequence that binds to a sorting protein or chaperone that targets prohormones in the TGN to secretory granules. To date, searches for a common sequence in, or posttranslational modification of, prohormones that might direct sorting to secretory vesicles have not been successful. For example, the pro region preceding the $Arg^{57}Arg^{58}$ site in human progastrin is homologous to progastrins in other species, but does not have significant homology in primary or secondary structure with the pro regions of other gastrointestinal hormones. Nevertheless, evidence that the pro regions of some hormones such as prosomatostatin can redirect the sorting of constitutively secreted proteins to the regulated pathway indicates that sorting information is contained in the pro region (123). Recently, a hairpin loop structure containing two disulfide bridges has been identified within the pro region of proopiomelanocortin (POMC) that directs its sorting to the regulated pathway of secretion (17). Unfortunately, this hairpin loop is not found in other prohormone precursors such as gastrin. Because a pro region binding protein has not been found, some hypothesize that proteins destined for the regulated pathway are selectively aggregated or condensed in the $Ca^{2+}$-rich, acidic milieu of the TGN (89). In this model, proteins that remain soluble are sorted to the constitutive pathway. Regardless of the mechanism of sorting, prohormones such as progastrin are processed further by the enzymes found in the secretory granules, and the nature of the resultant product(s) is dependent upon the enzymes present in the granules.

## Events in the Secretory Granule

After exiting the TGN, progastrin is concentrated in secretory granules that contain several processing enzymes (Figure 1). Selective endoproteolytic cleavage is perhaps the most important posttranslational processing step for gastrointestinal peptide hormones because virtually all undergo this reaction in one form or another. Not all dibasic sites in a given prohormone are cleaved, and different tissues may process the same prohormone at different dibasic sites because of the differential expression of the various prohormone convertases (PCs) in neuroendocrine tissues. The most frequent cleavage reactions occur at pairs of basic amino acid residues although mono-, tri-, and tetra-basic sites also serve as cleavage sites. Cleavages usually occur on the carboxyl-terminal side of a dibasic pair. Although in vitro studies have shown that trypsin can perform dibasic cleavages, the exact nature of the enzymes responsible for cleavage of prohormones in situ has been difficult to ascertain because of their presence in low quantities as compared with the relative abundance of other cellular proteases. A breakthrough came when Julius et al (60) described a mutation in the *kex2* gene of yeast that prevented the synthesis of a mating prohormone, which required cleavage at dibasic sites for biologic activity. The *kex2* gene was found to encode a $Ca^{2+}$-dependent serine protease that was not related to trypsin, as many had expected, but rather related to the bacterial subtilisins (41). A mammalian homologue of *kex2*, termed furin or PACE (Paired basic Amino acid residue Cleaving Enzyme) was identified by its homology to *kex2*. Furin is expressed in almost all mammalian cells and is responsible for processing proteins secreted via the constitutive pathway but not in prohormone processing in the regulated pathway in neuroendocrine cells (121). PACE or other members of the PC family may, however, partially cleave prohormones in non-endocrine cells in the constitutive secretory pathway. Other members of the PC family (PC1/PC3 and PC2) are $Ca^{2+}$-dependent serine proteases related to PACE, and the bacterial subtilisins and are expressed only in neuroendocrine cells (41, 116, 117). The acidic pH optimum (pH 5.5) of both enzymes is consistent with their activity in secretory granules. Other related family members that may play a role in proprotein processing in some tissues include PC4, which is expressed mainly in the testis, and PC5/PC6A, which is found in epithelial but not neuroendocrine cells of the small intestine.

Progastrin contains three dibasic cleavage sites $Arg^{57}Arg^{58}$, $Lys^{74}Lys^{75}$, and $Arg^{94}Arg^{95}$. Cleavages at $Arg^{57}Arg^{58}$ and $Arg^{94}Arg^{95}$ result in the formation of G34, whereas cleavages at $Lys^{74}Lys^{75}$ and $Arg^{94}Arg^{95}$ result in the formation of G17 (Figure 1). To determine if PC2 or PC1/PC3 was capable of processing progastrin, we heterologously expressed the gastrin cDNA in GH3 cells that express only PC2 and in AtT-20 cells that express PC1/PC3 and little, if any, PC2. Both cell lines produced mature carboxyl-terminal amidated gastrin, suggesting that either PC was capable of processing progastrin at the $Arg^{94}Arg^{95}$ site (24, 73). However, the PC2-expressing GH3 cells primarily produced G17, whereas the major molecular form of gastrin in the AtT-20 cells was G34, suggesting that PC2 but not PC1/PC3 was capable of cleaving the $Lys^{74}Lys^{75}$ site. To answer this question, we cotransfected AtT-20 cells with PC2 and noted the PC2-expressing AtT-20 cells primarily produced G17. These results are consistent with the finding that PC2 but not PC1/PC3 is expressed in canine antral G cells that contain primarily G17 (26). Further support for these observations can be found in results obtained from studies of the human duodenum, which expresses G34 as the major molecular form and contains much more PC1/PC3 than PC2 (12, 46, 110). Thus it appears that the tissue-specific expression of a member of the PC family may be responsible for the differential processing of the gastrin precursor.

After endoproteolytic cleavages at the carboxyl-terminal side of basic residues, the remaining basic residues are removed via the action of a carboxypeptidase (Figure 1) (80). The eukaryotic enzyme thought to be responsible for this action in neuroendocrine cells has been extensively characterized and is alternatively known as carboxypeptidase E (CPE), carboxypeptidase H, or enkephalin convertase. An obese mouse (fat/fat) was recently discovered to have a defect in prohormone processing related to a mutant CPE gene that rendered CPE biologically inactive (82). Because these mice also have increased amounts of gastrins extended at the carboxyl terminus by Arg residues, it confirms the role of CPE in progastrin processing (45).

Removal of $Arg^{94}Arg^{95}$ by CPE results in the formation of $Gly^{93}$-extended gastrins (G-Gly) that serve as substrates for the amidation enzyme, peptidylglycine $\alpha$-amidating monooxygenase (PAM) (6). Approximately 50% of all bioactive peptides are characterized by the presence of a carboxyl-terminal amide moiety that is often essential for biological activity. PAM requires $Cu^{2+}$, ascorbic acid, and molecular oxygen for full activity (34). Antral PAM is similar to that found in the pituitary, but PAM has selective affinity for certain substrates that may provide a mechanism for the differential amidation of various hormones within a given tissue or cell (28).

Region-specific antisera that recognize glycine-extended gastrins (G-Gly) as well as progastrins extended by the $Arg^{94}$ and $Arg^{95}$ residues show that progastrin, G-Gly, and amidated gastrin are colocalized within G cells of the stomach (124). The presence of these molecular forms is in accord with the hypothesis that these posttranslational processing reactions take place in a single enclosed cellular compartment such as the secretory granule (96). Further confirmation of the notion that G-Gly is converted to amidated gastrin in the secretory vesicle is the finding that G-Gly and gastrin are co-secreted from isolated G cells (125, 126). Recent gastrin biosynthetic studies suggest that the majority of amidated G17 arises from the amidation of G34-Gly to $G34-NH_2$ followed by conversion of $G34-NH_2$ to $G17-NH_2$ rather than by amidation of G17-Gly (135). This suggests that G17-Gly may be a second distinct endproduct in progastrin processing (Figure 1).

## GASTRIN RECEPTORS

Gastrin requires its carboxyl-terminal amide moiety for full biological activity (51, 77). Thus the isolation of a cDNA encoding the receptor that recognizes this motif represented a major advance in our understanding of gastrin physiology (65, 120). This discovery allowed investigators to more fully elucidate signal transduction mechanisms, structure/activity relationships, tissue distribution, and biological significance of gastrin. See Reference 141 for an excellent review of this subject; however, several points are important to note here.

The gastrin/CCK$_B$ receptor is a seven-transmembrane serpentine receptor that is similar to the CCK$_A$ receptor. The human gastrin/CCK$_B$ receptor gene consists of four introns and five exons (120). Differential processing of the fourth exon in the human gene can result in the formation of two transcripts that differ by five amino acids in the third intracytoplasmic loop that is important for signal transduction. Although the shorter transcript overwhelmingly predominates in human parietal cells, the physiologic significance of this five amino acid block is unknown. Some authors suggest that it has no effect on ligand binding or signal transduction (142), but in other studies, ligand binding to the long form of the receptor results in a sustained increase in intracellular calcium that is not seen in the short form (86). Other forms of the gastrin/CCK$_B$ receptor, truncated at the amino terminus, have been identified in colon cancer cell lines (81). Unfortunately, the biological significance of any of these altered forms of the gastrin/CCK$_B$ receptor is unknown.

Upon ligand binding, the gastrin/CCK$_B$ receptor binds to a G protein; the result being the activation of phospholipase C (PLC), which catalyzes the formation of inositol-1,4,5-trisphosphate (IP$_3$) and diacylglycerol (DAG) (65). IP$_3$ stimulates the release of intracellular calcium, and DAG activates protein kinase C (PKC). Unlike CCK binding to the CCK$_A$ receptor, gastrin binding to its receptor does not result in the accumulation of cAMP (141, 147). Moreover, release of intracellular Ca$^{2+}$ and activation of PKC occur in the parietal cell as well as in other gut cells that respond to the trophic actions of gastrin (21, 113). Several studies have shown that gastrin can stimulate the proliferation of gut cells as measured by an increase in either cell number, [$^3$H]-thymidine incorporation, ornithine decarboxylase (ODC) activity, or expression of two genes known to regulate cell proliferation (c-*fos* and c-*jun*) (59). Clinical examples of this effect can be seen with the overproduction of gastrin in tumors in the Zollinger-Ellison syndrome, which produces significant gastric hyperplasia (144). Many of these trophic effects can be blocked by gastrin/CCK$_B$ receptor antagonists, suggesting that they are mediated by this receptor.

Although much work remains, progress has been made at characterizing the intracellular events that occur between the initial events at the cell membrane and the resultant actions in the nucleus (Figure 2). It appears that in addition to activating PKC at the cell membrane, gastrin also activates tyrosine kinases that phosphorylate an adapter protein (Shc) (112, 115). Phosphorylated Shc then associates with two other proteins (Grb2 and a Ras activator, Sos). This

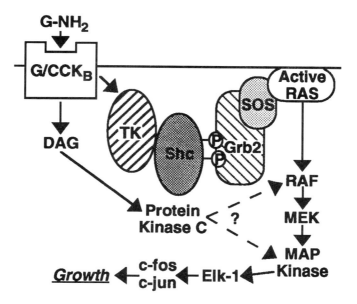

*Figure 2*   Model of gastrin's signal transduction mechanisms.   Binding of amidated gastrin
(G-NH$_2$) to the gastrin/CCK$_B$ receptor results in the generation of diacylglycerol (DAG) or activation of an unknown tyrosine kinase (TK). The TK then phosphorylates an adapter protein (Shc),
which associates with Grb2 and the RAS activator, SOS. Activated RAS begins the cascade of
kinase activation through RAF, MEK, MAP kinase, and Elk-1, which induces the expression of the
early responses genes c-*fos* and c-*jun*. In some systems, DAG can also activate PKC, which may
phosphorylate either RAF or MAP kinase via a second pathway that leads to cell growth.

complex can stimulate the Ras-dependent activation of the mitogen-activated
protein (MAP) kinase as well as the upstream activator of MAP kinase (MAP
and ERK kinase or MEK) (130).  MAP kinase phosphorylates a nuclear transcription factor (Elk-1) that enhances c-*fos* expression.  c-*fos* then combines
with c-*jun* to induce transcription of other genes that regulate growth.  Although
gastrin receptor antagonists completely reverse the effects on c-*fos* expression,
PKC inhibitors result in only a 40–50% reduction in gastrin-induced c-*fos* expression in a pancreatic cell line AR4-2J (130).  This suggests that the trophic
effects of gastrin are mediated by PKC-dependent and -independent pathways.
Conversely, other investigators have examined the trophic effects of gastrin in
a fibroblast cell line that heterologously expresses the gastrin/CCK$_B$ receptor
and found that gastrin's trophic effects are mediated solely by PKC-independent
pathways (137).  It is anticipated that these and other mechanisms will soon
be elucidated and aid in our understanding of gastrin's potentially important
growth-promoting effects.

# PHYSIOLOGIC RELEVANCE OF OTHER PROGASTRIN-PROCESSING PRODUCTS

The isolation of a cDNA encoding the gastrin/CCK$_B$ receptor illuminated the mechanisms by which gastrin exerts its regulatory effects on some gastrointestinal cells. However, determination of the role amidated gastrin plays in growth of some tumors such as colon cancers has been difficult to resolve (97). Numerous studies have been performed with conflicting results, but a recent large study suggests that prolonged hypergastrinemia may play a role in the development of some human colonic and gastric tumors (90, 129). The issue is complicated by the fact that some of the trophic effects of amidated gastrin may be mediated by receptors other than gastrin/CCK$_B$ or CCK$_A$ receptors (2, 5). Surprisingly, clarification of this issue may come from studies on the posttranslational processing of progastrin that provide new insights into the relationship of gastrin processing to the action of gastrin mediated by different gastrin receptors (23).

As mentioned above, gastrin (G-NH$_2$) requires its carboxyl-terminal amide moiety for full biological activity mediated by gastrin/CCK$_B$ receptors. Indeed, removal of the carboxyl-terminal amide in gastrin completely abolishes its acid stimulatory effects mediated by standard gastrin/CCK$_B$ receptors, and the immediate precursor of amidated gastrins, G-Gly, is at least four orders of magnitude less potent than G-NH$_2$ in stimulating acid secretion from gastric parietal cells (51, 77). Nevertheless, interest in the physiologic effects of G-Gly has been fueled by the observations that G-Gly is stored in brain and gut tissues (20, 124), is secreted with G-NH$_2$ from antral G cells into the circulation (125), and achieves concentrations in plasma roughly equivalent to those of G-NH$_2$ (19). Moreover, G-Gly is seen in greater concentrations than G-NH$_2$ during development and in some malignant tissues that express gastrin such as Zollinger-Ellison tumors and colon cancers (16, 20, 63, 72, 132). Finally, biosynthetic studies suggested that G17-Gly may be a distinct endproduct of progastrin processing (135). Thus the evidence pointed to G-Gly's role as a growth factor but not as a direct acid secretagogue.

To understand the role of amidated gastrin's immediate precursor, G-Gly, we conducted studies in which the gastrin-amidating enzyme (PAM) was inhibited by a copper chelator (25). As expected, this decreased amidated gastrin in the stomach and increased G-Gly in the stomach and plasma. However, plasma levels of amidated gastrin were maintained. Associated with these changes were increased basal and maximal gastric acid outputs, suggesting that chronically elevated levels of G-Gly in the presence of normal G-NH$_2$ plasma concentrations might up-regulate gastric acid secretory mechanisms.

To further characterize the potential trophic effects of G17-Gly, we examined whether G17-Gly might function as a growth factor in a fashion that could be distinguished from its relatively weak effects on the standard gastrin/CCK$_B$ receptor (111). We compared the abilities of G17-NH$_2$ and G17-Gly to stimulate DNA synthesis in the exocrine pancreatic AR4-2J cell line. Both G17-NH$_2$ and G17-Gly stimulated [$^3$H]thymidine incorporation in a dose-dependent fashion (Figure 3). As expected, the stimulation induced by G17-NH$_2$ was completely reversed by selective gastrin/CCK$_B$ receptor antagonists. In contrast, neither antagonist decreased the [$^3$H]thymidine uptake stimulated by G17-Gly (Figure 3). These data suggested that G-Gly might act through a mechanism independent of the gastrin/CCK$_B$ receptors. If G-Gly has a specific effect on AR4-2J proliferation that is independent of gastrin/CCK$_B$ receptors, we reasoned that it should be

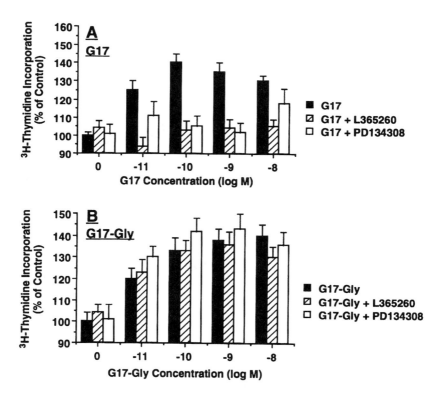

*Figure 3*   G-NH$_2$ and G-Gly trophic effects. Effects of the gastrin/CCK$_B$ receptor antagonists L365, 260 (*hatched bars*) and PD-134308 (*open bars*) on incorporation of [$^3$H]thymidine stimulated by (*A*) amidated G17 or (*B*) G17-Gly in pancreatic AR4-2J cells. Results are expressed as percent of control unstimulated [$^3$H]thymidine incorporation, means ±SE. (Reprinted with permission from Reference 111. Copyright © 1994, Am. Assoc. Adv. Sci.)

possible to demonstrate the presence of G-Gly–selective receptors. Competitive binding studies showed that unlabeled G-Gly displaced $^{125}$I-labeled G-Gly bound to AR4-2J cells, but G17-NH$_2$, cholecystokinin octapeptide, and the gastrin/CCK$_B$ receptor antagonists had no effect. As expected, unlabeled G17-NH$_2$ and both gastrin/CCK$_B$ receptor antagonists completely inhibited binding of $^{125}$I-labeled G17-NH$_2$ to AR4-2J cells. However, G-Gly, in concentrations as high as 1 $\mu$M had no effect on $^{125}$I-labeled G17-NH$_2$ binding.

These results demonstrated for the first time that both amidated gastrin and its glycine-extended posttranslational processing intermediates induce AR4-2J cell proliferation. Other data help to confirm the role that G-Gly may play in gastrointestinal physiology. G-Gly is also secreted from AR4-2J cells and can stimulate growth in an autocrine fashion (83). Although acute administration of G-Gly has no effect on gastric acid secretion (51, 77), chronic administration of G-Gly markedly enhances stimulated but not basal acid secretion from isolated parietal cells and in vivo via an increase in the expression of H$^+$, K$^+$-ATPase within gastric parietal cells (49, 61). Recent data suggest that G17-Gly but not G17-NH$_2$ promotes proliferation of fetal rabbit gastric epithelial cells (42). Moreover, G-Gly enhances the growth of a human hepatoma cell line and may contribute to gastrointestinal mucosal proliferation (64, 140). G-Gly receptors are also found on several human colon cancer cell lines that do not express gastrin/CCK$_B$ receptors (122). Because significant quantities of G-Gly are found in human colon cancers, it has been suggested that G-Gly may play a role in growth of these tumors (23).

If gastrin/CCK$_B$ and G-Gly receptors are distinct, one might expect that they would have distinct signal transduction mechanisms. Binding of G17-NH$_2$ to gastrin/CCK$_B$ receptors stimulates the mobilization of intracellular Ca$^{2+}$, whereas G17-Gly binding does not appear to alter intracellular Ca$^{2+}$ or cAMP concentrations (61). Although tyrosine kinase inhibitors block the effects of G17-Gly on parietal cells, the exact nature of its signal transduction awaits the isolation of a cDNA encoding the receptor and further study. G-Gly and G-NH$_2$ appear to act cooperatively to stimulate growth of AR4-2J cells in that G-NH$_2$, but not G-Gly, stimulates the expression of c-*fos* and c-*jun*. G-Gly, however, enhances jun kinase activity, which phosphorylates and thus bioactivates c-jun by allowing the c-fos/c-jun heterodimer to bind to the serum response element (131) (Figure 4).

Taken together, these observations suggest that growth-related receptors for G-Gly may mediate physiologic or pathophysiologic effects of progastrin processing products. Furthermore, this suggests for the first time that the precursor and the product of a key posttranslational processing reaction—peptide $\alpha$-amidation—have distinct biological actions mediated through separate receptors. Indeed, the posttranslational processing of a prohormone may define

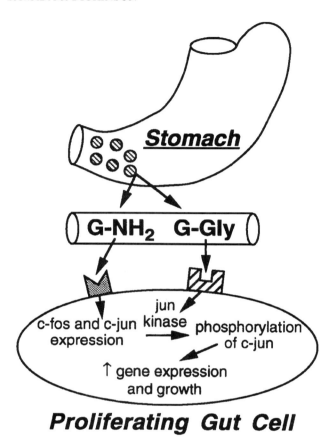

*Figure 4*   Mechanisms of G-NH$_2$ and G-Gly trophic effects.  Amidated gastrin (G-NH$_2$) and its glycine-extended precursor (G-Gly) are released from G cells in the gastric antrum into the circulation.  G-NH$_2$ acts through gastrin/CCK$_B$ receptors to enhance the expression of c-*fos* and c-*jun*.  G-Gly, via another distinct receptor and jun kinase, phosphorylates and thus bioactivates c-jun. c-fos and phosphorylated c-jun then induce the expression of other genes necessary for the proliferation of gut cells.

the ultimate physiologic effects of its products.  Because other peptide hormone-processing intermediates are also found in high concentrations in tumors and during development, we anticipate that these intermediates may have physiologic effects that will be defined by future studies. Other fruitful areas of investigation likely include identification of possible receptors for progastrin, and precise identification of the enzymes responsible for the generation of these and other products of progastrin posttranslational processing in various cell types.

# GASTRIN AND PEPTIC ULCER DISEASE

## Overview

The studies reviewed here have expanded our knowledge of mechanisms of gastrin biosynthesis, release, and receptor/ligand interactions. However, the central clinical issue that initially drove these studies was elucidation of the mechanisms of peptic ulcer formation. For many years, peptic ulcer disease was a major cause of morbidity and mortality and early studies seemed to confirm the notion that gastric acid was requisite to the formation of duodenal ulcers. Thus it was hoped that a more thorough understanding of the regulation of gastric acid secretion would elucidate the pathogenesis of peptic ulcer disease. Early investigators identified gastrin as the primary postprandial regulator of gastric acid secretion (40). However, to understand the regulation of acid secretion, it is necessary to show interactions of the gastrin-producing G cells in the antrum with other cells involved in the regulation of acid secretion (Figure 5).

The G cell is a classic gut endocrine cell organized with microvilli on a lumenal surface that allow the G cell to detect the presence of food within the stomach. Gastrin released from G cells into the circulation has three major effects mediated by gastrin/CCK$_B$ receptors. First, gastrin can stimulate the

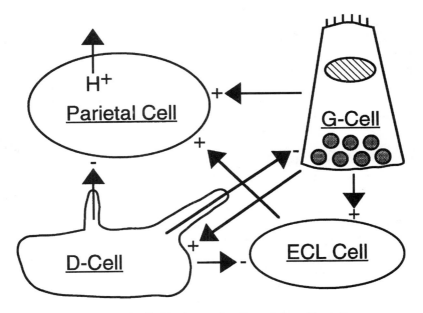

*Figure 5*    Interaction of the G cell with other gastric cells regulating acid secretion.

release of acid directly from the parietal cell. Second, gastrin can also stimulate acid secretion by enhancing the release of histamine from enterochromaffin-like (ECL) cells, which then binds to H2 receptors on the parietal cell. Third, gastrin also stimulates the release of somatostatin from gastric D cells. These D cells are distinct from those found in pancreatic islets in that they contain cytoplasmic processes that end in a bulbous swelling overlying adjacent parietal and G cells. Thus the actions of gastric somatostatin are primarily paracrine in nature, and physiologic stimulation of somatostatin release from these cells does not always result in a rise in plasma somatostatin levels. Somatostatin is a potent inhibitor of gastric acid secretion, acting directly on the parietal cell or blocking the continued release of gastrin from G cells and histamine release from ECL cells. Although more detailed reviews on the regulation of gastrin release have been published elsewhere (136), a summary is provided below.

## Neural

During the cephalic and oropharyngeal phases of a meal, gastrin release is directly stimulated by acetylcholine (ACh) released from vagal fibers via muscarinic receptors (48, 71). ACh released from other vagal fibers also inhibits the release of somatostatin from antral D cells, thereby indirectly enhancing gastrin secretion (48, 71, 76, 100, 106). As a consequence, sham feeding induces gastrin release that is inhibited by selective antral vagotomy (128). Interestingly, selective fundic vagotomy results in an enhancement of gastrin release, suggesting that there are fundic vagal inhibitory pathways of gastrin release (53). Because the antral excitatory and the fundic inhibitory effects are abolished by atropine, vagal cholinergic pathways are involved in both pathways (52, 53).

In addition to ACh, gastrin-releasing peptide (GRP) is also secreted from postganglionic vagal nerve fibers and directly stimulates gastrin release (31) via GRP receptors on G cells (102, 126). In the isolated perfused rat stomach, gastrin release in response to electrical field stimulation, nicotinic stimulation, and $\beta$-adrenergic stimulation is blocked by anti-GRP antibodies (109, 114), consistent with the notion that these agents mediate their effects via GRP release from postganglionic vagal fibers. Vasoactive intestinal polypeptide (VIP) is also released from vagal postganglionic fibers by nicotinic stimulation, electrical field stimulation, and gastric distention (108). Unlike GRP, VIP does not have a direct effect on the G cell but rather stimulates somatostatin release (105) from D cells, which, in turn, inhibits gastrin secretion.

During the gastric phase of a meal, antral distention evokes low levels of gastrin release that is inhibited by low doses of atropine but enhanced by atropine at higher doses (103). Other studies show that low-dose atropine depresses gastrin release in response to feeding in both intact and vagotomized dogs, suggesting that this effect is mediated by local neural reflexes (53). Because the gastrin release in response to antral distention is depressed by the $\beta$-adrenergic antagonists, an adrenergic sympathetic reflex may be involved (91). Antral distention in humans also activates inhibitory pathways of gastrin release because it inhibits GRP-stimulated release by an unknown mechanism.

## Hormonal

A variety of peptide hormones also regulate gastrin release, but space does not permit a detailed discussion of all of the mechanisms. Somatostatin is released from bulbous swellings at the end of cytoplasmic extensions in antral D cells onto G cells in many species (66, 101). This intimate relationship of the D cell with the G cell provides a tonic inhibition to gastrin release and makes somatostatin the primary hormonal regulator of gastrin release. It also provides the mechanism for many of the indirect effects of other hormones on gastrin release. For example, CCK released from the small bowel during the intestinal phase of digestion does not have a direct effect on the G cell but rather enhances somatostatin secretion via $CCK_A$ receptors on D cells (9, 18, 104), which inhibits gastrin release. In a similar fashion, secretin, gastric inhibitory polypeptide, prostaglandin E2, and glucagon also stimulate the release of somatostatin and inhibit gastrin secretion (14, 54, 100).

## Chemical

In accord with the presence of G cell microvilli extending into the lumen of the stomach, the G cell responds to the presence of food within the stomach (94). In the perfused rat stomach or in antral mucosal segments, peptone stimulates gastrin and inhibits somatostatin release (107). Neurotoxins such as tetrodotoxin, GRP antagonists, and atropine abolish both stimulation of gastrin release and inhibition of somatostatin release, indicating that peptone-induced gastrin release is mediated, in part, by both cholinergic and GRP neurons. However, other groups have shown that amino acids and amines also stimulate gastrin release from isolated canine G cells. Amino acid–stimulated gastrin release from isolated G cells was not blocked by decarboxylase inhibitors but enhanced by bombesin, isobutylmethylxanthine, and dibutyryl cAMP (22). These studies suggested that the amino acids themselves were capable of stimulating G cell release. Consistent with this notion was the finding that this effect was reversed by somatostatin via a pertussis toxin–sensitive GTP-binding protein. However, gastrin secretion induced by decarboxlyated amino acids (amines) that are often found in food is not reversed by physiologic inhibitors such as somatostatin (22, 69). It is hypothesized that the amines diffuse directly into gastrin-containing secretory granules in the G cell, where they are trapped in the granule's acidic environment. This results in an increase in pH of the granules and subsequent release. Other substances such as ammonia, which can be found in the stomachs of patients infected with *Helicobacter pylori*, also evoke the release of gastrin from antral G cells in a similar fashion (70). Other chemical stimuli such as an increase in gastric acid production completely suppress gastrin release. However, this is not a direct effect on the G cell, but is mediated by an increase in somatostatin secretion (55).

## H. Pylori, Ulcers, and Gastrin

Studies on the regulation of gastric acid secretion led to the discovery of H2 receptor antagonists that blocked the actions of histamine on the parietal cell. Although these and other gastric acid–suppressive agents promoted the healing of the majority of duodenal ulcers with 6 to 8 weeks of therapy, the ulcer would generally reappear with cessation of therapy. Thus the search for the cause of peptic ulcers continued. The discovery of a spiral bacterium (*H. pylori*) in the inflamed stomachs of patients with duodenal ulcers has led to a revolution in our understanding of ulcer pathogenesis and therapy (39, 75, 92). Because so many people are afflicted with peptic complaints, this discovery received a great deal of attention from scientists and the lay press. Despite initial skepticism regarding the relevance of this discovery, it is now widely accepted that virtually all patients with duodenal ulcers and 60–70% of those with gastric ulcers are infected with *H. pylori*. Moreover, failure to eradicate the infection often results in recurrence of the ulcers even with optimal anti-secretory therapy. In contrast, eradication of *H. pylori* results in complete healing, with a very low recurrence rate in the absence of reinfection (56).

Initially, these observations were difficult to mesh with our long-standing view that ulcers were secondary to a disorder in the regulation of gastric acid secretion. Not surprisingly, the view today is that both infection and alterations in gastric acid secretion appear to play a role in peptic ulcer pathogenesis. In support of this is the observation that although *H. pylori* is almost always present in patients with duodenal ulcers, the bacterium is more likely to be found in an inflamed gastric antrum than in the duodenum (50). Although initial infection with *H. pylori* is associated with gastritis and hyposecretion of acid, chronic infection leads to a moderate hypersecretion of gastric acid (1, 74, 78, 95). It is believed that this chronic hypersecretion of acid results in ulcer formation. Because patients with *H. pylori* have higher serum gastrins and decreased levels of antral somatostatin than non-infected controls, this finding suggests that *H. pylori* has some effect on the cells regulating gastrin release and acid secretion (11, 43, 44, 67, 68). Thus recent investigations have focused on the mechanisms by which chronic *H. pylori* infection alters the regulation of gastric acid secretion.

When compared with *H. pylori*-negative subjects, patients with duodenal ulcers and *H. pylori* infection have several abnormalities in the regulation of gastric acid secretion (35, 87). These include a two to fourfold increase in basal acid secretion, an increased maximal response to exogenous gastrin, a marked increase in acid secretion to GRP, and an increased ratio of basal acid output to maximal gastrin-stimulated acid output. Interestingly, although *H. pylori*–infected patients have increased acid secretion and moderate hypergastrinemia, the level of hypergastrinemia cannot fully account for the increase in acid secretion (35). *H. pylori*–positive duodenal ulcer patients also have impaired acid-inhibitory mechanisms. For example, antral distention inhibits gastric acid secretion in *H. pylori*–negative subjects but not in duodenal ulcer patients (87). Because somatostatin-producing D cells mediate many of the gastric acid inhibitory pathways, the reduced amounts of antral somatostatin seen with chronic infection can contribute to the reduced acid inhibition seen with antral distention, the loss of GRP-stimulated inhibitory control, hypergastrinemia, and enhanced acid secretion. All these abnormalities resolve within one year after eradication of infection except for the increased acid response to exogenous gastrin (35, 43, 87). It is doubtful that this response is the result of up-regulated acid secretory mechanisms due to prolonged hypergastrinemia because the *H. pylori*-induced hypergastrinemia resolves completely within one month after eradication. Furthermore, in patients with hypergastrinemia secondary to a gastrinoma, the enhancement of parietal cell mass fully resolves within six months after tumor resection (93). It is interesting to note *H. pylori*-positive patients without duodenal ulcers have all the same abnormalities that also correct with *H. pylori* eradication but to a lesser degree than those with ulcers. *H. pylori*-positive patients without ulcers do not, however, have elevated acid secretion in response to gastrin after eradication in some studies (35, 87). Thus it is supposed that patients who develop duodenal ulcers with *H. pylori* infection may have factors that increase their gastrin-stimulated acid secretory response. Although it is possible that duodenal ulcer patients may have other ways of up-regulating gastric acid secretory mechanisms in response to *H. pylori* infection, new attention is being given to possible differences in gastrin receptors and post-receptor mechanisms in duodenal ulcer patients.

To determine how *H. pylori* produces these effects in infected gastric mucosa, investigators have focused on the effects of bacterial products or inflammatory mediators on acid secretion. For example, *H. pylori* produces large amounts of urease and ammonia that modify the acidic milieu of the stomach. Although urease has little effect on gastric mucosa (109), ammonia ions can penetrate into the G cell's secretory granules where they become trapped in the acidic environment. As ammonia accumulates within the granule, the pH rises and the cells degranulate. Chronic administration of ammonia to rats has led to hypergastrinemia and gastric acid hypersecretion (70). Because *H. pylori* infection is associated with an underlying gastritis, investigators have examined the effects of inflammatory mediators on the regulation of acid secretion (37, 38, 58, 143). Interleukin-1$\beta$, interleukin 8, and tumor necrosis factor-$\alpha$ augment gastrin release from G cells. These and other cytokines are elevated in infected gastric mucosa, but much more study is needed before investigators can fully understand the effects of *H. pylori* infection on the regulation of acid secretion (11).

## SUMMARY

The study of gastrin has served as an excellent model for studies of gastrointestinal regulatory physiology. The pioneering studies of Bayliss & Starling (e.g. 2)—isolation of the peptide, development of a gastrin radioimmunoassay, isolation of a gastrin cDNA and subsequent biosynthetic studies, characterization the role of gastrin in peptic ulcer disease, and isolation of a cDNA encoding the receptor—are important milestones along the road to deeper understanding of gastric physiology. Emerging lines of gastrin investigation will include the unique biological activity of gastrin posttranslational processing intermediates, the intracellular mechanisms that mediate gastrin's effects on cell growth and differentiation, and the interaction of *H. pylori* and gastrin-producing G cells in peptic ulcer disease pathogenesis.

*Literature Cited*

1. Axon ATR. 1994. Acute infection with *H. pylori*. In *Helicobacter pylori: Basic Mechanisms to Clinical Cure*. pp. 407–12. Lancaster, England: Kluwer
2. Baldwin GS. 1994. Antiproliferative gastrin/cholecystokinin receptor antagonists target the 78-kDa gastrin-binding protein. *Proc. Natl. Acad. Sci. USA* 91(16):7593–97
3. Bayliss WM, Starling EH. 1902. The mechanism of pancreatic secretion. *J. Physiol.* 28:325–53
4. Boel E, Vuust J, Norris F, Norris K, Wind A, et al. 1983. Molecular cloning of human gastrin cDNA: evidence for evolution of gastrin by gene duplication. *Proc. Natl. Acad. Sci. USA* 80:2866–69
5. Bold RJ, Ishizuka J, Townsend CMJ, Thompson JC. 1994. Gastrin stimulates growth of human colon cancer cells via a receptor other than CCK-A or CCK-B. *Biochem. Biophys. Res. Commun.* 202(3):1222–26
6. Bradbury A, Finnie M, Smyth D. 1982. Mechanism of C-terminal amide formation by pituitary enzymes. *Nature* 298:686–88

7. Brand SJ, Klarlund J, Schwartz TW, Rehfeld JF. 1984. Biosynthesis of tyrosine-O-sulfated gastrins in rat antral mucosa. *J. Biol. Chem.* 259:13246–52
8. Bundgaard JR, Vuust J, Rehfeld JF. 1995. Tyrosine O-sulfation promotes proteolytic processing of progastrin. *EMBO J.* 14(13):3073–79
9. Burckhardt B, Delco F, Ensnick J, Meier R, Bauerefind P, et al. 1994. Cholecystokinin is a physiological regulator of gastric acid secretion in man. *Eur. J. Clin. Invest.* 24(6):370–76
10. Burgess TL, Kelly RB. 1987. Constitutive and regulated secretion of proteins. *Annu. Rev. Cell. Biol.* 3:243–93
11. Calam J. 1995. The somatostatin-gastrin link of *Helicobacter pylori* infection. *Ann. Med.* 27(5):569–73
12. Calam J, Dockray GJ, Walker R, Tracy HJ, Owens D. 1980. Molecular forms of gastrin in peptic ulcer: comparison of serum and tissue concentrations of G17 and G34 in gastric and duodenal ulcer subjects. *Eur. J. Clin. Invest.* 10:241–47
13. Chen LJ, Rosenquist GL. 1990. Enzymatic sulfation of gastrin in rat gastric mu-

cosa. *Biochem. Biophys. Res. Commun.* 170:1170–76

14. Chiba T, Taminato T, Kadowaki S, Able H, Chihara K, et al. 1980. Effects of glucagon, secretin, and vasoactive intestinal polypeptide on gastric somatostatin and gastrin release from isolated perfused rat stomach. *Gastroenterology* 79:67–71

15. Chowdhury JR, Berkowitz JM, Praissman M, Fara JW. 1976. Effect of sulfated and non-sulfated gastrin and octapeptide-cholecystokinin on cat gall bladder in vitro. *Experientia* 32:1173–75

16. Ciccotosto GD, McLeish A, Hardy KJ, Shulkes A. 1995. Expression, processing and secretion of gastrin in patients with colorectal carcinoma. *Gastroenterology* 109:1142–53

17. Cool DR, Fenger M, Snell CR, Loh YP. 1995. Identification of the sorting signal motif within proopiomelanocortin for the regulated secretory pathway. *J. Biol. Chem.* 270(15):8723–29

18. DelValle J, Chiba T, Park J, Yamada T. 1993. Distinct receptors for cholecystokinin and gastrin on canine fundic D-cells. *Am. J .Physiol.* 264(5):G811–15

19. DelValle J, Sugano K, Yamada T. 1989. Glycine-extended processing intermediates of gastrin and cholecystokinin in human plasma. *Gastroenterology* 97:1159–63

20. DelValle J, Sugano K, Yamada T. 1987. Progastrin and its glycine-extended post-translational processing intermediates in human gastrointestinal tissues. *Gastroenterology* 92(6):1908–12

21. DelValle J, Tsunoda Y, Williams JA, Yamada T. 1992. Regulation of $[Ca^{2+}]_i$ by secretagogue stimulation of canine gastric parietal cells. *Am. J. Physiol.* 262(3Pt 1):G420–26

22. DelValle J, Yamada T. 1990. Amino acids and amines stimulate gastrin release from canine antral G-cells via different pathways. *J. Clin. Invest.* 85:139–43

23. Dickinson CJ. 1995. Relationship of gastrin processing to colon cancer. *Gastroenterology* 109:1384–88

24. Dickinson CJ, Daugherty D, Guo Y, Hughes P, Yamada T. 1992. Molecular analysis of dibasic endoproteolytic cleavage signals. *J. Biol. Chem.* 267:21795–801

25. Dickinson CJ, Marino LR, Yamada T. 1990. Inhibition of the alpha-amidation of gastrin: effects on gastric acid secretion. *Am. J. Physiol.* 258:G810–14

26. Dickinson CJ, Sawada M, Guo YJ, Finniss S, Yamada T. 1995. Specificity of prohormone convertase endoproteolysis of progastrin in AtT-20 cells. *J. Clin. Invest.* 96:1425–31

27. Dickinson CJ, Takeuchi T, Guo Y-J, Stadler BT, Yamada T. 1993. Expression and processing of prohormones in nonendocrine cells. *Am. J. Physiol.* 264:G553–60

28. Dickinson CJ, Yamada T. 1991. Gastrin-amidating enzyme in the porcine pituitary and antrum: characterization of molecular forms and substrate specificity. *J. Biol. Chem.* 266:334–38

29. Dockray GJ. 1973. The action of gastrin and cholecystokinin-related peptides on pancreatic secretion in the rat. *Q. J. Exp. Physiol. Cogn. Med. Sci.* 58:163–69

30. Dockray GJ, Vaillant C, Hopkins CR. 1978. Biosynthetic relationships of big and little gastrins. *Nature* 273:770–72

31. Dockray GJ, Vaillant C, Walsh JH. 1979. The neuronal origin of bombesin-like immunoreactivity in the rat gastrointestinal tract. *Neuroscience* 4:473–80

32. Edkins JS. 1906. The chemical mechanism of gastric secretion. *J. Physiol.* 34:133–44

33. Edkins JS, Tweedy M. 1909. The natural channels of absorption evoking the chemical mechanism of gastric secretion. *J. Physiol.* 38:263–67

34. Eipper BA, Mains RE, Glembotski CC. 1983. Identification in pituitary tissue of a peptide $\alpha$-amidation activity that acts on glycine-extended peptides and requires molecular oxygen, copper and ascorbic acid. *Proc. Natl. Acad. Sci. USA* 80:5144–48

35. El-Omar EM, Penman ID, Ardill JES, Chittajallu RS. 1995. *Helicobacter pylori* infection and abnormalities of acid secretion in patients with duodenal ulcer disease. *Gastroenterology* 109(3):681–91

36. Evans EA, Gilmore R, Blobel G. 1986. Purification of microsomal signal peptidase as a complex. *Proc. Natl. Acad. Sci. USA* 83:581–85

37. Fan X, Chua A, Fan X, Keeling P. 1995. Increased gastric production of interleukin-8 and tumour necrosis factor with *Helicobacter pylori* infection. *J. Clin. Pathol.* 48(2):133–36

38. Fan X, Chua A, Shahi C, McDevitt J, Keeling P, Kelleher D. 1994. Gastric T lymphocyte responses to *Helicobacter pylori* in patients with *H. pylori* colonisation. *Gut* 35(10):1379–84

39. Feldman M. 1994. The acid test. Making clinical sense of the Consensus Conference on *Helicobacter pylori* [editorial;

comment]. *J. Am. Med. Assoc.* 272(1):70–71

40. Feldman M, Walsh JH, Wong HC, Richardson CT. 1978. Role of gastrin heptadecapeptide in the acid secretory response to amino acids in man. *J. Clin. Invest.* 61:308–13

41. Fuller RS, Brake A, Thorner J. 1989. Yeast prohormone processing enzyme (KEX2 gene product) is a $Ca^{2+}$-dependent serine protease. *Proc. Natl. Acad. Sci. USA* 86:1434–38

42. Glasgow RE, Kong W, Mulvihill SJ. 1996. Glycine-extended gastrin-17, but not gastrin-17-amide, promotes DNA synthesis in fetal rabbit gastric epithelial cells in vitro. *Gastroenterology* 110(4):A1074 (Abstr.)

43. Graham DY. 1996. *Helicobacter pylori* and perturbations in acid secretion: the end of the beginning. *Gastroenterology* 110:1647–49

44. Graham DY, Opekum A, Lew GM, Klein PD, Walsh JH. 1991. *Helicobacter pylori*-associated exaggerated gastrin release in duodenal ulcer patients. The effect of bombesin infusion and urea ingestion. *Gastroenterology* 100:1571–75

45. Greeley GHJ, Song L, Varlamov O, Leiter E, Fricker L. 1996. Localization of carboxypeptidases CP-D and CP-E in the gut and involvement of CP-E in processing progastrin. *Gastroenterology* 110(4):A1075( Abstr.)

46. Gregory RA, Tracy HJ. 1964. The constitution and properties of two gastrins extracted from hog antral mucosa. I. The isolation of two gastrins from hog antral mucosa. II. The properties of two gastrins isolated from hog antral mucosa. *Gut* 5:103–14

47. Gregory RA, Tracy HJ. 1961. The preparation and properties of gastrin. *J. Physiol.* 156:523–43

48. Gutzman S, Chayvialle JA, Banks WA, Rayford PL, Thompson JC. 1979. Effect of vagal stimulation on pancreatic secretion and on blood levels of gastrin, cholecystokinin, secretin, vasoactive intestinal peptide, and somatostatin. *Surgery* 86:329–36

49. Higashide S, Gomez G, Greeley GHJ, Townsend CM, Thompson JC. 1996. Glycine-extended gastrin potentiates gastrin-stimulated gastric acid secretion in rats. *Am. J. Physiol.* 33:G220–24

50. Hilsden RJ, Meddings JB, Sutherland LR. 1996. Intestinal permeability changes in response to acetylsalicylic acid in relatives of patients with Crohn's disease.

*Gastroenterology* 110:1395–403

51. Hilsted L, Hint K, Christiansen J, Rehfeld JF. 1988. Neither glycine-extended gastrin nor the 1–13 fragment of gastrin 17 influences gastric acid secretion in humans. *Gastroenterology* 94:96–110

52. Hirschowitz BI, Gibson RG. 1978. Stimulation of gastrin release and gastric secretion: effect of bombesin and a nonapeptide in fistula dogs with and without fundic vagotomy. *Digestion* 18:227–39

53. Hirschowitz BI, Gibson RG, Molina E. 1981. Atropine suppresses gastrin release by food intact and vagotomized dogs. *Gastroenterology* 81:838–43

54. Holst JJ, Jensen SL, Knuhtsen S, Nielsen OV, Rehfeld JF. 1978. Effect of vagus, gastric inhibitory polypeptide, and HCl on gastrin and somatostatin release from perfused pig antrum. *Am. J. Physiol.* 244:G515–22

55. Holst JJ, Ørskov C, Seier-Poulsen S. 1992. Somatostatin is an essential paracrine link in acid inhibition of gastrin secretion. *Digestion* 51(2):95–102

56. Hopkins RJ, Girardi LS, Turney EA. 1996. Relationship between *Helicobacter pylori* eradication and reduced duodenal and gastric ulcer recurrence: a review. *Gastroenterology* 110(4):1244–52

57. Hortin G, Folz R, Gordon JI, Strauss AW. 1986. Characterization of sites of tyrosine sulfation in proteins and criteria for predicting their occurrences. *Biochem. Biophys. Res. Commun.* 141:326–33

58. Huang J, O'Toole P, Doing P, Trust T. 1995. Stimulation of interleukin-8 production in epithelial cell lines by *Helicobacter pylori. Infect. Immun.* 63(5):1732–38

59. Johnson LR, McCormack SA, Wang J-Y. 1993. Regulation of gastrointestinal mucosal growth. In *Gastrin,* ed. J Walsh, pp. 285–300. New York: Raven

60. Julius D, Brake A, Blair L, Kunisawa R, Thorner J. 1984. Isolation of the putative structural gene to the lysine-arginine-cleaving endopeptidase required for processing of yeast prepro-$\alpha$-factor. *Cell* 37:1075–89

61. Kaise M, Muraoka A, Seva C, Takeda H, Dickinson CJ, Yamada T. 1995. Glycine-extended progastrin intermediates induce $H^+,K^+$-ATPase $\alpha$-subunit gene expression through a novel receptor. *J. Biol. Chem.* 270:11155–60

62. Kenner GW, Moore S, Ramachandran KL, Ramage R, Dockray GJ, et al. 1981. Porcine big gastrin: sequence, synthe-

sis and immunochemical studies. *Bioorg. Chem.* 10:152–60

63. Kochman ML, DelValle J, Dickinson CJ, Boland CR. 1992. Post-translational processing of gastrin in neoplastic human colonic tissues. *Biochem. Biophys. Res. Comm.* 189:1165–69

64. Koh TJ, Nicholls PJ, Wang TC. 1996. Glycine-extended gastrin promotes growth of a human hepatoma cell line. *Gastroenterology* 110(4):1089

65. Kopin AS, Lee YM, McBride EW, Miller LJ, Lu M, et al. 1992. Expression cloning and characterization of the canine parietal cell gastrin receptor. *Proc. Natl. Acad. Sci. USA* 89(8):3605–9

66. Larssen LI, Goltermann N, De Magistris L, Rehfeld JF. 1979. Somatostatin cell processes as pathways for paracrine secretion. *Science* 205:1393–95

67. Levi S, Beardshall K, Swift I, Foulkes W, Playford R, et al. 1989. Antral *Helicobacter pylori,* hypergastrinaemia and duodenal ulcers: effect of eradicating the organism. *Br. Med. J.* 299:1504–5

68. Levi S, Beardshall K, Swift I, Foulkes W, Playford R, et al. 1989. *Campylobacter pylori* and duodenal ulcers: the gastrin link. *Lancet* 1:1167–68

69. Lichtenberger LM, Delansorne R, Graziani LA. 1979. Importance of amino acid uptake and decarboxylation in gastrin release from isolated G cells. *Nature* 295:698–700

70. Lichtenberger LM, Dial EJ, Romero JJ, Lechago J, Jarboe LA, Wolfe MM. 1995. Role of luminal ammonia in the development of gastropathy and hypergastrinemia in the rat. *Gastroenterology* 108:320–29

71. Madaus S, Bender H, Schusdziarra V, Keh K, Munzert G, et al. 1990. Vagally induced release of gastrin, somatostatin and bombesin-like immunoreactivity from perfused rat stomach. Effect of stimulation on frequency and cholinergic mechanism. *Regul. Pep.* 30:179–92

72. Marino LR, Sugano K, Yamada T. 1988. Development of gastrin synthesis and posttranslational processing mechanisms in rats. *Am. J. Physiol.* 254:G87–92

73. Marino LR, Takeuchi T, Dickinson CJ, Yamada T. 1991. Expression and posttranslational processing of progastrin in heterologous endocrine cell lines. *J. Biol. Chem.* 266:6133–36

74. Marshall BJ, Armstrong JA, McGechie DB, Glancy RJ. 1985. Attempt to fulfill Koch's postulates for pyloric campylobacter. *Med. J. Aust.* 142:436–39

75. Marshall BJ, Warren JR. 1984. Unidentified curved bacilli in the stomach of patients with gastritis and peptic ulceration. *Lancet* 1(8390):1311–15

76. Martindale R, Kauffman GL, Levin S, Walsh JH, Yamada T. 1982. Differential regulation of gastrin and somatostatin secretion from isolated perfused rat stomachs. *Gastroenterology* 83:240–44

77. Matsumoto M, Park J, Sugano K, Yamada T. 1987. Biological activity of progastrin posttranslational processing intermediates. *Am. Physiol. Soc.* 87:G315–19

78. McGowan CC, Clover TL, Blaser MJ. 1996. *Helicobacter pylori* and gastric acid: biological and therapeutic implications. *Gastroenterology* 110:926–38

79. McGuigan JE. 1968. Immunochemical studies with synthetic human gastrin. *Gastroenterology* 54:1005–11

80. Merchant JL, Dickinson CJ, Yamada T. 1994. Molecular biology of the gut: model of gastrointestinal hormones. In *Physiology of the Gastrointestinal Tract,* ed. LR Johnson, pp. 295–350. New York: Raven. 3rd ed.

81. Miyake A. 1995. A truncated isoform of human CCK-B/gastrin receptor generated by alternative usage of a novel exon. *Biochem. Biophys. Res. Commun.* 208(1):230–37

82. Naggert JK, Fricker LD, Varlamov O, Nishina PM, Rouille Y, et al. 1995. Hyperproinsulinaemia in obese fat/fat mice associated with a carboxypeptidase E mutation which reduces enzyme activity. *Nat. Genet.* 10(2):135–42

83. Negre F, Fagot-Revurat P, Bouisson M, Rehfeld JF, Vaysse N. 1996. Autocrine stimulation of AR4–2J rat pancreatic tumor cell growth by glycine-extended gastrin. *Int. J. Cancer* 66:653–58

84. Nemeth J, Taylor B, Pauwels S, Varro A, Dockray GJ. 1993. Identification of progastrin derived peptides in colorectal carcinoma extracts. *Gut* 34(1):90–95

85. Nothwehr SF, Gordon JI. 1990. Targeting of proteins into the eukaryotic secretory pathway: signal peptide structure/function relationship. *BioEssays* 12:479–84

86. Ohtaki T, Park J, Song I, Guo Y, Hoeltzel M, et al. 1996. Short and long isoforms of the human CCKB receptor couple to post receptor signaling pathways in a differential manner. *Gastroenterology* 110(4):A1104 (Abstr.)

87. Olbe L, Hamlet A, Dalenback J, Fandriks L. 1996. A mechanism by which *Helicobacter pylori* invection of the antrum contributes to the development of duodenal ulcer. *Gastroenterology* 110:1386–94

88. Palade G. 1975. Intracellular aspects of the process of protein synthesis. *Science* 189:347–58

89. Palmer DJ, Christie DL. 1992. Identification of molecular aggregates containing glycoproteins III, J, K (carboxypeptidase H) and H (Kex2-related proteases) in the soluble and membrane fractions of adrenal medullary chromaffin granules. *J. Biol. Chem.* 267:19806–12

90. Parsonnet J, Kim P, Yang N, Orentreich JH, Vogelman JH, Friedman GD. 1996. Gastrin and gastric adenocarcinoma: a prospective evaluation. *Gastroenterology* 110(4):574

91. Peters MN, Walsh JH, Ferrari J, Feldman M. 1982. Adrenergic regulation of distention-induced gastrin release in humans. *Gastroenterology* 82:659–63

92. Peura DA. 1996. *Helicobacter pylori* and ulcerogenesis. *Am. J. Med.* 100(5A):19–25S (Suppl.)

93. Pisegna JR, Norton JA, Slimak GG, Metz DC, Maton PN, et al. 1992. Effect of curative gastrinoma resection on gastric secretory function and antisecretory drug requirement in the Zollinger-Ellison syndrome. *Gastroenterology* 102:767–78

94. Porak J. 1989. Endocrine cells of the gut. In *Handbook of Physiology. The Gastrointestinal System. Neural and Endocrine Biology,* 6:79–96. Bethesda: Am. Physiol. Soc.

95. Pounder RE. 1996. *Helicobacter pylori* and gastroduodenal secretory function. *Gastroenterology* 110:947–49

96. Rahier J, Pauwels S, Dockray GJ. 1987. Biosynthesis of gastrin. Localization of the precursor and peptide products using electron microscopic-immunogold methods. *Gastroenterology* 92:1146–52

97. Rehfeld JF. 1995. Gastrin and colorectal cancer: a never-ending dispute? *Gastroenterology* 108:1307–09

98. Rothman JE, Orci L. 1992. Molecular dissection of the secretory pathway. *Nature* 355(6359):409–15

99. Rothman JE, Wieland FT. 1996. Protein sorting by transport vesicles. *Science* 272(5259):227–34

100. Saffouri B, Weir G, Bitar K, Grider JR, Makhlouf GM. 1980. Gastrin and somatostatin secretion by perfused rat stomach: functional linkage of antral peptides. *Am. J. Physiol.* 238:G495–501

101. Saffouri B, Weir G, Bitar K, Makhlouf GM. 1979. Stimulation of gastrin secretion from perfused rat stomach by somatostatin antiserum. *Life Sci.* 25:1749–54

102. Schepp W, Prinz C, Hakanson R, Schusdziarra V, Classen M. 1990. Bombesin-like peptides stimulate gastrin release from isolated rat G-cells. *Regul. Pept.* 28:241–53

103. Schiller LR, Walsh JH, Feldman M. 1980. Distension-induced gastrin release. *Gastroenterology* 78:912–17

104. Schmidt W, Schenk S, Nustede R, Holst J, Folsch U, Creutzfeld W. 1994. Cholecystokinin is a negative regulator of gastric acid secretion and postprandial release of gastrin in humans. *Gastroenterology* 107(6):1610–20

105. Schubert ML. 1991. The effect of vasoactive intestinal polypeptide on gastric acid secretion is predominantly mediated by somatostatin. *Gastroenterology* 100:1195–200

106. Schubert ML, Bitar KN, Makhlouf GM. 1982. Regulation of gastrin and somatostatin secretion by cholinergic and noncholinergic intramural neurons. *Am. J. Physiol.* 243:G442–47

107. Schubert ML, Coy DH, Makhlouf GM. 1992. Peptone stimulates gastrin secretion from the stomach by activating bombesin/GRP and cholinergic neurons. *Am. J. Physiol.* 262:G685–89

108. Schubert ML, Makhlouf G. 1993. Gastrin secretion induced by distention is mediated by gastric cholinergic and vasoactive intestinal peptide neurons in rats. *Gastroenterology* 104:834–39

109. Schubert ML, Saffouri B, Walsh JH, Makhlouf GM. 1985. Inhibition of neurally mediated gastrin secretion by bombesin antiserum. *Am. J. Physiol.* 248:G456–62

110. Scopsi L, Gullo M, Rilke F, Martin S, Steiner DF. 1995. Proprotein convertases (PC1/PC3 and PC2) in normal and neoplastic tissues: their use as markers of neuroendocrine differentiation. *J. Clin. Endocrinol. Metab.* 80:294–301

111. Seva C, Dickinson CJ, Yamada T. 1994. Growth promoting effects of glycine-extended progastrin. *Science* 265:410–12

112. Seva C, Kowalski-Chauvel A, Blanchet JS, Vaysse N, Pradayrol L. 1996. Gastrin induces tyrosine phosphorylation of Shc proteins and their association with the Grb2/Sos complex. *FEBS Lett.* 378(1):74–78

113. Seva C, Scemama JL, Pradayrol L, Sarfati PD, Vaysse N. 1994. Coupling of pancreatic gastrin/cholecystokinin-B (GCCKB) receptors to phospholipase C and protein kinase C in AR4-2J tumoral cells. *Reg. Pept.* 52(1):31–38

114. Short GM, Reel GM, Doyle JW, Wolfe MM. 1985. Effect of GRP on β-adrenergic-stimulated gastrin and so-

matostatin release in the isolated rat stomach. *Am. J. Physiol.* 249:G197–202

115. Singh P, Narayan S, Adiga RB. 1994. Phosphorylation of pp62 and pp54 src-like proteins in a rat intestinal cell line in response to gastrin. *Am. J .Physiol.* 87:G315–19

116. Smeekens SP, Avruch AS, LaMendola J, Chan SJ, Steiner DF. 1991. Identification of a cDNA encoding a second putative prohormone convertase related to PC2 in AtT20 cells and islets of Langerhans. *Proc. Natl. Acad. Sci. USA* 88:340–44

117. Smeekens SP, Steiner DF. 1990. Identification of a human insulinoma cDNA encoding a novel mammalian protein structurally related to the yeast dibasic processing protease Kex2. *J. Biol. Chem.* 265:2997–3000

118. Soll AH. 1977. Studies on the actions and interactions of secretagogues on isolated mammalian parietal cells as reflected in changes in oxygen consumption and aminopyrine uptake. *Gastroenterology* 73(4 Pt2):899

119. Soll AH, Yamada T, Park J, Thomas LP. 1984. Release of somatostatinlike immunoreactivity from canine fundic mucosal cells in primary culture. *Am. J. Physiol.* 247(5 Pt1):G558–66

120. Song I, Brown DR, Wiltshire RN, Gantz I, Trent JM, Yamada T. 1993. The human gastrin/cholecystokinin type B receptor gene: alternative splice donor site in exon 4 generates two variant mRNAs. *Proc. Natl. Acad. Sci. USA* 90(19):9085–89

121. Steiner DF, Smeekens SP, Ohagi S, Chan SJ. 1992. The new enzymology of precursor processing endoproteases. *J. Biol. Chem.* 267:23435–38

122. Stepan VM, Sawada M, Yamada T, Dickinson CJ. 1995. Glycine-extended gastrin exerts growth-promoting effects on colon cancer cell lines. *Gastroenterology* 110:A1122 (Abstr.)

123. Stoller TJ, Shields D. 1989. The propeptide of preprosomatostatin mediates intracellular transport and secretion of α-globin from mammalian cells. *J. Cell Biol.* 108:1647–55

124. Sugano K, Aponte GW, Yamada T. 1985. Identification and characterization of glycine-extended post-translational processing intermediates of progastrin in porcine stomach. *J. Biol. Chem.* 260(21):11724–29

125. Sugano K, Park J, Dobbins WO, Yamada T. 1987. Glycine-extended progastrin processing intermediates: accumulation in cultured G-cells and cosecretion with gastrin. *Am. J. Physiol.* 253(4.1):G502–7

126. Sugano K, Park J, Soll AH, Yamada T. 1987. Stimulation of gastrin release by bombesin and canine gastrin-releasing peptides. Studies with isolated canine G cells in primary culture. *J. Clin. Invest.* 79(3):935–42

127. Sugano K, Park J, Yamada T. 1984. Biosynthesis of gastrin: studies with isolated enriched canine antral G-cells in primary culture. *Dig. Dis. Sci.* 29:835

128. Tepperman BL, Walsh JH, Preshaw RM. 1972. Effect of antral denervation on gastric release by sham feeding and insulin hypoglycemia in dogs. *Gastroenterology* 63:973–80

129. Thorburn CM, Friedman GD, Orentreich N, Vogelman JH, Parsonnet J. 1996. High gastrin levels increase risk for colorectal carcinoma. *Gastroenterology* 110(4):603

130. Todisco A, Takeuchi J, Yamada A, Urumov A, Yamada T. 1996. Molecular mechanisms for the growth factor actin of gastrin. *J. Invest. Med.* 40:318A (Abstr.)

131. Todisco A, Takeuchi Y, Seva C, Dickinson CJ, Yamada T. 1995. Gastrin and glycine-extended processing intermediates induce different programs of early gene activation. *J. Biol. Chem.* 270:28337–41

132. van Solinge WW, Neilsen FC, Friis-Hansen L, Falkmer U, Rehfeld JF. 1994. Expression but incomplete processing of progastrin in colorectal carcinoma. *Gastroenterology* 104:1099–107

133. Varro A, Henry J, Vaillant C, Dockray GJ. 1994. Discrimination between temperature- and brefeldin A-sensitive steps in the sulfation, phosphorylation, and cleavage of progastrin and its derivatives. *J. Biol. Chem.* 269(32):20764–70

134. Varro A, Nemeth J, Bridson J, Lee C, Moore S, Dockray GJ. 1990. Processing of the gastrin precursor. Modulation of phosphorylated, sulfated, and amidated products. *J. Biol. Chem.* 265(35):21476–81

135. Varro A, Voronina S, Dockray GJ. 1995. Pathways of processing of the gastrin precursor in rat antral mucosa. *J. Clin. Invest.* 95(4):1642–49

136. Walsh J. 1993. *Gastrin.* New York: Raven. 432 pp.

137. Walsh JH, Bouzyk M, Rozengurt E. 1993. Homologous desensitization of bombesin-induced increases in intracellular $Ca^{2+}$ in quiescent Swiss 3T3 cells involves a protein kinase C-independent

mechanism. *J. Cell Physiol.* 156(2):330–40

138. Walsh JH, Yallow RS, Berson SA. 1971. The effect of atropine on plasma gastrin response to feeding. *Gastroenterology* 60:16–21

139. Walter P, Gilmore R, Blobel G. 1984. Protein translocation across the endoplasmic reticulum. *Cell* 38:5–8

140. Wang TC, Koh TJ, Varro A, Cahill R, Fox JG, Dockray GJ. 1996. Processing and functional significance of human progastrin in transgenic mice. *Gastroenterology* 110(4):A1132 (Abstr.)

141. Wank SA. 1995. Cholecystokinin receptors. *Am. J. Physiol.* 269(5 Pt1):G628–46

142. Wank SA, Pisegna JR, Poirot SS. 1994. Functional significance of potential splice variants of the human cholecystokinin (CCK) B receptor. *Gastroenterology* 106(4):A850 (Abstr.)

143. Weigert N, Schaffer K, Schusdziarra V, Classen M, Schepp W. 1996. Gastrin secretion from primary cultures of rabbit antral G cells: stimulation by inflammatory cytokines. *Gastroenterology* 110:147–54

144. Wolfe MM, Jensen RT. 1987. Zollinger-Ellison syndrome. Current concepts in diagnosis and management. *N. Engl. J. Med.* 317(19):1200–09

145. Yalow RS, Berson SA. 1971. Future studies on the nature of immunoreactive gastrin in human plasma. *Gastroenterology* 60:203–14

146. Yoo OJ, Powell CT, Agarwal KL. 1982. Molecular cloning and nucleotide sequence of full-length cDNA coding for porcine gastrin. *Proc. Natl. Acad. Sci. USA* 79:1049–53

147. Yu DH, Noguchi M, Zhou ZC, Villanueva ML, Gardner JD, Jensen RT. 1987. Characterization of gastrin receptors on guinea pig pancreatic acini. *Am. J. Physiol.* 253:G793–801

*Annu. Rev. Physiol. 1997. 59:299–323*

# EVOLUTION AND REGULATION OF UREA SYNTHESIS AND UREOTELY IN (BATRACHOIDID) FISHES

## Patrick J. Walsh

Division of Marine Biology and Fisheries, NIEHS Marine and Freshwater Biomedical Sciences Center, Rosenstiel School of Marine and Atmospheric Science, University of Miami, 4600 Rickenbacker Causeway, Miami, Florida 33149-1098

KEY WORDS:  urea excretion, fish, ornithine-urea cycle, toadfish, elasmobranchs

### ABSTRACT

Selected teleostean (bony) fish species of the family Batrachoididae (toadfishes and midshipmen) possess high titers of all enzymes of the ornithine-urea cycle in their livers. These species have proven valuable in understanding the short-term regulation of urea synthesis, urea permeability, and transport across epithelial tissues, and how urea synthesis and excretion have evolved among vertebrates. One species in particular, the gulf toadfish (*Opsanus beta*), has been shown to rapidly switch from ammonia excretion to urea synthesis and excretion during a variety of stress conditions (including confinement). The transition is accompanied by an upregulation of hepatic glutamine synthetase activity, and a switch to pulsatile urea excretion from the anterior end of the fish. In fact, a single day's excretion can be voided in a period of <3 h. Hypotheses on the environmental significance of these patterns of urea synthesis and excretion are discussed.

## INTRODUCTION: THE COMPARATIVE UTILITY OF PISCINE STUDIES

Excretion of specialized waste nitrogen compounds (e.g. urea and uric acid) is well developed in tetrapod vertebrates as an adaptation for terrestrial existence (16, 17, 97). However, the ability to synthesize and excrete urea is well documented for fish, indicating that these abilities were likely present well before vertebrate emergence onto land. By examining how fish are similar to, or

299

different from, higher vertebrates, we can elucidate the evolutionary changes in nitrogen metabolism that took place in adapting to a terrestrial environment.

Fish also present alternative metabolic regulatory systems for comparative study. Most terrestrial organisms synthesize urea and/or uric acid obligately. For example, in humans, typical venous blood/plasma ammonia concentrations are kept very low (5–40 $\mu$M) by hepatic urea synthesis via the ornithine-urea cycle (O-UC); increasing blood levels by as little as 50 to 100% results in observable neural impairment and other pathologies (23, 56, 57). Such obligate dependence on urea production means that regulation of urea synthesis and excretion in most vertebrate species is inherently a process of fine-scale tuning of a constantly functioning pathway (56, 57). One obvious exception is the coarse-scale (i.e. off to on) regulation during development (e.g. see Reference 27 for mammals or Reference 6 for the amphibian transition from tadpole to tetrapod). In contrast to most vertebrates, teleostean (higher bony) fishes have higher tolerances to elevated plasma ammonia levels and present a greater range of synthesis and excretion patterns (18, 103). Both obligate ammonotely and obligate ureotely are seen in fish species, but also evident are rapid (e.g. within a 24 h time frame) shifts between ammonotely and ureotely (103). Thus fish give us the opportunity to study coarse-scale, but rapid, regulation typically not seen in other adult vertebrates.

Bearing in mind the comparative utility of piscine nitrogen metabolism and excretion, this article reviews recent studies on fish (particularly the toadfishes and midshipmen, Family Batrachoididae) and develops several themes, namely that (a) the O-UC is an ancient trait in animals; (b) the genes for the O-UC probably remain in many modern fish, but are silenced in most species in the adult phase; (c) the urea molecule can be retained because its epithelial permeability and transport can be tightly governed; (d) this trait of urea as a retainable molecule is still poorly understood from a mechanistic standpoint. However, this trait is critical to understanding why the metabolically expensive urea is synthesized by some fish. Finally, (e) when ammonia excretion is not directly cut off by the physical environment (e.g. air-exposure, high water pH), and urea is made by species remaining in aquatic environs where ammonia could still be easily excreted, fish need to employ specific mechanisms to retain the highly diffusible ammonia molecule so that it can be conserved for urea synthesis.

The topic of nitrogen metabolism and excretion in fish has been reviewed recently (2, 18, 34, 35, 51, 52, 62, 103). This review is meant to build on these works with recent discoveries and perspectives, focusing largely on a single family of teleostean fish, but drawing upon selected studies of other fish species. (For more general and mammalian perspectives the reader is referred to References 16, 56, 57, 99.) This review follows the terminology as initially applied to fish (41), where variable proportions of two or more of the three main nitrogenous waste products (ammonia, urea, uric acid) can be found in excreta. Thus ureotelic means the majority (i.e. >50%) of nitrogen is excreted as urea (41). Diverse biochemical processes contribute to the generation of nitrogenous waste. For example, many ammonotelic teleosts excrete 10 to 30% of their total waste nitrogen as urea, which typically comes from direct cleavage of the dietary amino acid arginine, or from breakdown of purines, rather than from de novo synthesis of urea from a central pool of ammonia via the O-UC (65, 103). Strictly speaking, even though most teleost fish make and excrete some urea, they would not be called ureogenic in that this term is reserved for those possessing a complete O-UC (41). These shorthand terms, although convenient, tend to classify organisms absolutely, when in fact the processes vary across a spectrum of types.

# UREOGENESIS IN TELEOSTS: A RETAINED OR REINVENTED TRAIT?

## Carbamoyl Phosphate Synthetase Isozyme Type

Modern-day cartilaginous fish (elasmobranchs) are well known for their abilities to generate urea via the O-UC, utilizing the mitochondrial enzyme carbamoyl phosphate synthetase III (CPSase III) to synthesize the first critical pathway intermediate, carbamoyl phosphate (1, 2). The isozyme's properties give important clues to the evolutionary history of ureogenesis. Unlike the mitochondrial isozyme in tetrapods, CPSase I, which prefers ammonia as a nitrogen donor, CPSase III in fish prefers glutamine (1, 2, 62). Although the extant descendants of the most primitive fishes, the agnathans (lampreys and hagfish), do not appear to be ureogenic (70, 72), CPSase III was in fact first discovered in modern descendants of groups more primitive than fish, e.g. four species (three phyla) of ureogenic invertebrates (87, 88). Griffith's (35) interpretation of this phylogenetic distribution is that the genes of the O-UC evolved more than once. However, the pathway characteristics, and specifically the CPSase III isozyme characteristics, are so highly conserved (3) that it seems more likely that the potential for ureogenesis was already a characteristic of the root-stock for all fish and that its absence in modern agnathans is a secondary loss. Although modern adult agnathans lack the expressed enzymes, no information exists on the presence or absence of O-UC genes in them. Furthermore, in the fishes more advanced than elasmobranchs, where mitochondrial CPSase is expressed (above basal levels of the cytosolic CPSase II used by all metazoans in pyrimidine biosynthesis), and where it has been characterized, CPSase III activity is present in all cases except one, the Dipnoans (lungfishes), where CPSase I is the sole isozyme present (2). These findings have been interepreted by us to mean that ureogenesis in fishes shares common evolutionary ancestry, but that the switch to an exclusively CPSase I-based O-UC took place in the Dipnoan lineage and that tetrapods share evolutionary history with the Dipnoans. However, substantial activities of ammonia-dependent activity have been reported for coelacanths (*Latimeria chalumnae*) (33) in addition to glutamine-dependent activity (62). More recently, for the air-breathing teleost *Heteropneustes fossilis*, activities with characteristics of both isozymes have been found in crude preparations (76). A common problem with many of these studies (including our own) is that it is difficult to interpret data on substrate preferences for crude preparations because, for example, CPSase III can have some activity with ammonia. Also, in studies where only ammonia is added, it is possible that glutamine could be synthesized from endogenous glutamate catalyzed by glutamine synthetase to fuel a substantial CPSase III activity. Clearly, for species where mixed isozyme types (*Heteropneustes fossilis*) or conflicting results (coelacanths) have been reported, careful examination of purified CPSases for isozyme type is warranted (see 2).

## Which Fish are Ureogenic and Why?

The occurrence of the enzymes of ureogenesis among fish species also gives clues to the evolutionary history of the trait. Elasmobranchs and coelacanths are ureoosmotic (41), i.e. they retain urea to levels of 400 mM or more in both plasma and tissues to bring their osmotic concentration close to that of seawater (34, 51, 103). A common, but anecdotal, evolutionary rationale ascribed to this use (not by the prior authors!) is that urea is a waste product that would be produced anyway, and by retaining a waste product, these fish are evolutionarily superior to the aquatic invertebrates that retain as osmolytes amino acids and other nitrogenous compounds, which by and large are costly to synthesize. This interpretation, however, ignores three important facts. First, urea synthesis is costly in terms of ATP requirements (63, 65). Notably, Kirschner (48) has recently assessed the relative theoretical cost of osmoregulation in elasmobranchs versus teleosts and found them to be about equally efficient. Second, although urea is less neurotoxic than ammonia (23), at the high concentrations associated with significant osmoregulatory benefit, urea may have destabilizing effects on macromolecules and thus must be counteracted by the simultaneous accumulation of high concentrations of stabilizing solutes (e.g. trimethylamine oxide; generally a 2:1 ratio of urea:TMAO) (7, 85). Lastly, elasmobranchs and coelacanths are fully aquatic and have no need to be ureotelic because they could theoretically avoid neurotoxicity by excreting nitrogenous waste across the gills as the freely diffusible ammonia. Surprisingly, however, few studies have critically focused on whether elasmobranchs excrete predominantly urea or ammonia (see Routes and Patterns of Urea Excretion).

Expression of the O-UC and/or ureotely is known for fewer than a dozen species of teleosts, which are spread across nine families and five orders from four continents (62, 69, 74, 75, 77). Surprisingly, ureotely has been extensively studied in only two species (see The Gulf Toadfish and The Lake Magadi Tilapia below) and has been confirmed for only an additional four species in very limited measurements (reviewed by 18, 75; see also 74). With the exception of the tilapia, these species are amphibious and can breathe air for long periods. In these amphibious species, ureogenesis is believed to be facultative, and its role is similar to that in the modern Dipnoan lungfish and to the primordial role that urea synthesis played in terrestrial colonization; namely, when ammonia excretion is cut off because the gills are no longer bathed in water, fish accumulate less neurotoxic waste, one that can be concentrated in excreta to minimize water loss during amphibious forays. Although the debate continues on the importance of ureogenesis in bicarbonate disposal in higher vertebrates (see e.g. references in 49, 56), it is clear that avoidance of ammonia intoxication, not acid-base regulation, is the root explanation for ureogenesis in fish (104). The more extensive study of ureogenesis in two teleost fish species leads to the emergence of additional rationales for why fish make urea.

THE LAKE MAGADI TILAPIA    Lake Magadi in Kenya's Rift Valley, is extremely alkaline (pH 10), containing massive levels of carbonates ($\geq 180$ mM) (105, 108). The high pH and buffering capacity of these waters would preclude ammonia excretion by typical teleosts under current models proposing that external protons at the gill-water boundary layer trap $NH_3$ (which has diffused across the gill epithelium) into the form of $NH_4^+$, keeping the outwardly directed ammonia partial pressure ($P_{NH3}$) gradient from blood to water high (102). The Lake Magadi tilapia (*Oreochromis alcalicus grahami*), the only fish in the lake, excrete no nitrogen metabolic waste as ammonia, but all as urea, generated by a complete hepatic O-UC (69). This species is not ureoosmotic, and because it is entirely aquatic, urea synthesis is not in response to terrestriality. Studies of this species have shown that the role of ureogenesis in acid-base regulation is minimal and that nitrogen load drives ureogenesis (105). Although this fish's adaptation to its environmental demands are dramatic, one could argue that the Lake Magadi tilapia is an extended example of what is believed to occur in air-exposed fish; namely that they resort to ureotelism when pathways of ammonia excretion are precluded by environmental parameters. Nonetheless, continued study of the mechanisms of regulation of ureogenesis in this clearly unique and obligate teleostean ureotele will likely lead to insights into regulation of ureogenesis in obligately ureotelic higher vertebrates.

THE GULF TOADFISH    Earlier studies with the oyster toadfish (*Opsanus tau*) demonstrated that it possessed a complete hepatic O-UC (71). Later it was shown that the gulf toadfish (*O. beta*) also had these enzymes (62) and that it could be facultatively ureotelic when challenged in the laboratory by exposure to ammonium chloride or air (90). These and subsequent experiments ruled out the possibilities that ureogenesis is important for osmoregulation in normal strength seawater (62) or acid-base balance (8, 93). These initial observations led us to suspect that gulf toadfish were similar to other facultatively ureotelic teleosts, making and excreting urea to avoid ammonia toxicity and desiccation during, for example, air-exposure at low tide. However, recent estimations of the degree of ureogenesis in toadfish freshly collected from the field (using two proxies, activities of hepatic glutamine synthetase, GSase, and plasma cortisol levels) suggest that tidal air-exposure/desiccation is not necessary to induce ureogenesis (TE Hopkins et al, unpublished observations). This suggestion was confirmed by laboratory experiments demonstrating that moderate stress (e.g. crowding or simple confinement, even without accumulation of ammonia in the water) is sufficient to trigger the rapid shift to ureotely in this species (94). Thus gulf toadfish appear to be an interesting model with which to study the rapid and coarse-scale regulation of urea synthesis and the mechanisms of urea release to the environment (see Regulation of Ureogenesis in the Gulf Toadfish and Sites and Mechanisms of Urea Excretion). These sections aid in developing a unique hypothesis on why (toad)fish make urea. However, before leaving the topic of evolutionary aspects, new discoveries in teleost embryos are addressed below.

TELEOST EMBRYOS    The above sections suggest that the O-UC cycle is an ancient trait in fish and that the genes are retained, not reinvented, by more advanced fish, albeit ostensibly in only a handful of species. Recently, however, interest has been rekindled in early life history stages of fish (35, 51, 52). Much earlier, Dépêche et al (26) showed that one species of teleost, the guppy (*Poecilia reticulata*), expressed the O-UC and made urea during selected embryonic stages. However, it was believed that this was a peculiarity of an ovoviviparous (live-bearing) reproductive strategy (26, 35). More recently, however, Wright et al (100) studied rainbow trout (*Oncorhynchus mykiss*), an ammonotelic aquatic teleost. Through careful measurements, they discovered that there is a brief window in development when rainbow trout embryos express CPSase III and OCTase activities and produce substantial amounts of urea. The activity measurements have been confirmed by sequencing cDNA for CPSase III prepared from rainbow trout, and by demonstration of expression of CPSase III mRNA very early in development (J Korte et al, unpublished observations). These findings for this teleost open up the possibility of a new evolutionary perspective. It is tempting to speculate that not only is the trait of ureogenesis monophyletic within the fishes, but that O-UC genes are still present in all or most species of fish and are simply silenced for most fish during the adult phase (100). Interestingly, there is one known example of an adult teleost (largemouth bass *Micropterus salmoides*) for which modest hepatic CP-Sase III and OCTase activities are expressed, a puzzling observation because the adult is ammonotelic (4, 19, 20). Note also that largemouth bass possess substantial intestinal and muscle CPSase III activity, a finding that should stimulate similar measurements in other species (4). These observations further support the notion that the O-UC genes may be present in most and perhaps all teleosts. Some relatively straightforward investigations to test this hypothesis include a broad survey of embryonic fish for expression of CPSase III, but more importantly, a broad survey of fish for the presence or absence of the CP-Sase III gene. Given that the CPSase III cDNA for dogfish shark and rainbow trout have been sequenced (39; J Korte et al, unpublished observations), this latter survey is within sight. These surveys should include not only primitive adult agnathans (lampreys and hagfishes), but also their larvae and *Amphioxus*, which are reminiscent of selected invertebrate larval forms believed to share ancestry with the stem vertebrates (35). A complete O-UC has been demonstrated in several invertebrate taxa (15), so examination of key higher invertebrates (e.g. echinoderms, urochordates, etc) for CPSase isozyme types is also called for.

# REGULATION OF UREOGENESIS IN THE GULF TOADFISH

In order to understand how gulf toadfish can rapidly activate ureogenesis, it is instructive to take a comparative approach to determine if and how their biochemical machinery differs from non-ureogenic confamilial species (family Batrachoididae). First, a second key feature of fish ureogenesis must be discussed. The requirement of CPSase III for glutamine as a nitrogen donor dictates that a second vital enzyme, GSase, must be located upstream in the pathway to supply CPSase III with glutamine made from a central ammonia pool. This is in contrast to mammals (CPSase I) where hepatic GSase is relegated to the perivenule (downstream) hepatocytes (45) and plays the fail-safe role of removing any ammonia not trapped in the O-UC by CPSase I (56). Generally, intrahepatic metabolic compartmentation is less pronounced in fish (59, 66), and in gulf toadfish liver, GSase appears to be distributed in all hepatocytes (64). Thus, in fish, GSase is believed to have regulatory responsibilities at least equal to, if not greater than, CPSase III (5, 63). For example, in *O. beta*, hepatic total GSase activity statistically can account for about 60% of

**Table 1**  Correlation between degree of ureotely and biochemical characteristics of O-UC enzymes for members of the family Batrachoididae

| Species | Ureotelic? | CPSase activity (units g$^{-1}$) | GSase activity | | |
|---|---|---|---|---|---|
| | | | Total (units g$^{-1}$) | Soluble (%) | Mitochondrial (%) |
| *Porichthys notatus* (Plainfin midshipman)[a] | No[b] | 0.02 | 1.3 | 86 | 6 |
| *Opsanus tau* (Oyster toadfish)[a] | No | 0.15 | 1.3 | 79 | 6 |
| *Opsanus beta* (Gulf toadfish) | Yes[c] | 0.50[a] | 1 → 13[a,c] | 37 → 77[a,c] | 43 → 15[a,c] |

[a]Reference 5; [b]TP Mommsen, unpublished data; [c]Reference 91. Note that distribution of GSase activity between soluble and mitochondrial compartments does not add up to 100%, as the remainder is in the debris fraction. Note also that the range given for *O. beta* GSase is for unconfined → confined conditions, respectively.

the variability in degree of ureotely versus ammonotely, with GSase increasing as percent ureotely increases as a curvilinear function (40) (see below).

In batrachoidids, substantial activities of all O-UC enzymes, save two, are found in the livers of two common batrachoidids, which appear to be non-ureotelic under laboratory conditions (Table 1). Predictably, where the non-ureotelic species differ markedly from the facultatively ureotelic *O. beta* is in the expression of CPSase III and GSase (Table 1). Non-ureotelic species, *O. tau* (the oyster toadfish) and *Porichthys notatus* (the plainfin midshipman), express low (probably subthreshold for O-UC) activities of CPSase III and low activities of GSase (in the cytosol only). The ureotelic *O. beta* expresses higher CPSase III activities, as well as high and variable GSase; notably, GSase is present in both mitochondrial and cytosolic compartments in *O. beta*.

## Moderate Stress Activates GSase and Ureogenesis in O. beta

With this intrafamilial variation in CPSase III and GSase in mind, we examined their activities in the facultatively ureotelic *O. beta* under different conditions. In the laboratory, *O. beta* excretes mostly ammonia (60% of total nitrogen) when held in large volumes of water (e.g. 100 g fish in 80 liter seawater) (91). However, ureotely predominates when gulf toadfish are air-exposed for 8 to 12 h and then reimmersed in a smaller water volumes (i.e. <8 liter), or when transferred to smaller water volumes (e.g. <8 liter) containing 150 $\mu$M ammonium chloride (90). In performing control experiments for effects of the small water volume only, we discovered that simply transferring toadfish to small water volumes makes them ureotelic (94). When the maximal activities of hepatic O-UC and affiliated enzymes were measured following confinement, there were changes in maximal activities for GSase only, which increased five-to sixfold in activity in 24 h (91, 94). The in vivo importance of this activity increase was confirmed by an increase in the hepatic glutamine:glutamate ratio (91) and the observation that plasma ammonia levels do not increase in confined fish (106). Surprisingly, when toadfish were transferred to the same small water volume, but with continuous flow through of seawater to prevent ammonia buildup, GSase activities were again elevated (91, 94). For obvious reasons, urea and ammonia excretion could not be measured during these latter experiments, but the experiments strongly suggested that the switch to ureotely, and the accompanying increase in GSase activity, could be activated by confinement alone and that the activation had a psychological or stress component.

In recent years, cortisol has received considerable study as an important hormone in coordinating the stress response in vertebrates including fish (10, 68). In fish, elevated plasma cortisol can be detected within 10 to 30 min following acute stress (e.g. crowding, netting, brief air-exposure), with peak cortisol levels reached at 1–2 h. A second hallmark of the stress response in vertebrates is elevated plasma glucose levels (from hepatic gluconeogenesis using amino acids generated at the periphery). With this literature in mind, and the observations that ureogenesis in toadfish appeared to be unresponsive to a classic battery of hormones (60), but was responsive to dexamethasone (a synthetic glucocorticoid) (61), we examined the effect of confinement on plasma cortisol levels in *O. beta*. A moderate plasma cortisol surge (37 ng ml$^{-1}$) was evident following confinement, peaking at approximately 2 h and returning to normal by 24 h (40); the cortisol surge preceded the maximal activation of GSase. When the confinement-induced cortisol surge was prevented by pre-injection with the cortisol synthesis blocker metyrapone, the activation of GSase was also prevented, indicating that cortisol release is necessary for GSase activation (40).

How relevant are these laboratory experiments to natural conditions? Toadfish undergo natural periods of confinement (e.g. under rocks, in large empty shells, buried in sediments) during reproductive and brooding activities, as well as during more routine predator avoidance (9, 12, 24, 25, 84). Interestingly, cortisol concentrations measured in freshly collected *O. beta* range from 0 to 44 ng ml$^{-1}$ (TE Hopkins et al, unpublished observations), indicating that cortisol levels in confinement experiments closely duplicate natural levels. Extreme cortisol levels (e.g. >60 ng ml$^{-1}$) were observed only in selected supraphysiological laboratory experiments (e.g. restraint of fish by a latex membrane) (106) or infectious disease (40) and were not seen in freshly collected fish. Furthermore, under these extreme laboratory stresses, toadfish revert to periods of complete ammonotely, but with very elevated excretion rates, indicative of a highly proteolytic state (106). Extreme stress in *O. beta* is probably a rare event in nature, but moderate cortisol elevation is probably an important natural cue in triggering ureogenesis.

## GSase and Glutaminase

In elasmobranchs studied to date, hepatic GSase is exclusively mitochondrial (18), and thus colocalized specifically with CPSase III, underscoring its importance and close linkage to CPSase in fish. In other elasmobranch tissues, GSase activity is expressed in either cytoplasm or mitochondria but has never been reported for both compartments in a single tissue. In this regard, the gulf toadfish system yielded another interesting observation. *O. beta* possesses GSase activity in both cytoplasm and mitochondria of its liver (in addition to the anticipated exclusive localization of CPSase III to the mitochondria) (5), and mitochondrial GSase expression is one key difference between the ureogenic *O. beta* and non-ureogenic confamilials. Surprisingly, however, during confinement-related activation of ureogenesis, it is exclusively cytosolic GSase activity that is upregulated (91). This observation raises a number of questions. If cytosolic GSase is responsible for generating glutamine for the O-UC, instead of, or in addition to, mitochondrial GSase, are there specific glutamine transporters in toadfish facilitating its mitochondrial uptake?

A second evident question is why generate glutamine at a site removed from CPSase III? A related question is what is the role of mitochondrial GSase if it is not important in generating glutamine during stress? An answer to both questions may lie with the enzyme glutaminase (GLNase), which breaks down glutamine to glutamate and ammonia. In higher vertebrates, glutamine, synthesized by GSase in both the brain and the perivenule hepatocytes, is an important circulatory nitrogen store. Glutamine arriving at periportal hepatocytes must be deaminated by GLNase for its ammonia moiety to enter the O-UC. In fishes, ammonia and alanine, not glutamine, are believed to be the main source of waste nitrogen transported from the periphery, and given CPSase III's requirement for glutamine, hepatic GLNase was believed to play a minor role in fish (63). Nonetheless, recent measurements of mitochondrial GLNase activities in toadfish liver show that they are not trivial and are on par with mitochondrial GSase activities (synthetic assay; 5). Thus the flow of glutamine through the mitochondrial GSase/GLNase branch point toward CPSase III may depend critically on the ratio of these two enzyme activities, and GLNase deactivation may be another important regulatory prerequisite for O-UC activation. Changes in GLNase activities during confinement stress have yet to be measured in *O. beta*. These studies may reveal that the presence of glutaminase (and a mitochondrial glutamine transporter) may afford the toadfish with additional layers of fine-scale control over glutamine flow to CPSase III.

In eukaryotes, mitochondrial proteins encoded in the nucleus (e.g. glutamate dehydrogenase) are targeted for translocation into mitochondria by an N-terminal leader sequence of between 20 and 70 amino acids, which is cleaved by mitochondrial proteases (36). Thus, depending upon an organism's needs, an enzyme activity could theoretically be differentially targeted to cytoplasm or mitochondria in one of two ways: (*a*) by two separate genes, one with and one without the leader sequence; or (*b*) by a single gene with either two alternative transcription or translation start sites. Campbell & Anderson (18) have applied these models to data on fish GSase (including unpublished observations of Ritter; 73), which suggest that in elasmobranchs there is a single GSase gene. Recently, Laud & Campbell (55) sequenced GSase cDNA and presented a model in which initiation of translation at an upstream site yields the larger mitochondrial protein, whereas initiation at a downstream site yields the smaller cytosolic protein, depending upon the tissue in question. The gulf toadfish, with its novel expression of hepatic GSase activity in both cytoplasm and mitochondria, would appear to present an interesting opportunity to further understand the molecular evolution of the architecture of the GSase gene(s) and the exact genetic mechanisms underpinning the trait of ureogenesis within the batrachoidids.

Recently we undertook the purification and initial structural characterization of hepatic GSase isozymes of the gulf toadfish (89a). As for elasmobranch GSase (80), both toadfish GSase isozymes had micromolar $K_m$ values for $NH_3/NH_4^+$. If intracellular $[NH_3/NH_4^+]$ are reflective of bulk plasma and tissue ammonia levels, this finding suggests that the enzyme is largely saturated with respect to $NH_3/NH_4^+$ in vivo. When coupled with observations that fish and other metazoan GSases are apparently not subject to allosteric regulation, the apparent in vivo saturation of GSase with ammonia may indicate that the toadfish has only a coarse-type of regulation over GSase activity, i.e. changes in concentration of enzyme. This hypothesis needs to be tested with direct measurements of GSase protein to confirm activity measurements, and these experiments are within reach as toadfish GSases can be quantified (89a) with rabbit antibodies to chicken GSase (81). In particular, it will be interesting to see if the differential responses of cytoplasmic and mitochondrial activities to stress are reflected in their concentrations. This antibody could also be used to verify the apparent homogeneous distribution of GSase in toadfish liver cell populations.

Another observation on the toadfish GSase proteins is that although they are the same size (approximate subunit $M_r = 42$ K) and have the same kinetic properties, they differ substantially in other (perhaps not physiologically relevant) characteristics (e.g. degree of inhibition by methionine sulfoximine) (89a). A reasonable hypothesis is that toadfish possess two GSase genes, a suggestion testable by current molecular methods (as were applied to dogfish shark GSase, 55). Also useful in this molecular examination would be the identification of differences in the binding of nuclear protein factors to upstream promoter regions, which would likely provide an explanation for why cytosolic GSase appears to be so much more readily synthesized, relative to mitochondrial GSase and to the cytosolic GSase of other non-ureogenic batrachoidid species. These molecular examinations will be especially informative when coupled to DNA-based phylogenetic techniques quantifying the genetic distances involved in evolutionary physiological change (31). Lastly, because the stress hormone cortisol appears to be one coordination point for GSase activation, promoter analyses may clarify the role of cortisol in GSase gene activation. In this regard, there may be parallels with the (temperature) stress response (86): (*a*) both heat shock proteins (HSPs) 70 and 90 have been implicated in the regulation of the steroid hormone receptor (98); and (*b*) HSP70 is essential for the proper folding, oligomerization, and translocation of newly synthesized proteins (98), a process of obvious importance to the proper routing of GSase(s) and activation of ureogenesis.

## A Role for Allosteric Activation of CPSase III in Regulation of Ureogenesis?

Despite the importance of GSase activation in the onset of ureogenesis in toadfish and the lack of in vitro maximal activity change in CPSase III during this transition, it is likely that CPSase III allosteric activation is important under many circumstances. First, the purified enzyme from elasmobranch and bass liver (1) and semipurified extracts from toadfish liver (5) show marked allosteric activation by *N*-acetyl glutamate. Second, during either confined or unconfined states in the toadfish, feeding markedly increases rates of urea excretion, regardless of the percent contribution of urea to the total nitrogen excretion budget (91). Increases in absolute rates of urea excretion occur even in fed, but unconfined toadfish, where total GSase activities are relatively low and do not change as the result of feeding (91). Therefore, allosteric regulation of CPSase III must be postulated. Unfortunately, *N*-acetyl glutamate levels have yet to be quantified in fish livers, and *N*-acetyl glutamate synthetase, which catalyzes the formation of *N*-acetyl glutamate from glutamate and acetyl CoA, remains to be characterized in fish.

From the findings presented thus far, a testable model of activation of ureogenesis in toadfish emerges (Figure 1). Among its elements are (*a*) overall coarse-scale control occurs by changes in GSase concentration. The accumulation of GSase is key to switching off ammonotely and in setting the overall tone for ammonia and nitrogen retention (see Why Do Toadfish Make Urea?). Several fine-scale control layers would be added by (*b*) allosteric activation of CPSase III by increases in *N*-acetyl glutamate formed as the result of activation of *N*-acetylglutamate synthetase or increases in intracellular concentrations

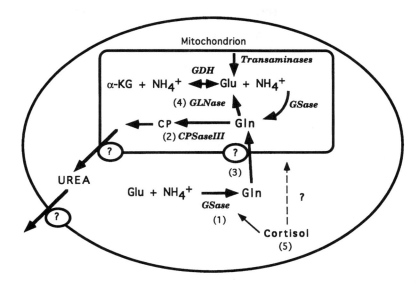

*Figure 1*   Schematic of proposed regulatory points (*a—e*; see text) for upregulation of ureogenesis in gulf toadfish *O. beta* liver. Abbreviations: Gln, glutamine; Glu, glutamate; αKG, α-ketoglutarate; CP, carbamoyl phosphate; CPSaseIII, carbamoylphosphate synthetase III; GSase, glutamine synthetase; GDH, glutamate dehydrogenase; GLNase, glutaminase. Downstream regions of O-UC and Krebs' cycle omitted for clarity. Also depicted are putative urea transporters.

of glutamate; (*c*) activation of a mitochondrial glutamine uptake system; and (*d*) deactivation of mitochondrial GLNase. (*e*) Lastly, this response is controlled, at least in part, by the stress hormone cortisol, with possible involvement of stress proteins.

## SITE AND MECHANISMS OF UREA EXCRETION

### Routes and Patterns of Urea Excretion

In earlier studies of urea retention in elasmobranchs, much focus was placed on the kidney's ability to actively reabsorb urea (38, 46, 83). Kidney urea retention in elasmobranchs results from an active transport mechanism (37, 78, 79) in concert with complex countercurrent exchanger anatomy (53, 54). Much less was known about elasmobranch gill urea permeability (11), but the putative low permeability of gills was believed to be primarily a structural adaptation (35, 103), with urea retention being favored in elasmobranchs because of their large size (and low surface area:volume ratio) and low oxygen consumption requirements correlated with relatively thick gill diffusive distances. Furthermore, although it was commonly believed that elasmobranchs are ureotelic (e.g. 67), some authors (63) assumed that elasmobranchs would be ammonotelic via the gills. It is only recently that investigators have more closely examined urea and ammonia excretion dynamics in elasmobranchs. In a study of spiny dogfish (*Squalus acanthias*), Wood and colleagues (107) found that >90% of excreted nitrogen was as urea across the gills and confirmed that resting gill permeabilities to urea must be extremely low. Based on experiments where urea analogues injected into the bloodstream enhanced urea excretion rates, they speculated that urea retention may involve a membrane back-transport mechanism at the gill basolateral membrane.

In teleosts, few studies have closely examined the route of urea excretion. In a study of the ammonotelic tidepool sculpin (*Oligocottus maculosus*), it was concluded that the small quantity of urea exiting the fish did so primarily at the anterior end (101). Studies of the Lake Magadi tilapia confirm that the bulk of urea is excreted at the anterior end of the fish (105). In both of these teleosts and in the spiny dogfish, no hints of pulsatile urea excretion were detected. In our earlier studies of toadfish, we had noticed that urea excretion appeared to be pulsatile (90), which we and other authors (35) attributed to periodic micturation of the urinary bladder. Recently, substantial evidence argues against this route of excretion as a significant pathway. Wood and colleagues (106) first documented that post-absorptive and confined *O. beta* (i.e. ureagenic, excreting 84% of nitrogen as urea) released 94% of excretory urea nitrogen in a single pulse, approximately once in 24 h. The rather pronounced pulse (up to 2500 $\mu$mols urea-N kg$^{-1}$) typically lasted <3 h (sample collection design precluded determining if the pulse was of even shorter duration) (Figure 2). Subsequent experiments using catheters for the urinary bladder and the rectum showed that these routes contributed less than 10% of total nitrogen excreted. When toadfish were placed in a divided chamber apparatus (82) with a latex membrane placed just behind the gill operculum opening to separate the anterior and posterior body, nearly all urea was excreted from the anterior end during ureotelic periods (106). The experimental protocol did not allow determination of which path the urea was taking, but gills and/or skin of the head are likely candidates.

## Urea Transporters in Fish Tissues?

The previous excretion data for fish strongly implicate the gills as a site of urea excretion. In order to appreciate the potential mechanisms involved in the pulse of urea excretion in toadfish, the permeabilities of urea should be addressed. A common misconception is that biological membranes are highly permeable to urea. However, membranes are intrinsically relatively impermeable to urea: permeability in artificial bilayers is $4 \times 10^{-6}$ cm s$^{-1}$ (30), and the olive oil-water partition coefficient for urea is close to $10^{-4}$ (22). By contrast, typical

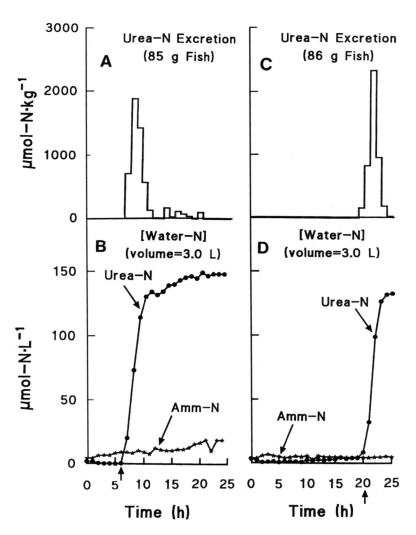

*Figure 2*   Typical hourly records of urea-N and ammonia-N excreted in ureotelic gulf toadfish, *O. beta*. Hourly urea-N excretion rates (*A, C*) were calculated from hourly water concentrations (*B, D*). Note the predominant single pulse of urea excretion (arrow on x-axis) and low ammonia accumulation (from 106).

permeabilities of membranes to ammonia (as $NH_3$) are two orders of magnitude higher (14, 103). Consequently, in order to explain the abilities of some mammalian tissues (e.g. the liver and kidney) to efficiently shuttle urea, many investigators have focused on specific transporters, with results leading to the view that urea is transported by facilitated diffusion and perhaps also by secondary active cotransport with $Na^+$ (32, 43). Urea transport by kidney tubules is inhibited by phloretin and a variety of competitive urea analogues (21, 110). The cDNA for a specific transport protein (UT-2) has been cloned and characterized (109), and this transport protein appears to be the vasopressin-sensitive component seen in kidney tubule studies (49).

For the toadfish, more recent experiments also implicate a specific membrane transporter. First, we have established that there is a precipitous drop in plasma [urea] during the excretory pulse and that the drop in whole body [urea] estimated from the plasma [urea] decrease closely matches the size of the pulse detected in the water (CM Wood et al, unpublished observations; Figure 3). Following an excretory pulse, plasma levels built back up at a more or less linear rate (Figure 3) similar to maximal urea production rates by toadfish hepatocytes in vitro (8, 62, 93). The predictability of the pulse and corresponding drop in plasma concentration enabled experiments to examine the control mechanism more closely. Immediately following a natural pulse, catheterized toadfish were injected with a urea bolus equal to the size of a typical pulse. This injection raised plasma [urea] to pre-pulse levels but did not immediately induce urea excretion (CM Wood et al, unpublished observations; Figure 4). The result was the same for control fish (either saline injected or not injected) and indicated that the urea excretion pulse was not cued by a threshold plasma [urea], but by some other mechanism. Our current working model is that a specific urea transporter is activated by a neural or hormonal signal. Recently, using low stringency Northern analyses of poly A+ RNA (3 ug/lane), we have detected an mRNA ($\approx$2.0 kb) in toadfish gill that hybridizes to rat UT2 cDNA (CP Smith et al, unpublished observations). Furthermore, using degenerate PCR primers based on the coding region of rat and rabbit UT2, we have amplified a 484-bp cDNA from reverse transcribed toadfish gill mRNA. Subsequent sequencing and computer analysis has revealed that the PCR product encodes a protein with high homology to rat and rabbit UT2 (CP Smith et al, unpublished observations).

Thus at least for toadfish and spiny dogfish, a picture is emerging of epithelia that manifest an ability for selective urea permeability. In the toadfish, a working hypothesis is that permeability may be rapidly increased for a short period and just as rapidly turned off, creating extremely tight control over the excretory fate of urea. Future experiments will surely involve characterization of what effectors turn the transporter on and off. For all fish, the comparison of DNA

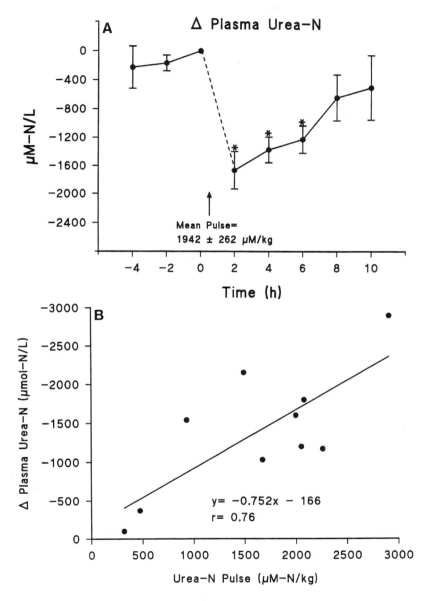

*Figure 3* Gulf toadfish *O. beta*. (*A*) Time course of mean decrease in plasma [urea] during urea excretion pulse (starting at time = 0). Values are means ±SE (N = 8). (*B*) Correlation of size of decrease in plasma [urea] with size of urea excretion pulse appearing in water, y = 0.752x + 166.34, r = 0.76 (CM Wood et al, unpublished observations).

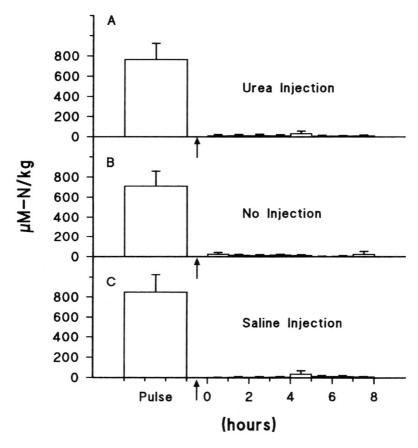

*Figure 4*   Urea-N excretion in groups of toadfish following injection of (A) a urea bolus of 2500 $\mu$mol kg$^{-1}$, (B) no injection, or (C) saline; all immediately after a natural pulse of urea excretion (*arrow*). The natural urea-N pulse in sham is the mean rate over 3 h, the resolution time of the detection system. Note that nearly no excretion was detectable following injection (CM Wood et al, unpublished observations).

and amino acid sequences of any urea transporters with other vertebrates will be useful in examining the evolutionary relationships of ureotely. Another area of research is the characterization of urea transport mechanisms in other tissues. Recent evidence suggests that urea carriers also occur in vertebrate liver; phloretin sensitivity of urea efflux has been documented in rat (28) and *O. beta* (95, 96) hepatocytes, although there has been no distinction between plasma membrane or mitochondrial membrane transport. At least in toadfish, rapid liver clearance may be important in contributing to the linear plasma rise after an excretory burst. Future studies could also concentrate on whether transport mechanisms at gill and liver are coordinated.

## WHY DO TOADFISH MAKE AND EXCRETE UREA?

Comparative studies with fish teach us that mechanisms to control urea transport across epithelia were in place early in the vertebrate lineage. Urea is the molecule of choice to be synthesized when control over excretion/loss is essential, not only because it is less neurotoxic than ammonia, but because its compartmentation can be easily controlled. We do not know the evolutionary and ecological rationale for why toadfish make and excrete urea, but it is reasonable to hypothesize that ureogenesis/ureotely can be useful to the toadfish (and perhaps other fish species) in at least two ecological contexts. First, when toadfish are hiding out, a continuous stream of ammonia leaking from the gills would leave a chemosensory trail that a predator could easily follow directly to the shelter. Strict control of urea excretion as pulses, and placement of this mechanism at the anterior end, while generally avoiding routine fouling of the shelter, would allow toadfish to poke only its head out of its shelter to excrete for a brief period when it perceives its environment to be relatively safe. Furthermore, a restricted time requirement of <3 h for a full day's worth of nitrogen excretion would enable the toadfish to excrete while briefly out of its shelter, e.g. while foraging. Both strategies would minimize predator encounter frequency. Batrachoidid fishes in general may require this excretory advantage because they are highly vocal at selected times of the year and thus advertise their location to predators more so than non-vocal benthic fishes (92). Additionally, gulf toadfish in particular can be found in habitats that facilitate predation (mudflats and grassbeds) (84), relative to other family members.

A second advantage of ureotely for aquatic organisms may lie in nitrogen conservation. When confined to its shelter, a toadfish is not able to feed extensively and might shift to a proteolytic state. Notably, when toadfish are ureotelic during laboratory confinement, total nitrogen excretion rate drops to approximately one third unconfined rates (91). Synthesis and retention of urea would allow the fish to temporarily retain and store nitrogen in a relatively nontoxic form that could later be broken down by gut microbes expressing urease activity, as hypothesized by Mommsen & Walsh (62). Note that we did not continue to apply this hypothesis to the toadfish because antibiotic treatment of toadfish did not alter plasma urea levels or urea excretion patterns (90). However, it is likely that these experiments were naively constructed in light of more recent information on the extreme pulsatility of urea excretion. The nitrogen conservation view is supported by the more recent observation that under fed conditions, toadfish typically continue to excrete substantial quantities of ammonia even during confined conditions (91). Many elasmobranchs are apex predators, tending to go days between large meals. Urea retention would enable them to hold onto nitrogen during fasting. Notably, elasmobranchs also have bacterial urease activity (50) that could aid in nitrogen recycling. The nitrogen conservation hypothesis clearly deserves more detailed experimental revisitation, and use of $^{15}N$ isotopes to trace nitrogen fluxes (44) may be particularly useful. Both the predator avoidance and nitrogen retention scenarios are stress related, and at least in the case of the toadfish, it is likely that the urea synthesis and retention mechanisms will prove to be largely coordinated through the hypothalamus-pituitary-interrenal axis.

## Reducing Gill Ammonia Permeability

Synthesis and retention of urea as an osmolyte, for nitrogen conservation, or control of chemosensory signals all have in common the need to reduce ammonia efflux. Thus toadfish and elasmobranchs have needed to solve a different problem than ammonotelic teleosts, whose need is to maximize ammonia efflux, or other ureotelic fish, whose ammonia excretion has been cut off for them by an environmental parameter. In their study of dogfish, Wood and colleagues (107) also discovered a very low gill ammonia permeability. Furthermore, when toadfish switch from ammonotely to ureotely, their ability to shut off ammonia excretion is nearly absolute (Figure 2). Certainly, activation of hepatic GSase contributes to this ability by maintaining plasma ammonia levels at pre-ureotelic values. So, how do toadfish and dogfish decrease gill ammonia permeability? In the mammalian kidney, selected sections of nephrons are made ammonia impermeable, and it is believed that the mechanism is incorporation of specialized lipids into plasma membranes (47). This strategy is unlikely to be useful in fish gill because it would likely lower the diffusing capacities for oxygen and carbon dioxide. However, toadfish and dogfish both have relatively low oxygen consumption requirements (13, 89), and part of the reduction in ammonia permeability could be met by a slightly thicker blood-water diffusion barrier (42). Nonetheless, this mechanism would still not account for the extremely low ammonia excretion rates. Wood et al (107) speculated that dogfish ammonia retention was by gill enzyme scavenging (e.g. GSase and GDH). Indeed, both toadfish and dogfish have measurable activities of these enzymes in gill (106, 107). However, calculation of gill ammonia trapping potential versus quantity of ammonia perfused through gills can be only approximate at present. First, cardiac output has been estimated for dogfish to be roughly 25 mls min$^{-1}$ kg$^{-1}$ (29), and similar values likely apply to the toadfish (29). Blood ammonia values for the hepatic vein (i.e. in the circulation after the liver and before the gill) are not readily available for either species; however, a representative venous value (e.g. caudal vein, which is pre-liver in the circulation) for toadfish is 100–200 $\mu M$ (106). Typical values for toadfish gill GDH and GSase (synthetase reaction) are 1.6 and 0.07 $\mu$mols min$^{-1}$ g$^{-1}$ fresh tissue (including weight of filaments, but not arches), respectively (106). Lastly, gill filament weight in toadfish is approximately 6 g kg$^{-1}$ (PJ Walsh, unpublished observations). These estimates indicate that toadfish gill has the capacity to enzymatically remove nearly 10 $\mu$mols ammonia min$^{-1}$ kg$^{-1}$ body weight, which is in excess of the value of 5 $\mu$mols ammonia min$^{-1}$ kg$^{-1}$ body weight passing through gill calculated from cardiac output and plasma ammonia values stated above. Despite the apparent low activity of GSase, however, its importance may lie in its micromolar $K_m$ for ammonia, and GSase and GDH may provide a combined high- and low-affinity tandem for ammonia scavenging. Clearly, gill metabolism should be experimentally examined to see if it is responsible for reducing apparent ammonia permeabilities in ureotelic fish (e.g. through perfused gill arches, with and without enzyme inhibitors). For fish in general, ammonia excretion and the relationship between circulating metabolites and the gill's ability to metabolically modify them has perplexed researchers for many years (58). This area will be especially challenging for researchers examining these interrelationships in ureotelic fish.

ACKNOWLEDGMENTS

Research for this article was supported by grants from the National Science Foundation (IBN-9507239) and National Institutes of Health (ES05075). I wish to thank Drs. PM Anderson, TE Hopkins, TP Mommsen, CM Wood, and PA Wright for examining an earlier draft of this article and for access to their unpublished data. I also wish to thank M Heitz and Drs. MA Hediger, JE Serafy, and CP Smith for access to their unpublished results and to Jimbo Luznar for making toadfish research possible.

*Literature Cited*

1. Anderson PM. 1991. Glutamine-dependent urea synthesis in elasmobranch fishes. *Biochem. Cell Biol.* 69:317–19
2. Anderson PM. 1995. Urea cycle in fish: molecular and mitochondrial studies. In *Fish Physiology,* Ser. eds. WS Hoar, DJ Randall, TJ Farrell, Vol. 14. *Ionoregulation: Cellular and Molecular Approaches,* eds. CM Wood, TJ Shuttleworth, pp. 57–83. New York: Academic
3. Anderson PM. 1995. Molecular aspects of carbamoyl phosphate synthesis. See Ref. 97, pp. 33–49
4. Anderson PM, Salo WL, Korte JJ, Wright PA, Felskie. 1996. Expression of urea cycle-related carbamoyl-phosphate synthetase III (CPSase III) in mus-

cle of rainbow trout (*Oncorhynchus mykiss*) and largemouth bass (*Micropterus salmoides*) and in trout embryos. *FASEB J.* 10:A1371 (Abstr.)
5. Anderson PM, Walsh PJ. 1995. Subcellular localization and biochemical properties of the enzymes of carbamoyl phosphate and urea synthesis in the batrachoidid fishes *Opsanus beta, Opsanus tau* and *Porichthys notatus. J. Exp. Biol.* 198:755–66
6. Atkinson BG. 1995. Molecular aspects of ureogenesis in amphibians. See Ref. 97, pp. 133–46
7. Ballantyne JS, Moyes CD, Moon TW. 1987. Compatible and counteracting solutes and the evolution of ion and os-

moregulation in fishes. *Can. J. Zool.* 65:1883–88

8. Barber ML, Walsh PJ. 1993. Interactions of acid-base status and nitrogen excretion and metabolism in the ureogenic gulf teleost *Opsanus beta. J. Exp. Biol.* 185:87–105

9. Barros NB. 1989. *Food habits of the bottlenose dolphin (Tursiops truncatus) in the southeastern United States, with special reference to Florida waters.* PhD thesis. Univ. Miami. 139 pp.

10. Barton BA, Iwama GK. 1991. Physiological changes from stress in aquaculture with emphasis on the response and effects of corticosteroids. *Annu. Rev. Fish Dis.* 1:3–26

11. Boylan J. 1967. Gill permeability in *Squalus acanthias.* In *Sharks, Skates and Rays,* ed. PW Gilbert, RF Mathewson, DP Rall, pp. 197–206. Baltimore: Johns Hopkins Univ. Press

12. Breder CM. 1941. On the reproduction of *Opsanus beta* Goode & Bean. *Zoologica* 26:229–32

13. Brett JR, Blackburn JM. 1978. Metabolic rate and energy expenditure in the spiny dogfish, *Squalus acanthias. J. Fish. Res. Bd. Can.* 35:816–21

14. Cameron JN, Heisler N. 1985. Ammonia transfer across fish gills: a review. In *Circulation, Respiration, and Metabolism,* ed. R Gilles, pp. 91–100. Berlin: Springer-Verlag

15. Campbell JW. 1965. Arginine and urea biosynthesis in the land planaria: its significance in biochemical evolution. *Nature* 208:1299–301

16. Campbell JW. 1991. Excretory nitrogen metabolism. In *Environmental and Metabolic Animal Physiology, Comparative Animal Physiology,* ed. CL Prosser, pp. 277–324. New York: Wiley-Liss. 4th ed.

17. Campbell JW. 1995. Excretory nitrogen metabolism in reptiles and birds. See Ref. 97, pp. 147–78

18. Campbell JW, Anderson PM. 1991. Evolution of mitochondrial enzyme systems in fish: the mitochondrial synthesis of glutamine and citrulline. In *Biochemistry and Molecular Biology of Fishes,* ed. PW Hochachka, TP Mommsen, 1:43–75. Amsterdam: Elsevier

19. Cao X, Kemp JR, Anderson PM. 1991. Subcellular localization of two glutamine-dependent carbamoyl-phosphate synthetases and related enzymes in liver of *Micropterus salmoides* (largemouth bass) and properties of isolated

liver mitochondria: comparative relationships with elasmobranchs. *J. Exp. Zool.* 258:24–33

20. Casey CA, Anderson PM. 1983. Glutamine and *N*-acetyl-L-glutamate-dependent carbamoyl phosphate synthetase from *Micropterus salmoides. J. Biol. Chem.* 258:8723–32

21. Chou C-L, Knepper M. 1989. Inhibition of urea transport in inner medullary collecting duct by phloretin and urea analogs. *Am. J. Physiol.* 257:F359–65

22. Collander R. 1937. The permeability of plant protoplasts to non-electrolytes. *Trans. Faraday Soc.* 33:985–90

23. Cooper AJL, Plum F. 1987. Biochemistry and physiology of brain ammonia. *Physiol. Rev.* 67:440–519

24. Cortes E. 1987. *Diet, feeding habits, and daily ration of young lemon shark, Negaprion brevirostris, and the effect of ration size on their growth and conversion efficiencies.* PhD thesis. Univ. Miami. 145 pp.

25. Cummings MV. 1987. *The feeding energetics of the double-crested cormorant in Biscayne Bay, Florida.* PhD thesis. Univ. Miami. 143 pp.

26. Dépêche J, Gilles R, Daufresne S, Chiapello H. 1979. Urea content and urea production via the ornithine-urea cycle pathway during the ontogenic development of two teleost fishes. *Comp. Biochem. Physiol. A.* 63:51–56

27. Dingemanse MA, Lamers WH. 1995. Gene expression and development of hepatic nitrogen metabolic pathways. See Ref. 97, pp. 229–42

28. Effros RM, Jacobs E, Hacker A, Murphy C. 1993. Reversible inhibition of urea exchange in rat hepatocytes. *J. Clin. Invest.* 91:2822–28

29. Farrell AP, Jones DR. 1992. The heart. In *Fish Physiology Vol. XIIA, The Cardiovascular System,* ed. WS Hoar, DJ Randall, AP Farrell, pp. 1–88. New York: Academic

30. Galluci E, Micelli S, Lippe C. 1971. Non-electrolyte permeability across thin lipid membranes. *Arch. Int. Physiol. Biochim.* 79:881–87

31. Garland T Jr, Carter PA. 1994. Evolutionary physiology. *Annu. Rev. Physiol.* 56:579–621

32. Gillin AG, Sands JM. 1993. Urea transport in the kidney. *Sem. Nephrol.* 13:146–54

33. Goldstein L, Harley-DeWitt S, Forster RP. 1973. Activities of ornithine-urea cycle enzymes and trimethylamine oxidase in the ceolacanth, *Latimeria*

*chalumnae. Comp. Biochem. Physiol.* 44B:357–62

34. Goldstein L, Perlman DF. 1995. Nitrogen metabolism, excretion, osmoregulation, and cell volume regulation in elasmobranchs. See Ref. 97, pp. 91–104

35. Griffith RW. 1991. Guppies, toadfish, lungfish, coelacanths, and frogs: a scenario for the evolution of urea retention in fishes. *Environ. Biol. Fish* 32:199–218

36. Grivell LA. 1988. Protein import into mitochondria. *Int. Rev. Cytol.* 111:107–41

37. Hays RM, Levine SD, Meyers JD, Heinemann HO, Kaplan MA, et al. 1977. Urea transport in the dogfish kidney. *J. Exp. Zool.* 199:309–16

38. Hickman CP, Trump BF. 1969. The kidney. In *Fish Physiology,* ed. WS Hoar, DJ Randall, 1:91–239. New York: Academic

39. Hong J, Salo WL, Lusty CJ, Anderson PM. 1994. Carbamoyl phosphate synthetase III, an evolutionary intermediate in the transition between glutamine-dependent and ammonia-dependent carbamoyl phosphate synthetases. *J. Mol. Biol.* 243:131–40

40. Hopkins TE, Wood CM, Walsh PJ. 1995. Interactions of cortisol and nitrogen metabolism in the ureogenic gulf toadfish *Opsanus beta. J. Exp. Biol.* 198:2229–35

41. Huggins AK, Skutch G, Baldwin E. 1969. Ornithine-urea cycle enzymes in teleostean fishes. *Comp. Biochem. Physiol.* 28:587–602

42. Hughes GM, Morgan M. 1976. The structure of fish gills in relation to their respiratory function. *Biol. Rev.* 48:419–75

43. Isozaki T, Lea JP, Tumlin JA, Sands JM. 1994. Sodium-dependent net urea transport in rat initial inner medullary collecting ducts. *J. Clin. Invest.* 94:1513–17

44. Iwata K, Deguchi M. 1995. Metabolic fate and distribution of $^{15}$N-ammonia in an ammonotelic amphibious fish, *Periophthalmus modestus,* following immersion in $^{15}$N-ammonium sulfate: a long term experiment. *Zool. Sci.* 12:175–84

45. Jungermann K, Katz N. 1989. Functional specialization of different hepatocyte populations. *Physiol. Rev.* 69:708–64

46. Kempton RT. 1953. Studies of the elasmobranch kidney. II. Reabsorption of urea by the smooth dogfish, *Mustelis canis. Biol. Bull.* 104:45–56

47. Kikeri D, Sun A, Zeidel ML, Hebert SC.

48. Kirschner LB 1993. The energetics of osmotic regulation in ureotelic and hypoosmotic fishes. *J. Exp. Zool.* 267:19–26

49. Knepper M, Chou C-L. 1995. Urea and ammonium transport in the mammalian kidney. See Ref. 97, pp. 205–27

50. Knight IT, Grimes DJ, Colwell RR. 1988. Bacterial hydrolysis of urea in the tissues of carcharhinid sharks. *Can. J. Fish. Aq.* 45:357–60

51. Kormanik GA. 1995. Maternal-fetal transfer of nitrogen in chondrichthyans. See Ref. 97, pp. 243–58

52. Korsgaard B, Mommsen TP, Wright PA. 1995. Nitrogen excretion in teleostean fish: adaptive relationships to environment, ontogenesis, and viviparity. See Ref. 97, pp. 259–87

53. Lacy ER, Reale E. 1991. Fine structure of the elasmobranch renal tubule: neck and proximal segments of the little skate. *Am. J. Anat.* 190:118–32

54. Lacy ER, Reale E, Schlusselburg DS, Smith WK, Woodward DJ. 1985. A renal countercurrent system in marine elasmobranch fish: a computer-aided reconstruction. *Science* 227:1351–54

55. Laud PR, Campbell JW. 1994. Genetic basis for tissue isozymes of glutamine synthetase in elasmobranchs. *J. Mol. Evol.* 39:93–100

56. Meijer AJ. 1995. Urea synthesis in mammals. See Ref. 97, pp. 193–204

57. Meijer AJ, Lamers WH, Chamuleau RAFM. 1990. Nitrogen metabolism and ornithine cycle function. *Physiol. Rev.* 70:701–48

58. Mommsen TP. 1984. Metabolism of the fish gill. In *Fish Physiology,* ed. WS Hoar, DJ Randall, pp. 203–38. New York: Academic. Vol. XB

59. Mommsen TP, Danulat E, Gavioli ME, Foster GD, Moon TW. 1991. Separation of enzymatically distinct populations of trout hepatocytes. *Can. J. Zool.* 69:420–26

60. Mommsen TP, Danulat E, Walsh PJ. 1991. Hormonal regulation of metabolism in hepatocytes of the ureogenic teleost *Opsanus beta. Fish Physiol. Biochem.* 9:247–52

61. Mommsen TP, Danulat E. Walsh PJ. 1992. Metabolic actions of glucagon and dexamethasone in liver of the ureogenic teleost *Opsanus beta. Gen. Comp. Endocrinol.* 85:316–26

62. Mommsen TP, Walsh PJ. 1989. Evolution of urea synthesis in vertebrates: the

piscine connection. *Science* 243:72–75

63. Mommsen TP, Walsh PJ. 1991. Urea synthesis in fishes: evolutionary and biochemical perspectives. In *Biochemistry and Molecular Biology of Fishes,* ed. PW Hochachka, TP Mommsen, 1:137–63. Amsterdam: Elsevier

64. Mommsen TP, Walsh PJ. 1991. Metabolic and enzymatic heterogeneity in the liver of the ureogenic teleost *Opsanus beta. J. Exp. Biol.* 156:407–18

65. Mommsen TP, Walsh PJ. 1992. Biochemical and environmental perspectives on nitrogen metabolism in fishes. *Experientia* 48:583–93

66. Ottolenghi C, Ricci D, Gavioli ME, Puviani AC, Fabbri E, et al. 1991. Separation of two populations of fish hepatocytes by digitonin infusion: some metabolic patterns and hormonal responsiveness. *Can. J. Zool.* 69:427–35

67. Perlman DF, Goldstein L. 1988. Nitrogen metabolism. In *Physiology of Elasmobranch Fishes,* ed. TJ Shuttleworth, pp. 253–76. Berlin: Springer-Verlag

68. Pickering AD, Pottinger TG. 1995. Biochemical effects of stress. In *Biochemistry and Molecular Biology of Fishes,* ed. PW Hochachka, TP Mommsen, 5:349–79. Amsterdam: Elsevier

69. Randall DJ, Wood CM, Perry SF, Bergman HL, Maloiy GMO, et al. 1989. Urea excretion as a strategy for survival in a fish living in a very alkaline environment. *Nature* 337:165–66

70. Read LJ. 1968. A study of ammonia and urea production and excretion in the freshwater-adapted form of the Pacific lamprey, *Entosphenus tridentatus. Comp. Biochem. Physiol.* B 26:455–66

71. Read LJ. 1971. The presence of high ornithine-urea cycle enzyme activity in the teleost *Opsanus tau. Comp. Biochem. Physiol.* B 39:409–13

72. Read LJ. 1975. Absence of ureogenic pathways in the liver of the hagfish, *Bdellostoma cirrhatum. Comp. Biochem. Physiol.* B. 51:139–41

73. Ritter NM. 1988. *Elasmobranch glutamine synthetase: synthesis and subcellular location of tissue-specific isozymes.* PhD thesis. Rice Univ., Houston, TX

74. Rozemeijer MJC, Plaut I. 1993. Regulation of nitrogen excretion of the amphibious blenniidae *Alticus kirki* (Guenther, 1868) during emersion and immersion. *Comp. Biochem. Physiol. A* 104:57–62

75. Saha N, Chakravorty J, Ratha BK. 1988. Diurnal variation in renal and extra-renal excretion of ammonia-N and urea-N in a freshwater air-breathing teleost, *Heteropneustes fossilis. Proc. Indian Acad. Sci. (Anim. Sci.)* 97:529–37

76. Saha N, Dkhar J, Anderson PM, Ratha BK. 1996. Carbamoyl phosphate synthetases in an air-breathing teleost, *Heteropneustes fossilis. Comp. Biochem. Physiol. B.* In press

77. Saha N, Ratha BK. 1989. Comparative study of ureogenesis in freshwater, air-breathing teleosts. *J. Exp. Zool.* 252:1–8

78. Schmidt-Nielsen B, Rabinowitz L. 1964. Methylurea and acetamide: active reabsorption by elasmobranch renal tubules. *Science* 146:1587–88

79. Schmidt-Nielsen B, Truniger B, Rabinowitz L. 1972. Sodium-linked urea transport by the renal tubule of the spiny dogfish *Squalus acanthias. Comp. Biochem. Physiol.* 18:271–81

80. Shankar RA, Anderson PM. 1985. Purification and properties of glutamine synthetase from liver of *Squalus acanthias. Arch. Biochem. Biophys.* 239:248–59

81. Smith DD Jr, Vorhaben JE, Campbell JW. 1983. Preparation and cross-reactivity of anti-avian glutamine synthetase antibody. *J. Exp. Zool.* 226:29–35

82. Smith HS. 1929. The excretion of ammonia and urea by the gills of fish. *J. Biol. Chem.* 81:727–42

83. Smith HS. 1936. The retention and physiological role of urea in the Elasmobranchii. *Biol. Bull.* 11:49–82

84. Sogard S, Powell GVN, Holmquist JG. 1987. Epibenthic fish communities on Florida Bay banks: relations with physical parameters and seagrass cover. *Mar. Ecol. Prog. Ser.* 40:25–39

85. Somero GN. 1986. Protons, osmolytes, and fitness of internal milieu for protein function. *Am. J. Physiol.* 251:R197–213

86. Somero GN. 1995. Proteins and temperature. *Annu. Rev. Physiol.* 57:43–68

87. Trammell PR, Campbell JW. 1970. Carbamyl phosphate synthesis in a land snail, *Strophocheilus oblongus. J. Biol. Chem.* 245:6634–41

88. Trammell PR, Campbell JW. 1971. Carbamyl phosphate synthesis in invertebrates. *Comp. Biochem. Physiol. B* 40:395–406

89. Ultsch GR, Jackson DC, Moalli R. 1981. Metabolic oxygen conformity among lower vertebrates: the toadfish revisited. *J. Comp. Physiol.* 142:439–43

89a. Walsh PJ. 1996. Purification and properties of hepatic glutamine synthetases from the ureotelic gulf toadfish, *Opsanus beta. Comp. Biochem. Physiol. B.* In press

90. Walsh PJ, Danulat EM, Mommsen TP. 1990. Variation in urea excretion in the gulf toadfish *Opsanus beta. Mar. Biol.* 106:323–8

91. Walsh PJ, Milligan CL. 1995. Effects of feeding and confinement on nitrogen metabolism and excretion in the gulf toadfish *Opsanus beta. J. Exp. Biol.* 198:1559–66

92. Walsh PJ, Mommsen TP, Bass AH. 1995. Biochemical and molecular aspects of singing in batrachoidid fishes. In *Biochemistry and Molecular Biology of Fishes,* ed. PW Hochachka, TP Mommsen, 4:279–89. Amsterdam: Elsevier

93. Walsh PJ, Parent JJ, Henry RP. 1989. Carbonic anhydrase supplies bicarbonate for urea synthesis in toadfish (*Opsanus beta*) hepatocytes. *Physiol. Zool.* 62:1257–72

94. Walsh PJ, Tucker BC, Hopkins TE. 1994. Effects of confinement/crowding on ureogenesis in the gulf toadfish *Opsanus beta. J. Exp. Biol.* 191:195–206

95. Walsh PJ, Wood CM. 1996. Interactions of urea transport and synthesis in hepatocytes of the gulf toadfish, *Opsanus beta. Comp. Biochem. Physiol. B* 113:411–16

96. Walsh PJ, Wood CM, Perry SF, Thomas S. 1994. Urea transport by hepatocytes and red blood cells of selected elasmobranch and teleost fishes. *J. Exp. Biol.* 193:321–35

97. Walsh PJ, Wright PA, eds. 1995. *Nitrogen Metabolism and Excretion.* Boca Raton, FL: CRC Press. 337 pp.

98. Welch WJ. 1992. Mammalian stress response: cell physiology, structure/function of stress proteins, and implications for medicine and disease. *Physiol. Rev.* 72:1063–81

99. Wright PA. 1995. Nitrogen excretion: three end products, many physiological roles. *J. Exp. Biol.* 198:273–81

100. Wright PA, Felskie A, Anderson PM. 1995. Induction of ornithine-urea cycle enzymes and nitrogen metabolism and excretion in rainbow trout (*Oncorhynchus mykiss*) during early life stages. *J. Exp. Biol.* 198:127–35

101. Wright PA, Pärt P, Wood CM. 1995. Ammonia and urea excretion in the tidepool sculpin (*Oligocottus maculosus*): sites of excretion, effects of reduced salinity and mechanisms of urea transport. *Fish Physiol. Biochem.* 14:111–23

102. Wright PA, Randall DJ, Perry SF. 1989. Fish gill water boundary layer: a site of linkage between carbon dioxide and ammonia excretion. *J. Comp. Physiol.* 158:627–35

103. Wood CM. 1993. Ammonia and urea metabolism and excretion. In *The Physiology of Fishes,* ed. DH Evans, pp. 379–425. Boca Raton, FL: CRC Press

104. Wood CM. 1996. Is there a relationship between urea production and acid-base balance in fish? In *Physiology and Biochemistry of Fishes of the Amazon,* ed. AL Val, VMF Almeida-Val, DJ Randall. Manaus, Brazil: INPA Press. In press

105. Wood CM, Bergman HL, Laurent P, Maina JN, Narahara A, Walsh PJ. 1994. Urea production, acid-base regulation and their interactions in the Lake Magadi tilapia, a unique teleost adapted to a highly alkaline environment. *J. Exp. Biol.* 189:13–36

106. Wood CM, Hopkins TE, Hogstrand C, Walsh PJ. 1995. Pulsatile urea excretion in the ureagenic toadfish *Opsanus beta*: an analysis of rates and routes. *J. Exp. Biol.* 198:1729–41

107. Wood CM, Pärt P, Wright PA. 1995. Ammonia and urea metabolism in relation to gill function and acid-base balance in a marine elasmobranch, the spiny dogfish (*Squalus acanthias*). *J. Exp. Biol.* 198:1545–58

108. Wood CM, Perry SF, Wright PA, Bergman HL, Randall DJ. 1989. Ammonia and urea dynamics in the Lake Magadi tilapia, a ureotelic teleost fish adapted to an extremely alkaline environment. *Respir. Physiol.* 77:1–20

109. You G, Smith CP, Kanai Y, Lee W-S, Stelzner M, Hediger MA. 1993. Cloning and characterization of the vasopressin-regulated urea transporter. *Nature* 365:844–47

110. Zhang R, Verkman AS. 1990. Urea transport in freshly isolated and cultured cells from rat inner medullary collecting duct. *J. Membr. Biol.* 117:253–61

*Annu. Rev. Physiol. 1997. 59:325–47*

# THE CHLORIDE CELL: Structure and Function in the Gills of Freshwater Fishes

*Steve F. Perry*

Department of Biology, University of Ottawa, 30 Marie Curie, Ottawa, Ontario K1N 6N5, Canada

KEY WORDS: gill, fish, lamella, ion regulation, gas transfer, pavement cell, acid-base balance, morphometry, proton pump

## ABSTRACT

This review focuses on the structure and function of the branchial chloride cell in freshwater fishes. The mitochondria-rich chloride cell is believed to be the principal site of *trans*-epithelial $Ca^{2+}$ and $Cl^-$ influxes. Though currently debated, there is accruing evidence that the pavement cell is the site of $Na^+$ uptake via channels linked electrically to an apical membrane vacuolar $H^+$-ATPase (proton pump).

Chloride cells perform an integral role in acid-base regulation. During conditions of alkalosis, the surface area of exposed chloride cells is increased, which serves to enhance base equivalent excretion as the rate of $Cl^-/HCO_3^-$ exchange is increased. Conversely, during acidosis, the chloride cell surface area is diminished by an expansion of the adjacent pavement cells. This response reduces the number of functional $Cl^-/HCO_3^-$ exchangers.

Under certain conditions that challenge ion regulation, chloride cells proliferate on the lamellae. This response, while optimizing the $Ca^{2+}$ and $Cl^-$ transport capacity of the gill, causes a thickening of the blood-to-water diffusion barrier and thus impedes respiratory gas transfer.

## INTRODUCTION

The fish gill chloride cell was first identified by Keys & Wilmer (41) to describe the mitochondria-rich cells responsible for $Cl^-$ secretion in seawater-adapted teleosts. The exact origin of the name chloride cell is unclear but may have arisen in the study of Copeland (9). The specific involvement of the branchial chloride cell in $Cl^-$ secretion in seawater fishes, although originally disputed (5), was later confirmed in an elegant series of experiments (20). The underlying

0066-4278/97/0315-0325$08.00

mechanisms of both $Na^+$ and $Cl^-$ excretion across the gills of marine teleost fish are now well established (89; reviewed by 2, 19, 39, 60, 88, 98, 99).

Mitochondria-rich cells, resembling the $Cl^-$-secreting cells of marine teleosts, also occur on the gill epithelia of freshwater fishes, and these cells are also termed chloride cells. Strictly speaking, this nomenclature may be inappropriate because the structure and, in part, the function of these cells in marine and freshwater fishes are markedly different. Consequently the chloride cells of freshwater fishes are also referred to as mitochondria-rich cells or ionocytes. Unlike the situation for seawater fish, there is marked debate as to the physiological function of the branchial chloride cell in freshwater environments. To some degree, the lack of certainty as to the role of the chloride cell in freshwater fishes has arisen from the absence of suitable model systems equivalent to the chloride cell-rich opercular membrane and other skin preparations of numerous seawater-adapted species (60, 64).

In recent years, considerable progress has occurred in our understanding of gill chloride cell function in freshwater fishes. This review focuses on the structure and function of the chloride cell in freshwater teleosts and summarizes recent advances related to its role in ionic regulation, acid-base balance, and gas transfer.

## STRUCTURE OF THE CHLORIDE CELL IN FRESHWATER FISHES

The chloride cell is one of four differentiated cell types comprising the gill epithelium (reviewed in 45–47, 51, 77, 85). The other cell types are the pavement cells (termed respiratory cells in the older literature), mucus cells, and neuro-epithelial cells (4, 12). In most teleost species that have been examined under so-called normal conditions, the chloride cell occupies only a small fraction (generally less than 15%) of the total surface area of all epithelial cells exposed to the environment. Moreover, there is great diversity with respect to the numbers and fractional surface area of exposed chloride cells in teleost fish. For example, Anguillid eels typically exhibit very few chloride cells on their gill epithelia, whereas salmonids display a relative abundance of branchial chloride cells (e.g. 74). The reasons for such pronounced interspecific variability in the distribution of gill chloride cells are unknown but may reflect marked interspecific differences in the "leakiness" of the gills to ions (see below).

The gill is composed of two distinct epithelial surfaces, the lamellar and filament epithelia [also termed the secondary and primary epithelia, respectively, in the older literature (47)]. The chloride cells are largely confined to the trailing edge of the filament epithelium and in particular are concentrated in the

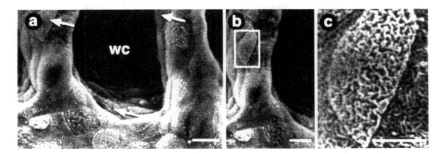

*Figure 1*  Scanning electron micrographs showing the distribution of chloride cells on the filamental and lamellar epithelia of rainbow trout (*Oncorhynchus mykiss*). The chloride cells are most abundant on the leading edge of the filament at the bases of lamellae and in the inter-lamellar regions. Panels *b* and *c* illustrate the appearance of the apical membrane of a highlighted lamellar chloride cell as viewed under moderate (*b*) and high-power (*c*) magnification. Arrows indicate a few representative chloride cells; wc = inter-lamellar water channel. The scale bars represent 10 $\mu$m. Modified from Laurent & Perry (52).

inter-lamellar regions and at the junctions between the filament and lamella (see Figure 1). Usually, the chloride cells are only sparsely distributed on the lamellae. However, under conditions of proliferation, the lamellae may be inundated with chloride cells and consequently impede the diffusion of respiratory gases (see below).

The surface structure of the chloride cell apical membrane has been revealed by numerous electron microscopy studies (e.g. 11, 21, 33–35, 42, 47, 67, 73, 74, 94). A striking feature of the apical membrane surface morphology is the profound variation among the species that have been examined. Figure 2 illustrates representative chloride cell apical membrane surfaces in four freshwater species (*Ictalurus nebulosus, Anguilla rostrata, Oncorhynchus mykiss, Oreochromis mossambicus*) as revealed by scanning electron microscopy (SEM) (74). In each instance, the apical membrane of the chloride cell has a distinct appearance that allows relatively simple designation of these cells from the surrounding pavement and mucus cells. In the brown bullhead (*Ictalurus nebulosus*), the apical membrane is characterized by a sponge-like appearance (Figure 2*a*) owing to the unusual arrangement of plasma membrane microplicae. In the American eel (*Anguilla rostrata*), the apical membrane has a carpet-like appearance resulting from an extremely dense array of microplicae. This serves to raise the apical membrane above the adjoining pavement cells (Figure 2*b*). In rainbow trout (*Oncorhynchus mykiss*), the convex apical membrane structure is more variable; some chloride cells exhibit a smooth surface whereas others, ornamented with more microplicae, appear rougher in their appearance

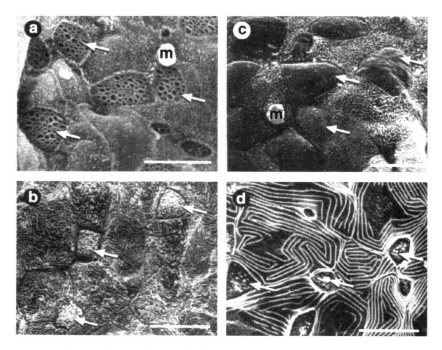

*Figure 2* Scanning electron micrographs showing the characteristic apical surface structure of gill filamental chloride cells in four freshwater teleost species: (*a*) brown bullhead (*Ictalurus nebulosus*), (*b*) American eel (*Anguilla rostrata*), (*c*) rainbow trout (*Oncorhynchus mykiss*), and (*d*) tilapia (*Oreochromis mossambicus*). In each panel, arrows indicate a few representative chloride cells; m = mucus cell. The scale bars represent 10 $\mu$m. Modified from Perry et al (74).

(Figure 2*c*). In the tilapia (*Oreochromis mossambicus*), the apical membrane may be substantially recessed below the adjacent pavement cells to form an apical crypt (Figure 2*d*), a structure usually associated with the chloride cells of marine fish (see also Figures 3 and 4).

The marked interspecific differences in the structure of the apical membrane precludes the absolute identification of chloride cells, in previously untested species, on the basis of their surface topology alone. Moreover, it demonstrates the limitation of estimating apical membrane surface area (a three-dimensional structure) using two-dimensional analysis. Thus comparisons (using two-dimensional analysis) of apical membrane surface areas between two or more species exhibiting differences in the degree of apical membrane ornamentation (e.g. Figure 2) may not accurately depict differences in the true apical membrane surface area.

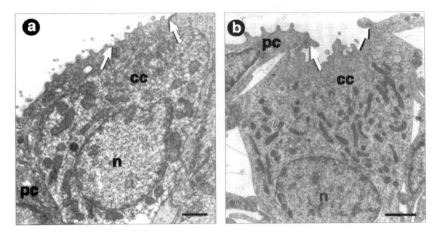

*Figure 3*  Transmission electron micrographs illustrating the typical chloride cell (*cc*) ultrastructure in (*a*) rainbow trout (*Oncorhynchus mykiss*) and (*b*) tilapia (*Oreochromis mossambicus*). In both species, the cells are characterized by numerous mitochondria, a tubular system, and a basal ovoid nucleus (*n*). In trout, the portion of the apical membrane exposed to the water (*arrows*) is slightly convex while in tilapia, the exposed apical membrane is recessed beneath the adjacent pavement cells (*pc*) to form an apical crypt. Scale bars in both panels represent 1.0 μm. Modified from Perry et al (74).

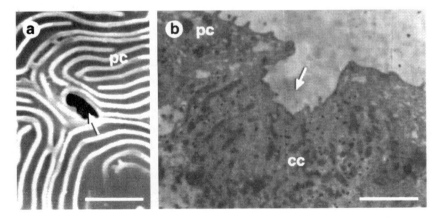

*Figure 4*  Scanning (*a*) and transmission (*b*) electron micrographs of tilapia (*Oreochromis mossambicus*) filamental epithelia showing the characteristic chloride cell (*cc*) and apical crypt (*arrows*) in this species. In panel *b*, antibodies against $Na^+/K^+$-ATPase and immunogold labeling (*black dots*) were used to demonstrate that this enzyme is predominantly localized to the chloride cell relative to the pavement cell (*pc*); scale bars in (*a*) and (*b*) represent 1.0 and 2.0 μm, respectively; modified from Lee et al (53). The original photo was provided courtesy of PP Hwang.

Unlike the diversity of its surface structure, the ultrastructure of the chloride cell is well conserved among the various species (11, 40, 45, 85, 94, 96, 97). The ubiquitous features of chloride cell ultrastructure are its abundance of mitochondria, an extensive tubular system emanating from the basolateral membrane, an array of sub-apical vesicles, and a large ovoid nucleus (see Figure 3). The three-dimensional tubular network is distributed throughout most of the cell to form an expansive surface area. Because the tubular/basolateral membranes are thought to be the sites of the transport enzyme $Na^+$, $K^+$-ATPase (10), the chloride cell is also characterized by an abundance of this particular enzyme (Figure 4). However, the specific role of the chloride cell $Na^+$, $K^+$-ATPase (biochemical correlate of the sodium pump) in *trans*-epithelial ion transport in freshwater fishes is uncertain (see below).

A variety of techniques are routinely utilized to identify chloride cells because of their characteristic ultrastructure and enzymatic composition. These techniques include the use of fluorescent mitochondrial markers (e.g. 39, 55, 80) and histochemical (55, 63) or immunocytochemical (53) localization of $Na^+$, $K^+$-ATPase, as well as standard staining of lipid membranes (3, 23). The results of recent studies, however, indicate that a subset of pavement cells, especially under conditions of respiratory acidosis, may also exhibit an abundance of mitochondria (e.g. 24, 29), and thus under certain conditions, mitochondrial markers may not be entirely specific for branchial chloride cells.

## Chloride Cell Sub-Types

It is well established (e.g. 11) that chloride cells exhibit subtle ultrastructural differences when viewed under the transmission electron microscope (TEM). Perhaps most notable is the presence of electron-dense (osmophilic) and light chloride cells (11, 96, 97). An intriguing question is whether these different ultrastructural characteristics reflect different chloride cell sub-types or simply different developmental stages of a common cell type (e.g. 97). On the basis of extensive TEM examination of teleost gills, Pisam and co-workers (82–85) have postulated the presence of two cell sub-types, the $\alpha$ and $\beta$ chloride cells that differ in their location and apical/sub-apical membrane properties (see Figure 5). The $\alpha$ cells are located predominantly at the base of the lamella and are believed to be the precursors of the chloride cells of seawater-adapted teleosts. The $\beta$ cells are found primarily in the inter-lamellar regions of the gill filament and occur only in teleosts inhabiting freshwater. The apical membrane of the $\alpha$ cell is characterized by extensive folding and projections, whereas the sub-apical cytoplasm contains numerous lightly staining vesicles that are distinct from the tubular system (Figure 5). Conversely, the apical membrane of the $\beta$ cell is smooth and the sub-apical cytoplasm contains heavily staining apical structures that, although independent of the tubular system, penetrate

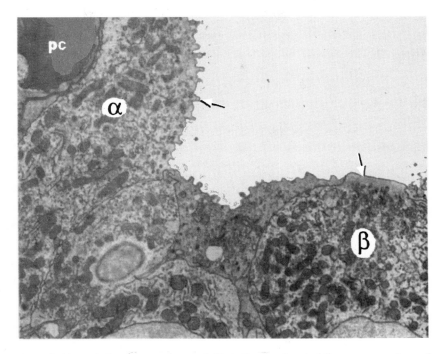

*Figure 5* Transmission electron micrograph illustrating the characteristic appearance of α- and β-type chloride cells in the gill of freshwater adapted Atlantic salmon (*Salmo salar*). Note in particular the differences in the structure of the apical membrane (*arrows*). In the β-type cells, the apical membrane is smooth, whereas in the α-type cells, the apical membrane is characterized by wavy projections (*folds*). Pc = pillar cell; see text for further details. Modified from Pisam et al (84). The original photo was provided courtesy of M Pisam.

deep within the tubular network of the cell (Figure 5). The SEM observations of smooth- and rough-appearing chloride cell apical membranes in salmonids (21, 22, 50, 74) are consistent with the description of α and β cells, respectively (see also Figure 2). The physiological functions of the α and β cells in freshwater fish are not known.

Although the evidence for different chloride cell sub-types in the freshwater fish gill is compelling (see above) and while there is evidence for mitochondria-rich cell sub-types in other secretory epithelia (e.g. 90), the possibility that these cells represent different activity or developmental stages of a single cell type cannot be excluded. Wendelaar Bonga and co-workers (96, 97) showed convincingly that chloride cells undergo apoptosis and that different developmental stages of the chloride cell are reflected by strikingly different ultrastructural properties. These findings do not refute the conclusions of Pisam and co-workers (e.g. 83), but they do suggest alternate explanations for the different morphologies of the freshwater chloride cell.

# THE ROLE OF THE CHLORIDE CELL
# IN IONIC REGULATION

There is much uncertainty surrounding the role of the chloride cell in ionic regulation in freshwater fishes. In the freshwater environment, fish continually lose ions across their permeable body surfaces of which the gill, owing to its large surface area, is the most significant. Ionic equilibrium is achieved, however, as a result of a more-or-less equivalent absorption of ions ($Ca^{2+}$, $Cl^-$, $Na^+$) from the water. Although it has been widely assumed that the chloride cell is responsible for the uptake of $Ca^{2+}$, $Cl^-$, and $Na^+$ from the water, this assumption is based largely on indirect evidence and likely is an oversimplification of the true situation.

## Trans-Epithelial Calcium Uptake

Several comprehensive reviews have been written on the mechanisms of gill *trans*-epithelial $Ca^{2+}$ uptake in freshwater fishes (13, 15, 16). The current model (71) contends that *trans*-epithelial $Ca^{2+}$ uptake is a multistep *trans*-cellular process that relies on active transport. The first step is the passive entry of $Ca^{2+}$ into the cell through presumptive apical membrane $Ca^{2+}$ channels. Some of the entering $Ca^{2+}$ is buffered by $Ca^{2+}$-binding proteins or sequestered within intracellular organelles. The final step is the energy-dependent movement of $Ca^{2+}$ across the basolateral membrane via a high-affinity $Ca^{2+}$-ATPase (17, 18, 71; reviewed in 15) and/or a lower-affinity $Na^+/Ca^{2+}$ exchanger (15, 95).

There is compelling indirect and correlative data, stemming from an array of studies employing widely varying techniques, that link the chloride cell to *trans*-epithelial $Ca^{2+}$ uptake. Importantly, the rates of $Ca^{2+}$ uptake in vivo (73) or in vitro (61, 65) are strongly correlated with the surface area and/or numbers of chloride cells. Moreover, treatments known to elicit proliferation of chloride cells such as cortisol therapy (14, 73, 81) or exposure to softwater (62, 73) are associated with an increased $Ca^{2+}$-transporting capacity of the gill. Ishihara & Mugiya (37) provided histological evidence for the involvement of the goldfish (*Carassius auratus*) chloride cell in $Ca^{2+}$ uptake by demonstrating oxalate-induced precipitates of $Ca^{2+}$ only in the vicinity of chloride cell apical openings. Using a perfused head preparation, Payan et al (69) showed that the uptake of $Ca^{2+}$ occurred across the arterio-venous circulation and thus concluded that the chloride cells of the filament epithelium were involved. Using a similar preparation, however, Perry & Wood (81) showed that the uptake of $Ca^{2+}$ was

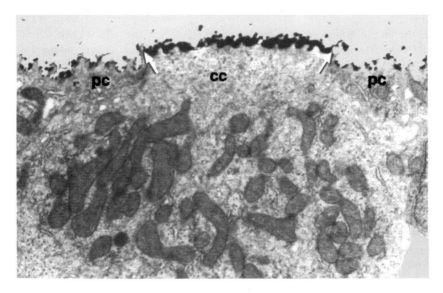

*Figure 6*  Transmission electron micrograph of rainbow trout (*Oncorhynchus mykiss*) gill illustrating the more-or-less specific deposition of lanthanum (a calcium channel antagonist) on the exposed apical membrane (*arrows*) of the centrally located chloride cell (*cc*); pc = pavement cell. Modified from Perry & Flik (71).

restricted to the arterio-arterial circulation but also concluded that chloride cells, albeit the lamellar chloride cells, are the sites of $Ca^{2+}$ uptake.

The feature of the chloride cell enabling its role in *trans*-branchial $Ca^{2+}$ uptake and distinguishing it from the other epithelial cell types of the gill is believed to be the presence of apical membrane $Ca^{2+}$ channels. Figure 6 illustrates the more-or-less specific deposition of $LaCl_3$, a potent $Ca^{2+}$ channel antagonist, on the apical membrane of the chloride cell. Current theory contends that the activity of the basolateral $Ca^{2+}$-ATPase exceeds the $Ca^{2+}$-transporting requirements of the chloride cell and thus the factor limiting $Ca^{2+}$ uptake in fish may be the numbers and/or conductive properties of the apical membrane $Ca^{2+}$ channels. Indeed, the principal hormone influencing $Ca^{2+}$ uptake in fish, stanniocalcin, is believed to exert its hypocalcaemic effect by influencing these apical membrane $Ca^{2+}$ channels (16).

Given that the chloride cell is the site of $Ca^{2+}$ uptake in fish and that the exposed surface area of these cells is modified during acid-base disturbances to regulate blood pH (see below), investigations are currently ongoing to ascertain the consequences of acid-base disturbances on branchial $Ca^{2+}$ uptake. As predicted from theory, the increased exposure of chloride cells that accompanies metabolic alkalosis (28, 72) in rainbow trout is associated with marked increases in the rate of branchial $Ca^{2+}$ uptake (58a). However, the reduced exposure of chloride cells associated with respiratory acidosis (28) is not accompanied by a reduction in $Ca^{2+}$ uptake; indeed $Ca^{2+}$ uptake is increased markedly (58b). This infers that fish are able to invoke compensatory mechanisms to counteract the effects of reduced chloride cell surface area on branchial $Ca^{2+}$ uptake. Alternatively, these data may indicate that the pavement cell also plays a role in $Ca^{2+}$ uptake, especially under conditions of reduced chloride cell availability.

## Trans-Epithelial Chloride Uptake

The nature of $Cl^-$ uptake across the fish gill has not been firmly established. However, there is substantial indirect evidence suggesting that absorption from the water occurs via an apical membrane electroneutral $Cl^-/HCO_3^-$ exchanger (e.g. 60). For example, addition of anionic exchanger inhibitors to the water (75, 78) or removal of external $Cl^-$ reduces the rate of $Cl^-$ uptake and results in the retention of $HCO_3^-$ and the development of metabolic alkalosis (e.g. 75). Furthermore, the addition of $HCO_3^-$ to the water also reduces branchial $Cl^-$ uptake and elicits internal metabolic alkalosis. It is unclear, however, as to how such an electroneutral exchanger would operate given the obvious unfavorable chemical gradient for $Cl^-$ across the apical membrane. One possibility is that the exchanger is driven by a favorable chemical gradient for $HCO_3^-$. Recent estimates of $[Cl^-]$ in chloride cells (40 mmol $l^{-1}$) (66), suggest that estimated intracellular $HCO_3^-$ levels (2 mmol $l^{-1}$; CM Wood, personal communication) may be insufficient to overcome the unfavorable $Cl^-$ gradient. It is important to note, however, that the activity of intracellular $Cl^-$ may be significantly lower than the measured concentration. Furthermore, the concentration of $Cl^-$ in the boundary layer water immediately adjacent to the gill epithelium has not yet been determined. Clearly, the nature of $Cl^-$ uptake across the apical membrane of fish gill epithelia requires reevaluation. Although previous studies implicating the involvement of an apical membrane anion-dependent ATPase (10) have largely been discounted, the potential involvement of such a $Cl^-/HCO_3^-$-ATPase in $Cl^-$ uptake should be reexamined. The exit step for $Cl^-$ from the cell cytosol to the extracellular compartment has not been elucidated although current models depict its movement through presumptive basolateral membrane $Cl^-$ channels (60).

It is generally assumed that the chloride cell is the site of $Cl^-$ uptake in freshwater fish although direct evidence is still lacking. The indirect evidence, however, is persuasive. For example, correlation analysis has revealed that inter- and intraspecific variation in the rates of $Cl^-$ uptake among and within species can be accounted for entirely by similar variation in the surface area of chloride cell apical membranes exposed to the water (50, 74, 76). Indeed, the proliferation of branchial chloride cells in fish exposed to ion-poor water (76) appears to be a response that increases the transporting capacity of the gill for both $Ca^{2+}$ and $Cl^-$.

Recently, Sullivan et al (92), using in situ hybridization, demonstrated the presence of messenger RNA (mRNA) for the $Cl^-/HCO_3^-$ anion exchanger in the trout gill. The hybridization signal was localized on both the lamellar and filament epithelia but was most abundant on the inter-lamellar regions of the filament. These regions contain the highest density of chloride cells and thus these data offer additional evidence that the chloride cell is the site of $Cl^-$ uptake via an apical membrane $Cl^-/HCO_3^-$ exchanger. During metabolic alkalosis, the amount of $Cl^-/HCO_3^-$ exchanger mRNA increases markedly (92) on both the filament and lamellar epithelia, which is consistent with the pronounced proliferation of chloride cells occurring during alkalosis (see below).

The numbers and surface area of exposed chloride cells differ widely among the species examined. For example, eels are characterized by an exceptionally low surface area of exposed chloride cells, whereas in trout the relative area of the gill covered by exposed chloride cells is comparatively high. Given the apparent crucial role of the chloride cell in both $Ca^{2+}$ and $Cl^-$ uptake in freshwater fishes, it seems likely that the surface area of exposed chloride cells in the various species is set by the intrinsic leakiness of the gill (and other permeable body surfaces) to these ions. Thus the eel displays an extremely low rate of ionic efflux, whereas in the trout, the ionic efflux rate is extremely high. Consequently, situations that accelerate the rate of ion loss are typically accompanied by branchial chloride cell proliferation.

## Trans-Epithelial Sodium Uptake

The classical model for $Na^+$ uptake in freshwater fish (43) incorporates an epithelial apical membrane electroneutral $Na^+/H^+$ exchanger. Although this model went essentially unchallenged for 50 years, it is now apparent that the presumed chemical gradients across the apical membrane of gill epithelial cells could not support such an exchanger. Consequently, Avella & Bornancin (1) proposed an alternate model for $Na^+$ uptake in freshwater fish that depicts the inward entry of $Na^+$ through apical membrane $Na^+$ channels. In this model the movement of $Na^+$ is driven by an electrochemical gradient supplied by an apical membrane vacuolar type $H^+$-ATPase (V-ATPase). In recent years, substantial evidence had accumulated to support this alternate model of $Na^+$ uptake (56–58, 66, 86, 91, 92). Although both models can adequately explain the tight coupling between $Na^+$ uptake and acid excretion across the gill, as well as the saturation kinetics displayed by $Na^+$ uptake (86), the available evidence would seem to favor the newer scheme and thus it should be viewed as a working model for $Na^+$ uptake across the freshwater fish gill.

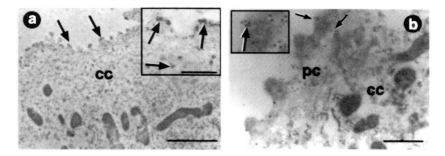

*Figure 7*  Transmission electron micrographs of rainbow trout (*Oncorhynchus mykiss*) gill illustrating the immunolocalization (*black dots*) of the vacuolar type proton ATPase (V-ATPase). The left panel (J Wilson, previously unpublished data) shows that immunoreactivity (*arrows*) against the 70-kDa subunit of the bovine brain V-ATPase is localized to the apical region of a chloride cell (*cc*). The right panel (G Sullivan, J Fryer & S Perry, previously unpublished data) shows that immunoreactivity (*arrows*) against the 31-kDa subunit of bovine renal V-ATPase is localized to the apical region of a pavement cell (*pc*) while the underlying chloride cell displays no immunoreactivity.

The V-ATPase is associated with the apical membrane and sub-apical regions of both chloride and pavement cells (Figure 7). In addition, carbonic anhydrase, an essential component of the proton pump/$Na^+$ uptake mechanism also is distributed within both cell types (87). However, it is not entirely clear which of these two gill cell types is responsible for $Na^+$ uptake in freshwater fishes, although several lines of evidence suggest that the pavement cell, rather than the chloride cell, is the principal site. First, Sullivan et al (91), using immunocytochemistry in conjunction with electron microscopy, demonstrated (in the tissues that were examined) that the V-ATPase was located exclusively in the apical regions of pavement cells. Figure 7*b* corroborates this finding and shows a pavement cell containing abundant V-ATPase immunoreactivity overlying a chloride cell that displays no immunoreactivity. Second, during periods of internal acidosis, the surface area of exposed chloride cells is reduced concurrently with an increased rate of $Na^+$ uptake and acid excretion. Thus there is no correlation between chloride cell surface area and $Na^+$ uptake/acid excretion, at least during acid-base disturbances. Indeed, in brown bullheads experiencing hypercapnic acidosis, the surface area of exposed chloride cell apical membranes can be reduced by as much as 90% without any effect on the rate of $Na^+$ uptake. Third, X-ray microanalysis studies of brown trout (*Salmo trutta*) gills revealed that changes in the environmental $Na^+$ concentration influenced the intracellular $Na^+$ levels in pavement cells without affecting the chloride cells (66).

Although Figure 7*a* (J Wilson, unpublished data) demonstrates pronounced V-ATPase immunoreactivity associated with the apical region of an exposed chloride cell, the physiological significance is unclear given the recent findings concerning $Na^+$ uptake in freshwater fishes (see above). Further, the reasons for the discrepant results from the studies immunolocalizing the V-ATPase (e.g. Figure 7) also remain unresolved.

A further confounding issue is the high activities of $Na^+/K^+$-ATPase in the chloride cells relative to the pavement cells (e.g. 44); the relative abundance of $Na^+/K^+$-ATPase in the chloride cell is illustrated clearly in Figure 4 (PP Hwang, personal communication). Although essential in seawater teleosts for the secretion of $Cl^-$ (89), the role of a basolateral membrane $Na^+/K^+$-ATPase in the chloride cells of freshwater fish is not immediately obvious if one assumes that the pavement cell is the site of *trans*-epithelial $Na^+$ uptake (see above). It is possible that the high activity of this enzyme in the chloride cell simply reflects the expansive surface area of the basolateral membrane in these cells in comparison with the low basolateral membrane surface area in the pavement cells. Although the $Na^+/K^+$-ATPase activity, and thus the specific $Na^+$ transport capacity of individual pavement cells, is low, the overall $Na^+$ transport capacity of the gill pavement cells is high owing to their abundance.

# THE ROLE OF THE CHLORIDE CELL IN ACID-BASE REGULATION

Cameron & Iwama (8) first suggested that morphological modifications to the gill epithelium, involving redistribution of chloride cells, might play a significant role in piscine acid-base regulation. In recent years, there has been considerable progress surrounding the possible role of chloride cells and epithelial remodeling in the amelioration of acid-base disturbances. It is clear that the chloride cells do indeed perform significant direct and indirect roles in acid-base regulation although current models (reviewed by 28, 29, 52) differ markedly from the original scheme proposed by Cameron & Iwama (8).

## Responses to Alkalosis

During metabolic alkalosis, rainbow trout experience marked proliferation of lamellar and filamental chloride cells (27, 30, 72). This response occurs concomitantly with a marked increase in the rates of $Cl^-$ uptake and base excretion, effects that have been attributed to stimulation of $Cl^-/HCO_3^-$ exchange. It is believed that the proliferation of chloride cells at such times is directly responsible for the increased $Cl^-/HCO_3^-$ exchange activity owing to an increased number of exchange sites exposed to the external environment. Indeed, in support of this idea, Perry & Goss (72) demonstrated that trout displaying prior chloride cell proliferation exhibited an enhanced ability to compensate metabolic alkalosis (when compared with normal trout) owing to increased branchial base excretion. Furthermore, Sullivan et al (92) demonstrated a pronounced increase in the amount of mRNA for the $Cl^-/HCO_3^-$ exchanger in alkalotic trout. Finally, the American eel possesses an extremely low surface area of exposed branchial chloride cells (e.g. 2%) (27), and unlike the situation in trout, the cell population in eels is insensitive to alkalosis (27). As a result, the eel is unable to increase $Cl^-$ uptake (presumably via $Cl^-/HCO_3^-$ exchange) but instead uses a different strategy, $Cl^-$ efflux modulation (27), to regulate blood pH during alkalosis. Although insufficient numbers of species have been examined to permit generalization, it is possible that the strategy of chloride cell expansion/proliferation to modulate $Cl^-/HCO_3^-$ exchange for compensation of alkalosis may be utilized only by those species possessing large chloride cell surface areas.

## Responses to Acidosis

In response to respiratory acidosis, brown bullheads and rainbow trout display marked reductions in the surface area of chloride cells exposed to the water owing to physical covering by adjacent pavement cells (24–26, 30). The response is rapid; for example in bullheads the chloride cell fractional area is reduced by 50% after only 6 h of hypercapnic acidosis (24). The covering of the chloride cells is believed to uncouple $Cl^-/HCO_3^-$ exchange sites from the external environment and thus reduce the rate of $Cl^-/HCO_3^-$ exchange, which is the predominant mechanism of compensating acidosis in these species. In this way, the chloride cell plays an indirect role in the compensation of acidosis. This strategy cannot be exploited by species such as eels, which display low branchial chloride cell surface areas and thus low and inflexible rates of $Cl^-/HCO_3^-$ exchange. Instead, eels regulate acidosis exclusively by adjusting $Na^+$-coupled acid equivalent fluxes (36).

The covering of the chloride cells during acidosis in trout and bullheads, at times of intense acid excretion and normal (or enhanced) rates of $Na^+$ uptake, casts doubt on a role for the chloride cell in apical membrane proton pumping and $Na^+$ uptake. Indeed, there is growing evidence that the pavement cell, rather than the chloride cell, performs the predominant direct role in the regulation of internal acid-base disturbances. For example, in hypercapnic brown bullheads, the pavement cells undergo pronounced transformation involving changes to both the apical membrane surface structure and cellular ultrastructure (24, 25, 52). These changes, including proliferation of apical membrane microplicae and sub-apical mitochondria, are indicative of increased cellular activity. The increased density of microplicae is consistent with an expansion of the apical plasma membrane. It has been argued that the changes to the apical membrane reflect increased traffic to, and fusion of proton pump vesicles with, the plasma membrane. In support of this idea, Laurent et al (48) have identified proton pump vesicles in the pavement cells of brown bullheads that are more abundant in the sub-apical regions of the cell during hypercapnic acidosis. Using immunocytochemistry, Sullivan et al (91) demonstrated a marked increase in the activity of the V-ATPase (proton pump) during hypercapnia in trout in the apical regions of pavement cells. Using in situ hybridization, Sullivan et al (92) reported an increase in the activity of proton pump mRNA in trout during hypercapnia that was localized almost exclusively to the lamellar epithelia.

Although the results of the many studies mentioned above implicate the pavement cell in $H^+$ excretion and $Na^+$ uptake and support the pavement cell's presumed role in acid-base regulation during acidosis, a direct role for the chloride cell cannot be excluded. Indeed, the results of experiments partitioning acid-equivalent fluxes across the lamellae and filamental epithelia in trout during hypercapnia (38) do suggest a possible direct involvement of the chloride cell. Recent advances in the in vitro culture of pavement cells (68) may provide a new avenue to investigate the relative roles of the pavement cell and chloride cell in acid-base regulation.

## CHLORIDE CELLS AND GAS TRANSFER

Under normal conditions, the chloride cells are distributed but sparsely on the lamellar surfaces. However, under conditions that challenge ionic regulation such as exposure of fish to softwater (81) or toxicants (54), chloride cells proliferate on both the filamental and lamellar surfaces of the gill (reviewed by 51, 77). Relative to the pavement cells, the spherical chloride cells are larger in diameter and often display convex apical membranes causing them to protrude into the inter-lamellar water channels. Although the proliferation of lamellar chloride cells during ionoregulatory challenges is presumed to increase the capacity of the gill to transport $Ca^{2+}$ (81) and $Cl^-$ (76), the inundation of the lamellae by proliferating cells might concurrently impair gas transfer owing to a thickening of the lamellar blood-to-water diffusion barrier.

### Effects of Chloride Cell Proliferation on Blood-to-Water Diffusion Distance

The impact of chloride cell proliferation on the lamellar blood-to-water diffusion distance has been assessed by applying standard morphometric techniques in comparisons of control fish with animals exposed to softwater (31, 49) or treated with morphogenetic hormones (6). These studies have yielded conflicting results. Laurent & Hebibi (49) reported a pronounced proliferation of chloride cells in rainbow trout exposed to softwater yet the blood-to-water diffusion distance was not increased nor was the "morphological diffusing capacity" reduced. In contrast, Greco et al (31) documented an approximate twofold increase in the thickness of the lamellar diffusion barrier that accompanied the chloride cell proliferation elicited by 1 to 4 weeks' exposure of trout to softwater. The dramatic impact of softwater exposure on chloride cell proliferation and the lamellar diffusion distance in the latter study is illustrated in Figure 8. The protrusion of convex chloride cells from the lamellar epithelium in this particular case, while increasing the diffusion distance for respiratory gases, also is likely to reduce the thickness of the water channels formed by adjacent lamellae.

Chronic treatment of fish with hormones including cortisol (50) and growth hormone (6, 59) elicits lamellar chloride cell proliferation and concomitantly elevates the ion transport capacity of the gill for $Ca^{2+}$ (14, 81) and NaCl (6, 50, 74). Thus cortisol and growth hormone may serve as osmoregulatory hormones in freshwater fish in addition to their well-known role in the adaptation of euryhaline fish to seawater (19). Bindon et al (6) demonstrated that chloride cell proliferation elicited by cortisol and/or ovine growth hormone caused an approximate doubling of the lamellar diffusion barrier with the degree of lamellar thickening positively correlated with the extent of the chloride cell proliferation. Figure 8c combines the morphometric data obtained from trout exposed to softwater (31) or injected with morphogenetic hormones (6). This figure clearly illustrates the tight coupling between the surface area of exposed chloride cells (an index of chloride cell proliferation) and the lamellar blood-to-water diffusion distance. Importantly, this relationship is independent of the method used to initiate chloride cell proliferation.

Although the conflicting results obtained by Laurent & Hebibi (49) are difficult to reconcile, the results of more recent studies, together with theoretical considerations (see above), strongly indicate that a thickening of the lamellar diffusion barrier is an obligatory consequence of lamellar chloride cell proliferation. Such lamellar thickening is likely to negatively influence respiratory gas transfer.

## Effects of Chloride Cell Proliferation on Respiratory Gas Transfer

Thomas et al (93) provided the first experimental evidence that respiratory gas transfer is impaired by chloride cell proliferation. In that study, two populations of rainbow trout were examined; one group was acclimated to relatively ion-rich water (approximately 1 mmol $l^{-1}$ [NaCl]), whereas another was acclimated to relatively ion-poor water (0.1 mmol $l^{-1}$ [NaCl]). The fish in ion-poor water displayed a pronounced proliferation of lamellar chloride cells and impairment of branchial oxygen transfer as indicated by the lowering of arterial $PO_2$. Moreover, these fish were less tolerant of hypoxia. Subsequent studies investigating the relationship between chloride cell proliferation and gas transfer

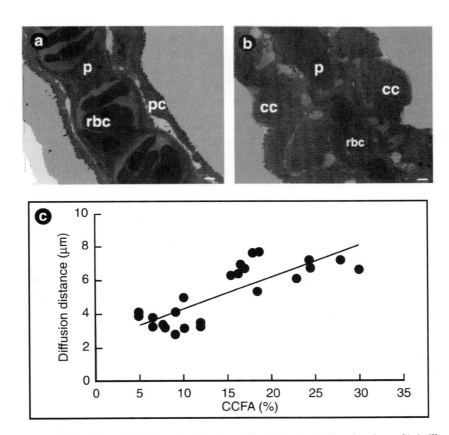

*Figure 8*    The effect of chloride cell proliferation on the rainbow trout (*Oncorhynchus mykiss*) gill lamellar blood-to-water diffusion barrier. The upper two panels, modified from Greco et al (31), illustrate that chloride cell (*cc*) proliferation, caused by exposure of fish to softwater (panel *b*), causes marked chloride cell proliferation and an obvious thickening of the blood-to-water diffusion barrier. Panel *c* [data compiled from Bindon et al (6) and Greco et al (31)] shows that the blood-to-water diffusion distance is positively correlated with chloride cell fractional area (CCFA; an index of chloride cell proliferation). Rbc = red blood cell, pc = pavement cell, p = pillar cell. Scale bars in (*a*) and (*b*) represent 1.0 μm.

(7, 32, 79) have confirmed and elaborated on the original findings of Thomas et al (93; reviewed in 70). Furthermore, it is now evident that fish invoke several compensatory mechanisms to minimize the degree of respiratory impairment associated with the thickening of the diffusion barrier elicited by chloride cell proliferation.

An important response accompanying chloride cell proliferation in rainbow trout is hyperventilation (79). Increased ventilation volume serves to raise $PaO_2$ and lower $PaCO_2$ and thereby partially offsets the increased diffusion limitations imposed by lamellar thickening. Such a response, although beneficial to gas transfer, will increase the energetic cost of gas exchange and prevent the usual hyperventilatory responses associated with exercise or exposure of fish to environmental disturbances. Perry et al (79) also recently showed in vitro that hemoglobin oxygen-binding affinity was increased in trout displaying chloride cell proliferation. This would serve to reduce the extent of the hypoxemia associated with any lowering of arterial $PO_2$.

In summary, chloride cell proliferation, although beneficial to ionic regulation, is a detriment to gas transfer owing to an increase in the thickness of the lamellar blood-to-water diffusion barrier. Compensatory adjustments, however, including hyperventilation and increased affinity of hemoglobin-oxygen binding partially offset the detrimental consequences on gas transfer and blood gas transport.

## CONCLUSION

Although there have been considerable advances in recent years concerning the role of the branchial chloride cell in freshwater fishes, there still remains substantial uncertainty in a number of important areas. Further advances in these areas will likely stem from studies incorporating a multidisciplinary approach in which cell culture techniques, molecular biology, histology, and electrophysiology are merged. Future research should address the following key issues:

1. the relative roles of the chloride cells and pavement cells in $Na^+$, $Cl^-$, and $Ca^{2+}$ uptake as well as acid-base regulation;

2. the mechanism of $Cl^-$ uptake across the apical membrane of gill chloride cells;

3. the physiological significance of the different chloride cell sub-types or their developmental stages;

4. the nature and localization of presumptive apical membrane $Na^+$ channels and their linkage to the proton pump.

ACKNOWLEDGMENTS

I am extremely grateful to the following individuals who gave permission to cite and present unpublished data or provided original plates of previously published material: Drs. Monique Pisam, Pung Pung Hwang, Pierre Laurent, David Randall, James Fryer, and Mr. Jonathan Wilson. I also thank Drs. Sjoerd Wendalaar Bonga, Gert Flik, and Chris Wood for faithfully answering (via electronic mail) my numerous questions relating to fish gill structure and function. I am indebted to the following graduate students and post-docs who gathered much of the data presented in this review: Drs. Greg Goss, Steve Reid, and Katie Gilmour; and Gary Sullivan, Shawn Bindon, and Anna-Maria Greco. I must also thank Drs. Jim Fenwick and Tom Moon for their helpful comments after reading an earlier version of the manuscript. Original work by SFP cited in this paper was funded by Natural Sciences and Engineering Research Council (NSERC) grants.

*Literature Cited*

1. Avella M, Bornancin M. 1989. A new analysis of ammonia and sodium transport through the gills of the freshwater rainbow trout (*Salmo gairdneri*). *J. Exp. Biol.* 142:155–75
2. Avella M, Bornancin M. 1990. Ion fluxes in the gills of freshwater and sea water salmonid fish. *Anim. Nutr. Transp. Process.* 26:1–13
3. Avella M, Masoni A, Bornancin M, Mayer-Gostan N. 1987. Gill morphology and sodium influx in the rainbow trout (*Salmo gairdneri*) acclimated to artificial freshwater environments. *J. Exp. Zool.* 241:159–69
4. Bailly Y, Dunel-Er S, Laurent P. 1992. The neuroepithelial cells of the fish gill filament—indolamine-immunocytochemistry and innervation. *Anat. Rec.* 233:143–61
5. Bevalander G. 1935. A comparative study of the branchial epithelium in fishes, with special reference to extrarenal excretion. *J. Morphol.* 57:335–51
6. Bindon SF, Fenwick JC, Perry SF. 1994. Branchial chloride cell proliferation in the rainbow trout, *Oncorhynchus mykiss:* implications for gas transfer. *Can. J. Zool.* 72:1395–402
7. Bindon SF, Gilmour KM, Fenwick JC, Perry SF. 1994. The effect of branchial chloride cell proliferation on gas transfer in the rainbow trout, *Oncorhynchus mykiss. J. Exp. Biol.* 197:47–63
8. Cameron JN, Iwama GK. 1987. Compen-

sation of progressive hypercapnia in channel catfish and blue crabs. *J. Exp. Biol.* 133:183–97
9. Copeland DE. 1948. The cytological basis of chloride transfer in the gill of *Fundulus heteroclitus. J. Morphol.* 82:201–27
10. De Renzis G, Bornancin M. 1984. Ion transport and gill ATPases. In *Fish Physiology,* ed. WS Hoar, DJ Randall, XB:65–104. New York: Academic
11. Doyle WH, Gorecki D. 1961. The so-called chloride cell of the fish gill. *Physiol. Zool.* 34:81–85
12. Dunel-Erb S, Bailly Y, Laurent P. 1982. Neuroepithelial cells in fish gill primary lamellae. *J. Appl. Physiol.* 53:1342–53
13. Fenwick JC. 1989. Calcium exchange across fish gills. In *Vertebrate Endocrinology: Fundamentals and Biomedical Implications,* ed. PKT Pang, MP Schreibman, 3:319–42. New York: Academic
14. Flik G, Perry SF. 1989. Cortisol stimulates whole body calcium uptake and the branchial calcium pump in freshwater rainbow trout. *J. Endocrinol.* 120:75–82
15. Flik G, Verbost PM. 1993. Calcium transport in fish gills and intestine. *J. Exp. Biol.* 184:17–29
16. Flik G, Verbost PM, Wendelaar Bonga SE. 1995. Calcium transport processes in fishes. In *Cellular and Molecular Approaches to Fish Ionic Regulation,* ed. CM

Wood, TJ Shuttleworth, pp. 317–36. New York: Academic

17. Flik G, Wendelaar Bonga SE, Fenwick JC. 1983. $Ca^{2+}$-dependent phosphatase and ATPase activities in eel gill plasma membranes-I. Identification of $Ca^{2+}$-activated ATPase activities with nonspecific phosphatase activities. *Comp. Biochem. Physiol. B* 76:745–54

18. Flik G, Wendelaar Bonga SE, Fenwick JC. 1985. Active $Ca^{2+}$ transport in plasma membranes of branchial epithelium of North-American eel, *Anguilla rostrata* LeSueur. *Biol. Cell* 55:265–72

19. Foskett JK, Bern HA, Machen TE, Conner M. 1983. Chloride cells and the hormonal control of teleost fish osmoregulation. *J. Exp. Biol.* 106:255–81

20. Foskett JK, Scheffey C. 1982. The chloride cell: definitive identification as the salt-secreting cell in teleosts. *Science* 215:164–66

21. Franklin GE. 1990. Surface ultrastructure changes in the gills of sockeye salmon (Teleostei: *Oncorhynchus nerka*) during seawater transfer: comparison of successful and unsuccessful seawater adaptation. *J. Morphol.* 206:13–23

22. Franklin GE, Davison W. 1989. S.E.M. observations of morphologically different chloride cells in freshwater-adapted sockeye salmon, *Oncorhynchus nerka. J. Fish Biol.* 34:803–4

23. Garcia-Romeu F, Masoni A. 1970. Sur la mise en evidence des cellules a chlorure de la branchie des poissons. *Arch. Anat. Microsc.* 59:289–94

24. Goss GG, Laurent P, Perry SF. 1992. Evidence for a morphological component in the regulation of acid-base balance in hypercapnic catfish (*Ictalurus nebulosus*). *Cell Tissue Res.* 268:539–52

25. Goss GG, Laurent P, Perry SF. 1994. Gill morphology during hypercapnia in brown bullhead (*I. nebulosus*): role of chloride cells and pavement cells in acid-base regulation. *J. Fish Biol.* 45:705–18

26. Goss GG, Perry SF. 1993. Physiological and morphological regulation of acid-base status during hypercapnia in rainbow trout (*Oncorhynchus mykiss*). *Can. J. Zool.* 71:1673–80

27. Goss GG, Perry SF. 1994. Different mechanisms of acid-base regulation in rainbow trout (*Oncorhynchus mykiss*) and American eel (*Anguilla rostrata*) during $NaHCO_3$ infusion. *Physiol. Zool.* 67:381–406

28. Goss GG, Perry SF, Laurent P. 1995. Gill morphology and acid-base regulation. In *Fish Physiology*, ed. CM Wood, TJ Shuttleworth, 14:257–84. New York: Academic

29. Goss GG, Perry SF, Wood CM, Laurent P. 1992. Mechanisms of ion and acid-base regulation at the gills of freshwater fish. *J. Exp. Zool.* 263:143–59

30. Goss GG, Wood CM, Laurent P, Perry SF. 1994. Morphological responses of the rainbow trout (*Oncorhynchus mykiss*) gill to hyperoxia, base ($NaHCO_3$) and acid (HCl) infusions. *Fish Physiol. Biochem.* 12:465–77

31. Greco AM, Fenwick JC, Perry SF. 1996. The effects of softwater acclimation on gill morphology in the rainbow trout, *Oncorhynchus mykiss. Cell Tissue Res.* 285:75–82

32. Greco AM, Gilmour KM, Fenwick JC, Perry SF. 1995. The effects of soft-water acclimation on respiratory gas transfer in the rainbow trout, *Oncorhynchus mykiss. J. Exp. Biol.* 198:2557–67

33. Hossler FE, Musil G, Karnaky KJJ, Epstein FH. 1985. Surface ultrastructure of the gill arch of the killifish, *Fundulus heteroclitus*, from seawater and freshwater, with special reference to the morphology of the apical crypts of chloride cells. *J. Morphol.* 185:377–86

34. Hossler FE, Ruby JR, McIlwain TD. 1979. The gill arch of the mullet, *Mugil cephalus* I. Surface ultrastructure. *J. Exp. Zool.* 208:379–98

35. Hwang PP. 1987. Tolerance and ultrastructural responses of branchial chloride cells to salinity changes in the euryhaline teleost *Oreochromis mossambicus. Marine Biol.* 94:643–49

36. Hyde DA, Perry SF. 1989. Differential approaches to blood acid-base regulation during exposure to prolonged hypercapnia in two freshwater teleosts: the rainbow trout (*Salmo gairdneri*) and the American eel (*Anguilla rostrata*). *Physiol. Zool.* 62:1164–86

37. Ishihara A, Mugiya Y. 1987. Ultrastructural evidence of calcium uptake by chloride cells in the gills of the goldfish, *Carassius auratus. J. Exp. Biol.* 242:121–29

38. Ishimatsu A, Iwama GK, Bentley TB, Heisler N. 1992. Contribution of the secondary circulatory system to acid base regulation during hypercapnia in rainbow trout (*Oncorhynchus mykiss*). *J. Exp. Biol.* 170:43–56

39. Karnaky KJJ. 1986. Structure and function of the chloride cell of *Fundulus heteroclitus* and other teleosts. *Am. Zool.* 26:209–24

40. Kessel RG, Beams HW. 1962. Electron microscope studies on the gill filaments of *Fundulus heteroclitus* from sea water and fresh water with special reference to the ultrastructural organization of the "chloride cell." *J. Ultrastruct. Res.* 6:77–87

41. Keys AB, Wilmer EN. 1932. Chloride secreting cells in the fills of fishes with special references to the common eel. *J. Physiol.* 76:368–77

42. King JAC, Hossler FE. 1991. The gill arch of the striped bass (*Morone saxatilis*). 4. Alterations in the ultrastructure of chloride cell apical crypts and chloride efflux following exposure to seawater. *J. Morphol.* 209:165–76

43. Krogh A. 1938. The active absorption of ions in some freshwater animals. *Z. Vergl. Physiol.* 25:335–50

44. Kültz D, Jürss K. 1993. Biochemical characterization of isolated branchial mitochondria-rich cells of *Oreochromis mossambicus* acclimated to fresh water or hyperhaline sea water. *J. Comp. Physiol. B* 163:406–12

45. Laurent P. 1984. Gill internal morphology. In *Fish Physiology*, ed. WS Hoar, DJ Randall, XA:73–183. New York: Academic

46. Laurent P. 1989. Gill structure and function: Fish. In *Comparative Pulmonary Physiology: Current Concepts*, ed. SC Wood. pp. 69–120. New York: Dekker

47. Laurent P, Dunel S. 1980. Morphology of gill epithelia in fish. *Am. J. Physiol.* 238:R147–59

48. Laurent P, Goss GG, Perry SF. 1994. Proton pumps in fish gill pavement cells? *Arch. Int. Physiol. Biochim. Biophys.*

49. Laurent P, Hebibi N. 1989. Gill morphometry and fish osmoregulation. *Can. J. Zool.* 67:3055–63

50. Laurent P, Perry SF. 1990. The effects of cortisol on gill chloride cell morphology and ionic uptake on the freshwater trout, *Salmo gairdneri. Cell Tissue Res.* 259:429–42

51. Laurent P, Perry SF. 1991. Environmental effects on fish gill morphology. *Physiol. Zool.* 64:4–25

52. Laurent P, Perry SF. 1995. Morphological basis of acid-base and ionic regulation in fish. In *Advances in Comparative and Environmental Physiology. Mechanisms of Systemic Regulation: Acid-Base Regulation, Ion Transfer and Metabolism*, ed. N Heisler, pp. 91–118. Heidelberg: Springer-Verlag

53. Lee T-H, Lin H-C, Yu M-J, Huang F-L, Hwang P-P. 1995. Mitochondria-rich cells in gills of the euryhaline teleost,

*Oreochromis mossambicus. Zool. Stud.* 34:239–40

54. Leino RL, McCormick JH, Jensen KM. 1987. Changes in gill histology of fathead minnows and yellow perch transferred to soft water or acidified soft water with particular reference to chloride cells. *Cell Tissue Res.* 250:389–99

55. Li J, Eygensteyn, J, Lock RAC, Verbost PM, van der Heijden AJH, et al. 1995. Branchial chloride cells in larvae and juveniles of freshwater tilapia *Oreochromis mossambicus. J. Exp. Biol.* 198:2177–84

56. Lin H, Pfeiffer DC, Vogl AW, Pan J, Randall DJ. 1994. Immunolocalization of $H^+$-ATPase in the gill epithelia of rainbow trout. *J. Exp. Biol.* 195:169–83

57. Lin H, Randall DJ. 1991. Evidence for the presence of an electrogenic proton pump on the trout gill epithelium. *J. Exp. Biol.* 161:119–34

58. Lin H, Randall DJ. 1993. $H^+$-ATPase activity in crude homogenates of fish gill tissue—inhibitor sensitivity and environmental and hormonal regulation. *J. Exp. Biol.* 180:163–74

58a. MacKenzie WM, Perry SF. 1996. Branchial and renal calcium fluxes in rainbow trout (*Oncorhynchus mykiss*) during metabolic alkalosis. *Comp. Biochem. Physiol. A.* In press

58b. MacKenzie WM, Perry SF. 1996. The effects of hypercapnia on branchial and renal calcium fluxes in the rainbow trout (*Oncorhynchus mykiss*). *J. Comp. Physiol. B.* In press

59. Madsen SS. 1990. Enhanced hypoosmoregulatory response to growth hormone after cortisol treatment in immature rainbow trout, *Salmo gairdneri. Fish Physiol. Biochem.* 8:271–79

60. Marshall WS. 1995. Transport processes in isolated teleost epithelia: opercular epithelium and urinary bladder. In *Cellular and Molecular Approaches to Fish Ionic Regulation*, ed. CM Wood, TJ Shuttleworth, pp. 1–23. New York: Academic Press

61. Marshall WS, Bryson SE, Wood CM. 1992. Calcium transport by isolated skin of rainbow trout. *J. Exp. Biol.* 166:297–316

62. Mayer-Gostan N, Bornancin M, De Renzis G, Naon R, Yee JA, et al. 1983. Extraintestinal calcium uptake in the killifish, *Fundulus heteroclitus. J. Exp. Zool.* 227:329–38

63. McCormick SD. 1990. Fluorescent labeling of $Na^+,K^+$-ATPase in intact cells by use of a fluorescent derivative of ouabain:

salinity and teleost chloride cells. *Cell Tissue Res.* 260:529–33

64. McCormick SD. 1994. Opercular membranes and skin. In *Analytical Techniques,* ed. PW Hochachka, TP Mommsen, pp. 231–38. Amsterdam: Elsevier

65. McCormick SD, Hasegawa S, Hirano T. 1992. Calcium uptake in the skin of a freshwater teleost. *Proc. Natl. Acad. Sci. USA* 89:3635–38

66. Morgan IJ, Potts WTW, Oates K. 1994. Intracellular ion concentrations in branchial epithelial cells of brown trout (*Salmo trutta* l) determined by x-ray microanalysis. *J. Exp. Biol.* 194:139–51

67. Olson KR, Fromm PO. 1973. A scanning electron microscope study of secondary lamellae and chloride cells of rainbow trout (*Salmo gairdneri*). *Z. Zellforsch.* 143:439–49

68. Part P, Norrgren L, Bergstrom E, Sjoberg P. 1993. Primary cultures of epithelial cells from rainbow trout gills. *J. Exp. Biol.* 17:219–32

69. Payan P, Mayer-Gostan N, Pang PKT. 1981. Site of calcium uptake in the freshwater trout gill. *J. Exp. Zool.* 216:345–47

70. Perry SF. 1997. Relationships between ionic regulation and gas transfer in freshwater fish. *Comp. Biochem. Physiol. A.* In press

71. Perry SF, Flik G. 1988. Characterization of branchial transepithelial calcium fluxes in freshwater trout *Salmo gairdneri.* *Am. J. Physiol.* 254:491–98

72. Perry SF, Goss GG. 1994. The effects of experimentally altered gill chloride cell surface area on acid-base regulation in rainbow trout during metabolic alkalosis. *J. Comp. Physiol. A* 164:327–36

73. Perry SF, Goss GG, Fenwick JC. 1992. The interrelationships between gill chloride cell morphology and calcium uptake in freshwater teleosts. *Fish Physiol. Biochem.* 10:327–37

74. Perry SF, Goss GG, Laurent P. 1992. The interrelationships between gill chloride cell morphology and ionic uptake in four freshwater teleosts. *Can. J. Zool.* 70:1737–42

75. Perry SF, Haswell MS, Randall DJ, Farrell AP. 1981. Branchial ionic uptake and acid-base regulation in the rainbow trout, *Salmo gairdneri. J. Exp. Biol.* 92:289–303

76. Perry SF, Laurent P. 1989. Adaptational responses of rainbow trout to lowered external NaCl concentration: contribution of the branchial chloride cell. *J. Exp. Biol.* 147:147–68

77. Perry SF, Laurent P. 1993. Environmental effects on fish gill structure and function.

In *Fish Ecophysiology*, ed. JC Rankin, FB Jensen, pp. 231–64. London: Chapman & Hall

78. Perry SF, Randall DJ. 1981. Effects of amiloride and SITS on branchial ion fluxes in rainbow trout, *Salmo gairdneri. J. Exp. Zool.* 215:225–28

79. Perry SF, Reid SG, Wankiewicz E, Iyer V, Gilmour KM. 1996. Physiological responses of rainbow trout (*Oncorhynchus mykiss*) to prolonged exposure to softwater. *Physiol. Zool.* In press

80. Perry SF, Walsh PJ. 1989. Metabolism of isolated fish gill cells: contribution of epithelial chloride cells. *J. Exp. Biol.* 144:507–20

81. Perry SF, Wood CM. 1985. Kinetics of branchial calcium uptake in the rainbow trout: effects of acclimation to various external calcium levels. *J. Exp. Biol.* 116:411–33

82. Pisam M, Auperin B, Prunet P, Rentierdelrue F, Martial J, Rambourg A. 1993. Effects of prolactin on alpha-chloride and beta-chloride cells in the gill epithelium of the saltwater adapted tilapia *Oreochromis niloticus. Anat. Rec.* 235:275–84

83. Pisam M, Caroff A, Rambourg A. 1987. Two types of chloride cells in the gill epithelium of a freshwater adapted euryhaline fish: *Lebistes reticulatus;* their modification during adaptation to seawater. *Am. J. Anat.* 179:40–50

84. Pisam M, Moal Le C, Auperin B, Prunet P, Rambourg A. 1995. Apical structures of "mitochondria-rich" $\alpha$ and $\beta$ cells in euryhaline fish gill: their behaviour in various living conditions. *Anat. Rec.* 241:13–24

85. Pisam M, Rambourg A. 1991. Mitochondria-rich cells in the gill epithelium of teleost fishes: an ultrastructural approach. *Int. Rev. Cytol.* 130:191–232

86. Potts WTW. 1994. Kinetics of sodium uptake in freshwater animals—a comparison of ion-exchange and proton pump hypotheses. *Am. J. Physiol.* 266:R315–20

87. Rahim SM, Delaunoy JP, Laurent P. 1988. Identification and immunocytochemical localization of two different carbonic anhydrase isozymes in teleostean fish erythrocytes and gill epithelia. *Histochemistry* 89:451–59

88. Shuttleworth TJ. 1989. Overview of epithelial ion-transport mechanisms. *Can. J. Zool.* 67:3032–38

89. Silva P, Stoff J, Field M, Fine L, Forrest JN, Epstein FH. 1977. Mechanism of active chloride secretion by shark rectal gland: role of Na-K-ATPase in chlo-

ride transport. *Am. J. Physiol.* 233:F298–306

90. Stetson DL, Steinmetz PR. 1985. $\alpha$ and $\beta$ types of carbonic anhydrase-rich cells in the turtles bladder. *Am. J. Physiol.* 249:F553–65

91. Sullivan GV, Fryer JN, Perry SF. 1995. Immunolocalization of proton pumps ($H^+$-ATPase) in pavement cells of rainbow trout gill. *J. Exp. Biol.* 198:2619–29

92. Sullivan GV, Fryer JN, Perry SF. 1996. Localization of mRNA for proton pump ($H^+$-ATPase) and $Cl^-/HCO_3^-$ exchanger in rainbow trout gill. *Can. J. Zool.* In press

93. Thomas S, Fievet B, Motais R. 1988. Adaptive respiratory responses of trout to acute hypoxia. I. Effects of water ionic composition on blood acid-base response and gill morphology. *Respir. Physiol.* 74:77–90

94. Threadgold LT, Houston AH. 1964. An electron microscope study of the "chloride cell" of *Salmo salar* L. *Exp. Cell Res.* 34:1–23

95. Verbost PM, Schoenmakers TJM, Flik G, Wendelaar Bonga SE. 1994. Kinetics of ATP- and $Na^+$-gradient driven $Ca^{2+}$ transport in basolateral membranes from gills of freshwater- and seawater-adapted tilapia. *J. Exp. Biol.* 186:95–108

96. Wendelaar Bonga SE, Flik G, Balm, PHM, van der Meij JCA. 1990. The ultrastructure of chloride cells in the gills of the teleost *Oreochromis mossambicus* during exposure to acidified water. *Cell Tissue Res.* 259:575–85

97. Wendelaar Bonga SE, van der Meij CJM. 1989. Degeneration and death, by apoptosis and necrosis, of the pavement and chloride cells in the gills of the teleost *Oreochromis mossambicus*. *Cell Tissue Res.* 255:235–43

98. Wood CM, Marshall WS. 1994. Ion balance, acid-base regulation, and chloride cell function in the common killifish, *Fundulus heteroclitus*—a euryhaline estuarine teleost. *Estuaries* 17:34–52

99. Zadunaisky JA. 1984. The chloride cell: the active transport of chloride and the paracellular pathways. In *Fish Physiology,* ed. WS Hoar, DJ Randall, XB:129–76. New York: Academic

*Annu. Rev. Physiol. 1997. 59:349–63*

# REGULATION OF OVARIAN FOLLICLE ATRESIA

## Antti Kaipia and Aaron J. W. Hsueh

Division of Reproductive Biology, Department of Gynecology and Obstetrics,
Stanford University School of Medicine, Stanford, California 94305-5317

KEY WORDS:   ovary, apoptosis, follicle, granulosa cell, gonadotropins

### ABSTRACT

The majority of ovarian follicles undergo atresia, a hormonally controlled apoptotic process. Monitoring apoptotic DNA fragmentation provides a quantitative and sensitive endpoint to study the hormonal regulation of atresia in ovarian follicles. During follicle development, gonadotropins, together with local ovarian growth factors (IGF-I, EGF/TGF-$\alpha$, basic FGF) and cytokine (interleukin-1$\beta$), as well as estrogens, activate different intracellular pathways to rescue follicles from apoptotic demise. In contrast, TNF-$\alpha$, Fas ligand, presumably acting through receptors with a death domain, and androgens are atretogenic factors. These diverse hormonal signals probably converge on selective intracellular pathways (including genes of the bcl-2 and ICE families) to regulate apoptosis. With a constant loss of follicles from the original stockpile, the ovary provides a unique model for studying the hormonal regulation of apoptosis.

## INTRODUCTION

### Apoptotic Cell Demise is a Physiological Process in Diverse Tissues

Apoptosis, a regulated form of cell death, is a physiological process essential for normal embryonic development and adult tissue homeostasis. In a developing embryo, widespread apoptosis actively sculptures the body shape during organogenesis (22). In adult tissues, apoptosis is also common, and its occurrence varies depending on the rate of tissue turnover. In the nervous system, heart, liver, and kidney, where the rate of cell proliferation is slow, little apoptosis is observed under physiological conditions (7). In tissues characterized

349

by constant stem cell proliferation, such as the hematopoietic system, intestinal epithelium, and testis, the rate of apoptosis is high (11, 82). In the ovary, a high rate of follicular cell apoptosis occurs during the reproductive life but without constant stem cell renewal ultimately leads to reproductive senescence (40).

It has been postulated that all differentiated cells in multicellular organisms are capable of undergoing apoptosis through a suicide program that is highly conserved during evolution (63, 64, 75). To stay alive, cells are probably dependent on survival signals acting on cellular receptors. If the survival signals are absent or insufficient, the apoptotic suicide program ensues by utilizing a set of death genes (75). Although the signals essential for cell survival are diverse and cell specific, the apoptotic death program in different tissues appears to be similar.

## Apoptotic Cell Death Exhibits Unique Morphological and Biochemical Features

Apoptosis of diverse cell types is distinguished by characteristic morphological changes both in the nucleus and the cytoplasm. A typical nuclear change is chromatin condensation, resulting in the formation of dense zones of heterochromatin underlying the nuclear membrane (82). As apoptosis continues, the nuclear membrane disrupts, and the nucleus disintegrates into spherical dense fragments, termed pyknotic nuclei. Independent of the chromatin condensation, calcium/magnesium-dependent endonuclease is activated, resulting in the cleavage of DNA between nucleosomal units (83). With electrophoretic fractionation, DNA from apoptotic nuclei shows a ladder pattern of oligonucleosomal DNA fragments with size multiples of 185–200 basepairs. The DNA ladder pattern has been regarded as the hallmark of apoptosis and provides a sensitive and specific biochemical marker for apoptotic cell death.

The cytoplasm of apoptotic cells is characterized by aggregation and disorientation of cytoplasmic organelles. Concomitantly, the plasma membrane shows shrinkage and blebbing, and the cell eventually breaks down into several membrane-bound apoptotic bodies that are recognized by neighboring phagocytotic cells.

## Apoptosis-Regulating Genes

Much of the present knowledge on the molecular mechanism of apoptosis is derived from genetic studies of *Caenorhabditis elegans*. During the development of this nematode, 131 of the 1090 somatic cells are destined to undergo apoptosis, and their death is under strict genetic control (27). Mutation analyses have identified at least ten genes that regulate apoptosis in *C. elegans* (25). Two of these genes, *ced-3* and *ced-4*, are necessary for apoptosis, and inactivating mutations of either can result in the accumulation of cells that normally should die (27). The *ced-3* gene encodes for a cysteine protease with functional and sequence similarity to mammalian cysteine proteases related to interleukin-1β-converting enzyme (ICE) (87). The *C. elegans* gene *ced-4* encodes for a calcium-binding protein that, unlike *ced-3*, shows no homology to any known mammalian gene (86). The *C. elegans ced-9* gene opposes the action of *ced-3* and *ced-4*, and inactivating mutations of *ced-9* result in massive cell death and lethality during development (34). Also, *ced-9* shares sequence and functional homology with members of mammalian bcl-2 proto-oncogene gene family (35). The evolutionary conservation of cell death effectors is evident, because both ICE and *ced-3* can cause apoptosis when overexpressed in mammalian cells (52), and overexpression of *bcl-2* inhibits apoptosis in nematode, insect, or mammalian cells (3, 35, 79).

ICE and bcl-2 are members of large gene families. The family of mammalian ICE-related proteases consists of at least six members, the expression of which is widespread, but tissue specific. The ICE-related proteases are key effectors of the suicide program and presumably mediate cell death by proteolytic cleavage of substrate proteins that are essential for cell viability, such as poly(ADP-ribose)polymerase (PARP) (31, 48). The bcl-2 family consists of at least seven positive and negative regulators of cell death that form dimers with each other (68, 85). The degree of homo- and heterodimerization of anti-/pro-apoptotic bcl-2-related proteins can act as a sensor to determine cell fate.

Several mammalian genes involved in the signaling of apoptosis contain a conserved death domain motif, which was initially identified within the intracellular region of tumor necrosis factor-α receptor type I (TNF-RI) and the Fas antigen as important in mediating apoptosis (53, 73). Since then, several intracellular proteins have been identified based on their interaction with the TNF-RI/Fas death domain (12, 18, 39, 71). Overexpression of TRADD (TNF-RI associating death domain protein) or FADD (Fas-associated death domain protein) in mammalian cells induces apoptosis, which suggests that they can mediate apoptotic signaling originating from plasma membrane receptors.

## APOPTOTIC CELL DEATH IN THE OVARY

### Both Somatic and Germ Cells in the Ovary Undergo Apoptotic Demise

Two major stages of cell degeneration can be distinguished in the ovary: degeneration of germ cells (attrition), which accounts for the largest loss of oocytes (6) and occurs mainly prenatally, and follicle degeneration (atresia), which occurs during postnatal reproductive life (Figure 1). In the human ovary, two million oocytes are found at birth, and at the onset of puberty approximately 400,000 follicles are present. However, only 400 follicles are ovulated during the female

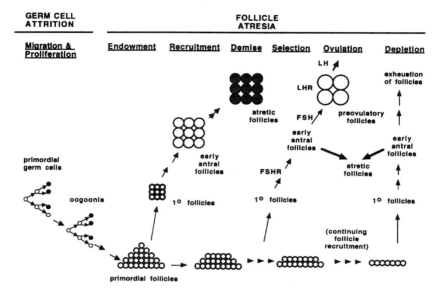

*Figure 1*  Germ cell attrition and follicle atresia. During fetal life, primordial germ cells migrate from the epithelium of the yolk sac to the genital ridge. During migration, primordial germ cells proliferate, and their survival is dependent on survival factors. In the fetal ovary, the oogonia continue to proliferate. The early stages of proliferation are characterized by massive germ cell apoptosis or atrition (dark cells). Close to birth in rodents, mitoses cease as the cells enter meiosis. During early postnatal life, most oocytes are surrounded by somatic follicular cells, and a fixed number of primordial follicles is endowed in the ovaries. Small fractions of the original stockpile of primordial follicles are recruited throughout the reproductive life, whereas most of the primordial follicles remain arrested at the initial stage of development. Once cohorts of follicles are recruited to grow, they are destined to undergo apoptosis at the early antral stage unless rescued by survival factors. The selected follicles mature and ovulate in response to the preovulatory gonadotropin surge. Following repeated cycles of recruitment, atresia, or ovulation, the follicle reserve is exhausted, thus signaling the onset of reproductive senescence. 1° follicles, primary follicles; FSHR, FSH receptor; LHR, LH receptor.

reproductive life (5). Therefore, of the potential pool of oocytes, only a small fraction will ever ovulate and the majority will undergo apoptotic demise. With a constant loss of cells from the original stockpile, the ovary provides a unique model for studying the regulation of apoptosis.

GERM CELL ATTRITION    In contrast to follicle atresia during neonatal and reproductive life, the germ cell is the main cell type undergoing apoptosis during fetal development. In humans, approximately three weeks after conception, the primordial germ cells are found in the epithelium of the yolk sac from which they migrate to the genital ridge. During migration, their survival and ongoing proliferation is dependent on survival factors. Primordial germ cell proliferation is stimulated in vitro by stem cell growth factor and basic fibroblast growth factor (bFGF), and withdrawal of these factors results in apoptotic demise of the germ cells (24, 61, 66).

Upon their arrival in the fetal ovary, the primordial germ cells, now termed oogonia, continue mitotic proliferation and some begin to undergo apoptosis (Figure 1) (6, 65). Close to birth in rodents, oogonia enter meiosis, and the meiotic process is arrested at the diplotene stage of prophase. During the first days of postnatal life, most oocytes are surrounded by somatic follicular cells to become primordial follicles, while those remaining naked, degenerate (57). Thus before the ovarian follicles are formed, massive apoptotic germ cell degeneration takes place and regulates the number of follicles endowed within the ovary. In transgenic mice with deletion of the apoptosis-suppressing gene *bcl-2*, the number of primordial follicles is reduced, and some follicle-like structures are devoid of germ cells, suggesting excessive germ cell loss in these animals (65).

FOLLICLE ATRESIA    Ovarian follicular degeneration or atresia is a hormonally controlled apoptotic prosess, whereby degenerating follicles are eliminated in a coordinated fashion (40). Using internucleosomal DNA fragmentation as a marker, follicle atresia in diverse species ranging from avian to human has been shown to result from apoptotic cell death (42, 45, 62, 77, 78). Most follicles remain in the resting pool of nongrowing primordial follicles, whereas a small fraction is recruited into the growing pool. The flattened granulosa cells around primordial follicles become cuboidal, and the oocyte grows as the follicle matures to become a primary follicle (58, 59). The granulosa cells lining the growing follicles acquire receptors for follicle-stimulating hormone (FSH) and proliferate to form two or three layers in secondary follicles (58, 59). Although follicle growth continues in the absence of circulating FSH during the preantral stage, FSH is necessary for the development of follicle antrum (54, 16). Atresia occurs at all stages of follicle development; the penultimate stage of follicle growth is the major branching point for cohorts of developing follicles (36) (Figure 1). Sufficient exposure of antral follicles to FSH is the most critical stimulus for the follicles to escape atresia and reach the preovulatory (Graafian) follicle stage (21, 30, 37, 70). The stage-dependent hormonal regulation of follicle cell apoptosis is discussed below.

## Regulation of Follicle Cell Apoptosis

FOLLICLE SURVIVAL FACTORS    In addition to triggering the ovulatory process, gonadotropins are required for the growth and development of ovarian follicles.

If preovulatory gonadotropin surges are blocked, or serum gonadotropins are decreased following hypophysectomy, follicles undergo atresia (14, 15, 74). Importantly, follicles can be rescued at early phases of atresia by exogenous gonadotropins (15, 33). Follicle atresia occurs via apoptosis (77), and the $Ca^{2+}/Mg^{2+}$-dependent endonuclease activity believed to be responsible for apoptotic DNA fragmentation can be detected in ovarian granulosa and luteal cells (13, 89).

To study the hormonal regulation of follicle atresia further, an in vitro culture model of isolated preovulatory follicles has been utilized. The culture of whole ovarian follicles provides a physiological model for the study of atresia because paracrine interactions between follicle cell types are not disrupted. In cultured preovulatory follicles, the spontaneous onset of apoptosis is suppressed by FSH and luteinizing hormone (LH)/human chorionic gonadotropin (19). Binding of gonadotropins to their membrane receptors in granulosa cells results in the activation of adenylate cyclase, accumulation of cAMP and, subsequently, activation of the protein kinase A signaling pathway (49) (Figure 2). The action of gonadotropins on follicle apoptosis can be mimicked by a cell-permeable cAMP analogue, which verifies that the signaling is via the protein kinase A pathway (28). Another pituitary hormone, growth hormone (GH), also affects follicular growth and differentiation and often augments the action of gonadotropins (44, 43). When tested in the follicle culture system, GH also suppresses the spontaneous onset of apoptosis (26).

In addition to pituitary endocrine hormones, locally produced growth factors such as insulin-like growth factor-I (IGF-I) may regulate folliculogenesis. Granulosa cells express receptors for IGF-I, and IGF-I synergizes with gonadotropins to promote granulosa cell differentiation (1, 23). Furthermore, similar to the action of gonadotropins, IGF-I suppresses follicle apoptosis (19). The action of IGF-I is locally modulated by IGF-binding proteins (IGFBPs), and IGFBP-3 in vitro effectively blocks the protective action of IGF-I on follicle apoptosis. IGFBP-3 also partially reverses the protective action of gonadotropins, indicating that the anti-atretogenic action of gonadotropins is partially mediated through locally produced IGF-I via the IGF-I receptor/tyrosine kinase signaling mechanism (19) (Figure 2). In addition, epidermal growth factor (EGF) and bFGF, both produced by follicular cells (47, 55, 80), inhibit spontaneous DNA fragmentation in preovulatory follicles (76), and their action can also be blocked by genistein, a tyrosine kinase inhibitor.

Interleukin-1$\beta$ (IL-1$\beta$), a cytokine initially identified as a regulator of the immune system, also affects ovarian functions (2). In many cell types, treatment with IL-1$\beta$ increases the synthesis of nitric oxide (NO), which, in turn, activates soluble guanyl cyclase (69). In the preovulatory follicle culture, treatment with IL-1$\beta$ increases NO production and inhibits apoptosis (20). Treatment with

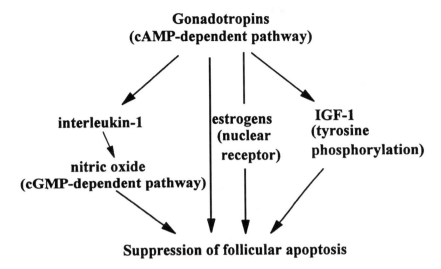

*Figure 2*    Multifactorial regulation of apoptosis in ovarian follicles. Gonadotropins are the major survival factors that suppress granulosa cell apoptosis through the activation of the cAMP-dependent pathway. The apoptosis-suppressing action of gonadotropins is augmented by local factors including interleukin-1β/nitric oxide, estrogens, and insulin-like growth factor-1, which in turn prevent apoptosis by activating the cGMP-dependent pathway, nuclear estrogen receptor, and tyrosine phosphorylation, respectively.

IL-1β receptor antagonist blocks both effects of IL-1β. Sodium nitroprusside, a NO donor, and an analogue of cGMP, the second messenger for NO, are also effective in inhibiting follicle apoptosis. Interestingly, the effect of gonadotropin is partially blocked by IL-1 receptor antagonist, indicating partial mediation of gonadotropin action via endogenous IL-1β and the NO-cGMP pathway in preovulatory follicles (20) (Figure 2).

Estrogens are indispensable for the growth and maturation of follicles. Treatment with estrogen increases the division of granulosa cells and increases ovarian weight (81). Atretic follicles exhibit decreased estrogen production and a lower estrogen/androgen ratio in the follicular fluid, suggesting the importance of local estrogens for the maintenence of healthy follicles (17). When immature, hypophysectomized rats are treated with an estrogen for two days, followed by estrogen removal, the ovary undergoes massive apoptosis (10). The apoptotic DNA fragmentation is confined to granulosa cells, indicating that it is the major cell type undergoing apoptosis. Progesterone, another ovarian steroid, may also inhibit follicle atresia, as it has been shown to decrease apoptosis in cultured granulosa cells (60).

ATRETOGENIC FACTORS    Several intraovarian factors induce atresia. Tumor necrosis factor-$\alpha$ (TNF-$\alpha$), a cytokine expressed in the oocyte and granulosa cells, signals through type I TNF-$\alpha$ receptor (TNF-RI), which contains a death domain (73). Treatment with TNF-$\alpha$ activates sphingomyelinase enzymes in target cells, resulting in the formation of ceramide, a lipid second messenger. Radiation and various forms of cell stress can also induce ceramide synthesis, and treatment with ceramide analogues induces apoptosis (56). In granulosa cells, TNF-$\alpha$ signaling is coupled to ceramide synthesis (67). When early antral follicles are cultured in the presence of FSH, a dose-dependent increase in apoptosis can be seen with increasing concentrations of TNF-$\alpha$ (46a). Furthermore, the TNF-$\alpha$ action on follicle cell apoptosis is mimicked by its second messenger, ceramide. Another death domain-containing receptor, Fas, has been identified in granulosa cells during early stages of atresia (32), and Fas ligand has been detected in the oocyte of atretic follicles. In cultured human granulosa/luteal cells, treatment with monoclonal anti-human Fas antibody induces apoptosis (62). Therefore, the activation of the Fas ligand-Fas system may also play a role in the initiation of follicle apoptosis.

IL-6, another cytokine produced by granulosa cells (29), also induces DNA fragmentation in cultured granulosa cells, suggesting its role as a potential atretogenic factor. In addition, the regulatory peptide gonadotropin releasing hormone (GnRH) inhibits follicle differentiation directly through specific receptors in granulosa and theca cells (41, 46). In vivo treatment of hypophysectomized, estrogen-treated rats with a GnRH agonist induces apoptotic DNA fragmentation (9).

In contrast to the role of estrogens as follicle survival factors, androgens promote ovarian follicle atresia (51, 88). Atretic follicles are characterized by reduced aromatase activity, leading to decreases of estrogen production and accumulation of androgen. Treatment of hypophysectomized, estrogen-treated rats with testosterone increases granulosa cell apoptosis (10), and endogenous androgens are likely atretogenic agents because androgen receptor blockers and testosterone antibodies can inhibit follicle atresia (50, 88).

Bcl-2 OVEREXPRESSION IN FOLLICULAR CELLS DECREASES ATRESIA AND PRO-MOTES GERM CELL TUMORIGENESIS    The apoptosis-suppressing protein bcl-2 has been overexpressed in ovarian cells under the control of the inhibin-$\alpha$ promoter/enhancer (38). Using an in vivo gonadotropin treatment protocol (42), these animals showed decreased apoptosis of ovarian follicles compared with wild-type animals. Following gonadotropin treatment, ovulation is enhanced, indicating that bcl-2 overexpression can rescue follicles that otherwise would become atretic (38). Bcl-2 overexpression in somatic follicular cells also increases the frequency of germ cell tumors (teratomas) in aging animals, suggesting that prolonged survival of somatic cells may stimulate tumorigenesis of germ cells (38). Alternatively, follicle atresia may also serve a protective function in normal animals by deleting follicles containing a defective oocyte with tumorigenic potential.

STAGE-SPECIFIC REGULATION OF FOLLICLE APOPTOSIS    Follicle selection, maturation, and ovulation are critically dependent on gonadotropins that work in concert with intraovarian paracrine factors to suppress the cell death program of granulosa cells. Although follicle cell apoptosis occurs at all stages of follicle development, the antral transition is the "bottle neck" for developing follicles (36). The pathways mediating survival signals during follicle development are redundant, and the potencies of different survival factors to suppress apoptosis are dependent on the developmental stage of the follicle (Figure 3).

Preantral follicles, although responsive to gonadotropins, can grow until the antral stage without gonadotropin support (36). Cultured preantral follicles, however, undergo spontaneous apoptosis, indicating their dependence on survival signals. In contrast to follicles at later developmental stages, gonadotropins or cAMP analogues are ineffective in rescuing preantral follicles from atresia. However, treatment with cGMP analogues inhibits spontaneous DNA fragmentation in these follicles, but the nature of the local or systemic hormones activating the cGMP pathway is unclear (Figure 3).

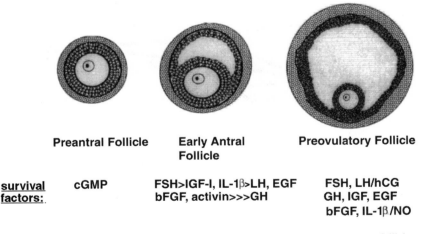

**Preantral Follicle**     **Early Antral**          **Preovulatory Follicle**
                           **Follicle**

survival      cGMP      FSH>IGF-I, IL-1β>LH, EGF      FSH, LH/hCG
factors:                bFGF, activin>>>GH            GH, IGF, EGF
                                                      bFGF, IL-1β/NO

*Figure 3*    Stage-dependent regulation of follicle demise. Preantral follicles, in contrast to follicles at later developmental stages, are not protected by gonadatropins, whereas an analogue of cGMP effectively inhibits apoptosis in these follicles. FSH is the major survival factor for early antral follicles. IGF-I, and IL-1β have a less pronounced rescuing effect, as do LH, EGF, bFGF, and activin. In preovulatory follicles, redundant mechanisms have evolved to prevent apoptosis mediated by cAMP (FSH, LH/hCG), tyrosine phosphorylation (IGF, EGF, bFGF), and cGMP (IL-1β/NO).

In early antral follicles, FSH is the major survival factor, and its action is mimicked by cAMP analogues. The apoptosis-suppressing effects of IGF-1, IL-1$\beta$, NO, and cGMP analogues are less pronounced than those of FSH. Likewise, LH, EGF, bFGF, and activin have a weak apoptosis-suppressing effect. At this developmental stage, the follicles are most vulnerable to undergo atresia, and sufficient exposure to FSH appears to be the most critical survival signal for their further development.

The preovulatory follicles have acquired redundant mechanisms to ensure their survival: Gonadotropins that stimulate cAMP production; IGF-1, EGF, and bFGF that act through tyrosine phosphorylation of specific receptors; IL-1$\beta$ and NO that activate cGMP synthesis, and estrogens. These hormones work in concert to prevent apoptosis of preovulatory follicles and allow subsequent ovulation (Figure 3).

## APOPTOSIS IS REGULATED BY DIVERSE HORMONAL MECHANISMS

Apoptosis in different tissues is controlled by various hormonal signaling mechanisms to maintain tissue homeostasis (Figure 4). A factor can promote cell

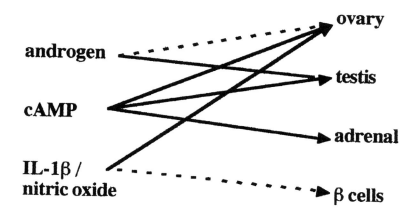

*Figure 4*  The extracellular signals capable of suppressing apoptosis are different in different cell types. Androgens are survival factors for testicular germ cells, whereas in the ovary, they promote apoptosis of granulosa cells. IL-1$\beta$/nitric oxide are survival factors for ovarian follicles but promote apoptosis in pancreatic $\beta$ cells. Activation of a cAMP-dependent pathway promotes survival of granulosa cells in the ovary, germ cells in the testis, and cortical cells in the adrenal. However, the extracellular signal activating the pathway varies: gonadotropins in the testis and ovary, and corticotropin (ACTH) in the adrenal. *Solid arrow,* suppression of apoptosis; *broken arrow,* promotion of apoptosis.

survival in one tissue and induce apoptosis in another: Androgens suppress apoptosis of testicular germ cells (11, 72) but promote apoptosis of ovarian granulosa cells (10). Likewise, IL-1$\beta$/NO are ovarian follicle survival factors (20) but promote apoptosis in pancreatic $\beta$ cells (4, 8). Different hormonal signals may suppress apoptosis in different cell types by activating the same intracellular pathways. Activation of cAMP-dependent pathway promotes survival of granulosa cells in the ovary (40), germ cells in the testis (11, 72), and cortical cells in the adrenal (84). However, the extracellular signal activating the pathway varies: gonadotropins in the testis and ovary and corticotropin (ACTH) in the adrenal.

## CONCLUDING REMARKS

Apoptosis is an important mechanism for the regulation of cell death. Atresia, the fate of most ovarian follicles, is a hormonally regulated apoptotic process. Acting through different second messenger systems, gonadotropins, together with local ovarian factors IGF-I and IL-1$\beta$/NO, as well as estrogens, serve as survival factors to rescue follicles from atresia. TNF-$\alpha$ and Fas ligand, presumably acting through receptors that posess a death domain, and androgens are atretogenic factors. It is believed that diverse second messenger systems may converge on selective intracellular pathways (including proteins belonging to the bcl-2 and ICE families) to regulate apoptosis. Elucidation of the molecular mechanisms and hormonal regulation of the suicide program in ovarian follicular cells should help in the design of new therapeutic modalities for the treatment of ovarian disorders characterized by excessive cell degeneration and infertility, such as premature ovarian failure and polycystic ovary syndrome. Study of the cellular mechanisms of apoptosis may also provide understanding of the pathogenesis of a variety of disease states such as cancer, viral infection, and neurodegenerative and autoimmune disorders (75).

ACKNOWLEDGMENTS

This study was supported by National Institutes of Health grant HD 31566.

*Literature Cited*

1. Adashi EY, Resnick CE, D'Ercole AJ, Svoboda ME, Van Wyk JJ. 1985. Insulin-like growth factors as intraovarian regulators of granulosa cell growth and function. *Endocr. Rev.* 6:400–20
2. Adashi EY, Resnick CE, Hernandez ER, Hurwitz A, Rosenfeld RG. 1990. Follicle-stimulating hormone inhibits the con-stitutive release of insulin-like growth factor binding proteins by cultured rat ovarian granulosa cells. *Endocrinology* 126:1305–7
3. Alnemri, ES, Robertson NM, Fernandes TF, Croce CM, Litwack G. 1992. Overexpressed full-length human bcl-2 extends the survival of baculovirus-infected Sf9

insect cells. *Proc. Natl. Acad. Sci. USA* 89:7295–99
4. Ankarcrona M, Dypbukt JM, Brune B, Nicotera P. 1994. Interleukin-1$\beta$-induced nitric oxide production activates apoptosis in pancreatic RINm5F cells. *Exp. Cell. Res.* 213:172–77
5. Baker TG. 1963. A quantitative and cytological study of germ cells in the human ovaries. *Proc. R. Soc. London, Ser. B* 158:417–33
6. Beaumont HM, Mandl AM. 1962. A quantitative and cytological study of oogonia and oocytes in the foetal and neonatal rat. *Proc. R. Soc. London Ser. B* 155:557–79
7. Benedetti, A, Jezequel AM, Orlandi F. 1988. A quantitative evaluation of apoptotic bodies in rat liver. *Liver* 8:172–77
8. Bergmann L, Kronke K-D, Suschek C, Kolb H, Kolb-Bachofern V. 1992. Cytotoxic action of IL-1$\beta$ against pancreatic islets is mediated via nitric oxide formation and is inhibited by $N^G$-monomethyl-L-arginine. *FEBS Lett.* 299:102–6
9. Billig H, Furuta I, Hsueh AJW. 1994. Gonadotropin releasing hormone (GnRH) directly induces apoptotic cell death in the rat ovary: biochemical and in situ detection of DNA fragmentation in granulosa cells. *Endocrinology* 134:245–52
10. Billig H, Furuta I, Hsueh AJW. 1993. Estrogens inhibit and androgens enhance ovarian granulosa cell apoptosis. *Endocrinology* 133:2204–12
11. Billig H, Furuta I, Rivier C, Tapanainen J, Parvinen M, et al. 1995. Apoptosis in testis germ cells: developmental changes in gonadotropin dependence and localization to selective tubule stages. *Endocrinology* 136:5–12
12. Boldin MP, Varfolomeev EE, Pancer Z, Met IL, Camonis JH, et al. 1995. A novel protein that interacts with the death domain of Fas/APO1 contains a sequence motif related to the death domain. *J. Biol. Chem.* 270:7795–98
13. Boone DL, Yan W, Tsang BK. 1995. Identification of a deoxyribonuclease I-like endonuclease in rat granulosa and luteal cell nuclei. *Biol. Reprod.* 53:1057–65
14. Braw RH, BarAmi S, Tsafriri A. 1981. Effect of hypophysectomy on atresia of rat preovulatory follicles. *Biol. Reprod.* 25:989–96
15. Braw RH, Tsafriri A. 1980. Effects of PMSG on follicular atresia in the rat ovary. *J. Reprod. Fertil.* 59:267–72
16. Cain L, Chatterjee S, Colling TJ. 1995. In vitro folliculogenesis of rat preantral follicles. *Endocrinology* 136:3369–77
17. Carson RS, Findlay JK, Clarke IJ, Burger HG. 1981. Estradiol, testosterone, and androstenedione in ovine follicular fluid during growth and atresia of ovarian follicles. *Biol. Reprod.* 24:105–13
18. Chinnaiyan AM, O'Rourke K, Tewari M, Dixit VM. 1995. FADD, a novel death domain-containing protein, interacts with the death domain of Fas and initiates apoptosis. *Cell* 81:505–12
19. Chun SY, Billig H, Tilly JL, Furuta I, Tsafriri A, et al. 1994. Gonadotropin suppression of apoptosis in cultured preovulatory follicles: mediatory role of endogenous IGF-I. *Endocrinology* 135:1845–53
20. Chun SY, Eisenhauer KM, Kubo M, Hsueh AJW. 1995. Interleukin-1$\beta$ suppresses apoptosis in rat ovarian follicles by increasing nitric oxide production. *Endocrinology* 136:3120–27
21. Chun SY, Eisenhauer K, Minami S, Billig H, Perlas E, Hsueh AJW. 1996. Hormonal regulation of apoptosis in early antral follicles: follicle-stimulating hormone as a major survival factor. *Endocrinology* 137:1447–56
22. Clarke PGH. 1990. Developmental cell death: morphological diversity and multiple mechanisms. *Anat. Embryol.* 181:195–213
23. Davoren JB, Kasson BG, Li CH, Hsueh AJW. 1986. Specific insulin-like growth factor I and II binding sites on rat granulosa cells: relation to IGF action. *Endocrinology* 119:2155–62
24. Dolci S, Pesce MD, De Felici M. 1993. Combined action of stem cell factor, leukemia inhibitory factor, and cAMP on in vitro proliferation of mouse primordial germ cells. *Mol. Reprod. Dev.* 35:134–39
25. Driscoll M. 1992. Molecular genetics of cell death in the nematode *Caenorhabditis elegans*. *J. Neurobiol.* 23:1327–51
26. Eisenhauer K, Chun SY, Billig H, Hsueh AJW. 1995. Growth hormone suppression of apoptosis in preovulatory follicles and partial neutralization by insulin-like growth factor binding protein (IGFBP). *Biol. Reprod.* 53:13–20
27. Ellis RE, Yuan J, Horvitz HR. 1991. Mechanisms and functions of cell death. *Annu. Rev. Cell Biol.* 7:663–98
28. Flaws JA, DeSanti A, Tilly KI, Roya JO, Kugu K, et al. 1995. Vasoactive intestinal peptide-mediated suppression of apoptosis in the ovary: potential mechanisms of action and evidence of a conserved antiatretogenic role through evolution. *Endocrinology* 136:4351–59
29. Gorospe WC, Hughes FMJ, Spangelo BL. 1992 Interleukin-6: effects on and

production by rat granulosa cells in vitro. *Endocrinology* 130:1750–52

30. Gougeon A. 1993. Dynamics of human follicular growth: a morphlogical perspective. In *The Ovary*, ed. EY Adashi, PCK Leung, pp. 21–31. New York: Raven

31. Gu Y, Sarnecki C, Aldape RA, Livingston DJ, Su MS. 1995. Cleavage of poly(ADP-ribose) polymerase by interleukin-1β converting enzyme and its homologs TX and Nedd2. *J. Biol. Chem.* 270:18715–18

32. Hakuno N, Koji T, Yano T, Kobayashi N, Tsutsumi O, et al. 1996. Fas/APO-1/CD95 system as a mediator of granulosa cell apoptosis in ovarian follicle atresia. *Endocrinology* 137:1938–48

33. Hay MF, Cran DG, Moor RM. 1976. Structural changes occurring during atresia in sheep ovarian follicles. *Cell Tissue Res.* 169:515–29

34. Hengartner MO, Ellis RE, Horvitz HR. 1992. *Caenorhabditis elegans* gene ced-9 protects cells from programmed cell death. *Nature* 356:494–99

35. Hengartner MO, Horvitz HR. 1994. *C. elegans* cell survival gene ced-9 encodes a functional homolog of the mammalian proto-oncogene bcl-2. *Cell* 76:665–76

36. Hirshfield AN. 1991. Development of follicles in the mammalian ovary. *Int. Rev. Cytol.* 124:43–101

37. Hirshfield AN, Midgley ARJ. 1978. The role of FSH in the selection of large ovarian follicles in the rat. *Biol. Reprod.* 19:606–11

38. Hsu SY, Lai RJM, Chun SY, Hsueh AJW. 1996. Targeted overexpression of Bcl-2 in ovaries of transgenic mice decreases follicel apoptosis, increases litter size, and enhances tumorigenesis. *Endocrinolog* 137:4837–43

39. Hsu H, Xiong J, Goeddel DV. 1995. The TNF receptor 1-associated protein TRADD signals cell death and NF-κB activation. *Cell* 81:495–504

40. Hsueh AJW, Billig H, Tsafriri A. 1994. Ovarian follicle atresia: a hormonally controlled apoptotic process. *Endocr. Rev.* 15:1–18

41. Hsueh AJ, Jones PB. 1981. Extrapituitary actions of gonadotropin-releasing hormone. *Endocr. Rev.* 2:437–61

42. Hughes FMJ, Gorospe WC. 1991. Biochemical identification of apoptosis (programmed cell death) in granulosa cells: evidence for a potential mechanism underlying follicular atresia. *Endocrinology* 129:2415–22

43. Hutchinson LA, Findlay JK, Herington AC. 1988. Growth hormone and insulin-like growth factor-I accelerate PMSG-induced differentiation of granulosa cells. *Mol. Cell. Endocrinol.* 55:61–69

44. Jia XC, Kessel B, Yen SS, Tucker EM, Hsueh AJ. 1986. Serum bioactive follicle-stimulating hormone during the human menstrual cycle and in hyper- and hypogonadotropic states: application of a sensitive granulosa cell aromatase bioassay. *J. Clin. Endocrinol. Metab.* 62:1243–49

45. Jolly PD, Tisdall DJ, Heath DA, Lun S, McNatty KP. 1994. Apoptosis in bovine granulosa cells in relation to steroid synthesis, cAMP response to FSH and follicular atresia. *Biol. Reprod.* 51:934–44

46. Jones PB, Conn PM, Marian J, Hsueh AJ. 1980. Binding of gonadotropin releasing hormone agonist to rat ovarian granulosa cells. *Life Sci.* 27:2125–32

46a. Kaipia A, Chun SY, Eisenhauer K, Hsueh AWJ. 1996. Tumor necrosis factor-α and its second messenger, ceramide, stimulate apoptosis in cultured ovarian follicles. *Endocrinology* 137:4864–70

47. Kudlow JE, Kobrin MS, Purchio AF, Twardzik DR, Hernandez ER, et al. 1987. Ovarian transforming growth factor-α gene expression: immunohistochemical localization to the theca-interstitial cells. *Endocrinology* 121:1577–79

48. Lazebnik YA, Kaufmann SH, Desnoyers S, Poirier GG, Earnshaw WC. 1994. Cleavage of poly(ADP-ribose) polymerase by a proteinase with properties like ICE. *Nature* 371:346–47

49. Leung PCK, Steele GL. 1992. Intracellular signaling in the gonads. *Endocr. Rev.* 13:476–98

50. Louvet JP, Harman SM, Ross GT. 1975. Effects of human interstitial cell stimulating hormone and human follicle-stimulating hormone on ovarian weights in estrogen-primed hypophysectomized immature male rats. *Endocrinology* 96:1179–86

51. Louvet JP, Harman SM, Schrieber JR, Ross GT. 1975. Evidence of a role of adrogens in follicular maturation. *Endocrinology* 97:366–72

52. Miura M, Zhu H, Rotello R, Hartwieg EA, Yuan J. 1993. Induction of apoptosis in fibroblasts by IL-1β-converting enzyme, a mammalian homolog of the C. elegans cell death gene ced-3. *Cell* 75:653–60

53. Nagata S, Golstein P. 1995. The Fas death factor. *Science* 267:1449–56

54. Nayudu PL, Osborn M. 1992. Factors influencing the rate of preantral and antral growth of mouse ovarian follicles in vitro. *J. Reprod. Fertil.* 95:349–62

55. Neufeld G, Ferrara N, Schweigerer L, Mitchell R, Gospodarowicz D. 1987.

Bovine granulosa cells produce basic fibroblast growth factor. *Endocrinology* 121:597–603

56. Obeid LM, Linardic CM, Karolak LA, Hannun YA. 1993. Programmed cell death induced by ceramide. *Science* 259:1769–71

57. Ohno S, Smith JB. 1964. Role of fetal follicular cells in meiosis of mammalian oocyte. *Cytogenetics* 3:324–33

58. Pedersen T, Peters H. 1968. Proposal for a classification of oocytes and follicles in the mouse ovary. *J. Reprod. Fertil.* 17:555–57

59. Peters H, Byskov AG, Grinsted J. 1978. Follicular growth in fetal and prepubertal ovaries of human and other primates. In *Gynecological Endocrinology,* ed. GT Ross, Lipsett MB, pp. 469–85. London: Saunders

60. Peluso JJ, Pappalardo A. 1994. Progesterone and cell adhesion interact to regulate granulosa cell apoptosis. *Biochem. Cell Biol.* 72:547–51

61. Pesce M, Farrace MG, Piacentini M, Dolci S, De Felici M. 1993. Stem cell factor and leukemia inhibitory factor promote primordial germ cell survival by suppressing programmed cell death (apoptosis). *Development* 118:1089–94

62. Quirk SM, Cowan RG, Joshi SG, Henrikson KP. 1995. Fas antigen-mediated apoptosis in human granulosa/luteal cells. *Biol. Reprod.* 52:279–87

63. Raff MC. 1992. Social controls on cell survival and cell death. *Nature* 356:397–400

64. Raff MC, Barres BA, Burne JF, Coles HS, Ishizaki Y, et al. 1993. Programmed cell death and the control of cell survival: lessons from the nervous system. *Science* 262:695–700

65. Ratts VS, Flaws JA, Kolp R, Sorenson CM, Tilly JL. 1995. Ablation of bcl-2 gene expression decreases the number of oocytes and primordial follicles established in the post-natal female mouse gonad. *Endocrinology* 136:3665–68

66. Resnick JL, Bixler LS, Cheng L, Donovan PJ. 1992. Long-term proliferation of mouse primordial cells in culture. *Nature* 359:550–51

67. Santana P, Llanes L, Hernandez I, Gallardo G, Quintana J, et al. 1995. Ceramide mediates tumor necrosis factor effects on P450-aromatase activity in cultured granulosa cells. *Endocrinology* 136:2345–48

68. Sato T, Hanada M, Bodrug S, Irie S, Iwama N, et al. 1994. Interactions among members of the bcl-2 protein family analyzed with a yeast two-hybrid system.

*Proc. Natl. Acad. Sci. USA* 91:9238–42

69. Schmidt HHHW, Walter U. 1994. NO at work. *Cell* 78:919–25

70. Schwartz NB. 1974. The role of FSH and LH and of their antibodies on follicular growth and on ovulation. *Biol. Reprod.* 10:236–76

71. Stanger BZ, Leder P, Lee TH, Kim E, Seed B. 1995. RIP: a novel protein containing a death domain that interacts with Fas/APO-1 (CD95) in yeast and causes cell death. *Cell* 81:513–23

72. Tapanainen JS, Tilly JL, Vihko KK, Hsueh AJW. 1993. Hormonal control of apoptotic cell death in the testis: gonadotropins and androgens as testicular cell survival factors. *Mol. Endocrinol.* 7:643–50

73. Tartaglia LA, Rothe M, Hu YF, Goeddel DV. 1993. Tumor necrosis factor's cytotoxic activity is signaled by the p55 TNF receptor. *Cell* 73:213–16

74. Terranova PF. 1981. Steroidogenesis in experimentally induced atretic follicles of the hamster: a shift from estradiol to progesterone synthesis. *Endocrinology* 108:1885–90

75. Thompson CB. 1995. Apoptosis in the pathogenesis and treatment of disease. *Science* 267:1456–62

76. Tilly JL, Billig H, Kowalski KI, Hsueh AJW. 1992. Epidermal growth factor and basic fibroblast growth factor suppress the spontaneous onset of apoptosis in cultured rat granulosa cells and follicles by a tyrosine kinase-dependent mechanism. *Mol. Endocrinol.* 6:1942–50

77. Tilly JL, Kowalski KI, Johnson AL, Hsueh AJW. 1991. Involvement of apoptosis in ovarian follicular atresia and postovulatory regression. *Endocrinology* 129:2799–801

78. Tilly JL, Kowalski KI, Schomberg DW, Hsueh AJW. 1992. Apoptosis in atretic ovarian follicles is associated with selective decreases in messenger RNA transcripts for gonadotropin receptors and cytochrome p450 aromatase. *Endocrinology* 131:1670–76

79. Vaux DL, Weissman IL, Kim SK. 1992. Prevention of programmed cell death in *Caenorhabditis elegans* by human bcl-2. *Science* 258:1955–57

80. Westergaard LG, Andersen CY. 1989. Epidermal growth factor (EGF) in human preovulatory follicles. *Hum. Reprod.* 4:257–60

81. Williams PC. 1940. Effect of stilbestrol on ovaries of hypophysectomized rats. *Nature* 145:388–89

82. Wyllie AH. 1987. Apoptosis: cell death in tissue regulation. *J. Pathol.* 153:313–16

83. Wyllie AH, Kerr JFR, Currie AR. 1980. Cell death: the significance of apoptosis. *Int. Rev. Cytol.* 68:251–306

84. Wyllie AH, Kerr JFR, Macaskill IAM, Currie AR. 1973. Adrenocortical cell deletion: the role of ACTH. *J. Pathol.* 111:85–94

85. Yin X, Oltvai ZN, Korsmeyer SJ. 1994. BH1 and BH2 domains of bcl-2 are required for inhibition of apoptosis and heterodimerization with BAX. *Nature* 369:321–23

86. Yuan J, Horvitz HR. 1992. The *Caenorhabditis elegans* cell death gene ced-4 encodes a novel protein and is ex-pressed during the period of extensive programmed cell death. *Development* 116:309–20

87. Yuan J, Shaham S, Ledoux S, Ellis HM, Horvitz HR. 1993. The C. elegans cell death gene ced-3 encodes a protein similar to mammalian interleukin-1β-converting enzyme. *Cell* 75:641–52

88. Zeleznik AJ, Hillier SG, Ross GT. 1979. Follicle stimulating hormone-induced follicular development: an examination of the role of androgens. *Biol. Reprod.* 21:673–81

89. Zeleznik AJ, Ihrig L, Bassett SG. 1989. Developmental expression of $Ca^{2+}/Mg^{2+}$-dependent endonuclease activity in rat granulosa and luteal cells. *Endocrinology* 125:2218–20

*Annu. Rev. Physiol. 1997. 59:365–93*

# SPECIFIC, NONGENOMIC ACTIONS OF STEROID HORMONES

## M. Wehling

Institute of Clinical Pharmacology, Faculty for Clinical Medicine at Mannheim, University of Heidelberg, 68135 Mannheim, Germany

KEY WORDS:   steroids, membrane receptors, rapid effects, second messengers

## ABSTRACT

Traditionally, steroid hormone action has been described as the modulation of nuclear transcription, thus triggering genomic events that are responsible for physiological effects. Despite early observations of rapid steroid effects that were incompatible with this theory, nongenomic steroid action has been widely recognized only recently. Evidence for these rapid effects is available for steroids of all clones and for a multitude of species and tissues. Examples of nongenomic steroid action include rapid aldosterone effects in lymphocytes and vascular smooth muscle cells, vitamin $D_3$ effects in epithelial cells, progesterone action in human sperm, neurosteroid effects on neuronal function, and vascular effects of estrogens. Mechanisms of action are being studied with regard to signal perception and transduction, and researchers have developed a patchy sketch of a membrane receptor-second messenger cascade similar to those involved in catecholamine and peptide hormone action. Many of these effects appear to involve phospholipase C, phosphoinositide turnover, intracellular pH and calcium, protein kinase C, and tyrosine kinases. The physiological and pathophysiological relevance of these effects is unclear, but rapid steroid effects on cardiovascular, central nervous, and reproductive functions may occur in vivo. The cloning of the cDNA for the first membrane receptor for steroids should be achieved in the near future, and the physiological and clinical relevance of these rapid steroid effects can then be established.

## INTRODUCTION

According to the traditional theory of steroid hormone action, steroids are thought to primarily affect the transcription of mRNA and, subsequently, protein synthesis. The physiological significance of these genomic actions of

365

0066-4278/97/0315-0365$08.00

steroids was established by documenting their sensitivity to inhibitors of transcription and translation, e.g. actinomycin D and cycloheximide. Researchers have characterized and cloned (15, 37, 41) the cDNAs that encode the intracellular steroid-binding proteins. They serve as transcription regulatory factors and constitute the main players in the genomic theory of steroid action; however, a direct interaction of steroids with nuclear DNA is also possible (49, 50, 127).

In the case of mineralocorticoids, long-term effects on blood pressure and on electrolyte and water balances are believed to result from genomic effects in the distal tubule of the kidneys (129). Cytoplasmic type-I receptors (mineralocorticoid receptors) (8, 34, 42) are distinct from type-II receptors (glucocorticoid receptors). As with other steroids, the receptor-ligand complex acts as a transcription factor and initiates the transcription of specific mRNA encoding for aldosterone-induced proteins (84). Cortisol can also act with type-I receptors to induce similar effects. Therefore, a concept based on these receptors alone is insufficient to explain physiological differences in the action of glucocorticoids and mineralocorticoids.

In the past few years, evidence for membrane-bound steroid receptors has been generated by studies of the rapid actions of various steroids, for example, rapid aldosterone effects in nonepithelial cells, human lymphocytes, and rat vascular smooth muscle cells. The findings from these and similar studies on rapid effects of steroids from all groups are incompatible with genomic steroid action. This review summarizes these phenomena and their potential physiological relevance.

## CRITERIA FOR THE CLASSIFICATION OF NONGENOMIC STEROID EFFECTS

The latency of genomic steroid action is believed to be the consequence of a series of events induced by steroids starting with mRNA production and modification, followed by protein synthesis, protein translocation and transport, and protein actions. Among the earliest known genomic steroid effects is the increased rate of transcription of mouse mammary tumor virus long terminal repeat (MMTV LTR) in L tk- aprt- cells first seen 7.5 min after glucocorticoid application (47); for mineralocorticoids, a similar effect is evident within 30 min and peaks after 3 h in a feline renal cell line (24). This process is insensitive to cycloheximide because it does not require new protein synthesis. Though even more rapid effects of steroids on transcriptional processes are known, most actinomycin D– or cycloheximide-sensitive effects occur after a lag phase of 10 min or more. The additional delay at the effector level is probably the result of the time required for the processing of newly synthesized protein molecules from their site of synthesis to their final location in the cell. The modification of intracellular steroid receptors by other agonists (e.g. dopamine, EGF, IGF-1; 52, 53, 93) through intracellular signaling can modify a genomic steroid action.

In light of these considerations, a steroid effect that occurs between a few seconds and 1–2 min after steroid application is likely due to a nongenomic rather than a genomic effect. To support the designation of steroid effects as nongenomic in nature, the response should not be blocked by inhibitors of DNA transcription or protein synthesis (e.g. actinomycin D or cycloheximide). A second tool separating genomic and nongenomic effects is the use of steroid coupled to macromolecules such as bovine serum albumin, which prevents the steroid from entering the cell. If these compounds are still active, the site of action is likely to be the plasma membrane, although endocytosis of the conjugated steroid into the cell might obscure this conclusion.

In summary, the rapid time-course and the insensitivity of the signals to inhibitors of transcription or protein synthesis are the main types of evidence for the classification of a response as a nongenomic event.

## SPECIFIC AND NONSPECIFIC NONGENOMIC EFFECTS OF STEROIDS

Rapid, nongenomic effects may occur by two mechanisms: (a) interaction of steroids with specific receptors and (b) interaction of steroids with nonspecific proteins and/or membrane lipids. The methods of traditional pharmacology have been applied to characterize the affinity and specificity of the putative receptors involved in rapid steroid effects until the receptors can be purified and their cDNAs cloned. Thus the hypothesis of specific receptors must be tested for each observation in the field.

Criteria for the involvement of specific receptor proteins include high affinity and low capacity of binding sites, selectivity for a particular ligand or agonist, inhibition by specific antagonists, saturability of binding, and inhibition of binding by proteolytic agents. Not all criteria have been evaluated for all nongenomic steroid effects described below, but many of the effects fulfill these requirements and, thus, likely represent specific, nongenomic steroid effects.

Nonspecific, nongenomic effects of steroids occur at high steroid concentrations; partial steroid specificity of these effects may be due to variable lipophilicity and polarity. These steroid-membrane interactions affect physico-chemical properties such as fluidity and the microenvironment of proteins in the membrane. The effects of steroids on all membranes were recognized in 1961 (147), and effects of estradiol and progesterone on membrane fluidity have been described in breast cancer (29), vaginal epithelial cells (105), and human spermatozoa (113). In particular, progesterone decreases the fluidity of sperm membranes, aggregates membrane vesicles, induces fusion of membrane vesicles, and renders vesicles permeable to hydrophilic molecules such as carboxyfluorescein (113). In contrast, testosterone and estradiol at the same concentration have little effect on membrane fluidity, membrane aggregation, fusion, and leakage.

However, given the specificity of many rapid steroid effects and their occurrence at low steroid concentrations, it is difficult to explain rapid effects on the basis of nonspecific interactions, although membrane protein receptors may be modulated by changes in the surrounding lipid environment that mimic specificity at the effector level. Also, in many instances, steroid concentrations required to elicit these effects are not achieved physiologically or pharmacologically, and the significance of these effects is, therefore, questionable. Neurosteroids, which are locally produced (14, 65), may reach concentrations necessary for most of the nonspecific, nongenomic steroid effects addressed here. In contrast, as steroids move freely through lipid barriers, major chemical gradients are not expected to exist, and local production may not produce major gradients in the steady state.

## SPECIFIC, NONGENOMIC STEROID EFFECTS

In 1942, Hans Selye described anesthetic effects of progesterone (111) that occur almost immediately after exposure to the hormone, an effect that constitutes one of the best characterized specific nongenomic steroid effects.

Among the early data that suggested that steroids have nongenomic actions was the finding that aldosterone has in vitro effects on sodium exchange in dog erythrocytes at physiological aldosterone concentrations (114). Because these cells lack a nucleus and thus a genomic pathway, the effects must depend on a nongenomic effector mechanism. Subsequently, direct membrane effects of glucocorticoids were demonstrated in isolated synaptosomes (36) and were possibly the cellular counterpart for the negative feedback effect of plasma cortisol on ACTH secretion, which occurs within a few minutes and may not be generated by genomic action. In addition, Pietras & Szego (99) demonstrated another example of an early steroid effect, that of rapid estrogen action on calcium flux in endometrial cells. Subsequently, putative nongenomic effects have been described for all groups of steroids and related compounds such as vitamin $D_3$ and triiodothyronine.

### Neurosteroids

The actions of $5\alpha$-pregnan-$3\alpha$,21-diol-20-one and $5\alpha$-pregnan-$3\alpha$-OH-20-one on chloride currents (72, 121, 151), the effects of pregnanolone on release of gonadotropin-releasing hormone (GnRH) (104), and certain neural effects induced by the local application of steroids (72) have led researchers to use the term neurosteroids.

Intracellular microelectrodes were used to demonstrate the effects of $5\alpha$-pregnan-$3\alpha$,21-diol-20-one in pyramidal neurons in an in vitro slice preparation of the adult rat frontal neocortex (121). This neurosteroid (at high concentrations, 10 $\mu$M) increased and prolonged the inhibitory postsynaptic potential and increased the mean maximal synaptic conductance of the early, GABA$_A$ receptor–mediated inhibitory postsynaptic potential by more than 700% and increased the mean synaptic conductance at the maximum of the late, partially GABA$_B$ receptor–mediated, inhibitory postsynaptic potential by approximately 400%. The progesterone-glucocorticoid receptor antagonist mifepristone did not prevent this increase. At a concentration of 1 $\mu$M, $5\alpha$-pregnan-$3\alpha$,21-diol-20-one increased only the early inhibitory postsynaptic potential to about 125%. Responses to the iontophoretically applied specific GABA$_A$ receptor agonist muscimol, but not to the specific GABA$_B$ receptor agonist $L$-baclofen, were enhanced by $5\alpha$-pregnan-$3\alpha$,21-diol-20-one. Excitatory postsynaptic potentials, resting membrane potential, input resistance, and action potential amplitude were not affected by this steroid. Thus in neocortical tissue of the rat, $5\alpha$-pregnan-$3\alpha$,21-diol-20-one enhances GABAergic inhibition by interacting with postsynaptic GABA$_A$ receptors, while synaptic excitation and parameters of electric excitability remain unchanged.

Neuroactive steroid modulation of GABA$_A$ receptors has also been investigated in the peptidergic nerve terminals of the posterior pituitary using patch-clamp techniques (151). The function of nerve terminal GABA$_A$ receptors as determined by Cl$^-$ currents was potentiated by the synthetic progestogen alfaxalone and by physiological concentrations of the progesterone metabolite allopregnanolone, indicating that the nerve terminal GABA$_A$ receptor responds similarly to the GABA$_A$ receptors of nerve cell bodies and endocrine cells. The nerve terminal GABA$_A$ receptors may provide a pathway by which gonadal steroids regulate peptide secretion from neurosecretory neurons.

Neurosteroids may be produced locally (14, 65), and high concentrations of the steroids may interact with GABA$_A$ receptors and other potential receptors (72). Antagonists of progesterone that interfere with binding of the hormone to intracellular receptors do not block these effects (121). Anesthetic effects of related steroids (e.g. althesin) have been used clinically and are still in use for veterinary purposes. It is not clear which anesthetic effects are mediated through those specific interactions with the GABA$_A$-receptor complex and which reflect nonspecific effects on lipid bilayers or membrane proteins (128) at high steroid concentrations. However, the analgesic effects of progesterone appear to be mediated through the GABA$_A$-receptor complex (40). These effects may involve a specific binding site for the steroids on the GABA$_A$ receptor, but also require the presence of GABA.

## Mineralocorticoids

The usual receptor-effector cascade includes a receptor that triggers intracellular second messengers (with no other ligand required). An example of this phenomenon is the nongenomic action of aldosterone in certain cells. Though early observations (62, 114) suggested that aldosterone may have nongenomic actions, research on the mechanisms for this action is relatively recent (82, 91). Rapid actions of aldosterone, which are insensitive to actinomycin D and cycloheximide and thus are presumably nongenomic, include an early ouabain- and actinomycin D–independent efflux of $^{22}$Na in rat arterial smooth muscle (82). Aldosterone effects also cause a rapid increase in free intracellular calcium levels in toad bladder (98). The immediate effect, along with that in lymphocytes (140a), represents the first reported evidence for nongenomic effects of aldosterone on free intracellular calcium.

Oberleithner et al (91) reported that aldosterone induces changes in intracellular pH in the distal tubule of the toad kidney, although the onset (15–20 min) is compatible with an early genomic event. Because the effect was blocked by amiloride, the effect was attributed to an increased activity of the sodium-proton exchanger.

Similar effects of aldosterone on electrolyte transport, including changes of intracellular electrolytes, cell volume, and an activation of the sodium-proton exchanger of the cell membrane, have been reported in human mononuclear leucocytes (HML), vascular smooth muscle cells (VSMC), and porcine aortic endothelial cells (PAEC). In HML, aldosterone raises intracellular sodium, potassium, and calcium concentrations and the cell volume within 1 h at an $EC_{50}$ of approximately 0.1 nM (137a, 140a, 141a). The first step in this effect, activation of the sodium-proton exchanger, occurs after only 1–2 min of incubation and, thus, is presumably nongenomic in nature; the $EC_{50}$ was 0.04 nM. In contrast to their nonselectivity with regard to classical intracellular type-I receptors, cortisol and other glucocorticoids were active at supramicromolar concentrations only, and the type-I mineralocorticoid receptor antagonist canrenone was ineffective as an inhibitor (141). A similar effect of aldosterone on sodium-proton exchange occurs in cultured VSMC from rat aortas after 4 min of incubation. The apparent $EC_{50}$ was approximately 0.2 nM—a concentration close to the physiological level of free aldosterone in rats [$\sim$0.2 nM (74)] and humans [$\sim$0.1 nM (2)]. The synthetic mineralocorticoid fludrocortisone was nearly as active as aldosterone, whereas cortisol was ineffective at micromolar concentrations. As in HML, canrenone did not block aldosterone effects at 1000-fold excess concentrations (25).

The role of phosphoinositide hydrolysis [producing inositol-1,4,5-tris phosphate ($IP_3$) and diacylglycerol (DAG)] as an important second messenger system in the rapid effects of aldosterone was documented both in HML and VSCM.

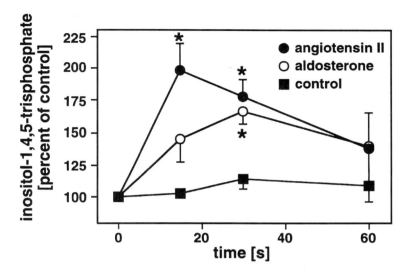

*Figure 1* Time course of IP$_3$ stimulation in vascular smooth muscle cells by aldosterone and angiotensin II: Cells were incubated in HEPES-buffered WM-752/H-F12 medium plus 0.01% ethanol (maximum vehicle concentration during steroid stimulation) alone (control), with 10 nmol/L aldosterone, or with 100 nmol/L angiotensin II. IP$_3$ levels were measured by a specific radioreceptor assay kit (from Reference 25 with permission).

Aldosterone and fludrocortisone significantly stimulated the generation of IP$_3$ within approximately 30 s at an EC$_{50}$ of approximately 0.1 nM. Cortisol and dexamethasone were weak agonists, with an EC$_{50}$ of approximately 1 $\mu$M (Figure 1). Canrenone did not block aldosterone effects at 100-fold excess concentrations (25, 26). Similarly, DAG production was increased in VSMC by subnanomolar concentrations of aldosterone but only by supramicromolar concentrations of cortisol (27). Angiotensin II induced similar effects, although aldosterone action was more prolonged.

Because IP$_3$ releases calcium from intracellular stores through IP$_3$-receptors in the endoplasmic reticulum (16), effects of aldosterone on free intracellular calcium concentration [Ca$^{2+}$]$_i$ were investigated in VSCM and PAEC (144, 145). An almost immediate increase of [Ca$^{2+}$]$_i$ was seen after addition of aldosterone; [Ca$^{2+}$]$_i$ reached a plateau after 2–3 min (Figures 2 and 3). Again, the EC$_{50}$ for aldosterone was approximately 0.1 nM, whereas cortisol and other glucocorticoids were active only at or above micromolar concentrations. Pretreatment with the aldosterone antagonist spironolactone (10 $\mu$M) for 5 or 30 min did not block the effect of aldosterone (10 nM), but the aldosterone-dependent release of calcium was blocked by depletion of intracellular calcium

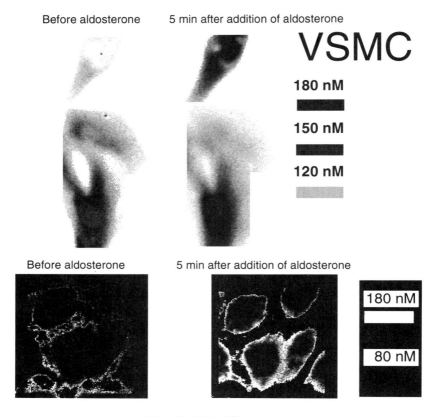

*Figure 2* Calcium images of rat vascular smooth muscle cells (VSMC) and porcine aortic endothelial cells (PAEC) before and 5 min after addition of 100-nM aldosterone. Free intracellular calcium was measured by dual-wavelength fluorescence of Fura2 in a microscopic cell-imaging system (modified from Reference 145 with permission).

stores. The sequence of this effect apparently involves an initial release of calcium from intracellular stores and a secondary influx of extracellular calcium. However, the relative importance of each source to the final effect on intracellular calcium appears to differ among various cell types. For example, release of calcium from intracellular stores is the predominant effect of aldosterone in VSMC, which contain a large compartment of stored calcium in the endoplasmic reticulum. In contrast, calcium influx is more prominent in PAEC, as shown by single-cell imaging (Figure 3) and by the more pronounced

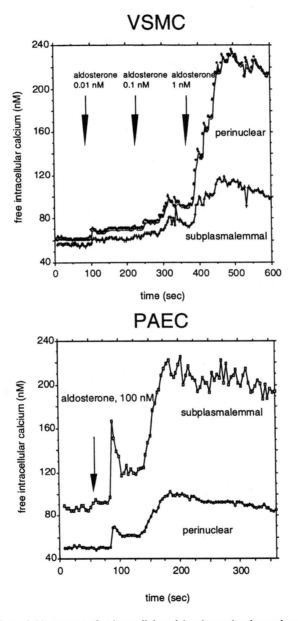

*Figure 3*   Effects of aldosterone on free intracellular calcium in a perinuclear and a subplasmalemmal region of interest in a vascular smooth muscle cell (VSMC) and a porcine aortic endothelial cell (PAEC) (modified from Reference 145 with permission).

blunting by removal of external calcium on $[Ca^{2+}]_i$ (145). Another feature of nongenomic steroid effects in PAEC is that $EC_{50}$ values of both aldosterone and hydrocortisone are lower by two orders of magnitude than are those in VSMC (M Wehling, unpublished results).

An unusual feature of rapid steroid action on $[Ca^{2+}]_i$ in both VSMC and PAEC is that the maximum increase (~50 nmol/L) is small even at high steroid concentrations. In contrast, angiotensin II causes a several-fold increase of $[Ca^{2+}]_i$ (e.g. from 100 to 800 nM). These dramatic increases in $[Ca^{2+}]_i$, at least after repeated applications, may impair cellular integrity, which would not occur in the case of aldosterone effects.

The rapid effect of aldosterone on free intracellular calcium is blocked by neomycin, genistein, indomethacin, and short-term treatment with phorbol esters, but it is augmented by staurosporine, indicating involvement of a tyrosine kinase, phospholipase C, and protein kinase C. Rapid effects of aldosterone on protein kinase C have also been demonstrated in VSMC by immunostaining, including translocation of the protein from the cytosol to the plasma membrane (27). Aldosterone also has rapid effects on neuronal activity in rat brain cortex (122), but the pharmacology of these central effects has yet to be elaborated.

## Glucocorticoids

Early observations on rapid glucocorticoid action on synaptosomes were described above (36). In cichlid fish pituitary, rapid suppression of prolactin release was attributed to a nongenomic effect of cortisol on cAMP and intracellular calcium levels (21).

Rapid behavioral effects of corticosterone have been described in the amphibian *Taricha granulosa* (78, 95). For example, stress-induced courtship is affected within a few minutes, presumably through a corticosterone receptor in neuronal membranes. There is a strong correlation between a given steroid's capacity to inhibit the behavior and its capacity to inhibit corticosterone binding (79, 94, 95). Furthermore, in caudal brain-stem neurons, corticosterone rapidly modulates neuronal activity and suppresses sensory processing. This is a rare example of a rapid steroid action for which congruent data have been obtained both at the subcellular and the physiological levels. The rapid increase of $IP_3$ production in VSMC (116) induced by hydrocortisone may involve the same mechanism.

Effects of cortisol on transmembrane currents in guinea pig ventricular myocytes have been linked to positive inotropic effects of steroids (148). However, high steroid concentrations (1–10 $\mu$M) are needed to produce this effect, and the effect may be nonspecific.

The mechanism of the anti-anaphylactic effect of high doses of glucocorticoids has not been defined. However, because the effect occurs within a few minutes and is resistant to actinomycin D, nongenomic steroid action may be involved (54). Membrane-stabilizing effects are thought to be involved (48, 67). It remains to be determined whether nonspecific (membrane stabilization) or specific nongenomic events are responsible.

## Gonadal Steroids

Gonadal steroids produce a wide array of nongenomic actions that are specific for different steroids from those subgroups discussed below.

PROGESTERONE    The action of progesterone on oocyte maturation and the spermatozoan acrosome reaction (18, 126, 134) are examples of nongenomic steroid effects that occur at physiological concentrations of progesterone with $EC_{50}$ values of 0.1–3 $\mu M$.

The action of progesterone on maturation of the amphibian oocyte (*Xenopus laevis*) has been explained in terms of its effects on $[Ca^{2+}]_i$ and chloride conductance (134). Though this progesterone-induced maturation has been studied extensively, the mechanism by which the arrest in prophase is released is not well understood but may involve inactivation of a cAMP-dependent protein kinase. However, oocyte maturation may occur independently from cAMP.

Progesterone in human sperm has effects on membrane receptors, second messengers, and the acrosome reaction. In this system, rapid steroid action appears to be mediated by a dual mechanism: direct activation of a calcium channel (presumably a receptor-operated channel, thus not dissimilar from the putative calcium channel involved in rapid aldosterone action) and an independent stimulation of tyrosine kinase (75, 120). However, calcium release from intracellular stores may be responsible for enhancing tyrosine kinase. In addition, protein kinase C may be involved in rapid progesterone action in human sperm (38). Again, the proposed evidence that at least two different membrane receptors influence different signaling systems will need to be revisited when the receptor(s) are cloned .

Rapid steroid effects may play an important role in at least one human disease. In infertile men with teratozoospermia, the progesterone-induced influx of calcium and the acrosome reaction were both impaired (92). Furthermore, Baldi et al (9) demonstrated a positive correlation between the extent of the progesterone-induced calcium response and the fertilization rate in oligozoospermic men. Pentoxifylline enhances progesterone action on acrosome reaction, and even a pharmacotherapeutic approach to infertility utilizing this compound is based on the nongenomic steroid action (58). However, the rapid nongenomic effect of progesterone on the spermatozoan acrosome reaction has been questioned recently (23), and future research must delineate the conditions under which progesterone activates the acrosome reaction, if at all.

Other nongenomic effects of progesterone include the control of mating behavior in female hamsters (31), and electrophysiological effects on synaptic transmission, membrane potential, and potassium or calcium conductances in rat hepatocytes, natural killer cells, and CA1 hippocampal neurons (55, 56, 71, 73, 131).

ESTROGEN    Estrogen induces rapid calcium influx into myometrial cells (99), and rapid responses to $17\alpha$-estradiol or $17\beta$-estradiol have been demonstrated in preoptic septal area or neostriatal neurons (60, 76), pituitary cells (33), and maturing human oocytes and granulosa cells (81, 118). Increases of cAMP, as in vascular smooth muscle, breast cancer, and uterine cells (7, 37a), may be related to rapid estrogen-induced activation of membrane adenylate cyclase, but confirmation is lacking. $EC_{50}$ values for these effects range from 0.1 to 1 nM.

Ethinyl estradiol or $17\alpha$-estradiol causes acute relaxation of human and pig coronary arteries in vivo (106, 107, 149), an effect that may be linked to the cardioprotective action of estrogens in postmenopausal women. However, the underlying mechanism for this effect is not clear. It may involve direct calcium-antagonistic effects on VSMC. In vitro concentrations of estrogens necessary for this relaxant effect (in the supramicromolar range) exceed physiological or pharmacological levels of these compounds; therefore, the effect may be categorized as nongenomic, possibly of a nonspecific origin. The same holds true for in vivo studies in which supramicromolar estrogen concentrations have been injected into coronary arteries; intracellular calcium and the paracrine action of nitrogen oxide, endothelin 1, and eicosanoids have been suggested as potential mediators of this effect (146).

ANDROGENS    Testosterone rapidly stimulates $[Ca^{2+}]_i$ in rat osteoblasts (68) (within 5 s via enhanced $Ca^{2+}$ influx, as shown by the effects of EGTA and the $Ca^{2+}$-channel blockers nifedipine and verapamil) and enhances $Ca^{2+}$ mobilization from the endoplasmic reticulum, as shown by the effects of thapsigargin and neomycin. Testosterone also increases formation of $IP_3$ and DAG within 10 s. Testosterone linked to bovine serum albumin [testosterone (O-carboxymethyl)oxime/bovine serum albumin] and its derivative, (O-carboxymethyl)oxime, have the same effects, although they are less potent than the free steroid. Cyproterone acetate, an androgen receptor antagonist, does not block the increase in $[Ca^{2+}]_i$, $IP_3$, and DAG formation induced by testosterone, whereas neomycin and pertussis toxin abolished the effects of testosterone on $IP_3$ and DAG. These results suggest that male rat osteoblasts bear nongenomic cell-surface receptors for testosterone that may be coupled to a phospholipase C via a pertussis toxin–sensitive G protein. This study awaits confirmation. The androgen effect is similar to that of aldosterone in VSMC with regard to time course, second messengers involved ($[Ca^{2+}]_i$, $IP_3$, and DAG), and molecular mechanisms of calcium release from intracellular stores.

In Sertoli cells, rapid effects of testosterone and dihydrotestosterone on $[Ca^{2+}]_i$ are also seen with a testosterone-BSA conjugate, suggesting a membrane effect (46). In contrast, the anti-androgen hydroxyflutamide or the $5\alpha$-reductase inhibitor finasteride inhibit the rapid effects of testosterone on $[Ca^{2+}]_i$, pointing to an additional effect of $5\alpha$-reduction and a potential involvement of intracellular androgen receptors in this process.

## Vitamin $D_3$

For rapid effects of vitamin $D_3$ on intracellular calcium, both the release and influx of calcium have been identified as sources of changes in calcium levels, and the relative contributions of the two sources depend on the cell type studied (88). In chicken myoblasts, $IP_3$ and DAG trigger the calcium response (80), wheras rapid cGMP responses have been seen in human fibroblasts (13). Extensive studies have been conducted to determine structural features of vitamin D analogues with regard to their differential activities in the genomic and nongenomic pathways in chick intestine and osteoblasts (10, 12, 32, 61, 90). The 6-s-*cis* analogue of 1,25-dihydroxy vitamin $D_3$ stimulates nongenomic effects but not genomic biological responses. $EC_{50}$ values for these effects are in the subnanomolar (i.e. physiological) range.

In a pancreatic beta-cell line, 1,25-dihydroxy vitamin $D_3$ induces oscillations of $[Ca^{2+}]_i$ through nonselective calcium channels that are blocked by lanthanum ions (112). In these cells, equilibrated at a steady-state glucose concentration of 5.5 mM, 1,25-dihydroxy vitamin $D_3$ (2–20 nM) rapidly (5–10 s) increases $[Ca^{2+}]_i$ and evokes sinusoidal $[Ca^{2+}]_i$ oscillations. The $[Ca^{2+}]_i$ oscillations are acutely dependent on extracellular $Ca^{2+}$ but not on extracellular glucose. The 1,25-dihydroxy vitamin $D_3$–evoked $[Ca^{2+}]_i$ oscillations are mediated by nonselective $Ca^{2+}$ channels that are permeable to $Mn^{2+}$ and suppressed by extracellular $La^{3+}$. Blockage of voltage-dependent $Ca^{2+}$ channels by nifedipine decreases the amplitude of the oscillations. Unlike its effect on the aldosterone-induced response of $[Ca^{2+}]_i$ in VSMC, depletion of intracellular $Ca^{2+}$ stores with thapsigargin did not affect the 1,25-dihydroxy vitamin $D_3$–stimulated $Ca^{2+}$ entry estimated by the $Mn^{2+}$ entry and Fura2 fluorescence quench. This observation implies that the hormone directly activates nonselective $Ca^{2+}$ channels. The 1,25-dihydroxy vitamin $D_3$–evoked increase in the background $Ca^{2+}$ influx appears to generate $[Ca^{2+}]_i$ oscillations by triggering $Ca^{2+}$ release through the ryanodine receptor/$Ca^{2+}$-release channel but not through activation of $IP_3$. These findings are consistent with a role of a membrane vitamin D receptor coupled to the plasma membrane $Ca^{2+}$ channels in mediating rapid effects of the hormone

(112). They also show that rapid steroid effects may share major similarities with regard to distal effects, for example, on $[Ca^{2+}]_i$; however, the proximal parts of signaling pathways involved in different steroid effects may vary widely.

## Triiodothyronine

Triiodothyronine acts genomically through receptors that are members of the superfamily of intracellular steroid receptors, but triiodothyronine also has rapid, nongenomic effects in various cells. Most known effects involve calcium membrane transport or $[Ca^{2+}]_i$, as shown for effects of triiodothyronine in thymocytes (110), rat liver cells (51), red blood cells lacking a nucleus (30), and rat myocytes (69). The similarity of these effects to rapid effects of steroid hormones is striking, and common distal pathways of intracellular activation may be involved for the two types of hormones.

## MEMBRANE-BINDING SITES FOR STEROIDS

These rapid steroid effects and classical intracellular steroid receptor effects differ in almost all regards; therefore, alternative receptors have been sought to provide a better match between steroid binding and rapid steroid effects. Given the phenomena described above that indicate similar receptor–second messenger–effector pathways, as for peptide hormones or catecholamines, most of these alternative binding sites are assumed to be localized in the plasma membrane.

Membrane-binding sites for steroids have been described for mineralocorticoids on kidney plasma membranes, glucocorticoids on liver and pituitary membranes, and estrogen on endometrial membranes (39, 63, 100, 117). However, a convincing match between these binding sites and rapid steroid effects, thus supporting a causal relation, is rarely obtained.

## Mineralocorticoids

In addition to classical type-I mineralocorticoid receptors in HML (4) and classical target tissues such as kidney tubules (42), membrane-binding sites for aldosterone have been found in HML and pig kidneys by the use of an iodinated aldosterone analogue. This analogue has a specific activity high enough to detect binding sites in the subnanomolar affinity range. Specific saturable binding of the radioligand to plasma membranes was demonstrated at a $K_d$ of approximately 0.1 nM for the radioligand and for nonradioactive aldosterone (28, 138). Cortisol was inactive up to micromolar concentrations, whereas the mineralocorticoids fludrocortisone and desoxycorticosterone acetate had an intermediate activity. Canrenone did not block the binding of aldosterone. These findings are the first to demonstrate membrane binding that is specific for mineralocorticoids. The findings thus match the functional data obtained in the same cells. To determine the size of the receptor protein, HML plasma membranes were covalently photolabeled with the same [$^{125}$I]-aldosterone derivative in the presence or absence of 1000-fold excess amounts of either unlabeled aldosterone or cortisol. Subsequent analysis by SDS-PAGE demonstrated significant aldosterone binding at a molecular mass of approximately 50 kDa (139). Binding was inhibited by aldosterone but not by cortisol (139).

Aldosterone-specific membrane-binding sites have also been found in pig liver membranes using the radioligand [1,2,6,7-$^{3}$H] aldosterone ([$^{3}$H] aldosterone) (77). Maximum binding capacity is approximately 700 fmol/mg microsomal protein. The reversible binding of [$^{3}$H] aldosterone was saturable, and Scatchard analysis (Figure 4) identified two apparent dissociation constants, $K_{d1} \leq 11$ nM and $K_{d2} = 118$ nM. The latter binding site most likely represents a nonspecific interaction, presumably with lipids. The high-affinity site $K_{d1}$ was obtained only as an upper estimate. Extrapolation of the asymptotic biphasic Scatchard plot would apparently give a much steeper slope at low tracer concentrations, indicating a lower true $K_{d1}$ value, which then might be fully compatible with $K_d$ values obtained with the iodinated tracer in HML and pig kidney membranes. Binding was optimal at pH 7.2, was thermolabile, and was reduced by more than 70% when membrane vesicles were pretreated with trypsin.

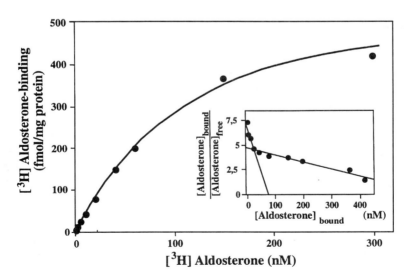

*Figure 4*  Saturation analysis of binding of [$^{3}$H] aldosterone to microsomal membranes from porcine liver. The Scatchard plot is inset. Straight lines represent data for high- and low-affinity binding sites (from Reference 77 with permission).

Two earlier studies of aldosterone binding to plasma membranes reported affinity constants for aldosterone binding of 3–13 nM for plasma membranes from rat kidneys in one (96) and of 100 nM in the other (39). Those $K_d$ values appear to be far from physiologically relevant, but since iodinated aldosterone was not yet available, an overestimation of the $K_d$ might apply here as well.

Important kinetic and pharmacological properties of the aldosterone membrane-binding sites, the rapid aldosterone effects on electrolyte transport, cell volume, and intracellular second messengers in those cells are similar, and these membrane binding sites are likely to represent the receptor that mediates rapid aldosterone effects. Key features of the classical type-I mineralocorticoid receptor, such as its nonselectivity for aldosterone, cortisol, and canrenone, and its lower affinity for aldosterone ($K_d$ value $\sim 1$ nM) are different from those of the membrane receptor. In addition, the affinity of membrane-binding sites for aldosterone and the $EC_{50}$ values for rapid aldosterone effects of about 0.1 nM match with the physiological concentration of free aldosterone in human [0.1 nM (2)] or rat [0.2 nM (74)] plasma, pointing to a possible physiological relevance of these effects (see below).

## Glucocorticoids

Glucocorticoids bind to amphibian neuronal (78, 79, 95) and rat liver (102, 124) membranes. There is a close correlation between a corticosterone membrane receptor in amphibian brain and rapid modification of reproductive behavior; the potential physiological relevance of this receptor is further underlined by its low $K_d$ value of 0.5 nM. G proteins may be involved in the receptor-protein interaction (94). In contrast to the high affinity of the neuronal-binding sites for corticosterone, rat liver membrane-binding sites for dexamethasone have a $K_d$ value of $\cong 400$ nM (102).

A glucocorticoid receptor–like antigen was detected by antibodies in human lymphoma cells (44, 45) and was correlated with cell death in these cells. Because this approach utilized epitopes of the classical intracellular glucocorticoid receptor (type II) for the immunostaining of steroid membrane receptors, a close relationship (if not identity) between these receptors has to be assumed. This relationship is unique in that all other putative steroid membrane receptors share little more than the main ligand with their intracellular counterpart, so an antigenic crossreactivity is remarkable.

## Gonadal Steroids

As for rapid effects, membrane-binding sites specific for steroids of this subgroup have been defined in various tissues.

PROGESTERONE    Membrane-binding sites specific for progesterone, second messengers for the progesterone effect (cAMP and intracellular calcium), and a physiological effect of progesterone (oocyte maturation) were described relatively early in *X. laevis* oocytes (20, 134), and their causal interaction, as judged from the consistency of data, appears to be likely. However, the synthetic progesterone R5020, which has both gestagen and glucocorticoid activities, was used in these experiments. In a different study, the binding of progesterone was demonstrated in membranes from frog oocytes (66).

Progesterone binding to human sperm surfaces has been investigated because rapid progesterone effects occur in these cells (see above). Blackmore & Lattanzio (18) and Tesarik et al (119) used progesterone-BSA-fluorescein isothiocyanate to demonstrate progesterone membrane binding in the head of human sperm. Iodinated progesterone-BSA has been used to detect membrane binding in rat brain (59, 123). In mouse brain membranes, four protein bands labeled by a progesterone analogue had apparent molecular weights ranging from 29 to 64 K (22a). Pregnenolone sulfate binding to rat brain membranes has been explained in terms of an interaction with $GABA_A$ receptors, which are thought to represent a major target for this neurosteroid (70).

ESTROGEN    Early observations showed estrogen binding to plasma membranes from myometrium, liver, and a breast cancer cell line (MCF-7) at $K_d$ values of approximately 1 nM (17, 100). More recent studies showed linking of estradiol and 2-OH-estradiol to pituitary plasma membranes at low $K_d$ values of 0.04 and 0.4 nM (22, 108). Similar results have been reported with dendritic hypothalamic membranes from guinea pigs (19).

As with glucocorticoid binding, estrogen membrane receptors have been detected in GH3/B6 rat pituitary tumor cells by antibodies to epitopes of the classical intracellular receptors (97). These cells exhibit rapid prolactin release (within 5 min) when treated with nanomolar amounts of estrogen. Using antibodies against a peptide corresponding to the hinge region of the intracellular estrogen receptor, researchers demonstrated that these cells contain a membrane estrogen receptor. These cells also specifically bind a fluorescent estrogen-BSA conjugate. Coincubation of cells with anti-estrogen receptor antibody and the fluorescent estrogen-BSA conjugate shows the colocalization of these labels on cells. As with the glucocorticoid receptor detected by a similar approach, these results suggest that the membrane estrogen receptor may be structurally similar to the intracellular estrogen receptor. This suggestion has been supported by a study (57) showing that 20 nM estrogen caused dissociation of the estrogen receptor from the plasma membrane of goat uterine cells. Again, because this approach starts from structures in the classical intracellular receptor and given the pharmacological diversity of nongenomic and genomic estrogen action, one might ask whether those membrane-binding sites actually transmit rapid estrogen effects.

## Vitamin D₃

*Vitamin D₃*

Membrane-binding sites for vitamin $D_3$ have been described in chick intestine (86, 87) and ROS 24/1 cells (10–12). In chick intestine, studies with analogues of vitamin $D_3$ [particularly 1,25(OH)2-7-dehydrocholesterol and 1,25(OH)2-lumisterol3] have provided convincing correlations between the protein binding to the solubilized membrane receptor and its ability to initiate the rapid hormonal stimulation of calcium transport. Rapid effects (15 s to 5 min) of vitamin $D_3$ occur in osteoblast-like cells that lack the intracellular vitamin D receptor, ROS 24/1, suggesting that a separate signaling system mediates the rapid actions. These nongenomic actions include rapid activation of phospholipase C and opening of calcium channels, pointing to a membrane localization of this signaling system. The 1 beta epimer of 1 alpha,25-dihydroxyvitamin $D_3$ can block these rapid actions, indicating that the 1 beta epimer may bind to the receptor responsible for the rapid actions in a competitive manner. The analogue 1 alpha,25-dihydroxyvitamin $D_3$ displaced $^3H$-1 alpha,25-dihydroxyvitamin $D_3$ from the membranes. Similarly, 1 beta,25-dihydroxyvitamin $D_3$ displaced 1 alpha,25-dihydroxyvitamin $D_3$ binding, while 25-hydroxyvitamin $D_3$ did not. The apparent $K_d$ for 1 alpha,25-dihydroxyvitamin $D_3$ was 0.8 $\mu M$ and for the 1 beta epimer was 0.5 $\mu M$. These binding sites match with rapid effects of vitamin $D_3$ in that the selectivity of vitamin $D_3$ analogues mirrors the activity of these compounds in rapid effects on electrolyte transport.

## Triiodothronine

*Triiodothronine*

High-affinity, specific binding sites for triiodothyronine (T3) in membranes from human placenta and rat liver (1, 101) have properties compatible with an involvement in rapid, nongenomic effects of T3 on electrolyte transport (see above). In human placenta, the binding site was solubilized after affinity labeling, and two classes of T3-binding sites were detected. One class had high affinity ($K_d = 2.0$ nM) and low capacity (approximately 320 fmol/mg protein); the other had low affinity ($K_d = 18.5\mu M$) and high capacity (approximately 2.2 pmol/mg protein). The binding sites were found to be specific for T3 in that other thyroid hormone analogs (D-T3, rT3, D-T4, and L-T4) were less effective or ineffective in displacing the bound [$^{125}I$]T3. The affinity labeling ligand BrAc[$^{125}I$]T3 labeled a protein with an apparent molecular mass of 65 kDa.

# A COMPLEX MODEL COMPRISES BOTH THE GENOMIC AND NONGENOMIC ASPECTS OF STEROID ACTION

To be comprehensive, any model of steroid hormone action must explain both rapid, nongenomic and delayed, genomic effects of steroids and related

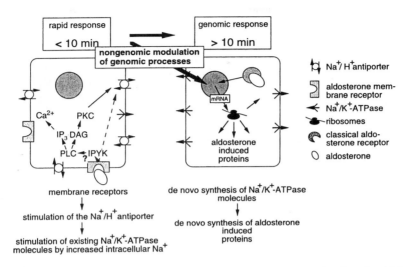

*Figure 5* Schematic presentation of a two-step model of mineralocorticoid action. In addition to the scheme representing the classical genomic theory of mineralocorticoid action (*right*), the nongenomic pathway is shown (*left*) comprising observations on rapid effects of aldosterone on the sodium-proton exchanger ($Na^+/H^+$ antiporter), intracellular second messengers (intermediate tyrosine kinase: IPYK; inositol-1,4,5-trisphosphate: IP₃; diacylglycerol: DAG; free intracellular calcium: $[Ca^{2+}]_i$; protein kinase C: PKC), and aldosterone binding to membrane receptors (from Reference 140 with permission).

hormones. A two-step model of steroid action (Figure 5) has been proposed (135–137). This model not only adds a new nongenomic part to the traditional theory but also addresses possible interactions between its components. This model is not intended to challenge the traditional model, but rather to provide a more complete coverage of steroid effects. For the sake of clarity, it does not treat other dimensions of steroid action, such as nonspecific, nongenomic action and nongenomic modification of genomic steroid effects by nonsteroidal compounds (e.g. dopamine) (93).

In the sequential model proposed here, a new component describes the nongenomic pathway of steroid action that involves steroid binding to putative membrane receptors resulting in almost-instant effects on second messengers and electrolyte transport. An important facet of this model is the interaction of the nongenomic and genomic pathways. Steroid hormones obviously could act through both mechanisms simultaneously, and these mechanisms appear to be important co-mediators of the wide range of cellular steroid effects. Note that there is increasing evidence for second messenger–related modulation of some steroid-induced transcriptional processes (83) as shown, for example, for agonist activity of the progesterone antagonist mifepristone that has been unmasked by independent stimulation of protein kinase A (89). In light of these considerations, steroids may control their own genomic effects through nongenomic actions. This gating function of the nongenomic pathway for the genomic effect would attach pharmacological properties of the nongenomic component (e.g. steroid specificity) to the genomic component of action (e.g. response augmentation).

The model presented here for mineralocorticoids has—with minor modifications—also been applied successfully to the action of other steroids, for example, to neurosteroids (72). This model offers a possible explanation of the complex action of steroids from all groups.

## PHYSIOLOGICAL AND CLINICAL SIGNIFICANCE OF RAPID STEROID ACTION

Examples of clinically relevant observations of rapid steroid effects are rare for most steroids. Modification of reproductive behavior by corticosterone (95) or progesterone (31) and anesthetic or sedative effects of progesterone (111) and neurosteroids (72) are among the exceptions. The negative feedback between plasma cortisol and CRH/ACTH levels (85) within a few minutes may be the result of nongenomic steroid action.

The only convincing in vivo evidence for rapid aldosterone action is on baroreceptor neuron discharge frequency in the dog (Figure 6), which occurs

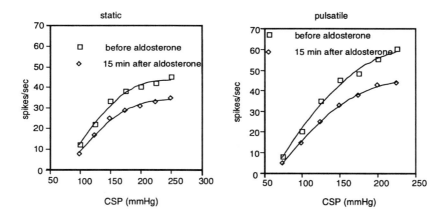

*Figure 6*  Effect of aldosterone on the baroreceptor reflex as measured in neurons of the carotid sinus (spiking frequency) in dogs. Effects were determined for static and pulsatile pressure conditions (modified from Reference 132 with permission).

as early as 15 min after application of the steroid, and on cardiovascular effects in humans (62, 132). In the latter case, Klein & Henk demonstrated that in humans increased peripheral vascular resistance and blood pressure and decreased cardiac output occurred within 5 min after administration of aldosterone (62).

In our clinic, a similar study is being conducted in the cardiac catheterization laboratory to confirm those early results by modern invasive techniques. In addition, a clinical study has been performed in 10 healthy volunteers (M Wehling, unpublished observation) in whom calf muscle phosphocreatine levels were monitored by nuclear magnetic resonance spectroscopy at rest and under stress. The administration of 1 mg of aldosterone intravenously facilitated phosphocreatine recovery after stress, an effect starting within 8 min after application of the steroid. Those effects were demonstrated despite the presence of normal endogenous aldosterone levels.

The selectivity of rapid in vitro effects and membrane binding of aldosterone may provide an additional explanation for differential effects of glucocorticoids versus mineralocorticoids in clinical settings. Thus if both major aspects of action—genomic and nongenomic pathways—are taken into account, a better match with clinical observations is obtained than is provided by the traditional theory of corticosteroid action alone. This traditional genomic theory has specific weaknesses, especially with regard to the nonselectivity of the classical type-I receptors involved. Those receptors have been cloned and, strikingly, do not separate aldosterone from cortisol (8). Clinical observations on the differential effects of glucocorticoid versus mineralocorticoid action reveal specificity conferring mechanisms for genomic mineralocorticoid action such as the enzyme protection of type-I receptors by 11-$\beta$-hydroxysteroid dehydrogenase (35, 43). This enzyme metabolizes cortisol, but not aldosterone, thus preventing cortisol from occupying type-I receptors. Enzyme protection would thus be supplemented by these nongenomic mineralocorticoid effects, which represent an additional specificity-conferring mechanism.

The possible physiological significance of nongenomic aldosterone actions, as in other cases of rapid steroid effects observed at low concentrations, is further highlighted by the low $EC_{50}$ or $K_d$ for both the rapid in vitro effects and membrane binding of aldosterone. These values are in perfect agreement with the physiological concentration of free aldosterone [$\sim$0.1 nM (2)].

Impairment of rapid aldosterone effects has been proposed for patients with pseudohypoaldosteronism (142, 143) in whom type-I receptors appear to be structurally normal (3, 5, 64, 150). These results have been obtained for defects of sodium and potassium transport in HML and are presently being investigated by measurements of $[Ca^{2+}]_i$ in epithelial cells. A preliminary evaluation of these data shows a reduced response of $[Ca^{2+}]_i$ to aldosterone in cells from patients with pseudohypoaldosteronism (M Wehling, unpublished observation).

Another condition that may be explained by a defect in rapid steroid action is human infertility, as described above (9, 58, 92).

## FUTURE TASKS IN NONGENOMIC STEROID RESEARCH

Cloning of the first membrane receptor for steroids remains the major challenge. It would enable researchers to devise agonists; to search for antagonists; to study proximal parts of signaling, which still represent an enigma; and to validate many of the assumptions drawn on the grounds of binding data and traditional cell physiology.

As described in the section on membrane-binding sites for steroids, various attempts to purify these receptor proteins have been undertaken. At the moment, photoaffinity labeling with characterization of the molecular weight and the determination of the specificity of those binding proteins have been achieved. In our laboratory (77), solubilization of aldosterone membrane receptors was partially successful for the ligand-protected complex only. The yield was very low, and the binding was labile, probably explaining the delay between characterization of membrane-binding sites and the cloning of the cDNAs that encode the receptors. In our laboratory, analogous work on the progesterone membrane receptor is progressing satisfactorily, and a partial sequence has been derived (77a).

If direct sequencing and subsequent cloning is difficult, low stringency cloning could be an alternative, although this approach presents major difficulties as well. Steroid- binding proteins that might share homologies with genuine steroid membrane receptors could be $Na^+/K^+$-ATPase (digitalis-binding site) and the $GABA_A$-receptor complex, although the steroid-binding site has not been identified. Certain opioid receptors bind steroids, and thus opioid receptors might serve as starting structures for homology cloning as well (103, 109).

## CONCLUSION

The facts summarized in this review should facilitate future analyses of rapid steroid action in human physiology and pathophysiology. Potential new strategies for therapeutic procedures derived from these developments should emerge, such as antagonists that might block both the genomic and nongenomic aspects of steroid action.

ACKNOWLEDGMENTS

Part of the author's studies included in this review are supported by the Wilhelm-Sander-Stiftung Foundation (88.015.3) and the Deutsche Forschungsgemeinschaft (We 1184/4-1/2, We 1184/6-1, Sc 4/9-4).

*Literature Cited*

1. Alderson R, Pastan I, Cheng S. 1985. Characterization of the 3,3',5-triiodo-L-thyronine-binding site on plasma membranes from human placenta. *Endocrinology* 116:2621–30
2. Al-Dujaili EAS, Edwards CRW. 1978. The development and application of direct radioimmunoassay for plasma aldosterone using [131]I-labelled ligand-comparison of three methods. *J. Clin. Endocrinol. Metab.* 46:105–13
3. Arai K, Tsigos C, Suzuki Y, Irony I, Karl M, et al. 1994. Physiological and molecular aspects of mineralocorticoid receptor action in pseudohypoaldosteronism: a responsiveness test and therapy. *J. Clin. Endocrinol. Metab.* 79:1019–23
4. Armanini D, Strasser T, Weber PC. 1985. Characterization of aldosterone binding sites in circulating human mononuclear leukocytes. *Am. J. Physiol.* 248:E388–90
5. Armanini D, Wehling M, Da Dalt L, Zennaro M, Scali U, et al. 1991. Pseudohypoaldosteronism and mineralocorticoid receptor abnormalities. *J. Steroid Biochem. Mol. Biol.* 40:363–65
6. Aronica M, Katzenellenbogen BS. 1993. Stimulation of estrogen receptor-mediated transcription and alteration in phosphorylation state of rat uterine ER by estrogen cAMP and IGF-1. *Mol. Endocrinol.* 7:743–52
7. Aronica M, Katzenellenbogen BS, Kraus WL. 1994. Estrogen action via the cAMP signalling pathway: stimulation of adenylate cyclase and cAMP regulated gene transcription. *Proc. Natl. Acad. Sci. USA* 91:8517–21
8. Arriza LA, Weinberger C, Cerelli G, Glaser TM, Handelin BL, et al. 1987. Cloning of human mineralocorticoid receptor complementary DNA: structural and functional kinship with the glucocorticoid receptor. *Science* 23:268–75
9. Baldi E, Krausz C, Luconi M, Bonaccorsi L, Maggi M, et al. 1995. Actions of progesterone on human sperm: a model of non-genomic effects on steroids. *J. Steroid Biochem. Mol. Biol.* 53:199–203
10. Baran DT. 1994. Nongenomic actions of the steroid hormone 1 alpha,25-dihydroxyvitamin D3 *J. Cell Biochem.* 56:303–6
11. Baran DT, Ray R, Sorensen AM, Honeyman T, Holick MF. 1994. Binding characteristics of a membrane receptor that recognizes 1 alpha,25-dihydroxyvitamin D3 and its epimer, 1 beta,25dihydroxyvitamin D3. *J. Cell Biochem.* 56:510–17
12. Baran DT, Sorensen AM. 1994. Rapid actions of 1 alpha–25-dihydroxyvitamin physiologic role. *Proc. Soc. Exp. Biol. Med.* 207:175–79
13. Barsony J, Marx SJ. 1991. Rapid accumulation of cyclic GMP near activated vitamin D receptors. *Proc. Natl. Acad. Sci. USA* 88:1436–40
14. Baulieu EE. 1991. Neurosteroids: a new function in the brain. *Biol. Cell* 71:3–10
15. Beato M. 1989. Gene regulation by steroid hormones. *Cell* 56:335–44
16. Berridge MJ. 1993. Inositol trisphosphate and calcium signalling. *Nature* 361:315–25
17. Berthois Y, Pourreau-Schneider N, Gandilhon P, Mittre H, Tubiana M, et al. 1986. Estradiol membrane binding sites of human breast cancer cell lines. Use of a fluorescent estradiol conjugate to demonstrate plasma membrane binding systems. *J. Steroid Biochem.* 25:963–72
18. Blackmore JP, Lattanzio F. 1991. Cell surface localization of a novel nongenomic progesterone receptor on the head of human sperm. *Biochem. Biophys. Res. Commun.* 81:331–36
19. Blaustein JD, Lehman MN, Turcotte JC, Greene G. 1992. Estrogen receptors in dendrites and axon terminals in the guinea pig hypothalamus. *Endocrinology* 131:281–90
20. Blondeau JP, Baulieu EE. 1984. Progesterone receptor characterized by photoaffinity labelling in the plasma membrane of *Xenopus laevis* oocytes. *Biochem. J.* 219:785–92
21. Borski RJ, Helms LMH, Richman NH III, Grau EG. 1991. Cortisol rapidly reduces prolactin release and cAMP and [45]Ca[2+] accumulation in the cichlid fish pituitary in vitro. *Proc. Natl. Acad. Sci. USA* 88:2758–62
22. Bression D, Michard M, LeDafniet M, Pagesy P, Peillon F. 1986. Evidence for a specific estradiol binding site on rat pituitary membranes. *Endocrinology* 119:1048–51
22a. Bukusoglu C, Krieger NR. 1994. Photoaffinity labeling with progesterone-11 alpha-hemisuccinate-(2-[[125]I] iodohistamine) identifies four protein bands in mouse brain membranes. *J. Neurochem.* 63:1434–38
23. Carver-Ward JA, Hollanders JMG,

Jaroud KA, Einspenner M, Al-Sedairy ST, Sheth KV. 1996. Progesterone does not potentiate the acrosome reaction in human spermatozoa: flow cytometri analysis using CD46 antibody. *Hum. Reprod.* 11:121–26

24. Cato ACB, Weinmann J. 1988. Mineralocorticoid regulation of transcription of transfected mouse mammary tumor virus DNA in cultured kidney cells. *J. Cell. Biol.* 106:2119–25

25. Christ M, Douwes K, Eisen C, Bechtner G, Theisen K, Wehling M. 1995. Rapid nongenomic effects of aldosterone on sodium transport in rat vascular smooth muscle cells: involvement of the $Na^+/H^+$-antiport. *Hypertension* 25:117–23

26. Christ M, Eisen C, Aktas J, Theisen K, Wehling M. 1993. The inositol-1,4,5-trisphosphate system is involved in rapid nongenomic effects of aldosterone in human mononuclear leukocytes. *J. Clin. Endocrinol. Metab.* 77:1452–57

27. Christ M, Eisen C, Meyer C, Theisen K, Wehling M. 1995. Immediate effects of aldosterone on diacylglycerol production and protein kinase C translocation in vascular smooth muscle cells. *Biochem. Biophys. Res. Commun.* 213:123–29

28. Christ M, Sippel K, Eisen C, Wehling M. 1994. Non-classical receptors for aldosterone in plasma membranes from pig kidneys. *Mol. Cell. Endocrinol.* 99:R31–34

29. Clarke R, van den Berg HW, Murphy RF. 1990. Reduction of the membrane fluidity of human breast cancer cells by tamoxifen and 17β-estradiol. *J. Natl. Cancer Inst.* 82:1702–5

30. Davis FB, Davis PJ, Blas SD. 1983. The role of calmodulin in thyroid hormone stimulation in vitro of human red blood cell $Ca^{2+}$-ATPase activity. *J. Clin. Invest.* 71:579–86

31. DeBold JF, Frye CA. 1994. Genomic and non-genomic actions of progesterone in the control of female hamster sexual behaviour. *Horm. Behav.* 28:445–53

32. Dormanen MC, Bishop JE, Hammond MW, Okamura WH, Nemere I. 1994. Nonnuclear effects of the steroid hormone 1 alpha,25(OH)2-vitamin $D_3$: analogs are able to functionally differentiate between nuclear and membrane receptors. *Biochem. Biophys. Res. Commun.* 201:394–401

33. Dufy B, Vincent JD, Fleury H, DuPasquier P, Gourdji D, Tixier-Vidal A. 1979. Membrane effects of thyrotropin-releasing hormone and estrogen shown by intracellular recording from pituitary cells. *Science* 204:509–11

34. Edelman IS, Fimognari GM. 1968. Modes of hormone action: on the biochemical mechanism of action of aldosterone. *Recent Prog. Hormone Res.* 24:1–44

35. Edwards CRW, Stewart PM, Burt D, Brett L, McIntyre MA, et al. 1988. Localisation of 11β-hydroxysteroid dehydrogenase-tissue specific protector of the mineralocorticoid receptor. *Lancet* 2:986–89

36. Edwardson JA, Bennett GW. 1974. Modulation of corticotrophin-releasing factor release from hypothalamic synaptosomes. *Nature* 251:425–27

37. Evans RM. 1988. The steroid and thyroid hormone receptor superfamily. *Science* 240:889–95

37a. Farhat MY, Abiyounes S, Dingaan B, Vargas R, Ramwell PW. 1996. Estradiol increases cyclic adenosine monophosphate in rat pulmonary vascular smooth muscle cells by a nongenomic mechanism. *J. Pharmacol. Exp. Ther.* 276:652–57

38. Foresta C, Rossato M, Virgilio F. 1995. Differential modulation by protein kinase C of progesterone-activated responses in human sperm. *Biochem. Biophys. Res. Commun.* 206:408–13

39. Forte LR. 1972. Effect of mineralocorticoid agonists and antagonists on binding of 3H-aldosterone to adrenalectomized rat kidney plasma membranes. *Life Science* 11:461–73

40. Frye CA, Duncan JE. 1994. Progesterone metabolites, effective at the $GABA_A$ receptor complex, attenuate pain sensitivity in rats. *Brain Res.* 643:194–203

41. Fuller PJ. 1991. The steroid receptor superfamily: mechanisms of diversity. *FASEB J.* 5:3092–99

42. Funder JW. 1993. Mineralocorticoids, glucocorticoids, receptors and response elements. *Science* 259:1132–36

43. Funder JW, Pearce PT, Smith R, Smith AI. 1988. Mineralocorticoid action: target tissue specificity is enzyme, not receptor, mediated. *Science* 242:583–85

44. Gametchu B. 1987. Glucocorticoid receptor-like antigen in lymphoma cell membranes: correlation to cell lysis. *Science* 236:456–61

45. Gametchu B, Watson CS, Wu S. 1993. Use of receptor antibodies to demonstrate membrane glucocorticoid receptor in cells from human leukemic patients. *FASEB J.* 7:1283–92

46. Gorczynska E, Handelsman DJ. 1995. Androgens rapidly increase the cytosolic calcium concentration in Sertoli cells. *Endocrinology* 136:2052–59

47. Groner B, Hynes NE, Rahmsdorf J, Ponta H. 1983. Transcription initiation of transfected mouse mammary tumor virus LTR DNA is regulated by glucocorticoid hormones. *Nucleic Acids Res.* 11:4713–25

48. Hammerschmidt DE, Knabe AC, Silberstein PT, Lamche HR, Coppo PA. 1988. Inhibition of granulocyte function by steroids is not limited to corticoids. Studies with sex steroids. *Inflammation* 12:277–84

49. Hendry LB. 1988. Stereochemical complimentary of DNA and steroid agonists and antagonists. *J. Steroid Biochem.* 31:493–523

50. Hendry LB, Witham FH, Chapman OL. 1977. Gene regulation: the involvement of stereochemical recognition in DNA-small molecule interactions. *Perspect. Biol. Med.* 21:120–30

51. Hummerich H, Soboll S. 1989. Rapid stimulation of calcium uptake into rat liver by *L*-tri-iodothyronine. *Biochem. J.* 258:363–67

52. Ignar-Thornbridge DM, Nelson KG, Bidwell MC, Curtis SW, Washburn TF, et al. 1992. Coupling of dual signalling pathways: EGF action involves the estrogen receptor. *Proc. Natl. Acad. Sci. USA* 88:4658–62

53. Ignar-Thornbridge DM, Terng CT, Ross CA, Parker MC, Korach KS, McLachlan JA. 1993. Peptide growth factors elicit estrogen receptor dependent transcriptional activation of an estrogen-responsive element. *Mol. Endocrinol.* 7:992–98

54. Inagaki N, Miura T, Nakajima T, Yoshida K, Nagai H, Koda A. 1992. Studies on the anti-allergic mechanism of glucocorticoids in mice. *J. Pharmacobiodyn.* 15:581–87

55. Joels M, de Kloet ER. 1994. Mineralocorticoid and glucocorticoid receptors in the brain. Implications for ion permeability and transmitter systems. *Prog. Neurobiol.* 43:1–36

56. Joels M, Karst H. 1995. Effects of estradiol and progesterone on voltage-gated calcium and potassium conductances in rat CA1 hippocampal neurons. *J. Neurosci.* 15:4289–97

57. Karthikeyan N, Thampan RV. 1996. Plasma membrane is the primary site of localization of the nonactivated estrogen receptor in the goat uterus: hormone binding causes receptor internalization. *Arch. Biochem. Biophys.* 325:47–57

58. Kay VJ, Coutts DR, Robertson L. 1994. Effects of pentoxifylline and progesterone on human sperm capacitation and acrosome reaction. *Hum. Reprod.* 9:2318–23

59. Ke FC, Ramirez VD. 1990. Binding of progesterone to nerve cell membranes of rat brain using progesterone conjugated to $^{125}$I-bovine serum albumin as a ligand. *J. Neurochem.* 54:467–72

60. Kelly MJ, Moss RL, Dudley CA, Fawcett CP. 1977. The specificity of the response of preoptic-septal area neurons to estrogen: $17\alpha$-estradiol versus $17\beta$-estradiol and the response of extrahypothalamic neurons. *Brain Res.* 30:53–64

61. Khoury RS, Weber J, Farach-Carson MC. 1995. Vitamin D metabolites modulate osteoblast activity by $Ca^{2+}$ influx-independent genomic and $Ca^{2+}$ influx-dependent nongenomic pathways. *J. Nutr.* 125:1699S–1703S

62. Klein K, Henk W. 1964. Klinisch-experimentelle Untersuchungen über den Einfluss von Aldosteron auf Hämodynamik und Gerinnung. *Z. Kreisl. Forsch.* 52:40–53

63. Koch B, Lutz-Bucher B, Briaud B, Mialhe C. 1978. Specific interaction of corticosteroids with binding sites in the plasma membranes of the rat anterior pituitary gland. *J. Endocrinol.* 79:215–22

64. Komesaroff PA, Verity K, Fuller PJ. 1994. Pseudohypoaldosteronism: molecular characterization of the mineralocorticoid receptor. *J. Clin. Endocrinol. Metab.* 79:27–31

65. Korneyev A, Pan BS, Polo A, Romeo E, Guidotti A, Costa E. 1993. Stimulation of brain pregnenolone synthesis by mitochondrial diazepam binding inhibitor receptor ligands in vivo. *J. Neurochem.* 61:1515–24

66. Kostellow AB, Weinstein SP, Morelli GA. 1982. Specific binding of progesterone to the cell surface and its role in the meiotic divisions of rana oocytes. *Biochem. Biophys. Acta* 720:356–63

67. Lamche HR, Silberstein PT, Knabe AC, Thomas DD, Jacob HS, Hammerschmidt DE. 1990. Steroids decrease granulocyte membrane fluidity, while phorbol ester increases membrane fluidity. Studies using electron paramagnetic resonance. *Inflammation* 14:61–70

68. Lieberherr M, Grosse B. 1994. Androgens increase intracellular calcium

concentration and inositol 1,4,5-tris-phosphate and diacylglycerol formation via a pertussis toxin-sensitive G-protein. *J. Biol. Chem.* 269:7217–23

69. Lomax RB, Cobbold PH, Allshire AP, Cuthbertson KS, Robertson WR. 1991. Tri-iodothyronine increases intracellular calcium levels in single rat myocytes. *J. Mol. Endocrinol.* 7:77–79

70. Majewska MD, Demirgoren S, London ED. 1990. Binding of pregnenolone sulfate to rat brain membranes suggests multiple sites of steroid action at the GABA$_A$ receptor. *Eur. J. Pharmacol. Mol. Pharmacol. Sec.* 189:307–15

71. Mandler RN, Seamer LC, Domalewski MD, Bankhurst AD. 1993. Progesterone but not estrogen depolarizes natural killer cells. *Nat. Immun.* 12:128–35

72. McEwen BS. 1991. Non-genomic and genomic effects of steroids on neural activity. *Trends Pharmacol. Sci.* 12:141–47

73. Meiri H. 1986. Is synaptic transmission modulated by progesterone? *Brain Res.* 385:193–96

74. Menachery A, Braley LM, Kifor I, Gleason R, Williams GH. 1991. Dissociation in plasma renin and adrenal ANG II and aldosterone responses to sodium restriction in rats. *Am. J. Physiol.* 261:E487–49

75. Mendoza C, Soler A, Tesarik J. 1995. Nongenomic steroid action: independent targeting of plasma membrane calcium channel and a tyrosine kinase. *Biochem. Biophys. Res. Commun.* 210:518–23

76. Mermelstein PG, Becker JB, Surmeier DI. 1996. Estradiol reduces calcium currents in rat neostriatal neurons via a membrane receptor. *J. Neurosci.* 16:595–604

77. Meyer C, Christ M, Wehling M. 1995. Characterization and solubilization of novel aldosterone binding proteins in porcine liver microsomes. *Eur. J. Biochem.* 229:736–40

77a. Meyer C, Schmid R, Scriba PC, Wehling M. 1996. Purification and partial sequencing of a putative progesterone-receptor from porcine liver membranes. *Eur. J. Biochem.* 239:726–31

78. Moore FL, Orchnik M. 1994. Membrane receptors for corticosterone: a mechanism for rapid behavioural responses in an amphibian. *Horm. Behav.* 28:512–19

79. Moore FL, Orchnik M, Lowry C. 1995. Functional studies of corticosterone receptors and neuronal membranes. *Receptor* 5:21–28

80. Morelli S, Boland ARD, Boland RL. 1993. Generation of inositol phosphates, diacylglycerol and calcium fluxes in myoblasts treated with 1,25-dihydroxyvitamin D$_3$. *Biochem. J.* 289:675–79

81. Morley P, Whitfield JF, Vanderhyden BC, Tsang BK, Schwartz JL. 1992. A new, nongenomic estrogen action–the rapid release of intracellular calcium. *Endocrinology* 131:1305–12

82. Moura AM, Worcel M. 1984. Direct action of aldosterone on transmembrane Na$^+$ efflux from arterial smooth muscle. *Hypertension* 6:425–30

83. Moyer ML, Borror KC, Bona BJ, DeFranco DB, Nordeen SK. 1993. Modulation of cell signaling pathways can enhance or impair glucocorticoid-induced gene expression without altering the state of receptor phosphorylation. *J. Biol. Chem.* 268:22933–40

84. Myers JH, Bohr D. 1985. Mechanisms responsible for the pressure elevation in sodium dependent mineralocorticoid hypertension. In *Endocrinology of Hypertension*, ed. F Mantero, EG Biglieri, CRW Edwards, pp. 131–48. New York: Raven

85. Myles AB, Daly JR, eds. 1974. *Corticosteroid and ACTH Treatment.* London: Edward Arnold. 216 pp.

86. Nemere I. 1995. Nongenomic effects of 1,25-dihydroxyvitamin D$_3$: potential relation of a plasmalemmal receptor to the acute enhancement of intestine calcium transport in chick. *J. Nutr.* 125:1695–98 (6 Suppl.)

87. Nemere I, Dormanen MW, Hammond WH, Okamura WH, Norman AW. 1994. Identification of a specific binding protein for 1α,25 dihydroxyvitamin D$_3$ in basal lateral membranes of chick intestinal epithelium and relationship to transcaltachia. *J. Biol. Chem.* 269:23750–56

88. Nemere I, Zhou LX, Norman AW. 1993. Nontranscriptional effects of steroid hormones. *Receptor* 3:277–91

89. Nordeen SK, Bona BJ, Moyer ML. 1993. Latent agonist activity of the steroid antagonist, RU486, is unmasked in cells treated with activators of protein kinase A. *Mol. Endocrinol.* 7:731–41

90. Norman AW, Okamura WH, Farach-Carson C, McAllewaert K, Branisteanu D, et al. 1993. Structure-function studies of 1,25-dihydroxyvitamin D$_3$ and the vitamin D endocrine system. 1,25-dihydroxy-pentadeuterio-previtamin D$_3$ (as a 6-s-*cis* analog) stimulates nongenomic but not genomic biological responses. *J. Biol. Chem.* 268:13811–19

91. Oberleithner H, Weigt M, Westphale HJ, Wang W. 1987. Aldosterone activates $Na^+/H^+$ exchange and raises cytoplasmic pH in target cells of the amphibian kidney. *Proc. Natl. Acad. Sci. USA* 84:1464–68

92. Oehninger S, Blackmore P, Morshedi M, Acosta AA, Alexander NJ. 1994. Defective calcium influx and acrosome reaction (spontaneous and progesterone-induced) in spermatozoa of infertile men with severe teratozoospermia. *Fertil. Steril.* 61:349–54

93. O'Malley BW, Tsai SY, Bagchi M, Weigel NL, Schrader WT, et al. 1991. Molecular mechanism of action of a steroid hormone receptor. *Recent Prog. Horm. Res.* 47:1–26

94. Orchinik M, Murray TF, Franklin PH, Moore FL. 1992. Guanyl nucleotides modulate binding to steroid receptors in neuronal membranes. *Proc. Natl. Acad. Sci. USA* 89:3830–34

95. Orchinik M, Murray TF, Moore FL. 1991. A corticosteroid receptor in neuronal membranes. *Science* 252:1848–51

96. Ozegovic B, Dobrovic-Jenik D, Milkovic S.1988. Solubilization of rat kidney plasma membrane proteins associated with $^3$H-aldosterone. *Exp. Clin. Endocrinol.* 92:194–98

97. Pappas TC, Gametchu B, Watson CS. 1995. Membrane estrogen receptors identified by multiple antibody labeling and impeded-ligand binding. *FASEB J.* 9(5):401–10

98. Petzel D, Ganz MB, Nestler EJ, Lewis JJ, Goldenring J, et al. 1992 Correlates of aldosterone-induced increases in $Ca_i^{2+}$ and Isc suggest that $Ca_i^{2+}$ is the second messenger for stimulation of apical membrane conductance. *J. Clin. Invest.* 89:150–56

99. Pietras RJ, Szego CM. 1975. Endometrial cell calcium and oestrogen action. *Nature* 253:357–59

100. Pietras RJ, Szego CM. 1977. Specific binding sites for oestrogen at the outer surfaces of isolated endometrial cells. *Nature* 265:69–72

101. Pliam NB, Goldfine ID. 1977 High affinity thyroid hormone binding sites on purified rat liver plasma membranes. *Biochem. Biophys. Res. Commun.* 79:166–72

102. Quelle FW, Smith RV, Hrycyna CA, Kaliban TD, Crooks JA, O'Brien JM. 1988. [$^3$H]-dexamethasone binding to plasma membrane-enriched fractions from liver of nonadrenalectomized rats. *Endocrinology* 123:1642–51

103. Ramamoorthy JD, Ramamoorthy S, Mahesh VB, Leibach FH, Ganapathy V. 1995. Cocaine-sensitive sigma-receptor and its interaction with steroid hormones in the human placental syncytiotrophoblast and in choriocarcinoma cells. *Endocrinology* 136:924–32

104. Ramirez VD, Dluzen D. 1987. Is progesterone a pre-hormone in the CNS? *J. Steroid Biochem.* 27:589–98

105. Reddy AG, Shivaji S, Gupta PD. 1989. Effect of estradiol on the membrane fluidity of the rat vagina endothelial cells. *J. Steroid Biochem.* 33:1229–33

106. Reis SE, Gloth ST, Blumenthal RS, Resar JR, Zacur HA, et al. 1994. Ethinyl estradiol acutely attenuates abnormal coronary vasomotor responses to acetylcholine in postmenopausal women. *Circulation* 89:52–60

107. Salas E, Lopez MG, Villarroya M, Sanchez-Garcia P, De Pascual R, et al. 1994. Endothelium-independent relaxation by 17-alpha-estradiol of pig coronary arteries. *Eur. J. Pharmacol.* 258:47–55

108. Schaeffer JM, Stevens S, Smith RG, Hsueh AJ. 1980. Binding of 2-hydroxyestradiol to rat anterior pituitary cell membranes. *J. Biol. Chem.* 255:9838–43

109. Schwarz S, Pohl P. 1994. Steroids and opioid receptors. *J. Steroid Biochem. Mol. Biol.* 48:391–402

110. Segal J, Ingbar SH. 1984. An immediate increase in calcium accumulation by rat thymocytes induced by triiodothyronine: its role in the subsequent metabolic response. *Endocrinology* 115:160–66

111. Selye H. 1942. Correlation between the chemical structure and the pharmacological actions of the steroids. *Endocrinology* 30:437–53

112. Sergeev IN, Rhoten WB. 1995. 1,25 Dihydroxyvitamin $D_3$ evokes oscillation of intracellular calcium in pancreatic beta-cell line. *Endocrinology* 136:2852–61

113. Shivaji S, Jagannadham MV. 1992. Steroid-induced pertubation of membranes and its relevance to sperm acrosome reaction. *Biochem. Biophys. Acta* 1108:99–109

114. Spach C, Streeten DH. 1964. Retardation of sodium exchange in dog erythrocytes by physiological concentrations of aldosterone, in vitro. *J. Clin. Invest.* 43:217–27

115. Speaker MG, Butcher FR. 1977. Cyclic nucleotide fluctuations during steroid induced meiotic maturation of frog

oocytes. *Nature* 267:848–50

116. Steiner A, Vogt E, Locher R, Vetter W. 1988. Stimulation of the phosphoinositide signalling system as a possible mechanism for glucocorticoid action in blood pressure control. *J. Hypertension* 6:S366–68

117. Suyemitsu T, Terayama H. 1975. Specific binding sites for natural glucocorticoids in plasma membranes of rat liver. *Endocrinology* 96:1499–508

118. Tesarik J, Mendoza C. 1995. Nongenomic effects of 17β-estradiol on maturing human oocytes: relationship to oocyte developmental potential. *J. Clin. Endocrinol. Metab.* 80:1438–43

119. Tesarik J, Mendoza C, Moos J, Carreras A. 1992. Selective expression of a progesterone receptor on the human sperm surface. *Fertil. Steril.* 58:784–92

120. Tesarik J, Moos J, Mendoza C. 1993. Stimulation of protein tyrosine phosphorylation by a progesterone receptor on the cell surface of human sperm. *Endocrinology* 133:328–35

121. Teschemacher A, Zeise ML, Holsboer F, Zieglgänsberger W. 1995. The neuroactive steroid 5-alpha-tetrahy-drodeoxycorticosterone increases GABAergic postsynaptic inhibition in rat neocortical neurons in vitro. *J. Neuroendocrinol.* 7:233–40

122. Thornton SN, Nicolaidis S. 1994. Long-term mineralocorticoid-induced changes in rat neuron properties plus interaction of aldosterone and ANG II. *Am. J. Physiol.* 266:R564–71

123. Tischkau SA, Ramirez VD. 1993. A specific membrane binding protein for progesterone in rat brain: sex differences and induction by estrogen. *Proc. Natl. Acad. Sci. USA* 90:1285–89

124. Trueba M, Ibarolla I, Ogiza K, Marino A, Macarulla JM. 1991. Specific binding sites for corticosterone in isolated cells and plasma membranes from rat liver. *J. Membrane Biol.* 120:115–24

125. Deleted in proof

126. Turner KO, Meizel S. 1995. Progesterone-mediated efflux of cytosolic chloride during the human sperm acrosome reaction. *Biochem. Biophys. Res. Commun.* 213:774–80

127. Uberoi NK, Hendry LB, Muldoon TG, Myers RB, Segaloff A, et al. 1985. Structure-activity relationships of some unique estrogens related to estradiol are predicted by fit into DNA. *Steroids* 45:325–40

128. Ueda I, Tatara T, Chiou JS, Krishna PR, Kamaja H. 1994. Structure-selective anaesthetic potency and effects on lipid and protein. *Anesth. Analg.* 78:718–25

129. Vander AJ, Malvin RL, Wilde WS, Lapides J, Sullivan LP, McMurray VM. 1958. Effects of adrenalectomy and aldosterone on proximal and distal tubular sodium reabsorption. *Proc. Soc. Exp. Biol. Med.* 99:323–25

130. Varnold RL, Smith LD. 1990. Protein kinase C and progesterone-induced maturation in *Xenopus* oocytes. *Development* 109:597–604

131. Waldegger S, Beisse F, Apfel H, Breit S, Kolb HA, et al. 1995. Electrophysical effects of progesterone on hepatocytes. *Biochem. Bophys. Acta* 1266:186–90

132. Wang W, McChain J, Zucker I. 1992. Aldosterone reduces baroceptor discharge in the dog. *Hypertension* 19:270–77

133. Wasserman WJ. 1992. The rapid transient decrease of sn-1,2-diacylglycerol in progesterone-stimulated *Xenopus laevis* oocytes is the result of an ethanol artifact. *Dev. Biol.* 154:223–25

134. Wasserman WJ, Pinto LH, O'Connor CM, Smith LD. 1980. Progesterone induces a rapid increase in $[Ca^{2+}]$ in *Xenopus laevis* oocytes. *Proc. Natl. Acad. Sci. USA* 77:1534–36

135. Wehling M. 1994. Nongenomic actions of steroid hormones. *Trends Endocrinol. Metab.* 5:347–53

136. Wehling M. 1995. Looking beyond the dogma of genomic steroid action: insights and facts of the 1990s. *J. Mol. Med.* 73:439–47

137. Wehling M. 1995. Rapid effects of aldosterone: a novel concept of non-genomic steroid action evolves. In *Genomic and Nongenomic Effects of Aldosterone*, ed. M Wehling, pp. 109–49. Boca Raton, FL: CRC

137a. Wehling M, Armanini D, Strasser T, Weber PC. 1987. Effect of aldosterone on the sodium and potassium concentrations in human mononuclear leukocytes. *Am. J. Physiol.* 252:E505–8

138. Wehling M, Christ M, Theisen K. 1992. Membrane receptors for aldosterone: a novel pathway for mineralocorticoid action. *Am. J. Physiol.* 263:E974–79

139. Wehling M, Eisen C, Aktas J, Christ M, Theisen K. 1992. Photoaffinity labeling of plasma membrane receptors for aldosterone from human mononuclear leucocytes. *Biochem. Biophys. Res. Commun.* 189:1424–28

140. Wehling M, Eisen C, Christ M. 1993. Membrane receptors for aldosterone:

a new concept of nongenomic mineralocorticoid action. *News Physiol. Sci.* 8:241–43

140a. Wehling M, Käsmayr J, Theisen K. 1990. Aldosterone influences free intracellular calcium in human mononuclear leukocytes in vitro. *Cell Calcium* 11:565–71

141. Wehling M, Käsmayr J, Theisen K. 1991. Rapid effects of mineralocorticoids on sodium-proton exchanger: genomic or nongenomic pathway? *Am. J. Physiol.* 260:E719–26

141a. Wehling M, Kuhls S, Armanini D. 1989. Volume regulation of human lymphocytes by aldosterone in isotonic media. *Am. J. Physiol.* 257:E170–74

142. Wehling M, Kuhnle U, Keller U, Weber PC, Armanini D. 1989. Inheritance of mineralocorticoid effector abnormalities of human mononuclear leukocytes in families with pseudoaldosteronism. *Clin. Endocrinol.* 31:597–605

143. Wehling M, Kuhnle U, Weber PC, Armanini D. 1988. Lack of effect of aldosterone on intracellular sodium and potassium in mononuclear leukocytes from patients with pseudohypoaldosteronism. *Clin. Endocrinol.* 28:67–74

144. Wehling M, Neylon CB, Fullerton M, Bobik A, Funder JW. 1995. Nongenomic effects of aldosterone on intracellular calcium in vascular smooth muscle cells. *Circ. Res.* 76:973–79

145. Wehling M, Ulsenheimer A, Schneider M, Neylon C, Christ M. 1994. Rapid effects of aldosterone on free intracellular calcium in vascular smooth muscle and endothelial cells: subcellular localization of calcium release by single cell imaging. *Biochem. Biophys. Res. Commun.* 204:475–81

146. White MM, Zamudio S, Stevens T, Tyler R, Lindenfeld J, et al. 1995. Estrogen, progesterone, and vascular reactivity: potential cellular mechanisms. *Endocr. Rev.* 16:739–51

147. Willmer EN. 1961. Steroids and cell surfaces. *Biol. Rev.* 36:368–98

148. Yano K, Tsuda Y, Kaji Y, Kanaya S, Fujiino T, et al. 1994. Effects of hydrocortisone on transmembrane currents in guinea pig ventricular myocytes–possible evidence for positive inotropism. *Jpn. Circ. J.* 58:836–43

149. Yue P, Chatterjee K, Beale C, Poole-Wilson PA, Collins P. 1994. Testosterone relaxes rabbit coronary arteries and aorta. *Circulation* 91:1154–60

150. Zennaro MC, Borensztein P, Jeunemaitre X, Armanini D, Soubrier F. 1994. No alteration in the primary structure of the mineralocorticoid receptor in a family with pseudohypoaldosteronism. *J. Clin. Endocrinol. Metab.* 79:32–38

151. Zhang SJ, Jackson MB. 1994. Neuroactive steroids modulate GABA$_A$ receptors in peptidergic nerve terminals. *J. Neuroendocrinol.* 6:533–38

*Annu. Rev. Physiol. 1997. 59:395–412*

# BIOLOGICAL FUNCTIONS OF ANGIOTENSIN AND ITS RECEPTORS

## *T. Matsusaka and I. Ichikawa*

Vanderbilt University Medical Center, Nashville, Tennessee 37232-2584

KEY WORDS:   aldosterone, JG cells, extracellular matrix, heart failure, renal failure

### ABSTRACT

Angiotensin receptors are present in a number of organs and systems including heart, kidney, gonad, and placenta; pituitary and adrenal glands; the peripheral vessels, and the central nervous system. This octapeptide exerts diverse effects that include induction of cell hypertrophy and/or hyperplasia and a stimulation of hormone synthesis and ion transport in the heart, kidney, and adrenal, primarily through type 1 (AT1) receptors. In the kidney, several heterogeneous cell populations—endothelial, epithelial, and vascular—carry AT1 receptors. Some studies suggest that AT2 receptors are also functional, but the cell type carrying this receptor and the nature of its specific function have not been fully elucidated. Although studies indicate that AT1 receptors are affected in response to physiological and pathophysiological manipulations, the functional significance of these modulations remains largely uncertain. Nevertheless, recent human genetic studies indicate that polymorphisms in AT1 receptors, as well as in other angiotensin-related genes, have significant impact on organ remodeling processes of the heart and the kidney.

## *A Wide Variety of Renal Cells Have Angiotensin Receptors*

A decade ago, Mendelsohn et al examined localization of angiotensin (Ang) II receptors in the adult rat kidney by using $^{125}$I-labeled [Sar$^1$] Ang II as a probe (57). High-density Ang II binding was observed in the glomerulus and in the inner zone of the outer medulla, outlining vasa recta bundles. The glomerular binding is consistent with mesangial localization. A recent electron microscope autoradiography study revealed that the medullary binding is localized exclusively to type 1 renomedullary interstitial cells (99). Studies have failed to demonstrate a similar signal in the inner stripe of the outer medulla of mice (37). Moderate to low binding occurred in tubules of the cortex and within the

395

inter bundle area of the inner zone of the outer medulla (57). An Ang type 1 receptor (AT1) antagonist, losartan, almost completely inhibits the binding of $^{125}$-I[Sar$^1$, Ile$^8$] Ang II in adult rat kidneys, whereas type 2 receptor (AT2) antagonist PD123177 has little effect, which indicates that most of the Ang II receptors in adult kidneys are AT1 receptors, with a limited number of AT2 receptors (81).

Mice and rats, but not humans, have two subtypes of AT1, namely, AT1A and AT1B. These receptor subtypes are likely the result of gene duplication, which occurred in rodents prior to the phylogenic divergence between the mouse and the rat (96). Gasc et al studied AT1A and AT1B expression in rats by in situ hybridization using specific probes for the 3' noncoding region of their mRNAs (28). AT1A mRNA was observed in mesangial cells, juxtaglomerular (JG) cells, epithelial cells of the proximal tubule, in the vasa recta, and occasionally in a few interstitial cells of the kidney cortex. AT1B mRNA was expressed at a lower level in mesangial cells, in JG cells, and in smooth muscle cells of the renal pelvis. It should be noted, however, that a negative result does not necessarily mean absence of the receptor but instead may reflect technical limitations in demonstrating expression.

## In Vivo Function of AT1 Receptors on JG Cells Needs Further Clarification

The highly expressed AT1 receptor on JG cells is closely associated with renin expression (43, 55a), consistent with the possibility that Ang II directly suppresses the release and production of renin (i.e. via short-loop feedback). Indeed, it was shown that Ang II suppresses renin release from rat kidney slices (61) and isolated perfused JG apparatus (54). Moreover, losartan was shown to induce renin mRNA in freshly isolated renin-producing cells cultured in vitro (88). A sub-pressor dose of Ang II infusion partially attenuated the renal renin mRNA stimulated by treatment with enalapril, an Ang I-converting enzyme (ACE) inhibitor (ACEi) (40). However, the in vivo significance of this short-loop feedback mechanism has not been established because the release and production of renin can be regulated primarily by baroreceptor and macula densa mechanisms (Figure 1). In fact, in renovascular hypertension or during dietary sodium restriction, renin release and production continues to be stimulated despite a marked increase in Ang II. In this connection, marked hyperplasia and hypertrophy of renin-producing cells have been noted in angiotensinogen null-mutant mice (64). The effect of removing Ang II's inhibition on renin-producing cells cannot be distinguished from systemic effects such as low blood pressure, which characterize the angiotensinogen null-mutant mice. Thus the biological significance of short-loop feedback and the functional role of the intense expression of AT1 on the renin production by JG cells remain unclear (55a).

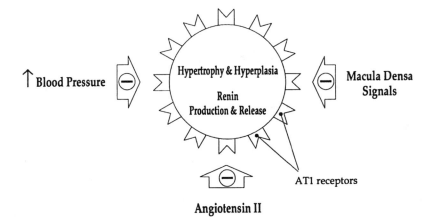

*Figure 1* Regulatory mechanism of renin production and release. AT1 receptor is by far the most intensely expressed in renin-producing cells. The renin release and production are regulated primarily by baroreceptor and macula densa mechanisms. The significance of the direct feedback regulation by Ang II has not been confirmed in vivo. It remains to be determined why renin-producing cells need to express high-density AT1.

## The Pathogenic Role of Angiotensin in Progressive Renal Disease Is Multifactorial

In addition to regulating systemic and local hemodynamics, Ang II may be involved in the accumulation of extracellular matrix (ECM), the hallmark of glomerulosclerosis and interstitial fibrosis, which are ubiquitous in progressive renal diseases. During advancement of glomerulosclerosis, both the quantity and the quality of ECM change. Administration of a dose of AT1 receptor antagonist (which did not lower blood pressure), to stroke-prone spontaneous hypertensive rats and deoxycorticosterone acetate-salt hypertensive rats, remarkably attenuated the typical morphological pattern of nephrosclerosis and the elevation of renal mRNA of TGF-$\beta$, type I, III, and IV collagens, and fibronectin, which occur in untreated controls (46). These observations suggest that Ang II can enhance gene expression of ECM components by a blood pressure-independent action. Indeed, in in vitro experiments, Ang II was found to stimulate synthesis of mRNA and protein of type I collagen, fibronectin and biglycan in mesangial cells via the AT1 receptor, and this was shown to be mediated, at least in part, by secretion of TGF-$\beta$ (42). Lee et al have shown that in the rat remnant kidney, angiotensinogen mRNA as well as TGF-$\beta$ 1, fibronectin and laminin B1 transcripts are abnormally expressed in endothelial cells, particularly in dilated glomerular capillaries prior to the development of sclerosis

(48). The AT1 receptor antagonist inhibited this gene expression. These findings suggest that Ang II is locally up-regulated in the injured endothelium and may trigger a cascade involving TGF-$\beta$ and ECM protein synthesis.

Other studies suggest that Ang II is also involved in interstitial fibrosis. Klahr and colleagues observed that ACEi and AT1 antagonist significantly blunted the increase of TGF-$\beta 1$ and collagen IV mRNAs in experimentally obstructed rat kidneys, in which a marked interstitial fibrosis would otherwise develop (45). Johnson et al showed that a chronic infusion of Ang II led to development of tubulointerstitial injury with type IV collagen deposition (41). In vitro studies by Wolf et al demonstrated that Ang II can induce type IV collagen and TGF-$\beta$ in MCT cells, a proximal tubular cell line (94). It was further shown that interstitial cells express a high level of AT1 receptors (28, 99). In fibroblasts of cardiac origin, Ang II was shown to induce hypertrophy and hyperplasia along with the expression of TGF-$\beta 1$ mRNA (77). Ang II may, therefore, stimulate the synthesis of ECM proteins in the renal interstitium directly, or via induction of growth factors.

Ang II may also modulate degradation of ECM. The importance of degradation mechanisms in the advancement of glomerulosclerosis is supported by the experimental demonstration that attenuation of ECM accumulation could lead to a reversal of established glomerulosclerosis (35). ECM proteins are degraded by a number of proteinases, among which matrix metalloproteinases (MMPs) play major roles. MMPs are secreted in inactive form, and plasmin is required for their conversion to active enzymes. Plasmin is generated from plasminogen by the action of plasminogen activators (PAs), which are also activated by plasmin, thereby forming a positive feedback loop. This system, which also plays a central role in fibrinolysis, is tightly regulated by PA inhibitors (PAIs). The importance of PAI-1 in ECM degradation in the kidney was shown by a study in which administration of PAI-1-neutralizing antibodies to cultured mesangial cells resulted in a several-fold increase in ECM degradation (6). It has been shown that Ang II increases PAI-1 mRNA in cultured vascular smooth muscle cells and vascular endothelial cells (26). In vivo infusion of Ang II in humans resulted in increased circulating levels of PAI-1 (75). Moreover, ACEi administration lowers plasma PAI-1 levels in humans (95). Thus Ang II has a capacity to attenuate fibrinolytic activity and ECM degradation via the PAI-1-PA-plasmin cascade. Overall, Ang II has the potential to attenuate ECM degradation via induction of PAI-1.

## Angiotensin Is Required for Kidney Ontogeny

AT1 is expressed in maturing glomeruli of the mouse fetus at day 16 (out of 20) of gestation (44). Ang II exerts a potent mitogenic action on mesangial cells isolated from the fetus but not on cells derived from the adult (72). The possibility thus exists that Ang II may participate in the proliferation of glomerular mesangial cells during nephrogenesis. This hypothesis has been proven in angiotensinogen null-mutant mice, which had a modest delay in glomerular maturation (64). Because glomerular maturity was comparable between homozygous-mutant neonates produced by homozygous versus heterozygous mothers, Ang II in the maternal circulation appears to have little impact on fetal glomerular maturation. The delay of glomerular maturity was most prominent at 1 week of age, and there was no difference in maturity at 3 weeks of age, indicating that Ang II is necessary for full glomerular maturation in the early postnatal period. Gomez and colleagues found that administration of an AT1 antagonist to newborn rats induced an arrest in nephrovascular maturation and attenuated the increase in glomerular size and number (89) and thus proposed that Ang II is a renal vascular growth factor. In angiotensinogen null-mutant mice, the glomerular number was found to be unaffected, however (64).

AT2 is intensely expressed in mesenchymal cells in the fetal mouse kidney (44). Moreover, the site of AT2 expression closely overlaps with that of a group of cells undergoing apoptosis following nephrogenesis. In this regard, it has been shown that AT2 exerts antiproliferative and apoptotic functions in some experimental settings (62). Therefore, the possibility was raised that AT2 receptors might be involved in nephrogenesis by eliminating undifferentiated mesenchymal cells surrounding the stalk of the ureter epithelium (44). Gomez and colleagues reported that an AT2 antagonist increased glomerulogenesis in organ culture (65). However, AT2 null-mutant mice were found to lack a comparable abnormality in glomerular morphology (34) (Table 1). Although the fate of fetal mesenchymal cells in the AT2 null-mutant mice has not been examined in full, the AT2 receptor does not appear to be essential for normal nephrogenesis in vivo.

## Significance of Local Production and Action of Angiotensin in the Heart Awaits In Vivo Verification

In 1979, an ACEi, captopril, was found to have a remarkable inhibitory effect on the myocardial hypertrophy of spontaneous hypertensive rats (SHR), which cannot be achieved by normalization of blood pressure with hydralazine (5). This early finding echoed a number of in vitro studies showing trophic effects of Ang II on cells, including cardiomyocytes and vascular smooth muscle cells, and led to the notion that Ang II is a cardiovascular growth factor. The anti-cardiovascular-hypertrophic effect of ACEi or AT1 antagonist was also observed in rats with abdominal aorta constriction (51). Moreover, Ang II infusion in rats was shown to induce cardiac hypertrophy, which can be prevented by

**Table 1**  Phenotypes of homozygous angiotensinogen null-mutant mice

Hypotension
Growth failure
Glomerulus
  Delayed maturation
  Resistance to glomerular sclerosis
  Impaired size autoregulation
Tubulointerstitium
  Interstitial fibrosis
  Tubular dilatation
  Hypoplastic papilla
  Reduced Na/K ATPase
Renal vasculature
  JGA hypertrophy
  Arterial wall thickening
Adrenal
  Hyperkalemia

an AT1 antagonist, but not by hydralazine (24). Although it is difficult to distinguish systemic versus local effects of Ang II in vivo, these studies suggest that inhibition of Ang II may have a salutary effect on cardiac hypertrophy to a degree greater than expected from its systemic blood pressure–lowering effect.

In addition to preventing cardiac hypertrophy accompanied by pressure overload, AT1 antagonists and ACEi preserve cardiac function after myocardial infarction both in rats and in humans (68). The salutary effect of ACEi may reflect the capacity of ACEi to reduce not only afterload but also preload; both effects becoming evident shortly after the start of ACEi treatment. One potentially important mechanism through which Ang II may be involved in the process of heart failure is the regulation of ECM turnover. Pressure overload causes not only cardiomyocyte hypertrophy but also reactive fibrosis (93). However, a disproportional accumulation of collagen leads to increased ventricular stiffness and hence diastolic dysfunction (93). As in the kidney, Ang II was shown to promote fibrosis in the heart. Sadoshima et al showed that Ang II induces a mitogenic response and up-regulation of TGF-$\beta$1 mRNA in cultured neonatal cardiac fibroblasts via AT1 receptor (77). Chronic infusion of Ang II into rats induces fibrosis and increases the content of type I collagen and fibronectin mRNA in the heart (21). It was shown that treatment with ACEi attenuates the reactive fibrosis in rats following myocardial infarction (58).

In these settings, Ang II is thought to be generated locally in the heart because a discrepancy exists between the concentration of plasma Ang II and that required for biological responses (25). Although it is controversial whether cardiovascular tissues can synthesize functionally significant amounts of renin (92, 25), the cardiovascular tissue can uptake circulating renin or utilize circulating Ang I (25). In vitro experiments showed that stretch induces Ang II release from cultured neonatal cardiomyocytes and that AT1 antagonist attenuates the expression of c-*fos*, which is activated by the stretch, thus indicating that Ang II can become an autocrine mediator for stretch-induced hypertrophy (78). A possible mechanism of Ang II up-regulation in cardiovascular diseases is an overproduction of ACE in the lesion. In this regard, ACE has been shown to be produced in an abnormally high amount in the reactive fibrous heart tissue of rats undergoing renovascular hypertension, myocardial infarction, or pericardiotomy (15, 82). It remains uncertain, however, whether the locally activated ACE is sufficient to account for the cardiovascular lesion.

## Stimulatory Effect of Angiotensin on Aldosterone Occurs Through AT1 Receptors and Involves Activation of Synthesis and Cell Proliferation

Ang II is the major regulator of aldosterone synthesis, and this function is mediated by the AT1 receptor (16). Consistent with this function, AT1 is intensely expressed in the adrenal gland. Gasc et al showed AT1A and AT1B expression in the rat adrenal by in situ hybridization (28). Zona glomerulosa cells express a high level of AT1A and AT1B mRNA, with AT1B mRNA expression being higher than that of At1a.

Ang II is thought to stimulate the secretion of aldosterone in at least three ways: (*a*) induction of enzymes that are required for aldosterone synthesis, (*b*) stimulation of the proliferation of adrenocortical cells, (*c*) induction of AT1 receptors (Figure 2). Cholesterol side chain cleavage (P450scc) and aldosterone synthase (P450aldo) catalyze the early and late rate-limiting steps, respectively. ACEi was shown to almost completely attenuate the enzyme activity, mRNA, and protein of both P450scc and P450aldo, which are increased during dietary sodium restriction in rats (2, 86). Holland et al, utilizing an adrenocortical cell line (33), showed that the Ang II response element is present within the initial 425 base pairs (bp) of the mouse P450aldo gene promoter.

In dietary sodium-restricted rats, the number of glomerulosa cells is increased, and enalapril completely inhibits the increase, indicating that Ang II has a proliferative effect on zona glomerulosa cells in vivo (59). Tian et al showed that Ang II stimulates thymidine incorporation and proliferation in cultured bovine glomerulosa cells via the AT1 receptor (84). In rats fed a low-sodium diet, the major site of cell replication (assessed by BrdU-incorporation) was not in the zona glomerulosa but in the transitional zone, which is located

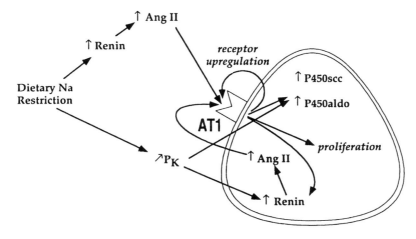

**Zona Glomerulosa Cells**

*Figure 2*  Postulated mechanism of stimulation of aldosterone synthesis during dietary sodium restriction. Dietary sodium restriction activates the renin-angiotensin system. Ang II stimulates aldosterone synthesis by increasing P450scc and P450aldo, inducing cell proliferation, and up-regulation of AT1 receptors. Sodium restriction may lead to a mild hyperkalemia, which in turn stimulates aldosterone secretion independently of the intra-adrenal renin-angiotensin system.

between the zona glomerulosa and zona fasciculata (59). This finding indicated that under sodium-deficient conditions, the major proliferating adrenal cells are not the glomerulosa cells, which are already differentiated, but stem cells, which are localized in the transitional zone.

Dietary sodium deficiency is the most common stimulus for increasing aldosterone secretion under physiological conditions. As discussed above, blockade of Ang II markedly attenuates aldosterone secretion, as well as expression of P450scc and P450aldo, and glomerulosa cell proliferation during sodium restriction. Ang II is, therefore, a potent mediator of aldosterone secretion during sodium depletion, although it is not known whether the increase in aldosterone is entirely dependent on Ang II. Several early observations discounted this notion. For example, plasma renin and Ang II levels often dissociate from aldosterone secretion (9). Nephrectomized rats respond to sodium depletion with a significant rise in aldosterone secretion (66). However, more recently these phenomena have been attributed to either one or a combination of the two mechanisms involving Ang II; that is, activation of the intra-adrenal renin-angiotensin system (23, 71) and/or alteration of the adrenal sensitivity to Ang II (1).

## *Potassium's Stimulatory Effect on Aldosterone Is Believed to Involve Activation of Adrenal Renin-Angiotensin and/or AT1 Receptor Up-Regulation*

Twenty-five years ago, potassium was proposed to be an important mediator for the zona glomerulosa response to sodium depletion (11). Indeed, extracellular potassium concentration is a major modulator of aldosterone synthesis. Nevertheless, studies have shown that the presence of Ang II is required for a full steroidgenic effect of potassium (Figure 2). Thus treatment of rats with captopril inhibits the potassium-induced increase in aldosterone and P450aldo, but not P450scc (86, 63). Moreover, although potassium supplement decreases plasma renin activity, it increases adrenal renin (63). Therefore, it has been proposed that locally generated Ang II in the adrenal glomerulosa cells mediates the aldosterone secretion induced by potassium. Local Ang II is shown to be necessary not only for potassium-stimulated aldosterone secretion but also for basal ACTH-stimulated and sodium depletion-induced aldosterone secretion (29, 66).

## *Data on Renal AT1 Receptor Regulation Are Inconsistent, and Its Biological Significance Remains Uncertain*

In classic terms, renin was thought to be the only rate-limiting factor for the renin-angiotensin system (RAS). Recently, it was shown that angiotensinogen, as well as ACE, is a rate-limiting factor. The importance of the number of Ang II receptors in regulating the activity of RAS has not been established. However, recent gene targeting studies have shown that the mice heterozygous for the AT1A receptor gene null mutation have blood pressure that is intermediate between wild-type and homozygous-mutant mice (37, 55a), suggesting that receptor regulation is functionally important.

Radioligand receptor-binding studies in rats showed that dietary sodium restriction leads to a decrease in glomerular Ang II receptor binding (7, 17). Because this down-regulation by sodium restriction can be aborted by a concurrent administration of an ACEi (79), it is speculated that the down-regulation is driven by the high plasma Ang II prevailing during sodium-restricted conditions. Indeed, both acute and chronic infusion of Ang II was shown to cause a significant reduction in Ang II binding sites in the rat glomerulus (8, 17). Because the same stimulus does not alter cardiac Ang II receptor binding (22) and increases adrenal receptor binding (see below), this down-regulation appears unique to the glomerulus. In concert with these in vivo observations, several-day exposure of glomerular mesangial cells to Ang II down-regulated Ang II binding sites by 23% (17). Because the in vivo down-regulation of Ang II binding sites could not be reversed experimentally by dissociation of bound endogenous Ang II, the Ang II receptor down-regulation was attributed to a phenomenon other than increased prior occupancy of the receptor by endogenous Ang II (8).

Although it is widely believed that the Ang II receptor in adult rat or human kidneys is AT1, it remains inconclusive whether the down-regulation of glomerular Ang II binding sites is entirely reflective of AT1 because there is currently no perfect receptor subtype-specific ligand available for study. Losartan, the most widely used synthetic AT1 receptor antagonist, binds to rat glomeruli and human mesangial cells; however, the number of sites and the dissociation constant value are greater than those for Ang II itself (17). These findings suggest that losartan binds not only to AT1 but also to non-Ang II receptor(s). This explains why chronic Ang II administration down-regulates Ang II-binding sites but not those of losartan (17).

The changes in renal Ang II receptor-binding characteristics in response to dietary salt restriction or Ang II infusion are not necessarily accompanied by parallel changes in receptor mRNA. Indeed, the studies are highly conflicting. In vitro exposure of mesangial cells to Ang II for up to 24 h does not affect AT1 mRNA expression (17). However, Makita et al reported a down-regulation of AT1 mRNA in rat mesangial cells exposed to Ang II (55). In rabbits, a sodium-deficient diet for 4 weeks led to a 43% increase in AT1 mRNA in glomeruli (18). These diverse observations on the level of AT1 gene transcripts may be attributed to (a) a technical difficulty in quantitating AT1 mRNA because the tissue level of mRNA is uniformly low, and thus commonly requires amplification of the message, which in itself may become a potential source of error; (b) heterogeneity of renal cells in which AT1 mRNA may be differentially regulated; and/or (c) activation of multiple factors during salt restriction, including reduced renal perfusion pressure, local Ang II release, and plasma aldosterone (90), which have various potentials to modulate AT1 at mRNA and/or protein levels.

In obstructed kidneys of the rat, renal AT1 mRNA began to fall appreciably within 6 h of the onset of obstruction (69). Similarly, a rat model of cyclosporine A toxicity characterized by hypertension and progressive renal scarring has been shown to down-regulate AT1 mRNA (87). In all these conditions, ACEi or AT1 antagonists can exert renal tissue-protective effects. Teleologically, therefore, down-regulation of Ang receptors may be viewed as an organ-specific homeostatic mechanism to minimize the unwanted actions of Ang II.

In models of hypertension, the status of renal Ang II receptors is less consistent. An elevated AT1 receptor density in the renal outer medulla of a rat hypertensive strain of SHR was noted by a ligand-binding assay (80). By quantitative autoradiography, however, Correa et al (19) reported that, whereas Ang II receptor density is significantly higher in 1 week old SHR rats than in age-matched Wistar-Kyoto (WKY) controls, the density at the glomeruli and the outer stripe of outer medulla decreases to the level below that of adult WKY controls. In contrast, in a rat model of renovascular hypertension, AT1 mRNA was found to be decreased in clipped kidneys (i.e. kidneys with a high local Ang II level), and unchanged in contralateral kidneys (22). In a similar study, AT1A mRNA was lower in both kidneys of models of hypertensive rats (30). However, in another study by Modrall et al (60), although AT1 mRNA was down-regulated shortly after the onset of hypertension, it increased seven- to eightfold in both clipped and unclipped kidneys when a marked hypertension was fully developed.

Overall, as in physiological conditions, the current literature is somewhat confusing with regard to the status of renal Ang II receptors in pathophysiological conditions. Several factors may contribute to this confusion. Most fundamentally, it has been neither established nor tested whether the alterations in Ang II receptor density reported for various experimental conditions, either physiological or pathophysiological, are of any biological significance.

## Cardiac AT1 Receptors May Be Up-Regulated During the Process of Hypertrophy

Several studies indicate that when the heart is undergoing hypertrophy, Ang receptors, particularly AT1, are up-regulated. Thus during the neonatal period, rat cardiac AT1A mRNA and the number of Ang II-binding sites are elevated two- to fourfold over adult levels (83). Moreover, the cardiac hypertrophy induced in rats with 2-kidney 1-clip Goldblatt hypertension is associated with increased cardiac AT1A mRNA and Ang II-binding sites (83). Likewise, in spontaneously hypertensive rats, increased AT1B mRNA was shown in the cardiac ventricle (38). Following myocardial infarction in rats, Meggs et al (56) documented cellular hypertrophy in the non-infarcted myocardium. In these cells, a nearly twofold increase in the density of Ang II was also noted. In contrast to these observations, Lopez et al (53) found decreased AT1 binding capacity and decreased AT1/AT2 ratio in the hypertrophied left ventricle following a partial aortic banding. Thus it is likely that, in addition to physical forces, other factors including the level of Ang II, impact on the status of myocardial Ang II receptors in different in vivo models of cardiac hypertrophy.

## ECF Volume Depletion and Angiotensin Up-Regulation of Adrenal AT1

Aguilera et al first documented that dietary salt restriction in rats increases the sensitivity of the adrenal gland to release aldosterone in response to Ang II. This adaptation was accompanied by increased binding of Ang II to the adrenal (3). Subsequently, a greater than fourfold increase in Ang II receptor-binding sites was documented in the adrenal zona glomerulosa of rats placed on a salt-restricted diet (12). These changes in Ang II binding capacity are accompanied by parallel changes in the transcript of the AT1 gene, the predominant Ang II receptor in the adrenal gland. Thus dietary salt restriction increases adrenal AT1A and AT1B mRNA by 60 and 110%, respectively (52). Of note, the Ang II receptor number in the rat adrenal gland was shown to be up-regulated by Ang II infusion, whereas it was down-regulated by administration of an ACEi (74). Moreover, an infusion of Ang II in rats in vivo up-regulates AT1 mRNA without altering its expression in other organs, and losartan administration reduces AT1 mRNA (36). Kitami et al further showed that AT1B mRNA in the rat adrenal was down-regulated by an AT1 antagonist (47). The up-regulation of Ang II receptor in the adrenal during salt restriction is, therefore, attributed to high Ang II levels.

In contrast to these results from the rat, where Ang II leads to up-regulation of its own receptors on glomerulosa cells and increases steroidgenic responsiveness, addition of this peptide to cultured bovine fasciculata and glomerulosa cells was shown to result in both down-regulation and desensitization (67). Moreover, in monkeys, sodium restriction causes reduction in Ang II receptors in the zona glomerulosa (70). Thus the response of adrenal AT1 receptors to salt restriction and Ang II appears to be different between rodents and bovine/primate groups. One notion is that a gene duplication occurred in AT1 to produce two subtypes (i.e. AT1A and AT1B) in rodents before the species divergence between these two groups (96) and that AT1A and AT1B in rodents are regulated differently. Thus it appears that the different responses of the two species groups reflect a phylogenic divergence that occurred in the regulatory regions of the AT1 receptor genes.

## Certain Gene Polymorphisms in the Renin Angiotensin System May Significantly Impact Organ Remodeling Processes in the Kidney and Heart

Rigat et al identified a polymorphism within intron 16 of the human ACE gene, consisting of the presence or absence of an Alu sequence 287 bp fragment (76). The presence of this fragment defines the insertion or the I allele, whereas its absence defines the deletion or the D allele. This ACE genotype was thus classified as II, ID, or DD. The ACE polymorphism has a significant association not only with the plasma level of ACE, but also with intracellular ACE as measured by ACE activity in T lymphocytes (20). Cambien et al proposed that the ID polymorphism is a marker for increased risk of myocardial infarction (MI) (13). Adult males with the DD genotype were found to have one-and–one-third times the risk for MI when compared with those with other genotypes. Similar findings have been reported by several subsequent studies (73), whereas some showed variant results (10, 50). The DD genotype has also been associated with idiopathic dilated cardiomyopathy and idiopathic ischemic cardiomyopathy (73). Some studies (50) refute these observations, however.

Tiret et al found a synergistic effect of ACE ID polymorphism and angiotensin II type 1 receptor gene polymorphism on the risk for MI (85). The polymorphism studied by Tiret consists of a nucleic acid substitution of A to C at position 1166 (A1166C) in the 3' untranslated region of an AT1 exon (85). A1166C homozygosity, which is, by itself, not predictive of MI, is, in a synergistic fashion with the ACE gene DD genotype, associated with increased risk of MI. Because this A to C substitution does not alter a potential mRNA polyadenylation or destabilization signal, this polymorphic locus is, as the ACE ID locus, believed to be a marker for an adjacent functional variant locus.

Genetic variations in several RAS genes have been evaluated for potential association with hypertension. Although the ACE, renin, and AT1 receptor genes have heretofore failed to be linked or associated with hypertension, Jeunemaitre et al showed that variation in the angiotensinogen gene is linked to hypertension (39). The mutation in which threonine (T) is substituted for methionine (M) at residue 235 was significantly more frequent in hypertensives than in controls in two genetically distinct human populations in Salt Lake City and Paris. The prevalence of the T variant was 36% in control, 47% in unrelated index cases, and 51% in severely hypertensive individuals (39). Moreover, T allele homozygotes had $\approx$20% higher levels of plasma angiotensinogen.

The significance of ACE gene polymorphism varies among different organs or tissues depending on the local availability of Ang I for conversion to Ang II by ACE. It has been shown that the Ang II/Ang I ratio is markedly higher in the kidney; this ratio averaged 0.3 and $\sim$2.0 in the plasma and kidney, respectively (4). It is possible, therefore, that the ACE ID polymorphism may be particularly relevant at the renal tissue level. Diabetic nephropathy and IgA nephropathy are recognized as the two most common causes of chronic renal failure. In both diseases, 30–50% of patients end up with chronic renal failure. Moreover, several studies (14, 49) have shown that ACE inhibitor effectively attenuates the progressive decline in renal function even in normotensive patients. The RAS is, therefore, believed to be involved in the progressive process of renal tissue destruction in these diseases. Several recent studies have shown a significant association in IgA nephropathy between ACE gene polymorphism and the progression to chronic renal failure. A study of 53 Japanese patients with IgA nephropathy (98) showed that, whereas the frequency of ACE DD genotype in patients with stable renal function (16%) was not significantly different from that in the general Japanese population ($\sim$10%), the ACE DD genotype in patients with declining renal function was significantly more frequent (43%). Other studies (32) reached similar conclusions, although variant results have also been obtained (27). Similar results were obtained in patients with diabetic nephropathy (97).

The DD genotype was shown in preliminary studies to serve as a significant risk factor for progressive loss of renal function in polycystic kidney disease (31) and other renal diseases (91).

ACKNOWLEDGMENTS

Our scientific endeavors are supported by the Center of Excellence in Pediatric Nephrology and Urology and funded by National Institutes of Health grant DK 44747. Some of the studies cited in this article were also supported in part by National Institutes of Health grant DK 37868. TM is the recipient of a fellowship from the National Kidney Foundation.

*Literature Cited*

1. Aguilera G. 1993. Factors controlling steroid biosynthesis in the zona glomerulosa of the adrenal. *J. Steroid Biochem. Mol. Biol.* 45:147–51
2. Aguilera G, Catt KJ. 1978. Regulation of aldosterone secretion by the renin-angiotensin system during sodium restriction in rats. *Proc. Natl. Acad. Sci. USA* 75:4057–61
3. Aguilera G, Hauger RL, Catt KJ. 1978. Control of aldosterone secretion during sodium restriction: adrenal receptor regulation and increased adrenal sensitivity to angiotensin II. *Proc. Natl. Acad. Sci. USA* 75:975–79
4. Allan DR, McKnight JA, Kifor I, Coletti CM, Hollenberg NK. 1994. Converting enzyme inhibition and renal tissue angiotensin II in the rat. *Hypertension* 24:516–22
5. Antonaccio MJ, Rubin B, Horovitz ZP, Laffan RJ, Goldberg ME, et al. 1979. Effect of chronic treatment with captopril (SQ 14,225), an orally active inhibitor of angiotensin I-converting enzyme in spontaneously hypertensive rats. *Jpn. Pharmacol.* 29:285–94
6. Baricos WH, Cortez SL, el-Dahr SS, Schnaper HW. 1995. ECM degradation by cultured human mesangial cells is mediated by a PA/plasmin/MMP-2 cascade. *Kidney Int.* 47:1039–47
7. Beaufils M, Sraer J, Lepreux C, Ardaillou R. 1976. Angiotensin II binding to renal glomeruli from sodium-loaded and sodium-depleted rats. *Am. J. Physiol.* 230:1187–93
8. Bellucci A, Wilkes BM. 1984. Mecha-

nism of sodium modulation of glomerular angiotensin receptors in the rat. *J. Clin. Invest.* 74:1593–600
9. Blair-West JR, Cain MD, Catt KJ, Coghlan JP, Denton DA, et al. 1971. The dissociation of aldosterone secretion and systemic renin and angiotensin II levels during the correction of sodium deficiency. *Acta Endocrinol.* 66:229–47
10. Bohn M, Berge KE, Bakken A, Erikssen J, Berg K. 1993. Insertion/deletion (I/D) polymorphism at the locus for angiotensin I-converting enzyme and myocardial infarction. *Clin. Genet.* 44:298–301
11. Boyd JE, Palmore WP, Mulrow PJ. 1971. Role of potassium in the control of aldosterone secretion in the rat. *Endocrinology* 88:556–65
12. Bradshaw B, Moore TJ. 1988. Abnormal regulation of adrenal angiotensin II receptors in spontaneously hypertensive rats. *Hypertension* 11:49–54
13. Cambien F, Poirier O, Lecerf L, Evans A, Cambou JP, et al. 1992. Deletion polymorphism in the gene for angiotensin-converting enzyme is a potent risk factor for myocardial infarction. *Nature* 359:641–44
14. Cattran DC, Greenwood C, Ritchie S. 1994. Long-term benefits of angiotensin-converting enzyme inhibitor therapy in patients with severe immunoglobulin A nephropathy: a comparison to patients receiving treatment with other antihypertensive agents and to patients receiving no therapy. *Am. J. Kidney Dis.* 23:247–54
15. Challah M, Nicoletti A, Arnal JF, Philippe M, Laboulandine I, et al. 1995. Cardiac

angiotensin converting enzyme overproduction indicates interstitial activation in renovascular hypertension. *Cardiovasc. Res.* 30:231–39

16. Chang RS, Lotti VJ. 1990. Two distinct angiotensin II receptor binding sites in rat adrenal revealed new by selective nonpeptide ligands. *Mol. Pharmacol.* 37:347–51

17. Chansel D, Bizet T, Vandermeersch S, Pham P, Levy B, Ardaillou R. 1994. Differential regulation of angiotensin II and losartan binding sites in glomeruli and mesangial cells. *Am. J. Physiol.* 266:F384–93

18. Cheng HF, Becker BN, Burns KD, Harris RC. 1995. Angiotensin II upregulates type-1 angiotensin II receptors in renal proximal tubule. *J. Clin. Invest.* 95:2012–19

19. Correa FM, Viswanathan M, Ciuffo GM, Tsutsumi K, Saavedra JM. 1995. Kidney angiotensin II receptors and converting enzyme in neonatal and adult Wistar-Kyoto and spontaneously hypertensive rats. *Peptides* 16:19–24

20. Costerousse O, Allegrini J, Lopez M, Alhenc-Gelas F. 1993. Angiotensin I converting enzyme in human circulating mononuclear cells: genetic polymorphism of expression in T lymphocytes. *Biochem J.* 290:33–40

21. Crawford DC, Chobanian AV, Brecher P 1994. Angiotensin II induces fibronectin expression associated with cardiac fibrosis in the rat. *Circ. Res.* 74:727–39

22. Della Bruna R, Ries S, Himmelstoss C, Kurtz A. 1995. Expression of cardiac angiotensin II AT1 receptor genes in rat hearts is regulated by steroids but not by angiotensin II. *J. Hypertens.* 13:763–69

23. Doi Y, Atarashi K, Franco-Saenz R, Mulrow PJ. 1984. Effect of changes in sodium or potassium balance, and nephrectomy on adrenal renin and aldosterone concentrations. *Hypertension* 6:I124–29

24. Dostal DE, Baker KM. 1992. Angiotensin II stimulation of left ventricular hypertrophy in adult rat heart. Mediation by the AT1 receptor. *Am. J. Hypertens.* 5:276–80

25. Dzau VJ, Re R. 1994. Tissue angiotensin system in cardiovascular medicine: a paradigm shift? *Circulation* 89:493–98

26. Feener EP, Northup JM, Aiello LP, King GL. 1995. Angiotensin II induces plasminogen activator inhibitor-1 and -2 expression in vascular endothelial and smooth muscle cells. *J. Clin. Invest.* 95:1353–62

27. Fukushima T, Nomura S, Kawai S, Osawa G. 1995. ACE genotype and progression

of IgA nephropathy. *Lancet* 346:571

28. Gasc JM, Shanmugam S, Sibony M, Corvol P. 1994. Tissue-specific expression of type 1 angiotensin II receptor subtypes. An in situ hybridization study. *Hypertension* 24:531–37

29. Gupta P, Franco-Saenz R, Mulrow PJ. 1995. Locally generated angiotensin II in the adrenal gland regulates basal, corticotropin-, and potassium-stimulated aldosterone secretion. *Hypertension* 25:443–48

30. Haefliger JA, Bergonzelli G, Waeber G, Aubert JF, Nussberger J, et al. 1995. Renin and angiotensin II receptor gene expression in kidneys of renal hypertensive rats. *Hypertension* 26:733–37

31. Harden PN, Geddes C, Boulton Jones M, Briggs JD, Junor JR, et al. 1994. Polymorphism in the ACE gene in patients with renal disease. *J. Am. Soc. Nephrol.* 5:330 (Abstr.)

32. Harden PN, Geddes C, Rowe PA, McIlroy JH, Boulton Jones M, et al. 1995. Polymorphisms in angiotensin-converting-enzyme gene and progression of IgA nephropathy. *Lancet* 345:1540–42

33. Holland OB, Carr BC, Braisier AR. 1995. Aldosterone synthase gene regulation by angiotensin. *Endocr. Res.* 21:455–62

34. Ichiki T, Labosky PA, Shiota C, Okuyama S, Imagawa Y, et al. 1991. Effect on blood pressure and exploratory behaviour of mice lacking angiotensin II type-2 receptor. *Nature* 377:748–50

35. Ikoma M, Kawamura T, Kakinuma Y, Fogo A. Ichikawa I. 1991. Cause of variable therapeutic efficiency of angiotensin converting enzyme inhibitor on glomerular lesions. *Kidney Int.* 40:195–202

36. Inagami T, Iwai N, Sasaki K, Guo DF, Furuta H, et al. 1993. Angiotensin II receptors: cloning and regulation. *Arzneim. Forsch.* 43:226–28

37. Ito M, Oliverio MI, Mannon PJ, Best CF, Maeda N, et al. 1995. Regulation of blood pressure by the type 1A angiotensin II receptor gene. *Proc. Natl. Acad. Sci. USA* 92:3521–25

38. Iwai N, Inagami T. 1992. Regulation of the expression of the rat angiotensin II receptor mRNA. *Biochem. Biophys. Res. Commun.* 182:1094–99

39. Jeunemaitre X, Soubrier F, Kotelevtsev YV, Lifton RP, Williams CS, et al. 1992. Molecular basis of human hypertension: role of angiotensinogen. *Cell* 71:169–80

40. Johns DW, Peach MJ, Gomez RA, Inagami T, Carey RM. 1990. Angiotensin II regulates renin gene expression. *Am. J. Physiol.* 259:F882–87

41. Johnson RJ, Alpers CE, Yoshimura A, Lombardi D, Pritzl P, et al. 1992. Renal injury from angiotensin II mediated hypertension. *J. Hypertens.* 19:464–74

42. Kagami S, Border WA, Miller DE, Noble NA. 1994. Angiotensin II stimulates matrix protein synthesis through induction of transforming growth factor-$\beta$ expression in rat glomerular mesangial cells. *J. Clin. Invest.* 93:2431–37

43. Kakinuma Y, Fogo A, Inagami T, Ichikawa I. 1993. Intrarenal localization of angiotensin II type 1 receptor mRNA in the rat. *Kidney Int.* 43:1229–35

44. Kakuchi J, Ichiki T, Kiyama S, Hogan BLM, Fogo A, et al. 1995. Developmental expression of renal angiotensin II receptor genes in the mouse. *Kidney Int.* 47:140–47

45. Kaneto H, Morrissey J, Klahr S. 1993. Increased expression of TGF-$\beta$1 mRNA in the obstructed kidney of rats with unilateral ureteral ligation. *Kidney Int.* 44:313–21

46. Kim S, Ohta K, Hamaguchi A, Omura T, Yukimura T, et al. 1994. Contribution of renal angiotensin II type 1 receptor to gene expressions in hypertension-induced renal injury. *Kidney Int.* 46:1346–58

47. Kitami Y, Okura T, Marumoto K, Wakamiya R, Hiwada K. 1992. Differential gene expression and regulation of type-1 angiotensin II receptor subtypes in the rat. *Biochem. Biophys. Res. Commun.* 188:446–52

48. Lee LK, Meyer TW, Pollock AS, Lovett DH. 1995. Endothelial cell injury initiates glomerular sclerosis in the rat remnant kidney. *J. Clin. Invest.* 96:953–64

49. Lewis EJ, Hunsicker LG, Bain RP, Rohde RD. 1993. The effect of angiotensin-converting enzyme inhibition on diabetic nephropathy. *N. Engl. J. Med.* 329:1456–62

50. Lindpaintner K, Lee M, Larson MG, Rao S, Pfeffer MA, et al. 1996. Absence of association or genetic linkage between the angiotensin converting-enzyme gene and left ventricular mass. *N. Engl. J. Med.* 334:1023–28

51. Linz W, Scholkens BA, Ganten D. 1989. Converting enzyme inhibition specifically prevents the development and induces regression of cardiac hypertrophy in rats. *Clin. Exp. Hypertens.* A11:1325–50

52. Llorens-Cortes C, Greenberg B, Huang H, Corvol P. 1994. Tissular expression and regulation of type 1 angiotensin II receptor subtypes by quantitative reverse transcriptase-polymerase chain reaction

analysis. *Hypertension* 24:538–48

53. Lopez JJ, Lorell BH, Ingelfinger JR, Weinberg EO, Schunkert H, et al. 1994. Distribution and function of cardiac angiotensin AT1- and AT2-receptor subtypes in hypertrophied rat hearts. *Am. J. Physiol.* 267:H844–52

54. Lorenz JN, Weihprecht H, He X, Skøtt O, Briggs JP, Schnermann J. 1993. Effect of adenosine and angiotensin on macula densa-stimulated renin secretion. *Am. J. Physiol.* 265:F187–94

55. Makita N, Iwai N, Inagami T, Badr K. 1992. Two distinct pathways in the downregulation of type-1 angiotensin II receptor gene in rat glomerular mesangial cells. *Biochem. Biophys. Res. Commun.* 185:142–46

55a. Matsusaka T, Nishimura H, Utsunomiya H, Kakuchi J, Niimura F, et al. 1996. Chimeric mice carrying regional targeted deletion of the angiotensin type 1A receptor gene: evidence against the role for local angiotensin in the in vivo feedback regulation of renin synthesis in juxtaglomerular cells. *J. Clin. Invest.* In press

56. Meggs LG, Coupet J, Huang H, Cheng W, Li P, et al. 1993. Regulation of angiotensin II receptors on ventricular myocytes after myocardial infarction in rats. *Circ. Res.* 72:1149–62

57. Mendelsohn FAO, Dunbar M, Allen A. Chou ST, Millan MA, et al. 1986. Angiotensin II receptors in the kidney. *Fed. Proc.* 45:1420–25

58. Michel JB, Lattion AL, Salzmann JL, de Lourdes Cerol M, Philippe M, et al. 1988. Hormonal and cardiac effects of converting enzyme inhibition in rat myocardial infarction. *Circ. Res.* 62:641–50

59. Mitani F, Suzuki H, Hata J, Ogishima T, Shimada H, Ishimura Y. 1994. A novel cell layer without corticosteroid-synthesizing enzymes in rat adrenal cortex: histochemical detection and possible physiological role. *Endocrinology* 135:431–38

60. Modrall JG, Quinones MJ, Frankhouse JH, Hsueh WA, Weaver FA, Kedes L. 1995. Upregulation of angiotensin II type 1 receptor gene expression in chronic renovascular hypertension. *J. Surg. Res.* 59:135–40

61. Naftilan AJ, Oparil S. 1978. Inhibition of renin release from rat kidney slices by the angiotensins. *Am. J. Physiol.* 235:F62–68

62. Nakajima M, Hutchinson HG, Fujinaga M, Hayashida W, Morishita R, et al. 1995. The angiotensin II type 2 (AT2) receptor antagonizes the growth effects of the AT1 receptor: gain-of-function study

using gene transfer. *Proc. Natl. Acad. Sci. USA* 92:10663–67

63. Nakamaru M, Misono KS, Naruse M, Workman RJ, Inagami T. 1985. A role for the adrenal renin-angiotensin system in the regulation of potassium-stimulated aldosterone production. *Endocrinology* 117:1772–78

64. Niimura F, Labosky PA, Kakuchi J, Okubo S, Yoshida H, Oikawa T, et al. 1995. Gene targeting in mice reveals a requirement for angiotensin in the development and maintenance of kidney morphology and growth factor regulation. *J. Clin. Invest.* 96:2947–54

65. Norwood VF, Garmey M, Gomez RA. 1995. Type 2 angiotensin receptor (AT-2) inhibits in vitro glomerulogenesis. *J. Am. Soc. Nephrol.* 6:704 (Abstr.)

66. Palmore WP, Marieb NJ, Mulrow PJ. 1969. Stimulation of aldosterone secretion by sodium depletion in nephrectomized rats. *Endocrinology* 84:1342–51

67. Penhoat A, Jaillard C, Crozat A, Saez J. 1988. Regulation of angiotensin II receptors and steroidogenic responsiveness in cultured bovine fasciculata and glomerulosa adrenal cells. *Eur. J. Biochem.* 172:247–54

68. Pfeffer JM, Fischer TA, Pfeffer MA. 1995. Angiotensin-converting enzyme inhibition and ventricular remodeling after myocardial infarction. *Annu. Rev. Physiol.* 57:805–26

69. Pimentel JL, Montero A, Wang S, Yosipiv I, El-Dahr S, Martinez-Maldonado M. 1995. Sequential changes in renal expression of renin-angiotensin system genes in acute unilateral ureteral obstruction. *Kidney Int.* 48:1247–53

70. Platia MP, Catt KJ, Hodgen GD, Aguilera G. 1986. Regulation of primate angiotensin II receptors during altered sodium intake. *Hypertension* 8:1121–26

71. Pratt RE, Bradshaw B, Moore TJ, Dzau VJ. 1988. Altered expression of the adrenal renin-angiotensin system in spontaneously hypertensive rats (SHR). *Circulation* 78:II59 (Abstr.)

72. Ray PE, Bruggerman LA, Horikoshi S, Aguilera G, Klotman PE. 1994. Angiotensin II stimulates human fetal mesangial cell proliferation and fibronectin biosynthesis by binding to AT1 receptors. *Kidney Int.* 45:177–84

73. Raynolds MV, Bristow MR, Bush EW, Abraham WT, Lowes BD, et al. 1993. Angiotensin-converting enzyme DD genotype in patients with ischemic or idiopathic dilated cardiomyopathy. *Lancet* 342:1073–75

74. Regitz-Zagrosek V, Auch-Schwelk W, Neuss M, Fleck E. 1994. Regulation of the angiotensin receptor subtypes in cell culture, animal models and human diseases. *Eur. Heart J.* 15:92–97 (Suppl. D)

75. Ridker PM, Gaboury CL, Conlin PR, Seely EW, Wiliams GH, Vaughan DE. 1993. Stimulation of plasminogen activator inhibitor (PAI-1) in vivo by infusion of angiotension II. Evidence of a potential interaction between the renin-angiotensin system and fibrinolytic function. *Circulation* 7:1969–73

76. Rigat B, Hubert C, Alhenc-Gelas F, Cambien F, Corvol P, Soubrier F. 1990. An insertion/deletion polymorphism in the angiotensin I-converting enzyme gene accounting for half the variance of serum enzyme levels. *J. Clin. Invest.* 86:1343–46

77. Sadoshima J, Izumo S. 1993. Molecular characterization of angiotensin II-induced hypertrophy of cardiac myocytes and hyperplasia of cardiac fibroblasts. Critical role of the AT1 receptor subtype. *Circ. Res.* 73:413–23

78. Sadoshima J, Xu Y, Slayter, HS, Izumo S. 1993. Autocrine release of angiotensin II mediates stretch-induced hypertrophy of cardiac myocytes in vitro. *Cell* 75:977–84

79. Skorecki KL, Ballerman BJ, Rennke HG, Brenner BM. 1983. Angiotensin II receptor regulation in isolated renal glomeruli. *Fed. Proc.* 42:3064–70

80. Song K, Kurobe Y, Kanehara H, Okunishi H, Wada T, et al. 1994. Quantitative localization of angiotensin II receptor subtypes in spontaneously hypertensive rats. *Blood Press* 5:21–26 (Suppl.)

81. Song K, Zhuo J, Allen AM, Paxinos G, Mendelsohn FAO. 1991. Angiotensin II receptor subtypes in rat brain and peripheral tissues. *Cardiology* 79:45–54 (Suppl. 1)

82. Sun Y, Cleutjens JPM, Diaz-Arias AA, Weber KT. 1994. Cardiac angiotensin converting enzyme and myocardial fibrosis in the rat. *Cardiovasc. Res.* 28:1423–32

83. Suzuki J, Matsubara H, Urakami M, Inada M. 1993. Rat angiotensin II (type 1A) receptor mRNA regulation and subtype expression in myocardial growth and hypertrophy. *Circ. Res.* 73:439–47

84. Tian Y, Balla T, Baukal AJ, Catt KJ. 1995. Growth responses to angiotensin II in bovine adrenal glomerulosa cells. *Am. J. Physiol.* 268:E135–44

85. Tiret L, Bonnardeaux A, Poirier O, Ricard S, Marques-Vidal P, et al. 1994. Synergistic effects of angiotensin-converting

enzyme and angiotensin II type 1 receptor gene polymorphisms on risk of myocardial infarction. *Lancet* 344:910–12

86. Tremblay A, Lehoux JG. 1992. Influence of captopril on adrenal cytochrome P-450s and adrenodoxin expression in high potassium or low sodium intake. *J. Steroid Biochem. Mol. Biol.* 41:799–808

87. Tufro-McReddie A, Gomez RA, Norling LL, Omar AA, Moore LC, Kaskel FJ. 1993. Effect of CsA on the expression of renin and angiotensin type 1 receptor genes in the rat kidney. *Kidney Int.* 43:615–22

88. Tufro-McReddie A, Johns DW, Geary KM, Dagli H, Everett AD, et al. 1994. Angiotensin II type 1 receptor: role in renal growth and gene expression during normal development. *Am. J. Physiol.* 266:F911–18

89. Tufro-McReddie A, Romano LM, Harris JM, Ferder L, Gomes RA. 1995. Angiotensin II regulates nephrogenesis and renal vascular development. *Am. J. Physiol.* 269:F110–15

90. Ullian ME, Schelling RJ, Linas SL. 1992. Aldosterone enhances angiotensin II receptor binding and inositol phosphate responses. *Hypertension* 20:67–73

91. van Essen GG, Rensma PL, Apperloo AJ, Scheffer H, Sluiter WJ, et al. 1995. ACE-gene polymorphism predicts rate of loss of renal function in non-diabetic chronic renal failure. *J. Am. Soc. Nephrol.* 6:407 (Abstr.)

92. von Lutterotti N, Catanzaro DF, Sealey JE, Laragh JH. 1994. Renin is not synthesized by cardiac and extrarenal vascular tissues: a review of experimental evidence. *Circulation* 89:493–98

93. Weber KT, Brilla CG. 1993. Structural basis for pathologic left ventricular hypertrophy. *Clin. Cardiol.* 16:II-10–14

94. Wolf G, Mueller E, Stahl RA, Ziyadeh FN. 1993. Angiotensin II-induced hypertrophy of cultured murine proximal tubular cells is mediated by endogenous transforming growth factor-$\beta$. *J. Clin. Invest.* 92:1366–72

95. Wright RA, Flapan AD, Alberti KG, Ludlam CA, Fox KA. 1994. Effects of captopril therapy on endogenous fibrinolysis in men with recent uncomplicated myocardial infarction. *J. Am. Coll. Cardiol.* 24:67–73

96. Yoshida H, Kakuchi J, Guo D, Furuta H, Iwai N, et al. 1992. Analysis of the evolution of angiotensin II type 1 receptor gene in mammals (mouse, rat, bovine and human). *Biochem. Biophys. Res. Commun.* 186:1042–49

97. Yoshida H, Kuriyama S, Atsumi Y, Tomonari H, Mitarai T, et al. 1996. Angiotensin I converting enzyme gene polymorphism in non-insulin dependent diabetes mellitus. *Kidney Int.* 50:657–64

98. Yoshida H, Mitarai T, Kawamura T, Kitajima T, Miyazaki Y, et al. 1995. Role of the deletion of polymorphism of the angiotensin converting enzyme gene in the progression and therapeutic responsiveness of IgA nephropathy. *J. Clin. Invest.* 96:2162–69

99. Zhuo J, Alcorn D, McCausland J, Mendelsohn FAO. 1994. Localization and regulation of angiotensin II receptors in renomedullary interstitial cells. *Kidney Int.* 46:1483–85

*Annu. Rev. Physiol. 1997. 59:413–36*

# RENAL K+ CHANNELS: Structure and Function

## Wenhui Wang

Department of Pharmacology, New York Medical College, Valhalla,
New York 10595

## Steven C. Hebert

Laboratory of Molecular Physiology and Biophysics, Renal Division,
Department of Medicine, Brigham and Women's Hospital and Harvard Medical
School, 75 Francis Street, Boston, Massachusetts 02115

## Gerhard Giebisch

Department of Cellular and Molecular Physiology, Yale University School of
Medicine, 333 Cedar Street, New Haven, Connecticut 06520-8026

KEY WORDS:   K channel, kidney, regulation, potassium secretion, volume regulation

### ABSTRACT

The activity of potassium ($K^+$) channels is intimately linked to several important transport functions in renal tubules. We review recent progress concerning the properties, site along the nephron, and physiological regulation of native $K^+$ channels, and compare their characteristics with those of recently cloned $K^+$ channels. We do not fully cover work on $K^+$ channels in amphibian tubules, cell cultures, and single tubule cells and do not review $K^+$ channels in mesangial cells.

## $K^+$ Channels in the Proximal Tubule

$K^+$ channels in the proximal tubule participate in generating the cell's negative membrane potential, which is a major driving force for the apical transport of positively charged carriers ($Na^+$-glucose cotransport, etc). $K^+$ channels are also responsible for potassium recycling across the basolateral membrane and are involved in cell volume regulation. Activation of $K^+$ channels in the proximal tubule has been shown to contribute to hypoxic injury (81).

413

0066-4278/97/0315-000413$08.00

## Apical $K^+$ Channels

GENERAL PROPERTIES    Two types of $K^+$ channels, with a single-channel conductance of 33 pS and 60 pS, respectively, have been identified (30–32). Whereas the 33 pS $K^+$ channel is inwardly rectifying and present in rabbit and mouse S3 segment (31), the 60 pS $K^+$ channel has a linear I-V relationship and is found only in the mouse kidney (30). A $Ca^{2+}$-activated 200 pS $K^+$ channel (19) and a 42 pS $K^+$ channel (75) have been observed in primary cultures of proximal tubule cells. Using brush border vesicles from rabbit kidney cortex and a lipid bilayer preparation, Zweifach et al also observed a $Ca^{2+}$-activated 100 pS $K^+$ channel (139). A $Ca^{2+}$-activated large-conductance $K^+$ channel has been described in amphibian proximal tubules (23, 50), and a 20 pS $K^+$ channel with lower selectivity for potassium is also present (50).

## Basolateral $K^+$ Channels

Several studies have shown the presence of an ATP-sensitive $K^+$ channel in the basolateral membrane of rat and rabbit proximal tubules (3, 32, 79, 109). The ATP-sensitive $K^+$ channel is inwardly rectifying (slope conductance of 46–60 pS), highly selective for potassium, and its open probability is increased by depolarization. Recently, an ATP-inhibitable $K^+$ channel was described in the basolateral membrane of ambystoma proximal tubule cells (70). In amphibian proximal tubules, two stretch-activated $K^+$ channels with conductances of 30 pS and 46 pS have been reported (50, 86). They are not sensitive to $Ca^{2+}$ but are activated by mechanical stretch (49, 84, 85, 86). A recent review covers the regulation of these stretch-activated $K^+$ channels (85).

## Regulation of Proximal $K^+$ Channels

ATP    Several lines of evidence indicate that the basolateral $K^+$ channel in the proximal tubule displays ATP-sensitivity. Figure 1 provides an overview of the localization of ATP-inhibitable $K^+$ channels along the nephron. $K^+$ channels in the mammalian proximal tubule are blocked by millimolar concentrations of ATP and contribute to the cell negative potential (29). These channels share several properties with apical ATP-modulated $K^+$ channels in the thick ascending limb (TAL) of the loop of Henle and in principal cells in the cortical collecting tubule (CCT). First, addition of glyburide, an agent that blocks the ATP-sensitive $K^+$ channel, reduced the basolateral $K^+$ conductance in the isolated perfused rat proximal tubule (109). Second, addition of ATP inhibited the activity of the 60 pS $K^+$ channel in both rat and rabbit proximal tubules (3, 45, 109). Finally, the 60 pS $K^+$ channel is activated by diazoxide, a putative opener of the ATP-sensitive $K^+$ channel (45). Several studies have shown that the ATP-sensitive $K^+$ channels may play an important role in linking basolateral $K^+$ conductance to the activity of the $Na^+$-$K^+$-ATPase. Inhibition of $Na^+$-$K^+$-ATPase decreases the activity of the 60 pS $K^+$ channel (3, 4, 45).

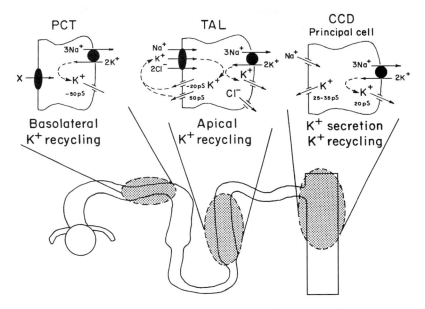

*Figure 1* Localization of ATP-sensitive K$^+$ channels along the mammalian nephron. PCT, proximal convoluted tubule; TAL, thick ascending limb of Henle; CCD, cortical collecting duct (7, 29, 37, 127).

Luminal addition of amino acid as a substrate for transport has been shown to decrease intracellular ATP concentration and to increase activity of the basolateral K$^+$ channel (3). In contrast, removal of luminal substrates has an opposite effect on intracellular ATP and channel activity.

pH    pH regulates the 60 pS K$^+$ channel in the basolateral membrane of rabbit proximal tubule (3, 30) and the luminal Ca$^{2+}$-activated large-conductance K$^+$ channel (75). These results are qualitatively consistent with the effect of acidosis on the macroscopic K$^+$ conductance of the proximal tubule (98).

STRETCH-STIMULATION    Although stretch-activated K$^+$ channels have not been identified in the native mammalian proximal tubule, stretch stimulation activates the apical K$^+$ channel in the amphibian kidney (23, 24), as well as in opossum kidney (OK) cell lines (110, 111). In addition, the stretch-activated K$^+$ channels have also been observed in the basolateral membrane of amphibian kidney (49, 82–86). The stretch-activated K$^+$ channels are involved in cell volume regulation (23, 24, 84, 85)

VOLTAGE    The apical Ca$^{2+}$-activated large-conductance K$^+$ channel is also activated by depolarization (30). Thus the large-conductance K$^+$ channel could play a role in maintaining the electrochemical driving force for sodium, because activation of the large-conductance $K^+$ channel tends to repolarize the apical cell membrane. The basolateral 60 pS $K^+$ channel is also activated by depolarization (31); however, its physiological significance is not known.

## $K^+$ Channels in the Thick Ascending Limb

GENERAL PROPERTIES    The TAL reabsorbs approximately 20–25% of the filtered sodium load and plays a key role in urinary concentrating ability. Apical $K^+$ channels are responsible for $K^+$ recycling, which is essential for maintaining the active NaCl reabsorption in the TAL. Inhibition of $K^+$ recycling has been shown to reduce $Cl^-$ reabsorption by 90% (38).

APICAL $K^+$ CHANNELS    Three types of $K^+$ channels, low-conductance (30 pS), intermediate-conductance (60–70 pS), and large-conductance (100–200 pS), have been identified in the apical membrane of the TAL (5, 34, 129). The low-conductance $K^+$ channel was first identified in the rabbit TAL (129) and subsequently identified in the rat TAL (116). The 30 pS $K^+$ channel is an inwardly rectifying channel that shares several biophysical properties with the low-conductance $K^+$ channel in the cortical collecting duct (CCD) (27, 128). The 70 pS $K^+$ channel has been observed only in the rat TAL (6). Although the 70 pS $K^+$ channel and 30 pS $K^+$ channel coexist in the same membrane, the 70 pS $K^+$ channel is predominant in the apical membrane of the TAL and may contribute to approximately 80% of the apical $K^+$ conductance under control conditions (124). Bleich et al have shown that the 70 pS $K^+$ channel is inhibited by millimolar concentrations of ATP, acidic pH, and millimolar concentrations of $Ca^{2+}$ (6). The large-conductance $K^+$ channel is observed in cultured TAL cells and is activated by $Ca^{2+}$ and depolarization (34). However, the channel open probability is very low (<0.01) at physiological cell membrane potential and resting intracellular $Ca^{2+}$ concentration. Thus it is unlikely that the $Ca^{2+}$-dependent $K^+$ channel plays a significant role in determining the apical $K^+$ conductance under physiological conditions.

   $Ca^{2+}$-activated $K^+$ channels have also been observed in apical membranes from TAL cells that had been incorporated into planar lipid bilayers (see 52). The calcium sensitivity of such high-conductance channels is dependent on the state of phosphorylation and is further modulated by changes in pH and membrane polarization: Calcium sensitivity is diminished following membrane hyperpolarization or acidification of the cytoplasmic surface of the channel (52). Of interest is the pronounced binding of calcium-calmodulin by the channel, and it has been suggested that both pH and potential sensitivity may have physiological significance (52).

APICAL $K^+$ CHANNEL IN THE MACULA DENSA CELLS    A 41 pS $K^+$ channel, believed to be involved in tubuloglomerular feedbacksignal transmission, has been identified in the rabbit macula densa cells. Several biophysical properties of the 41 pS K⁺ channel, such as voltage-independent high-open probability and pH sensitivity, are similar to those of the apical low-conductance K⁺ channel in the TAL (47). The 41 pS K⁺ channel is not sensitive to NaATP. However, in the reported study, the effects of MgATP were not investigated. The precise physiological role of this channel in the tubuloglomerular feedback mechanism has not been explored.

BASOLATERAL K⁺ CHANNEL    A basolateral K⁺ channel has been identified in the rabbit TAL (46). The channel has an inwardly rectifying conductance with an inward-slope conductance of 35 pS and an outward-slope conductance of 7 pS (46). However, its regulatory mechanism is unknown.

## Regulation of the K⁺ Channels in the TAL

Ca²⁺, pH AND ATP    Ca²⁺ plays an important role in the regulation of the apical K⁺ channel in the TAL (Figure 2). Increase in Ca²⁺ blocks the 70 pS K⁺ channel in inside-out patches. Increase in intracellular Ca²⁺ with ionomycin has been shown to inhibit the 41 pS K⁺ channel in the apical membrane of macula densa cells (47) and the 70 pS K⁺ channel (W Wang, unpublished

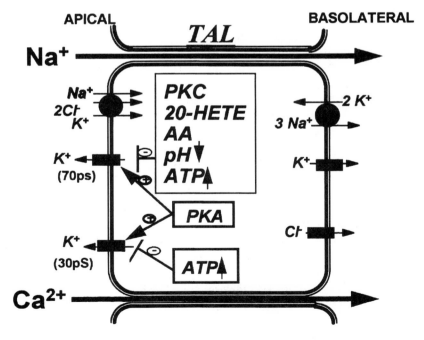

*Figure 2*    Regulation of K⁺ channel activity in cells of the TAL (6, 116, 118, 124, 125).

observations). The effect of $Ca^{2+}$ may be mediated by protein kinase C (PKC), because PKC inhibits the 70 pS $K^+$ channel (125). The apical $K^+$ channels of the TAL, except in rabbit TAL, are regulated by cell pH: alkalization increases, whereas acidic pH inhibits, the channel activity (5, 6). The apical $K^+$ channels in the TAL are inhibited by millimolar concentrations of ATP. However, the physiological importance of the ATP regulation needs further investigation.

ARACHIDONIC ACID (AA)    AA has been shown to inhibit the 70 pS $K^+$ channel in both cell-attached and inside-out patches (124). Several lines of evidence suggest that the effect of AA is mediated by a cytochrome P450 metabolite. First, the effect of AA was abolished by inhibitors of the cytochrome P450 monooxygenase. Second, addition of 20-HETE, a major product of the cytochrome P450-dependent pathway in the TAL (10), can mimic the effect of AA on the activity of the 70 pS $K^+$ channel. In addition, the inhibitory effect of 20-HETE can still be observed in the presence of inhibitors of P450 monooxygenase, indicating that the effect of AA is at a step prior to the formation of 20-HETE. The physiological significance of P450 metabolites has been recently explored. Increase in extracellular $Ca^{2+}$ from 1 to 5 mM reduces the activity of the 70 pS $K^+$ channel (125). It appears that the $Ca^{2+}$-sensing receptor (9) mediates the inhibitory effect of 5 mM extracellular $Ca^{2+}$, because neomycin, which has been shown to be a potent agonist for the $Ca^{2+}$-sensing receptor, can mimic the effect of 5 mM extracellular $Ca^{2+}$. However, addition of 17-octadecynoic acid completely abolishes the inhibitory effect of increase in extracellular $Ca^{2+}$, indicating that the P450-dependent metabolites mediate the effect of raising extracellular $Ca^{2+}$. Furthermore, it was demonstrated that addition of 50-pM angiotensin II inhibits the activity of the 70 pS $K^+$ channel (64). Because the inhibitory effect of angiotensin II can be abolished by suppression of the cytochrome P450 monooxygenase, it is suggested that the P450 metabolites are involved in mediating the inhibitory effect of angiotensin II. In addition, with use of gas chromatography/mass spectrometry, it was demonstrated that angiotensin II increased the production of 20-HETE two-fold (64).

PROTEIN KINASE A    A cAMP-dependent pathway such as protein kinase A (PKA) plays an important role in the regulation of the apical $K^+$ conductance and cell function in the TAL (38). The activity of the 30 pS $K^+$ channel was shown to be stimulated by vasopressin (116). Because cAMP can mimic the effect of vasopressin, data suggest that a cAMP-dependent pathway such as PKA mediated the vasopressin-induced stimulation of the 30 pS $K^+$ channel (116). The activity of the 70 pS $K^+$ channel decreased in an ATP-free solution and addition of ATP restored the channel activity (W Wang, unpublished observations). Furthermore, our unpublished observations show that addition of PKA catalytic subunits stimulates the activity of the 70 pS K$^+$ channel, suggesting that PKA is involved in the modulation of the 70 pS K$^+$ channel (W Wang, unpublished observations). The notion that PKA mediates the stimulatory effect of vasopressin is also confirmed by studies on renal medullary vesicles (80). In addition, previous measurements show that addition of vasopressin increased the apical macroscopic K$^+$ conductance (80). The PKA-induced stimulation of the activity of the apical K$^+$ channels may be involved in the vasopressin-induced stimulation of NaCl reabsorption in the TAL (38).

PROTEIN KINASE C    Several lines of evidence suggest that PKC is involved in the regulation of the 70 pS K$^+$ channel in the rat TAL (125). First, stimulation of PKC with phorbol ester decreased the activity of the 70 pS K$^+$ channel. Second, inhibition of PKC with calphostin C increased channel activity. Finally, application of exogenous PKC inhibited the channel activity in inside-out patches. The PKC may be responsible for mediating the inhibitory effect of Ca$^{2+}$ on the activity of the apical K$^+$ channels.

K$^+$ CHANNELS IN THE COLLECTING DUCT    K$^+$ channels in the basolateral membrane participate in generating the cell membrane potential involved in K$^+$ recycling across the basolateral membrane and could serve as an additional route for K$^+$ entering the cell during hyperaldosteronism.

## K$^+$ Channels in the Apical Membrane of Principal Cells

GENERAL PROPERTIES    Two types of K$^+$ channels have been identified in the apical membranes of principal cells in the rat and rabbit CCT: a large, single-conductance K$^+$ channel with low-open probability and a low-conductance K$^+$ channel with high-open probability. Besides their different conductances, these channels are also regulated by diverse mechanisms, and there is agreement that they serve different functions (28, 29, 39, 69, 127).

The first K$^+$ channel detected in mammalian principal cells was a Ca-$^{2+}$-activated, large-conductance K$^+$ channel (maxi-K$^+$ channel; see 26, 44) in the CCT with very low open probability at physiological levels of cytosolic Ca$^{2+}$ and cell potential. The channel is stimulated by membrane depolarization and high cytosolic Ca$^{2+}$ and inhibited by barium and millimolar concentrations of tetraethylammonium (TEA). Channel activity is reduced by lowering cytosolic pH or exposure to millimolar concentrations of ATP, but the channel becomes pH insensitive at high Ca$^{2+}$ concentrations (40). Stretch activation in excised patches occurs in a Ca$^{2+}$-independent manner when pipette suction is applied (77) but depends on extracellular Ca$^{2+}$ when cells are exposed to hypotonic media (40). Studies in rat everted collecting tubules also demonstrate the presence of an apical large-conductance K$^+$ channel whose activity increases with perfusion of either the lumen or bath with hypotonic saline solutions. However, the luminal effect depends on the presence of vasopressin (99). Large stretch-activated $K^+$ channels with the properties described above are also present in amphibian proximal tubules (see 85) and in other leaky epithelia (13, 110, 111). There is general agreement that the apical maxi-$K^+$ channel plays an important role in volume regulation (volume regulatory decrease) by initiating the release of potassium from tubule cells whose volume has been increased (see 100). Whether maxi-$K^+$ channels in principal cells could also modulate potassium secretion during changes in intratubule pressure is unknown.

The second channel in the apical membrane of principal cells of isolated CCTs is a small-conductance $K^+$ channel with high-open probability (12, 27, 128), and a channel with similar properties has also been found in primary cultures of rabbit CCTs (60). The characteristics of the channel include modest inward rectification and high selectivity of $K^+$ over $Na^+$, but the channel also conducts rubidium ($Rb^+$) ions (27) and thus may be involved in the secretion of $Rb^+$, which has been observed in isolated perfused rat CCTs (90, 91). Because the open probability of this $K^+$ channel is very high (95%) in physiological conditions (normal $K^+$ intake), activation of channel activity occurs largely by recruiting additional channels. The very rapid rate at which the channel pool increases, for instance by changes in cytosolic pH (see below), suggests that the activation process involves stimulation of dormant channels already present in the apical membrane.

REGULATION    Patch-clamp studies have shown that a high potassium intake increases the channel density of low-conductance $K^+$ channels (78, 128) (Figure 3). The mechanisms by which a high-potassium diet and the associated increased aldosterone levels lead to a long-term increase in $K^+$ channel activation are not fully understood but involve at least two separate pathways (78, 128): one that appears to be independent of aldosterone, which mediates increased potassium secretion when moderate loads of potassium are administered, and a second aldosterone-dependent mechanism that is activated by high loads of potassium. Of interest is the conclusion reached by both studies that a high-potassium diet per se is able to increase apical $K^+$ channel density, whereas high levels of circulating aldosterone alone, such as those observed in animals on a low-sodium diet, are insufficient to increase $K^+$ channel activity (78). Thus a rise in plasma potassium alone has emerged as an important signal for an increase in $K^+$ channel density.

One of the striking characteristics of the apical low-conductance $K^+$ channel is its exquisite sensitivity to changes in cell pH. Channel activity declines sharply when pH is decreased and reduction of pH from 7.4 to 7.0 effectively abolishes $K^+$ channel activity (128). A mathematical model has defined the contribution

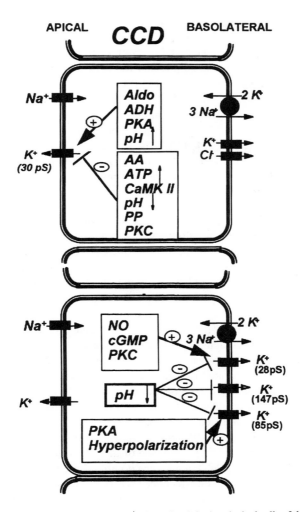

*Figure 3*   Regulation of apical secretory K$^+$ channel activity in principal cells of the CCD (*upper panel*) (11, 12, 27, 35, 60, 61, 78, 92, 112, 117, 119, 121–124, 127, 138). Regulation of basolateral K$^+$ channel activity in principal cells of the CCD (*lower panel*) (1–18, 41, 42, 92, 112, 118, 126).

of pH-induced changes in $K^+$ channel activity to the expected alterations in potassium secretion (101).

The apical $K^+$ channel is regulated by alterations in the cytosolic ATP/ADP ratio (117, 123). ATP-sensitive $K^+$ channels have also been defined in extrarenal tissues such as smooth, skeletal, and heart muscle and brain and pancreatic $\beta$-cells (1). Patch-clamp studies on apical $K^+$ channels in principal cells have shown that millimolar concentrations of ATP inhibit channel activity and that channel block is relieved by ADP. The inhibitory effect of ATP can also be reversed by $K^+$ channel openers such as chromakalim (117), whereas glyburide, an effective blocker of ATP-regulated $K^+$ channels ($K_{ATP}$), inhibits the small-conductance $K^+$ channel (114, 115). The sensitivity of the inhibitory effect of ATP is modulated by ADP, cAMP-dependent PKA, and cytosolic pH (122, 123). Thus both ADP and PKA increase the half-maximal inhibition ($K_d$) of ATP, whereas the $K_d$ is decreased at acidic cell pH. In the proximal tubule, basolateral ATP-sensitive $K^+$ channel activity is enhanced by stimulating transcellular $Na^+$ transport, which reduces intracellular [ATP] (109). Whether similar coupling of basolateral $K^+$ channel activity to $Na^+$-$K^+$-ATPase turnover via changes in cell [ATP] also occurs in principal cells of the CCT is presently unknown, but the cell ATP/ADP ratio has been demonstrated to be a key metabolic coupling mechanism between the rate of $Na^+$-$K^+$ pumping and $K^+$ recycling in principal cells of the frog skin, a tight epithelium sharing many properties with distal tubule nephron segments (112). An ATP-inhibitable K-selective channel has also been detected in inner medullary collecting duct (IMCD) cells (87).

The observation that changes in vasopressin levels stimulate potassium secretion in the initial collecting ducts of the rat kidney (21, 22, 91, 117) suggests that cAMP modulates apical $K^+$ channel activity. Indeed, patch-clamp studies of the low-conductance $K^+$ channel show that cAMP stimulates channel activity via a PKA-dependent pathway and that vasopressin significantly enhances channel activity in cell-attached patches (11, 122, 123). The role of submillimolar [ATP] in cAMP-induced activation of secretory $K^+$ channels is underscored by the $Mg^{2+}$ dependence of the ATP effect (ATP hydrolysis), because nonhydrolyzable ATP analogues do not mimic the effects of MgATP. Channel run-down can also be effectively overcome by exposing excised membrane patches to low concentrations of MgATP and PKA (123). cAMP has also been identified as activating low-conductance $K^+$ channels in A6 cells, a preparation sharing properties of mammalian principal cells (35).

An increase in cell calcium decreases the activity of the low-conductance $K^+$ channel. Such channel inhibition is not direct because exposure of the cytosolic surface of inside-out patches to high $[Ca^{2+}]$ does not diminish activity (128). However, when cell-attached membranes of principal cells are exposed to ionomycin, clamping of cell calcium at high concentrations occurs, and such maneuvers lead to complete suppression of channel activity (121). Exploration of the underlying mechanism showed that PKC and calcium-calmodulin-dependent kinases are involved in mediating the inhibitory effects of raising cell calcium on K$^+$ channel activity (57, 117, 122). Inhibition of apical K$^+$ channels following reduced basolateral Na$^+$-K$^+$-ATPase activity, a maneuver that increases cell calcium concentrations (121), has also been shown to involve calcium-dependent activation of PKC. Moreover, the inhibitory action of cyclosporin A on apical K$^+$ channels is also mediated by changes in cell calcium and activation of PKC (59).

These observations strongly suggest that channel activity is influenced by several separate phosphorylation processes that either stimulate or inhibit activity: PKA increases channel activity, whereas channel inhibition follows enhancement of Ca$^{2+}$-modulated PKC and calcium-calmodulin-dependent kinase II activity. Furthermore, a balance between such phosphorylation and dephosphorylation processes is strongly suggested by the presence of Mg$^{2+}$-dependent and Mg$^{2+}$-independent membrane-bound phosphatases in the apical membrane of principal cells whose activity diminishes channel activity (56). Thus the rapid decline of channel activity following patch excision (channel run-down) can be significantly delayed by exposure to Mg$^{2+}$-free solutions that contain submillimolar concentrations of ATP that permit phosphorylation yet are below the concentration that inhibits channels (56, 117, 123, 129).

The activity of apical low-conductance K$^+$ channels is reduced by AA (119). Because inhibitors of AA metabolism do not block the action of AA, a direct effect is suggested. An intact actin cytoskeleton is also required for normal K$^+$ channel activity (120). Embryonic development of K$^+$ channels lags behind that of sodium channels and has been implicated in low potassium secretion rates at birth (88).

THE ROLE OF K$^+$ CHANNELS IN CELL MIGRATION    An interesting series of studies on transformed Madin-Darby canine kidney cells (MDCK) has demonstrated that K$^+$ channels play an important role in cell mobility and migration (94–96). MDCK cells share several properties with mammalian principal and intercalated cells, and a Ca$^{2+}$-activated K$^+$ channel in their apical membrane has been functionally defined (93). Exposure to alkaline culture media leads to permanent transformation into cells that do not form polarized epithelia and are distinguished by vigorous migration. Migration of such transformed MDCK cells is intimately related to the activity of spontaneously oscillating Ca$^{2+}$-stimulated K$^+$ channels and their polar distribution along the cell axis (94–96).

## K$^+$ Channels in the Basolateral Membrane

GENERAL PROPERTIES    The most difficult aspect of studying basolateral K$^+$ channels in the CCD is exposing the basolateral membrane. Two techniques currently used to expose the basolateral membrane are mechanical and enzymatic approaches (41, 42, 126). Studying the basolateral $K^+$ channel in the collagenase-treated CCDs, Hirsch et al identified two types of basolateral $K^+$ channels with small and large conductances. The slope conductance of the small-conductance channel was 67 pS in cell-attached patches and 28 pS in excised patches. The conductance of the large-conductance $K^+$ channel was 147 pS in cell-attached patches, 85 pS in excised patches with asymmetrical KCl, and 198 pS in symmetrical high KCl solutions (41).

Using a split-open CCD, Wang et al were able to study the basolateral $K^+$ channel by mechanical removal of intercalated cells. Two types of $K^+$ channels with small conductance and intermediate conductance were identified in the lateral membrane of the CCD (126). The slope conductance of the small-conductance $K^+$ channel is 28 pS in an asymmetrical solution and 30 pS in symmetrical high KCl solutions, whereas the slope conductance of the intermediate-conductance $K^+$ channel is 85 pS in symmetrical high KCl solutions. Although the slope conductance of the small-conductance channel in the two studies is different, available evidence suggests that the channel observed in these studies is the same because both studies have found the same channel conductance in excised patches (41, 126). In addition, both studies show that cGMP stimulates this channel (41, 42, 63).

## Regulation of Basolateral $K^+$ Channels

NITRIC OXIDE (NO) AND cGMP    Several lines of evidence suggest that NO plays an important role in the regulation of the small-conductance channel in the basolateral membrane of the CCD (63). First, inhibition of nitric oxide synthase (NOS) reduces the channel activity. Second, the addition of exogenous NO donors restores the channel activity when it has been reduced by NOS inhibitors. Finally, application of a cGMP analogue stimulates channel activity, and cGMP also restores the channel activity blocked by NOS inhibitors, which indicates that the cGMP-dependent pathway may mediate the effect of NO. The mechanism by which cGMP stimulates channel activity is not fully understood. The fact that inhibition of cGMP-dependent protein kinase reduces channel activity suggests that the effect of cGMP may be mediated by cGMP-dependent protein kinase (40, 41). The physiological importance of cGMP-dependent regulation is best demonstrated by experiments in which addition of cGMP hyperpolarizes the cell membrane potential (40, 41). Because $Na^+$ reabsorption is an electrogenic process, alteration of the cell membrane potential could affect the apical $Na^+$ influx.

PROTEIN KINASE C    PKC has been shown to play an important role in modulating $K^+$ channels in the CCD (62, 118, 122). Stimulation of PKC blocks the apical low-conductance $K^+$ channel (29, 117, 122). In contrast, stimulation of

PKC increases the activity of the small-conductance K$^+$ channel in the CCD, whereas inhibition of PKC reduces the activity of the basolateral membranes. However, it is unlikely that the stimulatory effect of PKC is mediated by direct phosphorylation or a closely related protein because PKC has no effect on the activity of the small-conductance K$^+$ channel in excised patches. This suggests that the stimulatory effect of PKC observed in intact cells is mediated by an intermediator protein, which in turn activates the small-conductance K$^+$ channel. Further studies have revealed that the addition of an exogenous NO donor or cGMP analogue reversed the inhibitory effect of the PKC inhibitor on the channel activity, suggesting that NO may be involved in mediating the stimulatory effect of PKC (118). This view is further confirmed by experiments in which phorbol myristate acetate (PMA) has no stimulatory effect on channel activity when NOS is blocked. The PKC-induced stimulation of basolateral K$^+$ channels may play an important role in maintaining the function of principal cells. Increase in Na$^+$ influx transiently increases intracellular Na$^+$ concentration and accordingly raises intracellular Ca$^{2+}$, which could in turn activate PKC. Because an increase in Na$^+$ influx stimulates the Na$^+$-K$^+$-ATPase (25), K$^+$ influx across the basolateral membrane is enhanced. Thus PKC-induced stimulation of basolateral K$^+$ conductance could have a beneficial effect for K$^+$ recycling across the basolateral membrane of the cell.

PROTEIN KINASE A    PKA has been shown to stimulate the activity of the intermediate-conductance K$^+$ channel (118) whose open probability is increased by hyperpolarization. Application of PKA shifted the voltage-dependence curve to the right and made it more active at the given cell membrane potential. The PKA-induced stimulation could be important for the function of principal cells. The cAMP-dependent pathway has been shown to increase Na$^+$ reabsorption in the CCD (89). An increase in Na$^+$ reabsorption would stimulate the activity of Na$^+$-K$^+$-ATPase and consequently increase the basolateral K$^+$ conductance to enhance K$^+$ recycling. Because the activity of the intermediate-conductance K$^+$ channel is voltage dependent and because hyperpolarization increases the channel open probability, the hyperpolarization induced by stimulation of Na$^+$-K$^+$-ATPase would enhance the activity of this K$^+$ channel. In addition, direct PKA stimulation makes the intermediate-conductance K$^+$ channel less sensitive to the voltage changes and further increases the channel open probability.

CELL pH    The basolateral K$^+$ channel is sensitive to changes in cell pH (92). Data are consistent with macroscopic measurements in which acidosis reduces basolateral K$^+$ conductance.

## Molecular Structure of Renal K$^+$ Channels

Several channels have been cloned from renal tissues (see Table 1). These include K$^+$ channels from a renal papillary epithelial cell line (113): several

**Table 1**   Renal channels

| Type | Localization | General characteristics | Reference |
|------|--------------|------------------------|-----------|
| $I^a_{SK}$ | Proximal tubule | Slow activation | 106 |
| ROMK | CCD TAL | 30- to 40-pS inwardly rectifying ATP, pH-sensitive | 12, 27, 43, 124, 138 |
| RACTK$_1$ | CCD | 80 pS, pH-sensitive | 102 |
| Shaker (Kv1, Kv2, Kv3) | Medulla cell line, LLC-PK cell line | Voltage-gated, salicylamide-sensitive | 16, 18, 113 |
| K$_{CN}$1 | Rabbit kidney distal nephron | GMP-gated | 17, 135 |
| CCD-1RK$_3$ | Mouse CCD cell lines | 14 pS, inwardly rectifying | 130 |
| Shaker KC22 | Distal nephron | Voltage-gated | 18 |

$^a$Small conductance.

isoforms of voltage- and cGMP-gated Shaker-like potassium channels from renal libraries, cell cultures, and microdissected cortical collecting tubules (16–18); and a low-conductance, inwardly rectifying $K^+$ channel from cultured mouse CCT cells (130). Information on cell localization (apical versus basolateral), regulation, and physiological functions of these channels is emerging. Of interest is the observation that cGMP-stimulated $K^+$ channels have been identified in the basolateral membrane of native principal cells (41, 42, 118).

MOLECULAR IDENTIFICATION OF THE LOW-CONDUCTANCE $K^+$ SECRETORY CHANNEL   These $K^+$ channels are of special interest because they share many important properties with native apical $K^+$ channels in principal cells (see Table 2) and play an important role in potassium secretion (29).

An inwardly rectifying, ATP-regulated $K^+$ channel, ROMK1 ($K_{IR}$1.1a) (7, 37, 43), has been cloned from the outer medulla of rat kidney. ROMK, along with other subsequently discovered $K^+$ channel genes (2, 7, 15, 41, 53–55, 68, 102, 106, 138) defines a new class of inwardly rectifying $K^+$ channels, the $K_{IR}$ family. ROMK and other $K_{IR}$ family members encode proteins with the novel channel topology shown in Figure 4. The ROMK channel protein has two potential membrane-spanning helices (M1 and M2) (see Figure 4; 43) flanking a H5-like region, which forms part of the channel pore in the voltage-gated $K^+$ channels. ROMK is abundantly expressed in kidney and several other tissues (e.g. brain, spleen, lung, and eye) (43, 51).

The ROMK gene contains exons (43) yielding several alternatively spliced ROMK transcripts [ROMK1 ($K_{IR}$1.1), ROMK2 ($K_{IR}$1.1b), and ROMK3

**Table 2**  Comparison of ROMK ($K_{IR}$1.1) with the low conductance K$^+$ secretory channels in TAL and principal cells of CCD

| Property | ROMK | TAL | Principal cell in CCD |
|---|---|---|---|
| Channel conductance, ps | 35–45 | 30 | 25–35 |
| Selectivity | K$^+$ $\gg$ Na$^+$ | K$^+$ $\gg$ Na$^+$ | K$^+$ > Rb$^+$ $\gg$ Na$^+$ |
| Inward rectification | Yes | Yes | Yes |
| Open probability ($P_o$) | High (0.8–0.9 for > $-40$ mV) | High (0.8–0.9) | High (>0.9) |
| ATP inhibits (mM) | Yes [MgATP > Na$_2$ATP] | Yes [MgATP] | Yes [MgATP > Na$_2$ATP] |
| Run-down by phosphatase | Yes | ? | Yes |
| Re-activation by MgATP +PKA | Yes | Yes | Yes |
| pH-dependence (inhibited by $\downarrow$pH) | Yes | Yes | Yes |
| Arachidonate | Yes (ROMK1) | ? | Yes |
| PKC | Yes | ? | Yes |
| Glibenclamide | Yes (with CFTR) | Yes | Yes |

($K_{IR}$1.1c)]. All the protein products produced by these alternatively spliced transcripts form functional K$^+$ channels when expressed in *Xenopus laevis* oocytes (58, 97, 133). The alternative splicing at the 3'-noncoding region accounts for the $\approx$3 kb mRNA observed on northern blot analysis of rat kidney cortex and outer medulla RNA (58). In contrast, the 5' end splicing alters both the length and amino acid sequence of the NH$_2$-terminus of ROMK channels (8). The role of NH$_2$-terminal variations on ROMK channel function and regulation by phosphorylation-dephosphorylation processes is rapidly emerging (71–74).

It is evident that ROMK isoforms are differentially expressed along the nephron (58). ROMK2, which encodes the channel with the shortest NH$_2$-terminus, is the most widely distributed of the ROMK transcripts. The ROMK1 transcript is specifically expressed in collecting ducts [CCD, outer medullary (OMCD), and inner medullary (IMCD)], and ROMK3 is expressed in the earlier nephron segments [medullary thick ascending limb (MTAL), cortical thick ascending limb (CTAL), and distal convoluted tubule (DCT)]. Thus the distribution of ROMK channel isoforms suggests that ROMK channel-forming proteins represent the low-conductance secretory K$^+$ channel in the TAL and principal cells. It is also evident that all these loop and distal nephron segments, except the OMCD, appear to express two ROMK isoforms; ROMK2 and one of the isoforms (ROMK1 or ROMK3) encoding a channel protein

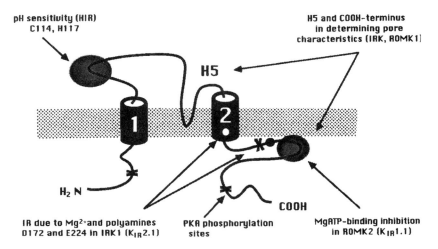

pH sensitivity (HIR)
C114, H117

H5 and COOH-terminus
in determining pore
characteristics (IRK, ROMK1)

H5

H₂ N

COOH

IR due to Mg²⁺and polyamines
D172 and E224 in IRK1 (K$_{IR}$2.1)

PKA phosphorylation
sites

MgATP-binding inhibition
in ROMK2 (K$_{IR}$1.1)

*Figure 4*   Structural model of ROMK channel protein.   HIR, hard inward rectifier; IR, inward rectification (7, 8, 37, 43, 61, 72, 74, 76, 132, 138).

with a longer $NH_2$-terminus. Whether ROMK channels form heteromultimeric complexes in some of these nephron segments, as has been demonstrated for the atrial G protein–gated, acetylcholine-activated inward rectifier $K^+$ channel [$K_{IR}3.1$(CIR) + $K_{IR}3.4$ (GIRK1)] (53) is presently unknown. However, recent studies have found that coexpression of ROMK2 ($K_{IR}1.1B$) with cystic fibrosis transmembrane conductance regulator (CFTR) confers increased sensitivity of ROMK2 channel to the $K^+$ channel inhibitor glibenclamide. Thus the glibenclamide sensitivity of the native low-conductance $K^+$ secretory channels in the TAL and principal cells may result from subunit interactions (72a).

Recent studies show that ROMK2 ($K_{IR}1.1b$) and ROMK1 ($K_{IR}1.1a$) have similar single-channel conductances of 30–40 pS in symmetrical 140-mM $K^+$ solutions (71–74). Thus ROMK does not appear to encode the intermediate-conductance (70 pS) $K^+$ secretory channel found in the rat TAL (116), although the possibility that ROMK could participate in a multisubunit complex forming the 70 pS channel has not been excluded. In a recent study, Hurst et al (47) examined the basic properties of the apical $K^+$ channel in rabbit macula densa cells and found a number of similarities between this channel and the apical $K^+$ secretory channel in CTAL and CCD (e.g. unitary conductance, nonvoltage dependency, and pH sensitivity). They suggested, however, that this was a different channel based in large part on the lack of channel inhibition by disodium ATP ($ATP^{-4}$); i.e. this channel appeared to lack ATP sensitivity. In this regard, Wang & Giebisch (123) and McNicholas et al (72–74) have shown that the low-conductance K$^+$ secretory channel in principal cells and ROMK2, respectively, can be reversibly inhibited by MgATP$^{-2}$, but are little affected by ATP$^{-4}$. Therefore the sensitivity of the macula densa K$^+$ channel to MgATP should be examined before concluding that it is insensitive to ATP. Finally, the expression of ROMK transcripts in DCT and OMCD suggests that this channel may contribute to K$^+$ secretion in these nephron segments. In this regard, Sansom et al (87) recently observed a low-conductance ($\approx$36 pS) K$^+$ channel in the mouse IMCD3 cell line with properties similar to those in rat TAL and principal cells.

## ROMK Channels: Correlation of Structure and Function

ROMK channels exhibit many of the ion permeation and regulatory properties of the low-conductance K$^+$ secretory channel observed on patch clamping of apical membranes of the TAL (5, 116, 117, 129) and principal cells (27, 29, 128). ROMK channels expressed in *Xenopus* oocytes have properties (see Table 1) that include a unitary conductance of 30–40 pS in symmetrical 140–150 mM KCl; high K$^+$:Na$^+$ selectivity (K$^+$ > Rb$^+$ > NH$^{4+}$ $\gg$ Na$^+$, Li$^+$) (121, 138); weak inward rectification resulting from block by internal Mg$^{2+}$ and/or polyamines such as spermine or spermidine (20, 61, 76); sensitivity to external Ba$^{2+}$, but not TEA$^+$ (138); marked sensitivity to cytosolic side reductions in pH (71, 72, 108); inhibition by arachidonic acid (66); run-down or loss of channel activity in excised patches in the absence of MgATP that involves dephosphorylation by a protein phosphatase (PP2C in *Xenopus* oocytes; 74); reactivation of channels after run-down by re-exposure to MgATP and the catalytic subunit of PKA (72, 74); sensitivity to inhibition by millimolar concentrations of MgATP (73, 70); and inhibition by glibenclamide (i.e. when ROMK2 is coexpressed with CFTR; 72a).

An amino acid segment between the two putative membrane-spanning helices in ROMK channels is homologous (59% similarity) to the pore-forming H5 region of voltage-gated K$^+$ channels (Figure 4). This suggests that ROMK1 and voltage- (cyclic nucleotide-) gated channels evolved from a common ancestral gene and supports an important role for the H5 region in forming the channel pore (33, 36, 67, 136, 137). In addition, this region contains the Gly-Try-Gly triplet that is conserved in channels with high K$^+$ selectivity (39, 48). However, whereas the H5-like region appears to contribute to the channel pore of K$_{IR}$ channels, Brown and coworkers (105) demonstrated the importance of the NH$_2$- and COOH-termini in determining the inward rectification characteristics of inwardly rectifying K$^+$ channels.

A characteristic of the low-conductance secretory K$^+$ channel found in principal cells is a lack of sensitivity to external tetraethyl-ammonium (TEA$^+$) (27, 28, 127, 128), and this ion has no effect on K$^+$ secretion by this nephron segment. Moreover, ROMK isoforms when expressed in *Xenopus* oocytes share this lack of TEA$^+$ sensitivity (up to 15 mM), consistent with a possible role for this cloned channel in K$^+$ secretion in the kidney. An aromatic amino acid, phenylalanine, at position 148 within the H5 region, might impart significant sensitivity to external TEA$^+$ in ROMK channels because site-directed mutagenesis studies in Shaker channels have shown that substitution of an aromatic amino acid at a similar position confers a high sensitivity to external TEA$^+$. Alternatively, the basic amino acid, arginine (R) at position 147 of ROMK1 might interfere with TEA$^+$ binding and explain the lack of high TEA$^+$ sensitivity in the ROMK1 channel (43).

Inward rectification is also a characteristic of the secretory K$^+$ channels in kidney. Inward rectifiers exhibit either strong (e.g. K$_{IR}$2.1; IRK1) (54) or weak (e.g. K$_{IR}$1.1; ROMK channels) rectification. Importantly, the K$^+$ secretory channels in kidney and ROMK channels both exhibit weak rectification—in other words, they have significant outward K$^+$ current—and thus can function in K$^+$ secretion. Inward rectification has been shown to depend on the blocking action of intracellular cations including Mg$^{2+}$ (76) and polyamines such as spermine and spermidine. Moreover, studies into the mechanism of rectification have begun to identify important amino acid residues or segments critical for both weak and strong rectification (65, 105, 131). Taglialatela et al (105) have shown that the COOH-, but not the NH$_2$-, terminus is critical for determining strong inward rectification. Recently, Taglialatela et al (104) identified a single, negatively charged amino acid (glutamine) within the COOH-terminus of the strong inward rectifier K$_{IR}$2.1 (IRK1), which contributes to the binding-interactions with Mg$^{2+}$ and could account for the role of the COOH-terminus in determining rectification properties. In addition, Lu & MacKinnon (65) and Wible et al (131) have shown that another negatively charged amino acid residue (aspartic acid) in the second membrane-spanning helix of K$_{IR}$2.1 (IRK1) is also important for strong rectification. In fact, mutating the asparagine in M2 of ROMK1 (Figure 2) to aspartic acid changes ROMK1 gating from the weak to strong type (Figure 4).

The finding of a potential nucleotide-binding site on ROMK1 provides support for the possibility that the ROMK channel might function as the renal ATP-sensitive low-conductance K$^+$ secretory channel. ROMK2 is, indeed, sensitive to MgATP (71, 72). A segment following the membrane-spanning M1 region contains a Walker A site motif [GXG(H in ROMK)XXGK] found to be involved in ATP binding in certain kinases (107). Moreover, a larger 27 amino acid region containing the Walker type A site, also exhibits significant similarity to the catalytic subdomain 1 of ERBB3, a member of the epidermal growth factor (EGF) receptor tyrosine kinase family (43). Based on this potential ATP-binding segment and the presence of several potential PKA and

PCK phosphorylation sites in the COOH-terminus of ROMK channel proteins, we suggest that this region is a regulatory domain on the channel. Indeed, we recently have shown by a combination of patch-clamping and site-directed mutagenesis that the Walker A segment in ROMK2 is involved in MgATP-binding-inhibition interactions. Direct evidence for cAMP-dependent PKA-mediated phosphorylation of ROMK2 has recently been obtained, and three phosphorylated serine residues have been identified (one on the NH$_2$-terminus and two on the COOH-terminus) (132). These PKA phosphorylation sites are degenerate in that any two are required for channel activity.

As discussed above, the native low-conductance K$^+$ secretory channels in the TAL and principal cells are quite sensitive to cytosolic acidification. ROMK channels expressed in *Xenopus* oocytes also show strong inhibition by reductions in cytosolic-side pH within the physiological range (7.4–7.0) (71, 97). This sensitivity could play an important role in altering K$^+$ secretion during acid-base disturbances. Recently moreover, Coulter et al (14) have shown that the strong inwardly rectifying K$^+$ channel HIR, found in heart and CNS, is sensitive to external pH. They localized the external pH sensitivity to a histidine residue in the Ml-H5-linker region of this channel. A histidine residue is also present in this same region of ROMK channels and could function in a similar fashion in external pH sensitivity in ROMK. This will require further investigation, however, because the K$^+$ secretory channel in principal cells can be exposed to quite low (<5.0) acid pH values (especially during acidosis). It is tempting to speculate that the tubular fluid pH may have a regulatory effect in K$^+$ secretion during acid-base disturbances.

ACKNOWLEDGMENTS

This work was supported by National Institutes of Health grants DK47402 and HL34300 (WW), NIH DK17433 (GG), and DK-37605 (SCH).

*Literature Cited*

1. Ashcroft SJH, Ashcroft FM. 1990. Properties and functions of ATP-sensitive K-channels. *Cell Signal* 2:197–214
2. Ashford MLJ, Bond CT, Blair TA, Adelman JP. 1994. Cloning and expression of a rat heart K$_{ATP}$ channel. *Nature* 370:456–59
3. Beck JS, Hurst AM, Lapointe J-Y, Laprade R. 1993. Regulation of basolateral K channels in proximal tubule studied during continuous microperfusion. *Am. J. Physiol.* F496–501
4. Beck JS, Laprade R, Lapointe J-Y. 1994. Coupling between transepithelial

Na transport and basolateral K conductance in renal proximal tubule. *Am. J. Physiol.* 266:F517–27
5. Bleich M, Kottgen M, Schlatter E, Greger R. 1995. Effect of NH$_4^+$/NH$_3$ on cytosolic pH and the K$^+$ channels of freshly isolated cells from the thick ascending limb of Henle's loop. *Pflügers Arch.* 429:345–54
6. Bleich M, Schlatter E, Greger R. 1990. The luminal K channel of the thick ascending limb of Henle's loop. *Pflügers Arch.* 415:449–60
7. Boim MA, Hebert HC. 1995. Renal potassium channels. In *Molecular Nephrology,*

ed. D Schlöndorff, JV Bonventre 25:335. New York/Basel/Hong Kong: Dekker

8. Boim MA, Ho K, Schuck ME, Bienkowski MJ, Block JH, et al. 1995. The ROMK inwardly rectifying ATP-sensitive K⁺ channel. II. Cloning and intra-renal distribution of alternatively spliced forms. *Am. J. Physiol.* 268:F1132–40

9. Brown EM, Gamba G, Riccardi D, Lombardi M, Butters R, et al. 1993. Cloning and characterization of an extracellular Ca-sensing receptor from bovine parathyroid. *Nature* 366:575–80

10. Carroll MA, Sala A, Dunn CE, McGiff JC, Murphy RC. 1991. Structural identification of cytochrome P450-dependent arachidonate metabolites formed by rabbit medullary thick ascending limb cells. *J. Biol. Chem.* 266:12306–12

11. Cassola AC, Giebisch G, Wang W. 1993. Vasopressin increases the density of apical low-conductance K channel in rat CCD. *Am. J. Physiol.* 264:F502–9

12. Chepilko S, Zhou H, Sackin H, Palmer LG. 1995. Permeation and gating properties of a cloned renal K⁺ channel. *Am. J. Physiol.* 168:C389–401

13. Christensen O, Zeuthen T. 1987. Maxi K⁺ channels in leaky epithelia are regulated by intracellular Ca²⁺, pH and membrane potential. *Pflügers Arch.* 408:249–59

14. Coulter KL, Perier F, Radeke CM, Vandenberg CA. 1995. Identification and molecular localization of a pH-sensing domain for the inward rectifier potassium channel HIR. *Neuron* 15:1157–69

15. Dascal N, Schreibmayer W, Lim NF, Wang W, Chavkin C, et al. 1993. Atrial G protein-activated K⁺ channel expression cloning and molecular properties. *Proc. Natl. Acad. Sci. USA* 90:10235–39

16. Desir GV. 1995. Molecular characterization of voltage and cyclic nucleotide-gated potassium channels in kidney. *Kidney Int.* 48:1031–35

17. Desir GV, Hamlin HA, Puente E, Reilly RF, Hildebrandt F, Igarashi P. 1992. Isolation of putative voltage-gated epithelial K-channel isoforms from rabbit kidney and LLC-PK1 cells. *Am. J. Physiol.* 262:F151–57

18. Desir GV, Velazquez H. 1993. Identification of a novel K-channel gene (KC22) that is highly expressed in distal tubule of rabbit kidney. *Am. J. Physiol.* 264:F128–33

19. Dubè L, Parent L, Sauvè R. 1990. Hypotonic shock activates a maxi K channel in primary cultured proximal tubule cells. *Am. J. Physiol.* 259:F348–56

20. Ficker E, Taglialatela M, Wible BA, Henley CM, Brown AM. 1994. Spermine and spermidine as gating molecules for inward rectifier K⁺ channels. *Science* 266:1068–72

21. Field M, Giebisch G. 1985. Hormonal control of renal potassium excretion. *Kidney Int.* 27:379–87

22. Field MJ, Stanton BA, Giebisch GH. 1984. Influence of ADH on renal potassium handling: a micropuncture and microperfusion study. *Kidney Int.* 25:502–11

23. Filipovic D, Sackin H. 1990. Stretch-activated calcium currents in renal proximal tubule. *Am. J. Physiol.* 160:F119–29

24. Filipovic D, Sackin H. 1992. Stretch- and volume-activated channels in isolated proximal tubule cells. *Am. J. Physiol.* 262:F857–70

25. Flemmer A, Doerge A, Thurau K, Beck FX. 1993. Transcellular sodium transport and basolateral rubidium uptake in the isolated perfused cortical collecting duct. *Pflügers Arch.* 424:250–54

26. Frindt G, Palmer LG. 1987. Ca-activated K channels in apical membrane of mammalian CCT and their role in K secretion. *Am. J. Physiol.* 252:F458–67

27. Frindt G, Palmer LG. 1989. Low-conductance K channels in apical membrane of rat cortical collecting tubule. *Am. J. Physiol.* 256:F143–51

28. Geibel J, Zweifach A, White S, Wang W, Giebisch G. 1990. K⁺ channels of the mammalian collecting duct. *Renal Physiol. Biochem.* 13:59–69

29. Giebisch G. 1995. Renal potassium channels: an overview. *Kidney Int.* 48:1004–9

30. Gögelein H. 1990. Ion channels in mammalian proximal renal tubules. *Renal Physiol. Biochem.* 13:8–25

31. Gögelein H, Greger R. 1984. Single channel recordings from basolateral and apical membranes of renal proximal tubules. *Pflügers Arch.* 401:424–26

32. Gögelein H, Greger R. 1987. Properties of single K channels in the basolateral membrane of renal proximal tubules. *Pflügers Arch.* 410:424–26

33. Goulding EH, Tibbs GR, Liu D, Siegelbaum SA. 1993. Role of H5 domain in determining pore diameter and ion permeation through cyclic nucleotide-gated channels. *Nature* 364:61–64

34. Guggino SE, Guggino WB, Green N, Sacktor B. 1987. Blocking agents of Ca²⁺-activated K⁺ channels in cultured medullary thick ascending limb cells. *Am. J. Physiol.* 252:C128–37

35. Hamilton KL, Eaton DC. 1991. cAMP-induced potassium channel activity in apical membrane of cultured A6 kidney cells. *Am. J. Physiol.* 261:F1055–62

36. Hartmann HA, Kirsch GE, Drewe JA, Taglialatela M, Joho RH, Brown AM. 1991. Exchange of conduction pathways between two related K+ channels. *Science* 251:942–44

37. Hebert SC. 1995. An ATP-regulated, inwardly rectifying potassium channel from rat kidney (ROMK). *Kidney Int.* 48:1010–16

38. Hebert SC, Andreoli TE. 1984. Effects of antidiuretic hormone on cellular conductive pathways in mouse medullary thick ascending limbs of Henle: II. Determinants of the ADH-mediated increases in transepithelial voltage and in net Cl absorption. *J. Membr. Biol.* 80:221–33

39. Heginbotham L, Abramson T, MacKinnon R. 1992. A functional connection between the pores of distantly related ion channels as revealed by mutant K+ channels. *Science* 258:1152–55

40. Hirsch J, Leipziger J, Fröbe U, Schlatter E. 1993. Regulation and possible physiological role of the Ca²⁺-dependent K+ channel of cortical collecting ducts of the rat. *Pflügers Arch.* 422:492–98

41. Hirsch J, Schlatter E. 1995. K channels in the basolateral membrane of rat cortical collecting duct are regulated by a cGMP-dependent protein kinase. *Pflügers Arch.* 429:338–44

42. Hirsch J, Schlatter E. 1995. K channels in the basolateral membrane of rat cortical collecting duct. *Kidney Int.* 48:1036–46

43. Ho K, Nichols CG, Lederer WJ, Lytton J, Vassilev PM, et al. 1993. Cloning and expression of an inwardly rectifying ATP-regulated potassium channel. *Nature* 362:31–38

44. Hunter M, Lopes AG, Boulpaep EL, Giebisch GH. 1986. Regulation of single potassium ion channels from apical membrane of rabbit collecting tubule. *Am. J. Physiol.* 251:725–33

45. Hurst AM, Beck JS, Laprade R, Lapointe J-Y. 1993. Na+ pump inhibition downregulates an ATP-sensitive K+ channel in rabbit proximal convoluted tubule. *Am. J. Physiol.* 264:F760–64

46. Hurst AM, Duplain M, Lapointe J-Y. 1992. Basolateral membrane potassium channels in rabbit cortical thick ascending limb. *Am. J. Physiol.* 263:F262–67

47. Hurst AM, Lapointe J-Y, Laamarti A, Bell PD. 1994. Basic properties and potential regulators of the apical K+ channel

in macula densa cells. *J. Gen. Physiol.* 103:1055–70

48. Jan LY, Jan YN. 1994. Potassium channels and their evolving gates. *Nature* 371:119–22

49. Kawahara K. 1990. A stretch-activated K channel in the basolateral membrane of *Xenopus* kidney proximal tubule cells. *Pflügers Arch.* 415:624–29

50. Kawahara K, Hunter M, Giebisch G. 1987. Potassium channels in *Necturus* proximal tubule. *Am. J. Physiol.* 253:F488–94

51. Kenna S, Röper J, Ho K, Hebert SC, Ashcroft SJH. 1994. Differential expression of the inwardly-rectifying K-channel ROMK1. *Mol. Brain Res.* 24:353–56

52. Klaerke DA. 1995. Purification and characterization of epithelial Ca²⁺-activated K+ channels. *Kidney Int.* 48:1047–56

53. Krapivinsky G, Gordon EA, Wickman K, Vellmirovic B, Krapivinsky L. 1995. K+ channel I_KACh is a heteromultimer of two inwardly rectifying K+-channel proteins. *Nature* 374:135–41

54. Kubo Y, Baldwin TJ, Jan YN, Jan LY. 1993. Primary structure and functional expression of a mouse inward rectifier potassium channel. *Nature* 362:127–33

55. Kubo Y, Reuveny E, Slesinger PA, Jan YN, Jan LY. 1993. Primary structure and functional expression of a rat G-protein-coupled muscarinic potassium channel. *Nature* 364:802–6

56. Kubokawa M, McNicholas CM, Higgins MA, Wang W, Giebisch G. 1995. Regulation of ATP-sensitive K+ channel by membrane-bound protein phosphatases in rat principal tubule cell. *Am. J. Physiol.* 269:F355–62

57. Kubokawa M, Wang W, McNicholas CM, Giebisch G. 1995. Role of Ca²⁺/CaMK II in Ca²⁺-induced K+ channel inhibition in rat CCD principal cell. *Am. J. Physiol.* 268:F211–19

58. Lee W-S, Hebert SC. 1995. The ROMK inwardly rectifying ATP-sensitive K+ channel. I. Expression in rat distal nephron segments. *Am. J. Physiol.* 268:F1124–31

59. Ling BN, Eaton DC. 1993. Cyclosporin A inhibits apical secretory K+ channels in rabbit cortical collecting tubule principal cells. *Kidney Int.* 44:974–84

60. Ling BN, Hinton CF, Eaton DC. 1991. Potassium permeable channels in primary cultures of rabbit cortical collecting tubule. *Kidney Int.* 40:441–52

61. Lopatin AN, Makhina EN, Nichols CG. 1994. Potassium channel block by cyto-

434 WANG, HEBERT & GIEBISCH

plasmic polyamines as the mechanism of intrinsic rectification. *Nature* 372:366–69

62. Lu M, Wang WH. 1996. Protein kinase C stimulates the small-conductance K channel in the basolateral membrane of the collecting duct of the rat kidney. *Am. J. Physiol.* In press

63. Lu M, Wang WH. 1996. Nitric oxide regulates the low-conductance K channel in the basolateral membrane of the cortical collecting duct. *Am. J. Physiol.* 270:C1336–42

64. Lu M, Zhu Y, Balazy M, Falck JR, Wang WH. 1996. Effect of angiotensin II on the apical K channels in the thick ascending limb of the rat kidney. *J. Gen. Physiol.* Submitted

65. Lu Z, MacKinnon R. 1994. Electrostatic tuning of $Mg^{2+}$ affinity in an inward-rectifier $K^+$ channel. *Nature* 371:243–46

66. Macica CM, Hebert SC, Wang W. 1994. Modulation of the renal ATP-sensitive $K^+$ channel, ROMK, by arachidonic acid. *J. Am. Soc. Nephrol.* 5:293, 1994 (Abstr.)

67. MacKinnon R, Yellen G. 1990. Mutations affecting TEA blockade and ion permeation in voltage-activated $K^+$ channels. *Science* 250:276–79

68. Makhina EN, Kelly AJ, Lopatin A, Mercer RW, Nichols CG. 1994. Cloning and expression of a novel human brain inward rectifier potassium channel. *J. Biol. Chem.* 269:20468–74

69. Malnic G, Aires MM, Giebisch G. 1971. Potassium transport across renal distal tubules during acid-base disturbances. *Am. J. Physiol.* 221:1192–208

70. Mauerer UR, Boulpaep EL, Segal AS. 1995. Properties of an inwardly rectifying $K_{ATP}$ channel on the basolateral membrane of renal proximal tubule. *J. Am. Soc. Nephrol.* 6:345, 1701 (Abstr.)

71. McNicholas CM, Giebisch G, Hebert SC. 1994. ATP- and pH-sensitivity of ROMK1 and ROMK2 $K^+$ channels. *J. Am. Soc. Nephrol.* 5:293, 1994 (Abstr.)

72. McNicholas CM, Giebisch G, Hebert SC. 1996. ROMK is an epithelial pH and ATP-sensitive $K^+$ channel. *Am. J. Physiol.* 40:F275–85

72a. McNicholas CM, Guggino WB, Schwiebert EM, Hebert SC, Giebisch G, Egan ME. 1996. Sensitivity of a renal $K^+$ channel (ROMK2) to the inhibitory sulfonylurea compound, glibenclamide, is enhanced by co-expression with the ATP-binding cassette transporter CFTR. *Proc. Natl. Acad. Sci. USA.* 93:8083–88

73. McNicholas CM, Hebert SC, Giebisch G. 1994. ATP-sensitivity of cloned epithelial $K^+$ channels ROMK1 and ROMK2. *J. Gen. Physiol.* 104:13a, 1994 (Abstr.)

74. McNicholas CM, Wang W, Ho K, Hebert SC, Giebisch G. 1994. Regulation of ROMK1 $K^+$ channel activity involves phosphorylation processes. *Proc. Natl. Acad. Sci. USA* 91:8077–81

75. Merot J, Bidet M, Lemaout S, Tauc M, Poujeol P. 1989. Two types of K channel in the apical membrane of rabbit proximal tubule in primary culture. *Biochim. Biophys. Acta* 978:134–44

76. Nichols CG, Ho K, Hebert SC. 1994. $Mg^{2+}$-dependent inward rectification of ROMK1 potassium channels expressed in *Xenopus* oocytes. *J. Physiol.* 476:399–409

77. Pacha J, Frindt G, Sackin H, Palmer LG. 1991. Apical maxi K channels in intercalated cells of CCT. *Am. J. Physiol.* 261:F696–705

78. Palmer LG, Antonian L, Frindt G. 1994. Regulation of apical K and Na channels and Na/K pumps in rat cortical collecting tubule by dietary K. *J. Gen. Physiol.* 104:693–710

79. Parent L, Cardinal J, Sauvé R. 1988. Single-channel analysis of a K channel at basolateral membrane of rabbit proximal convoluted tubule. *Am. J. Physiol.* 254:F105–13

80. Reeves WB, McDonald GA, Mehta P, Andreoli TE. 1989. Activation of K channel in renal medullary vesicles by cAMP-dependent protein kinase. *J. Membr. Biol.* 109:65–72

81. Reeves WB, Shah SV. 1994. Activation of potassium channels contributes to hypoxic injury in proximal tubules. *J. Clin. Invest.* 94:2289–94

82. Sackin H. 1987. Stretch-activated potassium channels in renal proximal tubule. *Am. J. Physiol.* 253:F1253–62

83. Sackin H. 1989. A stretch-activated K channel sensitive to cell volume. *Proc. Natl. Acad. Sci. USA* 86:1731–35

84. Sackin H. 1990. Regulation of renal proximal tubule basolateral potassium channels. In *Potassium Channels: Basic Function and Therapeutic Aspects*, ed. T Colatsky, pp. 231–49. New York: Liss

85. Sackin H. 1995. Mechanosensitive channels. *Annu. Rev. Physiol.* 57:333–53

86. Sackin H, Palmer LG. 1987. Basolateral potassium channels in renal proximal tubule. *Am. J. Physiol.* 253:F476–87

87. Sansom SC, Mougouris T, Ono S, Dubose TD Jr. 1994. ATP-sensitive $K^+$-selective channels of inner medullary collecting duct cells. *Am. J. Physiol.* 267:F489–96

88. Satlin LM. 1994. Postnatal maturation of potassium transport in rabbit cortical collecting duct. *Am. J. Physiol.* 266:F57–65
89. Schafer JA, Hawk CT. 1992. Regulation of Na channels in the cortical collecting duct by AVP and mineralocorticoids. *Kidney Int.* 41:255–68
90. Schafer JA, Troutman SL. 1986. Effect of ADH on rubidium transport in isolated perfused rat cortical collecting tubules. *Am. J. Physiol.* 250:F1063–72
91. Schafer JA, Troutman SL, Schlatter E. 1990. Vasopressin and mineralocorticoid increase apical membrane driving force for K secretion in rat CCD. *Am. J. Physiol.* 258:F199–210
92. Schlatter E, Haxelmans S, Hirsch J, Leipziger J. 1994. pH dependence of K conductances of rat cortical collecting duct principal cells. *Pflügers Arch.* 428:631–40
93. Schwab A, Geibel J, Wang W, Oberleithner H, Giebisch G. 1993. Mechanism of activation of K⁺ channels by minoxidil-sulfate in Madin-Darby canine kidney cells. *J. Membr. Biol.* 132:125–36
94. Schwab A, Oberleithner H. 1996. Plasticity of renal epithelial cells: the way a potassium channel supports migration. *Pflügers Arch.* 432(3):R87–93 (Suppl.)
95. Schwab A, Westphale H-J, Wojnowski L, Wünsch S, Oberleithner H. 1993. Spontaneously oscillating K⁺ channel activity in transformed Madin-Darby canine kidney cells. *J. Clin. Invest.* 92:218–23
96. Schwab A, Wojnowski L, Gabriel K, Oberleithner H. 1994. Oscillating activity of a Ca²⁺-sensitive K⁺ channel—a prerequisite for migration of alkali-transformed Madin-Darby canine kidney (MDCK-F) cells. *J. Clin. Invest.* 93:1631–36
97. Shuck ME, Block JH, Benjamin CW, Tsai T-D, Lee KS, et al. 1994. Cloning and characterization of multiple forms of the human kidney ROM-K potassium channel. *J. Biol. Chem.* 269:24261–70
98. Steels PS, Boulpaep EL. 1987. pH-dependent electrical properties and buffer permeability of the *Necturus* renal proximal tubule cell. *J. Membr. Biol.* 100:165–82
99. Stoner LC, Morley GE. 1995. Effect of basolateral or apical hypoosmolarity on apical maxi K⁺ channels of everted rat collecting tubule. *Am. J. Physiol.* 268:F569–80
100. Strange K. 1990. Volume regulation following Na⁺ pump inhibition in CCT principal cells: apical K⁺ loss. *Am. J. Physiol.* 258:F732–40
101. Strieter J, Weinstein AM, Giebisch G, Stephenson J. 1992. Regulation of K transport in a mathematical model of the cortical collecting tubule. *Am. J. Physiol.* 242:F544–51
102. Suzuki MK, Takahashi K, Ikeda M, Hayakawa H, Ogawa A, et al. 1994. Cloning of a pH-sensitive K⁺ channel possessing two transmembrane segments. *Nature* 367:642–45
103. Suzuki M, Takigawa T, Kimura K, Koseki C, Imai M. 1995. Immunohistochemical localization of pH-sensitive K⁺ channel, RACTK1. *Am. J. Physiol.* 269:C496–503
104. Taglialatela M, Ficker E, Wible BA, Brown AM. 1995. C-terminus determinants for Mg²⁺ and polyamine block the inward rectifier K⁺ channel IRK1. *EMBO J.* 14:5532–41
105. Taglialatela M, Wible BA, Caporaso R, Brown AM. 1994. Specification of pore properties by the carboxyl terminus of inwardly rectifying K⁺ channels. *Science* 264:844–47
106. Takumi T, Ohkubo H, Nakanishi S. 1988. Cloning of a membrane protein that induces a slow voltage-gated potassium current. *Science* 242:1042–45
107. Taylor SS, Knighton DR, Zheng J, Sowadski JM, Gibbs CS, Zoller MJ. 1993. A template for the protein kinase family. *Trends Biol. Sci.* 18:84–89
108. Tsai TD, Shuck ME, Thompson DP, Brenkowski MJ, Cie KC. 1995. Intracellular H⁺ inhibits a cloned rat outer medullary K⁺ channel expressed in *Xenopus* oocytes. *Am. J. Physiol.* 268:C1173–78
109. Tsuchiya K, Wang W, Giebisch G, Welling PA. 1992. ATP is a coupling modulator of parallel Na,K-ATPase-K-channel activity in the renal proximal tubule. *Proc. Natl. Acad. Sci. USA* 89:6418–22
110. Ubl J, Murer H, Kolb H-A. 1988. Hypotonic shock evokes opening of Ca-activated K channels in opossum kidney cells. *Pflügers Arch.* 412:551–53
111. Ubl J, Murer H, Kolb H-A. 1988. Ion channels activated by osmotic and mechanical stress in membranes of opossum kidney cells. *J. Membr. Biol.* 104:223–32
112. Urbach V, Van Kerkhove E, Maguire D, Harvey BJ. Cross-talk between ATP-regulated K⁺ channels and Na⁺ transport via cellular metabolism in frog skin principal cells. *J. Physiol.* 491:99–109
113. Volk KA, Husted RF, Pruchno CJ, Stokes JB. 1994. Functional and molecular evidence for Shaker-like K⁺ channels in rabbit renal papillary epithelial cell line.

*Am. J. Physiol.* 267:F671–78

114. Wang T, Wang W, Klein-Robbenhaar G, Giebisch G. 1995. Effects of a novel K$_{ATP}$ channel blocker on renal tubule function and K channel activity. *J. Pharm. Exp. Therap.* 273:1382–89

115. Wang T, Wang W, Klein-Robbenhaar G, Giebisch G. 1995. Effects of glyburide on renal tubule transport and potassium-channel activity. *Renal Physiol. Biochem.* 18:169–82

116. Wang W. 1994. Two types of K$^+$ channel on TAL of rat kidney. *Am. J. Physiol.* 267:F599–605

117. Wang W. 1995. View of K$^+$ secretion through the apical K channel of cortical collecting duct. *Kidney Int.* 48:1024–30

118. Wang WH. 1995. Regulation of the hyperpolarization-activated K channel in the lateral membrane of the CCD. *J. Gen. Physiol.* 106:25–43

119. Wang W, Cassola AC, Giebisch G. 1992. Arachidonic acid inhibits the secretory K channel of cortical collecting duct of rat kidney. *Am. J. Physiol.* 264:F554–59

120. Wang W, Cassola AC, Giebisch G. 1995. Involvement of the cytoskeleton in modulation of apical K channel activity in rat CCD. *Am. J. Physiol.* 267:F591–98

121. Wang W, Geibel J, Giebisch G. 1993. Mechanism of apical K channel modulation in principal renal tubule cells: effect of inhibition of basolateral Na-K-ATPase. *J. Gen. Physiol.* 101:673–94

122. Wang W, Giebisch G. 1991. Dual modulation of renal ATP-sensitive K-channel by protein kinase A and C. *Proc. Natl. Acad. Sci. USA* 88:9722–25

123. Wang W, Giebisch G. 1991. Dual effect of adenosine triphosphate on the apical small conductance K$^+$ channel of the rat cortical collecting duct. *J. Gen. Physiol.* 98:35–61

124. Wang WH, Lu M. 1995. Effect of arachidonic acid on activity of the apical K channel in the thick ascending limb of the rat kidney. *J. Gen. Physiol.* 106:727–43

125. Wang WH, Lu M, Hebert SC. 1996. P450 metabolites mediate extracellular Ca$^{2+}$-induced inhibition of apical K$^+$ channels in the thick ascending limb of the rat kidney. *Am. J. Physiol.* 271:C103–11

126. Wang WH, McNicholas CM, Segal AS, Giebisch G. 1994. A novel approach allows identification of K channels in the lateral membrane of rat CCD. *Am. J. Physiol.* 266:F813–22

127. Wang W, Sackin H, Giebisch G. 1992. Re-

nal potassium channels and their regulation. *Annu. Rev. Physiol.* 54:81–96

128. Wang W, Schwab A, Giebisch G. 1990. Regulation of small-conductance K channel in apical membrane of rat cortical collecting tubule. *Am. J. Physiol.* 259:F494–502

129. Wang W, White S, Geibel J, Giebisch G. 1990. A potassium channel in the apical membrane of rabbit thick ascending limb of Henle's loop. *Am. J. Physiol.* 258:F244–53

130. Welling PA. 1996. Primary structure and functional expression of a cortical collecting duct K$_{IR}$ channel. *Am. J. Physiol.* Submitted

131. Wible BA, Taglialatela M, Ficker E, Brown AM. Gating of inwardly rectifying K$^+$ channels localized to a single negatively charged residue. *Nature* 371:246–49

132. Xu Z-C, Yang Y, Hebert SC. 1996. Phosphorylation of the ATP-sensitive, inwardly-rectifying K$^+$ channel, ROMK, by cyclic AMP-dependent protein kinase. *J. Biol. Chem.* 271:9313–19

133. Yano H, Philipson LH, Kugler JL, Tokuyama Y, Davis EM, et al. 1994. Alternative splicing of human inwardly rectifying K$^+$ channel ROMK1 mRNA. *Mol. Pharmacol.* 45:854–60

134. Yao X, Chang AY, Boulpaep EL, Segal AS, Desir GV. 1996. Molecular cloning of a glibenclamide-sensitive voltage-gated potassium channel expressed in rabbit kidney. *J. Clin. Invest.* 97:225–33

135. Yao X, Segal AS, Welling P, Zhang X, McNicholas CM, et al. 1995. Primary structure and functional expression of a cGMP-gated potassium channel. *Proc. Natl. Acad. Sci. USA* 92:11711–15

136. Yellen G, Jurman ME, Abramson T, MacKinnon R. 1991. Mutations affecting internal TEA blockade identify the probable pore-forming region of a K$^+$ channel. *Science* 251:939–42

137. Yool AJ, Schwarz, TL. 1991. Alteration of ionic selectivity of a K$^+$ channel by mutation of the H5 region. *Nature* 349:700–4

138. Zhou HS, Tate S, Palmer LG. 1994. Primary structure and functional properties of an epithelial K channel. *Am. J. Physiol.* 266:C809–24

139. Zweifach A, Desir G, Aronson P, Giebisch G. 1991. A Ca-activated K channel from rabbit brush border membrane vesicles in planar lipid bilayers. *Am. J. Physiol.* 261:F187–96

*Annu. Rev. Physiol. 1997. 59:437–55*

# REGULATION OF GENE EXPRESSION BY HYPERTONICITY[1]

*Maurice B. Burg, Eugene D. Kwon, and Dietmar Kültz*

National Heart, Lung and Blood Institute, National Institutes of Health, Bethesda, Maryland 20892-0951

KEY WORDS:    sorbitol, aldose reductase, betaine, inositol, taurine

### ABSTRACT

Adaptation of cells to hypertonicity often involves changes in gene expression. Since the concentration of salt in the interstitial fluid surrounding renal inner medullary cells varies with operation of the renal concentrating mechanism and generally is very high, the adaptive mechanisms of these cells are of special interest. Renal medullary cells compensate for hypertonicity by accumulating variable amounts of compatible organic osmolytes, including sorbitol, *myo*-inositol, glycine betaine, and taurine. In this review we consider how these solutes help relieve the stress of hypertonicity and the nature of transporters and enzymes responsible for their variable accumulation. We emphasize recent developments concerning the molecular basis for osmotic regulation of these genes, including identification and characterization of osmotic response elements. Although osmotic stresses are much smaller in other parts of the body than in the renal medulla, similar mechanisms operate throughout, yielding important physiological and pathophysiological consequences.

## INTRODUCTION

Hypertonicity, which ordinarily results from a high concentration of salt, stresses animal cells because the ensuing osmotic efflux of water shrinks the cells and concentrates their contents. This shrinkage causes mechanical stresses. Concentration of intracellular salts and crowding of large intracellular molecules greatly affect the structure and activity of proteins, DNA, and other cellular macromolecules (19, 34). Cells adapt to hypertonicity by a variety of

---

[1]The US Government has the right to retain a nonexclusive, royalty-free license in and to any copyright covering this paper.

mechanisms that act to restore cell volume and normalize intracellular salt concentration (25, 69).

Most cells in mammals are not normally stressed by hypertonicity because the concentration of NaCl is closely controlled in virtually all extracellular body fluids. The renal inner medulla is a striking exception. As a consequence of its participation in the urinary concentrating mechanism, cells in the renal medulla are routinely exposed to variably high levels of NaCl that may reach molal concentrations. An important part of the adaptation of renal medullary cells to hypertonicity involves altered expression of a number of genes. In this review we focus on some of those genes that have been extensively studied, summarizing present knowledge of how hypertonicity regulates their expression and how the resultant gene products protect against hypertonicity.

## COMPATIBLE ORGANIC OSMOLYTES IN THE RENAL MEDULLA

When the urine is concentrated and medullary interstitial salt concentration is high, cells in the inner renal medulla accumulate large amounts of certain osmotically active organic solutes (called compatible organic osmolytes), predominantly sorbitol, *myo*-inositol (inositol), glycine betaine (betaine), taurine, and glycerophosphocholine (GPC) (18). The level of these solutes varies directly with the urinary and renal medullary interstitial salt concentration. These organic osmolytes help protect the cells from hypertonicity. Accumulation of compatible organic osmolytes in response to hypertonicity is a general response, found in virtually all prokaryotic and eukaryotic organisms that have been examined (69). The different organic osmolytes that are accumulated by cells fall into three classes: methylamines, polyols, and amino acids or amino acid derivatives. The predominant renal medullary organic osmolytes fit into these classes.

### How Compatible Organic Osmolytes Help Cells Adapt to Hypertonicity

A frequent initial response of cells that are shrunken by hypertonicity is rapid uptake of inorganic salts, accompanied by osmotic influx of water. This is referred to as regulatory volume increase (RVI) (25). RVI helps restore cell volume, alleviating the mechanical consequences of cell shrinkage and reducing molecular crowding. However, the intracellular level of inorganic salts remains high. Because noncovalent interactions of macromolecules depend strongly on the concentration of inorganic ions (69), the high intracellular salt concentration may perturb the structure and function of proteins and DNA, thus impairing cell function. Accumulation of compatible organic osmolytes reduces intracellular inorganic salt concentration toward a normal level. Because compatible organic osmolytes generally do not perturb cellular macromolecules, cells can safely accumulate large amounts of these organic osmolytes, whereas such high concentrations of inorganic salts may be harmful, at least over time (69).

This theory is supported by the strong effects that inorganic salts exert on many biochemical reactions in vitro, compared with much smaller effects of compatible organic osmolytes. There is also direct evidence for a beneficial effect of organic osmolyte accumulation on survival and growth of renal epithelial cells in culture, as measured by cloning efficiency. Hypertonicity greatly reduces cloning efficiency of renal cells under conditions in which they cannot accumulate organic osmolytes, and the cloning efficiency is restored when the compatible organic osmolytes do accumulate (39, 60, 68).

## GENES WHOSE EXPRESSION IS AFFECTED BY HYPERTONICITY

The known processes by which the renal medullary organic osmolytes are accumulated are summarized in Figure 1. The regulated steps are emphasized by heavy lines. Betaine, inositol, and taurine are taken up by $Na^+$ and $Na^+$ plus $Cl^-$-dependent transporters. Sorbitol is synthesized from glucose catalyzed by aldose reductase. GPC is synthesized from phosphatidylcholine. The abundance of both aldose reductase and the transporters for betaine inositol and taurine is regulated in response to high tonicity through changes in gene expression. In what follows, these processes are considered in detail with emphasis on recent findings concerning the regulation of the genes involved.

### *Aldose Reductase*

HYPERTONICITY INCREASES RENAL CELL SORBITOL    Hypertonicity increases renal cell sorbitol by raising the activity of aldose reductase, an enzyme that catalyzes synthesis of sorbitol from glucose (Figure 1) (18). The amount of aldose reductase enzyme rises because its rate of synthesis increases without any change in its degradation. Synthesis of aldose reductase rises because its mRNA is more abundant. The increased abundance of aldose reductase mRNA occurs because its rate of transcription (measured by nuclear run-on) rises markedly without any significant change in the rate of its degradation (52). Thus hypertonicity increases the transcription of the aldose reductase gene. The question is how.

THE ALDOSE REDUCTASE GENE    This gene has been cloned from several different species including rat (21), human (20, 62), and rabbit (15). The 5'-flanking region immediately adjacent to the structural gene contains a TATA box, a

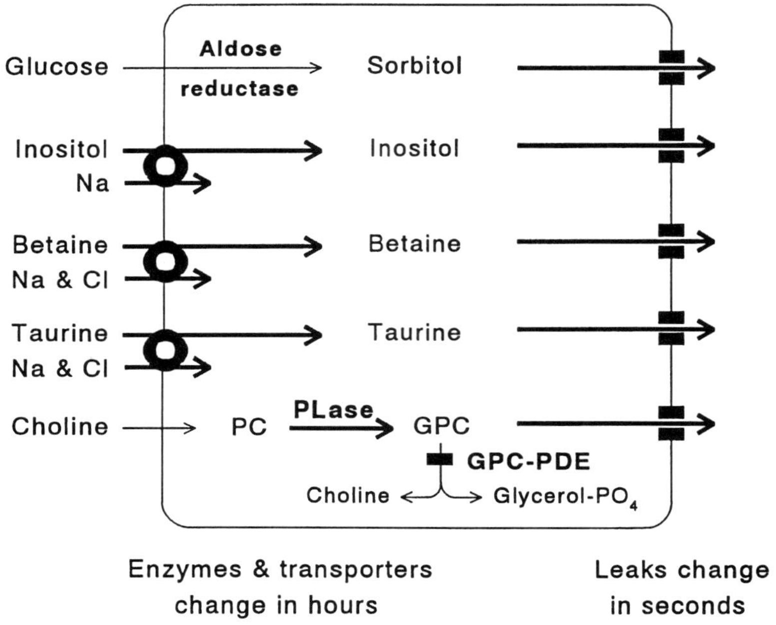

*Figure 1*  Mechanisms by which renal cells accumulate compatible organic osmolytes. Osmotically regulated processes are indicated by bold lines. PC, phosphatidylcholine; GPC, glycerophosphocholine; GPC-PDE, GPC:choline phosphodiesterase; PLase, phospholipase (from 3 with permission).

CCAAT box, and a GA-rich region, all of which contribute to promoter activity (15, 62), but do not individually or collectively confer osmotic regulation to reporter constructs.  In contrast, when a larger piece of the 5′-flanking region extending upstream of the promoter is added, there is strong osmotic regulation, suggesting that an element or elements conferring osmotic regulation reside in the 5′-flanking region (15).

THE ALDOSE REDUCTASE OSMOTIC RESPONSE ELEMENT   By testing progressively smaller pieces of the 5′-flanking region, incorporated into constructs containing a luciferase reporter gene, a 12-bp minimal essential osmotic response element (ORE) spanning positions $-1105$ to $-1094$ was defined in the rabbit aldose reductase gene (Figure 2) (14). This is the smallest part of the 5′-flanking region that yields increased luciferase activity in renal cells, transiently transfected with these constructs, and then exposed to hypertonicity. With similar methods an ORE was defined in the human aldose reductase gene

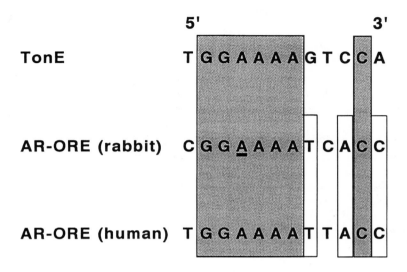

*Figure 2*  Comparison of the sequences for the canine TonE and rabbit and human aldose-reductase OREs. Replacement of adenosine in the rabbit ORE (position -1102, *underscored*) with guanosine to match the NFκB consensus sequence abolishes the ORE response to hypertonicity.

(48). Ten of twelve nucleotides are identical comparing the rabbit and human aldose reductase OREs (Figure 2). Furthermore, when a 17-bp fragment containing the rabbit ORE is incubated with nuclear extracts from cells exposed to hypertonicity, a slowly migrating band is induced, as determined by electrophoretic mobility shift assay (14). This is consistent with osmotic regulation of aldose reductase by increased binding of *trans*-acting protein(s). Reporter constructs containing parts of the 5′-flanking region outside of the rabbit ORE do not display increased luciferase activity following hypertonicity. However, as the size of the DNA fragment containing the ORE is narrowed down, the amount by which hypertonicity increases luciferase activity gradually diminishes. Thus the ORE is apparently the only part of the 5′-flanking region that can independently confer osmotic response, but the gradual drop in magnitude with decreasing fragment size suggests that other *cis*-elements may potentiate the osmotic response. The mechanism by which the interaction occurs between *cis*-elements and any *trans*-acting factors remains to be elucidated.

ABERRANT ALDOSE REDUCTASE GENE REGULATION IN DIABETES    The regulation of cell aldose reductase levels has garnered additional interest because, in subjects affected by diabetes mellitus, some cells may accumulate sorbitol to excess. This is associated with high blood glucose and is implicated in diabetic complications in the eye, peripheral nerves, and other tissues. Despite the abnormally high level of sorbitol, these cells continue to express aldose reductase, which exacerbates their condition. The normal role of aldose reductase in such cells is obscure, so the relation to osmoregulation is being scrutinized (4). Although the tissues damaged in diabetes are not normally exposed to the high levels of osmolality found in the renal inner medulla, cells from those (and other) tissues nevertheless respond to hypertonicity in culture by increasing aldose reductase gene expression (12, 18, 24, 44, 54). Human retinal epithelial cells in culture are similar to other types of cells in this regard (31). However, in a mutant line of these cells, the response is unregulated so expression of aldose reductase is constitutively high and does not increase with hypertonicity (24, 54). Thus the possibility has been raised that such abnormal aldose reductase expression could enhance the sensitivity of cells to the biochemical consequences of hyperglycemia, potentiating the development of diabetic complications (24).

## Betaine Transporter

HYPERTONICITY INCREASES BETAINE TRANSPORT    Betaine increases in renal medullary cells in vivo and in renal cells in tissue culture when the extracellular fluid becomes hypertonic (18). In the tissue cultures of renal cells [Madin-Darby renal canine kidney (MDCK) and PAP-HT25], the acute accumulation of betaine is entirely from an increased uptake from the medium. If no betaine is present in the medium, none accumulates in the cells, regardless of the osmolality. The transport is $Na^+$- and $Cl^-$-dependent (18, 66). Transport $V_{max}$ increases without significant change in $K_m$, consistent with an increase in the number of transporters. The osmotically regulated transporters are present at the basolateral surface of these epithelial cells (63). Freshly harvested renal medullary cells also take up betaine by transport (36), but the effect of osmolality on this transport has not been reported. Betaine is normally present in serum [mean of 38 $\mu$M in normal humans (1)], which provides a source of betaine for uptake into renal medullary cells. The betaine in serum comes from the diet and from synthesis, mainly in the liver and kidney cortex (18, 36). Thus it is plausible that betaine synthesized elsewhere in the body is taken up by renal medullary cells in vivo and that changes in transport account for its osmotic regulation.

BETAINE TRANSPORTER cDNA    The cDNA for a betaine transporter was cloned from MDCK cells by expression in *Xenopus* oocytes (66). This cell line was used because it expresses the increased $Na^+$- and $Cl^-$-dependent betaine transport in response to hypertonicity. Expression of cRNA derived from this clone produces both betaine and $\gamma$-amino-$n$-butyric acid GABA) transport by oocytes, hence the name *BGT1*. It encodes a single protein of 614 amino acids with 12 putative membrane-spanning regions. Additionally, it contains several consensus sequences for phosphorylation by protein kinase A and C and two glycosylation consensus sequences, suggesting possible posttranslational regulation. In fact, activators of protein kinase A and protein kinase C inhibit cell betaine uptake (46). *BGT1* mRNA levels are higher in the renal medulla than in other tissues tested, consistent with an important role for this transporter in osmotic regulation of medullary betaine levels in vivo.

HYPERTONICITY INCREASES TRANSCRIPTION OF THE BETAINE TRANSPORTER GENE   Hypertonicity rapidly increases transcription of *BGT1* in MDCK cells, followed by increases in *BGT1* mRNA and the rate of betaine uptake into the cells (61). Thus osmotic regulation of betaine accumulation by these renal cells occurs by changes in transcription of a gene coding for a betaine transporter. This mechanism is reminiscent of that used by *Escherichia coli*, which also accumulates betaine in response to high tonicity (32). However, the transporters are very different. The bacterial transporter is a three-component ATPase that directly energizes primary active betaine transport, whereas the mammalian transporter is a single protein that couples secondary active betaine transport to existing cellular $Na^+$- and $Cl^-$-gradients.

THE BETAINE TRANSPORTER GENE   The *BGT1* gene was cloned from canine DNA in order to investigate the mechanism by which hypertonicity increases its transcription (55). The gene extends over 28 kilobases and consists of 18 exons. The 5′ end of the gene has three different first exons that, together with alternative splicing, results in a complex mixture of mRNAs. Eight variants (divided into three main types) of the mRNA have been identified. They diverge considerably in their 5′ untranslated sequences. Each type is expressed in a tissue-specific manner, as determined by RT-PCR. Type A is detected only in kidney medulla. Type B is in brain, liver, kidney cortex, and medulla. Type C is in brain, kidney cortex, and medulla. The three alternative first exons each have an independent transcription initiation site that is under the control of an independent promoter. Hypertonicity induces all three types of mRNA in MDCK cells.

THE BETAINE TRANSPORTER TONICITY-RESPONSIVE ENHANCER ELEMENT   The 5′-flanking region of the *BGT1* gene contains a tonicity-responsive enhancer element (designated TonE) that spans −69/−50 of the sequence (56). MDCK cells transiently transfected with plasmid constructs containing TonE (either in its usual or reversed orientation), together with a downstream SV40 promoter and a luciferase reporter gene, demonstrate hypertonicity-induced increases in luciferase activity. Mobility shift assays expressing mutants of TonE have been used to narrow TonE activity to the $-60/-51$ region. In the mobility shift assays, nuclear extracts from MDCK cells exposed to hypertonicity produce a shifted band that is considerably more dense than the band from control cells. Thus hypertonicity induces greater binding of a protein or proteins to TonE. This presumably represents a *trans*-acting signal for increased transcription. The identity of the protein(s) and the mechanism by which binding is regulated by tonicity remain to be determined.

A comparison of the sequences for TonE and the OREs (Figure 2) reveals a considerable degree of similarity. Of the 12 bp in ORE, 7 (rabbit ORE) or 9 (human ORE) are identical to TonE, consistent with their potential interaction with similar *trans*-acting protein(s), but at this point it is not clear whether the same *trans*-acting proteins bind to and activate ORE and TonE, or whether there is a family of related factors.

The sequences of ORE and TonE also resemble the consensus sequence for the NF-$\kappa$B element (2) (GGGA/GNNC/TC/TC/A/TC), particularly with regard to the concentration of purines at the 5′ end. However, the ORE does not fit the NF-$\kappa$B consensus at nucleotide $-1102$ (of AR), where NF-$\kappa$B elements have a guanosine (G), rather than an adenosine (A), as in the ORE. To determine whether the ORE would retain osmotic responsiveness if its sequence were modified to include an NF-$\kappa$B element consensus base $-1102$ of the rabbit ORE, an adenosine (A) was replaced by a guanosine (G) (underlined in Figure 2), as is found in the NF-$\kappa$B element. Osmotic response is lost, apparently inconsistent with involvement of NF-$\kappa$B in the osmotic responsiveness of the aldose reductase gene (14).

BETAINE TRANSPORTER GENE REGULATION IN VIVO    The 5′-flanking region, which contains TonE, also mediates osmotic regulation of transcription in vivo (27). Transgenic mice harboring 2.4 kb of 5′-flanking region of the *BGT1* gene (including TonE) fused to the chloramphenicol acetyltransferase (CAT) reporter gene, express CAT activity in their renal medullas. Thirsting of these animals for 72 h produces a renal medullary CAT mRNA level that is fivefold higher than that in the medullas of mice that drink an excess of water for the same time. CAT mRNA is much lower in the renal cortex and does not change.

## Taurine Transporter

HYPERTONICITY INCREASES TAURINE TRANSPORT    Taurine increases in rat renal medullary cells in vivo following thirsting (42) or infusion of hypertonic saline (41). These conditions have in common an increase in the tonicity of the inner medulla. None of 25 other amino acids increases, except for a small rise in aspartic acid following saline infusion. Similarly, when MDCK cells are growing in medium containing 50 $\mu$M taurine, intracellular taurine approximately doubles within four to five days after making the medium hypertonic with mannitol (60). These results suggest that renal medullary cells respond to osmotic stress by accumulating taurine, which acts as a compatible organic osmolyte.

When no taurine is present in the medium, intracellular taurine falls, and the level of taurine no longer increases with hypertonicity (60). In the MDCK cells, the hypertonicity-induced accumulation of taurine is entirely due to increased transport from the medium across the basolateral side of the cells. Taurine transport is $Na^+$- and $Cl^-$-dependent. Hypertonicity increases the transport $V_{max}$ without changing $K_m$, consistent with an increase in the number of functioning transporters.

HYPERTONICITY INCREASES TRANSCRIPTION OF THE TAURINE TRANSPORTER GENE    The taurine transporter cDNA was cloned from MDCK cells based on its similarity to the betaine transporter (59). It encodes a single protein of 655 amino acids. Its deduced amino acid sequence places it in the same family of $Na^+$- and $Cl^-$-dependent transporters as the betaine transporter. Taurine transporter mRNA is present in dog renal medulla $\simeq$ renal cortex $>$ ileal mucosa $>$ brain $>$ liver $>$ heart $>$ epididymis. The taurine transporter cDNA has been used as a probe to measure the effect of hypertonicity on abundance of the transporter mRNA in MDCK cells (59). When the medium is made hypertonic, the abundance of taurine transporter mRNA rises. Thus the effect of hypertonicity to increase taurine uptake by MDCK cells (and by inference in the renal medulla, as well) is explained by increased expression of the taurine transporter gene.

## Inositol Transporter

HYPERTONICITY INCREASES INOSITOL TRANSPORT    Inositol increases in renal medullary cells in vivo and in renal cells in tissue culture when the extracellular fluid becomes hypertonic (18). In tissue cultures of renal epithelial cells, the acute accumulation of inositol is entirely from increased transporter-mediated uptake across the basolateral side of the cells. If inositol is absent from the medium, its increase in the cells in response to hypertonicity is much reduced. In contrast to betaine, however, cell inositol does not decrease to undetectable levels in inositol-free medium. Many types of cells require inositol in tissue culture medium; others do not. Nevertheless, it is routinely included in media. The inositol that persists in cells after several days in inositol-free medium might be a remnant of that which was initially present, either in a free form or incorporated in other compounds such as phospholipids. It might also represent de novo synthesis of inositol by a novel pathway. Whatever the case, the increase in inositol induced by hypertonicity is largely, if not entirely, due to uptake from extracellular fluid, not enhanced synthesis. Inositol is normally present in serum, which provides a source of inositol for uptake into renal medullary cells. Thus it is likely that inositol from the diet or synthesized elsewhere in the body is taken up by renal medullary cells in vivo and that changes in transport account for its osmotic regulation.

HYPERTONICITY INCREASES TRANSCRIPTION OF THE INOSITOL TRANSPORTER GENE    An inositol transporter cDNA was cloned from MDCK cells by expression in *Xenopus* oocytes (30) and named SMIT (s̲odium m̲yo-i̲nositol t̲ransporter). SMIT cDNA encodes a single protein of 718 amino acids, with 12 putative membrane-spanning regions. Based on its deduced amino acid sequence, SMIT belongs to a family that includes $Na^+$-dependent transporters for glucose (23) and nucleosides (43). Several potential protein kinase A and C phosphorylation sites are present in SMIT, consistent with possible posttranslational regulation of this transporter.

Transcription of SMIT begins to rise within a few hours after the medium is made hypertonic, followed by increased SMIT mRNA abundance and an increased rate of inositol transport into the cells (67). Thus hypertonicity regulates transcription of the inositol transporter gene, similar to the effect on the betaine transporter gene. The canine SMIT gene includes only two exons. The first exon contains 162 bp of the 5′ untranslated region, and the second exon contains the entire ($\approx$12 kb) open reading frame for the structural gene (47). These exons are interrupted by a large intron of $\approx$26 kb. Thus the overall genomic arrangement for SMIT is strikingly different from that of the betaine transporter. We anticipate that identification of the promoter and the regulatory sequences of the SMIT gene will yield important insights into mechanisms involved in its transcriptional regulation by hypertonicity.

INOSITOL TRANSPORTER GENE REGULATION IN VIVO    SMIT mRNA is more strongly expressed in the renal medulla than in other canine organs and tissues (30). Dehydration of rats increases SMIT mRNA in their renal medullas to a level approximately 2.5-fold higher than in rats drinking large quantities of fluid (65). It is of special interest that the mRNA increases as much in the outer as in the inner medulla (65), corresponding to inositol content that is as great, or even greater, in the outer than in the inner medulla (17, 65). Intraperitoneal injection of concentrated NaCl solution also induces SMIT mRNA in the rat renal medulla (64). The effect is rapid (within 3 h) and is significantly reduced by furosemide, a diuretic that minimizes renal medullary hypertonicity by inhibiting active NaCl transport out of the thick ascending limb of Henle's loop (TALH). The intrarenal distribution of SMIT mRNA was measured by in situ hybridization (64). It is present predominantly in the medullary and cortical TALHs and cortical macula densa cells, whereas medullary collecting ducts contain less. Intraperitoneal injection of concentrated NaCl solution increases labeling of

SMIT mRNA in the TALH and in the macula densa, but much less so in the inner medullary collecting duct. The interpretation is that increased NaCl transport by TALHs, following injection of NaCl, raises the tonicity of the interstitial fluid. The resultant hypertonicity, in turn, induces SMIT expression. Furosemide prevents the effect by inhibiting NaCl transport by the TALHs. It is not clear why the effect is smaller in the inner medullary collecting ducts. Perhaps their SMIT expression is intrinsically less sensitive to hypertonicity than in the TALH. Alternatively, the tonicity may rise less in the inner medulla than in the vicinity of the TALHs and macula densa cells under these experimental conditions.

## Heat Shock Proteins

HYPERTONICITY INCREASES EXPRESSION OF GENES FOR HEAT SHOCK PROTEINS Hypertonicity increases the abundance of mRNAs coding for heat shock proteins, including HSP-70 (7) and $\alpha$B-crystallin (9). This is of special interest because it suggests a relation between the response of cells to thermal stress and water stress. Thus elevated temperature and high salt concentration can adversely affect the structure and function of proteins, and both the heat shock proteins and compatible organic osmolytes that are produced in response to these stresses contribute protection by stabilizing proteins.

High temperature apparently triggers the heat shock response by altering cytoplasmic proteins (53). High inorganic salt concentration, which is the initial result of hypertonicity, also alters proteins (69). Thus modification of cell proteins could be the common factor that elevates HSP-70 both at high temperature and with hypertonicity. An adaptive value of induction of heat shock proteins in response to hypertonicity may be that this response precedes accumulation of organic osmolytes by several hours and could protect the cells as the organic osmolytes are accumulating (7).

RELATION BETWEEN HEAT SHOCK PROTEINS AND ORGANIC OSMOLYTES    Accumulation of organic osmolytes reduces the induction of HSP-70 by hypertonicity. Thus cellular accumulation of betaine and inositol, promoted by adding high concentrations of one or both of these solutes to the medium of cells in tissue culture, greatly attenuates the increase in HSP-70 mRNA abundance that otherwise occurs in response to hypertonicity (45, 51). The osmotic induction of betaine transporter mRNA that normally occurs in response to hypertonicity is similarly attenuated by the addition of high levels of betaine plus inositol to the medium (51). The induction of HSP-70 by elevated temperature is also reduced by accumulation of betaine, presumably because betaine stabilizes proteins (51).

These observations highlight the features that responses of genes primarily involved in response to heat shock and those primarily involved in response to osmotic stress have in common. Despite these similarities, there also is a major difference. Betaine transporter mRNA abundance is not affected by high temperature. Thus the betaine transporter is not a heat shock protein, and the mechanisms by which elevated temperature and hypertonicity affect gene expression must differ in important ways (51).

STIMULI FOR INDUCTION OF GENE EXPRESSION BY HYPERTONICITY IN MAMMAL-IAN CELLS    Studies in bacteria and yeast suggest that hypertonicity can induce alterations in gene expression through specific sensors and signaling pathways and by direct effects of intracellular salt concentration on DNA elements that regulate gene expression (5). Considering the large number of mammalian genes whose expression is affected by osmolality (3), it is possible that either or both of these mechanisms could be involved in the regulation of these genes. At present there is little information about the stimulus for osmotic regulation of any specific gene in a mammalian cell. However, some interesting inferences can be made based on what is known about the regulation of genes involved in organic osmolyte accumulation and heat shock factor expression in response to hypertonic stress.

## Intracellular Salt Concentration May Osmoregulate Gene Expression

Hypertonicity apparently stimulates increased aldose reductase gene transcription by elevating the total intracellular concentration of $Na^+$ and $K^+$ salts (or the intracellular ionic strength) (60). Increased osmolality per se is not sufficient because hyperosmolal addition of urea does not increase aldose reductase or sorbitol. Also, extracellular $Na^+$ and $Cl^-$ need not be elevated because hyperosmolal raffinose in the medium is as effective as NaCl. The important difference between urea, which does not elevate aldose reductase, and raffinose, which does, is that urea rapidly enters the cells so there is essentially no reduction in cell volume, whereas raffinose remains extracellular and causes the cells to shrink with a resultant rise in concentration of the $Na^+$ and $K^+$ salts that are retained in the cells. Thus increased expression of aldose reductase occurs when cell volume falls and intracellular concentrations of $Na^+$ and $K^+$ salts rise. Apparently, it is the increased ion concentration, not the decreased volume, that is the stimulus. When the two are dissociated by addition of ouabain during the exposure of a cell to hypertonicity, aldose reductase correlates almost perfectly with the sum of intracellular Na plus K concentration, but is not significantly related to cell volume (58).

With respect to the stimulus involved, the response to hypertonicity of the aldose reductase gene in mammalian cells is reminiscent of that of *proU* in *E. coli* (32). The stimulus in *E. coli* is elevated intracellular $K^+$ glutamate concentration, which is comparable to the increased concentrations of $Na^+$ and

$K^+$ salts in the mammalian cells. The lack of correlation between changes in cell volume and osmotic induction of aldose reductase is inconsistent with an important role for membrane sensors, which presumably would be responding to changes in pressure or membrane stretching.

There are also other findings suggesting that concentrations of intracellular $Na^+$ and $K^+$ salts are the primary stimulus for osmotic regulation of aldose reductase gene expression, as well as of some other genes involved in organic osmolyte accumulation. According to this model, as sorbitol and other organic osmolytes accumulate, the cells return to their initial volume, reversing the elevation of intracellular $Na^+$ and $K^+$ concentration and reducing the stimulus for increased transcription. Aldose reductase transcription rate peaks at a level approximately 18 times higher than control after 24 h of hypertonicity, then as sorbitol and other organic osmolytes accumulate, the transcription rate falls to a steady-state level approximately 5 times control (52). When aldose reductase activity is inhibited by Tolrestat, which prevents the accumulation of sorbitol, aldose reductase transcription rate does not fall after 24 h of hypertonicity, but rather continues to increase.

The hypertonicity-induced increase in the transcription of the genes coding for the betaine and inositol transporters probably also depends on increased intracellular $Na^+$ plus $K^+$. As is the case for sorbitol, hyperosmolal addition of urea does not induce accumulation of betaine or inositol (40), but hypertonic addition of raffinose or NaCl does, presumably because hypertonicity increases intracellular $Na^+$ plus $K^+$ salt concentration. Thus increased intracellular $Na^+$ plus $K^+$ salt concentration may not only elevate sorbitol by increasing transcription of aldose reductase but may also elevate betaine and inositol by increasing transcription of genes for their transporters. In addition, high betaine in the medium (and cells) inhibits osmotically induced transcription of aldose reductase (52), and high sorbitol, inositol or betaine inhibits osmotically induced expression of betaine transporter mRNA (13). These and similar interactions lead to reciprocal control of the renal organic osmolytes so that their total concentration is appropriate for the degree of hypertonicity (38). In addition, the interactions indirectly support identification of intracellular $K^+$ and $Na^+$ concentration as the stimulus for osmotic regulation of these genes. Sorbitol, inositol, and betaine are dissimilar enough chemically so that it is unlikely they all affect gene transcription directly in the same manner; rather, an indirect effect through changes in intracellular salt concentration seems more likely.

The same reasoning supports the idea that osmotic induction of heat shock genes also depends on intracellular inorganic ion concentration. As alluded to before, increased expression of HSP-70 mRNA in response to high NaCl is reduced when betaine and inositol are high in the medium (and cells), compared with the much greater and more prolonged elevation when there is no betaine or inositol in the medium (51).

## Coordinate Regulation of Genes
## for Organic Osmolyte Accumulation

Evidently there are mechanisms that coordinately regulate expression of the genes involved in organic osmolyte accumulation so that the total intracellular concentration of organic osmolytes is appropriate for the ambient tonicity. Pathological derangement of these mechanisms may contribute to the complications of diabetes. Poorly controlled diabetes is associated with a depletion of intracellular inositol, which may contribute to its complications (see 70 and the references therein). Extracellular glucose is high in poorly controlled diabetes. Excess of the substrate, glucose, drives the aldose reductase reaction in cells that express that enzyme. The resultant increase in cell sorbitol apparently suppresses accumulation of inositol. In rat lenses in vitro (35) and bovine lens epithelial cells in culture (6), high glucose raises cell sorbitol and reduces inositol transport. Some of the inhibition of transport persists for a time after the excess glucose is removed. Aldose reductase inhibitors reduce cell sorbitol and partially restore the inositol transport even in the continued presence of glucose. Therefore, at least part of the inhibition is due to sorbitol accumulation, consistent with the concept of coordinate regulation of total osmolyte amounts. The rest of the inhibition is apparently from direct competition by glucose for the inositol carrier, an effect that is shared by L-glucose. We conjecture that excess sorbitol inhibits inositol transport by reducing expression of the gene for the inositol transporter, but we are unaware of any direct tests of this hypothesis.

Macromolecular crowding is a stimulus for acute osmotic regulation of red cell transporters (8). However, there is no evidence that it is a stimulus for osmoregulation of gene expression in mammalian cells, and given that osmotic induction of aldose reductase does not correlate with cell volume, molecular crowding seems unlikely to be the direct stimulus in that system.

## SIGNALING PATHWAYS FOR OSMOREGULATION
## OF GENE ACTIVITY IN MAMMALIAN CELLS

Whereas many of the factors mentioned are likely involved in the regulation of genes by hypertonicity, it appears that interactions of various *trans*-acting proteins with their cognate DNA elements also play an important role in the regulation of these genes. Thus the question is raised as to how tonicity regulates association between these proteins and their DNA response elements. Alterations in the phosphorylation of these *trans*-acting proteins is an attractive possibility considering that a number of different types of mammalian cells

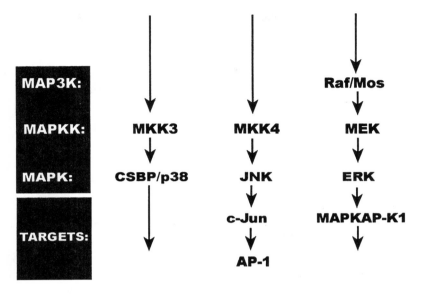

*Figure 3*  Mammalian MAPK signaling pathways that have been shown to be activated by hypertonicity. The diagram is simplified to emphasize the elements described in the text. MAP3K, MAP kinase kinase kinase; MAPKK, MAP kinase kinase; MAPK, MAP kinase.

have been shown to possess osmotically regulated kinase pathways similar to the HOG pathway described in yeast (5). To date, hypertonicity has been shown to induce at least three mammalian MAP kinase pathways (Figure 3). Every pathway consists of a kinase cascade in which each kinase sequentially activates the next by phosphorylation (50).

## Kinase Pathways

ERK    In the ERK pathway (49) (Figure 3) the MAPKKK isozymes, Raf (including Raf-1 and Raf-B) and c-Mos, activate the MAPKK, MEK, that in turn activates the ERKs, which are MAPKs. Hypertonic stress rapidly activates Raf-1, MEK (33, 57), and ERK (26, 29, 57) in tissue cultures. ERK, in turn, activates ribosomal S6 kinase (also known as MAPKAP kinase-1), which could extend the signal cascade into the nucleus (33). It is not clear, however, which genes, if any, are hypertonically induced through ERK. ERKs are also activated by phorbol esters via protein kinase C (PKC). TPA-induced depletion of PKC, which prevents osmotic activation of the ERK pathway, fails to block hypertonically induced transcription of the osmolyte transporter genes for *myo*-inositol and betaine (29).

JNK    The JNK pathway (Figure 3) is also induced by hypertonicity (16, 33). The JNK and ERK pathways differ in that the MEKs that activate ERK have little effect on JNK (10, 33). Instead, activation by hypertonicity is mediated by phosphorylation and activation of MKK4 (33, 37). One direct substrate of JNK is c-Jun, an AP-1 transcription factor (10), whose expression is increased in response to hypotonic stress (49). However, to date, the involvement of AP-1 in the regulation of gene expression by hypertonicity has not been shown.

p38    The p38 pathway (Figure 3) is also activated by hypertonicity (22). MKK3 activates the MAPK, p38 (11). Two human homologues of p38, CSBP1 and CSBP2, have been cloned (28). Like activation of p38, CSBP1 is activated by phosphorylation upon hyperosmotic stress. The role of the p38 pathway in gene regulation in response to hypertonicity remains to be determined.

Thus hypertonicity leads to phosphorylation and activation of numerous kinases in at least three different mammalian cascades. Presumably, at least some of these kinases are involved in osmotic regulation, but we do not know what their roles are, whether they osmoregulate any particular genes, nor whether any one cascade is necessary and sufficient to effect the organic osmolyte response. The availability of specific inhibitors and activators of these pathways should help answer these questions.

## CONCLUSIONS

The extremes of tonicity to which renal medullary cells are exposed elicit dramatic changes in transcription of genes coding for aldose reductase (which catalyzes the synthesis of sorbitol), and for transporters of betaine, inositol, and taurine. Accumulation of these compatible organic osmolytes benefits the cells by correcting cell volume and intracellular salt concentration. Similar osmotic response elements have recently been identified in the aldose reductase and betaine transporter genes. Hypertonicity seemingly increases the binding of one or more unidentified *trans*-acting regulatory proteins to these elements. The response apparently is elicited by increases in intracellular inorganic salt concentration. The signaling pathway remains uncertain but may be related to the complicated, interrelated protein kinase cascades that are activated by hypertonicity.

*Literature Cited*

1. Allen R, Stabler S, Lindenbaum J. 1993. Serum betaine, *N,N*-dimethylglycine and *N*-methylglycine levels in patients with cobalamin and folate deficiency and related inborn errors of metabolism. *Metabolism* 42:1448–60

2. Baeuerle PA. 1991. The inducible transcription activator NF-κB: regulation by distinct protein subunits. *Biochim. Biophys. Acta* 1072:63–80

3. Burg M. 1995. Molecular basis of osmotic regulation. *Am. J. Physiol.* 268:F983–96

4. Burg MB, Kador PF. 1988. Sorbitol, osmoregulation, and the complications of diabetes. *J. Clin. Invest.* 81:635–40

5. Burg MB, Kwon ED, Kültz D. 1996. Osmotic regulation of gene expression. *FASEB J.* In press

6. Cammarata P, Chen H-Q, Yang J, Yorio T. 1992. Modulation of myo-[$^3$H]inositol uptake by glucose and sorbitol in cultured bovine lens epithelial cells. I. Restoration of myo-inositol uptake by aldose reductase inhibition. *Invest. Ophthal. Vis. Sci.* 33:3561–71

7. Cohen D, Wasserman J, Gullans S. 1991. Immediate early gene and HSP70 expression in hyperosmotic stress in MDCK cells. *Am. J. Physiol.* 261:C594–601

8. Colclasure GC, Parker JC. 1992. Cytosolic protein concentration is the primary volume signal for swelling-induced [K-Cl] cotransport in dog red cells. *J. Gen. Physiol.* 100:1–10

9. Dasgupta S, Hohman TC, Carper D. 1992. Hypertonic stress induces α-B-crystallin expression. *Exp. Eye Res.* 54:461–70

10. Derijard B, Hibi M, Wu I-H, Barrett T, Su B, et al. 1994. JNK1: a protein kinase stimulated by UV light and Ha-Ras that binds and phosphorylates the c-Jun activation domain. *Cell* 76:1025–37

11. Derijard B, Raingeaud J, Barrett T, Wu I-H, Han J, et al. 1995. Independent human MAP kinase signal transduction pathways defined by MEK and MKK isoforms. *Science* 267:682–85

12. Ferraretto A, Negri A, Giuliani A, De Grada L, Conti A, Ronchi S. 1993. Aldose reductase is involved in long-term adaptation of EUE cells to hyperosmotic stress. *Biochim. Biophys. Acta* 1175:283–88

13. Ferraris JD, Burg M, Williams C, Peters E, Garcia-Perez A. 1996. Betaine transporter cDNA cloning and effect of osmolytes on its mRNA induction. *Am. J. Physiol.* 270:C650–54

14. Ferraris JD, Williams CK, Jung K-Y, Bedford JJ, Burg MB, Garcia-Perez A. 1996. ORE, a eukaryotic minimal essential osmotic response element: the aldose reductase gene in hyperosmotic stress. *J. Biol. Chem.* 271:18318–21

15. Ferraris JD, Williams CK, Martin BM, Burg MB, Garcia-Perez A. 1994. Cloning, genomic organization, and osmotic response of the aldose reductase gene. *Proc. Natl. Acad. Sci. USA* 91:10742–46

16. Galcheva-Gargova Z, Derijard B, Wu I-H, Davis RJ. 1994. An osmosensing signal transduction pathway in mammalian cells. *Science* 265:806–8

17. Garcia-Perez A, Burg M. 1991. Role of organic osmolytes in adaptation of renal cells to high osmolality. *J. Membr. Biol.* 119:1–13

18. Garcia-Perez A, Burg MB. 1991. Renal medullary organic osmolytes. *Physiol. Rev.* 71:1081–115

19. Garner MM, Burg MB. 1994. Macromolecular crowding and confinement in cells exposed to hypertonicity. *Am. J. Physiol.* 266:C877–92

20. Graham A, Brown L, Hedge PJ, Gammack AJ, Markham AF. 1991. Structure of the human aldose reductase gene. *J. Biol. Chem.* 266:6872–77

21. Graham C, Szpirer C, Levan G, Carper D. 1991. Characterization of the aldose reductase-encoding gene family in rat. *Gene* 107:259–67

22. Han J, Lee J-D, Bibbs L, Ulevitch RJ. 1994. A MAP kinase targeted by endotoxin and hyperosmolality in mammalian cells. *Science* 265:808–10

23. Hediger MA, Coady MJ, Ikeda TS, Wright EM. 1987. Expression cloning and cDNA sequencing of the Na$^+$/glucose co-transporter. *Nature* 330:379–81

24. Henry D, Del Monte M, Greene D, Killen P. 1993. Aldose reductase gene regulation in cultured human retinal pigment epithelial cells. *J. Clin. Invest.* 92:617–23

25. Hoffmann EK, Simonsen LO. 1989. Membrane mechanisms in volume and pH regulation in vertebrate cells. *Physiol. Rev.* 69:315–82

26. Itoh T, Yamauchi A, Miyai Y, Kameda T, Ueda N, Fujiwara Y. 1994. Mitogen-activated protein kinase and its activator are regulated by hypertonic stress in Madin-Darby canine kidney cells. *J. Clin. Invest.* 93:2387–92

27. Kaneko T, Takenaka M, Itoh T, Yoshimura Y, Okabe M, et al. 1995. Transcriptional activation by the tonicity responsive element of the canine betaine-GABA transporter gene in renal medulla of transgenic mice in response to high osmolarity. *J. Am. Soc. Nephrol.* 6:363

28. Kumar S, McLaughlin MM, McDonnell PC, Lee JC, Livi GP, Young PR. 1995. Human mitogen-activated protein kinase CSBP1, but not CBSP2, complements a *hog1* deletion in yeast. *J. Biol. Chem.* 270:29043–46

29. Kwon HM, Itoh T, Rim JS, Handler JS. 1995. The MAP kinase cascade is not essential for transcriptional stimulation of osmolyte transporter genes. *Biochem. Biophys. Res. Commun.* 213:975–79

30. Kwon HM, Yamauchi A, Uchida S, Preston AS, Garcia-Perez A, et al. 1992. Cloning of a Na$^+$/myo-inositol cotransporter, a hypertonicity stress protein. *J. Biol. Chem.* 267:6229–301

31. Lin L-R, Carper D, Yokoyama T, Reddy V. 1993. The effect of hypertonicity on aldose reductase, $\alpha$-$_B$-crystallin, and organic osmolytes in the retinal pigment epithelium. *Invest. Ophthamol. Vis. Sci.* 34:2352–59

32. Lucht JM, Bremer E. 1994. Adaptation of *Escherichia coli* to high osmolarity environments: osmoregulation of the high-affinity glycine betaine transport system ProU. *FEMS Microbiol. Rev.* 14:3–20

33. Matsuda S, Kawasaki H, Moriguchi T, Gotoh Y, Nishida E. 1995. Activation of protein kinase cascades by osmotic shock. *J. Biol. Chem.* 270:12781–86

34. Minton AP. 1983. The effect of volume occupancy upon the thermodynamic activity of proteins: some biochemical consequences. *Mol. Cell. Biochem.* 55:119–40

35. Mistry K, Beyer-Mears A, Diecke F. 1993. Mechanisms for D-glucose inhibition of myo-inositol influx into rat lens. *Diabetes* 42:1737–44

36. Moeckel G, Dasser H, Chen T, Schmolke M, Guder W. 1994. Bicarbonate-dependent betaine synthesis in rat kidney. *Contrib. Nephrol.* 110:46–53

37. Moriguchi T, Kawasaki H, Matsuda S, Gotoh Y, Nishida E. 1995. Evidence for multiple activators for stress-activated protein kinases/c-Jun amino-terminal kinases. *J. Biol. Chem.* 270:12969–72

38. Moriyama T, Garcia-Perez A, Burg MB. 1990. Factors affecting the ratio of the different organic osmolytes in renal medullary cells. *Am. J. Physiol.* 259:F847–58

39. Moriyama T, Garcia-Perez A, Olson A, Burg MB. 1991. Intracellular betaine substitutes for sorbitol in protecting renal medullary cells from hypertonicity. *Am. J. Physiol.* 260:F494–97

40. Nakanishi T, Turner RJ, Burg MB. 1990. Osmoregulation of betaine transport in mammalian renal medullary cells. *Am. J. Physiol.* 258:F1061–67

41. Nakanishi T, Uyama O, Sugita M. 1991. Osmotically regulated taurine content in rat renal inner medulla. *Am. J. Physiol.* 261:F957–62

42. Nakanishi T, Uyama O, Sugita M. 1992. Amino acids as well as polyols and methylamines accumulated in rat kidney during dehydration. *Amino Acids* 3:131–38

43. Pajor AM, Wright EM. 1992. Cloning and functional expression of a mammalian Na$^+$/nucleoside cotransporter. A member of the SGLT family. *J. Biol. Chem.* 267:3557–60

44. Petrash M, Flath M, Sens D, Bylander J. 1992. Effects of osmotic stress and hyperglycemia on aldose reductase gene expression in human renal proximal tubule cells. *Biochem. Biophys. Res. Commun.* 187:201–8

45. Petronini P, De Angelis W, Borghetti A, Wheeler K. 1993. Effect of betaine on HSP70 expression and cell survival during adaptation to osmotic stress. *Biochem. J.* 293:553–58

46. Preston AS, Yamauchi A, Kwon HM, Handler JS. 1995. Activators of protein kinase A and of protein kinase C inhibit MDCK cell myo-inositol and betaine uptake. *J. Am. Soc. Nephrol.* 6:1559–64

47. Rim JS, Preston AS, Takenaka M, Handler JS, Kwon HM. 1995. Cloning of the canine gene for the sodium/myo-inositol cotransporter (SMIT). *J. Am. Soc. Nephrol.* 6:368

48. Ruepp B, Bohren KM, Gabbay KH. 1996. Characterization of the osmotic response element of the human aldose reductase gene promoter. *Proc. Natl. Acad. Sci. USA* 93:8624–29

49. Schliess F, Schreiber R, Häussinger D. 1995. Activation of extracellular signal-regulated kinases Erk-1 and Erk-2 by cell swelling in H4IIE hepatoma cells. *Biochem. J.* 309:13–17

50. Seger R, Krebs EG. 1995. The MAPK signaling cascade. *FASEB J.* 9:726–35

51. Sheikh-Hamad D, Garcia-Perez A, Ferraris JD, Peters EM, Burg MB. 1994. Induction of gene expression by heat shock versus osmotic stress. *Am. J. Physiol.* 267:F28–F34

52. Smardo F, Burg M, Garcia-Perez A. 1992. Kidney aldose reductase gene transcription is osmotically regulated. *Am. J. Physiol.* 262:C776–82

53. Sorger P. 1991. Heat shock factor and the heat shock response. *Cell* 65:363–66

54. Stevens M, Henry D, Thomas T, Killen P, Greene D. 1993. Aldose reductase gene expression and osmotic dysregulation in cultured human renal pigment epithelial cells. *Am. J. Physiol.* 265:E428–38

55. Takenaka M, Bagnasco S, Preston A, Uchida S, Yamauchi A, et al. 1995. The canine betaine-GABA ($\gamma$-amino-*n*-butyric acid) transporter gene. Diverse mRNA isoforms are regulated by hypertonicity and are expressed in a tissue-

specific manner. *Proc. Natl. Acad. Sci. USA* 92:1072–76

56. Takenaka M, Preston AS, Kwon HM, Handler JS. 1994. The tonicity-sensitive element that mediates increased transcription of the betaine transporter gene in response to hypertonic stress. *J. Biol. Chem.* 269:29379–81

57. Terada Y, Tomita K, Homma MK, Nonoguchi H, Yang T, et al. 1994. Sequential activation of RAF-1 kinase, mitogen-activated protein (MAP) kinase kinase, MAP kinase, and S6 kinase by hyperosmolality in renal cells. *J. Biol. Chem.* 269:31296–301

58. Uchida S, Garcia-Perez A, Murphy H, Burg MB. 1989. Signal for induction of aldose reductase in renal medullary cells by high external NaCl. *Am. J. Physiol.* 256:C614–20

59. Uchida S, Kwon H, Yamauchi A, Preston A, Marumo F, Handler J. 1992. Molecular cloning of the cDNA for an MDCK cell $Na^+$ and $Cl^-$-dependent taurine transporter that is regulated by hypertonicity. *Proc. Natl. Acad. Sci. USA* 89:8230–34

60. Uchida S, Nakanishi T, Kwon H, Preston A, Handler J. 1991. Taurine behaves as an osmolyte in MDCK cells: protection by polarized, regulated transport of taurine. *J. Clin. Invest.* 88:656–62

61. Uchida S, Yamauchi A, Preston A, Kwon H, Handler J. 1993. Medium tonicity regulates expression of the $Na^+$- and $Cl^-$-dependent betaine transporter in Madin-Darby canine kidney cells by increasing transcription of the transporter gene. *J. Clin. Invest.* 91:1604–7

62. Wang K, Bohren K, Gabbay K. 1993. Characterization of the human aldose reductase gene promoter. *J. Biol. Chem.* 268:16052–58

63. Yamauchi A, Kwon H, Uchida S, Preston A, Handler J. 1991. *myo*-Inositol and betaine transporters regulated by tonicity are basolateral in MDCK cells. *Am. J. Physiol.* 261:F197–202

64. Yamauchi A, Miyai A, Shimada S, Minami Y, Tohyama M, et al. 1995. Localization and rapid regulation of $Na^+$/*myo*-inositol cotransporter in rat kidney. *J. Clin. Invest.* 96:1195–201

65. Yamauchi A, Nakanishi T, Takamitsu Y, Sugita M, Imai E, et al. 1994. In vivo osmoregulation of Na/*myo*-inositol cotransporter mRNA in rat kidney medulla. *J. Am. Soc. Nephrol.* 5:62–67

66. Yamauchi A, Uchida S, Kwon H, Preston A, Robey R, et al. 1992. Cloning of a $Na^+$ and $Cl^-$-dependent betaine transporter that is regulated by hypertonicity. *J. Biol. Chem.* 267:649–52

67. Yamauchi A, Uchida S, Preston AS, Kwon HM, Handler JS. 1993. Hypertonicity stimulates transcription of the gene for the $Na^+$/*myo*-inositol cotransporter in MDCK cells. *Am. J. Physiol.* 264:F20–F23

68. Yancey PH, Burg MB, Bagnasco SM. 1990. Effects of NaCl, glucose and aldose reductase inhibitors on cloning efficiency of renal medullary cells. *Am. J. Physiol.* 258:C156–63

69. Yancey PH, Clark ME, Hand SC, Bowlus RD, Somero GN. 1982. Living with water stress: evolution of osmolyte systems. *Science* 217:1214–22

70. Yorek M, Wiese T, Davidson E, Dunlap J, Stefani M, et al. 1993. Reduced motor nerve conduction velocity and $Na^+$-$K^+$-atpase activity in rats maintained on L-fucose diet. Reversal by myo-inositol supplementation. *Diabetes* 42:1401–6

## NOTE ADDED IN PROOF

Personal communication from K Gabbay: The human "aldose reductase" ORE (48) actually derives from some other, as yet unidentified human gene. Its inclusion in the aldose reductase 5′ flanking region resulted from an artifact contained in the clone isolated from a Clonetech human genomic DNA library. Nevertheless, the reported nucleotide sequence (48) does direct osmotic regulation, as described. The true human aldose reductase ORE is located at approximately 1150 bp from the transcription start site and differs in only 1 nucleotide from the earlier reported ORE. The authentic human aldose reductase ORE sequence (TGGAAAATCACC) is identical to the mouse aldose reductase ORE. The OREs from these two species direct osmotic regulation equally.

*Annu. Rev. Physiol. 1997. 59:457–82*

# CHEMICAL ACTIVATORS OF SENSORY NEURONS

## John N. Wood

Department of Anatomy and Developmental Biology, University College, Gower Street, London WC1E 6BT, United Kingdom

## Reginald Docherty

Department of Pharmacology, UMDS, St. Thomas Hospital, Lambeth Palace Road, London SE1 7EH, United Kingdom

KEY WORDS:   ligand-gated channels, nociception, dorsal root ganglia

### ABSTRACT

Chemical activation of sensory neurons plays an important role in the somatosensory system. The actions of both endogenous mediators such as excitatory amino acids, acetylcholine, bradykinin, and ATP, as well as selective exogenous activators of nociceptive sensory neurons are reviewed. The physiological significance of these mediators in both nociception and other types of sensation are discussed.

## INTRODUCTION

The chemical activation of sensory neurons through ligand-gated cation channels plays a critical role in the visual, olfactory, and somatosensory systems. In this review, we focus on the actions of extracellular activators of mammalian sensory neurons, with particular emphasis on nociceptive sensory neurons in the dorsal root ganglia (DRG), where the functional consequences of neuronal activation can be measured biochemically, electrophysiologically, and at the behavioral level.

Cyclic nucleotides play a pivotal role in visual and olfactory systems through their intracellular actions on an identified class of cation-selective ion channels. The G protein–coupled receptors that regulate cyclic nucleotide levels in response to photons or odorants have also been defined at the molecular level (25, 56). However, there is little evidence for an analogous role of cyclic nucleotide–gated channels in the somatosensory system. A variety of mechanically

457

0066-4278/97/0315-0457$08.00

activated channels or receptor systems that are activated by extracellular ligands appear to have a more significant role in these types of sensations.

## Sensory Neurons

The sensory neurons of the peripheral nervous system arise from migrating cells of the neural crest in the trunk, and from neural crest and ectodermal placodes in some cranial ganglia (75). Their eventual phenotype likely reflects both a form of predestination as they migrate to the sensory ganglia, as well as a response to local instructive signals and competition for target-derived trophic factors. Sensory neurons are activated by a variety of external stimuli (mechanical, thermal, and chemical). Some neurons are associated with specialized end organs such as Merkel cells, Pacinian corpuscles, or Meissner cells that are involved in mechanoreception; the signal transduction mechanisms between them are not well understood.

It has proved convenient to divide DRG sensory neurons into two broad populations: neurons with large-diameter cell bodies and fast-conducting myelinated axons (A-fibers) and neurons with small-diameter cell bodies and unmyelinated slowly conducting axons (C-fibers). Most of the small-diameter neurons are activated by tissue-damaging stimuli, whereas the large-diameter neurons are principally involved in mechanoreception or proprioreception, although $A\delta$ fibers have a nociceptive role. The sensory modalities defined electrophysiologically, as well as the expression of markers such as growth factor receptors, neuropeptides, or glycolipids, show many clearly distinct subpopulations of sensory neurons. Owing to practical constraints, the mechanism of chemical activation is much better understood than mechanical activation. Molecular biological techniques have allowed a catalogue of receptor and ligand-gated ion channel subunits expressed by sensory neurons to be drawn up. The present review, therefore, focuses on direct chemical activation of unmyelinated small-diameter C-fiber–associated sensory neurons.

## Ligand-Gated Ion Channels of Sensory Neurons

Ligand-gated ion channels can be grouped into three structurally distinct classes that have no obvious evolutionary relationship. The first group, exemplified by the nicotinic receptor family, has pentameric assemblies of subunits that traverse the cell membrane four times. This group includes the serotonin-gated $5HT_3$ receptor, as well as the anion channels gated by GABA and glycine. This group is known as the cysteine loop receptors due to a characteristic motif in the extracellular N-terminal region (68). The channel pore appears to be formed by an assembly of S2 domains (Figure 1, *hatched*). Neuronal nicotinic receptors comprise heteromultimers of agonist-binding subunits (alpha 2–7 subunits) and

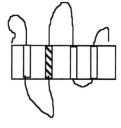

(a)   5-HT$_3$, Nicotinic alpha-2, 3, 4, 7 and beta-4

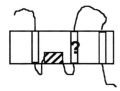

(b)   GluR1-4, GluR5 and Nr1 NMDA

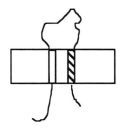

(c)   P2X 1, 2, 3, 4, 5, 6

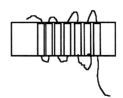

(d)   Bradykinin B2, prostaglandins PGE$_2$, PGl$_2$, tachykinins, vasopressin, 5HT-1A, 5HT-1D, 5HT-2

*Figure 1*   Subunit structure of DRG receptors and ion channels. (*a*) References 23, 87–89, 105, 107, 116, 130; (*b*) References 5, 11, 32, 40, 44, 52, 55, 58, 61, 64, 65, 79, 83, 100, 101, 103, 104, 111–113, 117, 131, 141, 147; (*c*) References 7, 10, 22, 30, 34, 71, 80, 97, 108, 133; (*d*) References 35, 36, 45, 53, 54, 67, 96, 109, 129, 132, 134.

accessory subunits, although the alpha-7 subunit alone is able to form functional channels.

The second class of ligand-gated channels is activated by glutamate and has three transmembrane domains, as judged by an analysis of glycosylation sites and protease sensitivity (62). These receptors have been divided into three groups based on agonist pharmacology: kainate-preferring, $\alpha$-amino-3-hydroxy-S-methyl-4-isoxalone (AMPA)-preferring, and N-methyl-D-aspartate (NMDA)-gated cation channels. The AMPA receptors, called GluRA-D or GluR1-4, are relatively impermeant to calcium and occur in alternatively spliced forms, known as flip and flop, throughout the nervous system. Kainate gates the GluR-5, -6, and -7 subunits. GluR-5 and -6 can form functional channels alone. NMDA receptors, which are usually multimeric, have significant permeability to calcium (147).

Recently, a new subset of ligand-gated channels comprising subunits with only two transmembrane domains has been found (9, 133). These ATP-gated cation channels have some secondary structural similarities to *Escherichia coli* mechanosensitive channels, *Caenorhabditis elegans* degenerins, and epithelial sodium channels, but the lack of sequence homology and distinct ion permeability suggests that these nonselective cation channels (classified as P2X receptors) form a distinct class of receptors.

## EXCITATORY AMINO ACID RECEPTORS

Primary afferent sensory neurons of the DRG are known to express functional ionotropic receptors for excitatory amino acids. At least two types of amino acid–gated channels are present: a non-NMDA kainate receptor and an NMDA receptor.

### Non-NMDA Kainate Receptors

Pharmacological studies in isolated preparations of dorsal roots with DRG attached have shown convincingly that exposing the nerve roots to ligands such as kainic acid causes depolarization of C-fibers but not of other afferent fiber types (2, 65, 104). Similar data have been obtained using an isolated tail-cord preparation, where the agonist ligands are applied to the peripheral processes of the sensory nerves while they remain functionally attached to the spinal cord (5). There is consensus from these studies as to the pharmacological profile of the C-fiber receptor, which is activated by a range of ligands such that domoic acid is the most potent known agonist, and domoate > kainate > quisqualate > glutamate > AMPA. Aspartate and NMDA are without activity. Therefore, the receptor is a non-NMDA amino acid receptor. A cation-specific ligand-gated ion channel that is activated by amino acids has been identified using patch-clamp techniques in a subpopulation of neurons (cell bodies) freshly isolated from neonatal or adult rat DRG (64). This ion channel has a pharmacological profile almost identical to that of the C-fiber response and probably represents the cellular basis of the C-fiber response. The ion channel discriminates poorly between different monovalent ions and has a linear I-V relation in the presence of extracellular Ca. No information is available as to whether the channel is permeable to divalent cations.

The unitary conductance and kinetic behavior of the non-NMDA channel in DRG is comparable to some non-NMDA AMPA/kainate-gated channels described in CNS neurons (for discussion, see 64). Also, the relative potency of agonists in C-fibers/DRG is similar to the relative affinity of these agonists at kainate-binding sites in the CNS (52, 55, 57). However, the DRG non-NMDA receptor(s) and the CNS non-NMDA receptor(s) differ in at least two important respects. First, the relative potency of agonists in functional assays is quite different; AMPA is a relatively weak agonist in C-fibers or DRG neurons (2, 64), whereas most non-NMDA receptors in the CNS are AMPA preferring (44). Second, in the CNS, agonists such as glutamate and AMPA induce a response that desensitizes, whereas kainate induces a response that does not desensitize (44, 72, but see also 101). In C-fibers and in voltage-clamped DRG neurons, responses to domoate and kainate, like the response to glutamate, desensitize, and in both preparations desensitization is strongly inhibited by concanavalin A (2, 64, 104). It has been suggested that relief of desensitization by concanavalin A is diagnostic for kainate-preferring non-NMDA receptors, distinguishing this subtype from AMPA-preferring non-NMDA receptors (100).

Heterologous expression in a mammalian cellular expression system of glutamate receptors from recombinant GluR-5 subunits (11, 113) yields a channel with a pharmacological profile very similar to that of the DRG kainate receptor. The mRNA encoding GluR-5 subunits may be alternatively spliced, giving rise to various forms that differ in both their C- and N-terminal regions (61). The splice variants may be further modified by RNA editing such that the final protein will have an arginine (R) rather than a glutamine (Q) residue in a particular position of its second transmembrane region. The unedited and edited forms of GluR-5 are termed GluR-5(Q) and GluR-5(R), respectively (113). It has recently been demonstrated that Q to R editing leads to a reduction in divalent cation permeability (61) and a large reduction in the conductance of ion channel(s) comprising recombinant GluR-5(R) (117). Homomeric expression of any of the splice variants gives rise to a kainate-binding site with a selectivity for ligands that is similar to that of the DRG kainate receptor. Only the GluR-5(Q) subunit gives rise to homomeric channels that may be activated in a functional (electrophysiological) assay. Activation of homomeric, GluR-5(Q) channels with kainate or domoate gives rise to a response that, like the DRG response, desensitizes, but unlike the DRG channel (64), the recombinant channel has a highly nonlinear I-V relation. Heterologous expression of homomeric GluR-5(Q) in mammalian (HEK) cells yields three single-channel conductances of 5, 9, and 14 pS (117), which compares well with the values of 4, 8, and 15–18 pS reported by Huettner for native kainate channels in DRG (64). Although homomeric GluR-5(R) expression does not give rise to functional channels, coexpression of GluR-5(R) with GluR-5(Q) yields heteromeric channels with a more linear I-V relation, consistent with the behavior of the channel activated by the DRG kainate receptor. Because DRGs express reasonably high levels of GluR-5 mRNA (11), Sommer et al (113) concluded that GluR-5 subunits are a major component of the DRG kainate receptor. Another strong candidate as a subunit in heteromeric non-NMDA receptors in the DRG is KA-2, a high-affinity kainate-binding protein that has 42% sequence identity with the GluR-5 subunit and a predicted structure similar to the other members of the ionotropic glutamate receptor family (58, 61). Similar to expression of GluR-5(R), heterologous expression of KA-2 yields a kainate-binding site but does not give rise to functional ligand-gated ion channels. Coexpression of KA-2 with GluR-5 or GluR-6 subunits (either Q or R editions) yields heteromeric channels that are activated by kainate and desensitize, i.e. have characteristics similar to the DRG kainate receptor. It is not clear whether the KA-2/GluR-5 or KA-2/GluR-6 heteromers have a pharmacological profile similar to the DRG kainate receptor in terms of their agonist selectivity, but otherwise the response of the heteromers to kainate is very similar to the DRG response. This is especially true of the heteromers KA-2 with the unedited GluR-5(R) or GluR-6(R) subunit channels, which have fairly linear I-V relations (58) over the voltage range tested (64) in native DRG receptors. We are not aware of any functional assays of a cellular response to amino acids in CNS neurons that has the same properties as the response described in DRG. Although mRNAs for most of the known glutamate receptor subunits (GluR-A to D and 5–7, KA-1 and KA-2) are expressed to some extent in DRG, GluR-5 mRNA is by far the most abundant subtype (100). Presumably, a relatively limited selection of non-NMDA receptor subunits expressed in DRG will give rise to channels with the characteristic pharmacology of the DRG kainate receptor.

There is some evidence that the DRG kainate receptor may be developmentally regulated, because responses to kainate are more easily demonstrated in neonatal than in adult tissue (2), but it is clear that the response can be evoked in adult tissue (2, 64). Consistent with this, GluR-5 mRNA is strongly expressed from embryonic day E16 through to postnatal day P21 (11) and presumably into adulthood. The kainate receptor in situ appears to be preferentially expressed on the afferent axons rather than on the DRG cell body because local administration of an agonist agent is less effective when applied at the DRG than elsewhere (2), which suggests that the receptor is involved in presynaptic control of transmitter release from C-fiber terminals in the spinal cord, presumably gated by glutamate released from other afferent fibers or from interneurons (2, 64). An alternative, or additional, physiological function may operate in the periphery, where glutamate released from damaged cells or during inflammatory processes may act on sensory nerve endings and contribute to nociceptive signaling mechanisms or neurogenic inflammation (5). Interestingly, the vagus nerve does not respond to excitatory amino acids, even though this preparation is rich in sensory C-fibers (2); thus the C-fiber kainate receptor may be selectively expressed in the sensory neurons of the DRG.

## NMDA Receptors

There is much evidence to implicate postsynaptic NMDA receptors on neurons in the spinal cord in sensory transmission mechanisms (132). In the present discussion, we are concerned not with the potential role of postsynaptic NMDA receptors in sensory transduction, but whether there are NMDA-activated ion channels on the primary sensory neurons and what function, if any, such receptors might have. Although some authors have found DRG neurons to be relatively unresponsive to NMDA (see above), there is considerable evidence suggesting that DRG neurons express NMDA receptors. Using freshly dissociated rat DRG neurons, Lovinger & Weight (83) found that glutamate or NMDA induced a depolarization and an inward current in most DRG neurons, whereas kainate induced a response in only 5 of 17 (about 30%) of neurons tested. No discrimination was made on the basis of the size of the neurons. This is not inconsistent with the data of Huettner (64), who found that 65% of small neurons ($<30$ $\mu$M diameter) responded to kainate but that larger neurons did not respond (see above). The NMDA receptor in DRG is not restricted to the C-fiber subpopulation of neurons. Indeed, it has been suggested that C-fibers express only non-NMDA receptors (104), which may mean that NMDA receptors are expressed selectively on large-diameter DRG neurons, i.e. those giving rise to A-fibers. Presumably, Lovinger & Weight (83) recorded mainly from the large-diameter DRG neurons. The recorded NMDA-induced membrane current (83) showed strong voltage-dependent rectification properties in the presence of extracellular $Mg^{2+}$ and was potentiated by glycine and blocked by the NMDA receptor antagonist 2-APV, which are physiological and pharmacological characteristics of the NMDA receptor (92). Experiments with heterologously expressed recombinant NMDA receptor subunits (see 61) have shown that NMDA receptors may be homomeric receptors made up solely of the NMDAR-1 subunit (or its many alternatively spliced variants) or heteromeric receptors consisting of NMDAR-1 and one or more of NMDAR-2A, -2B, -2C, or -2D. It has been suggested, at least in mice, that DRG NMDA receptors may be homomeric NMDAR-1 forms because mRNA for NMDAR-1 alone [not for NMDAR-2A, -2B, -2C, or -2D subunits (the equivalent subunits in mice are called $\zeta 1$, $\epsilon 1$, $\epsilon 2$, $\epsilon 3$, and $\epsilon 4$, respectively)] is expressed in this species (141). NMDAR-1 mRNA is expressed in adult rat DRG (112), but there is also evidence that NMDAR-2 subunits are expressed in this species (103).

It is unlikely that NMDA receptors are important in the acute activation mechanisms of primary afferent sensory neurons, because in intact tissue, NMDA does not appear to have any direct excitatory action, at least on C-fibers (2, 5, 104). Interestingly, it has been shown that activation of NMDA receptors stimulates neurite outgrowth in sensory neurons in culture (40). Presynaptic (i.e. on the primary afferent nerve terminals) NMDA receptors have been implicated as the mechanism of central sensitization associated with inflammatory hyperalgesia (46). Because synaptic remodeling in the spinal cord may be a feature of central sensitization mechanisms in chronic pain syndromes (43, 148), it is possible that presynaptic NMDA receptors on A-fiber inputs have a role in stimulating neuronal sprouting during the remodeling process. There is good evidence that A-fibers give rise to processes that can invade C-fiber territory in the substantia gelatinosa of the spinal cord following peripheral nerve injury (148). Interestingly, the NMDA antagonist MK-801 is capable of blocking the reorganization of dorsal horn input to create defined receptive fields after peripheral nerve section (77). This effect has been interpreted in terms of a block of postsynaptic receptors.

NMDA receptors may be present on sensory neurons other than DRG neurons. The $\zeta$ subunit (mouse equivalent of NMDAR-1) is expressed in the trigeminal ganglion (141). There is also evidence for the presence of presynaptic glutamate receptors on the central terminals of vagal afferents (80) and for transport of NMDA receptors in vagal axons (32). As far as we are aware, no detailed account of the responsiveness of other (i.e. not DRG) sensory neurons to NMDA has been published.

## NICOTINIC RECEPTORS

Functional nicotinic receptors are also expressed by subsets of DRG sensory neurons and are developmentally regulated. They have been detected in rat and chick. In the chick, responses to acetylcholine have been detected in ovo, and over 90% of DRG neurons are responsive by E18 (88). In situ hybridization, Northern blot analysis, and RNase protection have been used to classify the receptor subunits present in these cells. Both alpha-3 and alpha-4 neuronal nicotinic subunits are present (23). In the rat, about 50% of acutely dissociated DRG neurons respond to acetylcholine (116). In a study of nodose ganglion neurons, Mandelzys & Cooper found that only 40% of cells responded to acetylcholine but that this percentage could be increased by culturing the neurons in the absence of nonneuronal cells from the ganglion (87). Nerve growth factor (NGF) also exerts a regulatory role, increasing the current density sevenfold in neurons that are grown alone. There is some indirect evidence for an unusual nicotinic receptor in the peripheral nervous system, because an $\alpha$-bungarotoxin-binding complex that shows nicotinic pharmacology, but lacks known nicotinic subunits, has been detected. This complex is present in sympathetic, as well as sensory, ganglia but is absent in the CNS (105).

## ATP (P2X) RECEPTORS

ATP has been shown to evoke a sensation of pain on human blister bases (8a), and the molecular basis of this effect has been addressed by studies of sensory neurons in culture. Electrophysiological analysis indicates that up to 100% of DRG or nodose ganglion sensory neurons respond to ATP with elevated intracellular free-calcium concentrations or depolarizing responses (10, 22, 71). These effects are probably mediated by the third class of ligand-gated ion channels expressed by DRG neurons. Such P2X receptors comprise a family of glycosylated proteins of apparent $M_r$ about 60 K, that have intracellular N- and C-terminal domains, two membrane-spanning hydrophobic domains (the second of which lines the channel pore), and a large extracellular domain. The subunits are encoded by different genes, although alternatively spliced transcripts of particular subtype mRNAs also occur. The channels are 35–50% identical at the amino acid level and are permeant to both monovalent and divalent cations. These channels show some secondary structural similarities with amiloride-sensitive sodium channel subunits and *C. elegans* degenerins, but have a distinct pattern of expression of conserved cysteine residues in the predicted extracellular domain of the proteins. At present, six P2X receptors have been cloned and expressed either in *Xenopus* oocytes or in transfected HEK293 cells, and their distribution has been analysed by in situ hybridization (34). All six known P2X subtype mRNA transcripts have been found to be expressed in sensory neurons of the dorsal root, and nodose and trigeminal ganglia (reviewed in 97). However, only one subtype, P2X$_3$, is expressed selectively in small-diameter sensory neurons that generally subserve a nociceptive function (30, 79). An electrophysiological analysis of the properties of the expressed P2X$_3$ channel showed many similarities with rat sensory neurons in culture. Two-electrode voltage-clamp experiments showed that the P2X$_3$ channel is probably multimeric, as judged by a Hill slope of 1.4 at low agonist concentrations. Application of ATP resulted in an inward current and marked inward rectification, consistent with an inward cation flux. As the agonist concentration was increased, the current had a faster rise time and showed a more pronounced and faster sag in responses to sustained agonist application. The apparent $EC_{50}$ for ATP was 1.2 $\mu$M. The channel rapidly desensitizes and is activated by ATP congeners with the same rank order of potency as that described for sensory neurons in culture (at low concentrations 2-methyl thio ATP $\gg$ ATP $>$ $\alpha$-$\beta$ methylene ATP $>$ $\gamma$-thio ATP $>$ 2'deoxy ATP $>$ CTP $>$ADP $\gg$ UTP $\beta$, $\gamma$-methylene ATP $>$ GTP) (30). Indirect evidence for heteromultimeric channels in sensory neurons has been provided by coexpression studies of distinct P2X subunits in *Xenopus* oocytes. Some nodose ganglion cells desensitize slowly in response to $\alpha$-$\beta$ methylene ATP (71, 79). However, the oocyte-expressed $P2X_3$ receptor desensitizes rapidly. If $P2X_2$ (first identified in PC12 cells) is coexpressed with $P2X_3$ in oocytes, then a slowly desensitizing form of the receptor is formed (79). This evidence is consistent with, but does not prove, that heteromultimeric receptors exist in sensory neurons. There may be a heterogeneity in the composition of native ionotrophic ATP-gated channels; a recent paper reports that rat DRG neurons in culture desensitize rapidly, and the properties of the channel are very similar to those of homomeric $P2X_3$ (108) receptors expressed in *Xenopus* oocytes. In order to clarify this issue, specific antibodies to each P2X subunit will be required. Not only subunit composition, but distinct subcellular locations and the quaternary structure of these channels should be revealed with such reagents.

## 5HT

Binding and pharmacological studies have identified a number of 5HT receptor subtypes on sensory neurons. The G protein–coupled receptors $5HT_{1A}$ (36), $5HT_{1D}$ (94 ), and $5HT_2$ (130) are all found on these neurons. The $5HT_3$ receptor (previously classified as a nicotinic receptor beta-5 subunit) is the only directly gated cation channel present and is found on about 40% of DRG neurons grown in tissue culture (50, 107). $5HT_3$ is known to form a homomeric cation channel. Unmyelinated C-fibers seem to respond particularly well to 5HT (54).

Apart from the direct actions mediated through the $5HT_3$ receptor, the action of additional chemical activators of sensory neurons are enhanced by 5HT acting through other receptor subtypes (109). 5HT can also sensitize noxious mechanical stimulation (129). The effects of capsaicin and bradykinin on ventral horn depolarization are also strongly potentiated by perfusion of 5HT.

## CAPSAICIN (VANILLOID) RECEPTORS

Capsaicin is a plant-derived compound that excites some sensory nerves, but unlike other (known) sensory stimulants, it is highly specific in its actions. It has no significant effects on other neurons except at high concentrations, at least in the periphery. Physiologists have exploited this remarkable cellular specificity by using capsaicin as a probe to study sensory mechanisms. This work has been the subject of several comprehensive review articles (17, 26, 47, 63, 84, 93). Most of the biological actions of capsaicin in adult animals can be attributed to a single mechanism—activation of a specific receptor that opens cation-specific ion channels in the plasma membrane of a subpopulation of sensory neurons (12). The sensitive subpopulation includes a high proportion of C-fibers and some Aδ-fibers arising from neurons of the DRG, and nodose and trigeminal ganglia. The sensory modalities of the capsaicin-sensitive neurons are diverse and include polymodal nociceptors and thermosensitive neurons in the DRG and trigeminal (Gasserian) ganglia, and vagal (nodose and jugular ganglia) afferents that innervate the viscera but whose physiological function(s) is less well understood (see 63). There is also evidence suggesting that some neurons in the CNS and retina are sensitive to capsaicin (106), but there is little information available concerning the cellular mechanism of action at these sites.

The effects of capsaicin are strongly influenced by species, age of the animals, and concentration of the drug used. Sensory neurons in nonmammalian species tend to be weakly capsaicin sensitive at best (63), and chickens are not sensitive at all (66, 149, but see 60). The range of neurons that are sensitive to capsaicin is wider in fetal or neonatal animals than in adult animals (74). Also, fetal and neonatal animals are more sensitive than adults to the neurotoxic effects of capsaicin (146). Expression and maintenance of capsaicin responsiveness in adult DRG neurons is dependent on NGF (18, 144, 145). At quite modest concentrations (above 1 $\mu$M), capsaicin can exert nonspecific effects, in particular a pronounced voltage-dependent block of potassium channels (7, 70), that complicates analysis of the cellular effects of the drug. The diverse aspects of the biology of capsaicin, although interesting, are not considered in detail here. Instead, we focus on the putative capsaicin receptor and the ion channel associated with the receptor.

## Identification of the Vanilloid Receptor

To date, no endogenous capsaicinoid molecule has been identified. Nevertheless, the existence of a specific receptor for capsaicin is supported by various independent lines of evidence. First, several series of compounds have been discovered that show a distinct relationship between the chemical structure and pharmacological potency of capsaicin analogues (126, 127, 137–140). The existence of a well-defined structure-activity relationship suggests that the compounds interact with a specific binding site. Second, the development of capsazepine, a competitive antagonist of capsaicin responses (16), provides additional pharmacological evidence for a specific receptor for capsaicin. Third, resiniferatoxin (RTX), a naturally occurring structural analogue of capsaicin, has been used to define a ligand-binding site in DRG membranes (120) that has a distribution and range of characteristics consistent with its identification as the capsaicin receptor (21, 118, 123, 124, 145). RTX binding to DRG membranes is displaceable by either capsaicin or capsazepine (118, 119). RTX evokes physiological responses in a variety of assays that are similar to the effects of capsaicin, but RTX is about 100- to 200-fold, and in some assays up to 20,000-fold, more potent (21, 118, 143). Expression of the RTX-binding site, like capsaicin and RTX responsiveness, is dependent on NGF (145). The discovery of RTX as an ultra-potent capsaicin analogue (119–121) and the elucidation of a structure-activity relationship for the receptor has led to coining the term vanilloid receptor as more appropriate for the RTX/capsaicin-binding site (121).

## Subtypes of Vanilloid Receptor

Because capsaicin, RTX, and their analogues may have distinct analgesic and anti-inflammatory properties, as well as algesic and irritant features (27, 63, 125), the issue of whether vanilloid receptor subtypes exist is an important one. It may be possible to exploit some of the properties of RTX and its analogues for therapeutic ends by targeting vanilloid receptor subtypes. It is clear from in vitro studies that vanilloid receptor agonists have diverse pharmacological actions (37, 42, 86, 128). However, it is not clear whether the diversity is due to receptor heterogeneity or to differences in the pharmacokinetic properties and specificity of the drugs.

The vanilloid receptor, as revealed by binding studies or autoradiography, is present on the cell bodies, axons, and terminals of sensory neurons (145). This is consistent with physiological studies demonstrating sensitivity of all regions of sensory neurons to vanilloid agonists (63). In the rat, the affinity of the vanilloid receptor for RTX in different tissues has been found to differ by as much as 200-fold, leading to the suggestion that the vanilloid receptor may exist as more than one subtype. Specifically, it has been suggested that at least two distinct subtypes of vanilloid receptor exist, which are described loosely as a central type and a peripheral type (118). The central type is located predominantly on the cell bodies, central processes, and terminals of sensory neurons and in the urinary bladder (123), has a high affinity for RTX (estimates of $K_d$ 10–100 pM), and binds capsazepine relatively weakly ($K_i$ 3–5 $\mu$M). The peripheral type is located mainly on peripheral processes and terminals, notably in the airways (123), has a relatively low affinity for RTX ($K_d$ 100–3000 pM), and binds capsazepine strongly ($K_i \approx 0.1 \mu$M). Scatchard analysis of binding of RTX to the central-type vanilloid receptor yields a highly nonlinear relationship that may be indicative of positive cooperativity in binding. Binding of RTX to the peripheral-type receptor is noncooperative (see 118). On the other hand, Acs et al

(1), who also found that RTX binding shows positive cooperativity, could detect no significant differences in the binding properties of the vanilloid receptor in different regions of sensory neurons of the rat. The important question of whether more than one type of vanilloid receptor exists in a single species remains open (see section on Pharmacology of the Vanilloid-Activated Channel).

## Properties of the Vanilloid-Gated Ion Channel

Excitation of sensory neurons by capsaicin is accompanied by a decrease in membrane resistance, suggesting that the vanilloid receptor is linked to and opens an ion channel (6, 59, 90). Several voltage-clamp studies have shown that capsaicin activates an inward current at negative potentials in sensory neurons of the nodose ganglion (90), the DRG (12, 13, 17, 18, 20, 38, 41, 99, 102, 135, 142, 143), and trigeminal ganglion (82, 91). Single ion channels in membrane patches activated by vanilloids have been demonstrated in DRG (17, 41, 48, 99, 135) but not, so far as we are aware, in other sensory ganglia. All these studies are in broad agreement as to the basic properties of the vanilloid-activated conductance. The vanilloid-activated current is carried by cations, and the channel, which is probably impermeable to Cl, discriminates poorly between different monovalent cations (14, 17, 98, 149). Even large organic monovalent ions such as choline and arginine (144) can permeate the channel. It is generally held that the channel is permeable to $Ca^{2+}$ (17, 20, 41, 99, 135) and even large inorganic divalent ions such as $Co^{2+}$ (28, 38, 149). Comprehensive studies of capsaicin-induced ion fluxes in cultured DRG neurons support this view (149). Single-cell studies with calcium-sensitive fluorescent dyes, alone or with simultaneous electrophysiological recording (28, 31, 41), confirm the belief that the channel is permeable to $Ca^{2+}$. The channel may have a higher permeability to $Ca^{2+}$ than to monovalent ions (17), although a recent report (99) estimates the $Ca^{2+}$ permeability at only 0.24 that of $Na^{+}$. Published current-voltage relationships for vanilloid-induced current measured under a variety of conditions in intact voltage-clamped cells are usually linear and reverse close to 0 mV (13, 39, 143) or slightly more positively (135), as expected for a conductance of this type. The conductance-voltage relationship for single channels measured in isolated membrane patches is outwardly rectifying. Estimates of single-channel conductance vary from about 20 to 40 pS at membrane potentials between $-80$ and $-50$ mV (17, 48, 99, 135 ) and about 80 to 100 pS at $+60$ mV (17, 99). The probability of the channel being open $(P_o)$ in the presence of a vanilloid agonist is strongly voltage dependent (14), increasing by a factor of about 6 between $-60$ and $+60$ mV or e-fold for each 28.8 mV of depolarization (99). Taken together, the outward rectification of the single-channel conductance and the voltage dependence of $P_o$ would predict an outwardly rectifying current-voltage relationship for whole-cell currents; this is not what is generally observed (but see 20, 38). Given that vanilloids can activate channels in small cell-free membrane patches, it is reasonable to suppose that diffusable second messengers such as cAMP or cGMP are not involved in coupling the receptor to the ion channel. However, the discrepancy between the behavior of vanilloid-gated channels in isolated patches and whole cells suggests that some component of the cytosol modulates the behavior of the channels.

Capsaicin-induced currents in DRG neurons are quite slow to develop compared with currents evoked by ligands such as GABA or ATP (18, 135). This could mean that the binding site for capsaicin is not extracellular and access of capsaicin to its receptor is slowed by diffusion through the lipid membrane. Vlachová & Vyklicky (135) paid particular attention to the time course of capsaicin responses and showed that the rate of development of the inward current evoked by capsaicin (at $-50$ mV) is concentration dependent, which suggests that binding of capsaicin to its receptor, rather than diffusion, is the rate-limiting step in the capsaicin response. We confirmed this observation and found that (at $+40$ mV) capsaicin-induced outward current develops with a slow time constant that is concentration dependent ($2.8 \pm 0.6$ and $0.9 \pm 0.2$ s at 0.5 and 5 $\mu$M, respectively; R Docherty, unpublished observation). However, these data provide no insight into the location of the vanilloid receptor, be it intracellular, extracellular, or intramembranous. Vlachová & Vyklicky (135) also performed experiments where they included capsaicin (up to 50 $\mu$M) in their recording pipette, thereby allowing the drug access to the intracellular compartment, and found that this did not influence capsaicin responsiveness when the drug was applied extracellularly. This led them to suggest that the capsaicin-binding site is not intracellular. This is surprising because capsaicin is a lipophilic compound that can activate single channels in inside-out as well as outside-out patches (R Docherty, unpublished observation) and would therefore be expected to activate the vanilloid receptor from inside the cell irrespective of which side of the membrane the receptor is located. The sidedness of the vanilloid receptor is important because it informs ideas concerning the nature of potential capsaicinoid molecules and is, therefore, an issue that warrants further study.

## Pharmacology of the Vanilloid-Activated Channel

Estimates of the $EC_{50}$ for activation of the vanilloid-gated channel by capsaicin vary from about 1.1 $\mu$M in isolated membrane patches (99) to about 200 to 400 nM in voltage-clamped cells (12, 135). The Hill coefficient calculated by fitting a logistic equation to the dose-response data is 1.8 in each case [data from Oh et al (99) and Vlachová & Vyklicky (135) and calculated from data presented in figure 2 of Bevan & Docherty (12)]. It has been suggested that the steep slope of the dose-response curve yielding a value for the Hill slope close to 2 indicates that more than one vanilloid molecule must bind to the channel in order to activate it (135). These data recall the finding discussed above that RTX binding to the vanilloid receptor shows positive cooperativity with a cooperativity index close to 2 (118), which also has been interpreted as indicating that the vanilloid receptor displays two interacting binding sites. Interestingly, somewhat lower values of $\approx$60–70 nM have been determined for the $EC_{50}$ for capsaicin-induced $^{14}C$ guanidine efflux measurements (149) or for capsaicin-induced $Ca^{2+}$ uptake using $Ca^{2+}$-sensitive fluorescent dyes (31) in intact, cultured rat DRG neurons. Here the dose-response relationship is shallower, yielding Hill slopes close to 1 [logistic curves fitted to the data in figure 3a of Wood et al (149), and figure 1a of Cholewinski et al (31) yield values for the Hill coefficient of 0.94 and 0.99, respectively]. The $K_d$ for capsazepine calculated by Schild analysis from measurements of capsaicin-induced $^{86}Rb^+$ efflux in intact, cultured rat DRG neurons was 107 nM (16), which is very close to the value of 100 nM for the $K_i$ determined for binding of capsazepine to the peripheral type vanilloid receptor (see above). Unfortunately, no quantitative estimate for the antagonist potency of capsazepine on vanilloid-gated currents is available from electrophysiological studies, although it is clear that, at the relatively high concentration of 10 $\mu$M, capsazepine can block capsaicin-induced currents (16, 99). However, these numbers cannot be used to make a convincing case for vanilloid receptor subtypes underlying responses in the different assays, but the possibilities warrant further investigation.

## Desensitization Mechanisms

It is important to distinguish between two phenomena that are often included under a general heading of capsaicin desensitization. The first is a functional desensitization where a challenge with capsaicin leads to a reduction or loss of responsiveness of sensory neurons, not just to capsaicin, but to other stimuli as well. This functional desensitization may underlie the analgesic and anti-inflammatory effects of vanilloids. The second is a pharmacological desensitization where prolonged or repeated applications of capsaicin lead to a progressive decline in the size of subsequent responses to capsaicin itself (see 63). This feature of the capsaicin response has made the physiology and pharmacology of capsaicin and other vanilloids difficult to study quantitatively at the single-cell level. Both pharmacological desensitization to capsaicin (31, 39, 150, 151) and functional desensitization produced by capsaicin (110) depend largely on calcium uptake by the sensory neurons through the vanilloid-gated ion channel, but some degree of pharmacological desensitization occurs even in the absence of extracellular calcium (39, 82a, 151). It has recently been suggested (39, 151) that the mechanism activated by the increase in intracellular calcium concentration is stimulation of protein phosphatase 2B (calcineurin), a calcium- and calmodulin-dependent cytosolic enzyme. The suggestion was prompted by the observation that desensitization of capsaicin-induced inward currents in voltage-clamped DRG neurons is almost abolished when a complex of cyclosporin A and cyclophilin, which is a specific inhibitor of calcineurin (81), is introduced into the cytoplasm. Interestingly, responses of channels to vanilloid agonists in isolated inside-out membrane patches, when the cytosolic enzyme calcineurin is absent, are less subject to desensitization (99). The emergence of calcineurin as an intracellular mediator of pharmacological desensitization raises the interesting possibility that activation of vanilloid-gated channels may also lead to calcium-dependent dephosphorylation of other ion channels or intracellular proteins and may contribute to functional desensitization of sensory neurons. This hypothesis is consistent with the finding that functional desensitization of sensory neurons, as well as being calcium dependent, is blocked by ruthenium red (also calcium dependent) (4, 85), which blocks the activation of vanilloid-gated ion channels (41, 149).

Desensitization of capsaicin responses is a voltage-dependent phenomenon that is quite marked at negative membrane potentials but greatly reduced or even absent at positive membrane potentials (12, 82a, 151). This property is shared with other ligand-gated ion channels, in particular NMDA-gated channels (33) and $GABA_A$-gated channels (98), where calcineurin has also been implicated in their desensitization mechanisms (29, 76, 131). Whether the enzymatic action of calcineurin depends on membrane potential and the influx of extracellular calcium or whether calcineurin, by its action, alters the voltage dependence of the channel is an intriguing question.

## Protons as Activators of the Vanilloid-Gated Ion Channel

At present, there is no evidence for or against the notion that the vanilloid receptor is activated by an endogenous molecular ligand. An alternative hypothesis that protons are endogenous activators of the vanilloid-gated conductance has been proposed by Bevan (15). Protons (pH < 7.0) activate a transient inward current carried largely by sodium ions in many types of neurons, including sensory neurons, probably by transformation of the ion selectivity and voltage-dependence of voltage-activated calcium channels (73). An additional inward current is activated by protons (pH < 6.2) in sensory neurons. The latter current can be distinguished from the transient current because it activates more slowly, is persistent, has a lower pH threshold for activation and, although cation selective, has a wider ionic selectivity than the transient current (19). DRG neurons that express the persistent proton-gated conductance also respond to capsaicin with an inward current of similar kinetic and conductance properties (18). The persistent proton-gated conductance appears to be expressed only in the capsaicin-sensitive subpopulation of DRG neurons (19), and its expression, like expression of the vanilloid-gated ion channel (144, 145), is regulated by NGF (18). It is claimed in one study, using trigeminal ganglion neurons, that capsaicin can activate an additional transient current of character similar to the transient proton-activated conductance (82), although other workers have not noted such a response (91). Channels of similar amplitude and gating properties that are activated by either protons or capsaicin can be recorded in the same patch of DRG membrane (14). Also [$^3$H]-RTX-binding to the vanilloid receptor (see above) is pH sensitive (122). Taken together, these data present a convincing case that protons can activate the vanilloid-gated conductance and may therefore be an endogenous activator. Preliminary evidence also suggests that protons and capsaicin cause a calcium influx in the same neurons in DRG, presumably via the vanilloid-gated channel (16a). Recently, Oh et al (99) found that protons (pH 5.8–6.0) could neither activate the vanilloid-gated current in capsaicin-sensitive cells nor activate capsaicin-activated channels in isolated patches, although even the transient current evoked by low pH in these experiments was much smaller than those previously reported (19, 73). Similarly, Petersen & Lamotte (102) failed to elicit a response to protons in isolated DRG neurons, but in this case, the pH change was applied slowly as a deliberate strategy to avoid activating a proton-induced inward current because these authors were interested primarily in the effect of pH on capsaicin responsiveness (see below). Nevertheless, these studies show that support for the notion that protons open the vanilloid-gated channel is not unanimous.

In addition to direct activation of the vanilloid-gated conductance by low pH, protons have an indirect interaction with the conductance in that low extracellular pH causes a substantial potentiation of capsaicin responsiveness in DRG (73a, 102) and in trigeminal ganglion neurons (91). The threshold pH for potentiation is less acidic than for direct activation of the channel (102). Potentiation does not appear to be from changes in desensitization properties of the channel, nor is it likely to be from a change in the chemical properties of capsaicin itself. Because low pH either has no effect or reduces affinity and $B_{max}$ for vanilloid binding (122), it is not likely that effects on receptor binding lead to a potentiated response. Responses of frog DRG neurons to GABA are not potentiated by low pH (136). It would be interesting to know whether the potentiating effect is specific to capsaicin or whether responses to other agents, e.g. ATP or 5HT, in vanilloid-sensitive and -insensitive cells are also potentiated, since sensitization of sensory neurons in low extracellular pH conditions is not restricted to the vanilloid-sensitive subpopulation (114).

In studies on cultured DRG neurons where a vanilloid-like response to low pH is evident, the response is not blocked by capsazepine (16, 82), which suggests that if protons activate the channel, they do so by interacting at a site other than the vanilloid receptor. In general, ruthenium red, which blocks vanilloid-gated channels, blocks responses to both capsaicin and protons in cultured cells or intact tissues (see 15 for references). This view is reinforced by the finding that responses evoked by protons in the isolated vagus are not blocked by capsazepine at concentrations that block capsaicin responses (49). Other studies using intact preparations have shown that capsazepine blocks responses to acidic stimuli as well as capsaicin, which suggests that acidic stimuli may release an endogenous molecular vanilloid activator (49). Interpretation of data, especially in intact tissue preparations, is complicated by the possibility of nonspecific effects of capsazepine. For example, capsazepine blocks voltage-dependent calcium channels in rat DRG with an $EC_{50}$ of $\sim$8 $\mu$M (RJ Dochery, unpublished data). Nevertheless, even at modest concentrations (49), capsazepine blocks responses to protons and capsaicin, but not to other stimuli such as bradykinin.

## cAMP-GATED CATION CHANNELS

Activation of olfactory and photosensory neurons involves the regulation of cation channels by cyclic nucleotides. Surprisingly, there is no published information on the expression or significance of such channels in DRG neurons. Although the sensitivity of sensory neurons appears to be modulated through cAMP, after treatment with $PGE_2$, for example (45, 96), it seems likely that these effects are mediated by phosphorylation of ion channels and receptors rather than by direct gating of a cyclic nucleotide–dependent cation current (see below and 45, 51, 96).

## BRADYKININ

Bradykinin is a nonapeptide generated by proteolytic digestion of a high-molecular-weight kininogen precursor. It acts on a wide range of cell types and may play an important role in wound healing. The actions of bradykinin have been reviewed recently (115). Bradykinin B2 receptors and G protein–coupled seven-transmembrane receptors are known to be expressed on sensory neurons. The population of neurons that respond to bradykinin seem to be predominantly unmyelinated C-fibers, and bradykinin has been shown to be able to evoke a sensation of pain (67). Electrophysiological studies in spinal cord preparations with attached DRG neurons have suggested that the afferent fibers that depolarize dorsal horn neurons are TTX-resistant, again consistent with the selective action of bradykinin on nociceptors (67). Interestingly, bradykinin elevates cGMP levels in susceptible neurons, and this event has been linked to a subsequent desensitization. Recently, a role for nitric oxide (NO) in this process has been demonstrated, which suggests that activation of sensory neurons by bradykinin may also result in indirect effects on adjacent cells mediated by NO (8).

# REGULATION OF SENSORY NEURON SENSITIVITY

Perhaps as important as direct activation of sensory neurons by any single chemical entity is the regulation of sensitivity of these cells to depolarizing stimuli and subsequent action potential propagation. There is now strong evidence that hyperalgesic regulators, for example NGF, can increase the level of expression of receptors and channels that are intimately linked with nociceptor activation and input into the spinal cord (e.g. 18, 78). Such regulation could account for the alteration in sensitivity of these cells to noxious stimulation. In addition, it seems likely that short-term effects on the properties of channels and receptors by posttranslational modifications such as phosphorylation may explain some of the rapid actions of hyperalgesic mediators. Thus sensitization of some sodium channels and inhibition of potassium channel activity has been correlated with the actions of hyperalgesic mediators such as prostaglandins, which are known to elevate cAMP levels and may thus exert effects through protein kinase A activation (3, 45, 51). There is also evidence for regulation at the level of neurotransmitter release, as pretreatment with $PGE_2$ leads to a doubling in the release of substance P or calcitonin gene–related peptide (CGRP)–like immunoreactive material from sensory neurons in culture when bradykinin is added (134).

# FUTURE QUESTIONS

It seems clear that the pain-inducing properties of a number of chemical mediators such as bradykinin, ATP, or capsaicin can be explained by activation of cell surface receptors or ion channels on sensory neurons. In contrast, the functional significance of the expression of cation channels gated by excitatory amino acids or acetylcholine remains uncertain. The possibility exists that certain redundant components of a particular repertoire of genes may be switched on during the process of cell-type specification and have no significant functional role. Alternatively, excitatory amino acid and nicotinic receptors may be activated by glutamate or acetylcholine, although the peripheral source of these mediators is uncertain. Alternatively, some presynaptic role may be played by these receptors. Considerable insights into these problems will be provided by the generation and analysis of inducible null mutants for various receptor subtypes. The modalities that may be subserved by particular receptors are also of interest. Do chemical mediators play a role in proprioreception, mechanoreception, or thermoreception? Is there, for example, a temperature-regulated cation channel upon which the hot-pepper component capsaicin acts? The extensive electrophysiological and pharmacological literature on sensory neurons combined with the present cataloguing of receptor subtypes defined at the molecular level should soon provide answers to these intriguing questions.

ACKNOWLEDGMENTS

We thank the Wellcome Trust and the MRC for supporting this work. We apologize for many omissions owing to space limitations.

*Literature Cited*

1. Acs G, Palkovits M, Blumberg PM. 1994. Comparison of [$^3$H]-resiniferatoxin binding by the vanilloid (capsaicin) receptor in dorsal root ganglia, spinal cord, dorsal vagal complex, sciatic and vagal nerve and urinary bladder of the rat. *Life Sci.* 55:1017–26
2. Agrawal SG, Evans RH. 1986. The primary afferent depolarizing action of kainate in the rat. *Br. J. Pharmacol.* 87:345–55
3. Akins PT, McClesky EW. 1993. Characterisation of potassium currents in adult rat sensory neurons and modulation by opioids and cAMP. *Neuroscience* 56:759–69
4. Amann R, Donnerer J, Maggi CA, Giuliani S, DelBianco E, et al. 1990. Capsaicin desensitization in vivo is inhibited by ruthenium red. *Eur. J. Pharmacol.* 186:169–75
5. Ault B, Hildebrand LM. 1993. Activation of nociceptive reflexes by peripheral kainate receptors. *J. Pharmacol. Exp. Ther.* 265:927–32
6. Baccaglini PI, Hogan PG. 1983. Some rat sensory neurons in culture express characteristics of differentiated pain sensory cells. *Proc. Natl. Acad. Sci. USA* 80:594–98
7. Baker MD, Ritchie JM. 1994. The action of capsaicin on type I delayed rectifier K$^+$ currents in rabbit Schwann cells. *Proc. R. Soc. London Ser. B.* 255:259–65
8. Bauer MB, Murphy S, Gebhart GF. 1995. Stimulation of cyclic GMP production via a nitrosyl factor in sensory neuronal cultures by algesic or inflammatory agents. *J. Neurochem.* 65:363–72
8a. Bleehen T, Keele CA. 1977. Observations on the algogenic actions of adenosine compounds on the human blister base preparation. *Pain* 3:367–77
9. Brake AJ, Wagenbach MJ, Julius D. 1994. New structural motif for ligand-gated ion channels defined by an ionotropic ATP receptor. *Nature* 371:519–23
10. Bean BP. 1990. ATP-activated channels in rat and bullfrog sensory neurons. *J. Neurosci.* 10:1–10
11. Bettler B, Boulter J, Hermans-Borgmeyer I, O'Shea-Greenfield A, Deneris ES, et al. 1990. Cloning of a novel glutamate receptor subunit, GluR5: expression in the nervous system during development. *Neuron* 5:583–95
12. Bevan S, Docherty RJ. 1993. Cellular mechanisms of the action of capsaicin. See Ref. 148a, pp. 27–44
13. Bevan S, Forbes CA. 1988. Membrane effects of capsaicin on dorsal root ganglion neurones in cell culture. *J. Physiol.* 398:28P
14. Bevan S, Forbes CA, Winter J. 1993. Protons and capsaicin activate the same ion channels in rat isolated dorsal root ganglion neurones. *J. Physiol.* 459:401P
15. Bevan S, Geppetti P. 1994. Protons: small stimulants of capsaicin-sensitive sensory nerves. *Trends Neurosci.* 17:509–12
16. Bevan S, Hothi S, Hughes GA, James IF, Rang HP, et al. 1992. Capsazepine: a competitive antagonist of the sensory neurone excitant capsaicin. *Br. J. Pharmacol.* 107:544–52
16a. Bevan S, Richards DC. 1996. Modulation of intracellular Ca$^{2+}$ and pH by acid solutions and capsaicin in acutely dissociated rat DRG neurones. *J. Physiol.* 494:76P
17. Bevan S, Szolcsányi J. 1990. Sensory neuron-specific actions of capsaicin: mechanisms and applications. *Trends Pharmacol. Sci.* 11:330–33
18. Bevan S, Winter J. 1995. Nerve growth factor differentially regulates the chemosensitivity of adult rat cultured sensory neurons. *J. Neurosci.* 15:4918–26
19. Bevan S, Yeats J. 1991. Protons activate a cation conductance in a sub-population of rat dorsal root ganglion neurones. *J. Physiol.* 433:145–61
20. Bleakman D, Brorson JR, Miller RJ. 1990. The effect of capsaicin on voltage-gated calcium currents and calcium signals in cultured dorsal root ganglion cells. *Br. J. Pharmacol.* 101:423–31

21. Blumberg PM Szallasi A, Acs G. 1993. Resiniferatoxin—an ultrapotent capsaicin analogue. See Ref. 148a, pp. 45–62

22. Bouvier MN, Evans ML, Benham CD. 1991. Calcium influx induced by stimulation of ATP receptors on neurones from rat dorsal root ganglia. *Eur. J. Neurosci.* 3:285–91

23. Boyd RT, Jacob MH, McEachern AE, Caron S, Berg DK. 1991. Nicotinic acetylcholine receptor mRNA in dorsal root ganglion neurons *J. Neurobiol.* 22:1–14

24. Deleted in proof

25. Buck LB, Axel R. 1991. A novel multigene family may encode odorant receptors: a molecular basis for odor recognition. *Cell* 65:75–87

26. Buck SH, Burks TF. 1986. The neuropharmacology of capsaicin: review of some recent observations. *Pharmacol. Rev.* 38:179–226

27. Campbell E, Bevan S, Dray A. 1993. Clinical applications of capsaicin and its analogues. See Ref. 148a, pp.255–72

28. Chard PS, Bleakman D, Savidge JR, Miller RJ. 1995. Capsaicin-induced neurotoxicity in cultured dorsal root ganglion neurones: involvement of calcium-activated proteases. *Neuroscience* 65:1099–108

29. Chen QX, Stelzer A, Kay AR, Wong RKS. 1990. GABA$_A$ receptor function is regulated by phosphorylation in acutely dissociated guinea-pig hippocampal neurones. *J. Physiol.* 420:207–21

30. Chen CC, Akopian AN, Sivilotti L, Colquhoun D, Burstock G, Wood JN. 1995. A P2X purinoceptor expressed by a subset of sensory neurons. *Nature* 377:385–86

31. Cholewinski A, Burgess GM, Bevan S. 1993. The role of calcium in capsaicin-induced desensitization in rat cultured dorsal root ganglion neurones. *Neuroscience* 55:1015–23

32. Cincotta M, Beart PM, Summers RJ, Lodge D. 1989. Bidirectional transport of NMDA receptor and ionophore in the vagus nerve. *Eur. J. Pharmacol.* 160:167–71

33. Clark GD, Clifford DB, Zorumski CF. 1990. The effect of agonist concentration, membrane voltage and calcium on N-methyl-D-aspartate receptor desensitization. *Neuroscience* 39:787–97

34. Collo G, North RA, Kawshima E, Merlo-Pich E, Neidhardt S, et al. 1996. Cloning of P2X5 and P2X6 receptors, and the distribution and properties of an extended family of ATP-gated ion channels. *J. Neurosci.* 16:2495–507

35. Cui M, Nicol GD. 1995. cAMP mediates the prostaglandin E2 induced potentiation of bradykinin excitation in rat sensory neurones. *Neuroscience* 66:459–66

36. Daval G, Verge D, Basbaum AI, Bourgoin S, Hamon M. 1987. Autoradiographic evidence for 5HT1 binding sites on primary afferent fibres in the dorsal horn of the rat spinal cord. *Neurosci. Lett.* 83:71–76

37. Dickenson A, Hughes C, Rueff A, Dray A. 1990. A spinal mechanism of action is involved in the antinociception produced by the capsaicin analogue NE. 19550 (olvanil). *Pain* 43:353–62

38. Docherty RJ, Robinson B, Bevan S. 1991. Capsaicin causes prolonged inhibition of voltage-activated calcium currents in adult rat dorsal root ganglion neurons in culture. *Neuroscience* 40:513–21

39. Docherty RJ, Yeats JC, Bevan S, Boddeke HWGM. 1996. Inhibition of calcineurin inhibits the desensitization of capsaicin-evoked currents in cultured dorsal root ganglion neurones from adult rats. *Pflügers Arch.* 431:828–37

40. Dow KE, Riopelle RJ. 1990. Ethanol inhibits NMDA-stimulated neurite growth by sensory neurones in vitro. *NeuroReport* 1:111–14

41. Dray A, Forbes CA, Burgess GM. 1990. Ruthenium red blocks the capsaicin-induced increase in intracellular calcium and activation of membrane currents in sensory neurons as well as the activation of peripheral nociceptors in vitro. *Neurosci. Lett.* 110:52–59

42. Dray A, Patel I, Neem S, Rueff A, Urban L. 1992. Studies with capsazepine on peripheral nociceptor activation by capsaicin and low pH: evidence for a dual effect of capsaicin. *Br. J. Pharmacol.* 107:236P

43. Dubner R, Ruda MA. 1992. Activity-dependent neuronal plasticity following tissue injury and inflammation. *Trends Neurosci.* 15:96–103

44. Edmonds B, Gibb AJ, Colquhoun D. 1995. Mechanisms of activation of glutamate receptors and the time course of excitatory synaptic currents. *Annu. Rev. Physiol.* 57:495–519

45. England S, Bevan S, Docherty RJ. 1996. PGE2 modulates the TTX-resistant sodium current in neonatal rat DRG neurons via the cAMP-protein kinase A cascade. *J. Physiol.* 495:429–40

46. Ferreira SH, Lorenzetti BB. 1994. Glutamate spinal retrograde sensitization of primary sensory neurones associated with nociception. *Neuropharmacology* 33:1479–85

47. Fitzgerald M. 1983. Capsaicin and sensory neurones—a review. *Pain* 15:109–30

48. Forbes CA, Bevan S. 1988. Single channels activated by capsaicin in patches of membrane from adult rat sensory neurones in culture. *Neurosci. Lett. Suppl.* 32:S3

49. Fox AJ, Urban L, Barnes PJ, Dray A. 1995. Effects of capsazepine against capsaicin- and proton-evoked excitation of single airway C-fibres and vagus nerve from the guinea-pig. *Neuroscience* 67:741–52

50. Fozard JR. 1987. 5-HT, the enigma variations. *Trends Pharmacol. Sci.* 8:501–6

51. Gold MS, Reichling DB, Shuster MJ, Levine JD. 1996. Hyperalgesic agents increase a tetrodotoxin-resistant Na current in nociceptors. *Proc. Natl. Acad. Sci. USA* 93:1108–12

52. Gregor P, Eshhar N, Ortega A, Teichberg VI. 1988. Isolation, immunochemical characterization and localization of the kainate sub-class of glutamate receptor from chick cerebellum. *EMBO J.* 7:2673–79

53. Grubb BD, McQueen DS, Iggo A, Birrell GJ, Dutia MB. 1988. A study of 5-HT-receptors associated with afferent nerves located in normal and inflamed rat ankle joints. *Agents Actions* 25:216–18

54. Hamon M, Collin E, Chantrel D, Daval G, Verge D, et al. 1990. Serotonin receptors and the modulation of pain. In *Serotonin and Pain,* ed. JM Besson, pp. 53–72. Amsterdam: Excerpta Medica

55. Hampson, DR Huie D, Wenthold RJ. 1987. Solubilization of kainic acid binding sites from rat brain. *J. Neurochem.* 49:1209–15

56. Hargrave PA, Hamm HE, Hofmann KP. 1993. Interaction of rhodopsin with the G-protein, transducin. *BioEssays* 15:43–50

57. Henley JM, Barnard EA. 1991. Comparison of solubilised kainate and alpha-amino-3-hydroxy-5-methylisoxazolepropionate binding sites in chick cerebellum. *J. Neurochem.* 56:702–5

58. Herb A, Burnashev N, Werner P, Sakmann B, Wisden W, Seeburg PH. 1992. The KA-2 subunit of excitatory amino acid receptors shows widespread expression in brain and forms ion channels with distantly related subunits. *Neuron* 8:775–85

59. Heyman I, Rang HP. 1985. Depolarizing responses to capsaicin in a subpopulation of dorsal root ganglion cells. *Neurosci. Lett.* 56:69–75

60. Hiura A, Sakamoto Y. 1987. Effect of capsaicin on neurites of cultured dorsal root ganglia and isolated neurons of chick embryos. *Neurosci. Lett.* 73:237–41

61. Hollmann M, Heinemann S. 1994. Cloned glutamate receptors. *Annu. Rev. Neurosci.* 17:31–108

62. Hollmann M, Maron C, Heinemann S. 1994. N-glycosylation site-tagging suggests a three transmembrane domain topology for the glutamate receptor GluR1. *Neuron* 13:13441–43

63. Holzer P. 1991. Capsaicin: cellular targets, mechanisms of action, and selectivity for thin sensory neurones. *Pharmacol. Rev.* 43:143–201

64. Huettner JE. 1990. Glutamate receptor channels in rat DRG neurons: activation by kainate and quisqualate and blockade of desensitization by concanavalin A. *Neuron* 5:255–66

65. Ishida M, Shinozaki H. 1991. Novel kainate derivatives: potent depolarizing action on spinal motoneurones and dorsal root fibres in newborn rat. *Br. J. Pharmacol.* 104:873–78

66. Jancsó G, Ferencsik M, Such G, Kiràly E, Nagy A, Bujdosó M. 1985. Morphological effects of capsaicin and its analogues in newborn and adult mammals. In *Tachykinin Antagonists,* ed. R Hakanson, F Sundler, pp. 35–44. Amsterdam: Elsevier

67. Jeftinija S. 1994. Bradykinin excites tetrodotoxin-resistant primary afferent fibers. *Brain Res.* 665:69–76

68. Karlin A, Akabas MH. 1995. Toward a structural basis for the function of nicotinic acetylcholine receptors and their cousins. *Neuron* 15:1231–44

69. Deleted in proof

70. Kehl SJ. 1994. Block by capsaicin of voltage-gated $K^+$ currents in melanotrophs of the rat pituitary. *Br. J. Pharmacol.* 112:616–24

71. Khakh BS, Humphrey PPA, Surprenant A. 1995. Electrophysiological properties of P2X-purinoceptors in rat superior cervical, nodose and guinea-pig coeliac neurons. *J. Physiol.* 484:385–95

72. Kiskin NI, Krishtal OA, Tsyndrenko AY. 1986. Excitatory amino acid receptors in hippocampus: kainate fails to desensi-

tize them. *Neurosci. Lett.* 63:225–30

73. Konnerth A, Lux HD, Morad M. 1987. Proton-induced transformation of calcium channel in chick dorsal root ganglion cells. *J. Physiol.* 386:603–33

73a. Kress M, Fetzer S, Rech PW, Vyklicky L. 1996. Low pH facilitates capsaicin responses in isolated sensory neurons of the rat. *Neurosci. Lett.* 211:5–8

74. Lawson SN, Harper AA. 1984. Neonatal capsaicin is not a specific neurotoxin for sensory C-fibres or small dark cells in rat dorsal root ganglia. In *Antidromic Vasodilatation and Neurogenic Inflammation,* ed. LA Chahl, J Szolcsányi, F Lembeck, pp. 111–16. Budapest: Akademiai Kiado

75. Le Douarin NM, Kalcheim C, Teillet MA. 1992. The cellular and molecular basis of early sensory neuron development. In *Sensory Neurons,* ed. SA Scott, pp. 143–70. Oxford: Oxford Univ. Press

76. Leiberman DN, Mody I. 1994. Regulation of NMDA channel function by endogenous $Ca^{2+}$-dependent phosphatase. *Nature* 369:235–39

77. Lewin GR, McKintosh E, McMahon SB. 1994. NMDA receptors and activity dependent tuning of the receptive fields of spinal cord neurons. *Nature* 369:482–85

78. Lewin GR, Rueff A, Mendell LM. 1994. Peripheral and central mechanisms of NGF-induced hyperalgesia. *Eur. J. Neurosci.* 6:1903–12

79. Lewis C, Neidhart S, Holy C, North R A, Buell G, Surprenant A. 1995. Coexpression of P2X2 and P2X3 receptor subunits can account for ATP-gated currents in sensory neurons. *Nature* 377:432–35

80. Lewis SJ, Verberne AJ, Summers RJ, Beart PM, Cincotta M. 1988. Reduced glutamate binding in rat dorsal vagal complex after nodose ganglionectomy. *Brain Res. Bull.* 21:913–16

81. Liu J, Farmer JD Jr, Lane WS, Friedman J, Weissman I, Schrieber SL. 1991. Calcineurin is a common target of cyclophilin-cyclosporin A, FKBP-FK506 complexes. *Cell* 66:807–15

82. Liu L, Simon SA. 1994. A rapid capsaicin-activated current in rat trigeminal ganglion neurons. *Proc. Natl. Acad. Sci. USA* 91:738–41

82a. Liu L, Simon SA. 1996. Capsaicin-induced currents with distinct desensitization and $Ca^{2+}$ dependence in rat trigeminal gangion cells. *J. Neurophysiol.* 75:1503–14

83. Lovinger DM, Weight FF. 1988. Glutamate induces a depolarization of adult rat dorsal root ganglion neurones that is mediated predominantly by NMDA receptors. *Neurosci. Lett.* 94:314–20

84. Maggi CA, Meli A. 1988. The sensory-efferent function of capsaicin-sensitive sensory neurones. *Gen. Pharmacol.* 19:1–43

85. Maggi CA, Patacchini R, Santicioli P, Giuliani S, Geppetti P, Meli A. 1988. Protective action of ruthenium red towards capsaicin desensitization of sensory fibres. *Neurosci. Lett.* 88:201–5

86. Maggi CA, Patacchini R, Tramontana M, Amann R, Giuliani S, Santicioli P. 1990. Similarities and differences in the action of resiniferatoxin and capsaicin on central and peripheral endings of primary sensory neurons. *Neuroscience* 37:531–39

87. Mandelzys A, Cooper E. 1992. Effects of ganglionic satellite cells and NGF on the expression of nicotinic acetylcholine receptors by rat sensory neurons. *J. Neurophysiol.* 67:1213–21

88. Margiotta JF, Howard MJ. 1994. Eye-extract factors promote the expression of acetylcholine sensitivity in chick dorsal root ganglion neurons. *Dev. Biol.* 63:188–201

89. Maricq AV, Peterson AS, Brake AJ, Myers RM, Julius D. 1991. Primary structure and functional expression of the $5HT_3$ receptor, a serotonin-gated ion channel. *Science* 254:432–37

90. Marsh SJ, Stansfeld CE, Brown DA, Davey R, McCarthy D. 1987. The mechanism of action of capsaicin on sensory C-type neurons and their axons in vitro. *Neuroscience* 23:275–90

91. Martenson ME, Ingram SL, Baumann TK. 1994. Potentiation of rabbit trigeminal responses to capsaicin in a low pH environment. *Brain Res.* 651:143–47

92. McBain CJ, Meyer MM. 1994. N-methyl-D-aspartatic acid receptor structure and function. *Physiol. Rev.* 74:723–59

93. Monsereenosurn Y, Kongsamut S, Pezalla PD. 1982. Capsaicin—a literature survey. *CRC Crit. Rev. Toxicol.* 10:321–39

94. Moskowitz MA. 1992. Neurogenic versus vascular mechanisms of sumatriptan and ergto alkaloids in migraine. *Trends Pharmacol. Sci.* 13:307–11

95. Deleted in proof

96. Nicol GD, Cui M. 1994. Prostaglandin E2 enhaces bradykinin activation of embryonic rat sensory neurones. *J. Physiol.* 480:485–92

97. North RA. 1996. P2X purinoceptor

plethora. *Semin. Neurosci.* 8:187–94

98. Oh DJ, Dichter MA. 1992. Desensitization of GABA-induced currents in cultured rat hippocampal neurons. *Neuroscience* 49:571–76

99. Oh U, Hwang SW, Kim D. 1996. Capsaicin activates a nonselective cation channel in cultured neonatal rat dorsal root ganglion neurons. *J. Neurosci.* 16:1659–67

100. Partin KM, Patneau DK, Winters CA, Mayer ML, Buonanno A. 1993. Selective modulation of desensitization at AMPA versus kainate receptors by cyclothiazide and concanavalin A. *Neuron* 11:1069–82

101. Patneau DK, Vyklicky L, Mayer ML. 1993. Hippocampal neurons exhibit cyclothiazide-sensitive rapidly desensitizing responses to kainate. *J. Neurosci.* 13:3496–509

102. Petersen M, Lamotte RH. 1993. Effects of protons on the inward current evoked by capsaicin in isolated dorsal root ganglion cells. *Pain* 54:37–42

103. Petralia RS, Wang YX, Wenthold RJ. 1994. The NMDA receptor subunits NR2A, NR2B show histological and ultrastructural localization patterns similar to those of NR1. *J. Neurosci.* 14:6102–20

104. Pook P, Brugger F, Hawkins NS, Clark KC, Watkins JC, Evans RH. 1993. A comparison of the actions of agonists and antagonists at non-NMDA receptors of C-fibres and motorneurones of the immature rat spinal cord in vitro. *Br. J. Pharmacol.* 108:179–84

105. Pugh PC, Corriveau RA, Conroy WG, Berg DK. 1995. Novel subpopulation of neuronal acetylcholine receptors among those binding $\alpha$-bugarotoxin. *J. Pharmacol. Exp. Ther.* 47:717–25

106. Ritter S, Dinh JJ. 1993. Capsaicin-induced degeneration in rat brain and retina. See Ref. 148a, pp. 105–38

107. Robertson B, Bevan S. 1991. Properties of 5HT$_3$ receptor gated currents in adult rat DRG neurones. *Br. J. Pharmacol.* 102:272–76

108. Robertson SJ, Rae MG, Rowan EG, Kennedy C. 1996. Characterisation of a P2X purinoceptor in cultured neurones of the rat dorsal root ganglia. *Br. J. Pharmacol.* 118:951–56

109. Rueff A, Dray A. 1993. Pharmacological characterisation of the effects of 5-HT and prostaglandins on peripheral sensory neurons in vitro. *Agents Actions* 38:C13–15

110. Santicioli P, Patacchini R, Maggi CA,

Meli A. 1987. Exposure to calcium-free medium protects sensory fibres by capsaicin desensitization. *Neurosci. Lett.* 80:167–72

111. Sato K, Kiyama H, Park HT, Tohyama M. 1993. AMPA, kainate and NMDA receptors are expressed in the rat DRG neurones. *NeuroReport* 4:1263–65

112. Shigemoto R, Ohishi H, Nakanishi S, Mizuno N. 1992. Expression of the mRNA for the rat NMDA receptor (NMDAR1) in the sensory and autonomic ganglion neurones. *Neurosci. Lett.* 144:229–32

113. Sommer B, Burnashev, N, Verdoorn, TA Keinanen, K, Sakmann B, Seeburg PH. 1992. A glutamate receptor channel with a high affinity for domoate and kainate. *EMBO J.* 11:1651–56

114. Steen KH, Reeh PW, Anton F, Handwerker HO. 1992. Protons selectively induce lasting excitation and sensitization to mechanical stimulation of nociceptors in rat skin, in vitro. *J. Neurosci.* 12:86–95

115. Stewart JM. 1995. Bradykinin antagonists: development and applications. *Biopolymers* 37:143–55

116. Sucher NJ, Cheng TP, Lipton SA. 1990. Neural nicotinic acetylcholine responses in sensory neurons from postnatal rat. *Brain Res.* 533:248–54

117. Swanson GT, Feldmeyer D, Kaneda M, Cull-Candy S. 1996. Effect of RNA editing and sub-unit co-assembly on single channel properties of recombinant kainate receptors. *J. Physiol.* 492:129–42

118. Szallasi A. 1994. The vanilloid (capsaicin) receptor: receptor types and species differences. *Gen. Pharamcol.* 2:223–43

119. Szallasi A, Blumberg PM. 1989. Resiniferatoxin, a phorbol-related diterpene, acts as an ultrapotent analog of capsaicin, the irritant constituent in red pepper. *Neuroscience* 30:515–20

120. Szallasi A, Blumberg PM. 1990. Specific binding of resiniferatoxin, an ultrapotent capsaicin analog, by dorsal root ganglion membranes. *Brain Res.* 524:106–11

121. Szallasi A, Blumberg PM. 1990. Resiniferatoxin and its analogs provide novel insights into the pharmacology of the vanilloid (capsaicin) receptor. *Life Sci.* 47:1399–408

122. Szallasi A, Blumberg PM, Lundberg JM. 1995. Proton inhibition of [$^3$H]-resiniferatoxin binding to vanilloid (capsaicin) receptors in rat spinal cord. *Eur.*

*J. Pharmacol.* 289:181–87

123. Szallasi A, Goso C, Blumberg PM, Manzini S. 1993. Competitive inhibition by capsazepine of [$^3$H]-resiniferatoxin binding to central (dorsal root ganglia, spinal cord) and peripheral (urinary bladder, airways) vanilloid (capsaicin) receptors in the rat. *J. Pharmacol. Exp. Ther.* 267:728–33

124. Szallasi A, Nilsson S, Farkas-Szallasi T, Blumberg PM, Hökfelt T, Lundberg JM. 1995. Vanilloid (capsaicin) receptors in the rat: distribution in the brain, regional differences in the spinal cord, axonal transport to the periphery, and depletion by systemic vanilloid treatment. *Brain Res.* 703:175–83

125. Szolcsányi J. 1993. Actions of capsaicin on sensory receptors. See Ref. 148a, pp. 1–26

126. Szolcsányi J, Jancsó-Gàbor A. 1975. Sensory effects of sensory cogeners. I. Relationship between chemical structure and pain-producing potency of pungent agents. *Drug Res.* 25:1877–81

127. Szolcsányi J, Jancsó-Gàbor A. 1975. Sensory effects of sensory cogeners.II. Importance of chemical structure and pungency in desensitizing activity of capsaicin type compounds. *Drug Res.* 26:33–37

128. Szolcsányi J, Szallasi A, Szallasi Z, Joo F, Blumberg PM. 1990. Resiniferatoxin: an ultrapotent selective modulator of capsaicin-sensitive primary afferent neurons. *J. Pharmacol. Exp. Ther.* 255:923–28

129. Taiwo YO, Levine JD. 1992. Serotonin is a directly-acting hyperalgesic agent in the rat. *Neuroscience* 48:485–90

130. Todorovic SM, Anderson EG. 1990. Pharmacological characterisation of 5HT$_3$ receptors in rat DRG cells. *J. Pharmacol. Exp. Ther.* 254:109–15

131. Tong G, Shepherd D, Jahr CE. 1995. Synaptic desensitization of NMDA receptors by calcineurin. *Science* 267:1510–12

132. Urban L, Thomson SWN, Dray A. 1994. Modulation of spinal excitability: cooperation between neurokinins and excitatory amino acid neurotransmitters. *Trends Neurosci.* 17:432–38

133. Valera S, Hussy N, Evans RJ, Adami N, North RA, et al. 1994. A new class of ligand-gated ion channel defined by P2X receptors for ATP. *Nature* 371:519–23

134. Vasko MR, Campbell WB, Waite KJ. 1994. PGE2 enhances bradykinin-sti-mulated release of neuropeptides from rat sensory neurons in culture. *J. Neurosci.* 14:4987–97

135. Vlachová V, Vyklicky L. 1993. Capsaicin-induced membrane currents in cultured sensory neurons of the rat. *Physiol. Res.* 42:301–11

136. Vyklicky L, Philippi M, Kuffler DP, Orkand RK. 1993. GABA$_A$ membrane currents are insensitive to extracellular acidification in cultured sensory neurons of the frog. *Physiol. Res.* 42:313–17

137. Walpole CSJ, Wrigglesworth R. 1993. Structural requirements for capsaicin agonists and antagonists. See Ref. 148a, pp. 63–81

138. Walpole CSJ, Wrigglesworth R, Bevan S, Campbell EA, Dray A, et al. 1993. Analogues of capsaicin with agonist activity as novel analgesic agents; structure-activity studies. 1. The aromatic "A" region. *J. Med. Chem.* 36:2362–72

139. Walpole CSJ, Wrigglesworth R, Bevan S, Campbell EA, Dray A, et al. 1993. Analogues of capsaicin with agonist activity as novel analgesic agents; structure-activity studies. 2. The amide bond "B" region. *J. Med. Chem.* 36:2373–80

140. Walpole CSJ, Wrigglesworth R, Bevan S, Campbell EA, Dray A, et al. 1993. Analogues of capsaicin with agonist activity as novel analgesic agents; structure-activity studies. 3. The amide bond "C" region. *J. Med. Chem.* 36:2381–89

141. Watanabe M, Mishina M, Inoue Y. 1994. Distict gene expression of the N-methyl-D-aspartate receptor channel subunit in peripheral neurons of the mouse sensory ganglia and adrenal gland. *Neurosci. Lett.* 165:183–86

142. Williams JT, Zieglgansberger W. 1982. The acute effects of capsaicin on rat primary afferents and spinal neurones. *Brain Res.* 253:125

143. Winter J, Dray A, Wood JN, Yeats J, Bevan S. 1990. Resiniferatoxin: a potent sensory neuron excitotoxin. *Brain Res.* 520:131–40

144. Winter J, Forbes CA, Sternberg J, Lindsay RM. 1988. Nerve growth factor (NGF) regulates adult rat cultured dorsal root ganglion neuron responses to capsaicin. *Neuron* 1:973–81

145. Winter J, Walpole CS, Bevan S, James IF. 1993. Characterization of resiniferatoxin binding sites on sensory neurones: co-regulation of resiniferatoxin binding and capsaicin sensitivity in adult

rat dorsal root ganglia. *Neuroscience* 57:747–57

146. Winter J, Woolf C, Lynn B. 1993. Degenerative and regenerative responses of sensory neurones to capsaicin-induced damage. See Ref. 148a, pp. 139–60

147. Wisden W, Seeburg PH. 1993. Mammalian ionotropic glutamate receptors. *Curr. Opin. Neurobiol.* 3:291–98

148. Woolf CJ, Shortland P, Coggeshall RE. 1992. Peripheral nerve injury triggers central sprouting of myelinated afferents. *Nature* 355:75–78

148a. Wood JN, ed. 1993. *Capsaicin in the Study of Pain.* New York: Academic. 268 pp.

149. Wood JN, Winter J, James IF, Rang HP, Yeats J, Bevan S. 1988. Capsaicin-induced ion fluxes in dorsal root ganglion cells in clulture. *J. Neurosci.* 8:3208–20

150. Yeats JC, Boddeke HWGM, Docherty RJ. 1992. Capsaicin desensitization in rat dorsal root ganglion neurones is due to activation of calcineurin. *Br. J. Pharmacol.* 107:238P

151. Yeats JC, Docherty RJ, Bevan S. 1992. Calcium-dependent and independent desensitization of capsaicin-evoked responses in voltage-clamped adult rat dorsal root ganglion (DRG) neurones in culture. *J. Physiol.* 446:390P

*Annu. Rev. Physiol. 1997. 59:483–504*

# CONTROL OF M-CURRENT

*Neil V. Marrion*
Vollum Institute, Oregon Health Sciences University, Portland, Oregon 97201

KEY WORDS:   M-channel, potassium, modal gating, second messenger, modulation

### ABSTRACT

M-current is a non-inactivating potassium current found in many neuronal cell types. In each cell type, it is dominant in controlling membrane excitability by being the only sustained current in the range of action potential initiation. It can be modulated by a large array of receptor types, and the modulation can occur either by suppression or enhancement. Modulation of M-current has dramatic effects on neuronal excitability. This review discusses the numerous second messenger pathways that converge on regulation of this current: in particular, two forms of regulation of the M-current, receptor-mediated modulation and the control of macroscopic current amplitude by intracellular calcium. Both types of regulation are discussed with reference to the modulation of single-channel gating properties.

## INTRODUCTION

Stimulation of muscarinic receptors on sympathetic ganglion neurons causes a dramatic change in membrane excitability. Figure 1 illustrates how muscarine can cause a neuron to change from quiescent to tonically firing action potentials. Muscarinic receptor stimulation achieves this effect by suppressing a time-and voltage-dependent current called the M-current (15). This potassium current is slowly activated when the neuron is depolarized toward the threshold for action potential firing, hyperpolarizing the membrane back toward rest and reducing membrane excitability (3). M-current possesses the unique characteristic of sustained activation. Owing to its absence of inactivation, M-current has a major impact on neuronal excitability because it is the only current active at voltages near the threshold for action potential initiation.

Suppression of the M-current was the first clear example of neuromodulation of a potassium current in vertebrate nerve cells (15). Its suppression results in

483

+ muscarine

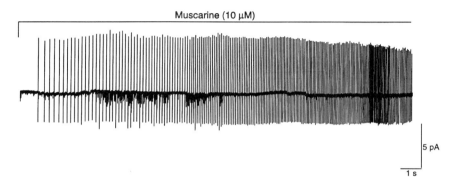

Muscarine (10 μM)

5 pA

1 s

*Figure 1*   Muscarinic receptor activation dramatically increases membrane excitability. Membrane excitability of a dissociated bullfrog sympathetic neuron was monitored by a cell-attached patch electrode containing 110 mM KCl (see inset). Cell was bathed in a sodium-based Ringers solution and had a membrane potential of −55 to −60 mV (determined from the reversal of potassium channel currents observed in the patch). Application of muscarine (10 μM) turned the cell from quiescent to tonically firing action potentials, with the frequency of firing increasing during the application of muscarine.

membrane depolarization and an increase in input resistance, which makes the cell more likely to fire action potentials (4) (Figure 1). The current is also synaptically regulated, with synaptic suppression of M-current underlying the slow excitatory postsynaptic potential (slow EPSP) in both frog (2) and rat (18) sympathetic neurons and in hippocampal CA3 neurons (22). Therefore, it is apparent that the presence of M-current exerts a powerful effect in regulating neuronal excitability (78).

Modulation of the M-current has long been of interest. Although the mechanisms of modulation remain elusive, we now know that this non-inactivating current is present in a huge variety of cell types, and it is dominant in regulating membrane excitability in each. A large array of receptor types can modulate this current, and the modulation can occur either by suppression or enhancement. Therefore, it is expected that modulation of the M-current will have dramatic effects on neuronal excitability. This review concentrates on recent findings, some controversial, that have explored the modulation and regulation of this current. First, receptor-mediated modulation of M-current is discussed, and then regulation of the M-current amplitude is explored.

# RECEPTOR-MEDIATED MODULATION OF M-CURRENT

Since the M-current was discovered by Brown & Adams in 1980 (15), its receptor-mediated suppression has been studied in different preparations by many workers. The current was named M for muscarinic because it was found to be suppressed by muscarinic receptor activation in bullfrog sympathetic ganglion neurons. M-current has since been found to be suppressed by a variety of receptor types, even within a single cell type. In bullfrog sympathetic ganglia, the M-current is suppressed by activation of receptors such as muscarinic (15), substance P (36), luteinizing hormone releasing hormone (LHRH) (1), purinergic (4), and $\beta$-adrenergic (5). In contrast, rat sympathetic neurons possess both muscarinic and angiotensin II receptors that are coupled to the suppression of M-current (26, 68). In hippocampal pyramidal neurons, the M-current is suppressed by activation of muscarinic (31), serotonin (25), opioid (54), and glutamate metabotropic receptors (23). M-current is also found in stomach smooth muscle, where it is suppressed by activation of muscarinic (70) and substance P (71) receptors. The convergence of such a large number of receptor types upon a single species of ion channel has been taken as evidence that a diffusible second messenger couples receptor activation to suppression of M-current. Suppression of M-current exhibits a marked delay and a slow time-course (Figure 2), which supports the likelihood that the messenger can diffuse. The finding that application of muscarine to rat or bullfrog sympathetic neurons can reduce M-channel activity isolated within a cell-attached patch (46, 67) is perhaps more compelling. This type of experiment suggests that the closure of M-channels by muscarinic receptor activation uses a diffusible second messenger.

The problem that has baffled investigators is the identity of the putative diffusible second messenger. This is partly because so many putative messengers can modulate the M-current, which has lead to many spurious hypotheses. A common finding is that any receptor coupled to the hydrolysis of $PIP_2$ and the generation of the messengers $(1,4,5)IP_3$ and diacylglycerol (DAG) suppresses the M-current. This is obviously not always the case because activation of $\beta$-adrenergic receptors will also suppress this current (5). However, many examples exist where this casual observation holds true. For example, activation of bradykinin receptors, producing a $(1,4,5)IP_3$-mediated increase in cytosolic calcium in NG108-15 neuroblastoma cells, suppresses the M-current (32). In elegant support of this casual observation is that only in those NG108-15 cells expressing $M_1$ or $M_3$ muscarinic receptors (which couple to this pathway) is the M-current suppressed by acetylcholine. In contrast, application of acetylcholine to NG108-15 cells expressing $M_2$ or $M_4$ receptors (which do not couple to the hydrolysis of $PIP_2$) had no effect on the M-current (29). In addition, native muscarinic $M_1$ receptors, which couple to the generation of these messengers,

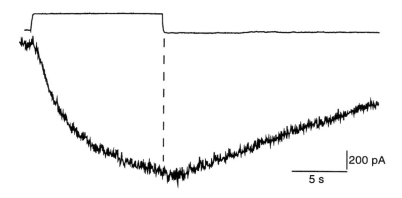

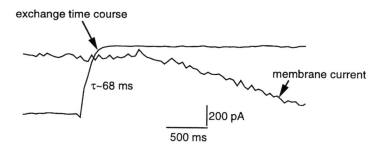

*Figure 2*  Fast application of muscarine reveals the delay and slow onset of M-current suppression. Application of muscarine (10 $\mu$M) to a bullfrog sympathetic neuron, voltage-clamped at $-30$ mV, using a fast exchange method. *Upper panel.* The time course of the application of muscarine is shown above the membrane-holding current response. Application of muscarine caused a net inward current as the sustained outward M-current was suppressed. *Lower panel.* The onset of the response to muscarine is shown on a faster time scale. Solution exchange was measured as the holding current change evoked by application of a 30 mM K$^+$ solution. The exchange occurred with an exponential time course, with time constant of 68 ms. At this time scale, the delay before onset of M-current suppression is obvious, $\approx$500 ms. (Experiment done at 22°C, in collaboration with B Bean.)

suppress the M-current in a number of cell types including sympathetic ganglia (50) and hippocampal pyramidal neurons (27). It seems obvious, therefore, that the messenger underlying the suppression of the M-current has to be related to this pathway. In this case, the candidates have to be either (1,4,5)IP$_3$ or DAG or one of their metabolites, or a rise of intracellular calcium. It has not been simple to resolve whether any of these candidates is the messenger.

## $(1,4,5)IP_3$

Direct intracellular injection of $(1,4,5)IP_3$ by iontophoresis or inclusion in the whole-cell pipette solution does not suppress the M-current in sympathetic ganglia. This has been found to be the case in bullfrog (59) and rat (20) neurons. In support of these data, intracellular application of heparin, an antagonist of $(1,4,5)IP_3$-mediated calcium release, does not block suppression of M-current by muscarine (24). In contrast, intracellular application of $(1,4,5)IP_3$ appears to suppress the M-current in CA1 hippocampal pyramidal cells, most likely independent of the release of intracellular calcium (27). Surprisingly, this result has not been confirmed and remains a single example of an effect of intracellular application of $(1,4,5)IP_3$ upon the M-current.

## *Activation of Protein Kinase C*

It has been proposed that activation of protein kinase C (PKC) underlies agonist-induced suppression of M-current (19). This was suggested because bradykinin induces the formation of $(1,4,5)IP_3$ and DAG, and suppression of M-current was observed with activators of PKC such as phorbol esters (19). Subsequently, M-currents in sympathetic (13, 16, 20, 46a), NG108-15 (62), and PC12 (77) cells have been found to be suppressed by addition of phorbol esters. The effect of phorbol esters is likely by activation of PKC, because their effect can be reduced by inhibitors of PKC (13, 46a). Support for the role of PKC mediating the effect of agonist comes from the finding that the suppression of M-current by ATP in bullfrog dorsal root ganglion (DRG) neurons is antagonized by staurosporine, an inhibitor of PKC (74). Also, down-regulation of PKC activity by chronic exposure of NG108-15 cells to phorbol ester reduces the response to bradykinin (62). However, the proposal has met opposition for several reasons. First, the response to phorbol esters is slow to plateau, a property not reflecting a problem of access (46a). Second, and much more compelling, is the finding that although the phorbol ester-induced suppression of M-current in frog and bullfrog sympathetic neurons could be antagonized by inhibitors of PKC, agonist-evoked suppression is unaffected (13, 46a). Third, the hippocampus is the only preparation where the M-current is not sensitive to phorbol esters (27). Although it would not be too surprising that second messenger control of a membrane current differs in various cell types, it seems curious that the hippocampus stands alone in this regard.

The action of phorbol esters on the M-current is more complicated than initially proposed. One problem concerning their action is that only a portion of the M-current was sensitive to the activators of PKC (13, 16, 20,). The M-current is also affected by intracellular calcium levels (see below). When dissociated sympathetic neurons are dialyzed with a free calcium concentration close to normal intracellular levels, all the M-current is sensitive to the phorbol ester (46a). It is also noted that partial suppression of M-current by low concentrations of agonist can antagonize the response to phorbol ester. These data suggest that two interconvertible populations of M-channels exist: one that is sensitive to both agonist and phorbol ester and another that can only be suppressed by agonist (46a). Even though the situation is less than clear, it is still tempting to suggest that this pathway is involved in the agonist-mediated suppression, because the M-current in so many preparations is sensitive to phorbol esters. Therefore, it is too early to exclude this pathway in mediating, at least in part, the effect of agonist upon the M-current.

## Arachidonic Acid

Another possible second messenger that may be liberated by the pathway forming $(1,4,5)IP_3$ and DAG is arachidonic acid (AA). It can be formed by the metabolism of DAG by diglyceride lipase or can be produced by the action of phospholipase $A_2$, which is activated by an increase in cytosolic calcium that occurs upon production of $(1,4,5)IP_3$. There is strong evidence that AA or one of its metabolites can modulate the M-current. For instance, enhancement of M-current in hippocampal neurons by somatostatin (53) is mimicked by AA. This work further showed that leukotriene $C_4$, a 5-lipoxygenase pathway metabolite of AA, can also augment the M-current and that the action of somatostatin can be blocked by a lipoxygenase inhibitor (64). However, if activation of muscarinic receptors causes the release of AA from hippocampal neurons (37), which presumably occurs following activation of somatostatin receptors, why do muscarinic agonists only induce suppression and not enhancement of the current?

AA also affects M-current in other preparations. For example, in frog and bullfrog sympathetic neurons, the M-current is enhanced by application of AA (12, 80). In contrast to the findings in the hippocampus, the effect of AA is not mimicked by leukotriene $C_4$, but by 12-HETE, a 12-lipoxygenase metabolite (80). The story is further complicated by findings from NG108-15 cells. AA was first reported to inhibit the M-current in these cells (61). Subsequently, it was reported that in some cells the M-current could be initially enhanced and then inhibited by AA. In the majority of cells only inhibition is observed (9). However, the inhibition of M-current is not blocked by inhibitors of AA metabolism (61) and has since been attributed to activation of PKC (63). It appears that some of the data obtained using AA, its metabolites, and inhibitors of AA metabolism may be confounded by the nonspecificity of their actions at the concentrations used. It is evident that the role of AA in receptor-mediated modulation of the M-current is still extremely unclear.

## Intracellular $Ca^{2+}$

It was first suggested by Kirkwood et al (40) that a rise of intracellular calcium ($[Ca^{2+}]_i$) couples receptor activation to suppression of M-current. $[Ca^{2+}]_i$ is an obvious candidate for a diffusible second messenger because the activation of $M_1$ receptors that mediate the production of $(1,4,5)IP_3$ (11) would be expected to evoke a rise in $[Ca^{2+}]_i$. However, the suggestion of Kirkwood et al (40) came at a time when the accepted idea held that a rise of $[Ca^{2+}]_i$ did not affect the M-current. For example, the pharmacology of M-current modulation was first outlined by Adams et al (4) and that study showed that the M-current is unaffected either by removal of extracellular $Ca^{2+}$ or by intracellular iontophoresis of $Ca^{2+}$. This finding was in contrast to the results in an intriguing paper by Tokimasa (73) who observed that the M-current is reduced following massive $Ca^{2+}$ entry from a Ca spike. The confusion was beginning to be apparent. For example, M-current is suppressed by extracellular divalent cations, such as $Ni^{2+}$ and $Co^{2+}$ (4, 75), but contrary to the findings of Adams et al (4), Tokimasa & Akasu (75) found that M-current is also reduced by removal of extracellular $Ca^{2+}$.

The role of a rise of $[Ca^{2+}]_i$ is still controversial because agonists that suppress the M-current do evoke a measurable rise of $[Ca^{2+}]_i$ in frog neurons (51, 59) but not in rat sympathetic or hippocampal neurons (8, 52, 55, 79). It is possible, however, that a rise of $[Ca^{2+}]_i$ in rat neurons is highly localized to the submembrane shell and is not resolvable by conventional $[Ca^{2+}]_i$ imaging techniques (28). In addition to the existence of a rise in $[Ca^{2+}]_i$, there is conflicting evidence as to whether receptor-mediated suppression of M-current can be blocked by intracellular calcium chelators. A high concentration of intracellular 1,2bis($O$-aminophenoxy)ethane-N,N',N'-tetraacetic acid (BAPTA) has been reported to block the effect of muscarinic receptor activation in both rat (8) and bullfrog (40) sympathetic neurons. However, the effect of intracellular BAPTA in rat neurons was proposed to result from the lowering of $[Ca^{2+}]_i$ to below resting levels rather than from the chelation of a $[Ca^{2+}]_i$ increase evoked by receptor activation (8). This interpretation suggests that the pathway coupling muscarinic receptors to M-channels requires a mininimum $[Ca^{2+}]_i$ for normal activation. A similar conclusion was reached for frog neurons by Yu et al (81), but not by Kirkwood et al (40). Other studies showed that the effect of agonist was not blocked by a high concentration of intracellular BAPTA (51, 59, 77, 81). These results suggest that there is not a role for a rise in $[Ca^{2+}]_i$ coupling receptor activation to M-current suppression. In addition, intracellular application of heparin, an antagonist of $(1,4,5)IP_3$-mediated calcium release, does not block suppression of M-current by muscarine but does prevent an enhancement (over-recovery) of M-current that follows wash-out of muscarine (see below) (24). Clarification of the role of $[Ca^{2+}]_i$ comes from studies using NG108-15 neuroblastoma x glioma cells. Upon differentiation, these cells express endogenous muscarinic receptors that couple the release of intracellular calcium to suppression of M-current (19). Chelation of the receptor-mediated increase in $[Ca^{2+}]_i$ prevents activation of a calcium-activated potassium current but not suppression of the M-current (61).

The putative role of an increase in $[Ca^{2+}]_i$ mediating suppression of M-current has been resurrected by the finding that application of $Ca^{2+}$ to inside-out excised patches from rat sympathetic neurons causes a reduction in M-channel activity (66). The effect of $[Ca^{2+}]$ reverses upon its removal, without the requirement for ATP. This result suggests that $[Ca^{2+}]$ acts directly on the M-channel and does not depend on the activity of an associated kinase or phosphatase (see below). This finding has important consequences in determining the role of $[Ca^{2+}]$ and has to be examined carefully. The effect of $[Ca^{2+}]$ declined both during the application and upon repeated application. In addition, not all patches responded (66), which is not to be expected if $[Ca^{2+}]$ acted directly on the M-channel. It appears more likely that the effect of $[Ca^{2+}]$ results from an action on a secondary protein that does not always remain associated with an excised patch. The effect of $[Ca^{2+}]$ inhibited M-channel activity with an $IC_{50}$ of 100 nM (66). This is close to the resting $[Ca^{2+}]_i$ for these neurons ($\approx$140 nM; 79), which suggests that at rest, the open probability $(P_o)$ of M-channels is only approximately 50% of the maximum value. This may allow some reserve in the amount of macroscopic M-current observed at any potential, implying that the amplitude of the M-current may be under control of $[Ca^{2+}]_i$ (see below). It is obviously too early to be convinced that the second messenger coupling to closure of M-channels is a rise in $[Ca^{2+}]_i$. A similar effect of $[Ca^{2+}]_i$ on M-channel $P_o$ is discussed below in the context of control of the amplitude of the M-current. It appears that the possible role of a rise in $[Ca^{2+}]_i$ mediating receptor-mediated suppression of M-current has to be examined in greater detail before a conclusion can be drawn.

Intriguing results from many investigators suggest several possible candidates for coupling receptor-activation to M-current suppression.

## G Proteins

Receptor-mediated suppression of the M-current acts through a pertussis toxin-insensitive G protein (20, 58), most probably a member of the $G_{\alpha q/11}$ class of G proteins (21). With use of the stable analogue of GDP, GDP$\beta$S, it was determined that three classes of receptors (LHRH, muscarinic, and substance P), coupling to suppress M-current in bullfrog sympathetic neurons, employ separate pools of presumably identical G proteins (69). This possible segregation of G proteins suggests that G protein activation may play a role in compartmentalizing a response to receptor activation. The rates of suppression and recovery of M-current are noted to be close to the in vitro rates of G protein activation and deactivation (45). This tempts the suggestion that the second messenger involves a direct association of the activated G protein with the M-channel or a closely associated substrate; however, this does not appear entirely plausible. A diffusible second messenger is assumed because suppression of M-current occurs with an obvious delay and is slow to develop (Figure 2). The role of a diffusible messenger is supported by the finding that application of muscarine modulates M-channel activity isolated within a cell-attached patch (46, 67). However, action on a cell-attached patch does not necessarily exclude the direct action of a G protein. It has been assumed that the interface between the membrane and the patch pipette glass prevents access of the activated G protein to its substrate. However, it is possible that the lifetime of the activated G protein would determine if it could travel far enough to cross this interface. It is not known if the $G\alpha q/11$ class of G proteins possesses the appropriate properties to allow for a direct action on the M-channel or a closely associated substrate. The only way to determine if this G protein can display such an interaction is to apply the preactivated (GTP-$\gamma$-S bound) $\alpha$ subunit to an inside-out patch containing M-channels. Considering the recent consensus that $\beta\gamma$, and not $\alpha$, subunits couple receptor activation to the effector (for example, activation of cloned inwardly rectifying potassium channels; 60), the $\beta\gamma$ subunits from Gq will also have to be tested. Until recently, this experiment could not be attempted because M-channel activity had not been recorded in the excised inside-out patch configuration. Now that M-channel activity can be supported in this patch configuration (47, 66), some interesting experiments should follow.

## Tyrosine Kinases

With use of heterologous expression systems, it was found that activation of $M_1$ muscarinic receptors causes suppression of Kv1.2, a cloned delayed rectifier channel (35). The effect of receptor activation is partially blocked by intracellular application of ethyleneglycol-bis($\beta$-aminoethyl)-N,N,N',N'-tetraacetic acid (EGTA) and is completely inhibited by the tyrosine kinase inhibitor genestein. These data suggest that a receptor-mediated increase in $[Ca^{2+}]_i$ activates a tyrosine kinase, which suppresses the potassium current. How can this finding relate to the suppression of M-current? As stated above, most data indicate that the effect of applied agonists is not blocked by intracellular calcium chelators, especially the relatively slow chelator EGTA. However, it is possible that a calcium-independent tyrosine kinase may be involved in receptor-mediated suppression of the M-current. This is made less likely by the finding that the response to muscarinic agonists is unaffected by either intracellular or extracellular application of genestein (18; N Marrion, unpublished results), although other suitable inhibitors must be tested to decide if this mechanism can be entirely discounted.

## Cyclic ADP-Ribose

Muscarinic receptor-mediated M-current suppression in NG108-15 cells is reduced when intracellular nicotinamide-adenine dinucleotide (NAD$^+$) levels are depleted by incubation with streptozotocin (33). NAD$^+$ is required for the production of cyclic adenosine diphosphate-ribose (ADP-ribose) (38). This cyclic nucleotide derivative enhances calcium-induced calcium release in bullfrog sympathetic neurons (34), a release mechanism that is blocked by ryanodine (48). Dialysis of NG108-15 cells with an electrolytic solution containing cyclic ADP-ribose causes an increase in [Ca$^{2+}$]$_i$ and loss of M-current (33). Chelation of this [Ca$^{2+}$]$_i$ increase does not prevent suppression of M-current, suggesting that cyclic ADP-ribose is capable of modulating M-current independently of a rise in [Ca$^{2+}$]$_i$ (33).

One obvious issue in ascribing a role for cyclic ADP-ribose in the suppression of M-current is determining whether it is generated by receptor activation. At present, only one second messenger cascade has been shown to increase intracellular levels of cyclic ADP-ribose, i.e. $3',5'$-cyclic guanosine monophosphate (cGMP) stimulates the formation of cyclic ADP-ribose from $\beta$-NAD$^+$ in sea urchin eggs (30). This result suggests a possible link with the intercellular messenger nitric oxide (NO) (14), which can stimulate the formation of cGMP. However, M-current is not sensitive to cGMP in sympathetic neurons (4, 20); additionally, an M-like current in rod photoreceptors (7) is not affected by application of the NO-generating substance S-nitrosocysteine (43).

To date, cyclic ADP-ribose is known only to enhance calcium release from ryanodine-sensitive calcium stores; no other effector roles have been described. This makes its putative role as a second messenger for M-current suppression questionable. As discussed above, the effect of cyclic ADP-ribose in NG108-15 cells occurs independently of a rise in [Ca$^{2+}$]$_i$ (33). In addition, the role of [Ca$^{2+}$]$_i$ in receptor-mediated suppression of M-current is in question (see above). Finally, it is assumed that any rise in [Ca$^{2+}$]$_i$ evoked by receptor activation arises from a (1,4,5)IP$_3$-sensitive store (24), which is likely to be separate from the ryanodine-sensitive store (10). Support for this assumption is that enhancement or over-recovery of M-current following agonist application is blocked by intracellular application of the (1,4,5)IP$_3$ receptor antagonist heparin (24). This suggests that the calcium rise evoked by agonists derives from an (1,4,5)IP$_3$-sensitive calcium store. However, M-current suppression by muscarinic receptor activation is reduced by preincubation of cells with caffeine (40). This protocol depletes the ryanodine-sensitive store, suggesting that the intracellular calcium store must also be accessible by muscarinic receptor activation. This seems surprising because the effect of muscarine is not blocked by ryanodine (N Marrion & PR Adams, unpublished observation). The exciting possibility remaining to be tested is whether cyclic ADP-ribose has a direct effect on M-channel activity.

## A Means to Discriminate the Identity of the True Second Messenger

From this discussion it is apparent that multiple second messenger candidates affect the M-current. However, the pharmacology of some of these putative second messenger systems is either rather sparse or not selective enough to be convincing. What is required is a baseline measure of the effect of receptor activation on the M-current with which to compare the effect of an applied messenger. Suppression of the M-current by muscarinic receptor activation does not change the macroscopic deactivation kinetics (4, 49). However, kinetic characterization of macroscopic kinetics is not a sufficient comparison, and a more convincing comparison can be made by examining the modulation of the single channel properties.

M-channels have been studied in detail from bullfrog and rat sympathetic ganglia. The channel displays complicated gating kinetics, which is in agreement with kinetic studies of the macroscopic current (49, 56). Macroscopic M-current deactivation is best described by the sum of two exponentials: an intermediate component with a voltage dependence (e-fold in 23 mV hyperpolarization) that dominates the characteristic macroscopic current relaxation and a slow component that is voltage insensitive. The intermediate kinetic component can also be resolved using stationary noise analysis, together with an additional, much faster kinetic component. This fast component is also voltage insensitive. Each kinetic component is sensitive to muscarinic receptor activation, but the fast component is the least affected (49). The properties of single M-channels have been studied extensively in bullfrog and rat sympathetic neurons (46, 47, 65, 66, 72). In general, minor differences may exist between cell types, but a consensus is rapidly being reached. For example, in both rat and bullfrog sympathetic neurons, the M-channel displays non-stationary kinetic behavior (46, 47, 66, 72). For the purpose of this review, only data from bullfrog sympathetic neurons are discussed.

The M-channel in bullfrog neurons displays two conductance levels (10 and 15 pS in isotonic potassium solutions), both of which exhibit similar gating behavior. Analysis of open state kinetics shows that each conductance level possesses two open states and have identical kinetic properties (46). The open state described by the longer open time constant has a value and a voltage dependence extremely close to that measured for the deactivation of the macroscopic current (46, 49). The exponential distribution with the fast time constant has a value close to that of the fast kinetic component resolved using stationary noise analysis. This open time constant, like that of the fast component, is voltage insensitive (46).

The M-channel exhibits modal gating, a behavior that permits the channel to exhibit two dominant behaviors: a short open time, low $P_o$ activity (mode 1); and a long open time, high $P_o$ behavior (mode 2) (46, 47). Channel openings described by the longer open time constant (see above) underlie mode 2 behavior, whereas activity giving rise to the faster time constant produces mode 1 behavior. It is proposed that the characteristic slow relaxations of macroscopic M-current arise principally from mode 2 gating of M-channels (46). Both conductance levels display spontaneous switching between mode 1 and 2 gating, which occurs on a much slower time scale than the gating kinetics of the channel. The apparent switches take place within 0.5- to 1-s segments of channel activity, and it is proposed that the slow kinetic component observed in macroscopic deactivation current relaxations arises from this mode switch. An example of the modal behavior of M-channels is shown in Figure 3. Patches are seen to display a predominance of either short or long duration openings. The time constants are well preserved, but the contribution of each time constant to the open duration histogram differs from patch to patch (Figure 3).

Application of muscarine lowers M-channel activity by causing a selective reduction in the number of openings contributing to mode 2 behavior, together with a relatively small increase in the number of mode 1 openings (46). Muscarine produces this effect only when applied outside the patch, suggesting that a diffusible second messenger is involved in this response. The macroscopic M-current results from mode 2 behavior (i.e. long open time, high $P_o$). Therefore, reduction of mode 2 activity by muscarine would reduce the macroscopic current with little change in the kinetics of M-current deactivation (46).

M-channel gating can be modeled using two sequential gating schemes, one for each mode, separated by a reversible transition (47). This model can replicate the different M-channel behaviors shown in Figure 3 by changing the transition rate constant for exiting mode 2 gating (47). This model can also be used to describe the effect of muscarine on M-channel gating (Figure 4). The model is run by allowing the control M-channel activity, with long open time events, to dominate the channel behavior (Figure 4A). The effect of muscarine is modeled with a tenfold reduction in the opening rate constant for entering the mode 2 open state. This gives rise to a biexponential open duration distribution where short open time behavior now dominates. Analysis of the $P_o$ distribution shows that this manipulation causes a loss of the $P_o$ peak corresponding to mode 2 activity and a small increase in the number of events underlying mode 1 behavior (46). Thus the effect of muscarine on M-channel kinetics can be

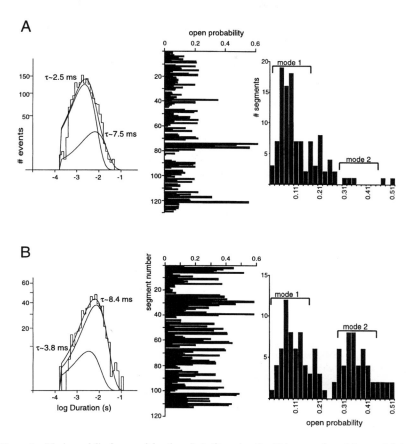

*Figure 3*   M-channel displays modal gating. *Left.* Open duration histograms for patches containing predominantly short (*left panel A*) or long (*left panel B*) openings. *Center.* Runs analysis for these patches (where $P_0$ within 0.5-s time segments is plotted against segment number) show the M-channel undergoes time segments of low $P_0$ activity and then switches to high $P_0$ behavior. For patch *center panel A*, the M-channel exhibits predominantly low $P_0$ ($-0.05$) activity with frequent brief sojourns to higher $P_0$ behavior. Patch *center panel B* exhibits mainly long duration openings and displays time segments of both low and high $P_0$ behavior, with the M-channel switching to high $P_0$ behavior more frequently and for longer times. *Right.* Measurement of $P_0$ within 0.5-s time segments demonstrates that this behavior represents discrete modes of open probability. Short duration openings display a single peak of low $P_0$ between 0.02 and 0.15 called mode 1 (*right panel A*). Longer duration openings, with short duration events present (which produce a peak corresponding to mode 1), give a higher $P_0$ peak between 0.27 and 0.44 (mode 2) (*right panel B*).

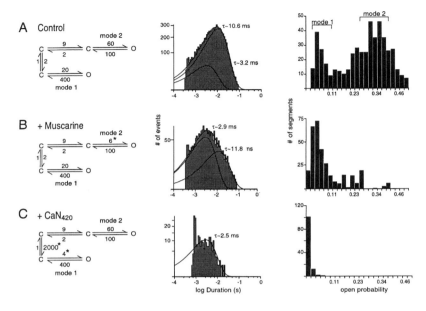

*Figure 4*   Modeling the effect of receptor activation and application of $CaN_{420}$ on the kinetics of M-channel gating. *A*. The model of M-channel gating favoring mode 2 activity is presented for comparison with the effects of muscarine and $CaN_{420}$. *B*. The open rate constant for mode 2 activity is reduced 10-fold from control (marked with an ∗) to approximate the effect of muscarine. This change produces channel behavior whose open duration histogram is best fit by the sum of two exponentials, with time constants similar to control, but with a reduction in the proportion of events giving mode 2 openings. *C*. The effect of $CaN_{420}$ is modeled with a 1000-fold increase in the rate constant for leaving mode 2 behavior and a 5-fold decrease in the opening rate constant for mode 1 activity (both marked with ∗). These manipulations produce channel behavior whose open duration distribution is best fit by a single exponential, corresponding to short open time activity. Analysis of $P_o$ gives a curtailed single peak, representing infrequent mode 1 activity.

used as a measure for comparison with the effect of a putative messenger. The effect of $[Ca^{2+}]$ on M-channel kinetics is very different from that of muscarine (Figure 4) and is discussed below in the context of control of the amplitude of the macroscopic M-current.

## REGULATION OF M-CURRENT AMPLITUDE

Enhancement of the M-current produces membrane hyperpolarization and a decrease in excitability. Suppression of the M-current increases membrane excitability, owing to the loss of the stabilizing influence exerted by this current. The effect of M-current suppression on cell firing (Figure 1) makes it clear that if

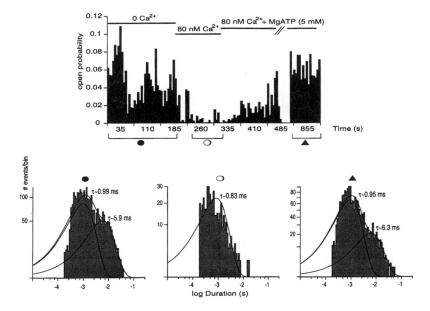

*Figure 5*   Regulation of M-channel activity by $[Ca^{2+}]_i$ and ATP. *Upper panel.* Patch $P_o$ is plotted against time, with $P_o$ calculated in 5-s time segments. Excision into nominally zero $Ca^{2+}$ solution supported M-channel activity. Within 20 s of increasing $[Ca^{2+}]$ bathing the inside-out patch to 80 nM, M-channel activity declined. Addition of ATP (5 mM), in the presence of 80 nM $Ca^{2+}$, caused a gradual return to sustained activity. *Lower panel.* Open duration histograms obtained from activity during the labeled time segments. In nominally zero $Ca^{2+}$ solution, M-channel open state kinetics were best described by a biexponential distribution with time constants appropriate for underlying mode 1 and 2 gating. Upon addition of 80 nM free $Ca^{2+}$, M-channel gating changed, with a complete loss of long open time events underlying mode 2 activity and a dramatic reduction in the number of openings contributing to mode 1 behavior. The subsequent addition of ATP allowed the return of the long time component to the open duration histogram and an increase in the number of openings underlying mode 1 behavior.

the amplitude of the M-current were under dynamic control, it would have major consequences for membrane excitability. As discussed above, the M-current has been shown to be both enhanced and suppressed. For example, application of somatostatin (53) or opioids (54) to hippocampal pyramidal neurons causes an enhancement of the M-current. Activation of $\beta$-adrenergic receptors on smooth muscle cells also augments the current (70). Suppression of M-current is seen with a myriad of receptor types (see above).

To date, direct receptor-mediated enhancement of the M-current has not been observed in sympathetic ganglion neurons. However, the M-current recorded from frog ganglionic neurons can be enhanced by application of AA (12, 80) as already discussed. In addition, the M-current is transiently augmented in frog sympathetic neurons following removal of agonist, a phenomenon termed over-recovery (58). Current data suggest that $[Ca^{2+}]_i$ levels play a large role in regulation of M-current amplitude. Agonists that suppress the M-current simultaneously increase $[Ca^{2+}]_i$ (51, 59). Chelation of this $[Ca^{2+}]_i$ rise blocks the occurrence of over-recovery (51). In addition, over-recovery is also blocked by intracellular application of the $(1,4,5)IP_3$ receptor antagonist, heparin, suggesting the calcium rise evoked by agonists derives from an $(1,4,5)IP_3$-sensitive calcium store (24). By raising $[Ca^{2+}]_i$ with a variety of methods, modest increases (from 50 to 150 nM) were found to enhance the current, whereas larger increases in $[Ca^{2+}]_i$ (>200 nM) inhibited M-current (51, 81). For example, calcium entry evoked by action potential firing enhances the M-current (39, 51). In contrast, suppression of M-current is observed following massive $Ca^{2+}$ entry from a $Ca^{2+}$ spike (73). The maintenance of M-current recorded at resting calcium levels, and its enhancement by a modest $[Ca^{2+}]_i$ rise, both require ATP in the whole-cell pipette solution (58, 81). This suggests that calcium-dependent phosphorylation may underlie both phenomena.

The distribution of M-channel modal gating has been suggested, in large part, to dictate the amplitude of the macroscopic current, with larger macroscopic currents resulting from longer periods spent in mode 2 channel behavior (46, 47). In addition, calcium-dependent events likely determine the amplitude of the macroscopic M-current by controlling the rate of transition between gating modes (46, 47). Calcium-dependent phosphorylation may promote mode 2 gating, thus producing the characteristic macroscopic M-current relaxations. Conversely, larger increases in $[Ca^{2+}]_i$ reduce the M-current by an increase in mode 1 activity, which may be favored by a calcium-dependent dephosphorylation. An increase in the time- and voltage-independent mode 1 openings would reduce the macroscopic M-current relaxations, thus producing an increase in apparent membrane leak conductance.

Support for the role of a kinase in the mediation of mode 2 M-channel behavior has been shown using inside-out patches excised from bullfrog sympathetic neurons (47). In approximately 60% of patches excised into a solution containing 80 nM free $[Ca^{2+}]$, M-channel activity rapidly declines. This concentration of $[Ca^{2+}]$ is close to the resting $[Ca^{2+}]_i$ concentration observed for these neurons (44). Application of ATP to the patch causes a return of M-channel activity (47), which has important implications, because if ATP is acting as a phosphate donor (see below), this suggests that a kinase must remain closely associated with the patch, even after excision. Hence, the initial loss of mode 2 activity upon patch excision into an ATP-free solution most likely suggests that an active phosphatase is associated with the patch. It is probable that the presence and activity of an associated kinase and/or phosphatase accounts for the observed variation in the persistence of M-channel activity after patch excision, its recoverability upon addition of ATP, and the distribution of M-channel modal gating behavior (47).

The presence of a calcium-dependent phosphatase following patch excision is shown in Figure 5. Excision of an inside-out patch into $Ca^{2+}$-free Ringer solution supports M-channel activity. Analysis of M-channel open times shows that the gating is best described by two exponentials, with time constants underlying both mode 1 and 2 activity. Increase of the $[Ca^{2+}]$ bathing the inside-out patch to 80 nM causes a loss of M-channel activity. This lowering of the patch $P_o$ is produced by a complete loss of mode 2 behavior and a dramatic reduction in the number of openings contributing to mode 1 activity (Figure 5). This effect is very different from that produced by application of muscarine (see Figure 4). The addition of ATP, in 80 nM free $[Ca^{2+}]$, causes an increase of M-channel $P_o$, by a return of long open time events underlying mode 2 activity and an increase in the number of mode 1 openings. This experiment demonstrates that both a kinase and a calcium-dependent phosphatase remain associated with the patch. After raising $[Ca^{2+}]$, the M-channel or a physically close substrate is dephosphorylated by the calcium-dependent phosphatase, promoting only mode 1 behavior. The effect of the phosphatase can be overcome by an associated kinase when ATP is added, producing a return of mode 2 openings. Therefore, at the resting $[Ca^{2+}]_i$ for these neurons, the action of the kinase is favored, yielding mode 2 M-channel openings and the characteristic slow macroscopic M-current relaxations.

An obvious candidate for the calcium-dependent phosphatase is calcineurin or phosphatase 2B (41). This possibility has been tested using a preactivated, calcium-independent form of calcineurin ($CaN_{420}$), produced by inclusion of a stop codon at residue 420 of rat brain calcineurin cDNA, to yield a truncated form lacking the autoinhibitory domain (57). Intracellular dialysis of bullfrog sympathetic neurons with $CaN_{420}$ causes an inhibition of the macroscopic M-current, an effect that would be predicted if the action of this phosphatase reduces mode 2 activity (47). The prediction was tested by applying $CaN_{420}$ to excised inside-out patches containing M-channels (47). The effect of $CaN_{420}$ mirrors what is observed following an increase of $[Ca^{2+}]_i$ applied to an inside-out patch (Figure 5), i.e. a complete loss of mode 2 behavior and a dramatic reduction in the number of mode 1 openings (47). M-channel $P_o$ is reduced by an increase of $[Ca^{2+}]_i$, application of $CaN_{420}$, and muscarinic receptor activation. Although the effect of $[Ca^{2+}]_i$ is identical to that seen on addition of $CaN_{420}$, neither of these treatments mimics the effect of muscarinic receptor activation. The effect of $CaN_{420}$ has also been modeled using the modal gating scheme discussed above (Figure 4C). To account for the effect of $CaN_{420}$ (and $[Ca^{2+}]_i$), the transition rate for exiting mode 2 behavior is significantly increased, and the opening rate constant for entering the mode 1 open state is reduced. These manipulations are very different from those required to model the effect of muscarine (Figure 4$B$). These data indicate that muscarine does not exert its effect on M-channel $P_o$ by raising $[Ca^{2+}]_i$ and activating calcineurin. This is supported by the finding that the suppression of M-current by muscarine is unaltered by intracellular dialysis with the autoinhibitory peptide to calcineurin (47).

The identity of the putative kinase is not known, although it cannot be PKA or PKC. Addition of cAMP derivatives or forskolin does not affect macroscopic M-current in either frog or rat sympathetic ganglia (4, 20). Furthermore, activation of PKC by phorbol esters or diacylglycerol analogues inhibits the M-current (13, 16, 20, 46a, 62), an effect opposite to that expected for the proposed kinase. Myosin light chain kinase (MCLK) is, however, a candidate. Intracellular perfusion of bullfrog sympathetic neurons with a preactivated form of MCLK enhances the M-current (6), which would be expected if this kinase were promoting mode 2 M-channel openings (46, 47). Endogenous MLCK is present in these neurons, and its inhibition by either a synthetic peptide or wortmannin suppresses both the agonist-induced over-recovery and the M-current measured at a $[Ca^{2+}]_i$ concentration of 100 nM (6, 76).

The endogenous phosphatase is likely to be calcineurin (47), mainly because it is the only $Ca^{2+}$-dependent phosphatase known, and its effect upon M-channel gating is identical to that seen by raising the $[Ca^{2+}]$ applied to an excised inside-out patch. In addition, the presence of endogenous calcineurin in bullfrog sympathetic neurons is indicated by the finding that the macroscopic M-current is augmented and that run-down is slowed in cells dialyzed with the autoinhibitory peptide to calcineurin (47).

It is certain that the amplitude of M-current is also highly regulated in other cell types. For example, in some experiments, run-down of the M-current in rat sympathetic neurons is so marked that stable recordings can only be obtained using the perforated patch technique in order to preserve the intracellular milieu (18). In addition, the M-like current in rod photoreceptors is maintained by a calcium-dependent phosphorylation that is blocked by inhibitors of calcium/calmodulin-dependent protein kinases (S Barnes, personal communication). Also, it is interesting to note that the augmentation of M-current observed following adrenergic stimulation in stomach smooth muscle cells (70) may reflect regulation of M-current amplitude by a kinase and phosphatase. It is entirely possible that M-channels may be regulated by the same phosphorylation/dephosphorylation cycle in different preparations, although the identity of the enzymes involved may be different. Some support for this idea comes from the kinetic change observed upon enhancement of M-current. Augmentation of the M-current in rod photoreceptors, stomach smooth muscle, and frog sympathetic ganglia is accompanied by a slowing of deactivation and a speeding up of activation (51, 70; S Barnes, personal communication), which suggests that M-current amplitude is regulated in a similar manner in these cell types but that the particular enzymes involved differ.

A simple mechanism for regulation of the macroscopic M-current is becoming clear. Observation of M-channel modal gating behavior allows a basic understanding of how the amplitude of the macroscopic current can be changed (46, 47). This phenomenon involves a very different mechanism from that of current suppression by receptor activation, with a reduction in the opening rate to mode 2 gating behavior a likely mechanism. Resolution of the mechanisms underlying M-channel single channel gating will provide a clearer understanding of control of the macroscopic current.

ACKNOWLEDGMENTS

I thank the many investigators who have worked on the M-current for providing their most recent material for this review. In addition, I thank Dr. Dawn Shepherd for the critical reading of this manuscript.

*Literature Cited*

1. Adams PR, Brown DA. 1980. Luteinizing hormone-releasing factor and muscarinic agonists act on the same voltage-sensitive $K^+$-current in bullfrog sympathetic neurones. *Br. J. Pharmacol.* 68:353–55

2. Adams PR, Brown DA. 1982. Synaptic inhibition of the M-current: slow excitatory post-synaptic potential mechanism in bullfrog sympathetic neurones. *J. Physiol.* 332:263–72

3. Adams PR, Brown DA, Constanti A. 1982. M-currents and other potassium currents in bullfrog sympathetic neurones. *J. Physiol.* 330:537–72

4. Adams PR, Brown DA, Constanti A. 1982. Pharmacological inhibition of the M-current. *J. Physiol.* 332:223–62

5. Akasu T. 1988. Adrenaline depolarization in paravertebral sympathetic neurones of bullfrogs. *Pflügers Arch.* 411:80–87

6. Akasu T, Ito M, Nakano T, Schneider CR, Simmons MA, et al. 1993. Myosin light chain kinase occurs in bullfrog sympathetic neurons and may modulate voltage-dependent potassium currents. *Neuron* 11:1133–45

7. Beech DJ, Barnes S. 1989. Characterization of a voltage-gated $K^+$ channel that accelerates the rod response to dim light. *Neuron* 3:573–81

8. Beech DJ, Bernheim L, Mathie A, Hille B. 1991. Intracellular $Ca^{2+}$ buffers disrupt muscarinic suppression of $Ca^{2+}$ current and M current in rat sympathetic neurons. *Proc. Natl. Acad. Sci. USA* 88:652–56

9. Béhé P, Sandmeier K, Meves H. 1992. The effect of arachidonic acid on the M current of NG108-15 neuroblastoma x glioma hybrid cells. *Pflügers Arch.* 422:122–28

10. Berridge MJ. 1993. A tale of two messengers. *Nature* 365:388–89

11. Bone EA, Fretten P, Palmer S, Kirk CJ, Michell RH. 1984. Rapid accumulation of inositol phosphates in isolated rat superior cervical ganglia exposed to VI-vasopressin and muscarinic cholinergic stimuli. *Biochem. J.* 221:803–11

12. Bosma MM, Bernheim L, Leibowitz MD, Pfaffinger PJ, Hille B. 1990. Modulation of M current in frog sympathetic ganglion cells. In *G Proteins and Signal Transduction.* pp. 43–59. New York: Rockefeller Univ. Press

13. Bosma MM, Hille B. 1989. Protein kinase C is not necessary for peptide-induced suppression of M current or for desensitization of the peptide receptors. *Proc. Natl. Acad. Sci. USA* 86:2943–47

14. Bredt DS, Snyder SH. 1992. Nitric oxide,

a novel neuronal messenger. *Neuron* 8:3–11

15. Brown DA, Adams PR. 1980. Muscarinic suppression of a novel voltage-sensitive $K^+$-current in a vertebrate neurone. *Nature* 283:673–76

16. Brown DA, Adams PR. 1987. Effects of phorbol dibutyrate on M currents and M current inhibition in bullfrog sympathetic neurons. *Cell. Mol. Neurobiol.* 7:255–69

17. Deleted in proof

18. Brown DA, Buckley NJ, Caulfield MP, Duffy SM, Jones S, et al. 1995. Coupling of muscarinic acetylcholine receptors to neural ion channels: closure of $K^+$ channels. In *Molecular Mechanisms of Muscarinic Acetylchloline Receptor Function*, ed. J Wess, pp. 165–80. Austin, TX: Landes

19. Brown DA, Higashida H. 1988. Voltage- and calcium-activated potassium currents in mouse neuroblastoma x rat glioma hybrid cells. *J. Physiol.* 397:149–65

20. Brown DA, Marrion NV, Smart TG. 1989. On the transduction mechanism for muscarine-induced inhibition of M-current in cultured rat sympathetic neurones. *J. Physiol.* 413:469–88

21. Caulfield MP, Jones S, Vallis Y, Buckley NJ, Kim G, et al. 1994. Muscarinic M-current inhibition via $G_{\alpha q}/11$ and $\alpha$-adrenoceptor inhibition of $Ca^{2+}$ current via $G_{\alpha o}$ in rat sympathetic neurones. *J. Physiol.* 477:415–22

22. Charpak S, Gähwiler BH. 1991. Glutamate mediates a slow synaptic response in hippocampal slice cultures. *Proc. R. Soc. London Ser. B* 243:221–26

23. Charpak S, Gähwiler BH, Do KQ, Knöpfel T. 1990. Potassium conductances in hippocampal neurons blocked by excitatory amino-acid transmitters. *Nature* 347:765–67

24. Chen H, Kurenny DE, Smith PA. 1993. Heparin prevents M-current over-recovery but not M-current suppression in bullfrog sympathetic ganglion neurones. *Brain Res.* 625:323–27

25. Colino A, Halliwell JV. 1987. Differential modulation of three separate K-conductances in hippocampal CAI neurons by serotonin. *Nature* 327:73–77

26. Constanti A, Brown DA. 1981. M-currents in voltage-clamped mammalian sympathetic neurones. *Neurosci. Lett.* 24:289–94

27. Dutar P, Nicoll RA. 1988. Classification of muscarinic responses in hippocampus in terms of receptor subtypes and second-messenger systems: electrophysiological

28. Eilers J, Callewaert G, Armstrong C, Konnerth A. 1995. Calcium signaling in a narrow somatic submembrane shell during synaptic activity in cerebellar Purkinje neurons. *Proc. Natl. Acad. Sci. USA* 92:10272–76

29. Fukuda K, Higashida H, Kubo T, Maeda A, Akiba I, et al. 1988. Selective coupling with $K^+$ currents of muscarinic acetylcholine receptor subtypes in NG108-15 cells. *Nature* 335:355–58

30. Galione A, White A, Willmott N, Turner M, Potter BVL, Watson SP. 1993. cGMP mobilizes intracellular $Ca^{2+}$ in sea urchin eggs by stimulating cyclic ADP-ribose synthesis. *Nature* 365:456–59

31. Halliwell JV, Adams PR. 1982. Voltage-clamp analysis of muscarinic excitation in hippocampal neurons. *Brain Res.* 250:71–92

32. Higashida H, Brown DA. 1986. Two polyphosphatidylinositide metabolites control two $K^+$ currents in a neuronal cell. *Nature* 323:333–35

33. Higashida H, Robbins J, Egorova A, Noda M, Taketo M, et al. 1995. Nicotinamide-adenine dinucleotide regulates muscarinic receptor-coupled $K^+$ (M) channels in rodent NG108-15 cells. *J. Physiol.* 482:317–23

34. Hua S-Y, Tokimasa T, Takasawa S, Furuya Y, Nohmi M, et al. 1994. Cyclic ADP-ribose modulates $Ca^{2+}$ release channels for activation by physiological $Ca^{2+}$ entry in bullfrog sympathetic neurons. *Neuron* 12:1073–79

35. Huang X-Y, Morielli AD, Peralta EG. 1993. Tyrosine kinase-dependent suppression of a potassium channel by the G-protein-coupled m1-muscarinic acetylcholine receptor. *Cell* 75:1145–56

36. Jones SW. 1985. Muscarinic and peptidergic excitation of bull-frog sympathetic neurones. *J. Physiol.* 366:63–87

37. Kanterman RY, Ma AL, Briley EM, Axelrod J, Felder CC. 1990. Muscarinic receptors mediate the release of arachidonic acid from spinal cord and hippocampal neurons in primary culture. *Neurosci. Lett.* 118:235–37

38. Kim H, Jacobson EL, Jacobson MK. 1993. Synthesis and degradation of cyclic ADP-ribose by NAD glycohydrolases. *Science* 261:1330–33

39. Kirkwood A, Lisman JE. 1992. Action potentials produce a long-term enhancement of M-current in frog sympathetic ganglion. *Brain Res.* 580:281–87

40. Kirkwood A, Simmons MA, Mather RJ,

Lisman JE. 1991. Muscarinic suppression of the M-current is mediated by a rise in internal $Ca^{2+}$ concentration. *Neuron* 6:1009–14

41. Klee CB, Draetta GF, Hubbard MJ. 1988. Calcineurin. *Adv. Enzymol.* 61:149–200

42. Deleted in proof

43. Kurenny DE, Moroz LL, Turner RW, Sharkey KA, Barnes S. 1994. Modulation of ion channels in rod photoreceptors by nitric oxide. *Neuron* 13:315–24

44. Lipscombe D, Madison DV, Poenie M, Reuter H, Tsien RW, Tsien RY. 1988. Imaging of cytosolic $Ca^{2+}$ transients arising from $Ca^{2+}$ stores and $Ca^{2+}$ channels in sympathetic neurons. *Neuron* 1:355–65

45. Lopez HS. 1992. Kinetics of G protein-mediated modulation of the potassium M-current in bullfrog sympathetic neurons. *Neuron* 8:725–36

46. Marrion NV. 1993. Selective reduction of one mode of M-channel gating by muscarine in sympathetic neurons. *Neuron* 11:77–84

46a. Marrion NV. 1994. M-current suppression by agonist and phorbol esters in bullfrog sympathetic ganglion cells. *Pflügers Arch.* 426:296–303

47. Marrion NV. 1996. Calcineurin regulates M-channel modal gating in sympathetic neurons. *Neuron* 16:163–73

48. Marrion NV, Adams PR. 1992. Release of intracellular calcium and modulation of membrane currents by caffeine in vertebrate sympathetic neurons. *J. Physiol.* 445:515–35

49. Marrion NV, Adams PR, Gruner W. 1992. Multiple kinetic states underlying macroscopic M-currents in bullfrog sympathetic neurons. *Proc. R. Soc. London Ser. B* 248:207–14

50. Marrion NV, Smart TG, Marsh SJ, Brown DA. 1989. Muscarinic suppression of the M-current in the rat sympathetic ganglion is mediated by receptors of the $M_1$-subtype. *Br. J. Pharmacol.* 98:557–73

51. Marrion NV, Zucker RS, Marsh SJ, Adams PR. 1991. Modulation of M-current by intracellular $Ca^{2+}$. *Neuron* 6:533–45

52. Marsh SJ, Trousland J, Leaney JL, Brown DA. 1995. Synergistic regulation of a neuronal chloride current by intracellular calcium and muscarinic receptor activation: a role for protein kinase C. *Neuron* 15:729–37

53. Moore SD, Madamba SG, Joëis M, Siggins GR. 1988. Somatostatin augments the M-current in hippocampal neurons. *Science* 239:278–80

54. Moore SD, Madamba SG, Schweitzer P, Siggins GR. 1994. Voltage-dependent effects of opioid peptides on hippocampal CA3 pyramidal neurons in vitro. *J. Neurosci.* 14:809–20

55. Müller W, Connor JA. 1991. Cholinergic input uncouples $Ca^{2+}$ changes from $K^+$ conductance activation and amplifies intradendritic $Ca^{2+}$ changes in hippocampal neurons. *Neuron* 6:901–5

56. Owen DG, Marsh SJ, Brown DA. 1990. M-current noise and putative M-channels in cultured rat sympathetic ganglion cells. *J. Physiol.* 431:269–90

57. Perrino BA, Ng LY, Soderling TR. 1995. Calcium regulation of calcineurin phosphatase activity by its B-subunit and calmodulin: role of the autoinhibitory domain. *J. Biol. Chem.* 270:340–46

58. Pfaffinger PJ. 1988. Muscarine and t-LHRH suppress M-current by activating an IAP-insensitive G-protein. *J. Neurosci.* 8:3343–53

59. Pfaffinger PJ, Leibowitz MD, Subers F-M, Nathanson NM, Aimers W, Hille B. 1988. Agonists that suppress M-current elicit phosphoinositide turnover and $Ca^{2+}$ transients, but these events do not explain M-current suppression. *Neuron* 1:477–84

60. Reuveny E, Slesinger PA, Inglese J, Morales JM, Iniguez-Lluhi JA, et al. 1994. Activation of the cloned muscarinic potassium channel by G protein $\beta\gamma$-subunits. *Nature* 370:143–46

61. Robbins J, Marsh SJ, Brown DA. 1993. On the mechanism of M-current inhibition by muscarinic m1 receptors in DNA-transfected rodent neuroblastoma x glioma cells. *J. Physiol.* 469:153–78

62. Schäfer S, Béhé P, Meves H. 1991. Inhibition of M current in NG108-15 neuroblastoma x glioma hybrid cells. *Pflügers Arch.* 418:581–91

63. Schmitt H, Meves H. 1993. Protein kinase C as mediator of arachidonic acid-induced decrease of neuronal M current. *Pflügers Arch.* 425:134–39

64. Schweitzer P, Madamba S, Siggins GR. 1990. Arachidonic acid metabolites as mediators of somatostatin-induced increase of neuronal M-current. *Nature* 346:464–67

65. Selyanko AA, Brown DA. 1993. Effects of membrane potential and muscarine on potassium M-channel kinetics in rat sympathetic neurones. *J. Physiol.* 472:711–24

66. Selyanko AA, Brown DA. 1996. Intracellular calcium directly inhibits potas-

sium M channels in excised membrane patches from rat sympathetic neurons. *Neuron* 16:151–62

67. Selyanko AA, Stansfeld CE, Brown DA. 1992. Closure of potassium M-channels by muscarinic acetylcholine-receptor stimulants requires a diffusible messenger. *Proc. R. Soc. London Ser. B* 250:119–25

68. Shapiro MS, Wollmuth LP, Hille B. 1994. Angiotensin-II inhibits calcium and M-current channels in rat sympathetic neurons via G-proteins. *Neuron* 12:1319–29

69. Simmons MA, Mather RJ. 1991. Selectivity of the effects of guanosine-5′-O-(2-thiodiphosphate) on agonist inhibition of the M-current in amphibian sympathetic neurons. *J. Neurosci.* 11:2130–34

70. Sims SM, Singer JJ, Walsh JV. 1988. Antagonistic adrenergic-muscarinic regulation of M-current in smooth muscle cells. *Science* 239:190–93

71. Sims SM, Walsh JV, Singer JJ. 1986. Substance P and acetylcholine both suppress the same $K^+$ current in dissociated smooth muscle cells. *Am. J. Physiol.* 251:C580–87

72. Stansfeld CE, Marsh SJ, Gibb AJ, Brown DA. 1993. Identification of M-channels in 'outside-out' patches excised from sympathetic ganglion cells. *Neuron* 10:639–54

73. Tokimasa T. 1985. Intracellular $Ca^{2+}$-ions inactivate $K^+$-current in bullfrog sympathetic neurons. *Brain Res.* 337:386–91

74. Tokimasa T, Akasu T. 1990. ATP regulates muscarine-sensitive potassium current in dissociated bull-frog primary afferent neurones. *J. Physiol.* 426:241–64

75. Tokimasa T, Akasu T. 1990. Extracellular calcium ions are required for muscarine-sensitive potassium current in bullfrog sympathetic neurons. *J. Auton. Nerv. Syst.* 29:163–74

76. Tokimasa T, Ito M, Simmons MA, Schneider CR, Tanaka T, et al. 1995. Inhibition by wortmannin of M-current in bullfrog sympathetic neurones. *Br. J. Pharmacol.* 114:489–95

77. Villarroel A, Marrion NV, Lopez H, Adams PR. 1989. Bradykin inhibits a potassium M-like current in rat pheochromocytoma PCI2 cells. *FEBS Lett.* 255:42–46

78. Wang HS, McKinnon D. 1995. Potassium currents in rat prevertebral and paravertebral sympathetic neurones. *J. Physiol.* 485:319–37

79. Wanke E, Ferroni A, Malgaroli A, Ambrosini A, Pozzan T, Meldolesi J. 1987. Activation of muscarinic receptors selectively inhibits a rapidly activated $Ca^{2+}$ current in rat sympathetic neurons. *Proc. Natl. Acad. Sci. USA* 84:4313–17

80. Yu SP. 1995. Roles of arachidonic acid, lipoxygenases and phosphatases in calcium-dependent modulation of M-current in bullfrog sympathetic neurons. *J. Physiol.* 487:797–811

81. Yu SP, O'Malley DM, Adams PR. 1994. Regulation of M current by intracellular calcium in bullfrog sympathetic ganglion neurons. *J. Neurosci.* 14:3487–99

*Annu. Rev. Physiol. 1997. 59:505–25*

# ENDOTHELIAL CELL REGULATION OF CONTRACTILITY OF THE HEART

## Saul Winegrad

Department of Physiology, University of Pennsylvania School of Medicine, Philadelphia, Pennsylvania 19104-6085

KEY WORDS:   contractility, endothelin, ATPase activity, contractile efficiency, cardiac myocytes

---

### ABSTRACT

Endocardial and coronary vascular endothelial cells release substances that modify the contraction of cardiac myocytes. The major and possibly the sole up-regulating substance is endothelin. Several down-regulating substances are secreted, but none has yet been specifically identified. The relative amounts of up- and down-regulating substances are related to tissue oxygen tension. As $pO_2$ rises, the concentration of up- and down-regulating substances, respectively, increases and decreases. Endothelin increases isometric force and decreases actomyosin ATPase activity thus increasing the economy of conversion of chemical to hydrodynamic energy. Beta-adrenergic agonists increase ATPase activity through an endothelial cell-dependent mechanism, leading to decreased economy. Therefore, two endothelial cell-dependent systems exist for regulating contractile efficiency: One involving endothelin appears to optimize the contraction for efficiency; the other, the beta-adrenergic-mediated system, optimizes for power.

---

## Introduction

In executing its function as part of the cardiovascular system, the heart must be able to vary its performance over a wide range in order to satisfy the needs of the organism. Requirements for cardiac output can vary by as much as 500%, and the response must be very rapid. In the healthy heart, the duration of the change in hemodynamic demands may be brief. In contrast, certain pathological states or long-term training by athletes alters the average requirement of the heart. The body responds differently to these two types of changes in functional requirements. For short-term alteration of function, transient post-translational modification of the appropriate organelles occurs, whereas alteration of long-term demands on the heart are met by changes in gene expression.

505

0066-4278/97/0315-0505$08.00

For the heart to adapt to either short- or long-term demands, there must be a set of input signals, mechanisms for sensing these signals and integrating the information, and ultimately pathways for modifying the contraction of the cardiac myocyte. The two most familiar input signals to the heart are its resting length and neuroendocrine transmitters from the autonomic nervous system. Some of the mechanisms for modulating the contraction, i.e. variation in the cytoplasmic concentration of activator $Ca^{2+}$ and in the sensitivity of the contractile proteins to cytoplasmic $Ca^{2+}$, both resulting in altered production of force, have received the most attention.

These mechanisms cannot account for all of the changes in cardiac contractility that have been observed nor the degree of sophistication with which the heart responds to certain stresses or changes in ambient conditions. Four sets of observations illustrate this point: (a) Dilated and hypertrophied hearts often have actomyosin with reduced ATPase activity even in the absence of any detectable change in the isoforms of myofibrillar proteins (6, 54). Although this change in function has been attributed to damage or impaired function, physiological post-translational modification of the proteins has not been ruled out. (b) Beta-adrenergic stimulation has been unanimously observed to increase the force of contraction, yet well-executed studies have found inconsistent changes in the velocity of unloaded shortening and the rate of ATP hydrolysis. In some studies, velocity and ATPase activity increase, and in others they do not change (16, 17, 49, 55). The differences can be reconciled if the regulation of cross-bridge kinetics exclusive of the regulation of force production can occur. (c) Alpha-adrenergic stimulation increases the force of contraction, but it decreases the velocity of unloaded shortening and the rate of the ATP hydrolysis by actomyosin showing that force development and the rate of cycling of cross-bridges can be regulated in opposite directions (46). (d) Endothelin enhances the force of contraction of both coronary vascular smooth and cardiac muscle at similar concentrations. Because contraction of vascular smooth muscle should decrease blood supply to the contractile cells, an increase in the force of contraction of the heart would be difficult to sustain, and it is likely that this situation does not normally occur.

The answer to these conundrums may come from an understanding of a third set of input and effector signals in the regulation of cardiac function that has only recently been identified and appreciated (5, 9, 12, 40). Endothelial cells in the endocardium and the coronary vasculature secrete substances that can modify the contractility of the heart. The nature and the rate of secretion of these cardioregulatory substances appear to be related to the energy supply to the heart and the rate at which the heart is working, making the system well suited to maintain a balance between energy supply and work performed (39). In this way, the viability of the cardiac myocytes can be maintained in the presence of changing demands on the heart by the organism. In the following discussion, the cellular and molecular bases for the regulation of cardiac contractility by endothelial-derived factors are considered, as well as the role that endothelium-based regulation of contraction plays in the integrated function of the heart in an organism. This review is limited to post-translational mechanisms and does not consider the role of endothelin (with angiotensin) in the modulation of cardiac contractility through the control of gene expression. The major goal is to examine the nature of the additional dimension that endothelial regulation of cardiac contraction provides for the heart and the cellular and molecular mechanisms involved in the modulation of myocyte function.

## Early Evidence of Endothelial Cell Regulation

Alteration of the shape of an isometric contraction by removal or disruption of the endocardial endothelium covering isolated papillary muscles was the first evidence that endothelial cells might modulate cardiac contractility (5). The rate of rise of force was unchanged, but relaxation began earlier, resulting in a shorter contraction with a lower peak force. The effect of disruption of the endocardium was progressively diminished by raising the concentration of extracellular $Ca^{2+}$ or increasing the resting length of the contractile cells towards their optimal length. The change in the shape of the contraction varied with animal species and temperature, but the constant theme was a briefer contraction with a lower peak developed force. When endocardial or vascular endothelial cells were cultured and the medium conditioned by the cultured cells was added to the medium bathing isolated cardiac tissue, the effect of disruption of the endocardium on the contraction of the cardiac cells was partially or completely reversed, indicating that the change in contractility dependent on the presence of the endothelial cells was due to some substances secreted or released by the endothelial cells (9, 44).

During normal perfusion of the coronary circulation, the ATPase activity of actomyosin in cardiac cells is uniform in all of the cells in the ventricles, but when the nature of the perfusion of the coronary vessels is changed, ATPase activity among the cells becomes non-uniform for a period of time (28). The heterogeneity of ATPase activity could not be explained simply by a change in the relative availability of oxygen to different cells because the lowest ATPase activity in isolated papillary muscles was at the surface of the tissue bundle where oxygen tension should have been the highest, and it was the highest near unperfused blood vessels. The distribution of relative ATPase activity could be reproduced by a model in which endothelial cells in the endocardium and in the walls of the small arteries released substances that could either raise or lower actomyosin ATPase activity (26). In the model, the rate at which up-regulating and down-regulating cardioactive substances were released depended on the local oxygen tension in the microenvironment of the blood vessels and the shear stress on the endothelial cells. These results not only show the importance of endothelial cells in regulating contractility but also imply that there is an important role for oxygen availability in modulating the system.

A major advantage of a cardiac regulatory system based on endothelial cell integration of information and release of regulatory factors is that it permits localized control based on local conditions. Regulation through neuroendocrine function and pressure-volume relations operates primarily globally, responding to input at the organ level. An endothelial cell–derived regulatory system would modulate the contractility of cardiac myocytes according to local metabolic and vascular conditions. This would allow less well perfused regions of the heart to function at a lower level without interfering with the normal function of well-perfused regions of the organ. This mechanism may be involved in the production of "hibernating" regions of the heart, a clinically observed phenomenon in which poorly perfused regions of the heart contract weakly or not at all but still remain viable. Function can be restored to normal by a return of normal blood perfusion.

## Requirements for Endothelial Cell Regulation of Cardiac Contractility

Vascular and endocardial endothelial cells appear to have similar functional capabilities in the isolated preparations that have been studied. Any useful model of regulation of myocardial function must consider how the specific locations and environments of the two types of endothelial cells influence their contributions to the modulation of contraction in the intact heart. For instance, arterial endothelial cells are well suited to sense the velocity and possibly the rate of blood flow directly. They are not well located to be good direct sensors of the rate of oxygen consumption or tissue $pO_2$ because they are normally exposed to fully oxygenated blood, but they could act as a focal point for the flow of information about the relative rate of use and supply of oxygen from the blood, vascular smooth muscle, and cardiac myocytes. Endocardial endothelial cells are well located to sense resting ventricular volume, a reflection of resting fiber length, but as with vascular endothelium, they are not well located for sensing the rate of oxygen use.

The potential diffusion pathways for substances released by endothelial cells must also be considered. The concentration of any endothelium-derived substance that has a similar effect on the force of contraction of vascular smooth muscle and the cardiac myocytes, as is the case for nitric oxide and endothelin (see below), cannot change in the same direction at both sites at the same time because this would cause a simultaneous, incompatible rise in contractility of the heart and decrease in coronary flow. Some type of functional diffusion barrier must exist between the two different sites. Substances secreted into the vascular or ventricular lumens would be heavily diluted by the flowing blood. There is evidence for preferential secretion of cardioactive factors by endothelial cells from the abluminal surface (38). There also is the problem of the distance that endothelium-derived substances must diffuse between cells and along surfaces with high concentrations of binding sites before they reach the cardiac myocytes. In view of these considerations, can these two locations of endothelial cells be the source of direct modulators of contractility of the cardiac myocytes, or is the major role for these cells to regulate contraction by exercising indirect control?

## Identity of the Regulatory Factors

Identification of the regulatory factors has been pursued by two different but complementary approaches: (a) analysis of the effluent of coronary perfusion in isolated working hearts (39, 40) and (b) analysis of the medium conditioned by cultured endocardial or vascular endothelial cells (44). Coronary effluent contains a combination of up- and down-regulating factors, as determined by assay on the contractility of isolated cardiac trabeculae from another heart. Both direct measurement and response to BQ 123, an endothelin receptor A antagonist, identified the major and possibly the sole up regulator as endothelin (30, 33, 34). The down regulator(s) are still unidentified, but because of its(their) stability, nitric oxide cannot account for the down-regulating effect.

The up-regulatory cardioactive factor produced by medium conditioned by endothelial cells has also been identified as endothelin by the loss of the effect in the presence of antibodies against endothelin. Additional down-regulating factors have been demonstrated by the effect of stimulation of an isolated heart by bradykinin and by the effect of endothelial cell superfusate on isolated cardiac myocytes. In neither case has a molecular identification been made.

## Oxygen and Shear Stress as Input Signals

The net effect of the combination of up- and down-regulating factors of endothelial cell origin in the coronary venous perfusate can be correlated with tissue oxygen tension. At higher concentrations of oxygen, the coronary venous perfusate increased the isometric force generated by trabeculae on which the effluent was assayed. The amplitude of the increase diminished and then became a decrease as the oxygen tension in the tissue of the heart donating the venous effluent decreased. At the higher and lower ends of the range of oxygen tensions, the regulatory substances in the effluent appeared, respectively, to be exclusively up- and down-regulating forces. In the middle of the range of oxygen tension, both factors were present but in different proportions. The role of oxygen tension as a factor in the rate of production of down-regulating factors by cultured endothelial cells has not been specifically addressed, and the down regulator in the culture medium has not yet been identified.

The modulation of contractility by endothelium-derived factors by oxygen tension does not consist only of the release of cardioregulatory substances by endothelial cells in accordance with the local tissue oxygen tension. There is cross-talk between the endothelial cells and the cardiac myocytes, and there is an effect of shear stress on the rate of synthesis and release of endothelin by the endothelial cells. This has been demonstrated by examining the effect of the venous effluent from an isolated perfused working heart after reoxygenation on the contractility of trabeculae dissected from another heart. In perfused hearts, the vascular endothelial cells can be either intact or disrupted, thus providing a reliable way to confirm that the cellular origin of the material producing any effect on contractility is the endothelial cell. Distinction between endothelial cells and cardiac myocytes as the target cells for producing an effect can be made because the majority of the endothelial cells in the isolated trabecula (85%) are located in the endocardium, and they can be disrupted either mechanically or by a very brief exposure to a low concentration of detergent. Trabeculae can be totally depleted of endothelial cells by perfusing the coronary circulation with a bolus of detergent before removing the trabeculae and disrupting the endocardial endothelium with detergent.

The effluent from the perfused heart can be assayed on the isolated trabecula in four ways, each of which provides different information depending on whether the endothelial cells in the perfused heart and isolated trabecula are intact (39). When both sets of endothelial cells are intact, there is change in the contractility of the trabecula that correlates with the tissue oxygen tension in the perfused heart. No change in contractility is seen when the endothelial cells in both perfused heart and trabecula have been disrupted. The first conclusion from these studies is that the origin of the regulatory substances is the endothelium. Myocytes do not release substances that enter the coronary circulation and then directly alter the contractility of other myocytes. Coronary venous effluent from perfused hearts with disrupted vascular endothelium modifies the contractility of trabeculae with intact endothelium in accordance with the tissue oxygen tension in the perfusate. On the other hand, the effect on the contractility of the trabecula is not correlated with tissue oxygen tension when the effluent is assayed on trabeculae with disrupted endothelial cells, even when the perfused heart has intact endothelium. The last two observations indicate that the oxygen sensor in this regulatory system is not located in the endothelial cell, but more likely in the cardiac myocytes. Because the vascular smooth muscle cell is located near the flow of well-oxygenated fluid, it is unlikely to be the oxygen sensor. Fibroblasts could also act as oxygen sensors. Their location is favorable for such a function, but there are no data to evaluate such a possibility. The second conclusion is that the oxygen-sensing cell, presumably the cardiac myocyte, releases a substance that stimulates or is required for the endothelial cells to secrete endothelin.

Shear stress modifies the synthesis and the secretion of endothelin by cultured endothelial cells (2, 25). The relation is nonlinear, complex, and depends on whether the level of shear stress is constant or pulsatile. Increasing nonpulsatile shear stress lowers the rate of secretion of endothelin, but secretion increases with pulsatile shear stress up to a maximum, beyond which secretion declines. Although several possible mechanisms for the increase in the endothelin formation have been proposed, including activation of stretch-sensitive ion channels, the formation of intracellular filaments, and the polymerization of actin, the causes have not been firmly identified.

The effect of shear stress on the synthesis and secretion of endothelin by intact vascular endothelial cells in the perfused heart was estimated from the effect of the rate of coronary flow on the endothelial cell content of endothelin and the concentration of endothelin in the venous effluent (30). Endothelial cell content was estimated by stripping off the vascular endothelium with high-pressure perfusion and measuring the amount of endothelin in the effluent (30). Endothelial cell content of endothelin was related to the rate of coronary perfusion similarly to the relation found between pulsatile shear stress and endothelin secretion in cultured cells. However, in the perfused isolated heart, the rate of coronary flow and the concentration of endothelin in the venous effluent are not consistently correlated. Apparently in the intact isolated heart, physical forces on the vascular endothelium are important in regulating the rate of synthesis of endothelin, but other factors, including presumably substances released by the oxygen-sensing myocytes, are also important in determining the rate of secretion of endothelin.

## Action of Endothelin

Endothelin, a peptide synthesized in endothelial cells and in cardiac myocytes, was first discovered by its effect on vasomotor tone, but it has subsequently been shown to have a profound effect on the cardiac myocytes themselves. The effect is complex and depends to a substantial extent on the concentration of endothelin, the preparation, and the parameter used to assess the contractility of the cardiac myocytes (15). When isometric force is measured in isolated trabeculae, the threshold for a change in maximum isometric force is almost 1 nM and the response increases up to 10–100 nM, although Endoh and colleagues (8, 20, 48) have detected small increases (10–15%) at picomolar concentrations. In isolated, freely suspended cardiac myocytes, in which the contractile parameters measured are the extent and the velocity of shortening, the threshold for a change is as low as 1 pM (18, 22). In the isolated myocytes, the resting sarcomere length is about 1.9 $\mu$m and in the isolated trabeculae it is generally about 2.2 $\mu$m. This may be important as discussed below. The effect on isolated cells is blocked by protein kinase C (PKC) inhibition (18). When actomyosin ATPase activity is the measured parameter in cryostatic sections of quickly frozen hearts, the response is even more complex (33). At concentrations between 1 to 50 pM, the extent and the velocity of shortening are increased, and the ATPase is increased. At concentrations above 100 pM, the ATPase activity is reduced, and the velocity of unloaded shortening is also reduced. The higher range coincides with the one where force is increased. Within the concentration range where force is increased and ATPase decreased, the amplitude of the decline in ATPase activity from endothelin increases progressively as sarcomere length is increased from 1.9 to 2.4 $\mu$m (33). The effect of endothelin on ATPase activity is very small at 1.9 $\mu$m, but it is approximately 35% at 2.4 $\mu$m. From these data, one can conclude that endothelin has multiple effects on the contraction and that they are probably independently controlled. Force and ATPase activity may change in the same or in the opposite directions or one can occur without the other (Figure 1).

The apparent binding constant of endothelin, which has been estimated to be from 0.005 to 1 nM based on non-equilibrium binding studies, is another property that remains unclear. Frelin & Guedin (11) argue that non-equilibrium conditions lead to an over-estimation of the true binding constant, which is actually in the 0.1 to 1.0 pM range. They claim that with the high concentration of binding sites on endothelial cells, their high affinity and the abluminal secretion of endothelin, a low concentration of endothelin in the region is maintained by what amounts to a buffer system. On the other hand, others claim that because of the very slow off rate for endothelin from its receptor, and the importance of internalization rather than release from the receptor as the major mechanism for reversal of its effect on contractility, the system does not lend itself to equilibrium analysis (14). Because endothelin stimulates the secretion of nitric oxide (NO), which opposes the action of endothelin in several ways (see below), the total effect of endothelin in the presence of endothelial cells is also heavily buffered by the action of NO. Because there is tonic secretion of endothelin in isolated preparations, these effects contribute to the variation in the response of cardiac muscle to endothelin depending on whether endothelial cells are present (31).

The cellular mechanisms for the increase in force and the changes in ATPase activity are different. The increase in the force of contraction is produced primarily by an increase in the sensitivity of the contractile system to $Ca^{2+}$. Two observations support this conclusion. The relation between intracellular $Ca^{2+}$ concentration and force is shifted to lower concentrations of $Ca^{2+}$, and the maximum $Ca^{2+}$-activated force is not changed (52). Although some of this shift in $Ca^{2+}$ sensitivity appears to be the result of alkalization of the cytoplasm by

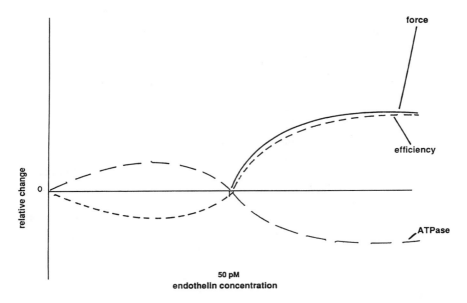

*Figure 1*   A composite dose-response relation for the concentration of endothelin and several of the contractile parameters of cardiac muscle. The shape of the relation is approximate to show that the relation for ATPase is biphasic and the threshold concentration for a major effect on force is higher than that required to change ATPase activity. The maximum speed of unloaded shortening is not shown, but it is very similar to the ATPase activity.

the effect of endothelin on the Na-H transporter, it cannot be entirely attributed to a pH change (24). In addition, there is some evidence for an increase in the inward $Ca^{2+}$ current during depolarization (36). The mechanism for the endothelin effect on ATPase activity must be the post-translational modification of the myofibrillar proteins, because this shift is observed even when the concentration of $Ca^{2+}$ is not limiting (33). The particular myofibrillar proteins that may participate in these kinetic changes are discussed below.

The rate of production of endothelin is sensitive to two different parameters that are likely to be input signals for an endothelium-based cardioregulatory system. Cyclical shear stress stimulates the synthesis of endothelin by endothelial cells as discussed above. Increased synthesis and binding by cardiac myocytes is also induced by myocardial ischemia or anoxia (19, 50). The concentration of mRNA for endothelin-1 rises in cardiac myocytes and not in endothelial cells following 90 min of localized ischemia. No change occurs in the non-ischemic zones of the heart. The concentration of endothelin in the venous effluent of isolated perfused hearts has the opposite response to changes in tissue $pO_2$. Elevated oxygen tension raises endothelial cell secretion and lower oxygen tension raises synthesis in the myocytes. The apparent difference in the response to oxygen may indicate that endothelin synthesis and secretion are regulated by oxygen tension in opposite directions in cardiac myocytes and endothelial cells. Endothelin produced in the cardiac myocytes might not reach the perfusion medium because of the high affinity of binding sites on the myocytes and the endothelial cells and, conversely, endothelin produced by vascular endothelial cells may not reach a very high concentration in the perfusion fluid or at the cardiac myocytes. The histochemical measurements of ATPase in isolated papillary muscle supports this inference.

Vascular smooth muscle in culture releases a substance that inhibits the rate of endothelin secretion by endothelial cells (45). The conditions controlling the rate of formation of the endothelin-regulating material are not known. It would be of considerable interest if control was related to the tension on the smooth muscle cells, as this is a parameter that would reflect an arterial cross-section area and therefore coronary flow. With the smooth muscle cells monitoring the arterial cross section and communicating that information to endothelial cells, which themselves monitor velocity of blood flow through shear stress, the vascular endothelial cells would be able to distinguish the rate of coronary flow accurately. This would be a useful supplement to the information about myocyte use of oxygen that is received from the cardiac myocytes.

A decrease in the ATPase activity of actomyosin in the presence of an increase or a constant level of contractile force, as occurs with endothelin at concentrations greater than 100 pM, means that force is developed and maintained with a lower rate of ATP hydrolysis and therefore with a greater economy of energy transduction (1). This action, which is different from the decrease in economy generally observed with beta-adrenergic stimulation, fits well into the overall function of the endothelial cell regulation of contractility, which seems to be closely tied to energy metabolism and the balance between energy supply and work performed (4). The increase in the economy becomes progressively greater with the longer sarcomere length in the range of 1.9 to 2.4 $\mu$m, making endothelin potentially more effective when the heart dilates and its work per contraction increases. A decrease in actomyosin ATPase activity due to a change in myosin isoforms occurs with chronic dilatation and hypertrophy as a result of altered gene expression (29), but the response of ATPase activity to endothelin is much faster, providing the cardiac cell with a rapidly responding post-translational mechanism for modifying the economy of the contraction that becomes more active as the workload on the heart increases.

## Nitric Oxide

Although there is still some controversy about the effects of NO on cardiac contractility at low concentrations (23), it is clear that NO can have a strong effect on the heart (13, 37). There is general agreement that NO can decrease the contractility of the heart, accelerate left ventricular relaxation, and increase diastolic distensibility. These changes are probably the result of the increased production of cGMP in as much as the addition of the membrane permeant form of cGMP, the 8-bromo analogue, can reproduce these effects (7, 43). Inhibitors of cGMP-dependent protein kinase inhibit the change in transmembrane $Ca^{2+}$ movement and block the decrease in contractility produced by NO donors at higher concentrations. At low concentrations of NO donors, there is an increase in cAMP and contractility that is similar to an increase in isoproterenol, presumably by cGMP inhibition of phosphodiesterase. It is difficult to use the membrane permeant 8-bromo analogue of cGMP to study the low concentration effects because although it strongly stimulates the protein kinase, it is only a poor inhibitor of the phosphodiesterase.

There is interaction between NO and other cardioregulatory mechanisms such as beta-adrenergic agonists and endothelin. Low concentrations of cGMP produced by low concentration of NO donors enhance the positive effects of beta-adrenergic agonists on contractility (23). High concentrations of cGMP from high concentrations of NO donors antagonize the beta-adrenergic effect. NO is also produced in cardiac myocytes, where its action is to diminish the increase in the extent of shortening of isolated myocytes produced by isoproterenol (3). In the absence of increased contractility from isoproterenol, inhibition of NO synthase in the cardiac myocyte had no effect on the extent of shortening.

NO also interacts with endothelin. Endothelin stimulates endothelial cell NO synthase, which results in a higher level of NO. In isolated cardiac myocytes, NO prevents the increase in intracellular $Ca^{2+}$ concentration that can be produced by endothelin without changing the increase in the extent of shortening (7). This observation is particularly interesting because it suggests that the increase in the extent of shortening is not due to an alteration in the sensitivity to $Ca^{2+}$, unlike the increase in force observed in isolated trabeculae. In isolated perfused hearts, NO does not alter endothelin's effects on the force of contraction, but it does prevent endothelin-induced increase in end diastolic pressure, consistent with the relaxing effect of NO seen in the absence of endothelin.

## Endothelium-Derived Down-Regulating Cardioactive Substances

There are negatively inotropic factors derived from vascular endothelial cells, but so far little progress has been made in identifying them. From the existing data, it is likely that there are multiple factors. The venous effluent from isolated perfused working hearts contains a factor(s) derived from the endothelial cells of the coronary arteries that decreases the peak isometric force of a trabecula removed from another heart. The apparent activity of the substance or substances increases as the tissue oxygen tension declines (39). This is partially from a decline in the concentration of the up-regulating endothelin, but also to an apparent increase of the down-regulating factor. This factor has not been identified, but its relative stability—its activity decreases by no more than 10-15% in the course of 40 min at room temperature—indicates that it is not NO. It can however completely prevent the positive effect of low concentrations of endothelin.

The existence of a down regulator from the coronary vascular endothelium has been demonstrated by another protocol. Perfusion of a heart with bradykinin causes a transient but significant decline in contractility that is blocked by prior disruption of the coronary endothelium (10). The effect was not blocked by nitro-arginine, which inhibits NO synthase, but it was blocked by the K channel inhibitor glibenclamide. Interestingly, the bradykinin caused a maintained elevation of cGMP but produced only a transient effect on contractility in a Langendorff preparation.

There has also been a report of a $Ca^{2+}$-desensitizing factor present in the superfusate of endothelial cells (42). It appears to be stable, resistant to trypsin, of very low molecular weight, and unchanged by the presence of either protein kinase A (PKA) and PKC inhibitors or pertussis toxin. It is not cGMP.

## The Molecular Basis of Regulation of Cardiac Contractile Proteins

In addition to possible changes in the amount of $Ca^{2+}$ made available for the activation of contraction, cardioactive factors modify the contractile proteins themselves. In almost every study of the action of endothelin on the contractility of the cardiac myocyte, an increase in the force at suboptimal concentration of intracellular $Ca^{2+}$ has been observed (22, 52). The same general response has been seen in bundles of intact cardiac cells, in permeabilized cardiac cells, and in isolated cardiac myocytes, using different intracellular indicators of $Ca^{2+}$ concentration. The pathway required to produce this change in the responsiveness of the contractile proteins involves G proteins and PKC because pertussis toxin and PKC inhibitors block the effect (18, 22).

The change in the contractile proteins is most likely to be the result of one or more phosphorylations. Three different phosphorylatable sites on the contractile proteins have been well documented. Phosphorylation of the inhibitory subunit of troponin (TNI) by PKA leads to a decrease in the sensitivity of the contractile proteins to $Ca^{2+}$ (35, 41). In intact myofibrils or cells, TNI phosphorylation is associated with an increase of actomyosin ATPase activity or cross-bridge cycling, although other phosphorylations may be required as well (17, 55). Both of these changes in function are the opposite of what endothelin produces as it increases the contractile force. Phosphorylation of the regulatory light chain of myosin (LC2) increases the sensitivity of the contractile proteins to $Ca^{2+}$ at low levels of activation without raising maximum $Ca^{2+}$-activated force (47). This phosphorylation is produced by either PKA or a $Ca^{2+}$-calmodulin-regulated enzyme but not by PKA. In isolated cardiac myofibrils and myocytes, PKC phosphorylates the same sites as PKA on C protein in the thick filament, but the two kinases phosphorylate different sites on TNI (51). Their effects on actomyosin ATPase activity are different as well (51). The rate at which ATP is hydrolyzed after treatment with PKC is decreased. This effect from PKC is the same as that produced by endothelin operating through PKC in the intact cell. Therefore, one may tentatively conclude that the different combinations of TNI and C protein phosphorylation from PKA and PKC are responsible for the opposite changes in ATPase activity.

In the study of the effects on actomyosin ATPase activity of phosphorylation by PKA, PKC, and the combination in response to alpha-, beta-, and combined alpha-beta-adrenergic stimulation, changes in phosphorylation of the cardiac contractile proteins were measured (32). There were changes in phosphorylation of C protein and of TNI, but no consistent changes in the extent of phosphorylation of LC2. Only the phosphorylation of C protein had a clear relation to the changes in ATPase activity. The rate of ATP hydrolysis doubled as phosphorylation of C protein increased from its lowest to its highest value, and the level of phosphorylation always changed in the same direction as the ATPase activity. These results suggest that phosphorylation of C protein is a necessary event in the regulation of ATPase activity. Because the phosphorylated sites on C protein are the same with PKA or PKC, C protein phosphorylation may be a permissive step that allows regulation of actomyosin ATPase activity to occur. The different phosphorylated sites on TNI may detemine the direction of the change in ATPase activity.

Changes in the structure of isolated thick filaments as distinct from these produced in the regulatory proteins of the thin filament occur in response to phosphorylations (53). These structural changes in the thick filament may be the basis for regulation of ATPase activity. Incubation of the thick filaments with PKA and ATP produces phosphorylation of C protein without affecting the LC2. The distance of the end of the cross-bridge, which contains the actin-binding site, from the backbone of the thick filament can be calculated from the difference between the widths of the thick filament where there are cross-bridges and the width in the central bare zone that contains no cross-bridges. The position of the reflections along the 43-nm layer line in the optical diffraction pattern indicates how far the center of mass of the cross-bridge lies from the axis of the thick filament.

In thick filaments with a low level of phosphorylation of C protein not exposed to PKA, the ends of a majority (>70% ) of cross-bridges lie 5–6 nm from the surface of the thick filament, and the center of mass of the cross-bridge is about 1.3 nm from the surface. After phosphorylation of C protein by PKA, the cross-bridges are extended by an additional 3 nm—both the end and the center of mass move about the same distance. If one assumes the normal interfilament spacing that exists in a filament lattice in an intact cell, the phosphorylation moves the average position of the actin attachment site at the end of the cross-bridge from a position about 3 nm away from the surface of the thin filament to the filament's surface. The observed change in intensity of the reflections indicates that the flexibility of the cross-bridge is probably reduced, increasing the percentage of time during the cross-bridge cycle that the cross-bridge is at or near the surface of the thin filament. This could increase the probability of attachment and the rate of ATP hydrolysis.

## Modulation of Adrenergic Effect on ATPase Activity

Although a majority of studies show that beta-adrenergic stimulation of the heart increases the velocity of unloaded shortening and the rate of ATP hydrolysis by actomyosin and decreases the efficiency of conversion of biochemical energy to mechanical work, a few studies from well-established laboratories have found no effect on the kinetics of the contraction even though contractile force has been increased (16, 49). The most rigorous study that failed to show an effect on ATPase activity was performed on skinned fibers. The differences are reconcilable if regulation of the kinetics and the force of contraction in cardiac muscle by beta-adrenergic stimulation have separate mechanisms, with regulation of kinetics requiring the presence of intact endothelial cells. This separation appears to be true when endothelial cells are present and there is an adequate supply of oxygen to the cells in the myocardium (29).

In the absence of endothelial cells, actomyosin ATPase activity is unchanged by cAMP. In the presence of endothelial cells, the degree to which ATPase activity can be raised by cAMP is related to oxygen tension (21, 32, 39). As oxygen tension rises, the amplitude of the increase in ATPase from the same concentrations of cAMP increases. At low oxygen tensions, the ATPase activity is refractory to cAMP. This suggests that an oxygen-dependent endothelial cell–derived factor is necessary for regulation of ATPase activity. The secretion of endothelin by endothelial cells has a similar relation to oxygen tension. As the tissue oxygen tension rises, the amount of endothelin added to the coronary perfusate increases. Together these observations can be explained if endothelin or some response to endothelin such as PKC activation is essential for the regulation of actomyosin ATPase activity. It may be necessary to alter the contractile proteins in a way that allows them to be regulated by cAMP-dependent

PKA. The existence of an endothelin-activated change in the contractile proteins that allows ATPase to be regulated has some experimental support (33). In the absence of endothelin, the apparent rate of ATP hydrolysis by cross-bridges overlapped by actin is unaffected by sarcomere length, in as much as ATPase activity declines linearly with increasing sarcomere length, just as does $Ca^{2+}$-activated force. In the presence of a concentration of endothelin that lowers ATPase activity, increasing sarcomere length from 1.9 to 2.4 $\mu$m progressively diminishes the apparent rate at which each overlapped cross-bridge hydrolyzes ATP. Endothelin seems to make the rate of cross-bridge cycling sensitive to the steric arrangement between cross-bridge and thin filament. ATPase regulation that is dependent on the steric arrangement may be a general mechanism.

Alpha-adrenergic stimulation, which also activates PKC, may have an effect similar to endothelin on the kinetics of cross-bridge cycling. For cAMP to produce an increase in actomyosin ATPase activity in thin sections of quickly frozen cardiac muscle, a low level of alpha-adrenergic activity is necessary (32). In the presence of alpha-adrenergic inhibition, 1 $\mu$M cAMP has either no effect or may decrease actomyosin ATPase activity. The effect of alpha-adrenergic stimulation, however, is biphasic like that of endothelin. At 10 $\mu$M, the optimal concentration of norepinephrine for its increase in force, the catecholamine decreases ATPase activity and blocks the increase that would have been seen with cAMP in the presence of low levels of alpha-adrenergic stimulation. These results are very similar to the increase in actomyosin ATPase activity produced by picomolar concentrations and the decrease by nanomolar concentrations of endothelin. Both alpha-adrenergic agonists and endothelin activate PKC, which decreases the actomyosin ATPase activity of isolated cardiac cells and myofibrils at high levels of activation.

## Summary and Scheme of Integrated Function of Endothelial Cells

In organizing and evaluating data from studies with isolated cells, bundles of cardiac tissue, and intact hearts, one must give careful consideration to the strengths and limitations of each type of preparation: the absence of any structural organization in isolated cell preparations; the unusually high endocardial cell to cardiac myocyte ratio with very short diffusion distances between the two in papillary muscle; and the difficulty of sorting out direct from indirect effects in the intact heart, in which the consequences of changes in coronary flow can be difficult to distinguish from direct effects on the cardiac myocytes.

Five general observations form the basis for a hypothetical endothelin-based regulatory system that responds to the metabolic state of the cardiac myocytes: (*a*) the separate regulation of force and kinetics of contraction; (*b*) the biphasic effect of endothelin on force, actomyosin ATPase activity, and efficiency of contraction—decreased efficiency at low concentrations and increased efficiency at high concentrations of endothelin; (c) the existence of a factor released by cardiac myocytes that modulates the secretion of endothelin by endothelial cells [myocyte-derived regulator of endothelin (MDRE)]: It is secreted at an increasing rate as tissue $pO_2$ rises; (d) the increased sensitivity of cardiac myocytes to endothelin with increasing sarcomere length; and (e) the increased secretion and increased binding of endothelin by cardiac myocytes as $pO_2$ at the myocyte decreases.

An increase in oxygen tension at the cardiac myocyte raises the secretion of MDRE and suppresses the secretion of endothelin by the cardiac myocytes. Because of the primarily unidirectional secretion of endothelin by vascular endothelial cells, the smooth muscle in the vessels is exposed to a high concentration of endothelin, which causes constriction and decreased blood flow. A much lower concentration of endothelin in the medium (blood in the intact heart) would produce a low concentration at the cardiac myocytes and result in a decrease in the efficiency of contraction and a reduction of oxygen tension at these cells. A decrease in oxygen tension at the cardiac myocyte causes increased secretion of endothelin and a reduced secretion of MDRE by cardiac myocytes, thereby producing an autocrine effect of endothelin on the myocytes. The increase in endothelin concentration at the cardiac myocytes is large enough to produce an increase in the efficiency and force of contraction, whereas the reduced secretion by the vascular endothelial cells causes vasodilatation and increased blood flow. Increased binding by cardiac myocytes minimizes the amount of endothelin reaching the vascular muscle. The resultant increase in blood flow and cardiac efficiency helps restore the balance between work done and energy or oxygen supplied to the heart (Figure 2). The effectiveness of this system is amplified by an increase in fiber length, as occurs when outflow falls below inflow to the heart. The result of the mechanisms proposed by this model is that cardiac efficiency and coronary blood flow move in complementary directions in response to the level of oxygen tension, and oxygen tension at the cardiac myocyte is maintained within a specific range of values, avoiding both low and high levels.

NO and NO donors decrease contractility by shortening and lowering the peak of the contraction at moderate concentrations and augmenting the contractility at low concentrations. High and low concentrations of cGMP have the same effect. Because these changes in the contraction resemble those produced in isolated papillary muscles by disrupting the endocardial endothelium, it has been suggested that NO operates as a physiological cardiac regulator. However, we do not know what controls NO's level of function in terms of modulation of cardiac contractility or how it fits into the normal regulation of

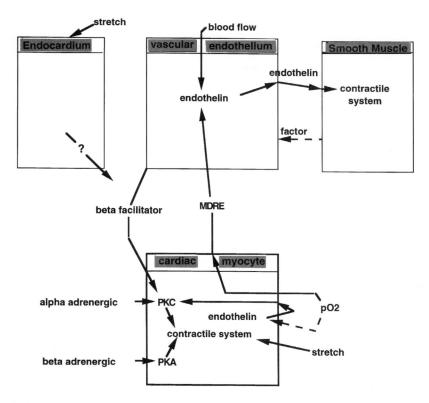

*Figure 2*   A proposed scheme for the interactions among endothelial cells and contractile cells in the heart. Solid lines indicate a positive effect and interrupted lines indicate a negative effect. The question mark indicates an effect demonstrated in isolated cells, but also the lack of an apparent way for this effect to occur in the intact heart.

cardiac activity. There is interaction between NO and endothelin. Endothelin stimulates the production of NO, which can reduce the further secretion of endothelin.

Endothelial cells are modulators of actions of alpha- and beta-adrenergic agonists, substance P, vasopressin, serotonin, atrial natriuretic peptides, and prostaglandins on certain parameters of the cardiac contraction. Endothelin and probably NO may keep the extent of change in contractility produced by these agents within the limits placed by energy supply, possibly through effects on phosphatase activity that result in a shift of balance between kinase activity and phosphorylation.

Although multiple down-regulating substances have been identified in the coronary venous effluent and in the incubation medium of endothelial cells, these substances have not yet been identified, and their cellular mechanisms have not been elucidated. These substances can be produced by endocardial endothelium and vascular endothelium proximal to the arterioles at a rate dependent primarily on ambient tissue $pO_2$. Because endothelial cells in the coronary arteries and left ventricular endocardium normally are exposed to only fully oxygenated blood, signals from elsewhere in the tissue would be required for the control of their secretion.

## Problems and Future Directions

At the present time very little is known about the negative or down-regulating factors in terms of identity, secretion, and action. It is very likely that more than one down-regulating factor exists. Until this ignorance has been removed, any endothelial cell scheme must perforce be preliminary.

More information is needed about the gradients of cardioactive substances around the endothelial cells and the actual concentrations of these factors produced at the cardiac myocyte (27). Important in the understanding is the possible existence of specialized diffusion pathways within the heart.

Cross-talk among the different cell types appears to be of considerable importance. More molecular conduits for this cross-talk probably exist than have already been identified. It is possible that the role of endothelial cells in collating and transmitting information within this cross-talk is equally important to any role as a direct source of effector substances.

Determining the role of smooth muscle in the interactions and the factors controlling its endothelin-regulating substances will be important in the overall scheme of intercellular regulation.

The changes in the contractile proteins responsible for the alteration in ATPase activity and cross-bridge kinetics need to be elucidated.

How can endocardial cells function as regulators of contractility in view of the diffusion distances to the myocytes and the enormous dilution that would occur with secretion of material into the cardiac chambers? These cells are ideally located to be sensors of cardiac size and distention and thus their function needs to be clarified.

*Literature Cited*

1. Alpert NR, Mulieri LA. 1983. Thermomechanical economy of hypertrophied hearts. In *Perspectives in Cardiovascular Research,* ed. NR Alpert, 7:619–30. New York: Raven
2. Awolesi M, Widmann M, Sessa W, Sum-
pio B. 1994. Cyclic strain increases endothelial nitric oxide synthase activity. *Surgery* 116:439
3. Balligrand J-L, Kelly RA, Marsden PA, Smith TW, Michel T. 1993. Control of cardiac muscle cell function by an endoge-

nous nitric oxide signalling system. *Proc. Natl. Acad. Sci. USA* 90:347–51

4. Breisch EA, Houser SR, Coulson RL. 1983. Reduced heat production in compensated pressure-overload hypertrophy of the left ventricle of the cat. In *Perspectives in Cardiovascular Research*, ed. NR Alpert, 7:587–99. New York: Raven

5. Brutsaert DL, Meulemans AL, Sipido KJ, Sys SU. 1988. Effect of damaging the endocardial surface on the mechanical performance of isolated cardiac muscle. *Circ. Res.* 62:358–66

6. Carey R, Natarajan G, Bove A, Coulson R, Spann J. 1979. Myosin adenosine-triphosphatase activity in the volume overloaded hypertrophied feline right ventricle. *Circ. Res.* 45:81–97

7. Ebihara Y, Haist JV, Karmazyn M. 1996. Modulation of endothelin-1 effects on rat hearts and cardiomyocytes by nitric oxide and 8-bromo cyclic GMP. *J. Mol. Cell. Cardiol.* 28:265–77

8. Endoh M, Takanashi M. 1991. Differential inhibitory action of phorbol-12,13-dibutyrate on the positive inotropic effect of endothelin-1 and Bay K8644 in the isolated rabbit papillary muscle. *Cardiovasc. Res.* 17(Suppl.7):25S165–68

9. Evans HG, Lewis MJ, Shah AM. 1994. Modulation of myocardial relaxation by basal release of endothelin from endocardial endothelium. *Cardiovasc. Res.* 28:1694–99

10. Fort S, Lewis MJ. 1993. A factor released from coronary vascular endothelium inhibits myocardial contractile performance. *Am. J. Physiol.* 264:H830–36

11. Frelin C, Guedin D. 1994. Why are circulating concentrations of endothelin-1 so low? *Cardiovasc. Res.* 28:1613–22

12. Furchgott R, Zawadski J. 1980. The obligatory role of endothelial cells in the relaxation of arterial smooth muscle of acetylcholine. *Nature* 288:373–76

13. Grocott-Mason RM, Anning PB, Evans H, Lewis MJ, Shah AM. 1994. Modulation of left ventricular relaxation in isolated ejecting heart by endogenous nitric oxide. *Am. J. Physiol.* 267:H1804–13

14. Hasenfuss G, Mulieri L, Leavitt B, Alpert N. 1994. Influence of isoproterenol on contractile protein function, excitation-contraction coupling, and energy turnover of isolated nonfailing human heart. *J. Mol. Cell. Cardiol.* 26:1461–69

15. Hilal-Dandan R, Urasawa K, Brunton L. 1992. Endothelin inhibits adenylate cyclase and stimulates phosphoinositide hydrolysis in adult cardiac myocytes. *J. Biol. Chem.* 267:10620–24

16. Hoffman PA, Lange JH III. 1994. Effects of phosphorylation of troponin I and C protein on isometric tension and velocity of unloaded shortening in skinned single cardiac myocytes from rats. *Circ. Res.* 74:718–26

17. Hoh JFY, Rossmanith GH, Hamilton AM. 1991. Effects of dibutyryl cyclic AMP, ouabain, and xanthine derivatives on crossbridge kinetics in rat cardiac muscle. *Circ. Res.* 68:702

18. Jones L, Rozick J, Tsutsui H, Cooper G IV. 1992. Endothelin stimulates multiple responses in isolated ventricular cardiac myocytes. *Am. J. Physiol.* 263:H1447–54

19. Kagamu, Suzuki T, Arakawa, Mitsui Y. 1994. Low oxygen enhances endothelin-1 (ET-1) production and responsiveness to ET-1 in cultured cardiac myocytes. *Biochem. Biophys. Res. Comm.* 202:1612

20. Kasai H, Takanashi M, Takasaki C, Endoh M. 1994. Pharmacological properties of endothelin receptors subtypes mediating positive inotropic effects in rabbit heart. *Am. J. Physiol.* 266:H2220–28

21. Kato NS, Weisberg A, Winegrad S. 1991. Effect of left atrial filling pressure on the activity of specific myosin isozymes in rat heart. *Circ. Res.* SSI:1582–90

22. Kelly R, Eid H, Kramer B, O'Neill M, Liang B, et al. 1990. Endothelin enhances the contractile responsiveness of adult rat ventricular myocytes to calcium by a pertussis toxin sensitive pathway. *Clin. Invest.* 86:1164–71

23. Kojda G, Kottenberg K, Nix P, Schluter KD, Piper HM, Noack E. 1996. Low increase in cGMP induced by organic nitrates and nitrovasodilators improves contractile response of rat ventricular myocytes. *Circ. Res.* 78:91–101

24. Kramer B, Smith T, Kelly R. 1991. Endothelium and increased contractility in adult rat heart myocytes. Role of intracellular alkalosis induced by activation of protein kinase C-dependent Na-H exchanger. *Circ. Res.* 68:269–79

25. Kuchen M, Frangos JA. 1993. Shear stress regulates endothelium 1 release via a protein kinase C and cGMP in cultured endothelial cells. *Am. J. Physiol.* 264:H150–56

26. Lin L-E, McClellan GM, Weisberg A, Winegrad S. 1991. A physiological basis for the variation in the contractile properties of isolated rat heart. *J. Physiol.* 441:73–94

27. Margulies K, Hildebrand F Jr, Lerman A, Perella M, Burnett J Jr. 1990. Increased endothelin in experimental heart failure. *Circulation* 82:2226

28. McClellan GM, Weisberg A, Kato N, Ramaciotti C, Sharkey A, Winegrad S. 1992. Contractile proteins in myocardial cells are regulated by factor(s) released by blood vessels. *Circ. Res.* 70:787–803
29. McClellan GM, Weisberg A, Lin LE, Winegrad S. 1993. Endothelial cells are required for cAMP regulation of cardiac contractile proteins. *Proc. Natl. Acad. Sci. USA* 90:2885–89
30. McClellan GM, Weisberg A, Rose D, Winegrad S. 1994. Endothelial cell storage and release of endothelin as a cardioregulatory mechanism. *Circ. Res.* 75:85–96
31. McClellan GM, Weisberg A, Winegrad S. 1995. Endothelin regulation of cardiac contractility in the absence of added endothelin. *Am. J. Physiol.* 268:H1621–27
32. McClellan GM, Weisberg A, Winegrad S. 1995. Cyclic AMP can raise or lower actomyosin ATPase. *Am. J. Physiol.* 267:H431–42
33. McClellan GM, Weisberg A, Winegrad S. 1996. Effect of endothelin-1 on actomyosin ATPase activity: implications for the efficiency of contraction. *Circ. Res.* 78:1044–50
34. Mebazaa A, Mayoux E, Maeda K, Martin L, Lakatta EG, et al. 1993. Paracrine effects of endocardial endothelial cells on myocyte contraction via endothelin. *Am. J. Physiol.* 265:H1841–46
35. Mope L, McClellan GM, Winegrad S. 1980. Calcium sensitivity of the contractile system and phosphorylation of troponin in hyperpermeable cardiac cells. *J. Gen. Physiol.* 75:271–82
36. Ono K, Tsuujimoto G, Sakamoto A, Eto K, Masaki T, et al. 1994. Endothelin-A receptor mediates cardiac inhibition by regulating calcium and potassium currents. *Nature* 370:301–4
37. Paulus WJ, Vantrimpont PJ, Shah AM. 1995. Paracrine coronary endothelial control of left ventricular function in humans. *Circulation* 92:2119–26
38. Pohl U, Buss R. 1989. Differential vascular sensitivity to luminally and adventitially applied endothelin-1 *J. Cardiovasc. Pharm.* 13(Suppl. 5)S188–90
39. Ramaciotti C, McClellan G, Sharkey A, Rose D, Weisberg A, Winegrad S. 1993. Cardiac endothelial cells modulate contractility of rat heart in response to oxygen tension and coronary flow. *Circ. Res.* 72:1044–64
40. Ramaciotti C, Sharkey A, McClellan GM, Winegrad S. 1992. Endothelial cells regulate cardiac contractility. *Proc. Natl. Acad. Sci. USA* 89:4033–36
41. Robertson S, Johnson D, Holroyde M, Kranias I, Potter J, Solaro J. 1982. The effect of troponin I phosphorylation on the Ca binding properties of the calcium regulatory site of bovine cardiac troponin. *J. Biol. Chem.* 257:160
42. Shah AM, Mebazaa A, Wetzel RC, Lakatta EG. 1994. Novel cardiac myofilament desensitizing factor released by endocardial and vascular endothelial cells. *Circulation* 89:2492–97
43. Shah AM, Spurgeon HA, Sollott SJ, Talo A, Lakatta EG. 1994. 8-bromo-cGMP reduces the myofilament response to Ca in intact cardiac myocytes. *Circ. Res.* 74:970–78
44. Smith JA, Shah AM, Lewis MJ. 1991. Factors released from the endocardium of the ferret and pig modulate myocardial contraction. *J. Physiol.* 439:1–14
45. Stewart DJ, Langleben D, Ceracek P, Cianflone K. 1990. Endothelin release is inhibited by co-culture of endothelial cells with cells of vascular media. *Am. J. Physiol.* 259:H1928
46. Strang KT, Moss RL. 1995. Alpha adrenergic receptor stimulation decreases the maximum shortening velocity of skinned single ventricular myocytes from rats. *Circ. Res.* 77:114–20
47. Sweeney L, Stull J. 1990. Alterations of cross bridge kinetics by myosin light chain phosphorylation in rabbit skeletal muscle: implications for regulation of actin-myosin interactions. *Proc. Natl. Acad. Sci. USA* 87:414–18
48. Takanashi M, Endoh M. 1991. Characterization of positive inotropic effect of endothelin on mammalian ventricular myocardium. *Am. J. Physiol.* 261:H611–19
49. de Tombe PP, Stienen GJM. 1995. Protein kinase A does not alter economy of force maintenance in skinned cardiac rat trabeculae. *Circ. Res.* 76:734–41
50. Tonnessen T, Giaid A, Saleh D, Naess PA, Ynagisawa M, Christensen G. 1995. Increased in vivo expresssion and production of endothelin-1 by porcine cardiomyocytes subjected to ischemia. *Circ. Res.* 76:767–72
51. Venema RC, Kuo JF. 1993. Protein kinase C mediated phosphorylation of troponin I and C protein in isolated myocardial cells is associated with inhibition of myofibrillar actomyosin ATPase. *J. Biol. Chem.* 268:2705–11
52. Wang J, Paik G, Morgan J. 1991. Endothelin 1 enhances myofilament $Ca^{2+}$-responsiveness in aequorin loaded ferret

myocardium. *Circ. Res.* 69:582–89

53. Weisberg A, Winegrad S. 1996. Alteration of myosin crossbridges by phosphorylation of myosin-binding protein C in cardiac muscle. *Proc. Natl. Acad. Sci. USA* 93:8999–9003

54. Wikman-Coffelt J, Fenner C, Coffelt R, Sabel A, Kamiyama T, Mason D. 1975. Chronological effects of mild pressure overload on myosin ATPase activity in the canine right ventricle. *J. Mol. Cell. Cardiol.* 7:219–24

55. Winegrad S, Weisberg A, Lin L-E, McClellan G. 1986. Adrenergic regulation of myosin adenosine triphosphatase activity. *Circ. Res.* 58:83–95

*Annu. Rev. Physiol. 1997. 59:527–49*

# SPATIAL RELATIONSHIPS IN EARLY SIGNALING EVENTS OF FLOW-MEDIATED ENDOTHELIAL MECHANOTRANSDUCTION

*Peter F. Davies[1], Kenneth A. Barbee[2], Michael V. Volin[3], Andre Robotewskyj[3], Jai Chen[4], Loren Joseph[3], Melvin L. Griem[5], Miles N. Wernick[6], Elizabeth Jacobs[7], Denise C. Polacek[1], Natacha DePaola[8], and Abdul I. Barakat[3]*

[1]Institute for Medicine and Engineering, University of Pennsylvania, Philadelphia, Pennsylvania 19104; [2]Department of Neurosurgery, Hahnemann Medical College of Pennsylvania, Philadelphia, Pennsylvania 19102; Departments of [3]Pathology, [4]Radiology, and [5]Radiation and Cellular Oncology, University of Chicago, Chicago, Illinois 60637; [6]Department of Electrical and Computer Engineering, Illinois Institute of Technology, Chicago, Illinois 60616; [7]Department of Medicine, Medical College of Wisconsin, Milwaukee, Wisconsin 53226; and [8]Department of Biomedical Engineering, Rensselaer Polytechnic Institute, Troy, New York 12181

KEY WORDS: endothelium, biomechanics, hemodynamic shear stress, blood flow, vasoregulation, atherosclerosis

### ABSTRACT

Blood flow interactions with the vascular endothelium represent a specialized example of mechanical regulation of cell function that has important physiological and pathological cardiovascular consequences. The endothelial monolayer in vivo acts as a signal transduction interface for forces associated with flowing blood (hemodynamic forces) in the acute regulation of artery tone and chronic structural remodeling of arteries, including the pathology of atherosclerosis. Mechanisms related to spatial relationships at the cell surfaces and throughout the cell that influence flow-mediated endothelial mechanotransduction are discussed. In particular, flow-mediated ion channel activation and cytoskeletal dynamics are considered in relation to topographic analyses of the luminal and abluminal surfaces of living endothelial cells.

527

0066-4278/97/03 15-0527$08.00

## INTRODUCTION

As blood flows through arteries, it imparts physical forces to the vascular wall that regulate a number of important physiological responses in blood vessels and are also implicated in the development of arterial wall pathologies. Changes in blood flow are responsible for the acute regulation of vessel tone, the development of blood vessel structure during embryogenesis and early growth, and the chronic remodeling of adult blood vessels following interventions that alter the mechanical environment. Hemodynamic forces can be resolved into two principal vectors: first, shear stress, a frictional force acting at the interface between flowing blood and the vessel wall; and second, pressure acting normal to the vessel wall, which imposes circumferential stretch to the tissue (24, 33). It is now well accepted that hemodynamic shear stress acts through the endothelium to regulate both acute vessel tone and chronic restructuring of blood vessels (19, 23). Thus the endothelium is a complex mechanical signal-transduction interface between flowing blood and the vessel wall (70).

In contrast to physiological regulation, the role of hemodynamics in pathological events is less well understood. The most notable association is that regions of disturbed flow correlate with the distribution of atherosclerotic lesions in large arteries, a relationship that has been recognized since the 1850s (83). Some regions of the arterial tree never succumb to atherosclerosis, whereas others are highly susceptible. These areas usually coincide with regions of separation from unidirectional laminar flow that occur typically near branches, bifucations, regions of arterial narrowing, and curvatures in the arteries. The local hemodynamic forces generate complex gradients of shear stress and produce highly uneven stretch forces within the vessel wall. Consequently, theories of high shear stress, low shear stress, particle residence time in the bulk fluid, and differential arterial compliance and stretch have all gained a degree of credibility as causative factors of focal atherosclerosis (13, 32, 87). How the endothelium plays a dominant hemodynamic role in such a complex environment is unclear, although at least one major endothelial dysfunction is associated with the developing lesions: the failure of both flow-mediated and chemically regulated vasodilation (37). Other vascular pathologies in which blood flow plays an important role include the clotting and fibrinolytic cascades at the blood vessel surface, where critical concentrations of enzymes, substrates, and cofactors responsible for clot formation and dissolution are influenced by the local flow characteristics that regulate the convective delivery and removal of reagents (26, 35).

This article reviews spatial relationships that influence signaling responses initiated by hemodynamic shear stresses in endothelial cells. Cell imaging techniques, in providing geometric information at cell surfaces, have prompted a reexamination of the localization of mechanotransduction sites. The reader is also referred to a recent review of flow-mediated endothelial mechanotransduction mechanisms (19).

## Endothelial Bioresponses to Hemodynamic Forces: A Hierarchy

A sense of order can be created from the bewildering array of endothelial responses to shear stress by arranging them in order of response times; a hierarchy of potential relationships can then be postulated. A prominent feature is that they range across a variety of biological disciplines, from electrophysiology to biochemistry to cell biology, gene regulation and major changes of cell structure (Figure 1). These diverse responses are often contemporaneous. For example, very early electrophysiological changes of membrane potential (seconds) and the activation of potent biochemical cascades appear to have similar time constants (8). The latter include G protein activation, the mobilization of phosphoinositide derivatives, release of intracellular free calcium,

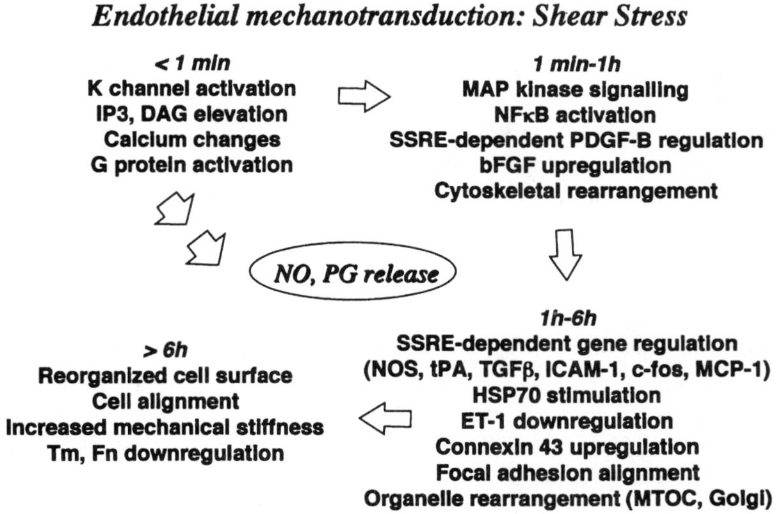

### Endothelial mechanotransduction: Shear Stress

*Figure 1* Endothelial mechanotransduction: shear stress. IP$_3$, inositol-1,4,5-trisphosphate; DAG, diacylglycerol; PG, prostaglandins; NO, nitric oxide; MAP, mitogen-activated protein; NFκB, nuclear factor kappa B; SSRE, shear stress response element; PDGF-B, platelet derived growth factor B chain; bFGF, basic fibroblast growth factor; NOS, nitric oxide synthase; tPA, tissue plasminogen activator; TGFβ, transforming growth factor beta; ICAM-1, intercellular adhesion molecule-1; MCP-1, monocyte chemoattractant protein-1; HSP-70, 70-kDa heat shock protein; ET-1, endothelin-1; MTOC, microtubule-organizing center; Tm, thrombomodulin; Fn, fibronectin.

and cyclic nucleotide phosphorylation (9, 30). Structural changes, such as re-arrangements of actin and vimentin filaments, which are generally observed much later in the sequence of mechanotransduction events and are associated with changes of cell shape, are also detectable by sensitive techniques soon after the initiation of a change of mechanical load (19, 31). The time constants are similar to those associated with activation of some of the known early transcription factors (49). Although many responses support an ordered sequence of initial signaling leading to transcription factor activation, gene regulation and cellular structural adaptation (associated with the synthesis of new proteins), there are also shorter signaling pathways. An example is shown in Figure 1 as release of the potent vasodilators nitric oxide (NO) and prostacyclin. By requiring only acute signaling, a vasoregulatory outcome can be stopped quickly or reversed if the mechanical environment changes. Therefore, it is not necessary for the cells to undergo major restructuring in response to reversible acute mechanical events. On the other hand, if the new mechanical environment is sustained, transcriptional, posttranscriptional, and posttranslational events cause an appropriate functional and/or structural reorganization that may be considered an adaptive response. For example, the alignment of endothelial cells in the direction of flow is a usual outcome of exposure to directional flow (25, 60).

Between these acute and chronic responses are many interacting components. Two transcription factor families that are present in the cytoplasm of most cells, including endothelium, are *Rel*-related nuclear factor kappa B (NFκB) and nuclear factor activator protein-1 (AP1). Both are stimulated by shear stress (49), and NFκB p50-p65 complex binds to a recently described shear stress response element (SSRE) identified as a consensus sequence found in several flow-responsive genes (68, 69). It has recently become apparent that there are multiple interactive SSREs in the endothelium. Shyy et al (77, 78) have shown that flow-induced expression of the endothelial early response gene, monocyte chemoattractant protein-1 (MCP-1), is regulated through shear stress–sensitive *cis*-acting sequences in the 5′ promoter. A phorbol ester response element that binds the transcription factor AP1 was found to be essential for shear responses. Furthermore, recent studies of gap junction connexin gene expression in cultured endothelial cells subjected to flow demonstrate upregulation of connexin 43 mRNA despite the absence of known SSREs in the connexin gene (DC Polacek et al, manuscript submitted). These experiments suggest that multiple *cis* response elements are involved in shear stress–induced gene regulation. By defining the temporal and spatial framework within which the bioresponses occur, a better understanding of the multiple interactions should follow.

There are four major areas currently under investigation within the general pathways of flow-mediated mechanotransduction. The first is to address the question: How is a mechanical force converted by the endothelium into an initial response? The second is to elucidate the pathways leading to rapid release of NO and other vasodilators and to determine if these initial pathways are also common to other downstream responses, particularly gene regulation. Studies of transcription factors activated by shear stress and their interactions with DNA of (mechanoresponsive) genes in the nucleus constitute the third research focus. The fourth area is the study of alterations of cell structure, particularly those involving the cytoskeleton. Following initial signaling, it is likely that these areas overlap and interact extensively, and cellular adaptation to flow, a slow process, may influence initial signaling. However, spatial relationships are currently most accessible for investigation of the first and fourth of these areas, the initial cell response and the cytoskeleton.

## IMAGING THE LUMINAL ENDOTHELIAL SURFACE

When hemodynamic shear stress acts at the endothelial cell surface, the stress distribution at the surface and throughout the cell is determined by the three-dimensional shape of the luminal surface (Figure 2). Most studies have assumed the shear stresses to be those calculated for a smooth surface without reference to the individual cell topography. However, each cell responds to the forces acting locally at its surface. Thus characterization of flow forces on a cellular

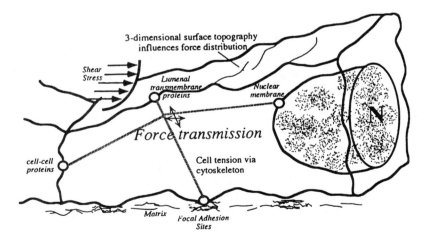

*Figure 2*   Schematic of an endothelial cell illustrating the importance of spatial considerations in relation to hemodynamic shear stress. The three-dimensional surface geometry determines stress concentratins at the cell surface that are transferred to the interior of the cell via the cytoskeleton. N, nucleus.

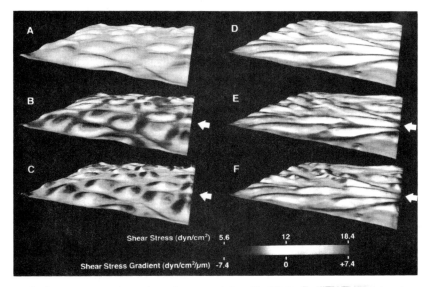

*Figure 3*    AFM images of part of a confluent monolayer of bovine aortic endothelial cells in culture. Panels *A, D*: Surface geometry before and after alignment with flow. Panels *B, E*: Three-dimensional distribution of shear stress over the luminal endothelial surface calculated by finite element analysis (bulk fluid shear stress 12 dyn/cm²). Panels *C, F*: Distribution of stress concentrations (shear stress gradients) at the luminal surface. (From Reference 6, reprinted with permission.)

scale, requiring detailed cell surface geometry, is essential. In a theoretical study of flow over a sinusoidal undulating surface simulating the endothelium, Satcher et al (73) demonstrated variations in shear stress over the model cell surface that were strongly dependent on the surface geometry. The model was extended to living cells in near real-time by Barbee et al (5, 6) using atomic force microscopy (AFM) to map out the real surface geometry. In the absence of flow, bovine aortic endothelial cells in confluent cultures were polygonal in shape with quite smooth surfaces. Boundaries between cells were visible and the average differential from the highest point of the cells (over the nuclear region) to the lowest point at junctions between cells was several μm (Figure 3*A*). After monolayers had been subjected to directional flow for 24 h, the cells aligned with the flow and AFM measurements were repeated. There was a small decrease in the average range of surface heights compared with control cells, but a significant decrease in the amplitude of surface undulations i.e. streamlining of the cells. An 11° average slope in control cells was reduced to an 8° incline in the flow-aligned cells with significant implications for the distribution of stresses.

## Stress Concentrations Determined by Surface Geometry

The AFM geometric data provided $\approx 10^5$ x, y, and z coordinates for each cell. By analyzing AFM data from a representative region of the confluent monolayer in a computer simulation of flow, the distribution of shear stress on a cell-by-cell basis was calculated using the computational fluid dynamics program NEKTON (6). As shown in Figures 3B and C, in which gray scales representing shear stress and shear stress gradients, respectively, in the flow direction were superimposed on the cell contours, it can be seen that the stress distribution is determined by the topographic undulations. This is true for both control cells and those aligned by flow. The average peak stress per cell was reduced in the aligned monolayers as was the peak shear stress gradient per cell. The relative areas exposed to extremes of both shear stress and shear stress gradient were smaller in aligned cells compared with non-aligned cells.

## Heterogeneity of Endothelial Flow Responses

A prominent feature of Figure 3, particularly in aligned cells, is the display of cell-to-cell differences in stress concentrations that arise from the heterogeneity of topography. The large variations in stress concentrations between neighboring cells may help explain the frequently observed differential endothelial responses to flow observed both in vivo and in vitro. Examples include the expression of VCAM-1 protein in vivo (84) and in vitro (63), VCAM-1 mRNA in vivo (56), ICAM-1 protein expression in vivo (84) and in vitro (58), elevation of intracellular calcium ($[Ca^{2+}]_i$) measured in vitro (34, 76) and in vivo (27), induction of synthesis and nuclear relocalization of c-fos protein in vitro (67), expression of major histocompatibility complex (MHC) antigens in vitro (55), inhibition of endothelial cell division in vitro (88), and relocalization of the Golgi apparatus and microtubule-organizing center (MTOC) in vitro (16). In each of these cases, high levels of response in one or a group of cells is accompanied by absent or diminished responses in adjacent cells of the same endothelial monolayer despite exposure to an identical flow field in vitro or location in a predicted uniform hemodynamic environment in vivo. Because the responses are specifically flow-related, very local regulatory mechanisms must be responsible for the differences. A plausible explanation is the heterogeneous topography that exists in the monolayer. The sensitivity of a cell may be determined by the fraction of cell surface exposed to stress concentrations above a critical threshold (20).

## Critical Factors in the Location of Flow Sensors

A similar argument can be made for individual flow sensors. In addition to cell-to-cell variations in stress distribution, variations in hemodynamic forces on a subcellular scale may also be important. Because the force distribution

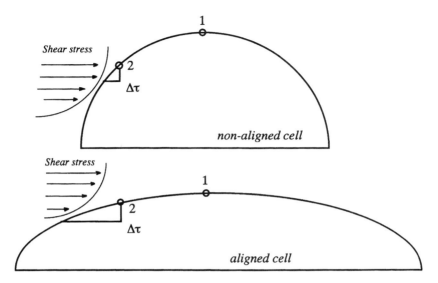

*Figure 4*  Proposed influence of endothelial surface topography upon the sensitivity of putative mechanosensors (*open circle*) at the lumenal cell surface following cell alignment by shear stress. At position 1, the shear stresses and stress gradients are similar, but at position 2, the stress concentration ($\Delta\tau$) is markedly reduced in the aligned cell. Cell responses may depend on both the distribution of mechanosensors (or surface elements linked to them) and the altered topography.

is spatially variable, the precise location of any primary flow sensor at the luminal endothelial surface is relevant to that particular cell's ability to respond. As shown simplistically in Figure 4, if there is a limited number of flow sensors at the luminal surface, those grouped at position 1 will be exposed to virtually identical (maximal) stress concentration whether aligned or not. If, however, sensors are located where the subcellular geometries in the two cell configurations are very different (position 2), the stress concentrations in one configuration may be above or below an activation threshold. The concept can be extended to any model of localized mechanical sensitivity involving a modest number of flow sensors per cell; e.g. flow-sensitive transmembrane proteins linked to the intracellular cytoskeleton that concentrate the stresses into and throughout the cell body (85). Thus varying surface geometries in a flow environment can directly influence cell tension (43, 44).

## Endothelial Surface Geometry Is Similar In Vitro and In Situ

To explore the relevance of in vitro measurements of cell topography to in vivo geometry, the endothelium of a rabbit aorta was imaged by AFM (20). At present, a limitation of this approach is the variable waviness of underlying arterial wall structures that often exceeds the range of vertical movement of the AFM stylus. This results in reliable imaging of only relatively small regions of the arterial surface; however, although limited in area, accurate detailed topographic data was recorded. An AFM image obtained from the abdominal aorta is shown in Figure 5 (*top panel*). The luminal surfaces of five cells are visible aligned in the direction of flow. They were of a size and shape that resembled those of cells aligned by flow in vitro. A comparison of selected longitudinal height profiles (*lower panels*) demonstrates the similarity of both the general shape of the profile (e.g. height-to-length ratio) and the relative smoothness of the surface in both in vivo and in vitro images (20). These images are the first detailed measurements of endothelial surface geometry in living arteries. They strongly suggest that the surface contours of endothelial cells maintained in culture are very similar to those observed in situ, a finding that supports the validity in vivo of conclusions derived from in vitro measurements of cell surface geometry.

## LOCATION OF FLOW-SENSITIVE K$^+$ CHANNELS

An important early endothelial response to shear stress, now known to be entirely or partly localized to the luminal membrane, is activation of inwardly rectifying K$^+$ (IRK) channels, first identified by Olesen et al (65). When flow was imposed, a membrane current developed as a function of shear stress with half-maximal activation at 0.7 dyn/cm$^2$. Channel activity reached a plateau near 20 dyn/cm$^2$. On the basis of ion selectivity and reversal potential, the current was identified as an inwardly rectifying K$^+$ current and was designated $I_{KS}$. The current was rapidly activated in response to flow, only slowly desensitized (minutes), and was inactivated when flow was stopped. Neither atrial myocytes nor vascular smooth muscle cells expressed $I_{KS}$. Subsequent studies of single IRK channel recordings in cell-attached patches (46) demonstrated flow-associated hyperpolarization and activation of large inward and small outward whole-cell currents, consistent with the previous whole-cell recordings and confirming localization to the luminal cell surface. The absence of large conductance single channel currents and insensitivity to charybdotoxin suggested that maxi-K channels did not contribute to flow responses. The open state probability of individual IRK channels was increased within minutes of exposure to shear stress, reflecting a delayed opening and closing response when compared with shear stress-activated whole cell currents. Considering that the recordings were made from patches that were not directly exposed to the shear stress (being protected by the micropipette), the findings suggest that the channel is activated secondarily to other signaling events initiated by shear stress elsewhere on the cell surface and transmitted to the channels in the micropipette.

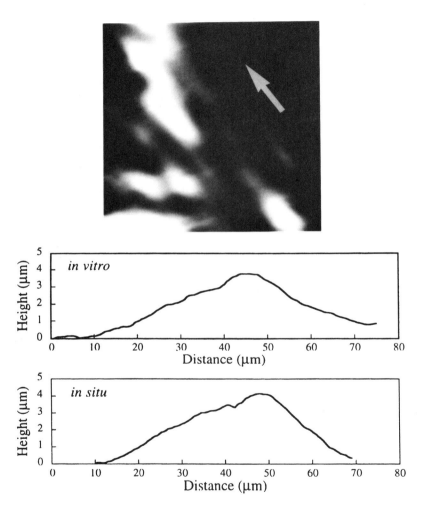

*Figure 5    Upper panel.* AFM raw image of the endothelium of rabbit aorta in situ. Cells are aligned with the longitudinal axis of the vessel in a straight segment with no branches. *Lower panels.* Longitudinal sections of a representative cell from an aligned culture (in vitro) and from rabbit aortic endothelium (in situ). The sections are similar in height-to-length ratio and in the shape of the profile. (Reprinted from Reference 20, with permission.)

This could occur by a dependence upon membrane hyperpolarization effected by IRK channels outside of the patch, or by mechanical (cytoskeletal) or chemical (e.g. G proteins, calcium) linking to primary mechanosensors elsewhere. Some evidence for a link to calcium was obtained by the finding that the open probability of endothelial IRK channels in inside-out patches excised from the cell surface was increased twofold by exposure to micromolar concentrations of calcium (46). Because these studies were limited to the luminal membrane, they confirm the existence of flow-sensitive IRK channels only at that site. It remains unclear, however, whether the channels themselves are flow sensors; the delayed IRK responses in patches may occur by activation secondary to an upstream sensor.

These studies are consistent with measurements of unidirectional $Rb^+$ efflux from endothelium that confirm a shear stress-dependent plasma membrane permeability to $K^+$ (2), and recordings of endothelial hyperpolarization during flow using potentiometric dyes (59). Cooke and colleagues (17, 62) used pharmacologic inhibitors to demonstrate the association of flow-sensitive endothelial $K^+$ channel activity with the release of an endogenous nitrovasodilator in arterial rings. They have also provided circumstantial evidence that activation of a $K^+$ channel is associated with G-protein coupling and the elevation of endothelial cGMP. Although voltage-gated calcium channels are not present in cultured endothelial cells (1, 64, 80), hyperpolarization can lead to increased calcium influx via a calcium/phosphatidylinositol/hyperpolarization-activated $Ca^{2+}$-permeable channel (51, 52, 64), and hyperpolarization increases the electrochemical gradient for calcium, resulting in calcium influx (39). The opposite effect, depolarization, attenuates cellular functions that rely upon calcium influx, e.g. NO release, vasodilation (14, 52).

Endothelial hyperpolarization as a function of shear stress was also reported using membrane potential–sensitive fluorescent dyes (59). Recent studies (A Barakat & PF Davies, manuscript submitted) using the voltage-sensitive dye bisoxonol have revealed a simultaneous activation by flow of hyperpolarizing and depolarizing responses. A dominant initial hyperpolarization was reversed so that the cell reached a net depolarized state after several minutes. If IRK channels were blocked with barium or cesium, immediate depolarization was recorded. Depolarization was blocked by chloride current inhibitors, suggesting the involvement of flow-sensitive chloride channels. When chloride channels were inhibited, a prolonged hyperpolarization resulted.

Olesen & Bundgaard (64) have demonstrated that an inwardly rectifying $K^+$ channel in bovine aortic endothelial cells requires phosphorylation in order to remain open. Inside-out patches required administration of ATP to the cytosolic side in order to maintain ion channel activity. These findings suggest that a prominent inwardly rectifying $K^+$ channel in endothelial cells has some similar characteristics to the rat kidney channel cloned by Ho et al (40) and for which a putative ATP-binding site implicated in phosphorylation was identified. Evidence that flow-activated $K^+$ channels may operate independently of chemically sensitive $K^+$ channels has recently been published (41).

Attempts to clone endothelial $K^+$ channels on the basis of structural homology to channels identified in other tissues have met with limited success. However, a IRK channel has recently been cloned from human umbilical vein endothelium that contains two transmembrane-spanning regions flanking a pore region and an extraordinarily long extracellular loop. The channel has been designated endothelial IRK (E-IRK; MV Volin et al, manuscript submitted). E-IRK mRNA is expressed strongly in Northern blots of cultured endothelial, but not smooth muscle cells, and exclusively in endothelial cells of rabbit arterial tissue probed by in situ hybridization. E-IRK is the first $K^+$ channel cloned from endothelial cells (subfamily KIR 2.3); further studies will determine if it is flow sensitive (see note added in proof).

## IMAGING THE ABLUMINAL ENDOTHELIAL SURFACE ADHESION SITES

### Focal Adhesion Dynamics

Whatever the stress distribution induced by flow on the luminal endothelial surface, resistance to cell detachment and rolling is localized to adhesion sites on the abluminal surface. We propose that some aspects of flow-mediated signaling in the endothelium could be located at adhesion sites, the stress forces being transferred across the cell body through the cytoskeleton (19, 21–23, 25). All anchorage-dependent cells, including the endothelial lining of blood vessels, attach to the extracellular matrix at specialized regions called focal adhesion sites (12, 45, 79). In both in vivo and in vitro at such sites, the extracellular domains of integral membrane proteins bind to adhesion proteins of the matrix or substratum. In vitro, the separation distances between a protein-coated glass surface and the cell approaches 10–15 nm, allowing imaging of the adhesion sites by interference reflection microscopy (IRM) made possible by differences in refractive index of the components (36). Following initial observations of cell-substratum adhesion sites in Swiss 3T3 cells by tandem scanning confocal microscopy (TSCM), the dynamic nature of these sites in living endothelial cells was demonstrated using TSCM, digital image processing, and three-dimensional image reconstruction (22, 23) (Figure 6). In the raw image, TSCM combines IRM principles with confocal optical sectioning capability. In an unperturbed confluent monolayer of endothelial cells adherent to a glass substratum coated with adhesion proteins, focal adhesion remodeling

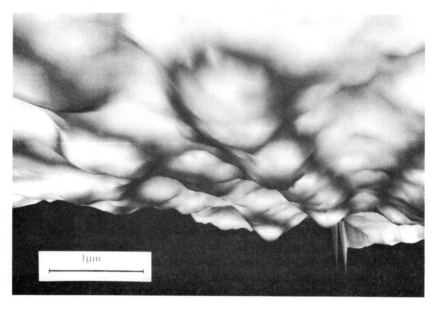

*Figure 6*    Endothelial abluminal cell surface geometry observed in real-time by tandem scanning confocal microscopy after image processing and computer enhancement. Reconstructed three-dimensional image of the abluminal surface of a living endothelial cell. The substratum has been removed from the image to expose the surface topography. Membrane projections represent focal adhesion sites where the cell is attached to the underlying (invisible) extracellular matrix.

occurred in a random fashion without any preferred orientation (21). Adhesion sites occasionally disappeared, sometimes in less than 1 min; in other cases, the area of contact remained constant but changed considerably in shape and size. The appearance of new sites was observed where contact had not previously existed between the cell and the adhesion proteins. Throughout these adhesion dynamics, the shape of individual cells in the monolayer remained unchanged, the overall effect being that of stationary cells constantly probing and reprobing the substratum. Observations during directional flow showed complex changes of focal adhesion site dynamics, the net effect of which was site remodeling related to the direction of the luminal shear stress (22).

Recently, quantitative analyses of site orientation and alignment during flow have been performed by expanding the use of the Fourier transform to quantify the complex nature of the changes in endothelial adhesion sites during continuous exposure to flow forces (M Wernick et al, manuscript submitted). Two-dimensional directional remodeling of adhesions in cells exposed to flow was analyzed for changes in the principal axis of alignment, $\theta$, and the degree of

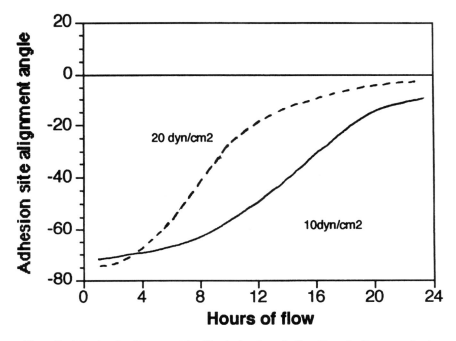

*Figure 7* Adhesion site alignment at the abluminal surface of cells subjected to flow at two levels. Adhesion sites moved toward alignment (zero value) more quickly in a shear stress field of 20 dyn/cm$^2$ than at 10 dyn/cm$^2$.

alignment (eccentricity), *e*. Quantitation was obtained by principal component analysis of the magnitude of the discrete Fourier transform of each image. The analyses revealed that adhesion site remodeling was progressively directional during flow, that the rates of site realignment and eccentricity ($d\theta/dt$ and $de/dt$) were related to the magnitude of the shear stress (Figure 7) and the composition of the extracellular matrix, and that changes of *e* could proceed at a markedly different rate than $\theta$. These real-time, live cell measurements confirm that adhesion site remodeling is part of the coordinated responses of endothelium to changes of cell tension, a finding consistent with the overall hypothesis that mechanical tension mediates cell function (41, 42).

## Biochemical Signaling at Adhesion Sites

At focal adhesion sites, a series of linker molecules provides direct structural communication between the cytoskeleton and the extracellular matrix through transmembrane proteins of the integrin family (10–12) allowing both inside-out and outside-in signaling between the cell and its matrices (42). The dynamic nature of adhesion sites in endothelial and other anchorage-dependent cells is best explained as a rapid turnover of one or more key structural elements such that the sites constantly rearrange in area and position (19). This is a particularly active mechanism in migrating cells. If adhesion sites are involved in hemodynamic signaling, timing is important because a delayed response may imply that the remodeling is occurring secondary to overall cytoskeletal reorganization, whereas a rapid response may imply a primary signaling role in mechanotransduction. The TSCM studies demonstrated directional remodeling of adhesion sites with variable time constants ranging from almost immediate responses to significant delays.

Potential flow-signaling molecules localized to focal adhesion sites include tyrosine, threonine, and serine kinases. The phosphorylation levels of intracellular proteins associated with adhesion sites, which are implicated in integrin-mediated cell adhesion, have been studied in endothelial cells subjected to flow. Anti-phosphotyrosine Western blots of abstracts of confluent endothelial cells demonstrated two prominent groups of protein at 120–130 kDa and 65–75 kDa that were identified as the proteins focal adhesion kinese (FAK) and paxillin, respectively. Both proteins were shown to be associated with endothelial focal adhesion sites by immunfluorescence. When compared with no-flow control endothelial monolayers, phosphorylation of paxillin in bovine aortic endothelial cells increased several-fold within 2 h of exposure to unidirectional laminar flow (12 dyn/cm$^2$ shear stress), whereas in contrast, FAK phosphorylation remained within 20% of control levels (Figure 8). This was confirmed in Western blots of immunoprecipitated FAK and paxillin. The enhanced tyrosine phosphorylation of paxillin was preceded by a 50% decrease during the first minute, suggesting enhanced phosphatase activity. Measurements of FAK enzyme activity during flow revealed no changes. However, in human umbilical vein endothelial cells, Berk et al (B Berk, personal communication) have observed enhanced FAK tyrosine phosphorylation several minutes after initiation of flow without significant changes in paxillin phosphorylation levels. Although these data are preliminary, they suggest that protein kinase activity at adhesion sites may be involved in the hemodynamic response of endothelial cells to shear stress.

## FLOW-SENSITIVE SIGNALING PATHWAYS FOR NITRIC OXIDE AND OTHER ACUTE VASOREGULATORS

The mechanism(s) of flow induced NO-mediated vasodilation are likely regulated by endothelial nitric oxide synthase (eNOS) activity. The enzyme is constitutively expressed at a basal level and its activity appears to be calcium/calmodulin-dependent (29, 50). Protoporphyrin IX, FAD, FMN, and tetrahydrobiopterin (74) are required cofactors (75). A unique feature of eNOS is

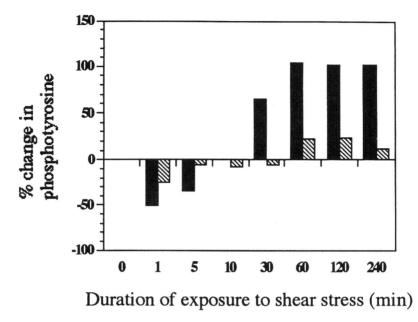

*Figure 8* Tyrosine phosphorylation of focal adhesion kinase (FAK; *hatched bars*) and paxillin (*solid bars*) in confluent endothelial cells subjected to unidirectional flow (shear stress = 12 dyn/cm$^2$).

a myristoylation site of unknown function at the N-terminus (54, 61, 73, 75) that may anchor it to the plasma membrane and in some way be involved in shear-activation of eNOS. The enzyme is subject to feedback regulation by NO (71). Flow activation of eNOS appears to involve increase of intracellular calcium. However, the mechanisms of shear stress transduction are unclear because of the large number of regulatory possibilities associated with the co-factors for activation of this enzyme, the presence of common transcription factor–binding sites in the 5'-flanking region, and the availability of recently identified phosphorylation sites that may be regulatory (74; see below).

eNOS mRNA and protein expression is significantly increased following ex-posure to shear stress in laminar flow (60, 82). The increase was prevented by inhibition of protein synthesis and was independent of PKC activation or inhi-bition. A potassium channel antagonist, tetraethyl ammonium chloride (TEA), blocked the response, suggesting some relationship with potassium channels. An inhibitor of microtubule polymerization, nocadozole, also abolished the flow-related eNOS effect. eNOS expression is sensitive to different flow char-acteristics at a fixed mean shear stress, i.e. enhanced expression follows step changes in flow. eNOS expression in vivo correlates well with situations of increased or decreased flow (47).

eNOS, in common with other NOSs, contains consensus sequences for phosphorylation by protein kinases A and C, and calmodulin kinase II (74). Rapidly increased phosphorylation of serine or threonine residues upon exposure to shear stress has been reported (18). In addition, there is a calcium/calmodulin-independent mechanism of activation of eNOS (66, 81). In cultured endothelium, flow-induced NO release is biphasic, with an initial rapid rise at the onset of flow followed by slow development of a sustained increased level of production (7). The initial peak NO release is $Ca^{2+}$ dependent but independent of shear stress magnitude. In contrast, the sustained phase is $Ca^{2+}$ independent but dependent on shear stress magnitude. Flow appears to stimulate $Ca^{2+}$-dependent NO release in periodic bursts at approximately 15 min intervals, whereas the $Ca^{2+}$-independent NO release is continuous and sustained. Recently, Ayajiki et al (4) reported that the $Ca^{2+}$-dependent phase may be an in vitro artifact. In excised segments of rabbit iliac artery, they at first found both $Ca^{2+}$-dependent and $Ca^{2+}$-independent responses to be similar to those noted in vitro. However, when the arterial segments were restored to their in vivo lengths, the $Ca^{2+}$-dependent phase was abolished and their data suggest that NO production proceeds principally through a $Ca^{2+}$-independent mechanism in vivo. If this is true, then the focus of eNOS control shifts toward other pathways. A prominent candidate pathway is the phosphorylation of mitogen-activated protein (MAP) kinases (81). MAP kineses are activated independently of $Ca^{2+}$. Activation is inhibited by interference with the activity of protein kinase C. A link to upstream G protein signaling was provided by the demonstration that MAP kinase activation is preventable by exposing the cells to nonhydrolyzable GDP analogues. In vivo, inhibition of protein tyrosine kinase by herbimycin abolishes flow-dependent NO release in intact arteries (4). All these studies suggest that tyrosine phosphorylation is required for the activation of eNOS but the spatial relationships remain unclear.

# THE ENDOTHELIAL CYTOSKELETON IN FLOW SIGNALING

## Stress Transmission

Cells rely upon a combination of structural and chemical elements for normal function; the two are closely intertwined. For example, cell shape determined by the cytoskeleton mediates cell growth and differentiation (42). The cytoskeleton determines the shape of anchorage-dependent cells and physically connects many cell components thereby generating cell tension. When endothelial cells are subjected to flow, the cytoskeletal tension is likely to change. This has not been directly measured (although it is now feasible), but is supported by a number of experiments.

Change in cell shape and cytoskeletal distribution was one of the earliest observations in cultured endothelium subjected to directional flow, resulting in cell alignment (24, 60). The reorganization of adhesion sites during flow is best explained by transfer of stress across the cell from the luminal to abluminal surfaces. At the luminal surface, Wang et al (85) have demonstrated the transfer of twisting forces across the luminal endothelial membrane via transmembrane integrins, resisted by cytoskeletal components. At adhesion sites on the abluminal surface, cytoskeletal elements are linked to integrins that bind extracellular adhesion proteins (11). Thus there is continuity of structural elements across the cell that are involved in mechanotransduction.

The cytoskeleton might be considered to be involved in shear stress mechanotransduction at every level. It determines cell geometry including the luminal topography. It maintains cell tension at (a) adhesion sites, critical locations regulating many aspects of cell function; (b) cell junctions, which regulate contact inhibition of endothelial growth and cell-cell communication; and (c) the nuclear membrane, which may be physically important for gene regulation. It interacts with biochemical pathways throughout the cell including those regulating its own turnover, and it is implicated in mechanosensitive ion channel activation (72). The three principal cytoskeletal groups of proteins—actin microfilaments, intermediate filaments, and microtubules—participate in poorly understood ways in flow-mediated mechanotransduction.

Actin has been most widely studied (24, 31, 38, 86). Microfilament reorganization in flow results in the assembly of bundles oriented in the direction of flow (38), possibly associated with new actin synthesis (31). Changes in actin distribution are detectable within minutes of the onset of flow (PF Davies, unpublished observations) and are probably faster, observations being limited only by technical constraints.

Endothelial intermediate filaments have recently been shown to respond to flow (28). The cells contain a dense, vimentin-containing intermediate filament network that extends throughout the cytoplasm and provides mechanical continuity between luminal and abluminal surfaces and the nucleus. Within 2 h of flow, the network loses some continuity and short discontinuous strands and globular foci of vimentin are present in many cases. With continued flow, this intermediate state resolved to a reorganized, less dense network aligned with the long axis of the cell (and flow direction). Two additional findings in this study were the association of intermediate filaments with focal adhesion sites and the rapid redistribution of an intermediate filament-binding protein. The latter may also associate with adhesion sites and be a link to actin filaments and other proteins located there (FW Flitney et al, unpublished studies).

Microtubules have not been extensively studied in mechanotransduction research. Recently, however, Malek & Izumo (53) have shown that microtubule disruption by nocodazole blocked cell alignment by flow and the induction of actin stress fibers. They extended these findings to show that cell shape change was dependent on tyrosine kinase activity and intracellular calcium concentration, although the precise link to the cytoskeleton was not identified. Cell alignment was not dependent on intermediate filaments.

## Three-Dimensional Imaging

Progress in understanding the role of the cytoskeleton in mechanotransduction is enhanced by direct observation of the spatial relationships within living endothelial cells, an approach applied to surfaces by AFM and TSCM techniques, as described above. Improvements in laser confocal microscopy and greater computational power applied to conventional fluorescence microscope images promises to revolutionize real-time visualization of spatial elements (15). Deconvolution of stacked images obtained by optical sectioning of individual cells removes out-of-focus information. Extension of these approaches to living cells looks promising with the introduction of green fluorescent protein gene constructs that provide endogenous fluorescence to the cytoskeleton.

## FLOW-MEDIATED CHEMICAL SIGNALING

The spatial relationships discussed throughout this review are most relevant to shear stress forces that result in displacement of specific localized membrane sensors and/or multiple connected components extending throughout the cell. However, labile chemicals at the cell surface may activate endothelial flow responses independently of physical displacement of the cell (reviewed in 19). Thus when high local concentrations of labile agonists are released close to the endothelial surface, the probability of interaction with endothelial receptors is greatly influenced by flow; increased flow improves convective delivery to the receptors, whereas decreased flow slows convection. When the removal rate exceeds convective and diffusive delivery rates from the bulk fluid, a steep concentration gradient exists between the fluid and the cell surface, and this in turn will be influenced by the flow characteristics. It appears that flow-mediated chemical responses and shear stress displacement responses may occur independently of each other. When shear stress was greatly increased by changing the fluid viscosity, with only small changes in mass transport, flow-mediated relaxation of intact arteries was enhanced, indicating that the physical force was the principal effector (48, 57). Ando et al (3) have also provided evidence for a direct mechanism of force transduction in evoking $[Ca^{2+}]_i$ responses that is additional to the effects of flow upon mass transport. Thus consideration of the potency of the local chemical environment should be included whenever possible in the interpretation of flow experiments, and the spatial relationships within chemical gradients near the cell surface can become a complex factor in flow-mediated cellular responses. Both physical displacement of the cell and chemical concentrations may interact to evoke a mechano-chemical transduction response.

ACKNOWLEDGMENTS

This work is supported by SCOR grant HL15062 and HL36049 MERIT Award (PFD) from the National Heart Lung and Blood Institute of the National Institute of Health, and Grant-in-Aid 91-1557 from the American Heart Association.

*Literature Cited*

1. Adams DJ, Barakeh J, Laskey R, van Breemen C. 1989. Ion channels and regulation of intracellular calcium in vascular endothelial cells. *FASEB J.* 3:2389–400
2. Alevriadou BR, Eskin SG, McIntire SV, Schilling WP. 1993. Effect of shear stress on $^{86}$Rb$^{+}$ efflux from calf pulmonary artery endothelial cells. *Ann. Biomed. Eng.* 21:1–7
3. Ando J, Ohtsuka A, Korenaga R, Kawamura T, Kamiya A. 1993. Wall shear stress rather than shear rate regulates cytoplasmic Ca$^{2+}$ responses to flow in vascular endothelial cells. *Biochem. Biophys. Res. Commun.* 190:716–23
4. Ayajiki K, Hindermann M, Hecker M, Fleming I, Busse R. 1996. Intracellular pH and tyrosine phosphorylation but not calcium determine shear stress-induced nitric oxide production in native endothelial cells. *Circ. Res.* 78:750–58
5. Barbee KA, Davies PF, Lal R. 1994. Shear stress induced reorganization of the surface topography of living endothelial cells imaged by atomic force microscopy. *Circ. Res.* 74:163–71
6. Barbee KA, Mundel T, Lal R, Davies PF. 1995. Subcellular distribution of shear stress at the surface of flow aligned and non-aligned endothelial monolayers. *Am. J. Physiol.* 268:1765–72
7. Berk BC, Corson MA, Peterson TE, Tseng H. 1995. Protein kinases as mediators of fluid shear stress stimulated signal transduction in endothelial cells: a hypothesis for calcium-independent events activated by flow. *J. Biomech.* 28:1439–50
8. Berthiaume F, Frangos JA. 1992. Flow-induced prostacyclin production is mediated by a pertussis toxin-sensitive G protein. *FEBS Lett.* 308:277–79
9. Bhagyalakshmi A, Berthiaume F, Reich KM, Frangos JA. 1992. Fluid shear stress stimulates membrane phospholipid metabolism in cultured human endothelial cells. *J. Vasc. Res.* 29:443–49
10. Buck C, Horwitz A. 1987. Integrin, a transmembrane glycoprotein complex mediating cell-substratum adhesion. *J. Cell Sci. Suppl.* 8:231–50
11. Burridge K. 1986. Substrate adhesions in normal and transformed fibroblasts: organization and regulation of cytoskeletal, membrane, and extracellular matrix components at focal contacts. *Cancer Res.* 4:18–78
12. Burridge K, Fath K, Kelly T, Nuckolls G, Turner C. 1988. Focal adhesions: transmembrane junctions between the extracellular matrix and the cytoskeleton. *Annu. Rev. Cell Biol.* 4:487–525
13. Caro CG, Fitzgerald JM, Schroter RC. 1969. Arterial wall shear and distribution of early atheroma in man. *Nature* 223:1159–61
14. Chand N, Altura MB. 1981. Acetylcholine and bradykinin relax intrapulmonary arteries by acting on endothelial cells: role in lung vascular disease. *Science* 213:1376–79
15. Chen J, Aarsvold J, Chen CT, Griem ML, Davies PF, et al. 1996. High performance image analysis and visualization for three-dimensional light microscopy. *Proc. IASTED Signal Image Process.* In press
16. Coan DE, Wechezak AR, Viggers RF, Sauvage LR. 1993. Effect of shear stress upon localization of the Golgi apparatus and microtubule organizing center in isolated cultured endothelial cells. *J. Cell Sci.* 104:1145–53
17. Cooke JP, Rossitch E, Andon NA, Loscalzo

J, Dzau V. 1991. Flow activates an endothelial potassium channel to release an endogenous nitrovasodilator. *J. Clin. Invest.* 88:1663–71

18. Corson MA, Berk BC, Navas JP, Harrison DG. 1993. Phosphorylation of endothelial nitric oxide synthase in response to shear stress. *Circulation* 88:1–183 (Abstr.)

19. Davies PF. 1995. Flow-mediated endothelial mechanotransduction. *Physiol. Rev.* 75:519–60

20. Davies PF, Mundel T, Barbee KA. 1995. A mechanism for heterogeneous endothelial responses to flow in vivo and in vitro. *J. Biomech.* 28:1553–60

21. Davies PF, Robotewskyj A, Griem ML. 1993. Endothelial cell adhesion in real-time. Measurements in vitro by tandem scanning confocal image analysis. *J. Clin. Invest.* 91:2640–52

22. Davies PF, Robotewskyj A, Griem ML. 1994. Quantitative studies of endothelial cell adhesion: directional remodeling of focal adhesion sites in response to flow forces. *J. Clin. Invest.* 93:2031–38

23. Davies PF, Tripathi SC. 1993. Mechanical stress mechanisms and the cell. An endothelial paradigm. *Circ. Res.* 72:239–45

24. Dewey CF. 1979. Dynamics of arterial flow. *Adv. Exp. Med. Biol.* 115:55–89

25. Dewey CF Jr, Bussolari SR, Gimbrone MA Jr, Davies PF. 1981. The dynamic response of vascular endothelial cells to fluid shear stress. *J. Biomech. Eng.* 103:177–88

26. Diamond SL, Sharefkin JB, Dieffenbach C, Frazier-Scott K, McIntire LV, Eskin SG. 1990. Tissue plasminogen activator mRNA levels increase in cultured human endothelial cells exposed to laminar shear stress. *J. Cell. Physiol.* 143:364–71

27. Falcone JC, Kuo L, Meininger GA. 1993. Endothelial cell calcium increases during flow-induced dilation in isolated arterioles. *Am. J. Physiol.* 264:H653–59

28. Flitney FW, Goldman RD, Skalli O, Mercurius K, Davies PF. 1996. Dynamic properties of intermediate filaments in cultured endothelial cells: effects of controlled fluid shear stress. In *The Biology of Nitric Oxide*, ed. S Moncada, J Stamler, S Gross, EA Higgs, p. 251. London: Portland

29. Forstermann U, Pollock JS, Schmidt HH, Heller M, Murad F. 1991. Calmodulin-dependent endothelium-derived relaxing factor synthase activity is present in the particulate and cytosolic fractions of bovine aortic endothelial cells. *Proc. Natl. Acad. Sci. USA* 88:1788–92

30. Frangos JA, Eskin SG, McIntire LV, Ives CL. 1985. Flow effects on prostacyclin production by cultured human endothelial cells. *Science* 227:1477–79

31. Franke RP, Grafe M, Schnittler H, Seiffge D, Mittermayer C, Drenckhahn D. 1984. Induction of human vascular endothelial stress fibers by fluid shear stress. *Nature* 307:648–50

32. Fry DL. 1973. Atherogenesis: initiating factors. In *Ciba Found. Symp. 12*, pp. 96–118. London: Ciba Found.

33. Fung YC, Liu SQ. 1993. Elementary mechanics of the endothelium of blood vessels. *J. Biomech. Eng.* 115:1–12

34. Geiger RV, Berk BC, Alexander RW, Nerem RM. 1992. Flow-induced calcium transients in single endothelial cells: spatial and temporal analysis. *Am. J. Physiol.* 262:C1411–17

35. Grabowski EF, Lam FP. 1995. Endothelial cell function, including tissue factor expression, under flow. *Thromb. Hemost.* 74:123–28

36. Heath JP, Dunn GA. 1978. Cell to substratum contacts of chick fibroblasts and their relation to the microfilament system. A correlated interference reflection and high voltage electronmicroscope study. *J. Cell Sci.* 29:197–12

37. Henry PD, Cabello OA, Chen CH. 1995. Hypercholesterolemia and endothelial dysfunction. *Curr. Opin. Lipidol.* 6:190–95

38. Herman IM, Brant AM, Warty VS, Bonaccorso J, Klein EC, et al. 1987. Hemodynamics and the vascular endothelial cytoskeleton. *J. Cell Biol.* 105:291–302

39. Himmel HM, Whorton AR, Strauss HC. 1993. Intracellular calcium, current, and stimulus-response coupling in endothelial cells. *Hypertension* 21:112–27

40. Ho K, Nichols CG, Lederer WJ, Lytton J, Vassilev PM, et al. 1993. Cloning and expression of an inwardly rectifying ATP-regulated potassium channel. *Nature* 362:31–38

41. Hutcheson IR, Griffith TM. 1994. Heterogeneous populations of K$^+$ channels mediate EDRF release to flow but not agonists in rabbit aorta. *Am. J. Physiol.* 266:H590–96

42. Hynes RO. 1992. Integrins: versatility, modulation, and signalling and cell adhesion. *Cell* 69:11–25

43. Ingber D. 1991. Integrins as mechanochemical transducers. *Curr. Opin. Cell Biol.* 3:841–48

44. Ingber DE, Jamieson JD. 1985. Cells as tensegrity structures: architectural regulation of histodifferentiation by physical forces transduced over basement membrane. In *Gene Expression During Normal and Malignant Differentiation*, ed. LC Andersson, CG Gahmberg, P Ekblom, pp. 13–32. Orlando FL: Academic

45. Izzard CS, Lochner LR. 1980. Formation of cell-to-substrate contacts during fibroblast motility: an interference-reflexion study. *J. Cell Sci.* 42:81–116

46. Jacobs ER, Cheliakine C, Gebremedhin D, Birks EK, Davies PF, Harder DR. 1995. Shear activated channels in cell-attached patches of cultured bovine aortic endothelial cells. *Pflügers Arch.* 431:129–31

47. Kaiser L, Spickard RC, Oliver NB. 1989. Heart failure depresses endothelium dependent responses in canine femoral artery. *Am. J. Physiol.* 259:H962–67

48. Koller A, Sun D, Kaley G. 1993. Role of shear stress and endothelial prostaglandins in flow- and viscosity-induced dilation of arterioles in vivo. *Circ. Res.* 72:1276–84

49. Lan QX, Mercurius KO, Davies PF. 1994. Stimulation of transcription factors NF-$\kappa$-B and AP1 in endothelial-cells subjected to shear-stress. *Biochem. Biophys. Res. Commun.* 201:950–56

50. Lopez-Jaramillo P, Gonzalez MC, Palmer RM, Moncada S. 1990. The crucial role of physiological calcium concentrations in the production of endothelial nitric oxide and the control of vascular tone. *Br. J. Pharmacol.* 101:489–93

51. Luckoff A, Busse R. 1990. Calcium influx into endothelial cells and formation of endothelium derived relaxing factor is controlled by the membrane potential. *Pflügers Arch.* 416:305–11

52. Luckhoff A, Clapham DE. 1992. Inositol 1, 3, 4,5-tetrakisphosphate activates an endothelial $Ca^{2+}$-permeable channel. *Nature* 355:356–58

53. Malek AM, Izumo S. 1996. Mechanism of endothelial cell shape change and cytoskeletal remodeling in response to fluid shear stress. *J. Cell Sci.* 109:713–26

54. Marsden PA, Heng HH, Scherer SW, Stewart RJ, Hall AV, Shi XM, et al. 1993. Structure and chromosomal localization of the human constitutive endothelial nitric oxide synthase. *J. Biol. Chem.* 268:17478–88

55. Martin-Mondiere CF, Caprani A, Desgranges PC, Loisance DY, Charron DJ. 1989. Shear stress affects expression of major histocompatibility complex antigens on human endothelial cells. *ASAIO Trans.* 35:288–90

56. McKinsey J, DePaola N, Cybulsky M, Davies PF, Polacek D. 1995. Increased venous endothelial VCAM-1 expression in disturbed flow regions associated with arteriovenous fistula in normal and hypercholesterolemic rabbits. *FASEB J.* 9:A343 (Abstr.)

57. Melkumyants AM, Balashov SA, Khayutin VM. 1989. Endothelium dependent control of arterial dismeter by blood viscosity. *Cardiovasc. Res.* 23:741–47

58. Nagel T, Resnick N, Atkinson WJ, Dewey CF Jr, Gimbrone MA Jr. 1994. Shear stress selectively up regulates ICAM-1 expression in cultured human vascular endothelial cells. *J. Clin. Invest.* 94:885–91

59. Nakache M, Gaub HE. 1988. Hydrodynamic hyperpolarization of endothelial cells. *Proc. Natl. Acad. Sci. USA* 85:1841–43

60. Nerem RM, Levesque MJ, Cornhill JF. 1981. Vascular endothelial morphology as an indicator of the pattern of blood flow. *J. Biomech. Eng.* 103:172–77

61. Nishida K, Harrison DG, Navas JP, Fisher AA, Dockery SP, et al. 1992. Molecular cloning and characterization of the constitutive bovine aortic endothelial cell nitric oxide synthase. *J. Clin. Invest.* 90:2092–96

62. Ohno M, Gibbons GH, Dzau V, Cooke JP. 1993. Shear stress elevates endothelial cGMP. Role of a potassium channel and G-protein coupling. *Circulation* 88:193–97

63. Ohtsuka A, Ando J, Korenaga R, Kamiya A, Toyama-Sorimaci N, Miyasaka M. 1993. The effect of flow on the expression of vascular adhesion molecule-1 by cultured mouse endothelial cells. *Biochem. Biophys. Res. Commun.* 193:303–10

64. Olesen SP, Bundgaard M. 1993. ATP-dependent closure and reactivation of inward rectifier $K^+$ channels in endothelial cells. *Circ. Res.* 73:492–95

65. Olesen SP, Clapham DE, Davies PF. 1988. Hemodynamic shear stress activates a $K^+$ current in vascular endothelial cells. *Nature* 331:168–70

66. Perry PB, O'Neill WC. 1993. Flow stimulates nitric oxide synthesis in endothelial cells through a calcium-independent mechanism. *Circulation* 88:1–134 (Abstr.)

67. Ranjan V, Diamond SL. 1993. Fluid shear stress induces synthesis and nuclear localization of c-*fos* in cultured human endothelial cells. *Biochem. Biophys. Res. Commun.* 196:79–84

68. Resnick N, Collins T, Atkinson W, Bonthron DT, Dewey CF Jr, Gimbrone MA Jr. 1993. Platelet-derived growth factor-B chain promoter contains a *cis*-acting fluid shear-stress-responsive element. *Proc. Natl. Acad. Sci. USA* 90:4591–95

69. Resnick N, Gimbrone MA Jr. 1995. Hemodynamic forces are complex regulators of endothelial gene expression. *FASEB J.* 9:874–82

70. Rodbard S. 1970. Negative feedback mechanisms in the architecture and function of the connective and cardiovascular tissues. *Perspect. Biol. Med.* 13:507–27
71. Rogers NE, Ignarro LJ. 1992. Constitutive nitric oxide synthase from cerebellum is reversibly inhibited by nitric oxide formed from L-arginine. *Biochem. Biophys. Res. Commun.* 189:242–49
72. Sachs F. 1988. Mechanical transduction in biological systems. *CRC Crit. Rev. Biomed. Eng.* 16:141–69
73. Satcher RL, Bussolari SR, Gimbrone MA, Dewey CF. 1992. The distribution of fluid forces on model arterial endothelium using computational fluid dynamics. *J. Biomech. Eng.* 114:309–16
74. Sessa WC. 1994. The nitric oxide synthase family of proteins. *J. Vasc. Res.* 31:131–43
75. Sessa WC, Pritchard K, Seyedi N, Wang J, Hintze TH. 1994. Chronic exercise increases coronary vascular nitric oxide production and endothelial cell nitric oxide synthase gene expression. *Circ. Res.* 74:349–53
76. Shen J, Luscinskas FW, Connolly A, Dewey CF Jr, Gimbrone MA Jr. 1992. Fluid shear stress modulates cytosolic free calcium in vascular endothelial cells. *Am. J. Physiol.* 262:C384–90
77. Shyy YJ, Hsieh HJ, Usami S, Chien S. 1994. Fluid shear stress induces a biphasic response of human monocyte chemotactic protein-1 gene expression in vascular endothelium. *Proc. Natl. Acad. Sci. USA* 90:4678–82
78. Shyy YJ, Li YS, Lin MC, Chen W, Yuan S, et al. 1995. Multiple *cis* elements mediate shear stress-induced gene expression. *J. Biomech.* 28:1451–57

79. Stehbens WE. 1966. The basal attachment of endothelial cells. *J. Ultrastruct. Res.* 15:388–400
80. Takeda K, Schini V, Stoeckel H. 1987. Voltage-activated potassium, but not calcium currents in cultured bovine aortic endothelial cells. *Pflügers Arch.* 410:385–93
81. Tseng H, Peterson TE, Berk BC. 1995. Fluid shear stress stimulates mitogen-activated protein kinase in endothelial cells. *Circ. Res.* 77:869–78
82. Uematsu M, Navas JP, Nishida K, Ohara Y, Murphy TJ, et al. 1995. Regulation of endothelial cell nitric oxide synthase mRNA expression by shear stress. *Am. J. Physiol.* 269:C1371–78
83. Virchow R. 1860. In *Cellular Pathology as Based Upon Physiological and Pathological Histology.* Transl. F Clance. London: Churchill (From German)
84. Walpola PL, Gotlieb AI, Cybulsky MI, Langille BL. 1995. Expression of ICAM-1 and VCAM-1 and monocyte adherence in arteries exposed to altered shear stress. *Arterioscler. Thromb. Vasc. Biol.* 15:2–10
85. Wang N, Butler JP, Ingber DE. 1993. Mechanotransduction across the cell surface and through the cytoskeleton. *Science* 260:1124–27
86. Wechezak AR, Viggers RF, Sauvage LR. 1985. Fibronectin and F-actin redistribution in cultured endothelial cells exposed to shear stress. *Lab. Invest.* 53:639–47
87. Zarins CK, Zatina MA, Giddens DP, Ku DN, Glagov S. 1987. Shear stress regulation of artery lumen diameter in experimental atherogenesis. *J. Vasc. Surg.* 5:413–20
88. Ziegler T, Nerem RM. 1994. Effect of flow on the process of endothelial cell division. *Arterioscler. Thromb.* 14:636–43

## NOTE ADDED IN PROOF

An additional $K^+$ channel cDNA cloned from endothelial cells has been reported (subfamily KIR 2.1) by Forsyth S, Hoger A, Hoger J. 1996. *FASEB J.* 10:A627 (Abst.)

*Annu. Rev. Physiol. 1997. 59:551–71*

# THE CELLULAR AND MOLECULAR RESPONSE OF CARDIAC MYOCYTES TO MECHANICAL STRESS

*Junichi Sadoshima and Seigo Izumo*

Cardiovascular Research Center, Division of Cardiology, University of Michigan
Medical Center, Ann Arbor, Michigan 48109-0644

KEY WORDS:    stretch, hypertrophy, angiotensin II, signal transduction, mechanoreceptor, cell
swelling

## ABSTRACT

External load plays a critical role in determining muscle mass and its phenotype in
cardiac myocytes. Cardiac myocytes have the ability to sense mechanical stretch
and convert it into intracellular growth signals, which lead to hypertrophy. Mechanical stretch of cardiac myocytes in vitro causes activation of multiple second
messenger systems that are very similar to growth factor-induced cell signaling
systems. Stretch of neonatal rat cardiac myocytes stimulates a rapid secretion
of angiotensin II which, together with other growth factors, mediates stretch-
induced hypertrophic responses in vitro. In this review, various cell signaling
mechanisms initiated by mechanical stress on cardiac myocytes are summarized
with emphasis on potential mechanosensing mechanisms and the relationship
between mechanical loading and the cardiac renin-angiotensin system.

## INTRODUCTION

Although it is well known that mechanical forces have many effects on the
structure and function of cells, little is known as to how mechanical stimuli
are converted into intracellular signals of gene regulation (24, 99). External
load plays a critical role in determining muscle mass and its phenotype in both
cardiac and skeletal muscle in vivo (56). Cultured primary skeletal muscle cells
grown on an elastic substrate have been shown to undergo an increase in protein synthesis in response to static stretch of the substrate (100). Similarly,
stretching adult cardiac myocytes or neonatal myocytes cultured in serum-free

551

media by 10 to 20% above resting length causes an increase in protein synthesis without DNA synthesis (hypertrophy) (38, 52, 74). This response clearly indicates that skeletal muscle cells and cardiac myocytes are able to sense external load in the absence of neuronal and hormonal factors. Mechanical stimuli also cause a rapid change in gene expression (38, 74). Linear stretch of cardiac myocytes in vitro causes transcriptional activation of immediate-early genes followed by an induction of the fetal genes—atrial natriuretic factor (ANF), skeletal $\alpha$-actin, and $\beta$-myosin heavy chain (MHC) (74). The phenotypic feature of stretched myocytes is very similar to that of pressure overload–induced hypertrophy in vivo (28). Analysis of cell signaling mechanisms shows that stretch activates multiple signal transduction pathways, similar to those activated by growth factors (68, 99). Recent evidence indicates that mechanical stretch has a close relationship with autocrine/paracrine growth factors in the heart such as the tissue (cardiac) renin-angiotensin system (4, 78). A question central to our understanding of the mechanism of load-induced hypertrophy is how cardiac myocytes sense mechanical stress and convert it into intracellular growth signals.

## SIGNAL TRANSDUCTION PATHWAYS ACTIVATED BY MECHANICAL STRETCH

### Gene Expression

The first group of genes activated by mechanical stretch are immediate-early genes such as c-*fos*, c-*jun*, *Egr-1*, and c-*myc* (38, 74). Among these, the mechanism of activation of the c-*fos* gene has been studied most extensively (39, 68, 77). Transfection of cultured neonatal cardiac myocytes with c-*fos* promoter-reporter gene constructs indicates that the serum response element (SRE) is both necessary and sufficient to confer stretch responsiveness to the c-*fos* promoter and that the Ets domain adjacent to the SRE core, a binding site of the ternary complex factor $p62^{TCF}$, is essential for transcriptional activation (68). This suggests that the signal generated by mechanical stretch activates the serum response factor (SRF)-$p62^{TCF}$ complex via the SRE, causing induction of c-*fos*. A similar finding was obtained by direct injection of c-*fos* promoter-reporter gene constructs into the intact adult rat heart, which were then subjected to pressure overload in a Langendorf (perfused) preparation. (2). Furthermore, c-*fos* induction by hypotonic cell swelling, another type of mechanical stress that increases membrane tension, is also mediated by activation of SRF-$p62^{TCF}$ in cardiac myocytes (76). Thus activation of SRF-$p62^{TCF}$ may be the general mechanism of c-*fos* activation in response to increased membrane tension in cardiac myocytes.

Cardiac hypertrophy is associated with upregulation of the fetal program (10, 28, 41, 56). Several *cis*-regulatory elements have been identified that may mediate inducibility of ANF, $\beta$-MHC, and skeletal-$\alpha$-actin after $\alpha$1-adrenergic or endothelin-1 stimulation in vitro (10). However, such elements have not been fully elucidated in the case of mechanical stretch. The ANF-CAT (chloramphenicol acetyltransferase) reporter construct containing a 3.4-kb ANF 5′ flanking sequence (including AP-1 and a putative $Ca^{2+}$/CRE site) in a neonatal rat ventricular myocytes failed to respond to mechanical stretch in transient transfection experiments (74). In transgenic mice harboring the luciferase reporter gene containing a 3.0-kb 5′ flanking sequence of the rat ANF gene, pressure overload did not significantly stimulate ANF-luciferase reporter activity, despite the fact that the same construct was significantly upregulated in $\alpha$1-adrenergic or endothelin-1 stimulated neonatal rat ventricular myocytes in vitro (36). These findings suggest either that induction of ANF mRNA in load-induced hypertrophy requires *cis*-acting elements that lie outside the 3.4 kb of the 5′ flanking region of the ANF gene or that induction of ANF mRNA expression is mediated by posttranscriptional mechanisms. Differences in *cis*-acting elements required for induction by humoral factors and mechanical stretch also have been observed in $\beta$-MHC induction. Although the sequence containing multimers of M-CAT elements was sufficient to confer $\alpha$1-adrenergic responsiveness onto heterologous neutral promoters in cultured neonatal cardiac myocytes (31), a $\beta$-MHC-CAT construct containing up to 673 base pairs 5′ flanking sequence of the rat $\beta$-MHC gene failed to respond to mechanical stretch when transfected into neonatal cardiac myocytes (74). These results suggest that stretch-induced cell signaling may utilize a mechanism distinct from the $\alpha$ receptor-mediated cell signaling used to regulate $\beta$-MHC or ANF gene expression. As for skeletal $\alpha$-actin gene regulation, the region between $-99$ and $-77$ of the 5′ flanking sequence, which contains SRE1, is necessary for the stretch-induced increase in skeletal-$\alpha$-actin promoter activity in avian skeletal muscle (8). However, SRE1 in the skeletal actin promoter does not contain the Ets domain but binds to YY1, another DNA-binding protein (8). Thus the mechanism of stretch-induced SRE activation of skeletal-$\alpha$-actin may not be identical to that of c-*fos*.

## Intracellular Signaling Molecules

In general, mechanical stress–induced signal transduction is characterized by simultaneous activation of multiple second messenger systems (68, 99). In cultured neonatal cardiac myocytes, mechanical stretch causes activation of phospholipases C, D, and $A_2$ (PLC, PLD, and $PLA_2$); tyrosine kinases; $p21^{ras}$; Raf-1; mitogen-activated protein (MAP) kinases and their activators; c-Jun N-terminal protein kinases (JNK); 90-kDa S6 kinase ($pp90^{RSK}$); protein kinase

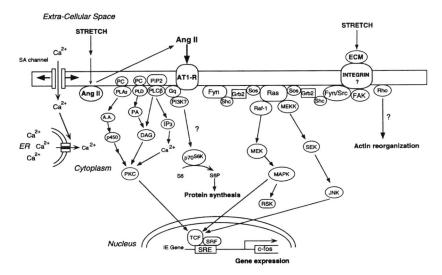

*Figure 1*  Model of a signal transduction pathway initiated by mechanical stretch in cardiac myocytes. The arrows provide the notion of directionality in the signaling processes, some of which
are still conjectural (marked with ?) or modeled after the known hierarchy of activation in other
cell systems. Abbreviations: A.A., arachidonic acid; Ang II, angiotensin II; AT1-R, angiotensin
II type 1 receptor; DAG, diacylglycerol; ECM, extracellular matrix; ER, endoplasmic reticulum;
FAK, focal adhesion kinase; IE gene, immediate-early gene; IP$_3$, inositol 1,4,5-trisphosphate;
JNK, c-jun N-terminal kinase; MAPK, mitogen-activated protein kinase; PA, phosphatidic acid;
PC, phosphatidylcholine; PKC, protein kinase C; PLA$_2$, phospholipase A2; PLC, phospholi-
pase C; PLD, phospholipase D; PIP$_2$, phosphatidyl inositol bisphosphate; PI3K, phosphatidyli-
nositol 3 kinase; RSK, 90-kDa ribosomal S6 kinase; SA channel, stretch-activated ion channel;
SEK, stress-activated protein kinase kinase; SRE, serum response element; SRF, serum response
factor.

C (PKC); and probably other molecules (40, 68, 77, 110, 111). Our current
model of signal transduction pathways activated by mechanical stretch in cardiac myocytes is summarized in Figure 1.

PHOSPHOLIPASES    Mechanical stretch of cardiac myocytes activates PI- and
PC-PLC within 1 min, the earliest time examined (39, 68). In addition to
PLC, mechanical stretch of cardiac myocytes also activates PLD and PLA$_2$,
and activation of these phospholipases generates various lipid-derived second
messengers such as inositol-1,4,5-trisphosphate (IP$_3$), diacylglycerol (DAG),
arachidonic acids, and phosphatidic acid (68). IP$_3$ causes Ca$^{2+}$ release from
intracellular Ca$^{2+}$ storage sites, and DAG activates PKC, which plays an important role in stretch-induced immediate-early gene expression, such as c-*fos* and
*Egr-1* (39, 68). Stretch-induced activation of multiple phospholipases has also

been reported in repetitive mechanical stimulation of cultured avian skeletal muscle (101).

There are several possible mechanisms for stretch-induced activation of phospholipases. First, in fetal lung cells, mechanical stress causes tyrosine phosphorylation and activation of PLC$\gamma$ through activation of c-*src* (47). However, this may not be the case in the heart because cardiac myocytes predominantly express PLC$\beta$3, not PLC$\gamma$ (19). Second, angiotensin II (Ang II) secreted by mechanical stretch could activate phospholipases (70). However, because secretion of Ang II by stretch takes place over 5 to 10 min (78), it may not mediate the initial rapid production of IP$_3$. Third, mechanical stress increases intracellular Ca$^{2+}$ by activating Gd$^{3+}$-sensitive, Ca$^{2+}$-permeable, stretch-activated cation channels (87), which in turn could activate Ca$^{2+}$-sensitive phospholipases. However, reducing extracellular [Ca$^{2+}$] by EGTA did not affect stretch-induced c-*fos* gene expression (68), which suggests that Ca$^{2+}$-influx is not essential for stretch-induced cell response. Fourth, stretch may enhance accessibility of membrane-associated phospholipases to their substrate (101). In lipid bilayer model systems, the phospholipase C activity can be increased by elevating surface pressure on the monolayer, which expands the space between phospholipid moieties and makes phospholipase accessible to the hydrophobic fatty acid portions of the phospholipid substrates (21). However, there has not been direct evidence to support this interesting hypothesis.

MAP KINASE CASCADES    Recent evidence suggests that cell growth stimuli as well as various environmental stresses, including UV radiation, osmotic stress, DNA damage, and heat shock, activate protein kinase cascades, which activate MAP kinases such as ERKs, JNKs, and p38/RK (30). These kinases are serine/threonine kinases and phosphorylate various cellular substrates important for cell growth and differentiation, including cardiac hypertrophy (92). Members of the MAP kinase family have been shown to phosphorylate the C-terminal region of Elk1/p62$^{TCF}$ transcription factor, thereby stimulating c-*fos* gene transcription (96). Mechanical stretch of neonatal cardiac myocytes has been shown to activate ERK1 and ERK2 and their downstream protein kinase pp90$^{RSK}$ (68, 111). Although the functional roles of these ERKs and pp90$^{RSK}$ in stretch-induced cardiac hypertrophy are unclear at present, they may be important in regulation of gene expression such as c-*fos* and ANF (95). Mechanical stretch of neonatal cardiac myocytes also activates the upstream regulators of ERKs, including MAP kinase kinase (MEK1) and MEK kinases (Raf-1 and MEKK1) (110). Thus mechanical stretch activates the MAP kinase cascade, which is also utilized by receptor tyrosine kinases and cytokine receptors. Recent evidence suggests that mechanical stretch also activates JNK1 in cardiac myocytes (40). Activation of JNK by stretch is relatively slow (15 min) compared with ERK activation (5 min). It remains to be determined which kinase among the MAP kinase family is responsible for stretch-induced activation of p62$^{TCF}$. Recently, hypotonic cell swelling of cardiac myocytes has been shown to activate ERKs and JNK1, but not p38/RK (76). Thus activation of ERK and JNK may be a common signaling mechanism in response to different types of increased membrane tension in cardiac myocytes. Activation of the MAP kinase cascade by mechanical stretch appears to be an evolutionarily well-conserved response, because the budding yeast cell activates PKC1 (homologue of mammalian PKC), BCK1 (a MEKK homologue), MKK1/2 (a MEK homologue), and MPK1 (an ERK homologue) in response to low osmolarity and heat shock, both of which cause an increase in membrane tension (29).

p21$^{ras}$ is a proto-oncogene that plays an essential role in cell growth, differentiation, and gene expression (1, 54). Constitutively active p21$^{ras}$ reproduces many aspects of cardiac hypertrophy in cultured cardiac myocytes, as well as in transgenic mice (22, 94). The dominant-negative p21$^{ras}$ has been shown to suppress phenylephrine-induced cardiac hypertrophic response (94). Mechanical stretch of cardiac myocytes has been shown to rapidly activate p21$^{ras}$ (68). The role of p21$^{ras}$ in stretch-induced cardiac hypertrophy remains to be elucidated.

PROTEIN SYNTHESIS REGULATORS    How mechanical stretch causes an increase in protein synthesis is not well understood. Protein synthesis is regulated by various molecules interacting with the translational machinery of the ribosome (35). S6, a component of 40S ribosomal proteins, is located at the interface between 40S and 60S ribosomal proteins and may interact directly with mRNA (90). Multiple serine phosphorylations of S6 at the carboxy-terminus regulate the rate of protein synthesis by stimulating initiation and elongation of protein translation (90). The S6 phosphorylation at the carboxy-terminus is mediated by a family of serine/threonine kinases, known as S6 kinases. Mechanical stretch of neonatal cardiac myocytes in vitro has been shown to cause activation of pp90$^{RSK}$ (68, 111). However, recent studies suggest that p70$^{S6K}$, not pp90$^{RSK}$, is the physiological kinase that phosphorylates S6 in vivo (11). At present, it is unknown whether mechanical stretch of cardiac myocytes activates p70$^{S6K}$. Ang II has been shown to activate p70$^{S6K}$ in neonatal cardiac myocytes in vitro (72).

Another potential protein synthesis regulator is the translation initiation factor eIF-4E, whose phosphorylation is rate limiting for translational initiation. A significant increase in eIF-4E phosphorylation was observed in response to ventricular pressure overload in a canine model in vivo (102). The molecular identity of the kinases responsible for eIF-4E phosphorylation in vivo is unknown. Activity of eIF-4E is also negatively regulated by its binding protein

PHAS-1. Phosphorylation of PHAS-1 prevents binding to eIF-4E, thereby removing its inhibitory effect on eIF-4E (59). It is not known if mechanical stretch causes phosphorylation of PHAS-1. In rat vascular smooth muscle, Ang II stimulates rRNA synthesis and increases overall translational capacity of the cell. This is mediated by increased transcriptional activation of rRNA, which is accompanied by serine phosphorylation of the upstream binding factor (UBF) (20). Neither the identity of the kinase for UBF nor whether mechanical stretch causes increase in rRNA synthesis is known.

## MECHANOSENSORS

The most obvious but perhaps most difficult question in the mechanotransduction of the heart is what is the stretch receptor. It is unlikely that cardiac myocytes possess specialized mechanosensing molecules similar to hair cells in the inner ear and touch sensors in the skin. Although mechanical stretch activates multiple second messenger systems as described above, it is unknown which molecules are directly activated by stretch and which molecules are indirectly activated by other upstream modulators. It is also not clear which molecules are activated by stretch at the earliest time point, because the very early time course of activation of each second messenger system has not yet been determined systematically. A mechanosensitive molecule is assumed to have some interaction with the plasma membrane in order to sense the tension of the membrane. Tension has long been recognized as a regulator of biochemical activity in skeletal muscle (23), and the subtle force generated by membrane tension seems sufficient to alter a variety of enzymatic activities (85). A similar mechanism has been proposed for the osmosensing mechanism of yeast cells, where SLN-1, a histidine kinase, and Sho1, a SH3-containing protein, independently regulate the MAP kinase family protein kinase cascade (PBS2-HOG1) in response to high osmolarity. Because SLN-1 and Sho1 are transmembrane proteins, it has been postulated that they work as a mechano-(osmo-) sensor (49). In *Caenorhabditis elegans,* 13 genes have been identified that play essential roles in mechanosensation (touch response). Interestingly, some of the genes encode ion channels, cytoskeleton and extracellular matrix proteins, or proteins that associate with these molecules (34). In this review, we discuss three putative mechanosensing mechanisms in the heart.

### Ion Channels

An increase in the end-diastolic volume accelerates the rate of repolarization and shortens the duration of the ventricular action potential with slight depolarization of the resting membrane potential (43). Therefore, it is likely that mechanical stress affects ion channels in the heart. Several kinds of stretch-activated ion (SA) channels have been found using the single-channel, patch-clamp technique, where the open probability of the channel is increased by negative pressure applied in the suction patch electrode. These channels include nonselective cation channels and $K^+$ channels with different ionic conductances (65, 77, 87). SA channels in the heart are sensitive to $Gd^{3+}$ (65, 77, 87), a known inhibitor of these channels. Opening of SA channels causes an increase in intracellular $Ca^{2+}$ because some of these channels are permeable to $Ca^{2+}$ and the influx causes $Ca^{2+}$-induced $Ca^{2+}$ release (65, 87). Opening of the nonselective cation channels at resting membrane potentials causes an inward current, thereby depolarizing the membrane and increasing membrane excitability (97).

It has been shown that treatment of myocytes with $Gd^{3+}$ does not affect stretch-induced c-*fos* expression or a stretch-induced increase in the rate of protein synthesis, suggesting that $Gd^{3+}$-sensitive SA channels are not involved in stretch-induced hypertrophic responses (77). It should be noted, however, that this does not exclude any possible involvement of $Gd^{3+}$-insensitive mechanosensitive ion channels in stretch-induced hypertrophic responses. Recent experiments using the whole-cell current recording suggest that mechanical stress caused by whole-cell stretch or hypotonic swelling in fact affects a wide variety of ionic channels and currents in the heart, such as the $K^+ATP$ channel (98), a delayed $K^+$ rectifier channel (79), a $Cl^-$ channel (15), a L type $Ca^{2+}$ channel (53), and the $Na^+/K^+$ pump current (80). Moreover, mechanical stress caused by direct uniaxial stretch and by hypoosmotic cell inflation affect different ionic currents in guinea pig ventricular myocytes (79), indicating that the nature of mechanical stimuli greatly affects its electrophysiological effects. Thus the electrophysiological response of the myocyte would be best estimated by the whole-cell recording during whole-cell uniaxial stretch. It has been shown that the whole-cell stretch of guinea pig ventricular myocytes causes a time-independent current with a reversal potential of $-15$ mV (79). The ionic selectivity and pharmacological properties of the channel responsible for the stretch-induced inward current have not been reported, although it is likely that a $Ca^{2+}$-activated nonselective cation channel or the $Na^+/Ca^{2+}$ exchanger mediate the inward current (79).

It remains to be determined whether SA channels can be the initial mechanosensor in stretch-induced cardiac hypertrophy. It is suggested that SA channels directly interact with the cytoskeleton and thus can intrinsically sense the cell stretch (17, 89). SA channels in vascular endothelial cells are activated within a few milliseconds by negative pressure applied in the suction patch pipette (42). A cloned renal epithelial $Na^+$ channel, whose mRNA expression is also observed in the heart, has been shown to display stretch-induced activation in planar lipid bilayers (3). Thus some SA channels are in fact directly activated in response to an increase in membrane tension. On the other hand, some whole-cell ionic conductance activated by stretch can be activated secondarily by other second messengers such as increased $[Ca^{2+}]$ (79). Moreover, fatty acids, generated by mechanically activated phospholipases (57), are suggested to be the intermediaries in activation of SA channels in toad smooth muscle cells. Isolation of SA channel genes (18), determination of their mechanosensitivity in the lipid bilayer system, and subsequent genetic approaches such as gene disruption (34) are essential to determine whether SA channels are the true mechanosensor in stretch-induced hypertrophy.

## Integrins

Integrins are heterodimeric transmembrane receptors that couple components of the extracellular matrix with the actin cytoskeleton (58). Multiple integrins are expressed in the heart and participate in a wide variety of biological processes (6). Integrins are important regulators in early cardiac development in vivo, providing positional information for migrating and differentiating cells (6) and are also an important determinant of morphology of cardiac myocyte in vitro (88). Because the cytoplasmic domain of the integrin physically associates with the cytoskeletal elements (58, 84), integrins can be a mechanosensor that transmits mechanical signals to the cytoskeleton. In fact, magnetic beads coated with an integrin ligand are capable of transferring mechanical stress to the cytoskeleton (103). Importantly, the cytoplasmic domain of the $\beta$-integrin interacts not only with actin-binding proteins such as talin and $\alpha$-actinin, but also with the amino-terminal domain of focal adhesion tyrosine kinase (FAK). FAK further interacts with various signaling molecules such as Src, Fyn, p130$^{Cas}$, Graf (GTPase regulator associated with FAK), Grb2, and PI-3 kinase (58, 84). These signaling molecules further activate various downstream protein kinase cascades, including p21$^{ras}$, MAP kinases, Rho/Cdc42, PIP-5 kinase, PKC, and p70$^{S6K}$ (58, 84). Thus integrins are very attractive candidates for a mechanotransducer that converts mechanical signals into intracellular second messenger signaling.

A subset of integrins such as $\alpha5\beta1$ specifically recognizes the amino acid sequence of Arg-Gly-Asp (RGD), and RGD peptide has been shown to inhibit integrin binding to the extracellular matrix (84). Pretreatment of neonatal rat cardiac myocytes on the stretchable substrate with RGD peptide does not inhibit c-*fos* gene induction by uniaxial stretch, suggesting that RGD-sensitive integrins are not essential for stretch-induced c-*fos* expression (77). The role of RGD-insensitive integrins in stretch-induced hypertrophy remains to be elucidated. Interestingly, tyrosine phosphorylation of FAK and paxillin by hypotonic cell swelling of cardiac myocytes was significantly attenuated by pretreatment with RGD peptide (71). This suggests that RGD-sensitive integrins play a role in swelling-induced tyrosine kinase activation. It remains to be determined whether integrins mediate some aspect of the stretch-induced cardiac hypertrophic response. Recently, the role of integrins in stretch-induced cellular responses has been suggested in other cell systems as well. In frog skeletal muscle, RGD peptide and an antibody against the integrin inhibited stretch-induced increase in release of neurotransmitters from the motor nerve terminals (9). RGD peptide or antibodies against $\beta3$ and $\alpha V \beta5$ integrins inhibited mitogenic response and production of PDGF in response to cyclical mechanical strain in rat vascular smooth muscle cells grown on a collagen substrate (106). Thus integrins appear to play a critical role in mediating stretch-induced cellular responses. Both collagen binding and mechanical stretch have been shown to independently potentiate the autocrine secretion of insulin-like growth factor-1 from skeletal muscle (61) and the mitogenic activity of angiotensin II in vascular smooth muscle cells (91). Therefore, it is possible that integrins also potentiate signals generated by other cellular mechanosensors.

## Tyrosine Kinases

Receptor type tyrosine kinases have transmembrane segments, and some of the nonreceptor-type tyrosine kinases, such as Src family tyrosine kinases, are anchored to the inner surface of cell membranes through their N-terminal myristoylation site. Thus it is possible that membrane stretch directly causes conformational changes of tyrosine kinases, thereby activating them. In support of this hypothesis, mechanical stretch of cardiac myocytes is shown to cause a rapid increase in phosphotyrosine content of proteins such as p42, p44, p60, p70, p85, p120, and p170 within 1 min (68). Hypotonic cell swelling of cardiac myocytes also causes rapid tyrosine phosphorylation of cellular proteins such as p42, p44, p70, p85, p120, p130, and p200 (76). Hypotonic swelling–induced c-*fos* gene expression was abolished by tyrosine kinase inhibitors but not by inhibitors of PKC, PLC, or Ang II antagonists (76). In contrast, stretch–induced c-*fos* gene induction was inhibited by inhibitors of tyrosine kinases, PKC and PLC, as well as by Ang II antagonists (68, 78). Thus although hypotonic cell swelling and linear stretch activate separate signaling mechanisms, tyrosine kinase activation is required for c-*fos* induction by both stimuli.

It is not known which tyrosine kinase is responsible for stretch-induced or hypotonic swelling–induced increases in tyrosine phosphorylation in cardiac myocytes. A recent report indicates that mechanical stretch of fetal lung cells caused activation of Src within 5 min; this was accompanied by translocation of Src from a Triton-soluble fraction to a cytoskeletal fraction (47). The tyrosine kinase inhibitor abolished stretch-induced DNA synthesis (47). Mechanical stretch caused an increase in tyrosine phosphorylation of FAK in mesangial cells (16). Although FAK is cytosolic and lacks a transmembrane domain, it can be localized to the focal adhesions through its interaction with the $\beta$-integrin.

The mechanism of tyrosine kinase activation by mechanical stress is unclear at present. However, it is interesting to note that mechanical stress activates tyrosine kinase very rapidly. In cardiac myocytes, hypotonic stress causes cell swelling within a few seconds. A significant increase in tyrosine phosphorylation can be observed in 5 s, the earliest time point examined (76). In the same preparation, hypotonic stress caused an increase in $[Ca^{2+}]$, but the onset of the increase in $[Ca^{2+}]$ was much slower compared with that of tyrosine phosphorylation (76). Thus activation of tyrosine kinases appears to be one of the earliest cellular responses observed at the whole-cell level in response to cell swelling. It is possible, however, that an activator of tyrosine kinases exists and can be activated by mechanical stress much earlier. Elucidation of the mechanism of mechanical stress–induced tyrosine kinase activation seems essential to determine whether tyrosine kinase is a direct mechanosensor.

## MECHANICAL STRESS AND GROWTH FACTORS

One of the most important characteristics of the cell signaling mechanism initiated by mechanical stretch of cardiac as well as skeletal myocytes is activation of multiple second messenger systems (68, 99, 101, 110, 111), as has been observed with intracellular signals induced by growth factors (64). Presence of autocrine/paracrine growth factors has been proposed as one of the important mechanisms in the pathogenesis of stretch-induced organ hypertrophy (99). During the past few years, accumulating evidence has demonstrated that in many cell systems, mechanical stretch stimulates production and/or secretion of growth factor(s) and that the growth factor(s) secreted in response to mechanical stretch mediate mechanical stretch-induced cell growth responses. Table 1 summarizes recent evidence of mechanical stretch-induced growth factor production/secretion in several cell types. Although different growth factors are involved, depending on the type of tissues as well as the type of mechanical

**Table 1**  Secretion of growth factors by mechanical stress

| Cell type | Species | Peptides | References |
|---|---|---|---|
| Cardiac myocytes | Rat (neonate) | Angiotensin II | (78, 44, 109) |
| Cardiac myocytes | Rat (neonate) | Endothelin-1 | (108) |
| Cardiac myocytes | Rat (adult) | Basic FGF | (32) |
| Skeletal muscle | Chicken | IGF-1 | (61) |
| Urinary tract SMC | Rat | NGF | (62) |
| Vascular SMC | Rat | PDGF | (105) |
| Vascular endothelial cells | Bovine | Endothelin-1 | (48) |
| Lung epithelial cells | Rat | PDGF | (46) |

stimuli, it is evident that autocrine/paracrine response is a common mechanism utilized in stretch-induced cell growth.

## Angiotensin II

Accumulating evidence suggests that Ang II may be a critical factor mediating load-induced hypertrophy in vivo. For example, treatment of rats having aortic coarctation with an angiotensin-converting enzyme (ACE) inhibitor or Ang II type I receptor antagonists (losartan and TCV 116) prevented (or caused regression of) left ventricular hypertrophy by pressure overload (5, 7, 37). An ACE inhibitor also prolonged survival of rats having pressure overload (104). Similarly, cardiac hypertrophy that occurs in rats with aortocaval shunt and volume overload can be prevented with losartan or an ACE inhibitor (quinapril) with high affinity for cardiac tissue ACE (66, 67). Treatment of patients suffering from myocardial infarction with ACE inhibitors prevented cardiac dilatation and reduced mortality (63). These results are consistent with the involvement of the renin-angiotensin system and its activation by hemodynamic loading in vivo. In fact, there is clear evidence for the existence of the cardiac renin-angiotensin system, which is supported by multiple findings from biochemical, immunohistochemical, and molecular biological demonstrations of all components of the renin-angiotensin system in the heart (4, 14, 45).

The role of Ang II as a critical mediator of stretch-induced hypertrophy has been shown in the neonatal rat cardiac myocyte system in vitro. Ang II receptor antagonists such as [Sar1 Ile8]Ang II (antagonist for the Ang II type I and II receptors) and losartan and TCV11974 (antagonists for the Ang II type I receptor) inhibit major markers of stretch-induced hypertrophy (e.g. c-*fos* gene expression, MAP kinase activation, an increase in the rate of protein synthesis, and induction of fetal type genes, such as ANF and skeletal-$\alpha$-actin), which suggests that Ang II plays a critical role in stretch-induced hypertrophy in the neonatal rat myocyte culture system (78, 109). Two groups reported the existence of the Ang II antagonist-uninhibitable component in a stretch-induced increase in the rate of protein synthesis (33) and MAP kinase activation (109). A part of the stretch-induced hypertrophic response may be mediated by other autocrine/paracrine growth factors, such as endothelin-1 (108), or by the signaling mechanism directly activated by stretch, although this Ang II–independent component of hypertrophic response seems variable depending on the cell density, types of extracellular matrix, nature of mechanical stress, and age of the experimental animals (33, 78, 109).

Mechanical stretch of neonatal rat cardiac myocytes in serum-free culture caused a more than 100-fold increase in Ang II concentrations in culture media ($\approx$500 pmol), peaking at 10 min (78). Mechanical stretch did not acutely stimulate production of Ang II, but significantly reduced intracellular Ang II content. This suggests that mechanical stretch causes secretion of preformed Ang II, although a stretch-induced increase in Ang II production is likely at a later stage. Ang II was found to be stored, at least in part, in the secretory granule-like structure in the ventricular myocytes (78). It is likely that ventricular myocytes also utilize the regulated type of secretion for stretch-induced secretion of Ang II. Recently ventricular myocytes were shown to be able to regulate secretion of ANF in response to endothelin or high KCl stimulation (25). Stretch-induced secretion of Ang II from neonatal rat cardiac myocytes has been confirmed by three other groups (44, 55, 109).

What is the signal transduction mechanism of mechanical stretch that causes secretion of Ang II from cardiac myocytes? Mechanical stretch-induced growth factor secretion in some cell systems shows a transient secretion peaking at about 10–120 min (48), suggesting the presence of growth factor stores that can be released in response to acute mechanical stress. In atrial myocytes, stretch causes secretion of ANF from stretch-sensitive, rapidly depletable pools that consist of newly synthesized ANF (51). Several possibilities can be considered as the mechanism of Ang II secretion. First, mechanical stretch activates PKC, $Ca^{2+}$, small GTP-binding proteins such as Rab, or other signaling mechanisms, which in turn may stimulate growth factor secretion (62, 107). Second, mechanical stress transiently causes an alteration in sarcolemmal permeability that allows release of cytosolic growth factors; recently, altered sarcolemmal permeability was shown to account for pacing-induced basic FGF release from adult rat ventricular cardiac myocytes (32). Finally, membrane tension may directly regulate membrane traffic and stimulate exocytosis/secretion (85).

Several lines of in vivo evidence suggest that the cardiac renin-angiotensin system is upregulated chronically in load-induced hypertrophy. mRNA expression of angiotensinogen, renin, ACE, and Ang II receptor are all upregulated in cardiac hypertrophy caused by pressure overload and ischemia (4, 82, 93, 112). At the protein level, upregulation of ACE activity and Ang II receptor binding were demonstrated (82, 93), and the percent of myocytes containing renin, Ang I, and Ang II was significantly increased in hypertrophied hearts (112). The upregulation of the cardiac renin-angiotensin system was also observed in mechanical stretch of neonatal rat cardiac myocytes in vitro (50, 86). Treatment of cultured cardiac myocytes with exogenous Ang II also upregulates mRNA expression of angiotensinogen, renin, and ACE, but not Ang II receptor (50, 69). This suggests that mechanical stretch initially causes acute secretion of preformed Ang II and that secreted Ang II may initiate a positive feedback mechanism, thereby upregulating the local renin-angiotensin system over time. It is likely, however, that upregulation of the Ang II receptor by mechanical stretch is mediated by an Ang II-independent mechanism.

**Table 2**  Comparison of the hypertrophic response of neonatal cardiac myocytes by stretch and Ang II

|  | Stretch | Ang II |
|---|---|---|
| Protein synthesis | ↑ | ↑ |
| Protein content | ↑ | ↑ |
| DNA synthesis | → | → |
| Immediate-early genes (c-$fos$, c-$myc$, $Egr$-$1$, etc) | ↑ | ↑ |
| Fetal genes (skeletal $\alpha$ actin, ANF, $\beta$-MHC, etc) | ↑ | ↑ |
| Growth factor genes (TGF-$\beta$, angiotensinogen, etc) | ↑ | ↑ |
| Blocked by $AT_1$ receptor blockers | yes | yes |

Ang II causes an increase in protein synthesis in adult rat heart in vivo or in isolated perfused heart independently of blood pressure (13, 83). In cultured neonatal rat cardiac myocytes, exogenously applied Ang II causes hypertrophy of cardiac myocytes and mitogenic response of cardiac fibroblasts (69, 81). These responses to Ang II are indistinguishable from those to mechanical stretch (Table 2), indicating that locally produced and/or secreted Ang II is sufficient to cause cardiac hypertrophy. Some investigators reported the apparent lack of hypertrophic effects by Ang II at low cell density conditions or in cultured adult myocytes (33, 60). AT1 receptor density may be very low in such culture conditions.

Table 3 summarizes the comparison of second messenger activation in response to stretch and exogenous Ang II. Although almost identical sets of signaling molecules are activated by stretch or Ang II (68, 70, 73, 75, 109,

**Table 3**  Comparison of second messengers activated by stretch or Ang II in cardiac myocytes

| Second messengers | Stretch | Ang II |
|---|---|---|
| Tyrosine kinases | ↑ | ↑ |
| MAP kinases | ↑ | ↑ |
| Ribosomal S6 kinases | ↑ | ↑ |
| $p21^{ras}$ | ↑ | ↑ |
| $IP_3$ (Pl-phospholipase C) | ↑ | ↑ |
| $Ca^{2+}$ | ↑ | ↑ |
| Diacylglycerol | ↑ | ↑ |
| Protein kinase C | ↑ | ↑ |
| Phosphatidic acid | ↑ | ↑ |
| Phospholipase D | ↑ | ↑ |
| Arachidonic acid release | ↑ | ↑ |
| cAMP | ± | ± |

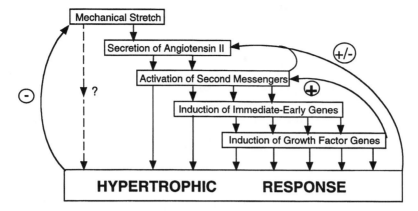

*Figure 2*    Roles of Ang II and other growth factors in stretch-induced cardiac hypertrophy in vitro. Solid arrows indicate experimentally defined processes. Broken arrows indicate unidentified effect by stretch.

111), it remains to be elucidated whether activation of the signaling molecules by mechanical stretch is exclusively mediated by Ang II. Precise comparison of activation kinetics and, more importantly, mechanical stretch in the presence of Ang II receptor antagonists seem to be essential to address this question.

Ang II has been shown to upregulate mRNA expression of various growth factors such as TGF$\beta$1, PDGF, basic FGF, endothelin-1, and insulin-like growth factor in the heart and vascular smooth muscle (12, 26, 27). Ang II and other growth factors such as PDGF and endothelin-1 mutually potentiate their growth-promoting effects (108). Although Ang II seems to be a primary mediator of stretch-induced hypertrophy in neonatal rat cardiac myocytes, other growth factors, whose expression is modulated by Ang II, may in concert mediate the stretch-induced cardiac hypertrophic response (Figure 2).

## Other Growth Factors

Recently, it has been reported that mechanical stretch causes secretion of endothelin-1 in neonatal rat cardiac myocytes. Although the amount of im-munoreactive endothelin-1 detected in the stretch-conditioned media was only 5 pmol/liter, a concentration well below that causing hypertrophic response by itself, it was shown to potentiate Ang II-induced activation of MAP kinase and Raf-1 through an endothelin-1 type A receptor-dependent mechanism (108). Stretch may therefore cause release of other growth factor(s), which may also be capable of causing some aspects of cardiac hypertrophy or of modulating action of Ang II. In isolated adult rat ventricular myocytes, release of basic FGF has been shown to play a critical role in pacing-induced cardiac hypertrophy (32).

## UNANSWERED QUESTIONS

Although studies using in vitro neonatal rat cardiac myocytes have clearly shown that autocrine secretion of Ang II plays an essential role in stretch-induced cardiac hypertrophy in vitro, many questions remain. First, it is not known if Ang II works as a primary mediator of stretch-induced hypertrophic responses in the hearts of different ages and species, as well as those in vivo. Specific growth factors that critically regulate load-induced hypertrophy have to be determined in each model system. Second, initial mechanosensing mechanisms that may cause secretion of growth factors need to be defined. Similarly, the stretch-induced signal transduction mechanism mediated by the Ang II-independent mechanism and its role in the hypertrophic response need to be defined. Third, the mechanism of intracardiac generation of Ang II still is not well understood. Although the existence of angiotensinogen, renin, and ACE mRNA has been shown in the heart, the level of mRNA expression is relatively low. Thus the relative role of the cardiac renin angiotensin system, compared with the systemic renin angiotensin system, remains to be determined. Moreover, intracellular production and storage of Ang II in stretch-releasable sites remains to be elucidated. Answers to these questions should provide a better understanding of the mechanism of load-induced hypertrophy and may lead to development of specific strategies leading to treatment and prevention of cardiac hypertrophy, remodeling, and failure.

ACKNOWLEDGMENTS

This work is in part supported by a National Institutes of Health grant. We thank Dr. TJ Kulik for critical reading of the manuscript.

*Literature Cited*

1. Abdellatif M, MacLellan WR, Schneider MD. 1994. p21 Ras as a governor of global gene expression. *J. Biol. Chem.* 269:15423–26
2. Aoyagi T, Izumo S. 1993. Mapping of the pressure response element of the c-*fos* gene by direct DNA injection into beating hearts. *J. Biol. Chem.* 268:27176–79
3. Awayda MS, Ismailov II, Berdiev BK, Benos DJ. 1995. A cloned renal epithelial Na$^+$ channel protein displays stretch activation in planar lipid bilayers. *Am. J. Physiol.* 268:C1450–59
4. Baker KM, Booz GW, Dostal DE. 1992. Cardiac actions of angiotensin II: role of an intracardiac renin-angiotensin system. *Annu. Rev. Physiol.* 54:227–41
5. Baker KM, Chernin MI, Wixson SK, Aceto JF. 1990. Renin-angiotensin system involvement in pressure-overload cardiac hypertrophy in rats. *Am. J. Physiol.* 259:H324–32
6. Baldwin HS, Buck CA. 1994. Integrins and other cell adhesion molecules in cardiac development. *Trends Cardiovasc. Med.* 4:178–87

7. Bruckschlegel G, Holmer SR, Jandeleit K, Grimm D, Muders F, et al. 1995. Blockade of the renin-angiotensin system in cardiac pressure-overload hypertrophy in rats. *Hypertension* 25:250–59a

8. Carson JA, Yan Z, Booth FW, Coleman ME, Schwarz RJ, Stump CS. 1995. Regulation of skeletal $\alpha$-actin promoter in young chickens during hypertrophy caused by stretch overload. *Am. J. Physiol.* 268:C918–24

9. Chen BM, Grinnell AD. 1995. Integrins and modulation of transmitter release from motor nerve terminals by stretch. *Science* 269:1578–80

10. Chien KR, Zhu H, Knowlton KU, Miller-Hance W, van-Bilsen M, et al. 1993. Transcriptional regulation during cardiac growth and development. *Annu. Rev. Physiol.* 55:77–95

11. Chung J, Kuo CJ, Crabtree GR, Blenis J. 1992. Rapamycin-FKBP specifically blocks growth-dependent activation of and signaling by the 70 kD S6 protein kinases. *Cell* 69:1227–36

12. Delafontaine P, Lou H. 1993. Angiotensin II regulates insulin-like growth factor I gene expression in vascular smooth muscle cells. *J. Biol. Chem.* 268:16866–70

13. Dostal DE, Baker KM. 1992. Angiotensin II stimulation of left ventricular hypertrophy in adult rat heart. Mediation by the AT1 receptor. *Am. J. Hypertens.* 5:276–80

14. Dostal DE, Rothblum KN, Chernin MI, Cooper GR, Baker KM. 1992. Intracardiac detection of angiotensinogen and renin: a localized renin-angiotensin system in neonatal rat heart. *Am. J. Physiol.* 263:C838–50

15. Hagiwara N, Masuda H, Shoda M, Irisawa H. 1992. Stretch-activated anion currents of rabbit cardiac myocytes. *J. Physiol.* 456:285–302

16. Hamasaki K, Mimura T, Furuya H, Morino N, Yamazaki T, et al. 1995. Stretching mesangial cells stimulates tyrosine phosphorylation of focal adhesion kinase pp125FAK. *Biochem. Biophys. Res. Commun.* 212:544–49

17. Hamill OP, McBride D Jr. 1992. Rapid adaptation of single mechanosensitive channels in *Xenopus* oocytes. *Proc. Natl. Acad. Sci. USA* 89:7462–66

18. Hamill OP, McBride D Jr. 1994. The cloning of a mechano-gated membrane ion channel. *Trends Neurosci.* 17:439–43

19. Hansen CA, Schroering AG, Robishaw JD. 1995. Subunit expression of signal transducing G proteins in cardiac tissue: implications for phospholipase C-beta regulation. *J. Mol. Cell. Cardiol.* 27:471–84

20. Hershey JC, Hautmann M, Thompson MM, Rothblum LI, Haystead TA, Owens GK. 1995. Angiotensin II-induced hypertrophy of rat vascular smooth muscle is associated with increased 18 S rRNA synthesis and phosphorylation of the rRNA transcription factor, upstream binding factor. *J. Biol. Chem.* 270:25096–101

21. Hirasawa K, Irvine RF, Dawson RM. 1981. The hydrolysis of phosphatidylinositol monolayers at an air/water interface by the calcium-ion-dependent phosphatidylinositol phosphodiesterase of pig brain. *Biochem. J.* 193:607–14

22. Hunter JJ, Tanaka N, Rockman HA, Ross J Jr, Chien KR. 1995. Ventricular expression of a MLC-2v-ras fusion gene induces cardiac hypertrophy and selective diastolic dysfunction in transgenic mice. *J. Biol. Chem.* 270:23173–78

23. Huxley AF, Simmons RM. 1971. Proposed mechanism of force generation in striated muscle. *Nature* 233:533–38

24. Ingber DE, Dike L, Hansen L, Karp S, Liley H, et al. 1994. Cellular tensegrity: exploring how mechanical changes in the cytoskeleton regulate cell growth, migration, and tissue pattern during morphogenesis. *Int. Rev. Cytol.* 150:173–224

25. Irons CE, Sei CA, Glembotski CC. 1993. Regulated secretion of atrial natriuretic factor from cultured ventricular myocytes. *Am. J. Physiol.* 264:H282–85

26. Ito H, Hirata Y, Adachi S, Tanaka M, Tsujino M, et al. 1993. Endothelin-1 is an autocrine/paracrine factor in the mechanism of angiotensin II-induced hypertrophy in cultured rat cardiomyocytes. *J. Clin. Invest.* 92:398–403

27. Itoh H, Mukoyama M, Pratt RE, Gibbons GH, Dzau VJ. 1993. Multiple autocrine growth factors modulate vascular smooth muscle cell growth response to angiotensin II. *J. Clin. Invest.* 91:2268–74

28. Izumo S, Nadal-Ginard B, Mahdavi V. 1988. Protooncogene induction and reprogramming of cardiac gene expression produced by pressure overload. *Proc. Natl. Acad. Sci. USA* 85:339–43

29. Kamada Y, Jung US, Piotrowski J, Levin DE. 1995. The protein kinase C-activated MAP kinase pathway of *Saccharomyces cerevisiae* mediates a novel aspect of the heat shock response. *Genes Dev.* 9:1559–71

30. Karin M, Hunter T. 1995. Transcriptional control by protein phosphorylation: sig-

nal transmission from the cell surface to the nucleus. *Curr. Biol.* 5:747–57

31. Kariya K, Karns LR, Simpson PC. 1994. An enhancer core element mediates stimulation of the rat beta-myosin heavy chain promoter by an alpha 1-adrenergic agonist and activated beta-protein kinase C in hypertrophy of cardiac myocytes. *J. Biol. Chem.* 269:3775–82

32. Kaye D, Pimental D, Prasad S, Maki T, Berger HJ, et al. 1996. Role of transiently altered sarcolemmal membrane permeability and basic fibroblast growth factor release in the hypertrophic response of adult rat ventricular myocytes to increased mechanical activity in vitro. *J. Clin. Invest.* 97:281–91

33. Kent RL, McDermott PJ. 1996. Passive load and angiotensin II evoke differential responses of gene expression and protein synthesis in cardiac myocytes. *Circ. Res.* 78:829–38

34. Kernan M, Zuker C. 1995. Genetic approaches to mechanosensory transduction. *Curr. Opin. Neurobiol.* 5:443–48

35. Kimball SR, Vary TC, Jefferson LS. 1994. Regulation of protein synthesis by insulin. *Annu. Rev. Physiol.* 56:321–48

36. Knowlton KU, Rockman HA, Itani M, Vovan A, Seidman CE, Chien KR. 1995. Divergent pathways mediate the induction of ANF transgenes in neonatal and hypertrophic ventricular myocardium. *J. Clin. Invest.* 96:1311–18

37. Kojima M, Shiojima I, Yamazaki T, Komuro I, Zou Z, et al. 1994. Angiotensin II receptor antagonist TCV-116 induces regression of hypertensive left ventricular hypertrophy in vivo and inhibits the intracellular signaling pathway of stretch-mediated cardiomyocyte hypertrophy in vitro. *Circulation* 89:2204–11

38. Komuro I, Kaida T, Shibazaki Y, Kurabayashi M, Katoh Y, et al. 1990. Stretching cardiac myocytes stimulates protooncogene expression. *J. Biol. Chem.* 265:3595–98

39. Komuro I, Katoh Y, Kaida T, Shibazaki Y, Kurabayashi M, et al. 1991. Mechanical loading stimulates cell hypertrophy and specific gene expression in cultured rat cardiac myocytes. Possible role of protein kinase C activation. *J. Biol. Chem.* 266:1265–68

40. Komuro I, Kudo S, Yamazaki T, Shiojima I, Hiroi Y, et al. 1995. Mechanical stretch activates JNK in cardiac myocytes. *Circulation* 92:I-239 (Abstr.)

41. Komuro I, Yazaki Y. 1993. Control of cardiac gene expression by mechanical stress. *Annu. Rev. Physiol.* 55:55–75

42. Lansman JB, Hallam TJ, Rink TJ. 1987. Single stretch-activated ion channels in vascular endothelial cells as mechanotransducers? *Nature* 325:811–13

43. Lerman BB, Burkhoff D, Yue DT, Franz MR, Sagawa K. 1985. Mechanoelectrical feedback: independent role of preload and contractility in modulation of canine ventricular excitability. *J. Clin. Invest.* 76:1843–50

44. Lin C, Baker KM, Thekkumkara TJ, Dostal DE. 1995. Sensitive bioassay for the detection and quantification of angiotensin II in tissue culture medium. *Biotechniques* 18:1014–20

45. Lindpaintner K, Ganten D. 1991. The cardiac renin-angiotensin system. An appraisal of present experimental and clinical evidence. *Circ. Res.* 68:905–21

46. Liu M, Liu J, Buch S, Tanswell AK, Post M. 1995. Antisense oligonucleotides for PDGF-B and its receptor inhibit mechanical strain-induced fetal lung cell growth. *Am. J. Physiol.* 269:L178–84

47. Liu M, Qin Y, Liu J, Tanswell K, Post M. 1996. Mechanical strain induces pp60$^{src}$ activation and translocation to cytoskeleton in fetal rat lung cells. *J. Biol. Chem.* 271:7066–71

48. MacArthur H, Warner TD, Wood EG, Corder R, Vane JR. 1994. Endothelin-1 release from endothelial cells in culture is elevated both acutely and chronically by short periods of mechanical stretch. *Biochem. Biophys. Res. Commun.* 200:395–400

49. Maeda T, Wurgler-Murphy SH, Saito H. 1994. A two-component system that regulates an osmosensing MAP kinase cascade in yeast. *Nature* 369:242–45

50. Malhotra R, Sadoshima J, Izumo S. 1994. Mechanical stretch upregulates expression of the local renin-angiotensin system genes in cardiac myocytes in vitro. *Circulation* 90:I-195 (Abstr.)

51. Mangat H, de Bold AJ. 1993. Stretch-induced atrial natriuretic factor release utilizes a rapidly depleting pool of newly synthesized hormone. *Endocrinology* 133:1398–403

52. Mann DL, Kent RL, Cooper GT. 1989. Load regulation of the properties of adult feline cardiocytes: growth induction by cellular deformation. *Circ. Res.* 64:1079–90

53. Matsuda N, Hagiwara N, Shoda M, Kasanuki H, Hosoda S. 1996. Enhancement of the L-tpe $Ca^{2+}$ current by mechanical stimulation in single rabbit cardiac myocytes. *Circ. Res.* 78:650–59

54. McCormick F. 1994. Activators and effectors of ras p21 proteins. *Curr. Opin. Genet. Dev.* 4:71–76
55. Miyata S, Haneda T, Nakamura Y, Fukuzawa J, Okamoto K, et al. 1993. The role of cardiac renin-angiotensin system in stretch-induced hypertrophy of cultured neonatal rat heart cells. *Circulation* 88:I–614 (Abstr.)
56. Morgan HE, Baker KM. 1991. Cardiac hypertrophy. *Circulation* 83:13–25
57. Ordway RW, Petrou S, Kirber MT, Walsh J Jr, Singer JJ. 1995. Stretch activation of a toad smooth muscle K$^+$ channel may be mediated by fatty acids. *J. Physiol.* 484:331–37
58. Parsons JT. 1996. Integrin-mediated signalling: regulation by tyrosine kinases and small GTP-binding proteins. *Curr. Opin. Cell Biol.* 8:146–52
59. Pause A, Belsham GJ, Gingras A-C, Donze O, Lin T-A, et al. 1994. Insulin-dependent stimulation of protein synthesis by phosphorylation of a regulator of 5'-cap function. *Nature* 371:762–67
60. Pennica D, King KL, Shaw KJ, Luis E, Rullamas J, et al. 1995. Expression cloning of cardiotrophin 1, a cytokine that induces cardiac myocyte hypertrophy. *Proc. Natl. Acad. Sci. USA* 92:1142–46
61. Perrone CE, Fenwick-Smith D, Vandenburgh HH. 1995. Collagen and stretch modulate autocrine secretion of insulin-like growth factor-1 and insulin-like growth factor binding proteins from differentiated skeletal muscle cells. *J. Biol. Chem.* 270:2099–106
62. Persson K, Sando JJ, Tuttle JB, Steers WD. 1995. Protein kinase C in cyclic stretch-induced nerve growth factor production by urinary tract smooth muscle cells. *Am. J. Physiol.* 269:C1018–24
63. Pfeffer JM, Fischer TA, Pfeffer MA. 1995. Angiotensin-converting enzyme inhibition and ventricular remodeling after myocardial infarction. *Annu. Rev. Physiol.* 57:805–26
64. Rozengurt E. 1991. Neuropeptides as cellular growth factors: role of multiple signaling pathways. *Eur. J. Clin. Invest.* 21:123–34
65. Ruknudin A, Sachs F, Bustamante JO. 1993. Stretch-activated ion channels in tissue-cultured chick heart. *Am. J. Physiol.* 264:H960–72
66. Ruzicka M, Leenen FH. 1995. Relevance of blockade of cardiac and circulatory angiotensin-converting enzyme for the prevention of volume overload-induced cardiac hypertrophy. *Circulation* 91:16–19
67. Ruzicka M, Yuan B, Harmsen E, Leenen FH. 1993. The renin-angiotensin system and volume overload-induced cardiac hypertrophy in rats. Effects of angiotensin converting enzyme inhibitor versus angiotensin II receptor blocker. *Circulation* 87:921–30
68. Sadoshima J, Izumo S. 1993. Mechanical stretch rapidly activates multiple signal transduction pathways in cardiac myocytes: potential involvement of an autorine/paracrine mechanism. *EMBO J.* 12:1681–92
69. Sadoshima J, Izumo S. 1993. Molecular characterization of angiotensin II-induced hypertrophy of cardiac myocytes and hyperplasia of cardiac fibroblasts: a critical role of the AT1 receptor subtype. *Circ. Res.* 73:413–23
70. Sadoshima J, Izumo S. 1993. Signal transduction pathways of angiotensin II induced c-*fos* gene expression in cardiac myocytes in vitro: roles of phospholipid-derived second messengers. *Circ. Res.* 73:424–38
71. Sadoshima J, Izumo S. 1994. Roles of integrins in cell swelling-induced tyrosine phosphorylation in cardiac myocytes. *Circulation* 90:I–305 (Abstr.)
72. Sadoshima J, Izumo S. 1995. Rapamycin selectively inhibits angiotensin II-induced increase in protein synthesis in cardiac myocytes in vitro; a potential role of 70 kDa S6 kinase. *Circ. Res.* 77:1040–52
73. Sadoshima J, Izumo S. 1996. The heterotrimeric Gq protein-coupled angiotensin II receptor activates p21$^{ras}$ via the tyrosine kinase-Shc-Grb2-Sos pathway in cardiac myocytes. *EMBO J.* 15:775–87
74. Sadoshima J, Jahn L, Takahashi T, Kulik TJ, Izumo S. 1992. Molecular characterization of the stretch-induced adaptation of cultured cardiac cells: an in vitro model of load-induced cardiac hypertrophy. *J. Biol. Chem.* 267:10551–60
75. Sadoshima J, Qiu Z, Morgan JP, Izumo S. 1995. Angiotensin II and other hypertrophic stimuli mediated by G protein-coupled receptors activate tyrosine kinase, mitogen-activated protein kinase, and 90-kD S6 kinase in cardiac myocytes: the critical role of Ca$^{2+}$-dependent signaling. *Circ. Res.* 76:1–15
76. Sadoshima J, Qiu Z, Morgan JP, Izumo S. 1996. Tyrosine kinase activation is an immediate and essential step in hypo-

tonic cell swelling-induced ERK activation and c-*fos* gene expression in cardiac myocytes. *EMBO J.* 15:5535–46

77. Sadoshima J, Takahashi T, Jahn L, Izumo S. 1992. Roles of mechanosensitive ion channels, cytoskeleton, and contractile activity in stretch-induced immediate-early gene expression and hypertrophy of cardiac myocytes. *Proc. Natl. Acad. Sci. USA* 89:9905–9

78. Sadoshima J, Xu Y, Slayter HS, Izumo S. 1993. Autocrine release of angiotensin II mediates stretch-induced hypertrophy of cardiac myocytes in vitro. *Cell* 75:977–84

79. Sasaki N, Mitsuiye T, Noma A. 1992. Effects of mechanical stretch on membrane currents of single ventricular myocytes of guinea-pig heart. *Jpn. J. Physiol.* 42:957–70

80. Sasaki N, Mitsuiye T, Wang Z, Noma A. 1994. Increase of the delayed rectifier $K^+$ and $Na(+)$-$K^+$ pump currents by hypotonic solutions in guinea pig cardiac myocytes. *Circ. Res.* 75:887–95

81. Schorb W, Booz GW, Dostal DE, Conrad KM, Chang KC, Baker KM. 1993. Angiotensin II is mitogenic in neonatal rat cardiac fibroblasts. *Circ. Res.* 72:1245–54

82. Schunkert H, Dzau VJ, Tang SS, Hirsch AT, Apstein CS, Lorell BH. 1990. Increased rat cardiac angiotensin converting enzyme activity and mRNA expression in pressure overload left ventricular hypertrophy. Effects on coronary resistance, contractility, and relaxation. *J. Clin. Invest.* 86:1913–20

83. Schunkert H, Sadoshima J, Cornelius T, Kagaya Y, Weinberg EO, et al. 1995. Angiotensin II-induced growth responses in isolated adult rat hearts. Evidence for load-independent induction of cardiac protein synthesis by angiotensin II. *Circ. Res.* 76:489–97

84. Schwartz MA, Schaller MD, Ginsberg MH. 1995. Integrins: emerging paradigms of signal transduction. *Annu. Rev. Cell Dev. Biol.* 11:549–99

85. Sheetz MP, Dai J. 1996. Modulation of membrane dynamics and cell motility by membrane tension. *Trends Cell Biol.* 6:85–89

86. Shyu KG, Chen JJ, Shih NL, Chang H, Wang DL, et al. 1995. Angiotensinogen gene expression is induced by cyclical mechanical stretch in cultured rat cardiomyocytes. *Biochem. Biophys. Res. Commun.* 211:241–48

87. Sigurdson W, Ruknudin A, Sachs F. 1992. Calcium imaging of mechanically induced fluxes in tissue-cultured chick heart: role of stretch-activated ion channels. *Am. J. Physiol.* 262:H1110–15

88. Simpson DG, Terracio L, Terracio M, Price RL, Turner DC, Borg TK. 1994. Modulation of cardiac myocyte phenotype in vitro by the composition and orientation of the extracellular matrix. *J. Cell. Physiol.* 161:89–105

89. Sokabe M, Sachs F. 1992. Towards molecular mechanism of activation in mechanosensitive ion channels. In *Advances in Comparative and Environmental Physiology,* ed. F Ito, 10:55–77. Berlin/Heidelberg: Springer-Verlag

90. Stewart MJ, Thomas G. 1994. Mitogenesis and protein synthesis: a role for ribosomal protein S6 phosphorylation? *BioEssays* 16:809–15

91. Sudhir K, Wilson E, Chatterjee K, Ives HE. 1993. Mechanical strain and collagen potentiate mitogenic activity of angiotensin II in rat vascular smooth muscle cells. *J. Clin. Invest.* 92:3003–7

92. Sugden PH, Bogoyevitch MA. 1995. Intracellular signalling through protein kinases in the heart. *Cardiovasc. Res.* 30:478–92

93. Suzuki J, Matsubara H, Urakami M, Inada M. 1993. Rat angiotensin II (type 1A) receptor mRNA regulation and subtype expression in myocardial growth and hypertrophy. *Circ. Res.* 73:439–47

94. Thorburn A, Thorburn J, Chen S-Y, Powers S, Shubeita HE, et al. 1993. HRas-dependent pathways can activate morphological and genetic markers of cardiac muscle cell hypertrophy. *J. Biol. Chem.* 268:2244–49

95. Thorburn J, Frost JA, Thorburn A. 1994. Mitogen-activated protein kinases mediate changes in gene expression, but not cytoskeletal organization associated with cardiac muscle cell hypertrophy. *J. Cell Biol.* 126:1565–72

96. Treisman R. 1996. Regulation of transcription by MAP kinase cascades. *Curr. Opin. Cell Biol.* 8:205–15

97. Tung L, Zou S. 1995. Influence of stretch on excitation threshold of single frog ventricular cells. *Exp. Physiol.* 80:221–35

98. van Wagoner DR. 1993. Mechanosensitive gating of atrial ATP-sensitive potassium channels. *Circ. Res.* 72:973–83

99. Vandenburgh HH. 1992. Mechanical forces and their second messengers in stimulating cell growth in vitro. *Am. J. Physiol.* 262:R350–55

100. Vandenburgh HH, Kaufman S. 1979. In vitro model for stretch-induced hypertrophy of skeletal muscle. *Science* 203:265–68

101. Vandenburgh HH, Shansky J, Karlisch P, Solerssi RL. 1993. Mechanical stimulation of skeletal muscle generates lipid-related second messengers by phospholipase activation. *J. Cell. Physiol.* 155: 63–71

102. Wada H, Ivester CT, Carabello BA, Cooper IVG, McDermott PJ. 1996. Translational initiation factor eIF-4E: a link between cardiac load and protein synthesis. *J. Biol. Chem.* 14:8359–64

103. Wang N, Butler JP, Ingber DE. 1993. Mechanotransduction across the cell surface and through the cytoskeleton. *Science* 260:1124–27

104. Weinberg EO, Schoen FJ, George D, Kagaya Y, Douglas PS, et al. 1994. Angiotensin-converting enzyme inhibition prolongs survival and modifies the transition to heart failure in rats with pressure overload hypertrophy due to ascending aortic stenosis. *Circulation* 90:1410–22

105. Wilson E, Mai Q, Sudhir K, Weiss RH, Ives HE. 1993. Mechanical strain induces growth of vascular smooth muscle cells via autocrine action of PDGF. *J. Cell Biol.* 123:741–47

106. Wilson E, Sudhir K, Ives HE. 1995. Mechanical strain of rat vascular smooth muscle cells is sensed by specific extracellular matrix/integrin interactions. *J. Clin.*

*Invest.* 96:2364–72

107. Wirtz HR, Dobbs LG. 1990. Calcium mobilization and exocytosis after one mechanical stretch of lung epithelial cells. *Science* 250:1266–69

108. Yamazaki T, Komuro I, Kudoh S, Zou Y, Shiojima I, et al. 1996. Endothelin-1 is involved in mechanical stress-induced cardiomycyte hypertrophy. *J. Biol. Chem.* 271:3221–28

109. Yamazaki T, Komuro I, Kudoh S, Zou Y, Shiojima I, et al. 1995. Angiotensin II partly mediates mechanical stress-induced cardiac hypertrophy. *Circ. Res.* 77:258–65

110. Yamazaki T, Komuro I, Kudoh S, Zou Y, Shiojima I, et al. 1995. Mechanical stress activates protein kinase cascade of phosphorylation in neonatal rat cardiac myocytes. *J. Clin. Invest.* 96:438–46

111. Yamazaki T, Tobe K, Hoh E, Maemura K, Kaida T, et al. 1993. Mechanical loading activates mitogen-activated protein kinase and S6 peptide kinase in cultured rat cardiac myocytes. *J. Biol. Chem.* 268:12069–76

112. Zhang X, Dostal DE, Reiss K, Cheng W, Kajstura J, et al. 1995. Identification and activation of autocrine renin-angiotensin system in adult ventricular myocytes. *Am. J. Physiol.* 269:H1791–802

# SPECIAL TOPIC: MOLECULAR MECHANISMS OF MECHANOTRANSDUCTION

## *Introduction,* Owen Hamill, *Special Topic Editor*

Mechanotransduction is the process by which mechanical energy is converted into electrical or biochemical signals. Over the last several years there have been numerous reviews written on the biophysical aspects of mechanotransduction in excitable and nonexcitable cells. Recently, however, significant developments have occurred in other areas of mechanotransduction. With this in mind, five topics have been selected to give flavor to the wide range of disciplines (cell biology, biophysics, and molecular biology) and preparations (bacterial to mammals) that are being employed to unravel the molecular mechanisms of mechanotransduction.

The initial chapter presents a conceptual framework by which one can look at cell structure and its response to mechanical loads. Ingber adopts an architectural principle known as tensegrity to explain how mechanical forces applied locally to a cell are integrated into a whole cell response via transmembrane molecules that connect extracellular and cytoskeletal structures. This model represents a significant and essential departure from earlier models that viewed the cell as a plasmalemma-enclosed bag of amorphous protoplasm.

The patch-clamp recording technique, by allowing the resolution of single mechano-gated (MG) channels, has played a dominant role in reenergizing interest in mechanotransduction over the last decade. However, in a chapter by Hamill & McBride, specific pitfalls are pointed out that can occur when physical limitations of the technique are exceeded. The resulting artifacts are due to mechanical over-stimulation of the patch resulting in pathological changes in both membrane function and morphology. Such artifacts, which can be avoided by careful attention to sealing and stimulation pressure/suction protocols, have in the past lead to misinterpretation of experimental results and confusion in the field.

Bourque & Oliet review the functional relevance of a specific class of MG channel in the central osmoregulation of mammalian extracellular fluids. Using

573

patch-clamp recording, they identify and characterize an osmosensitive cation channel in acutely dissociated magnocellular neurosecretory neurons of the hypothalmus. This channel displays a finite open probability ($P_o$) under isotonic conditions (i.e. the set point) but increases and decreases its $P_o$ under hypertonic and hypotonic conditions, respectively. The alteration of membrane conductance around this set point, as the neuron shrinks and swells, alters its firing properties, which in turn either increases or decreases the release of the natriuretic and diuretic hormones oxytocin and vasopressin.

Two chapters deal with the molecular biology of mechanotransduction in prokaryotes and eukaryotes. The chapter by Kung and colleagues focuses on MG channels in *E. coli*, which have recently been purified, cloned, and functionally reconstituted into pure liposomes. This technical achievement has allowed for the first time investigation of structure-function relations of an MG channel. Furthermore, with regard to the mechanisms of activation, it clearly demonstrates that tension developed within the membrane bilayer alone can gate the channel. The chapter by Tavernarakis & Driscoll reviews the genetic dissection of a supramolecular structure underlying gentle touch sensitivity in *C. elegans* and reinforces the idea that molecules in all three domains—extracellular, transmembrane, and cytoskeletal—play a role in conferring high mechanosensitivity on a specialized mechanoreceptor.

In combination, these chapters indicate that cells can be considered as mechanical entities with a number of parallel pathways involved in sensing various mechanical signals and mediating appropriate cellular responses. The emphasis of this special topic has been on the electrical aspect of mechanotransduction mainly because the patch-clamp technique has proven so powerful in stimulating and resolving single molecular events underlying mechanotransduction. Presumably the same general principles will prove useful in unravelling mechanisms underlying biochemical mechanotransduction. Although great advances have been made in dissecting out the various molecular components of different mechanotransduction pathways, new challenges now arise for improved functional studies. In particular, new biophysical techniques or approaches will be required to directly monitor interactions between molecular components either in situ or in reconstituted systems in order to fully appreciate how cells sense and respond to mechanical stimulation.

*Annu. Rev. Physiol. 1997. 59:575–99*

# TENSEGRITY: THE ARCHITECTURAL BASIS OF CELLULAR MECHANOTRANSDUCTION

## D. E. Ingber

Departments of Pathology and Surgery, Children's Hospital and Harvard Medical School, Boston, Massachusetts 02115

KEY WORDS: mechanoreceptor, cytoskeleton, integrins, signal transduction, extracellular matrix

### ABSTRACT

Physical forces of gravity, hemodynamic stresses, and movement play a critical role in tissue development. Yet, little is known about how cells convert these mechanical signals into a chemical response. This review attempts to place the potential molecular mediators of mechanotransduction (e.g. stretch-sensitive ion channels, signaling molecules, cytoskeleton, integrins) within the context of the structural complexity of living cells. The model presented relies on recent experimental findings, which suggests that cells use tensegrity architecture for their organization. Tensegrity predicts that cells are hard-wired to respond immediately to mechanical stresses transmitted over cell surface receptors that physically couple the cytoskeleton to extracellular matrix (e.g. integrins) or to other cells (cadherins, selectins, CAMs). Many signal transducing molecules that are activated by cell binding to growth factors and extracellular matrix associate with cytoskeletal scaffolds within focal adhesion complexes. Mechanical signals, therefore, may be integrated with other environmental signals and transduced into a biochemical response through force-dependent changes in scaffold geometry or molecular mechanics. Tensegrity also provides a mechanism to focus mechanical energy on molecular transducers and to orchestrate and tune the cellular response.

## INTRODUCTION

The question of how organisms sense mechanical signals and transduce them into biological responses has always intrigued biologists. At the beginning of this century, many scientists speculated that mechanical stresses played a

575

0066-4278/97/0315-0575$08.00

key role in the determination of tissue growth and form. More recent studies confirm that physical forces, including gravity, tension, compression, pressure, and shear, influence growth and remodeling in all living tissues and show that these effects are exerted at the cell level. Cell growth, differentiation, secretion, movement, signal transduction, and gene expression all can be altered by applying mechanical stresses directly to cultured cells. Yet, we still do not fully understand how individual cells perceive physical forces nor how they choreograph the molecular performance that results in mechanotransduction: the conversion of a physical signal into a biological or chemical response.

Although studies that analyze the effects of mechanical forces on cells commonly assume that other stimuli are constant, living cells likely receive many simultaneous inputs. For example, at the same time an endothelial cell is exposed to a change in fluid shear stress, it also may bind to a different growth factor or adhere to another extracellular matrix (ECM) molecule. Growth factors and ECM independently activate the same intracellular signaling pathways that mechanical stresses have been reported to influence through binding to their own cell surface receptors. Furthermore, many of the molecules that transduce these signals (e.g. ion channels, protein kinases, lipid kinases) are physically immobilized on the insoluble cytoskeleton (CSK), the major structural framework of the cell, which is itself highly sensitive to mechanical deformation. Nevertheless, living cells are able to simultaneously sense all these signals and yet produce only one concerted response: They grow, or differentiate, or die locally (32, 33). Thus to fully understand the mechanism of mechanotransduction and its relevance for regulation of tissue development and remodeling, we must explain how all these signals are integrated inside the cell.

The point of this chapter is not to provide an extensive review of recent experimental advances in the field of cellular mechanotransduction nor to enumerate the different signaling mechanisms that become activated when living cells are mechanically stressed. Excellent reviews of this type can be found in the recent literature (8, 13, 16, 27) and in the accompanying chapters in this volume. Instead, I hope to present a theoretical framework that places all the potential molecular mediators of mechanotransduction (e.g. ECM, stretch-sensitive ion channels, signaling molecules, CSK filaments) within the context of the structural complexity that exists in living cells and tissues.

In this chapter, I review work suggesting that the structural organization and interconnectedness of the CSK provides a physical basis for translating mechanical forces into a biochemical response, as well as a mechanism for integrating these signals with those generated by growth factors and ECM. This concept emerged from studies with cell models built from sticks and string using tensegrity architecture (28, 31, 34, 74). Tensegrity models predict that living cells and nuclei may be hard-wired to respond immediately to mechanical stresses transmitted over cell surface receptors that physically couple the CSK to ECM or to other cells. Tensegrity also offers a mechanism to explain how the CSK remodels in response to stress and, hence, how signaling molecules that are immobilized on this insoluble scaffold might change their distribution and function when force is applied to the cell surface. Results of studies with living cells that provide direct support for the tensegrity hypothesis are reviewed. Finally, I describe potential molecular mechanisms that cells may utilize to convert mechanical energy into chemical energy at the molecular level, as well as how tensegrity may be used to tune this transduction response.

## THE TENSEGRITY MODEL AND MECHANOTRANSDUCTION

The precise molecular mechanism of mechanotransduction remains unclear; however, there are a few clues. For example, cell surface ion channels have been identified that become activated or inactivated when the cell membrane is mechanically tensed in many cells. However, G protein activation, release of chemical second messengers (e.g. arachidonic acid, cyclic AMP, inositol trisphosphate, calcium), protein phosphorylation, secretion of growth factors, CSK alterations, remodeling of cell-ECM adhesions, and changes in gene expression also occur within seconds to minutes following mechanical perturbation (3, 9, 24, 43, 46, 59, 61–63, 73). In fact, activation of mechanosensitive ion channels is often not required for many of these effects (46, 62). Furthermore, the same mechanical stimulus may produce a different response depending on the presence of soluble hormones or the type of ECM substrate on which the cell adheres (63, 79). Thus it has been extremely difficult to dissect out cause and effect when analyzing the molecular basis of mechanotransduction.

In *C. elegans*, a genetic approach was used to map the mechanical signaling cascade that begins with a physical touch and ends with a change in movement. This work led to identification of multiple genes that encode the molecules required for mechanotransduction. Some of these genes encode new ion channels that may be stress sensitive; however, others encode ECM molecules and CSK proteins (12, 26). These elegant studies hit home the fact that molecules present in all three cellular domains—extracellular, membrane, and cytoplasmic—play critical roles in the mechanotransduction response. Biochemical analysis of the gravity-sensing mechanism in plants reveals a similar paradigm (11, 78). Thus we must place our current knowledge about molecular transducers within the structural framework that exists in living cells and tissues.

## Initial Assumptions

When my laboratory first approached this problem, we started with a few basic assumptions. The first was that to understand how individual cells sense and respond to forces, we must first map the molecular path by which mechanical signals are transferred across the cell surface. As in any architectural system, mechanical loads should be transferred across points where the structure is physically anchored to its underlying support foundation. Living cells are anchored to insoluble ECM scaffolds (e.g. basement membranes, interstitial matrix) that join together cells and mechanically stabilize all living tissues. They also interconnect with neighboring cells. We therefore assumed that mechanical stresses must be transferred to adherent cells through their adhesive contacts with surrounding ECM or through their junctions with neighboring cells (27, 34).

Our second assumption was that we could not answer the question of how cells sense and respond to mechanical forces if we viewed the cell as a viscous protoplasm surrounded by a membrane. Instead, we had to take into account that all cells contain an internal filamentous framework or CSK that stabilizes cell shape. Furthermore, the CSK is not a passive structure: All living cells generate active tension within their internal CSK via an actomyosin filament sliding mechanism similar to that used in muscle. This is not obvious in cells cultured on rigid plastic dishes; however, it is easily visualized by placing the same cells on malleable substrata such as silicone rubber, which they mechanically contract and pull up into folds (22). Isometric tension also can be measured in nonmuscle cells (e.g. endothelial cells, fibroblasts) cultured on flexible collagen gels (42), and release of these gels results in spontaneous contraction (24). These results indicate that all living cells have an internal prestress (pre-equilibrated stress) analogous to the stress within a tensed bow or catapult that is harnessed to send a projectile flying through space. This CSK prestress also corresponds to the basal tone that can be measured in resting muscle cells before being chemically stimulated to contract.

This conceptual approach led to a few observations that have important implications for cellular mechanotransduction. The first was that CSK tension is the major force acting on living cells, and thus all external mechanical loads are imposed on a pre-existing force balance. Therefore, the cellular response to stress is more like that of a violin string to tuning than a conventional stimulus-response coupling in which the signal (e.g. growth factor) is absent before it is added externally. This suggested that we must change the way we think about mechanosensation.

The second point was that forces may not be transmitted continuously across the entire cell surface, as assumed by conventional engineering models of cells that rely on continuum mechanics theory (17). This is because the membrane

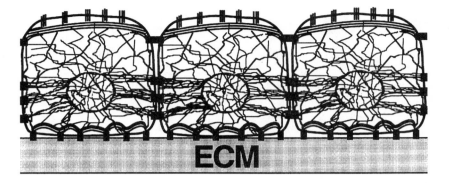

*Figure 1*  The intracellular cytoskeleton interconnects with the underlying extracellular matrix and neighboring cells through focal adhesion complexes at the cell base and specialized junctional complexes at the lateral cell borders, respectively.  Because of the presence of this molecular continuum, distant molecules in the ECM, cytoplasm, and nucleus may be mechanically coupled.

is not evenly glued to the ECM or to neighboring cells.  Rather, a cell anchors to underlying ECM and surrounding cells by physically coupling its tensed CSK filaments to specific receptors that cluster within localized adhesion sites (Figure 1).  These molecular spot welds are called focal adhesion complexes (FACs) when they mediate cell-ECM adhesion at the cell base (Figure 2) and junctional complexes (e.g. adherens junctions, desmosomes) when they mediate cell-cell adhesion along the lateral cell borders (18).

FACs contain clusters of transmembrane ECM receptors called integrins (1). Integrins are heterodimeric proteins comprised of different $\alpha$ and $\beta$ subunits. There are more than 20 different types of each chain (e.g. $\alpha2$, $\alpha5$, $\alpha V$, $\beta1$, $\beta2$, $\beta3$, etc); the specific combination of the different subunits defines the molecular binding specificity (e.g. integrin $\alpha5\beta1$ binds fibronectin, whereas $\alpha2\beta1$ binds collagen).  In addition, the FACs contain multiple actin-binding proteins (e.g. talin, vinculin, $\alpha$-actinin, paxillin) that also interact with the cytoplasmic tail of the integrin and thereby form a molecular bridge that stretches continuously from ECM to the internal CSK (18).  Intermediate filaments also may insert on these adhesion complexes in certain cells (5).

Specialized cell-cell adhesion molecules (e.g. cadherins, selectins, CAMs) use some of the same actin-associated proteins (e.g. vinculin, $\alpha$-actinin) to physically couple to the actin CSK, but not others (e.g. not talin) (18, 80). Specialized CSK linker proteins, known as catenins, also interconnect cadherins to the actin CSK within adherens junctions at the lateral cell borders (19). Desmosomes represent sites in which the intermediate filament systems of

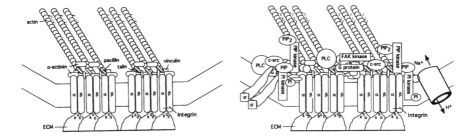

*Figure 2*   The cytoskeletal framework of the focal adhesion complex (*left*) comprised of clustered integrins and actin-associated molecules (e.g. vinculin, talin, paxillin, $\alpha$-actinin) physically interconnects the extracellular matrix to intracellular actin microfilaments (ends of stress fibers). These structural interconnections represent a preferred molecular pathway for transmembrane mechanical signal transfer. Many signal transducing molecules that mediate the cell's response to growth factors and ECM binding function when immobilized on the same molecular framework (*right*). Thus the focal adhesion complex may represent a major site for integration of chemical and mechanical signals.

neighboring cells are mechanically coupled; however, the molecular basis of transmembrane coupling is not as well understood.

Based on the above assumptions, we expected that both cell-generated stresses and external mechanical forces should converge on these localized adhesion sites. Thus we suggested that transmembrane receptors that physically couple internal CSK networks to external support scaffolds provided specific molecular pathways for mechanical signal transfer across the cell surface (27, 34). In other words, ECM receptors and cell-cell adhesion molecules could act as mechanoreceptors.

## Cellular Tensegrity

There was one final assumption: Cells are physically built to respond immediately to mechanical stress. The corollary is that understanding how cells stabilize their structure and shape may help to explain how cells sense and respond to mechanical signals. At the time we initiated our studies on cell structure, it was assumed that cell shape was controlled by either membrane surface tension, osmotic forces, CSK viscosity, or molecular polymerization. In contrast, we based our model of cell organization on the possibility that cells stabilize their extended forms by incorporating compression-resistant elements, either internal molecular struts or localized regions of the underlying ECM, to resist the otherwise global pull of the contractile CSK (34).

There is a known building system that self-stabilizes through use of isolated compression struts, which place the surrounding structural network under

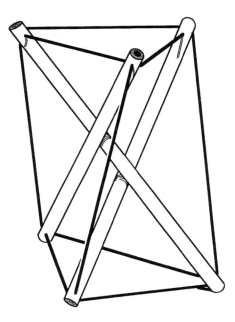

*Figure 3*    Tensegrity structures contain a series of isolated compression-resistant elements (*white struts*) that resist the pull of surrounding tensile elements (*black cables*) and impose a prestress that stabilizes the entire network. These structures may contain different size, shape, and number of building elements, and they may be organized hierarchically. Thus they can exhibit a wide range of forms that differ from this simple conceptual depiction.

tension and thereby create an internal prestress (Figure 3). This form of architecture is known as tensegrity because of its dependence on tensional integrity (30). In fact, this is the way our bodies are constructed: Our bones are held up against the force of gravity and mechanically stabilized through their tensile linkages with surrounding muscles and tendons. Even insects, which have an exoskeleton, and plants, which impose a global prestress through generation of local turgor pressures within individual cells, use a similar mechanism of structural stabilization.

Analysis of tensegrity cell models constructed by interconnecting multiple wood dowels with a continuous series of elastic strings revealed some interesting behavior (28, 31, 34). These cell models appeared round when unattached because of their internal tension; however, they spread out and flattened when they were attached to a rigid foundation. When the rigid foundation was then made flexible, the same model spontaneously contracted the substrate and returned to a round configuration, again because of the presence of internal tension. In other words, this simple stick and string tensegrity model mimicked the behavior of living cells cultured on malleable substrates.

These studies suggested that cell spreading may result from a transfer of CSK stresses onto the surrounding ECM and a concomitant shift in internal force distributions within the CSK, rather than from a net increase in the amount or length of CSK filaments. Mooney, working in my laboratory, recently approached this question directly by simultaneously measuring cell spreading kinetics and changes in microtubule and actin microfilament mass in liver epithelial cells (hepatocytes) plated on different ECM substrata (54). These studies demonstrated that spreading and flattening of the entire cell body is not driven directly by net polymerization of either microfilaments or microtubules. Instead, ECM proteins promote cell spreading by resisting cell tension and thereby promoting structural rearrangements within the CSK. These studies also provided evidence to suggest that microtubules do act as internal support struts (i.e. local compression elements) that resist the pull of the surrounding contractile actin CSK in these cells, as previously demonstrated in many other cell types (reviewed in 28). Stiffened (cross-linked) bundles of actin filaments also bear local compression when they push out against the surrounding tensed CSK and interconnected cortical membrane to form thin finger-like projections called filopodia in migrating cells (66). Thus living cells appear to use tensegrity to stabilize their form.

HIERARCHICAL FEATURES    Tissues are organized as a structural hierarchy; they are composed of groupings of individual cells that, in turn, contain specific arrangements of smaller organelles exhibiting their own mechanical stability. For example, the nucleus contains its own internal structural framework or nuclear matrix (56) and, in fact, nuclei can be physically transplanted from one cell to another without loss of function. Yet, when a cell spreads on a culture dish, its nucleus also extends in parallel (35).

Importantly, tensegrity can provide a mechanical basis for this hierarchical behavior. This can be visualized by constructing a model in which tensile threads are stretched from the surface of a large tensegrity structure to a smaller tensegrity sphere placed at its center. When this round model attaches and spreads on a rigid substrate, the cell and nucleus extend in a coordinated manner (Figure 4). The nucleus also polarizes basally because stress concentrates at the cell base. In vitro experiments confirm that living cells and nuclei spread and polarize in a similar manner when they adhere to ECM (36).

The tensegrity structures used here are conceptual models that represent a mechanism of form stabilization that should be independent of scale and thus may apply equally well at the organ, tissue, cell, organelle, or molecular levels (30). Furthermore, all the interconnected molecular elements in these hierarchical assemblies feel the same pull (albeit to varying degrees) and respond in

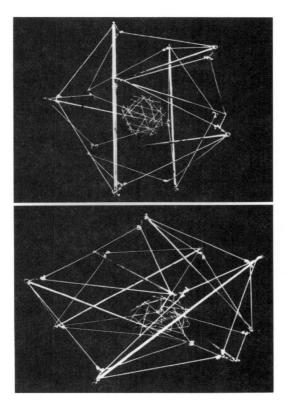

*Figure 4*   A two-tier hierarchical tensegrity model that mimics the behavior of nucleated cells. The larger model is constructed from aluminum struts and elastic cord. The smaller geodesic sphere at its center is composed of wooden sticks and thin white elastic thread. The two independently stable structures spread in a coordinated manner (bottom view vs top) and function as a single mechanically integrated unit because they are interconnected by thin black elastic threads that cannot be seen due to the black background.

an integrated manner, as visualized in the two-tier, nucleated tensegrity model (Figure 4). The flexibility and interconnectedness of this type of network could explain why large-scale movements (e.g. walking, running, sitting) can mechanically deform tissues, ECM, CSK, and nuclei without causing breaks or tears. More importantly in the present context, these modeling studies imply that living cells and nuclei might be hard-wired to respond directly to mechanical forces that are applied to specific cell surface receptors and, in particular, receptors that mediate cell adhesion. Thus we set out to test this hypothesis and to explore whether cells respond to external stresses through use of a tensegrity mechanism for force integration.

## *Molecular Pathways for Mechanical Signal Transfer*

ADHESION RECEPTORS AS MECHANORECEPTORS    To determine whether mechanical signals are transferred across the cell surface over discrete molecular pathways, we developed a device to apply controlled mechanical stresses directly to specific cell surface receptors without producing global changes in cell shape or altering fluid flow (74). Shear stress (torque) was applied to membrane-bound ferromagnetic microbeads (1–6 $\mu$m in diameter) that were coated with ligands or antibodies for different cell surface receptors by first magnetizing the beads in one direction and then applying a weaker twisting magnetic field that did not remagnetize the beads in the perpendicular orientation. The cellular deformation that resulted in response to stress application was determined by simultaneously quantitating bead rotation (angular strain) using an in-line magnetometer.

Using this magnetic twisting technique, we were able to demonstrate that applying shear stress to cell surface integrin receptors results in a stress-dependent increase in CSK stiffness (defined as the ratio of stress to strain) (Figure 5). As predicted by the tensegrity model, this response is mediated through higher order structural interactions between all the different CSK filament systems (i.e. microfilaments, microtubules, and intermediate filaments). In contrast, application of force to other transmembrane receptors that do not normally mediate adhesion (e.g. acetylated low-density lipoprotein receptor, HLA antigen) does not induce CSK stiffening (74, 80).

More recently, we confirmed that different integrins ($\beta$1, $\beta$3, $\alpha$V, $\alpha$5, $\alpha$2) and cell-cell adhesion molecules (e.g. E-selectin, PECAM) can mediate force transfer across the cell surface and to the CSK, although the efficiency of coupling varies considerably from receptor to receptor (76, 80). In addition, we have been able to demonstrate that similar mechanical coupling between integrins and CSK is observed in many cell types, that this stiffening response does not require membrane continuity, and that dynamic changes in cell shape are driven by actomyosin-based tension generation and accompanied by coordinated changes in CSK mechanics (67, 75, 76). Other laboratories also have demonstrated that integrins physically couple to the CSK (65) and that they transfer CSK tension to the ECM (64). Importantly, both mechanosensation in animal cells and gravitropism in plants can be inhibited by interfering with integrin binding, using soluble synthetic peptides that are specific for these receptors (7, 74, 78, 79). Taken together, these results support our hypothesis that adhesion receptors such as integrins act as mechanoreceptors because they are among the first cell surface molecules to sense mechanical stress and thereby transmit these signals across the cell surface over a specific molecular pathway.

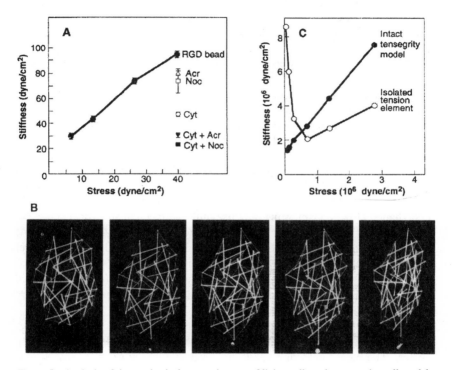

*Figure 5* Analysis of the mechanical responsiveness of living cells and a tensegrity cell model. (*A*) The stiffness (ratio of stress to strain) of the CSK of living cells was measured using magnetic twisting cytometry. Nocodazole (Noc; 10 $\mu$g/ml), cytochalasin D (Cyt; 0.1 $\mu$g/ml), and acrylamide (Acr; 4 mM) each independently suppress the CSK stiffening response by interfering with microtubules, microfilaments, and intermediate filaments, respectively. (*B*) A tensegrity cell model under different mechanical loads. This model consists of a geodesic spherical array of wood dowels (0.3 × 15 cm) and thin elastic threads (0.06 × 6 cm). The model was suspended from above and loaded, from left to right, with 0, 20, 50, 100, or 200 g weights on a single strut at its lower end. (*C*) Stiffness of the stick and string tensegrity model is defined as the ratio of applied stress to strain (linear deformation of the entire structure). Similar measurements were carried out using an isolated tension element, i.e. a single thin elastic thread of similar size to that found in the model. (Reprinted with permission from Reference 74.)

MECHANICAL COUPLING TO THE CYTOSKELETON    Transmembrane force transfer across integrins correlates with recruitment of the FAC proteins, vinculin,
$\alpha$-actinin, and talin and, thus, physical linkage of integrins to the actin CSK (74).
In collaboration with Ezzel (14), we recently compared the mechanical properties of mutant cells that lack vinculin with wild-type cells and two different
vinculin-transfected clones. Interestingly, cells that lacked vinculin retained the
ability to form filopodia and contained normal levels of total polymerized and
cross-linked actin, yet they could not form lamellipodia, assemble stress fibers,
or efficiently spread when plated on ECM. The loss of vinculin also resulted
in inhibition of FAC formation and in a decrease in the mechanical stiffness of
the integrin-CSK linkage, as measured using cell magnetometry. Furthermore,
when vinculin was replaced by transfection, the efficiency of transmembrane
mechanical coupling, stress fiber formation, and cell spreading were all restored
to near wild-type levels.

Vinculin, therefore, may represent one of the downstream molecules mediating the mechanical signaling cascade that begins with a tug on an integrin and
results in stress-dependent changes in CSK structure and associated changes in
cell shape. However, integrins may use multiple mechanisms for mechanical
coupling. For example, integrin $\alpha2$ appears to bind directly to actin filaments
(40). This integrin also exhibits an enhanced ability to mediate collagen gel
contraction when compared with other integrin subtypes (64). Future studies will be necessary to fully map the molecular pathways that mediate force
transfer within the FAC, as well as in cell-cell adhesion complexes.

A LOCAL SIGNAL PRODUCES A GLOBAL RESPONSE    Magnetic cytometry studies
show that living cells respond to increasing levels of applied stress by getting
stiffer. The most interesting result, however, is that the shape of the stiffening response is linear: the mechanical stiffness of the CSK increases in direct
proportion as the level of applied stress is raised (Figure 5). Cultured endothelium exhibits a similar response when exposed to fluid shear stress (71). This
behavior is also a fundamental property of many living tissues, including muscle, mesentery, cartilage, skin, and bone, yet there is no known mechanical or
mathematical explanation for this behavior (17).

When we applied mechanical stresses to a tensegrity model, we found that it
also exhibited linear stiffening (Figure 5) (74). This response was due to a novel
structural property of tensegrity systems: all the interconnected structural elements globally reorient in response to a local stress (Figure 5). Cells and tissues
may similarly exhibit high mechanical strength because stresses applied locally
are distributed over thousands of interconnected molecular support elements.
More recent modeling studies have revealed that tensegrity also can explain
how different mechanical stress distributions can generate specific molecular

patterns (e.g. stress fibers, triangulated nets, geodesic domes) within the actin CSK, independently of any change in filament polymerization (28, 31).

Working with Stamenovic (69), we have developed a mathematical basis for the linear stiffening response exhibited by living cell and tissues based on tensegrity, starting from first principles. This approach confirms that two major parameters determine the mechanical stability of tensegrity structures: prestress and architecture. Prestress determines the initial stiffness of the structure and assures that the system will respond immediately when externally stressed. It also determines the characteristic frequency of vibration (harmonic oscillation) that the structure will exhibit. In contrast, architecture refers to the number of building elements, as well as how they distribute forces in space. This geometric feature determines how the interconnected structural elements rearrange and thus how the entire structural assembly stiffens in response to stress.

Both the original stick and string tensegrity cell models and this mathematical analysis incorporate elastic tensile elements to model dynamic changes in filament length. Actin filaments and microtubules are non-extensible; however, intermediate filaments are highly entangled polymers that progressively extend and straighten as the cell spreads. Recent studies also show that a highly elastic protein filament called titin exists in the CSK of many cells (39). In any case, even tensegrity structures that contain non-extensible filaments exhibit a linear stiffening response, although over a narrower range of extension. Furthermore, a tensegrity network composed of non-extensible sticks and strings can exhibit both linear stiffening and high flexibility if the stiff compression elements are allowed to buckle like microtubules do in living cells (M Coughlin & D Stamenovic, personal communication).

LIVING CELLS AND NUCLEI ARE HARD-WIRED    If cell surface integrin receptors, CSK filaments, and nuclear scaffolds are hard-wired together, as suggested by the tensegrity model, then mechanical stresses could be transferred well into the depth of the cell over specific molecular pathways. Maniotis, Chen & Bojanowski, working in my laboratory, recently found that living cells and nuclei are indeed hard-wired such that a mechanical tug on cell surface integrin receptors can immediately change CSK organization and alter the arrangement of molecular assemblies in the depth of the nucleus, in time periods much faster than those necessary for polymerization (49). This ability to produce an action at a distance was found to be specific for integrins, independent of cortical membrane distortion, and mediated by discrete linkages between the CSK and nucleus. Also, filamentous linkages could be demonstrated between different nucleoli in interphase cells and different chromosomes in mitosis (48, 49).

Analysis of the molecular basis of this transcellular mechanical coupling reveals that actin microfilaments alone are sufficient to mediate force transfer to the nucleus at low strains; however, intermediate filaments are required to maintain mechanical coupling at high deformation. These CSK cables also function as molecular guy wires to anchor the central nucleus in place and to control its mechanical stiffness. In contrast, microtubules act to stabilize the cytoplasm and nucleus against lateral compression.

In summary, these studies confirm that although the CSK is surrounded by membranes and penetrated by viscous cytosol, it is this discrete filamentous network that provides cytoplasm's principal mechanical strength, as well as the main path for mechanical signal transfer from the cell surface to the nucleus. Furthermore, the efficiency of force transfer depends directly on the mechanical properties of the CSK and nucleus which, in turn, are determined through cooperative interactions between microfilaments, intermediate filaments, and microtubules, just as was predicted by the tensegrity model. This prestressed system of molecular connections may therefore provide a discrete path for mechanical signal transfer through cells, as well as a mechanism for producing integrated changes in cell and nuclear structure in response to stress.

## Mechanisms for Mechanochemical Transduction

Much of the cell's metabolic machinery functions in a solid state. The chemical reactions mediating protein synthesis, RNA transport, glycolysis, and DNA synthesis all appear to involve channeling of sequestered substrates and products from one immobilized enzyme to another along insoluble CSK filaments and nuclear matrix scaffolds (reviewed in 29). Signal transduction may be regulated in a similar manner. For example, we and others have shown that multiple signaling molecules that are activated by integrins and growth factors (e.g. phosphatidylinositol-3-kinase, $Na^+/H^+$ antiporter, phospholipase C, $_{pp}60^{c-src}$, $_{pp}125^{FAK}$) become physically associated with the CSK framework of the FAC within minutes after integrin clustering is induced (52, 57). A subset of growth factor receptors (e.g. FGF receptors) also can be found within the same insoluble complexes (57).

Thus the CSK framework of the FAC may represent a major site for signal integration between growth factor and ECM-based signaling pathways (Figure 2). Because these signaling molecules lie in the main path for mechanical force transfer, the FAC represents a potential site for translating mechanical stresses into biochemical responses and for integrating these responses with those activated by growth factor and ECM binding. This possibility is supported by the finding that mechanical stretch increases phosphorylation of the focal adhesion tyrosine kinase, $_{pp}125^{FAK}$ (21).

Some investigators have interpreted the finding that mechanical stresses can raise the level of inositol phosphates and release calcium from intracellular stores to indicate that the membrane-associated enzyme that produces this product, phospholipase C, may be mechanosensitive. This is because growth factors commonly regulate this pathway by activating this enzyme. However, integrins can increase inositol phosphate production by another mechanism: They control the synthesis and, hence, availability of the inositol lipid substrate, phosphatidylinositol-bisphosphate (50). Interestingly, the phosphatidylinositol kinases that mediate this effect also are immobilized on the CSK within the FAC (51). This provides an excellent example of how mechanical stresses may be able to generate chemical signals through a variety of mechanisms and how difficult it is to interpret the molecular basis of mechanochemical transduction.

The findings presented above suggest that living cells and nuclei are literally built to sense and respond immediately to mechanical stresses applied to specific cell surface receptors such as integrins. Because of the presence of discrete CSK interconnections, mechanical stresses and vibrations may be preferentially transferred to distinct structures inside the cell and nucleus, including signaling molecules in the FAC, ion channels in the membrane, ribosomes, nuclear pores, chromosomes, and perhaps even individual genes. By distributing force over a relatively small number of support elements, this type of hard-wiring provides a mechanism to concentrate stress and focus mechanical energy on specific molecular elements that physically associate with the CSK. If cell and nuclear metabolism functions in a solid state, then stress-induced changes in scaffold geometry or mechanics could provide a mechanism to regulate and orchestrate the cellular response to force. This long-range force transfer could explain, for example, how cell stretching results in extension of the nucleus, physical expansion of nuclear pores, and associated increases in nucleocytoplasmic transport (15, 35).

GEOMETRIC REARRANGEMENTS    Our studies with living cells demonstrate that pulling on integrins causes the internal CSK and nuclear scaffolds to immediately realign along the main axis of the applied tension field (48, 49). Resultant changes in the topology of these networks could alter cellular biochemistry directly. For example, mRNAs specifically localize to intersections between different actin filaments, rather than along their length (4). Vertices within highly triangulated microfilament networks (e.g. within actin geodesic domes) are also preferred sites for actin polymerization, as observed during formation of filopodia that lead cell movement (60). Thus stress-induced changes in CSK architecture (e.g. transformation of triangulated nets to linear bundles) could influence protein synthesis by destabilizing CSK-associated mRNAs or change the dynamics of actin polymerization and thereby alter cell spreading or movement.

Geometric remodeling of the CSK also may influence other biochemical or enzymatic reactions that channel along CSK or nuclear scaffolds (e.g. glycolysis, DNA synthesis) (Figure 6). For example, mechanical deformation of the

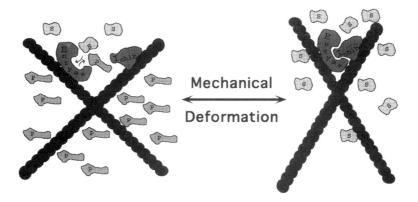

*Figure 6*  Mechanotransduction through geometric remodeling of CSK scaffolds. If biochemistry functions in a solid state, then changes in CSK network geometry may alter cell metabolism or signal transduction by changing the relative position of different regulatory molecules, hence altering their ability to chemically interact. Transduction also may be carried out through direct mechanical distortion of molecules that alters thermodynamic or kinetic parameters (not shown).

FAC may generate intracellular chemical signals by bringing immobilized kinases and substrates into direct juxtaposition, thereby facilitating downstream signaling. This type of direct mechanical coupling could explain how release of calcium and neurotransmitters from motor nerve terminals can be induced within 10 ms after integrins are stressed (7), as well as how $_{pp}125^{FAK}$ becomes phosphorylated in response to stretch (21).

CHANGES IN MOLECULAR MECHANICS    Molecules that are incorporated within insoluble macromolecular scaffolds bearing mechanical loads transmitted from integrins will feel a pull exerted on the cell surface, whereas neighboring soluble molecules only nanometers away will not. The transfer of focused mechanical energy to these molecules will therefore alter their chemical potential, as well as their shape (e.g. protein folding) and motion through mechanical distortion. These are the very features of molecules that determine their chemical behavior. In fact, chemical mechanisms for altering enzyme activity or signal transduction, such as protein tyrosine phosphorylation, actually manifest themselves at the biophysical level by altering protein flexibility and conformation (72). Thus mechanical energy could be converted directly into chemical energy through stress-induced changes in molecular shape or mechanics.

When a noncovalent adhesive bond between two proteins is either pulled or pushed, the chemical potential of that bond increases (i.e. the stable bond is at minimum energy) (reviewed in 45). Increasing the energy in the system may change chemical activities by effectively changing the activation energy, thus altering the rate constant for a reaction. If the association and dissociation constants are equally affected, the thermodynamics (ratio between the constants) will not be altered, and the equilibrium will remain the same, but the kinetics will change. If the forward and reverse reactions differ in their sensitivity to this deformation, then the thermodynamics will be altered and the equilibrium will shift. Finally, the oscillatory motion of molecules, a key kinetic determinant of how they behave chemically, also can be altered by altering molecular shape or stiffness. Thus stress-induced changes in molecular mechanics can produce direct mechanochemical transduction in a number of ways.

## Thermodynamic Regulation

An example of a thermodynamic transduction mechanism in living cells comes from analysis of the response of CSK microtubules to changes in mechanical stress. If the cytoplasm were entirely viscous, individual CSK filaments could not experience a tension or compression along their length. However, microtubules can feel compression because contractile microfilaments can insert at their ends or, in other words, because cells use tensegrity architecture.

A thermodynamic model was developed that incorporates tensegrity to explain how microtubule assembly is controlled within nerve cells (6). The formation of long nerve processes called neurites is mediated by elongation of CSK microtubules through polymerization. Microtubules are dynamic polymers of tubulin that rapidly polymerize and depolymerize in response to changes in the concentration of free tubulin monomer (41). Tensegrity predicts that each time a moving neurite forms a new adhesion, it transfers some compression from its internal microtubule struts to the external compression-resistant ECM. Decompressing a microtubule decreases its chemical potential, thereby lowering the critical concentration of tubulin required to maintain it in a polymerized form (25). Thus free tubulin monomers will be added to the ends of the microtubule until the tubulin monomer concentration decreases sufficiently to restore the equilibrium, or until the preexisting force balance is reestablished.

Analysis of living nerve cells has confirmed that microtubule polymerization is indeed sensitive to changes in tension in the surrounding actin CSK (38), as well as to alterations in cell-ECM adhesions (44). Microtubule assembly also can be induced by applying external tension directly to the surface membranes of these cells (10). Epithelial cells sense the same change in thermodyamic parameters in their microtubules when they attach and spread on ECM; however, they apparently have evolved a mechanism to produce a different molecular response (53). Rather than increasing microtubule polymerization, they react enzymatically by producing a concomitant increase in the rate of tubulin protein degradation when they transfer force from microtubules to the ECM. This results in a net decrease in the concentration of free tubulin monomer until it matches the new lower critical concentration for tubulin. The net effect is that the total mass of polymerized microtubules remains constant when epithelial cells spread, whereas it increases during neurite extension.

The sensitivity of tubulin to tensegrity-based thermodynamic alterations may play an important role in signal transduction because many cellular functions (e.g. production of cAMP, actin filament organization) can vary depending on the state of microtubule polymerization (46, 47). Furthermore, dimeric tubulin can bind to specific G proteins, such as those that mediate adenylyl cyclase activation, and activate their GTPase activity via direct transfer of GTP (58). This is one explanation of how mechanical stresses and receptors that are not directly coupled to G proteins (e.g. integrins) may activate this signaling pathway.

## Kinetic Regulation

One of the best examples of how mechanical stresses can alter reaction kinetics comes from analysis of cell adhesion and spreading (45). Because of the dynamics of cell adhesion, the equilibrium state may never be reached since the cell may not be able to form enough bonds fast enough to prevent detachment. This is particularly important in situations where cells that are trying to form new adhesions are exposed to mechanical stresses. For example, very fast on and off rates are required for leukocyte attachment and rolling on the endothelial cell surface at physiological shear stresses (2). Furthermore, all cells exert tractional forces on their adhesion receptors, and changes in receptor kinetics likely play a central role in most adhesive phenomena.

Analysis of how pulling or compressing the adhesive bond may alter chemical reaction rate constants has revealed that two types of dynamic behavior may result depending on the relative stiffness of the transition state and the bond (45). If the bond is stiffer than the transition state, bond dissociation will be accelerated by the application of stress and, hence, the bond will slip. If the bond is more flexible than its transition state, stressing the bond will actually decrease the dissociation rate and thus cause the bond to catch. Meanwhile, the forward rate constant (association rate) may or may not be altered. Analogous slide and catch bonds between different molecules may govern how higher order CSK scaffolds deform in response to stress. However, the main point is that mechanically stressing any molecule alters its behavior in a number of ways. The same mechanical stimulus may also produce an entirely different response depending on the structural properties of each molecular sensor.

Another kinetic feature that can be altered by mechanical stresses is molecular movement or vibration, one of the most important determinants of molecular function. To understand how mechanical stress alters molecular motion, think of a molecule as a semiflexible spring that is fixed at its lower end and contains a dense ball bearing at its center. This spring exhibits a characteristic frequency of lateral vibration (harmonic frequency) that is a function of the inherent stiffness of the spring and the placement of its center of mass. If temperature and energy are constant, then shifting the center of mass closer to the lower fixed end of the spring or shortening its length (e.g. by altering protein folding) will cause the frequency of oscillation to increase and the amplitude (range of motion) to decrease, much like shortening the cable on a pendulum. Another way to alter the rate of vibration is to change the stiffness of the spring; decreasing its flexibility (e.g. by distending the molecule) will cause it to vibrate more quickly over a narrower range, much like a violin string does when it is stiffened (tensed). Furthermore, application of vibrational motion of the same frequency as the natural harmonic of the structure will result in an increase in the amplitude of vibration (range of motion) without changing the rate. Thus different molecules may be sensitive to different vibration frequencies. Of course, both frequency and amplitude also may be altered by adding energy to the system.

Therefore, stress-induced changes in molecular shape and mechanics can change a reaction rate, such as transport of an anion through a channel, by varying the frequency of channel opening or closing, or by changing the size of the pore opening at a given rate of vibration. Interestingly, many mechanosensitive ion channels respond to stress kinetically by altering their opening or closing rates (23). Moreover, normal mechanosensitive ion channel sensitivity and adaptation responses become deregulated when membrane-CSK linkages are disrupted (23, 70).

## Tuning the Transduction Response

Tensegrity provides a mechanism to mechanically and harmonically couple interconnected structures at different size scales and in different locations throughout living cells and tissues (30, 34, 55). Thus cell and tissue tone may be tuned by altering the prestress in the system. This may be accomplished by altering the architecture of the system or the level of CSK tension (69). In either case, increasing the stiffness of the network will alter vibration frequencies and associated molecular mechanics of all the constituent support elements. This may, in part, explain how the part (molecule, cell) and whole (e.g. cell, tissue, organ, organism) can function as a single mechanically integrated system (30).

This tuning mechanism also may play an important role in mechanical signal amplification, as well as in the adaptation responses that are necessary to tune out certain signals. For example, recombinant mechanosensitive ion channels can be activated by direct mechanical deformation when placed in synthetic liposomes that lack any CSK interconnections (70). However, when compared with similar channels analyzed in in situ in living cells, these channels appear to be hypersensitive and to lack normal adaptive responses (23, 70). If the mechanically stressed liposome containing the ion channel is viewed like a sail luffing in the wind, then the addition of CSK connections and associated transfer of tension may act to winch in the membrane and thus alter its range of motion and frequency of vibration as well as its stiffness. Any one of these changes may feed back to tune the mechanotransduction response, as seen in studies with intact cells (23, 70).

On a larger scale, alterations in CSK stiffness or in the number of load-bearing elements in the system will change how stress dissipates in the network before it reaches the molecular transducer. A cell that is very stiff may be able to sense lower levels of stress more quickly than a more flexible cell. Conversely, the more flexible cell may be able to sense larger strains. This adaptability may contribute to the different sensitivities exhibited by specialized mechanosensory cells; for example, the stiff hair cells of the inner ear sense small vibrations, whereas more flexible spindle cells of muscle recognize changes in length (stretch). A similar mechanism may explain why osteocytes, which contain highly extended (and hence stiffened) processes, preferentially respond to high frequency and low amplitude strains (13).

In addition, the way in which the CSK is organized (i.e. the architectural feature in the mathematical model) will itself alter the way in which the cell senses and responds to stress. For example, the shape of the mechanosensory cell may alter how it vibrates and thus determine its ability to sense particular vibration frequencies. The hair cell of the inner ear provides a beautiful example of this type of structural specialization. These cells contain numerous cylindrical projections on their apices called stereocilia, which contain cross-linked bundles of CSK filaments surrounded by a tightly apposed surface membrane. These rigid struts are, in turn, interconnected at their lateral borders by filamentous tip links. The presence of these lateral tensile connections pull together the individual stiffened stereocilia and create a local tensegrity force balance, thereby stabilizing the entire apical region of the cell. Their disruption results in both disorganization of cell architecture and loss of mechanosensitivity. Although it is commonly assumed that these tip links directly interconnect with their target mechanosensitive ion channels, recent studies suggest that these transducing molecules are located at a more distant site (20). This long-range effect may be explained by the use of tensegrity. Interestingly, conditions that cause mechanoreceptor cells in the fishing tentacles of sea anemones to tune their sensitivity to different vibration frequencies also produce changes in the length of their stereocilia and in the shape of their CSK (77).

Finally, because the ECM physically interconnects with the CSK, its mechanical properties also may contribute significantly to the mechanotransduction response. If the ECM is highly flexible, then a rapid deformation may be sensed, whereas a sustained stress will dissipate before it reaches the cell. In fact, this very mechanism is used by Pacinian corpuscle mechanoreceptor cells of skin to filter out sustained signals (arising from continuous pressure or touch), a common form of receptor adaptation. If the ECM is less flexible, then stresses may be transmitted to and through the cell, only to be dissipated through movements in the CSK. For example, when fluid shear stress is applied to the apical membrane of endothelium, the cell and its CSK are immediately pulled against their fixed basal adhesions to ECM. This can be visualized by dynamic changes in FAC remodeling at the cell base, which occur within seconds to minutes after shear is exerted (9). The resistance imposed by the relatively inflexible ECM induces global rearrangements in the CSK through a tensegrity mechanism, as measured by a linear stiffening response (71). These changes in CSK mechanics, in turn, may serve to simultaneously modulate multiple signaling mechanisms. A similar response could be induced throughout the cell by a change in osmolarity that causes the cell membrane to pull outward or inward against its CSK tethers.

## CONCLUSIONS

The purpose of this chapter is to review the architectural and molecular basis of cellular mechanotransduction, with particular emphasis on the process of signal integration. The experimental studies reviewed suggest that cell surface adhesion receptors (e.g. integrins, cell-cell adhesion molecules), interconnected CSK networks, and associated nuclear scaffolds function as a structurally unified system. This system gains its mechanical stability and long-range flexibility from tensional continuity, discrete load-bearing members, and the presence of internal prestress. These are the fundamental requirements of tensegrity architecture. Use of tensegrity could serve to concentrate stresses and focus mechanical energy on mechanochemical and mechanoelectrical transducing molecules that physically associate with the insoluble CSK. It also may provide a mechanism to orchestrate and tune the entire cellular response to stress.

These studies also suggest that the specialized anchoring complexes or FACs that mediate mechanical coupling between CSK, integrins, and ECM may represent a potentially important site for signal integration because molecules that transduce signals from ECM, growth factors, and mechanical stresses all appear to concentrate in this location. Similar signal integration also may occur within junctional complexes at the lateral cell borders (18). Mechanochemical transduction may, in turn, result from changes in the CSK geometry or mechanics that alter local thermodynamic or kinetic parameters. This type of direct mechanical coupling could serve to modulate slower diffusion-based chemical signaling pathways and coordinate functional changes throughout the depth of the cytoplasm and nucleus. Thus, in simplest terms, the CSK may be viewed as mechanical filter: The same chemical or mechanical input will produce a different output (cellular response) depending on the geometry and mechanics of this structural framework. Use of tensegrity by cells may therefore help to explain how distortion of the cell or CSK caused by gravity, hemodynamic forces, pressure, stretch, or even cell tension (32, 37, 54, 68) can alter cellular biochemistry and switch cells between different genetic programs.

ACKNOWLEDGMENTS

I would like to thank Chris Chen and Doug Lauffenburger for their helpful discussions and Judah Folkman and Ramzi Cotran for their continued support. This research is funded by grants from NASA, NIH, and DOD. DEI is a recipient of a Faculty Research Award from the American Cancer Society.

*Literature Cited*

1. Albelda AM, Buck CA. 1990. Integrins and other cell adhesion molecules. *FASEB J.* 4:2868–80
2. Alon R, Hammer DA, Springer TA. 1995. Lifetime of the P-selectin-carbohydrate bond and its response to tensile force in hydrodynamic flow. *Nature* 374:539–42
3. Basdra EK, Papavassiliou AG, Huber LA. 1995. Rab and rho GTPases are involved in specific response of periodontal ligament fibroblasts to mechanical stretching. *Biochim. Biophys. Acta* 1268:209–13
4. Bassell GJ, Powers CM, Taneja KL, Singer RH. 1994. Single mRNAs visualized by ultrastructural in situ hybridization are principally localized at actin filament intersections in fibroblasts. *J. Cell Biol.* 126:863–76
5. Bershadsky AD, Tint IS, Svitkina TM. 1987. Association of intermediate filaments with vinculin-containing adhesion plaques of fibroblasts. *Cell Motil. Cytoskelet.* 8:274–83
6. Buxbaum RE, Heideman SR. 1988. A thermodynamic model for force integration and microtubule assembly during axonal elongation. *J. Theor. Biol.* 134:379–90
7. Chen BM, Grinnell AD. 1995. Integrins and modulation of transmitter release from motor nerve terminals by stretch. *Science* 269:1578–80
8. Davies PF. Flow-mediated endothelial mechanotransduction. *Physiol. Rev.* 75:519–60
9. Davies PF, Robotewsky JA, Griem ML.

1994. Quantitative studies of endothelial cell adhesion. Directional remodeling of focal adhesion sites in response to flow forces. *J. Clin. Invest.* 93:2031–38
10. Dennerll TJ, Joshi HC, Steel VL, Buxbaum RE, Heideman SR. 1988. Tension and compression in the cytoskeleton of PC-12 neurites II: quantitative measurements. *J. Cell Biol.* 107:665–74
11. Ding JP, Pickard BG. 1993. Mechanosensory calcium-selective cation channels in epidermal cells. *Plant J.* 3:83–110
12. Du H, Gu G, William CM, Chalfie M. 1996. Extracellular proteins needed for *C. elegans* mechanosensation. *Neuron* 16:183–94
13. Duncan RL, Turner CH. 1995. Mechanotransduction and the functional response of bone to mechanical strain. *Calcif. Tissue Int.* 57:344–58
14. Ezzell RM, Goldmann WH, Wang N, Parasharama N, Ingber DE. 1996. Vinculin promotes cell spreading by mechanically coupling integrins to the cytoskeleton. *J. Cell Biol.* Submitted
15. Feldherr CM, Akin D. 1993. Regulation of nuclear transport in proliferating and quiescent cells. *Exp. Cell Res.* 205:179–86
16. French AS. 1992. Mechanotransduction. *Annu. Rev. Physiol.* 54:135–52
17. Fung YC. 1988. *Biomechanics: Mechanical Properties of Living Tissues.* New York: Springer-Verlag
18. Geiger B, Yehuda-Levenberg S, Bershadsky AD. 1996. Molecular interactions in

the submembrane plaque of cell-cell and cell-matrix adhesions. *Ann. Anat.* In press

19. Gumbiner BM. 1993. Proteins associated with the cytoplasmic surface of adhesion molecules. *Neuron* 11:551–64

20. Hackney CM, Furness DN. 1995. Mechanotransduction invertebrate hair cells: structure and function of the stereociliary bundle. *Am. J. Physiol.* 268:C1–13

21. Hamasaki K, Mimura T, Furuya H, Morino N, Yamazaki T, et al. 1995. Stretching mesangial cells stimulates tyrosine phosphorylation of focal adhesion kinase pp125$^{FAK}$. *Biochem. Biophys. Res. Commun.* 212:544–49

22. Harris AK, Wild P, Stopak D. 1980. Silicone rubber substrata: a new wrinkle in the study of cell locomotion. *Science* 208:177–80

23. Hamill OP, McBride DW Jr. 1992. Rapid adaptation of single mechanosensitive channels in *Xenopus* oocytes. *Proc. Natl. Acad. Sci. USA* 89:7462–66

24. He Y, Grinnell F. 1994. Stress relaxation of fibroblasts activates a cyclic AMP signaling pathway. *J. Cell Biol.* 126:457–64

25. Hill TL. 1981. Microfilament and microtubule assembly or disassociation against a force. *Proc. Natl. Acad. Sci. USA* 78:5613–17

26. Hong K, Driscoll M. 1994. A transmembrane domain of the putative channel subunit MEC-4 influences mechanotransduction and neurodegeneration in *C. elegans. Nature* 367:470–73

27. Ingber DE. 1991. Integrins as mechanochemical transducers. *Curr. Opin. Cell Biol.* 3:841–48

28. Ingber DE. 1993. Cellular tensegrity: defining new rules of biological design that govern the cytoskeleton. *J. Cell Sci.* 104:613–27

29. Ingber DE. 1993. The riddle of morphogenesis: a question of solution chemistry or molecular cell engineering? *Cell* 75:1249–52

30. Ingber DE. 1997. The architecture of life. *Sci. Am.* In press

31. Ingber DE, Dike L, Hansen L, Karp S, Liley H, et al. 1994. Cellular tensegrity: exploring how mechanical changes in the cytoskeleton regulate cell growth, migration, and tissue pattern during morphogenesis. *Int. Rev. Cytol.* 150:173–224

32. Ingber DE, Folkman J. 1989. Mechanochemical switching between growth and differentiation during fibroblast growth factor-stimulated angiogenesis in vitro: role of extracellular matrix. *J. Cell Biol.* 109:317–30

33. Ingber DE, Folkman J. 1989. How does extracellular matrix control capillary morphogenesis? *Cell* 58:803–5

34. Ingber DE, Jamieson JD. 1985. Cells as tensegrity structures: architectural regulation of histodifferentiation by physical forces tranduced over basement membrane. In *Gene Expression During Normal and Malignant Differentiation,* ed. LC Andersson, CG Gahmberg, P Ekblom, pp. 13–32. Orlando, FL: Academic

35. Ingber DE, Madri JA, Folkman J. 1987. Extracellular matrix regulates endothelial growth factor action through modulation of cell and nuclear expansion. *In Vitro Cell Dev. Biol.* 23:387–94

36. Ingber DE, Madri JA, Jamieson JD. 1986. Basement membrane as a spatial organizer of polarized epithelia: Exogenous basement membrane reorients pancreatic epithelial tumor cells in vitro. *Am. J. Pathol.* 122:129–39

37. Ingber DE, Prusty D, Sun Z, Betensky H, Wang N. 1995. Cell shape, cytoskeletal mechanics and cell cycle control in angiogenesis. *J. BioMechanics* 28:1471–84

38. Joshi HC, Chu D, Buxbaum RE, Heideman SR. 1985. Tension and compression in the cytoskeleton of PC 12 neurites. *J. Cell Biol.* 101:697–705

39. Keller TC III. 1995. Structure and function of titin and nebulin. *Curr. Opin. Cell Biol.* 7:32–38

40. Kieffer JD, Plopper G, Ingber DE, Hartwig JH, Kupper TS. 1995. Direct binding of F-actin to the cytoplasmic domain of the $\alpha2$ integrin chain in vitro. *Biochem. Biophys. Res. Comm.* 217:466–74

41. Kirschner M, Mitchison T. 1986. Beyond self-assembly: from microtubules to morphogenesis. *Cell* 45:329–42

42. Kolodnoy M, Wysolmerski RB. 1992. Isometric contraction by fibroblasts and endothelial cells in tissue culture: a quantitative study. *J. Cell Biol.* 117:73–82

43. Kuchan MJ, Jo H, Frangos JA. 1994. Role of G proteins in shear stress-mediated nitric oxide production by endothelial cells. *Am. J. Physiol.* 267:C753–58

44. Lamoureux P, Steel VL, Regal C, Adgate L, Buxbaum RE, Heideman SR. 1990. Extracellular matrix allows PC-12 neurite elongation in the absence of microtubules. *J. Cell Biol.* 110:71–79

45. Lauffenburger DA, Linderman JJ. 1993. *Receptors: Models for Binding, Trafficking, and Signaling.* New York: Oxford Univ. Press.

46. Malek AM, Izumo S. 1996. Mechanism of endothelial cell shape change and cytoskeletal remodeling in response to fluid

shear stress. *J. Cell Sci.* 109:713–26

47. Manie S, Schmid-Alliana A, Kubar J, Ferrua B, Rossi B. 1993. Disruption of microtubule network in human monocytes induces expression of interleukin-1 but not that of interleukin-6 nor tumor necrosis factor-alpha. Involvement of protein kinase A stimulation. *J. Biol. Chem.* 268:13675–81

48. Maniotis A, Bojanowski K, Ingber DE. 1997. Mechanical continuity and reversable chromosome disassembly within intact genomes removed from living cells. *J. Cell. Biochem.* Submitted

49. Maniotis A, Chen C, Ingber DE. 1997. Direct evidence for mechanical connections between cell surface integrin receptors, cytoskeletal filaments and the nucleoplasm in living cells. *Proc. Natl. Acad. USA.* In press

50. McNamee H, Ingber D, Schwartz M. 1993. Adhesion to fibronectin stimulates inositol lipid synthesis and enhances PDGF-induced inositol lipid breakdown. *J. Cell Biol.* 121:673–78

51. McNamee HP, Liley HG, Ingber DE. 1996. Integrin-dependent control of inositol lipid synthesis in the focal adhesion complex. *Exp. Cell Res.* 224:116–22

52. Miyamoto S, Akiyama S, Yamada KM. 1995. Synergistic roles for receptor occupancy and aggregation in integrin transmembrane function. *Science* 267:883–85

53. Mooney D, Hansen L, Langer R, Vacanti JP, Ingber DE. 1994. Extracellular matrix controls tubulin monomer levels in hepatocytes by regulating protein turnover. *Mol. Biol. Cell* 5:1281–88

54. Mooney D, Langer R, Ingber DE. 1995. Cytoskeletal filament assembly and the control of cell shape and function by extracellular matrix. *J. Cell Sci.* 108:2311–20

55. Pienta KJ, Coffey DS. 1991. Cellular harmonic information transfer through a tissue tensegrity-matrix system. *Med. Hypoth.* 34:88–95

56. Pienta KJ, Getzenberg RH, Coffey DS. 1991. Cell structure and DNA organization. *Crit. Rev. Eukaryot. Gene Express.* 1:355–85

57. Plopper G, McNamee H, Dike L, Bojanowski K, Ingber DE. 1995. Convergence of integrin and growth factor receptor signaling pathways within the focal adhesion complex. *Mol. Biol. Cell* 6:1349–65

58. Popova JS, Johnson GL, Rasenick MM. 1994. Chimeric $G_{\alpha}s/G_{\alpha}i2$ proteins define domains on $G_{\alpha}s$ that interact with tubulin for $\beta$-adrenergic activation of adenylyl cyclase. *J. Biol. Chem.* 269:21748–54

59. Prasad AR, Logan SA, Nerem RM, Schwartz CJ, Sprague EA. 1993. Flow-related responses of intracellular inositol phosphate levels in cultured aortic endothelial cells. *Circ. Res.* 72:827–36

60. Rathke PC, Osborn M, Weber K. 1979. Immunological and ultrastructural characterization of microfilament bundles: polygonal nets and stress fibers in an established cell line. *Eur. J. Cell Biol.* 19:40–48

61. Resnick N, Collins T, Atkinson W, Bonthron DT, Dewey CF Jr, Gimbrone M Jr. 1993. Platelet-derived growth factor B chain promoter contains a *cis*-acting fluid stress-response element. *Proc. Natl. Acad. Sci. USA* 90:4591–95

62. Sadoshima J, Takahashi T, Jahn L, Izumo S. 1992. Roles of mechano-sensitive ion channels, cytoskeleton, and contractile activity in stretch-induced immediate-early gene expression and hypertrophy of cardiac myocytes. *Proc. Natl. Acad. Sci. USA* 89:9905–9

63. Sadoshima J, Xu Y, Slayter HS, Izumo S. 1993. Autocrine release of angiotensin II mediates stretch-induced hypertrophy of cardiac myocytes in vitro. *Cell* 75:977–84

64. Schiro JA, Chan BM, Roswit WT, Kassner PD, Pentland AP, et al. 1991. Integrin $\alpha 2\beta 1$ (VLA-2) mediates reorganization and contraction of collagen matrices by human cells. *Cell* 67:403–10

65. Schmidt CE, Horwitz AF, Lauffenburger DA, Sheetz MP. 1993. Integrin-regulated cytoskeletal interactions in migrating fibroblasts are dynamic, asymmetric and regulated. *J. Cell Biol.* 123:977–91

66. Sheetz MP, Wayne DB, Pearlman AL. 1992. Extension of filopodia by motor-dependent actin assembly. *Cell Motil. Cytoskelet.* 22:160–69

67. Sims J, Karp S, Ingber DE. 1992. Altering the cellular mechanical force balance results in integrated changes in cell, cytoskeletal and nuclear shape. *J. Cell. Sci.* 103:1215–22

68. Singhvi R, Kumar A, Lopez G, Stephanopoulos GN, Wang DIC, et al. 1994. Engineering cell shape and function. *Science* 264:696–98

69. Stamenovic D, Fredberg J, Wang N, Butler J, Ingber D. 1996. A microstructural approach to cytoskeletal mechanics based on tensegrity. *J. Theor. Biol.* In press

70. Sukharev SI, Martinac B, Arshavsky VY, Kung C. 1993. Two types of mechanosensitive channels in the *Escherichia coli* cell envelope: solubilization and functional reconstitution. *Biophys. J.* 65:177–83

71. Thoumine O, Ziegler T, Girard PR, Nerem RM. 1995. Elongation of confluent endothelial cells in culture: the importance of fields of force in the associated alterations of their cytoskeletal structure. *Exp. Cell Res.* 219:427–41

72. Urry D. 1992. Free energy transduction in polypeptides and proteins based on inverse temperature transitions. *Prog. Biophys. Mol. Biol.* 57:23–57

73. Vandenburgh HH, Shansky J, Solerssi R, Chromiak J. 1995. Mechanical stimulation of skeletal muscle increases prostaglandin F2$\alpha$ production, cyclooxygenase activity, and cell growth by a pertussis toxin-sensitive mechanism. *J. Cell. Physiol.* 163:285–94

74. Wang N, Butler JP, Ingber DE. 1993. Mechanotransduction across the cell surface and through the cytoskeleton. *Science* 260:1124–27

75. Wang N, Ingber DE. 1994. Control of cytoskeletal mechanics by extracellular matrix, cell shape, and mechanical tension. *Biophys. J.* 66:2181–89

76. Wang N, Ingber DE. 1995. Probing transmembrane mechanical coupling and cytomechanics using magnetic twisting cytometry. *Biochem. Cell. Biol.* 73:1–9

77. Watson GM, Hessinger DA. 1992. Receptors for N-acetylated sugars may stimulate adenylate cyclase to sensitize and tune mechanoreceptors involved in triggering nematocyst discharge. *Exp. Cell Res.* 198:8–16

78. Wayne R, Staves MP, Leopold AC. 1992. The contribution of the extracellular matrix to gravisensing in characean cells. *J. Cell Sci.* 101:611–23

79. Wilson E, Sudhir K, Ives HE. 1995. Mechanical strain of rat vascular smooth muscle cells is sensed by specific extracellular matrix/integrin interactions. *J. Clin. Invest.* 96:2364–72

80. Yoshida M, Westlin WF, Wang N, Ingber DE, Rosenweig A, et al. 1996. Leukocyte adhesion to vascular endothelium induces E-selectin association with the actin cytoskeleton. *J. Cell Biol.* 133:445–55

*Annu. Rev. Physiol. 1997. 59:601–19*

# OSMORECEPTORS IN THE CENTRAL NERVOUS SYSTEM

## Charles W. Bourque and Stéphane H. R. Oliet*

Centre for Research in Neuroscience, Montreal General Hospital and McGill University, Montreal, H3G 1A4, Canada; *present address: Department of Cellular and Molecular Pharmacology, University of California, San Francisco, California 94143

KEY WORDS:  mechanosensitivity, ion channels, cell volume, thirst, vasopressin

### ABSTRACT

Osmoreceptors regulate sodium and water balance in a manner that maintains the osmotic pressure of the extracellular fluid (ECF) near an ideal set point. In rats, the concerted release of oxytocin and vasopressin, which is determined by the firing rate of magnocellular neurosecretory cells (MNCs), plays a key role in osmoregulation through the effects of natriuresis and diuresis. Changes in excitatory synaptic drive, derived from osmosensitive neurons in the organum vasculosum lamina terminalis (OVLT), combine with endogenously generated osmoreceptor potentials to modulate the firing rate of MNCs. The cellular basis for osmoreceptor potentials has been characterized using patch-clamp recordings and morphometric analysis in MNCs isolated from the supraoptic nucleus of the adult rat. In these cells, stretch-inactivated cationic channels transduce osmotically evoked changes in cell volume into functionally relevant changes in membrane potential. The experimental details of these mechanisms are reviewed in their physiological context.

## INTRODUCTION

Among the physiological parameters whose short-term stability is most aggressively defended by vertebrates is the osmotic pressure of the extracellular fluid (ECF). Terrestrial mammals, in particular, have long been known to maintain a relatively constant ECF osmolality despite pronounced variations in salt and water intake (18). This observation implies that osmoregulatory responses present in these animals are subject to control by osmoreceptors, sensors specialized for the detection of small changes in fluid osmolality. In this review, we

601

0066-4278/97/0315-0601$08.00

focus on recent advances concerning the cellular and molecular basis for signal transduction in osmoreceptors of the central nervous system (CNS). The significance of the findings is best emphasized if considered in a relevant physiological context. We begin, therefore, with a brief historical overview of osmoreceptors and of their functional role in the regulation of body fluids.

## Osmoreceptors and Body Fluid Homeostasis

In mammals, CNS osmoreceptors are known to contribute to the concerted regulation of sodium and water balance in a manner that maintains the osmotic pressure of the ECF near an ideal set point (12). Thus the maintenance of an equilibrium between water intake and excretion is achieved largely through osmoreceptor-driven changes in thirst and diuresis. By analogy, sodium balance is maintained, in part, through osmotically regulated changes in sodium appetite and natriuresis (68). Not surprisingly, acute disturbances in either sodium or water balance can produce rapid shifts in ECF osmolality. The clinical consequences of such perturbations are mainly neurological (3, 4, 5) and include confusion, paralysis, coma, and convulsive seizures. When particularly severe, osmotically evoked brain swelling or shrinking can have traumatic or even lethal consequences (4, 5, 29, 46). Mechanisms underlying osmoreception and osmoregulation, therefore, are of considerable pathophysiological interest.

## Discovery of Central Osmoreceptors

In 1937, Gilman (26) observed that drinking in dogs could be provoked by systemic infusion of hypertonic sodium chloride, but not by equivalent osmotic loads of membrane-permeant urea. He concluded, therefore, that the sensation of thirst must arise as a consequence of cellular dehydration; the reduction of cell volume that results from water efflux upon increases in external osmotic pressure. At that time, however, investigators did not know whether the sensation of thirst resulted from a generalized decrease in the volume of all cells, or from the activation of specialized receptor cells or tissues.

The term osmoreceptor was first introduced by EB Verney in the discussion of his now classic series of experiments on the release of vasopressin (88), the antidiuretic hormone. Similar to Gilman's findings on thirst (26), Verney discovered that vasopressin release in dogs can only be evoked by hypertonic solutions comprising membrane-impermeant solutes, such as sodium chloride, sodium sulfate, or sucrose, but not by hypertonic urea. Further, by studying the effects of acute infusions of hyperosmotic solutions into different arteries and veins, Verney concluded that osmoreceptors regulating vasopressin secretion were located within the brain. In subsequent experiments featuring intracranial lesions and arterial ligations, Jewell & Verney established that central osmoreceptors controlling vasopressin release were located in the anterior region of the hypothalamus (31).

## Osmoreceptors Comprise Neuronal Elements

As indicated above, osmoreceptors in the CNS contribute not only to the regulation of water balance, but to sodium homeostasis as well (12). Moreover, most of the responses regulated by osmoreceptors are either directly or indirectly mediated by the brain. The osmotic regulation of sodium and water intake, for example, is achieved by changes in ingestive behavior brought about by variations in perceived thirst (2, 23, 67, 79–82) and appetite for salt (9, 75, 83, 92). Osmotic control of renal diuresis and natriuresis is also centrally mediated via the release of hormones by neurosecretory neurons (6, 13, 20, 42, 44, 61, 67). Because signals derived from osmoreceptors must ultimately be relayed to neurons mediating each of these responses, osmoreceptors themselves must comprise neuronal elements.

## Location of Central Osmoreceptors

There is no reason a priori why the brain should house only one osmoreceptor. In fact, signals derived from a variety of central and peripheral receptors may eventually converge on each of the osmoregulatory output systems (12), thereby providing useful redundancy in the osmotic control of body fluid balance. Moreover, because all cells in the brain are exposed to variations in ECF osmolality, neurons responsible for the activation of various osmoregulatory reflexes might themselves be intrinsically sensitive to changes in osmolality (12).

Lesion experiments by many investigators have suggested that structures near the anterior part of the hypothalamus are important not only for vasopressin secretion (25, 32, 34, 37, 38, 42, 49, 62, 69, 72, 80–82), as found by Jewell & Verney (88), but also for the osmotic regulation of thirst (25, 32, 36–38, 43, 80–82), sodium appetite (83), and natriuresis (6, 7, 41, 45, 78). Indeed, the results of these and other studies (12) suggest that osmotic control of most osmoregulatory responses is achieved through central pathways originating from neurons located in three structures associated with the lamina terminalis: the subfornical organ (SFO), the median preoptic nucleus (MnPO), and the organum vasculosum lamina terminalis (OVLT). Neurons in these areas, therefore, may effectively operate as cellular osmoreceptors. In agreement with this hypothesis, electrophysiological experiments in vivo have demonstrated the presence of osmoresponsive neurons in each of these loci (12). Moreover, recordings obtained in vitro under conditions blocking synaptic transmission have demonstrated that at least some of the neurons located in the SFO (12, 71), MnPO (65), and OVLT (65, 89) are intrinsically sensitive to changes in fluid osmolality.

Osmosensitive neurons, however, can only be recognized as functional osmoreceptors if they also can be shown to innervate and regulate neuronal
elements responsible for the genesis of specific osmoregulatory responses. Because the neural circuits mediating thirst and sodium appetite are unknown,
definitive proof concerning the location of cellular osmoreceptors regulating
these responses cannot be obtained presently. In contrast, pathways involved
in the osmotic control of neurohypophysial hormone release are well characterized (12) and offer a unique opportunity to investigate the cellular basis for
osmoreception.

## OSMOTIC CONTROL OF NEUROHYPOPHYSIAL HORMONE RELEASE

### Neurohypophysial Hormones and Osmoregulation

Vasopressin, the antidiuretic hormone, is one of the two neurohypophysial
peptides synthesized by distinct populations of magnocellular neurosecretory
cells (MNCs) in the mammalian hypothalamus (76, 85). The other product of
MNCs, oxytocin, is well known for its role as a humoral trigger for uterine
contractions at birth and for milk ejection during lactation (13, 61). In the
rat, however, oxytocin also contributes to sodium balance and osmoregulation
because it is potently natriuretic (17, 87) and because its release is regulated by
changes in osmolality (49, 86). Indeed, in this species, systemic concentrations
of both hormones increase as a function of plasma osmolality (20, 67, 86), from
an apparent threshold near 280 mosmol/kg. At the physiological osmotic set
point ($\approx$295 mosmol/kg in rats), both oxytocin and vasopressin are detectable in
blood at concentrations sufficient to contribute to basal natriuresis (17, 87) and
antidiuresis (20, 67), respectively. By suppressing neurohypophysial hormone
release, therefore, hypotonic stimuli simultaneously promote compensatory
sodium retention and water excretion. Systemic hypertonicity, in contrast,
enhances the release of both hormones, which promotes sodium excretion and
water retention. Thus the concerted osmotic control of vasopressin and oxytocin
secretion represents a powerful osmoregulatory response in the rat (12).

### Functional Organization of the Hypothalamo-Neurohypophysial System

Somata of MNCs are located in the paraventricular and supraoptic nuclei of the
hypothalamus (76, 85) from which they emit axons projecting toward the median eminence (13, 61). Collectively, these axons emerge from the base of the
brain, forming the infundibular stalk, and enter the neurohypophysis where they
individually branch into thousands of neurosecretory terminals (52). Peptides
released at this location reach the general circulation through the fenestrated

capillaries of the neurohypophysis (28). Experiments with the isolated neu-rointermediate lobe of the rat pituitary have shown that secretion of oxytocin and vasopressin from the secretory terminals depends on action potential dis-charge and that the rate of secretion increases as a function of firing frequency in the neurohypophysial axons (19). Because the axons and terminals of MNCs cannot sustain firing in the absence of somatic drive (11), hormone secretion is primarily determined by the rate at which MNC somata generate action poten-tials (11, 13, 61).

## Plasma Osmolality and Electrical Activity in MNCs

Electrophysiological recordings in anesthetized rats have revealed that the rates at which action potentials are discharged by the somata of both types of MNCs vary as positive functions of plasma osmolality (90, 91). Moreover, at the os-motic set point, both types of MNCs tend to display slow (2–3 Hz) irregular firing (61), consistent with the presence of low, but measurable, concentra-tions of plasma vasopressin and oxytocin under resting conditions. Intraperi-toneal injection of water, which reduces plasma osmolality, inhibits MNCs (14), whereas injection of hypertonic solutions provokes increases in firing rate (12, 13, 30, 35, 61). Functionally, therefore, osmoreceptor-mediated control of the rat hypothalamo-neurohypophysial system is achieved primarily via changes in the rate at which action potentials are discharged by the somata of MNCs.

## OSMORECEPTORS FOR NEUROHYPOPHYSIAL HORMONE RELEASE

A large number of central and peripheral sites may contribute to the osmotic regulation of neurohypophysial hormone release (12). Cellular osmoreceptors, however, are defined not only by their intrinsic sensitivity to changes in fluid osmolality, but also by their ability to regulate neuronal systems responsible for the production of specific osmoregulatory responses. With respect to such criteria, only two brain regions can presently be identified as comprising cellular osmoreceptors controlling neurohypophysial hormone secretion: the OVLT and the supraoptic nucleus.

## Osmoreceptors in the OVLT

Electrolytic lesions encompassing the OVLT have been found to impair os-motic control of neurohypophysial hormone release (62, 79–82). Moreover, anatomical studies have indicated that neurons in the OVLT send projections to hypothalamic nuclei containing MNCs (15, 63, 84, 93, 94). Because some OVLT neurons are intrinsically osmosensitive (65, 89), it is likely that these cells represent cellular osmoreceptors contributing to the osmotic control of neurohypophysial hormone release. Three additional experimental approaches support this hypothesis: First, OVLT neurons anatomically identified as projecting toward the supraoptic nucleus express the protein product of the activity-dependent immediate early gene *fos* following systemic hypertonic stimulation (53). Second, OVLT neurons antidromically identified as projecting to the supraoptic nucleus are excited by hypertonic stimuli in vitro (51). Third, localized hypertonic stimulation of the region of the OVLT in vivo (30) or in vitro (64, 66) excites hypothalamic MNCs.

Intracellular recordings (66) from MNCs maintained at a potential just below spike threshold by current injection revealed that changes in firing rate provoked by osmotic stimulation of the OVLT result from a selective modulation in the frequency of glutamatergic excitatory postsynaptic potentials (EPSPs). This observation is consistent with electrophysiological data indicating that axonal projections from the OVLT mediate glutamatergic excitation of MNCs in the rat supraoptic nucleus (63, 66, 96). Quantitative analysis in vitro (66) has shown that the frequency of spontaneous EPSPs recorded in MNCs increases as a function of the osmotic pressure of the solution superfusing the OVLT, with an apparent threshold near 280 mosmol/kg. Osmoreceptor neurons in the OVLT, therefore, contribute to the osmotic control of the hypothalamo-neurohypophysial system via changes in the synaptic excitation of hypothalamic MNCs (12, 64, 66). Based on these in vitro observations, the electrical activity of the OVLT neurons involved can be presumed to vary as a positive function of fluid osmolality with a threshold near 280 mosmol/kg, a value corresponding to the osmotic threshold for neurohypophysial hormone release in vivo (67, 86).

## Intrinsic Osmosensitivity of Hypothalamic MNCs

It was Verney himself who first suggested that MNCs might operate as osmoreceptors (88). The intrinsic osmosensitivity of MNCs, however, was first demonstrated by Mason (39) in a report revealing that neurons in the supraoptic nucleus are depolarized by hypertonic stimulation in the absence of chemical synaptic transmission. Surprisingly, the functional importance of this response has not been universally endorsed (62, 70, 81). The main argument against a physiological role for the intrinsic osmosensitivity of MNCs rests on the fact that whereas urea readily permeates cell membranes, it has only limited permeability across the blood-brain barrier (98). Thus systemic infusion of urea should cause water to move from the brain parenchyma to the circulation faster than urea can permeate in the opposite direction, thereby increasing the osmotic pressure on the neural side of the blood-brain barrier (62). Because systemic urea is ineffective as a stimulus for vasopressin release (88), it is argued that the osmoreceptors controlling release must lie outside the blood-brain barrier (62, 70,

81). Although the lack of effect of systemic urea provides indirect support for the involvement of the OVLT and other circumventricular organs (which lack a blood-brain barrier) in osmoregulation (70, 81), it does not prove that these sites comprise osmoreceptors. Furthermore, the observation does not exclude the possibility that the intrinsic osmosensitivity of MNCs represents an important, if not essential, aspect of osmotic control. Indeed, intrinsically generated changes in membrane potential in MNCs may be subthreshold for spike discharge during physiological osmotic stimulation (12, 35). If this is the case, functional excitation in response to systemic hypertonicity would necessitate that excitatory synaptic inputs (EPSPs) also be present to trigger the action potentials (12). Lack of vasopressin release in response to urea (88) or to hypertonic stimulation in OVLT-lesioned rats (80–82), therefore, simply could be due to the absence or loss of excitatory synaptic drive under the conditions of these experiments. This hypothesis is supported by the demonstration that in OVLT-lesioned rats, osmotically evoked increases in firing rate in MNCs can be restored by providing a constant excitatory drive through the sustained application of glutamate (34). By analogy, the total number of impulses discharged during individual milk-ejection bursts in oxytocinergic MNCs of lactating female rats can be enhanced by hypertonic stimulation (50). Finally, it is possible that the special properties of capillaries in the supraoptic nucleus (see below) allow a relatively high permeability to urea in this region of the CNS. Considering these results and those discussed below, it is likely that the intrinsic osmosensitivity of MNCs combines with osmotically regulated excitatory inputs, derived from the OVLT, to ensure adequate osmotic control of neurohypophysial hormone release in situ (12).

# FUNCTIONAL ANATOMY OF OSMORECEPTORS

## *The Supraoptic Nucleus*

The supraoptic nucleus comprises a compact array of MNC somata, glial cells, and capillaries (60, 77). Electron microscopic analysis (28) reveals that the vasculature of the nucleus bears the hallmark features of a functional blood-brain barrier. Thus the capillary endothelium is not fenestrated and features few cytoplasmic pits and vesicles. Moreover, the processes of glial cells are interposed between MNC somata and the endothelial cells of local capillaries. In agreement with these morphological features, the permeability of endothelial cells and *trans*-endothelial flux of some solutes (per unit area) are as low in the supraoptic nucleus as they are in other parts of the cerebral gray matter (28). It has long been recognized that the magnocellular nuclei of the hypothalamus feature an unusually dense vascularization (22). Indeed, morphometric analysis reveals that the density, volume fraction, and surface area of the capillary bed are four times greater in the rat supraoptic nucleus than in hypothalamic nuclei lacking MNCs (28). Furthermore, the average capillary diameter within the supraoptic nucleus is significantly smaller than in other regions. Thus while solute flux per unit area may be slow across the capillary endothelium of the supraoptic nucleus (28), the overall permeability of the tissue to water and various solutes (e.g. urea) may be relatively higher here than in other parts of the brain. Enhanced permeability to water, in fact, is suggested by the recent observation that this region expresses a high density of mRNA coding for aquaporin-4 (33), a member of the family of transmembrane water channels (21). The combination of a large capillary surface area, facilitated water flux, and low permeability to solutes, suggests that the supraoptic nucleus is optimized to promote rapid changes in tissue volume and parenchymal osmotic pressure during variations in systemic osmolality.

## The OVLT

The OVLT is a member of the specialized group of brain nuclei termed circumventricular organs. These structures are characterized by both the presence of a dense vascularization (95) and the absence of a functional blood-brain barrier (27). Indeed, the capillary endothelium in circumventricular organs is highly fenestrated and features numerous pits and vesicular profiles. The high rate of tissue perfusion supported by such features presumably facilitates solute exchange between the vascular and neuronal compartments of the tissue. A common feature of both osmoreceptors is the facilitated exposure of local neurons to changes in ECF osmolality.

## CELLULAR BASIS FOR OSMORECEPTION

Because the first cells identified as intrinsically osmosensitive were supraoptic neurons (39), and because such neurons are easily identifiable in various in vitro preparations from rat brain (13), most of what is currently known about the ionic basis for osmoreception has come from experiments in rat MNCs. The main features of the mechanism underlying the osmosensitivity of these cells are discussed below.

### Effects of Osmotic Stimuli on Membrane Voltage and Conductance

Intracellular recordings from supraoptic neurons in hypothalamic slices (1, 39) or explants (10) have revealed that MNCs become depolarized when exposed to hypertonic solutions. In the rat, this response is associated with a reduction of input resistance (10) and persists in the presence of tetrodotoxin or in $Ca^{2+}$-free solutions, suggesting a postsynaptic origin. Voltage-clamp measurements with sharp electrodes (10) reveal that at potentials near −60 mV, hypertonic stimuli provoke an inward current associated with an increase of membrane conductance. Although current reversal was not observed in those experiments, extrapolation of current voltage relations recorded in the presence and absence of osmotic stimuli suggested a null potential lying between spike threshold (≈−50 mV) and 0 mV. Because responses were not affected by chloride injections sufficient to invert the polarity of $Cl^-$-mediated inhibitory synaptic potentials, activation of a nonselective cationic conductance was suggested as underlying the effects of hypertonic solutions (10).

A procedure permitting the acute isolation of viable and identifiable MNCs from adult rats has provided the definitive demonstration that these cells behave as intrinsic osmoreceptors (55). Thus in the absence of any synaptic input, MNCs remain sensitive to small changes in fluid osmolality, a response that cannot be observed in neighboring non-neuroendocrine cells or in cortical neurons (56). A significant observation, first made in isolated neurons (56, 57), was that individual MNCs respond not only to increases in fluid osmolality, but to hypotonicity as well. Thus whereas hypertonic solutions provoke membrane depolarization, hypotonic stimuli elicit hyperpolarizing responses. Under whole-cell voltage clamp (56, 57), brief hypertonic stimulation of MNCs held at −60 mV elicited a reversible inward current. Current-voltage analysis indicates that this response results from an increase of membrane conductance and that the activated current reverses near −40 mV. In the same cells, application of hypotonic stimuli reduces membrane conductance, suppressing a current that also reverses near −40 mV. These observations suggest that a single membrane conductance might be differentially regulated by increases and decreases in fluid osmolality (58).

## Ionic Permeability of the Osmotically Regulated Conductance

During whole-cell recording experiments on isolated MNCs, changes in the concentration of extracellular or intracellular chloride did not noticeably affect the reversal potential of the current modulated by osmotic stimuli (54, 56, 57). However, removal of external $Na^+$ caused this potential to shift toward the equilibrium potential for $K^+$ (≈−100 mV) and raising the concentration of external $K^+$ ions caused the reversal potential to shift toward $E_{Na}$. Cationic channels permeable to both $Na^+$ and $K^+$ ions, therefore, mediate the responses of MNCs to changes in fluid osmolality. Under near-physiological conditions ($[K^+]_O$ ≈3 mM), the cationic conductance was found to favor $K^+$ over $Na^+$ with a ratio of about 5:1 (54). Because the resting potential of MNCs lies near −65 mV under resting osmotic conditions (54, 56), activation of this conductance tends to depolarize the cells toward spike threshold, whereas its suppression hyperpolarizes the cell and reduces membrane excitability (58).

## Role of Cell Volume in Osmoreception

As described above, centrally controlled osmoregulatory reflexes are believed to be activated as a consequence of the cellular dehydration that results from efflux of cytoplasmic water upon increases in external osmolality (26). In order to determine whether changes in cellular hydration are associated with the responses of MNCs to osmotic stimuli, we compared the time course of changes in cationic conductance with that of cell volume in response to the application of a brief (90 s) hypertonic stimulus. Morphometric analysis using confocal laser scanning microscopy, and whole-cell patch-clamp measurements revealed that the osmotically evoked decrease in cell volume occurred simultaneously with the changes in conductance provoked by the hypertonic stimulus (54, 56), supporting the notion that changes in cell volume play a key role in osmoreception. The close temporal relationship between changes in cell volume and cationic conductance further implied that generation of a long-lived second messenger was unlikely to participate in the production of these responses. Given such constraints, two mechanisms became apparent as possible candidates for the regulation of cationic conductance during changes in fluid osmolality. First, because variations in cell volume associated with osmotic stimulation result from transmembrane water flux, changes in solute concentration could play a role in signal transduction. Alternatively, changes in physical strain could mediate the osmotic regulation of a cationic conductance by modulating mechanosensitive channels.

## Effects of Isotonic Volume Changes on Membrane Conductance

To determine if changes in solute concentration are required for coupling changes in cell volume to the modulation of cationic conductance, the effects of cell swelling or shrinking were examined in the absence of osmotic stimulation (79, 82). Under whole-cell recording conditions, this was accomplished readily by modifying the pressure inside the recording pipette while monitoring cell size through the microscope. Current clamp recordings from potentials near rest revealed that a decrease in cell volume provoked by pipette suction elicits a depolarization (56), whereas pressure-evoked cell swelling results in a hyperpolarization (54). Although these results are consistent with those obtained during osmotically evoked changes in cell volume, the nature of the conductance underlying responses to variations in pipette pressure might have been different from that modulated by osmotic stimuli. Examination of current-voltage relations recorded during isotonic shrinking and swelling indicates that depolarizing and hyperpolarizing responses are associated, respectively, with increases and decreases in membrane conductance, and that the currents underlying both responses reverse near $-40$ mV (54, 56). Moreover, increases in external $[K^+]$ provoked identical changes in the reversal potential of the currents modulated by each of the four treatments (56). Finally, responses to hypertonic stimuli could be reversed by inflating the cells via increased pressure in the recording pipette, and responses to hypotonic stimuli could be reversed by applying suction to the pipette (54). The results of these experiments indicate that changes in cell volume, rather than variations in cytosolic solute concentration, are required for the osmotic modulation of cationic conductance.

## PROPERTIES OF SINGLE CHANNELS UNDERLYING OSMORECEPTION

The importance of changes in cell volume for osmoreception suggests that the activity of the channels responsible for variations in macroscopic conductance is physically regulated by cell swelling or shrinkage. Parameters involved in the regulation of individual cationic channels, therefore, were examined using single-channel recording techniques.

### Supraoptic MNCs Express Mechanosensitive Channels

Under cell-attached conditions, patch-clamp recordings obtained from acutely isolated MNCs revealed inward single-channel currents when membrane patches were held at $-100$ mV (56). Current-voltage analysis revealed a reversal potential near $-40$ mV and an open channel conductance of $\approx 32$ pS. The activity of these cationic channels could be reversibly modulated by changes in pipette pressure, or by modifying the osmolality of the solution surrounding the cell, thereby identifying these channels as possible mechanotransducers for osmoreception (56).

### Is Channel Mechanosensitivity Required for Osmoreception?

Although these observations suggest that the channels underlying osmoreception are mechanosensitive, they did not demonstrate that mechanical gating is involved in transducing osmoreception. As indicated by Morris (47), a number of criteria must be fulfilled to establish that single-channel mechanosensitivity is responsible for the generation of a macroscopic mechanoreceptor response. In the context of osmoreception, demonstration of the following items would be particularly important. First, the physical sensitivity of the channels should be consistent with the changes in tension that occur during the volume-dependent regulation of macroscopic conductance. Second, the kinetic features associated with the direct mechanical gating of channel activity should be similar to those provoked by osmotic stimulation of the cell. Third, the sensitivity of single channels to a pharmacological blocker should be comparable to that of the macroscopic osmoreceptor current. Fourth, the dynamic range of single-channel responsiveness should agree with that of the physiological response.

## Channel Mechanosensitivity Is Consistent with Macroscopic Osmoreception

Ideally, the assessment of physical parameters regulating a mechanosensitive channel would involve correlation of variations in measured channel activity with observed changes in membrane structure (74). Unfortunately, unless simultaneous high-resolution imaging can be performed (73), the precise geometry of a membrane patch cannot be determined during a cell-attached recording experiment. Moreover, while controlled changes in pipette pressure can be applied through a variety of devices (40), the absolute residual pressure on the pipette side of a patch is difficult to ascertain, even when the pipette is open to the atmosphere (48). Under resting conditions, therefore, the orientation of a patch (i.e. whether convex or concave) and its radius of curvature are unknown. Fortunately, these problems can be partly overcome by examining channel responses to a series of changes in pipette pressure (48). Thus assuming that application of a large negative pipette pressure establishes patch convexity with respect to the cell, stepwise removal of this pressure, followed by stepwise increases in positive pressure, should gradually flatten the patch and subsequently provoke increasing patch concavity.

In MNCs, the average opening probability ($P_O$) of the mechanosensitive channels was found to be maximal near zero pressure and to decrease in response to either increases or decreases in pipette pressure (54, 56, 58, 59). The existence of a symmetric relationship between channel activity and pipette pressure suggests that the channels expressed in MNCs are not regulated by forces perpendicular to the membrane, which would vary as a monotonic function of pipette pressure. Rather, the channels appear to be regulated by changes in force tangential to the plasma membrane, which would be minimal when the patch is flat and increase as a function of either patch convexity or concavity. Because their activity is inhibited by increases or decreases in pipette pressure, the channels expressed in MNCs are identified as stretch inactivated (SI) (48).

As illustrated in Figure 1, the presence of SI cationic channels in MNCs is consistent with the osmotic regulation of cell volume, macroscopic conductance, and membrane potential. Thus by increasing tangential force, hypotonic cell swelling suppresses SI channel activity, reduces whole-cell cationic conductance, and provokes membrane hyperpolarization. Conversely, relaxation of tangential forces upon hypertonic shrinkage increases channel activity and membrane cationic conductance, thereby depolarizing the cell (58).

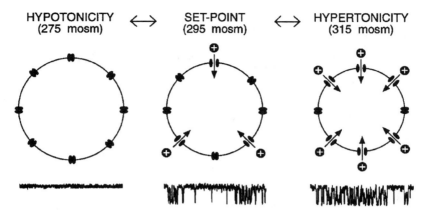

*Figure 1*  Stretch inactivated (SI) cationic channels transduce osmoreception. Under resting osmotic conditions (*middle panel*) a portion of the SI cationic channels is active and allows the influx of positive charge (diagram). Hypotonic stimulation (*left*) provokes cell swelling and inhibits channel activity, thereby hyperpolarizing the cell. In contrast, hypertonic stimulation (*right*) causes cell shrinking. Activation of an increased number of channels under this condition augments charge influx and results in membrane depolarization. Traces representing changes in the activity of a single SI channel are shown below.

## Common Changes in Channel Kinetics During Mechanical and Osmotic Stimulation

Kinetic analysis of recordings made from cell-attached patches containing single channels reveals that the distribution of channel open times recorded from SI cationic channels at rest can be described as an exponential function, with a mean time constant of $1.6 \pm 0.2$ ms (59). This value is not affected by changes in channel activity provoked either by osmotic stimulation of the cell or by modification of pipette pressure (59). Changes in channel $P_O$, therefore, are not mediated by variations in the duration of individual channel openings. Channel closed times observed at rest are distributed more broadly, with dwell time histograms approximating the sum of two or three exponentials (54, 59). Because the slowest components of such distributions have time constants exceeding 1000 ms, information concerning evoked changes in specific components has not been obtained. By simplifying the analysis to an examination of the mean channel closed time (16), however, we have observed that changes in channel closed time can explain the totality of changes in channel $P_O$ evoked by either variations of pipette pressure or osmotic stimulation (59). Although further analysis will be required to confirm that the kinetic schemes underlying changes in channel $P_O$ provoked by both types of stimuli are identical, available results support the hypothesis that mechanical and osmotic stimuli regulate channel gating through a common mechanism.

## Gadolinium Blocks Single SI Channels and Macroscopic Osmoreceptor Current

Previous studies have demonstrated that the trivalent inorganic cation gadolinium ($Gd^{3+}$) causes open channel blockade of many types of cationic mechanosensitive channels (8, 24, 97). In agreement with these reports, addition of varying concentrations of $Gd^{3+}$ to recording pipettes was found to cause a dose-dependent decrease in the mean open time of SI cationic channels in isolated MNCs (59). The concentration at which the mean duration of SI channel openings was reduced by 50% was ≈30 μM. In order to determine whether $Gd^{3+}$ interferes with other aspects of osmo-mechanical transduction, we examined whether high concentrations (100–300 μM) of the blocker affect osmotically evoked volume changes or the mechanical sensitivity of the SI channels themselves. Laser scanning microscopic imaging experiments revealed that neither the time course nor the amplitude of the volume decrease provoked by a 60 mosmol/kg stimulus was altered by the presence of 100 μM $Gd^{3+}$ in the external medium (54, 59). Moreover, recording of SI channels in cell-attached membrane patches, using pipettes containing 100 μM $Gd^{3+}$, revealed that the bell-shaped relationship between normalized channel $P_O$ and changes in pipette pressure was identical in the presence and absence of $Gd^{3+}$ (54, 59). At a concentration of 30 μM, $Gd^{3+}$ would be expected to reduce the mean duration of channel openings by 50% without affecting osmotically evoked changes in cell volume or mechanically evoked changes in channel closed time and relative $P_O$. Therefore, if SI channels underlie osmoreception, macroscopic osmoreceptor currents should be inhibited by comparable concentrations of $Gd^{3+}$. In agreement with this prediction, macroscopic current responses to hypertonic stimuli were inhibited with an $IC_{50}$ of ≈40 μM (54, 59). Moreover, under current clamp, depolarizing osmoreceptor potentials evoked by hypertonic stimuli were reversibly inhibited by adding 100–250 μM $Gd^{3+}$ to the external solution. The pharmacological effects of $Gd^{3+}$ on macroscopic responses, therefore, are consistent with those observed on single SI cationic channels.

## Dynamic Range of SI Channel Activity and Macroscopic Responses

Single-channel analysis has revealed that the activity of SI cationic channels in MNCs can be abolished by changes in pipette pressure as small as +3 cm $H_2O$ (54, 56, 58, 59). It is conceivable that complete suppression of channel activity might occur during modest hypotonic stimulation. Indeed, under whole-cell recording conditions, application of solutions of decreasing osmotic pressures has revealed that membrane conductance reaches a minimum at $\approx$275 mosmol/kg (57). Based on the changes in whole-cell conductance observed during osmotic stimulation (54), it is likely that under resting osmotic conditions (i.e. at 295 mosmol/kg) approximately 60% of the input conductance of MNCs is mediated through SI-cationic channels. In support of this proposal, $Gd^{3+}$ has been found to inhibit a current reversing near $-40$ mV when applied to MNCs bathed in a solution adjusted to 295 mosmol/kg (54). Application of $Gd^{3+}$ to MNCs under hypotonic conditions (275 mosmol/kg), however, was without effect (59). The apparent osmotic threshold for SI channel activity in vitro, therefore, corresponds to the threshold for oxytocin and vasopressin release in vivo (67, 86). Indeed, during hypertonic stimulation, increases in membrane conductance are first detected at 280 mosmol/kg (57).

## CONCLUDING REMARKS

Experiments on MNCs of the rat supraoptic nucleus have provided a unique opportunity to examine the mechanism underlying signal transduction in a CNS osmoreceptor. Our analysis reveals that cationic channels whose activity is reduced by membrane stretch may be the molecular mechanotransducers responsible for converting osmotically evoked changes in cell volume into functionally relevant changes in membrane potential (Figure 1). Although mechanisms underlying signal transduction may be different in osmoreceptors located elsewhere in the CNS or in the periphery (12), preliminary observations suggest that the intrinsic osmosensitivity of some cells in the SFO (12), MnPO (65), and OVLT (65) depends on a mechanism similar to that found in MNCs. However, a more detailed understanding of the biophysical aspects of osmo-mechanical transduction must await the identification of the molecular structure of the ion channels involved and the cytoskeletal molecules that presumably regulate their gating apparatus.

ACKNOWLEDGMENTS

We thank the Medical Research Council of Canada for supporting this work by providing operating support and an M.R.C. Scientist Award to CWB, and the Heart and Stroke Foundation of Canada for providing a Studentship Award to SHRO. The authors are also grateful to Drs. Thomas Fisher and Daniel Voisin for their helpful comments during the preparation of this manuscript.

*Literature Cited*

1. Abe H, Ogata N. 1982. Ionic mechanism for the osmotically induced depolarization in neurones of the guinea-pig supraoptic nucleus in vitro. *J. Physiol.* 327:157–71
2. Andersson B. 1978. Regulation of water intake. *Physiol. Rev.* 58:582–603
3. Andrew RD. 1991. Seizure and acute os-

motic change: clinical and neurophysiological aspects. *J. Neurol. Sci.* 101:7–18

4. Arieff AI. 1986. Hyponatremia, convulsions, respiratory arrest, and permanent brain damage after elective surgery in healthy women. *N. Engl. J. Med.* 314:1529–35

5. Arieff AI, Guisado R. 1976. Effects on the central nervous system of hypernatremic and hyponatremic states. *Kidney Int.* 10:104–16

6. Bealer SL. 1983. Hemodynamic mechanisms in CNS-induced natriuresis in the conscious rat. *Am. J. Physiol.* 244:F376–82

7. Bealer SL, Haywood JR, Gruber KA, Buckalew VM Jr, Fink GD, et al. 1983. Preoptic-hypothalamic periventricular lesions reduce natriuresis to volume expansion. *Am. J. Physiol.* 244:R51–57

8. Berrier C, Coulombe A, Szabo I, Zoratti M, Ghazi A. 1992. Gadolinium ion inhibits loss of metabolites by osmotic shock and large stretch-activated channels in bacteria. *Eur. J. Biochem.* 206:559–65

9. Blackburn RE, Samson WK, Fulton RJ, Stricker EM, Verbalis JG. 1993. Central oxytocin inhibition of salt appetite in rats: evidence for differential sensing of plasma sodium and osmolality. *Proc. Natl. Acad. Sci. USA* 90:10380–84

10. Bourque CW. 1989. Ionic basis for the intrinsic activation of rat supraoptic neurones by hyperosmotic stimuli. *J. Physiol.* 417:265–78

11. Bourque CW. 1990. Intraterminal recordings from the rat neurohypophysis in vitro. *J. Physiol.* 421:247–62

12. Bourque CW, Oliet SHR, Richard D. 1994. Osmoreceptors, osmoreception, and osmoregulation. *Front. Neuroendocrinol.* 15:231–74

13. Bourque CW, Renaud LP. 1990. Electrophysiology of mammalian magnocellular vasopressin and oxytocin neurosecretory neurons. *Front. Neuroendocrinol.* 11:183–12

14. Brimble MJ, Dyball REJ. 1977. Characterization of the responses of oxytocin- and vasopressin-secreting neurones in the supraoptic nucleus to osmotic stimulation. *J. Physiol.* 271:253–71

15. Camacho A, Phillips MI. 1981. Horseradish peroxidase study in rat of the neural connections of the organum vasculosum of the lamina terminalis. *Neurosci. Lett.* 25:201–4

16. Colquhoun D, Sigworth F. 1995. Fitting and statistical analysis of single channel records. In *Single Channel Recording,* ed. B Sakmann, E Neher, pp. 483–87. New York: Plenum. 2nd ed.

17. Conrad KP, Gellai M, North WG, Valtin H. 1986. Influence of oxytocin on renal hemodynamics and sodium excretion. *Ann. NY Acad. Sci.* 689:346–62

18. Darrow DC, Yannet H. 1935. The changes in the distribution of body water accompanying increase and decrease in extracellular electrolyte. *J. Clin. Invest.* 14:266–75

19. Dreifuss JJ, Kalnins I, Kelly JS, Ruf KB. 1971. Action potentials and release of neurohypophysial hormones in vitro. *J. Physiol.* 215:805–17

20. Dunn FL, Brennan TJ, Nelson AE, Robertson GL. 1973. The role of blood osmolality and volume in regulating vasopressin secretion in the rat. *J. Clin. Invest.* 52:3212–19

21. Engel A, Walz T, Agre P. 1994. The aquaporin family of membrane water channels. *Curr. Opin. Struct. Biol.* 4:545–53

22. Finley K. 1939. The capillary beds of the paraventricular and supra-optic nuclei of the hypothalamus. *J. Comp. Neurol.* 71:1–19

23. Fitzsimons JT. 1976. The physiological basis of thirst. *Kidney Int.* 10:3–11

24. Franco A Jr, Winegar BD, Lansman JB. 1991. Open channel block by gadolinium ion of the stretch-inactivated ion channel in mdx myotubes. *Biophys. J.* 59:1164–70

25. Gardiner TW, Stricker EM. 1985. Hyperdipsia in rats after electrolytic lesions of nucleus medianus. *Am. J. Physiol.* 248:R214–23

26. Gilman A. 1937. The relation between blood osmotic pressure, fluid distribution, and voluntary water intake. *Am. J. Physiol.* 120:323–28

27. Gross PM, Sposito NM, Pettersen SE, Fenstermacher JD. 1986. Differences in function and structure of the capillary endothelium in gray matter, white matter and a circumventricular organ of rat brain. *Blood Ves.* 23:261–70

28. Gross PM, Sposito NM, Pettersen SE, Fenstermacher JD. 1986. Differences in function and structure of the capillary endothelium in the supraoptic nucleus and pituitary neural lobe of rats: evidence for the supraoptic nucleus as an osmometer. *Neuroendocrinology* 44:401–7

29. Gullans SR, Verbalis JG. 1993. Control of brain volume during hyperosmolar and hypoosmolar conditions. *Annu. Rev. Med.* 44:289–301

30. Honda K, Negoro H, Higuchi T, Tadokoro Y. 1987. Activation of neurosecretory cells by osmotic stimulation of anteroventral third ventricle. *Am. J. Physiol.* 252:R1039–45

31. Jewell PA, Verney EB. 1957. An experimental attempt to determine the site of the neurohypophyseal osmoreceptors in the dog. *Philos. Trans. R. Soc. London Ser. B* 240:197–324

32. Johnson AK. 1985. Role of the periventricular tissue surrounding the anteroventral third ventricule (AV3V) in the regulation of body fluid homeostasis. See Ref. 70a, pp. 319–31

33. Jung JS, Bhat RV, Preston GM, Guggino WB, Baraban JM, Agre P. 1994. Molecular characterization of an aquaporin cDNA from brain: candidate osmoreceptor and regulator of water balance. *Proc. Natl. Acad. Sci. USA* 91:13052–56

34. Leng G, Blackburn RE, Dyball REJ, Russel JA. 1989. Role of anterior peri-third ventricular structures in the regulation of supraoptic neuronal activity and neurohypophyseal hormone secretion in the rat. *J. Neuroendocrinol.* 1:35–46

35. Leng G, Dyball REJ, Mason WT. 1985. Electrophysiology of osmoreceptors. See Ref. 70a, pp. 333–4

36. Lind RW, Thunhorst RL, Johnson AK. 1984. The subfornical organ and the integration of multiple factors in thirst. *Physiol. Behav.* 32:69–74

37. Mangiapane ML, Thrasher TN, Keil LC, Simpson JB, Ganong WF. 1983. Deficits in drinking and vasopressin secretion after lesions of the nucleus medianus. *Neuroendocrinology* 37:73–77

38. Mangiapane ML, Thrasher TN, Keil LC, Simpson JB, Ganong WF. 1984. Roles for the subfornical organ in vasopressin release. *Brain Res. Bull.* 13:43–48

39. Mason WT. 1980. Supraoptic neurones of rat hypothalamus are osmosensitive. *Nature* 287:154–57

40. McBride DW Jr, Hamill OP. 1995. A fast pressure-clamp technique for studying mechanogated channels. In *Single Channel Recording*, ed. B Sakmann, E Neher, pp. 329–40. New York: Plenum. 2nd ed.

41. McKinley MJ. 1992. Common aspects of the cerebral regulation of thirst and renal sodium excretion. *Kidney Int.* 41(Suppl. 37):S102–6

42. McKinley MJ, Denton DA, Coghlan JP, Harvey RB, McDougall JG, et al. 1987. Cerebral osmoregulation of renal sodium excretion—A response analogous to thirst and vasopressin release. *Can. J. Physiol. Pharmacol.* 65:1724–29

43. McKinley MJ, Denton DA, Leskell LG, Mouw DR, Scoggins BA, et al. 1982. Osmoregulatory thirst in sheep is disrupted by ablation of the anterior wall of the optic recess. *Brain Res.* 236:210–15

44. McKinley MJ, Denton DA, Park RG, Weisinger RS. 1983. Cerebral involvement in dehydration-induced natriuresis. *Brain Res.* 263:340–43

45. McKinley MJ, Lichardus B, McDougall JG, Weisinger RS. 1992. Periventricular lesions block natriuresis to hypertonic but not isotonic NaCl loads. *Am. J. Physiol.* 262:F98–107

46. McManus ML, Churchwell KB. 1994. Clinical significance of cellular osmoregulation. In *Cellular and Molecular Physiology of Cell Volume Regulation*, ed. K Strange, pp. 63–77. Boca Raton, FL: CRC Press

47. Morris CE. 1992. Are stretch-sensitive channels in molluscan cells and elsewhere physiological mechanotransducers? *Experientia* 48:852–58

48. Morris CE, Sigurdson WJ. 1989. Stretch-inactivated ion channels coexist with stretch-activated ion channels. *Science* 243:807–9

49. Negoro H, Higuchi T, Tadokoro Y, Honda K. 1988. Osmoreceptor mechanism for oxytocin release in the rat. *Jpn. J. Physiol.* 38:19–31

50. Negoro H, Honda K, Uchide K, Higuchi T. 1987. Facilitation of milk ejection-related activation of oxytocin-secreting neurones by osmotic stimulation in the rat. *Exp. Brain Res.* 65:312–16

51. Nissen N, Bourque CW, Renaud LP. 1993. Membrane properties of organum vasculosum lamina terminalis neurons recorded in vitro. *Am. J. Physiol.* 264:R811–15

52. Nordmann JJ. 1977. Ultrastructural morphometry of the rat neurohypophysis. *J. Anat.* 123:213–18

53. Oldfield BJ, Badoer E, Hards DK, McKinley MJ. 1994. Fos production in retrogradely labelled neurons of the lamina terminalis following intravenous infusion of either hypertonic saline or angiotensin II. *Neuroscience* 60:255–62

54. Oliet SHR. 1994. *Osmoreception in rat supraoptic neurons.* PhD thesis. McGill Univ., Montreal. 169 pp.

55. Oliet SHR, Bourque CW. 1992. Properties of supraoptic magnocellular neurones isolated from the adult rat. *J. Physiol.* 455:291–306

56. Oliet SHR, Bourque CW. 1993. Mechanosensitive channels transduce osmosensitivity in supraoptic neurons. *Nature* 364:341–43

57. Oliet SHR, Bourque CW. 1993. Steady-state osmotic modulation of cationic conductance in neurons of rat supraoptic nucleus. *Am. J. Physiol.* 265:R1475–79

58. Oliet SHR, Bourque CW. 1994. Osmoreception in magnocellular neurosecretory cells: from single channels to secretion. *Trends Neurosci.* 17:340–44

59. Oliet SHR, Bourque CW. 1996. Gadolinium uncouples mechanical detection and osmoreceptor potential in supraoptic neurons. *Neuron* 16:175–81

60. Perlmutter LS, Tweedle CD, Hatton GI. 1984. Neuronal/glial plasticity in the supraoptic dendritic zone: dendritic bundling and double synapse formation at parturition. *Neuroscience* 13:769–79

61. Poulain DA, Wakerley JB. 1982. Electrophysiology of hypothalamic magnocellular neurones secreting oxytocin and vasopressin. *Neuroscience* 7:773–808

62. Ramsay DJ, Thrasher TN, Keil LC. 1983. The organum vasculosum lamina terminalis: a critical area for osmoreception. In *The Neurohypophysis: Structure, Function and Control,* ed. BA Cross, G Leng, pp. 91–98. Amsterdam/Lausanne: Elsevier

63. Renaud LP, Cunningham JT, Nissen R, Yang CR. 1993. Electrophysiology of central pathways controlling release of neurohypophysial hormones: focus on the lamina terminalis and diagonal band inputs to the supraoptic nucleus. *Ann. NY Acad. Sci.* 689:122–32

64. Richard D, Bourque CW. 1992. Synaptic activation of rat supraoptic neurons by osmotic stimulation of the organum vasculosum lamina terminalis. *Neuroendocrinology* 55:609–11

65. Richard D, Bourque CW. 1994. Osmotic activation of neurons dissociated from the OVLT and median preoptic nucleus (MnPO). *Soc. Neurosci. Abstr.* 20:1567

66. Richard D, Bourque CW. 1995. Synaptic control of rat supraoptic neurones during osmotic stimulation of the organum vasculosum lamina terminalis in vitro. *J. Physiol.* 489:567–77

67. Robertson GL. 1985. Osmoregulation of thirst and vasopressin secretion: functional properties and their relationship to water balance. See Ref. 70a, pp. 203–12.

68. Rose BD. 1989. *Clinical Physiology of Acid-Base and Electrolyte Disorders,* pp. 153–208. New York: McGraw-Hill. 853 pp. 3rd ed.

69. Russel JA, Blackburn RE, Leng G. 1988. The role of the AV3V region in the control of magnocellular oxytocin neurons. *Brain Res. Bull.* 20:803–10

70. Share L. 1996. Control of vasopressin release: an old but continuing story. *News Physiol. Sci.* 11:7–13

70a. Shrier RW, ed. 1985. *Vasopressin.* New York: Raven. 506 pp.

71. Sibbald JR, Hubbard JE, Sirrett NE. 1988. Responses from osmosensitive neurons of the rat subfornical organ in vitro. *Brain Res.* 461:205–14

72. Sladek CD, Johnson AK. 1983. Effect of anteroventral third ventricle lesions on vasopressin release by organcultured hypothalamo-neurohypophyseal explants. *Neuroendocrinology* 37:78–84

73. Sokabe M, Sachs F. 1990. The structure and dynamics of patch-clamped membranes: a study using differential interference contrast light microscopy. *J. Cell. Biol.* 111:599–606

74. Sokabe M, Sachs F. 1992. Towards molecular mechanism of activation in mechanosensitive ion channels. In *Advances in Comparative and Environmental Physiology,* ed. F Ito, pp. 55–77. Berlin Heidelberg: Springer-Verlag

75. Stricker EM, Verbalis JG. 1988. Hormones and behavior: biological basis of thirst and sodium appetite. *Am. Sci.* 76:261–67

76. Swaab DF, Pool CW, Nijveldt F. 1975. Immunofluorescence of vasopressin and oxytocin in the rat hypothalamo-neurohypophyseal system. *J. Neural Trans.* 36:195–215

77. Theodosis DT, Poulain DA. 1984. Evidence for structural plasticity in the supraoptic nucleus of the rat hypothalamus in relation to gestation and lactation. *Neuroscience* 11:183–93

78. Thornborough JR, Passo SS, Rothballer AB. 1973. Forebrain lesion blockade of the natriuretic response to elevated carotic blood sodium. *Brain Res.* 58:355–63

79. Thrasher TN. 1985. Circumventricular organs, thirst and vasopressin secretion. See Ref. 70a. pp 311–18

80. Thrasher TN. 1989. Role of forebrain circumventricular organs in body fluid balance. *Acta Physiol. Scand.* 136(Suppl. 583):141–50

81. Thrasher TN, Keil LC. 1987. Regulation of drinking and vasopressin secretion: role of organum vasculosum lamina terminalis. *Am. J. Physiol.* 253:R108–20

82. Thrasher TN, Keil LC, Ramsay DJ. 1982. Lesions of the organum vasculosum of the lamina terminalis (OVLT) attenuate osmotically induced drinking and vasopressin secretion in the dog. *Endocrinology* 110:1837–39

83. Thunhorst RL, Ehrlrich KJ, Simpson JB. 1990. Subfornical organ participates in salt appetite. *Behav. Neurosci.* 104:637–42

84. Tribollet E, Amstrong WE, Dubois-Dauphin M. 1985. Extra-hypothalamic afferent inputs to the supraoptic area of the rat as determined by retrograde and anterograde tracing techniques. *Neuroscience* 15:135–48

85. Vandersande F, Dierickx K. 1975. Identification of the vasopressin producing and of the oxytocin producing neurons in the hypothalamic neurosecretory system of the rat. *Cell Tissue Res.* 164:153–62

86. Verbalis JG, Baldwin EF, Robinson AG. 1986. Osmotic regulation of plasma vasopressin and oxytocin after sustained hyponatremia. *Am. J. Physiol.* 250:R444–51

87. Verbalis JG, Mangione MP, Stricker EM. 1991. Oxytocin produces natriuresis in rats at physiological plasma concentration. *Endocrinology* 128:1317–22

88. Verney EB. 1947. The antidiuretic hormone and the factors which determine its release. *Proc. R. Soc. London Ser. B* 135:25–26

89. Vivas L, Chiaraviglio E, Carrer HF. 1990. Rat organum vasculosum lamina terminalis in vitro: responses to changes in sodium concentration. *Brain Res.* 519:294–300

90. Wakerley JB, Poulain DA, Brown D. 1978. Comparison of firing patterns in oxytocin and vasopressin-releasing neurones during progressive dehydration. *Brain Res.* 148:425–40

91. Walters JK, Hatton GI. 1974. Supraoptic neuronal activity in rats during five days of water deprivation. *Physiol. Behav.* 13:661–67

92. Weisinger RS, Considine P, Denton DA, McKinley MJ. 1979. Rapid effect of change in cerebrospinal fluid sodium concentration on salt appetite. *Nature* 280:490–91

93. Weiss ML, Hatton GL. 1990. Collateral input to the paraventricular and supraoptic nuclei in the rat. I. Afferents from the subfornical organ and anteroventral third ventricle region. *Brain Res. Bull.* 24:231–38

94. Wilkin LD, Mitchell LD, Ganten D, Johnson AK. 1989. The supraoptic nucleus: afferents from areas involved in control of body fluid homeostasis. *Neuroscience* 28:573–84

95. Yamaguchi K, Morimoto A, Murakami N. 1993. Organum vasculosum lamina terminalis (OVLT) in rabbit and rat: topographical studies. *J. Comp. Neurol.* 330:352–62

96. Yang CR, Senatorov VV, Renaud LP. 1994. Organum vasculosum lamina terminalis-evoked postsynaptic responses in rat supraoptic neurones in vitro. *J. Physiol.* 477:59–74

97. Yang XC, Sachs F. 1989. Block of stretch-activated ion channels in *Xenopus* oocytes by gadolinium and caesium ions. *Science* 243:1068–71

98. Yudilevich DL, de Rose N. 1971. Blood-brain transfer of glucose and other molecules measured by rapid indicator dilution. *Am. J. Physiol.* 220:841–46

*Annu. Rev. Physiol. 1997. 59:621–31*

# INDUCED MEMBRANE HYPO/ HYPER-MECHANOSENSITIVITY:
## A Limitation of Patch-Clamp Recording

*Owen P. Hamill and Don W. McBride, Jr.*

Department of Physiology and Biophysics, University of Texas Medical Branch, Galveston, Texas 77555

KEY WORDS:  mechanosensitivity, channel gating, hyper-mechanosensitivity, hypo-mechano-sensitivity, patch clamp

### ABSTRACT

Practical limitations of the patch-clamp technique when recording mechanogated membrane ion channels are considered. Mechanical overstimulation of the patch or the cell from excessive suction/pressure protocols induces morphological and functional changes. In particular, the plasma membrane becomes decoupled from the underlying cytoskeleton to form either membrane blebs (cell-attached) or ghosts (whole cell). As a consequence, a membrane ion channel may show either a decrease or an increase in its native mechanosensitivity or even acquire mechanosensitivity. The effect varies with ion channel and cell type and presumably arises because of a disruption of membrane-cytoskeleton interactions. We consider that such disruptions are a pathological consequence of excessive mechanical stress, either during or after seal formation, rather than an immutable consequence of patch-clamp recording. By careful attention to the suction/pressure protocols during sealing and throughout recording, such artifacts can be avoided.

## INTRODUCTION

From the time single mechanogated (MG) channels were first recognized using the patch-clamp technique, they have been shown to be widely, if not ubiquitously, expressed in cell types representative of all the living kingdoms (28). This apparent ubiquity has led to two different views with regard to the reality and function of these channels. On the one hand, it has been suggested that MG channels function as physiological mechanotransducers subserving

621

0066-4278/97/0315-0621$08.00

the obvious transduction role in mechanosensory cells (2, 3, 19); more general and basic roles such as cell volume and growth regulation in animal cells (15, 28, 35, 38–40); and gravitrophism and turgor control in plant cells (1, 5, 38). On the other hand, specific reports have questioned the reality of MG channels as biological transducers and propose that such channel activity is an artifact of patch-clamp recording (33, 34, 36; see Reference 6 for discussion). One approach in addressing the functional aspect of this controversy has been to correlate whole-cell mechanosensitive responses with single MG channel activities using pharmacological agents (for review, see 17). In this review, another aspect of the controversy is addressed by focusing on some of the practical limitations of stimulating and recording membrane ion channel currents using the patch-clamp technique. We conclude that, as with any technique, single-channel patch-clamp recording has its limitations, and when these limitations are exceeded, artifacts may result. In particular, we show that mechanical overstimulation of the patch, either during or after tight seal formation, may result in an ion channel either decreasing or increasing its native mechanosensitivity. The effect depends on the type of channel and cell type and presumably occurs because of disruption of membrane-cytoskeleton (MEM-CSK) interactions. In both cases, such artifacts can lead to misinterpretation of experimental data. By analogy, artifacts and misinterpretations arise in using the voltage-clamp technique when its inherent limitations (e.g. space clamp and series resistance) are overlooked and exceeded.

## MECHANICAL REQUIREMENTS OF PATCH-CLAMP RECORDING

A general feature of the patch-clamp technique is the typical requirement to apply suction to the patch pipette in order to draw membrane into the tip and thus promote tight seal formation (10). Once the seal is formed, suction is not necessary to maintain it and should be released. However, the ability to mechanically stimulate the patch by applying suction or pressure is retained. Furthermore, stronger suction can be used to rupture the patch and gain low-resistance access to measure whole-cell currents. In this configuration, pressure or suction can be used to inflate or deflate the cell. Although initial studies used mouth- or syringe-applied suction/pressure, recent methods have been developed that better control the suction/pressure with feedback or pressure-clamp systems (16, 30, 31, 32, 46). Pressure-clamp techniques also allow more reproducible and precisely controlled pressure/suction protocols for tight seal formation.

Clearly, every experimental technique has its limitations. Moreover, a researcher using a particular technique must be aware of its limitations and guard against situations in which the limitations are exceeded. Early in the development of the patch-clamp technique, concern was raised over whether any mechanical perturbation associated with tight seal formation would result in changes in the physiological properties of the patch (42). At the time, the general agreement between results from patch-clamp and conventional intracellular recording techniques indicated that there was no major alteration in functional membrane patch properties. However, these early comparisons were made on ligand- and voltage-gated channels where mechanical factors would presumably not be critical in the channels' gating. Subsequently, with the discovery of MG channels in which MEM-CSK interactions were hypothesized to be important (4), the issue regarding mechanical disturbance of the patch has warranted further critical examination.

During the course of a patch-clamp recording, the degree of preservation of MEM-CSK interactions is expected to depend on the overall mechanical history of the patch and includes both the initial care and gentleness of the sealing protocol, as well as postseal treatment of the patch associated with suction/pressure stimulation protocols. We see the degree of preservation of MEM-CSK interactions, in either the patch or the whole cell, represented by a continuum, from fully intact and functional, to partially then completely decoupled, and ultimately to rupture of the patch or the cell. Although the state of MEM-CSK interactions on this continuum is related to the overall patch (or cell) history involving both preseal and postseal mechanical contributions, these two components are discussed separately below.

## Gentle Versus Forceful Seals

Critical parameters describing the sealing protocol are the magnitude and duration of the applied suction necessary to obtain the tight seal, which appear to depend on pipette, solution, and cell characteristics. Unfortunately, these critical parameters are generally not reported. However, in an early study on frog erythrocytes, it was demonstrated that suction protocols necessary for tight seal formation could vary from so-called gentle or spontaneous seals, requiring little or no suction, respectively, to forceful seals requiring stronger and prolonged suction (see figure 24-3 in Reference 8). Although the terms gentle and forceful may seem arbitrary, more recent studies utilizing the pressure-clamp technique have revealed dramatic differences in both the functional and morphological properties of the membrane patch depending upon the sealing protocols (11). Specifically, it was shown in *Xenopus* oocytes, when recording with standard (i.e. 2 $\mu$m tip diameter) patch pipettes, that gentle seals obtained with less than 5 mmHg (1 mmHg = 133 Pa) suction for 10 s or less best preserved the high mechanosensitivity and rapid adaptation (i.e. channels close despite maintained stimulation) of the endogenous MG channel activity

(11, 13). On the other hand, forceful seals, obtained with suctions of >10–20 mmHg for >30 s, result in reduced or hypo-mechanosensitivity and the absence of adaptation in MG channel activity (11). Subsequently, in other preparations, mostly notably snail neurons (44), an opposite effect of gentle versus forceful seals has been seen. In this example, forceful seals resulted in increased rather than reduced mechanosensitivity and thus made the patch abnormally hyper-mechanosensitive. These two types of behavior indicate different interactions between membrane channels and their underlying CSK that are apparently subject to disruption by the mechanical stresses associated with forceful seals. The nature of the interactions and bases of the disruption are discussed below.

## Effects of Patch/Cell Mechanical Overstimulation

MORPHOLOGICAL CHANGES    Whereas the visible manifestations of mechanical overstimulation depend upon the patch recording configuration, there appears to be a commonality between the patch and whole-cell phenomena that involves MEM-CSK decoupling.

*Membrane blebbing*    In their initial study of membrane patch morphology, Sakmann & Neher (41) observed that tight seals obtained with applied suction display a characteristic omega-shaped membrane deformation as the membrane is drawn into the pipette. They also noted in those cases where tight seals formed spontaneously (i.e. without suction) that no membrane was drawn into the pipette and no membrane deformation was evident. In a subsequent study using high-resolution videomicroscopy, Sokabe & Sachs (45) observed a similar omega-shaped distortion in sealed membrane on chick cultured skeletal muscle. However, they further observed that with repetitive suction/pressure steps after seal formation, the plasma membrane could be made to separate or pull away from the underlying cytoplasm as evidenced by a clear space developing between the two. A similar decoupling or blebbing of the membrane from the underlying cytoplasm was seen after forceful seals or repetitive suction protocols were applied to a gently sealed patch from *Xenopus* oocytes (11).

Originally, the term membrane bleb was used to describe membrane surface vesicles or blisters that form on cells following applied mechanical or chemical stress (23, 43). Electron microscopy studies indicate that such membrane blebs are free of organelles and cytoplasmic structures and therefore most likely arise from localized decoupling of the plasma membrane from the underlying CSK (23, 43). By analogy, we consider membrane blebs that form in the patch pipette to be a pathological consequence of excessive mechanical stress, either during seal formation or subsequent overstimulation of the patch, rather than an immutable consequence of tight seal formation.

In contrast to the above view that regards membrane blebbing as a result of exceeding a limitation of patch-clamp recording, Milton & Caldwell have taken a more extreme view (33, 34). They hypothesize, "that a specific process, termed membrane blebbing, must occur in order for tight seals to form . . ." (34). They further propose that the suction required to draw the membrane into the pipette is sufficient to induce blebbing. In these studies, Milton & Caldwell have clearly pointed out that when using large pipettes (10–15 $\mu$m tip diameter), with suctions of 10–20 mmHg maintained even after seal formation, blebs readily form in the patch pipette (e.g. see their video sequences in Figures 1 and 2 in Reference 33). Although they report similar bleb formation using 2 $\mu$m tip pipettes, they give no details regarding the suction protocols used for sealing with these pipettes. Perhaps even more surprising, no mention is made of the tension that would be developed in the membrane patch when using such large pipettes. Presumably, it is the membrane tension that is the relevant stimulus rather than the pressure. According to Laplace's law, $T = Pr/2$ (where $T$ is tension, $P$ is pressure and, $r$ is the radius of patch curvature), and assuming a hemispherical patch, the membrane tension developed with 20 mmHg pressure using a 10 $\mu$m tip pipette would be equivalent to that developed with 100 mmHg in a 2 $\mu$m tip pipette. Clearly, this represents an excessive mechanical stress to the patch and must be considered overstimulation because pressures of this magnitude often cause membrane patch rupture (50). In this case, Milton & Caldwell have documented a pathological membrane condition that arises when certain limitations concerning the sealing protocol are exceeded. This result should be taken as a warning rather than a generality about the patch-clamp technique.

*Cell ghosting or ballooning*    A condition analogous to membrane blebbing in the patch can be induced in cells during whole-cell recording by the application of positive pressure to inflate the cell. At a certain pressure, the plasma membrane becomes detached from a core of cytoplasm and a clear space develops between the surrounding membrane and the cytoplasmic core. Presumably, this clear space is composed of cytoplasm diluted by injected pipette solution. Thus, the perimeter of the cell as defined by the plasma membrane takes on a halo or ghost-like appearance. The pressure required to initially detach the membrane and form such ghosts in mammalian cells (e.g. $BC_3H1$) is relatively large (>50 mmHg) and is dependent on duration and cell size. However, after detachment, much smaller pressures (<5 mmHg) are sufficient to reversibly inflate and deflate the cell. During such inflating or ballooning, the cell volume can be increased to several times its original volume without disrupting the tight seal. To date, the types of cells that display such ghosting or ballooning include $BC_3H1$ cells (12; O Hamill & D McBride, unpublished observations), GH3 cells (36), and mast cells (47).

FUNCTIONAL CHANGES    Accompanying the above morphological changes are functional changes in the mechanosensitivity of membrane currents. Specifically, overstimulation of the patch after gentle seal formation can induce either hypo- or hyper-mechanosensitivity depending on the channel and the cell type studied.

*Induced hypo-mechanosensitivity*    Suction steps applied to gently sealed cell-attached patches on *Xenopus* oocytes typically produce a rapid ($<1$ ms) activation of MG channel currents that show adaptation or channel closing even in the presence of sustained stimulation (11, 13). This adaptation is highly voltage dependent ($\tau = 100$ ms at $-100$ mV, and $\tau = 2500$ ms at $100$ mV) but does not require external $Ca^{2+}$. Furthermore, as long as suction pulses are small ($<20$ mmHg) and brief ($<5$ s), voltage-dependent adaptation is retained during repetitive pulses. However, if the stimulus is increased in magnitude or duration, there is a progressive and typically irreversible loss of adaptation and its voltage dependence. Accompanying this loss is a reduction in mechanosensitivity of the patch, seen as a shift to the right and a decrease in the slope of the stimulus-response (i.e. Boltzmann) relation. Continued stimulation of the patch can ultimately result in complete abolishment of patch mechanosensitivity without losing the tight seal. A labile voltage-sensitive adaptation and mechanosensitivity have also been reported for a nonselective MG channel activity in yeast plasma membrane (7). In oocytes, the induced hypo-mechanosensitivity of the patch can be correlated with the appearance of membrane blebbing of the patch in the pipette (11). If oocyte membrane is blebbed either chemically or mechanically, prior to sealing, MG channel activity displays no adaptation and reduced mechanosensitivity similar to that seen in membrane blebbed in the pipette (9, 51). However, the hypo-mechanosensitivity seen in preblebbed membrane is evident immediately, even with gentle sealing, rather than occurring progressively and, furthermore, does not require overstimulation. These basic observations of hypo-mechanosensitivity in blebbed membrane negate the hypothesis that MG channel activity is a consequence of membrane blebbing (34).

*Induced hyper-mechanosensitivity*    In contrast to the induced hypo-mechanosensitivity seen in the oocyte, other cell types show an induced hyper-mechanosensitivity in response to overstimulation of the whole cell or the patch. One example of this is the $BC_3H1$ cell, a smooth muscle cell line (12; O Hamill & D McBride, unpublished observations). In the whole-cell configuration, small pressure steps ($<20$ mm Hg) initially fail to elicit any mechanosensitive current. However, after ghosting or ballooning the cell as described above, the same small previously ineffective pressures can now reversibly activate a gadolinium-sensitive whole-cell current of hundreds of pAs. Thus the stimulus-response relation of the whole cell is permanently shifted to the left by overstimulation or mechanical priming, thereby making the cell abnormally hyper-mechanosensitive.

A similar hyper-mechanosensitivity related to mechanical overstimulation of the membrane patch occurs in snail (*Lymnaea stagnalis*) neurons. In these cells, mechanical priming is required to elicit mechanical activation of a $K^+$-selective channel in cell-attached patches (44). Furthermore, it was demonstrated that the latency for MG channel activation decreased from as long as 35 s with the first large ($\approx$100 mmHg with 2 $\mu$m tip pipettes) suction step to less than a second with repetitive large suction steps. The latency was also drastically reduced by pretreating the cell with cytochalasin to disrupt the actin CSK. These changes in latency, as a result of priming or treating with cytochalasin, are consistent with the membrane being decoupled from a constraining CSK such that more tension is sensed in the membrane (see below). This priming phenomenon appears to underlie the apparent discrepancy reported between experimentally measured whole-cell currents and those anticipated from cell-attached patch recordings (36). However, in hindsight, the discrepancy was not the result of failure to elicit whole-cell currents but rather was due to hyper-mechanosensitivity induced in the patch by mechanical priming and patch history. Again, this reflects a pathological situation in which the limitations of the patch-clamp technique were exceeded. In reality, the minimally perturbed (i.e. gently sealed) patch in this cell type is essentially non-mechanosensitive (44) in agreement with the whole-cell insensitivity (36). A remaining issue concerns the contribution of so-called stretch-inactivated channels to the whole-cell current. However, predicted contributions based on patch studies are complicated by recent findings that these channels may be sensitive to the direction of membrane curvature rather than membrane stretch itself (27).

## MECHANISMS OF MECHANOSENSITIVITY AND ITS MODULATION

Two broad classes of mechanisms have been implicated in conferring mechanosensitivity onto the gating of a channel protein. One relies on direct connections between the channel gate and proteins, in the extracellular matrix (ECM) and/or the CSK; we refer to this as the tethered model (4, 18–21). In this model, a shearing or relative displacement of the channel with respect to the CSK (or ECM) would cause channel gating. The other model relies on tensions developed purely within the bilayer, and we refer to this as the bilayer model (29, 37). Model systems in which purified or cloned channel proteins have been reconstituted into lipid vesicles devoid of a CSK have shown that MG channels can be activated by the bilayer mechanism (48, 49). However, in order for the bilayer tension to affect the channel open probability ($P_o$), there must be a change in the membrane area occupied by the channel ($\Delta A$) associated with the open-closed conformational change. In this case, $P_o$ would be tension ($t$) sensitive through the Boltzmann relation $P_o = 1/(1 + \exp[(\Delta G_o - t\Delta A)/kT])$ where $\Delta G_o$ is the difference in free energy between open and closed states in the absence of tension. Thus any channel, including voltage- and ligand-gated channels, that undergo an open-closed conformation area change are mechanosensitive, with the sensitivity increasing with the magnitude of the area change (14). Although the tethered and bilayer mechanisms are not mutually exclusive, in the ideal tether model there would be no need for an open-closed channel conformation area change.

## Mechanism of Induced Changes in Mechanosensitivity

The CSK underlying the membrane serves a basic role of supporting and constraining the lipid bilayer. Furthermore, the CSK, by providing a framework with localized attachment points with the membrane, organizes or divides it into microdomains. In addition, specific interactions between CSK elements and membrane channel proteins may also directly influence channel distribution and function. As discussed above, mechanical overstimulation during patch-clamp recording can result in decoupling or disruption of MEM-CSK interactions. With the bilayer no longer supported or constrained by the CSK, it is more easily distended by osmotic and hydrostatic pressures. This manifests itself by bleb formation in the cell-attached patches and ballooning or ghosting in the whole-cell configuration. Besides the general morphological effects, specific MEM-CSK interactions that are important for mechanosensitivity are also disrupted.

HYPO-MECHANOSENSITIVITY    A number of scenarios exist by which MEM-CSK disruption may result in changes in membrane mechanosensitivity. The first basic phenomenon is one in which a normally MG channel loses its mechanosensitivity. Although others can be envisioned, the simplest mechanism would involve the tethered model of gating, and loss of the tether (or gating spring) by MEM-CSK disruption, which would abolish mechanosensitivity. This mechanism explains the loss of mechanosensitivity seen in *Xenopus* oocytes. In contrast to the tethered model, it is difficult to envisage how a bilayer gated channel would become hypo-mechanosensitive with MEM-CSK disruption.

HYPER-MECHANOSENSITIVITY    This basic phenomenon involves either a normally MG channel, which increases its mechanosensitivity, or a normally non-MG channel (i.e. voltage, ligand or leak), which gains mechanosensitivity with MEM-CSK disruption. Because there are no CSK interactions in the blebbed or disrupted membrane, the channel must be able to be gated directly by tensions developed within the bilayer. As mentioned above, the CSK serves to constrain the bilayer while imposing microdomains in it. The constraining elements, by acting as parallel viscoelastic components, prevent the development of tension in the bilayer. Similarly, for a given pressure, tension is also reduced (according to Laplace's law) because of the smaller radius of curvature of the microdomains compared with the radii of the patch or the cell. Loss of the constraining elements and the microdomains therefore results in increased tension transmitted to the channel. This, coupled with the requisite open-closed channel area change, leads to hyper-mechanosensitivity. This mechanism may underlie the increased mechanosensitivity seen in $BC_3H1$ and snail cells resulting from overstimulation (12, 44). A similar mechanism accounts for the increased mechanosensitivity of bacterial MG channel activity when the peptidoglycan layer (the bacterial equivalent of the cytoskeleton) is disrupted (24) or when MG channel proteins are reconstituted into a peptidoglycan-free bilayer (48, 49). It is difficult to envisage how disruption of a tethered model channel could lead to hyper-mechanosensitivity.

Milton & Caldwell have suggested that hyper-mechanosensitivity seen in blebbed membrane may be due to lipid-lined pores that form in the CSK-free bilayer as a consequence of mechanical stress (34). Although such stress-induced lipid pores may account for increased and irregular current fluctuations immediately preceding patch rupture, they cannot account for the $K^+$-selective, unitary MG current events seen in snail neurons (44) and the gadolinium-sensitive, whole-cell-mechanosensitive current seen in $BC_3H1$ cells following mechanical overstimulation (12). Furthermore, such a general mechanism cannot account for hypo-mechanosensitivity as seen in blebbed membrane of *Xenopus* oocytes (9, 11, 51).

## CONCLUSIONS

It has been demonstrated that mechanical overstimulation of the cell membrane can produce two opposite phenomena: namely, induced hypo-mechanosensitivity or induced hyper-mechanosensitivity. We consider these phenomena pathological when they occur during patch-clamp recordings. However, it may be that MEM-CSK rearrangements occuring during physiological conditions such as cell growth and differentiation (22) and volume regulation (25, 26) also result in either up-regulation or down-regulation of the mechanosensitivity of specific membrane proteins. Although the focus of this review is on alterations in mechanosensitivity, any membrane enzymatic or channel function (e.g. ligand- or voltage-gating) that is dependent on either a conformational area change or tethering to the CSK may also be subject to alteration or modulation by the mechanisms discussed above.

ACKNOWLEDGMENTS

This work was supported by grants from the National Institute of Arthritis and Musculoskeletal and Skin Diseases, grant RO1-AR42782; the National Science Foundation; and the Muscular Dystrophy Association.

*Literature Cited*

1. Edwards KL, Pickard BG. 1987. Detection and transduction of physical stimuli in plants. In *The Cell Surface and Signal Transduction*, ed. E Wagner, H Greppin, B Millet, pp. 41–66. Heidelberg: Springer-Verlag
2. Erxleben C, Ubl J, Kolb H-A. 1991. Identifying and characterizing stretch-activated ion channels. In *Molecular Neurobiology. A Practical Approach,* ed. J Chad, H Wheal. pp. 75–91. Oxford: Oxford Univ. Press
3. French AS. 1992. Mechanotransduction. *Annu. Rev. Physiol.* 54:135–52
4. Guharay F, Sachs F. 1984. Stretch-activated single ion channel currents in tissue cultured embryonic chick skeletal muscle. *J. Physiol.* 352:685–701
5. Gustin MC. 1992. Mechanosensitive ion channels in yeast. Mechanisms of activation and adaptation. In *Advances in Comparative and Environmental Physiology,* ed. F Ito, 10:19–38. Berlin: Springer-Verlag
6. Gustin MC, Sachs F, Sigurdson WJ, Ruknudin A, Bowman C, et al. 1991. Technical comments. Single channel mechanosensitive currents. *Science* 253:1195–97
7. Gustin MC, Zhou X-L, Martinac B, Kung C. 1988. A mechanosensitive ion channel in the yeast plasma membrane. *Science* 242:762–63
8. Hamill OP. 1983. Potassium and chloride channels in red blood cells. In *Single Channel Recording*, ed. B Sakmann, E Neher, pp. 451–71. New York: Plenum
9. Hamill OP, Chen M, Zhang Y, McBride DW Jr. 1995. A cytoskeleton (CSK) deficient plasma membrane vesicle preparation from *Xenopus* oocytes for studying CSK affects on membrane ion channel gating. *J. Physiol.* 483:P162
10. Hamill OP, Marty A, Neher E, Sakmann B, Sigworth F. 1981. Improved patch clamp techniques for high current resolution from cells and cell-free membrane patches. *Pflügers Arch.* 391:85–100
11. Hamill OP, McBride DW Jr. 1992. Rapid adaptation of the mechanosensitive channel in *Xenopus* oocytes. *Proc. Natl. Acad. Sci. USA* 89(16):7462–66
12. Hamill OP, McBride DW Jr. 1993. Patch and whole-cell MG currents recorded from BC₃H-1 muscle cells. *Biophys. J.* 64:A93
13. Hamill OP, McBride DW Jr. 1994. Molecular mechanisms of mechanoreceptor adaptation. *News Physiol. Sci.* 9:53–59
14. Hamill OP, McBride DW Jr. 1994. The cloning of a mechano-gated membrane channel. *Trends Neurosci.* 17:439–43
15. Hamill OP, McBride DW Jr. 1995. Mechanoreceptive membrane ion channels. *Am. Sci.* 83:30–37
16. Hamill OP, McBride DW Jr. 1995. Pressure/patch-clamp methods. In *Patch Clamp Techniques and Protocols,* ed. AA Boulton, GB Baker, W Walz, pp. 75–87. New Jersey: Humana Press
17. Hamill OP, McBride DW Jr. 1996. The pharmacology of mechano-gated membrane ion channels. *Pharmacol. Rev.* 48(2):231–52
18. Hamill OP, McBride DW Jr. 1996. A supramolecular complex underlying touch sensation. *Trends Neurosci.* 19:1–5
19. Howard J, Roberts WM, Hudspeth AJ. 1988. Mechanoelectrical transduction by hair cells. *Annu. Rev. Biophys. Biophys. Chem.* 17:99–124
20. Huang M, Gu G, Ferguson EL, Chalfie M. 1995. A stomatin-like protein necessary for mechanosensation in *C. elegans*. *Nature* 378:292–95
21. Hudspeth AJ, Gillespie PG. 1994. Pulling strings to fine tune transduction: adaptation by hair cells. *Neuron* 12:1–9
22. Ingber DE, Prusty D, Sun Z, Betensky H, Wang N. 1995. Cell shape, cytoskeletal mechanics and cell cycle control in angiogenesis. *J. Biomech.* 28:1471–84
23. Jurkowitz-Alexander MS, Altschuld RA, Hohl CM, Johnson JD, McDonald JS, et al. 1992. Cell swelling, blebbing and death are dependent on ATP depletion and independent of calcium during hypoxia in a glial cell line (ROC-1). *J. Neurochem.* 59:344–52
24. Kubalski A, Martinac B, Ling KY,

Adler J, Kung C. 1993. Activities of a mechanosensitive ion channel in an *E. coli* mutant lacking the major lipoprotein. *J. Membr. Biol.* 131:151–60

25. Lascola CD, Kraig RP. 1996. Whole cell chloride currents in rat astrocytes accompany changes in cell morphology. *J. Neurosci.* 16:2532–45

26. Levitan I, Almonte C, Mollard P, Garber SS. 1995. Modulation of a volume-regulated chloride current by F-actin. *J. Membr. Biol.* 147:283–94

27. Marchenko SM, Sage SO. 1996. Mechanosenitive channels from endothelium of excised intact rat aorta. *Biophys. J.* 70:A365

28. Martinac B. 1992. Mechanosensitive ion channels: biophysics and physiology. In *Thermodynamics of Cell Surface Receptors,* ed. MB Jackson, pp. 327–52. Boca Raton, FL: CRC Press

29. Martinac B, Adler J, Kung C. 1990. Mechanosensitive ion channels of *E. coli* activated by amphipaths. *Nature* 348:261–63

30. McBride DW Jr, Hamill OP. 1992. Pressure clamp: a method for rapid step perturbation of mechanosensitive channels. *Pflügers Arch.* 421:606–12

31. McBride DW Jr, Hamill OP. 1993. Pressure-clamp technique for measurement of the relaxation kinetics of mechanosensitive channels. *Trends Neurosci.* 16:341–45

32. McBride DW Jr, Hamill OP. 1995. A fast pressure clamp technique for studying mechano-gated channels. In *Single Channel Recording,* ed. B Sakmann, E Neher, pp. 329–40. New York: Plenum. 2nd ed.

33. Milton RL, Caldwell JH. 1990. How do patch clamp seals form? A lipid bleb model. *Pflügers Arch.* 416:758–65

34. Milton RL, Caldwell JH. 1994. Membrane blebbing and tight seal formation: are there hidden artifacts in single-channel patch clamp recordings. *Comments Theor. Biol.* 3:265–284

35. Morris CE. 1990. Mechanosensitive ion channels. *J. Membr. Biol.* 113:93–107

36. Morris CE, Horn R. 1991. Failure to elicit neuronal macroscopic mechanosensitive currents anticipated by single channel studies. *Science* 251:1246–49

37. Opsahl LR, Webb WW. 1994. Transduction of membrane tension by the ion channel alamethicin. *Biophys. J.* 66:71–74

38. Pickard BG, Ding JP. 1992. Gravity sensing by higher plants. In *Advances in Comparative and Environmental Physiology,* ed. F Ito, 10:82–110. Berlin: Springer-Verlag

39. Sachs F. 1988. Mechanical transduction in biological systems. *CRC Crit. Rev. Biomed. Eng.* 16:141–69

40. Sackin H. 1995. Mechanosensitive channels. *Annu. Rev. Physiol.* 57:333–53

41. Sakmann B, Neher E. 1983. Geometric parameters of pipettes and membrane patches. In *Single Channel Recording,* ed. B Sakmann, E Neher, 37–51. New York: Plenum

42. Sakmann B, Neher E. 1984. Patch clamp techniques for studying ionic channels in excitable membranes. *Annu. Rev. Physiol.* 46:455–72

43. Scott RE. 1976. Plasma membrane vesiculation: a new technique for isolation of plasma membrane. *Science* 194:743–45

44. Small DL, Morris CE. 1994. Delayed activation of single mechanosensitive channels in *Lymnaea* neurons. *Am. J. Physiol.* 267:C598–606

45. Sokabe M, Sachs F. 1990. The structure and dynamics of patch-clamped membranes: a study using differential interference contrast light microscopy. *J. Cell Biol.* 111:599–606

46. Sokabe M, Sachs F, Jing Z. 1991. Quantitative video microscopy of patch clamped membranes stress, strain, capacitance and stretch channel activation. *Biophys. J.* 59:722–28

47. Solsona C, Fernandez J. 1996. Balloon patch clamp, a new configuration to study exocytosis. *Biophys. J.* 70:A151

48. Sukharev SI, Blount P, Martinac B, Blattner FR, Kung C. 1994. A large-conductance mechanosensitive channel in *E. coli* encoded by *mscL* alone. *Nature* 368:265–68

49. Sukharev SI, Martinac B, Arshasky VY, Kung C. 1993. Two types of mechanosensitive channels in the *E. coli* cell envelope: solubilization and functional reconstitution. *Biophys. J.* 65:177–83

50. Vandorpe DH, Small DL, Dabrowski AR, Morris CE. 1994. FMRF amide and membrane stretch as activators of the *Aplysia* S-channel. *Biophys. J.* 66:46–58

51. Zhang Y, Gao F, McBride DW, Hamill OP. 1996. On the nature of mechano-gated channel activity in cytoskeleton deficient vesicles shed from *Xenopus* oocytes. *Biophys. J.* 70(2):A349

*Annu. Rev. Physiol. 1997. 59:633–57*

# MECHANOSENSITIVE CHANNELS OF *ESCHERICHIA COLI*: The MscL Gene, Protein, and Activities

*Sergei I. Sukharev[1], Paul Blount[1], Boris Martinac[3], and Ching Kung[1,2]*

[1]Laboratory of Molecular Biology, and [2]Department of Genetics, University of Wisconsin, Madison, Wisconsin 53706; [3]Department of Pharmacology, The University of Western Australia, Perth, Australia 6907

KEY WORDS: MscL, stretch activated-channels, *E. coli*, patch clamp, osmotic forces

## ABSTRACT

Although mechanosensory responses are ubiquitous and diverse, the molecular bases of mechanosensation in most cases remain mysterious. MscL, a mechanosensitive channel of large conductance of *Escherichia coli* and its bacterial homologues are the first and currently only channel molecules shown to directly sense mechanical stretch of the membrane. In response to the tension conveyed via the lipid bilayer, MscL increases its open probability by several orders of magnitude. In the present review we describe the identification, cloning, and first sets of biophysical and structural data on this simplest mechanosensory molecule. We discovered a 2.5-ns mechanosensitive conductance in giant *E. coli* spheroplasts. Using chromatographies to enrich the target and patch clamp to assay the channel activity in liposome-reconstituted fractions, we identified the MscL protein and cloned the *mscL* gene. MscL comprises 136 amino acid residues (15 kDa), with two highly hydrophobic regions, and resides in the inner membrane of the bacterium. PhoA-fusion experiments indicate that the protein spans the membrane twice with both termini in the cytoplasm. Spectroscopic techniques show that it is highly helical. Expression of MscL tandems and covalent cross-linking suggest that the active channel complex is a homo-hexamer. We have identified several residues, which when deleted or substituted, affect channel kinetics or mechanosensitivity. Although unique when discovered, highly conserved MscL homologues in both gram-negative and gram-positive bacteria have been found, suggesting their ubiquitous importance among bacteria.

0066-4278/97/0315-0633$08.00

## INTRODUCTION

Contemporary physiology is anthropocentric and favors the use of animals as subjects. Therefore, activities of mechanosensitive (MS) channels have been documented electrophysiologically in more than 30 types of cells, mostly of animal origin (see 67–69 for reviews). Also, genetic dissection of touch response in *Caenorhabditis elegans* uncovered genes that appear to encode channel-like structures (see N Tavernarakis & M Driscoll this volume). However, the first and only MS channel that has been cloned and reconstituted, thereby allowing molecular biological and patch clamp characterization, is the mechanosensitive channel of large conductance (MscL) of the bacterium *Escherichia coli*.

Since the first demonstrations of MS channel activities in 1984, MS conductances have been shown by patch clamp in neurons and oocytes, and in cells of muscle, heart, kidney, blood, lens, plant roots, and leaves (12, 26). Reviews of these activities can be found in References 3, 36, 51, 63, 67–69, as well as in chapters in this volume. These various cells and tissues, however, are unsuitable for original genetic or molecular-biological research. On the other hand, there are genetically amenable animal species, such as *C. elegans* (21) and *Drosophila melanogaster* (39), where touch-insensitive mutants can be isolated and some of the genes corresponding to the mutations cloned. But even when the gene products are homologous to known ion channels, patch-clamp experiments have not yet been performed to determine if these products do form channels, let alone whether the channels are indeed mechanosensitive (3). Because of the previous lack of a model molecule such as the nicotinic acetylcholine receptor and the *shaker* $K^+$ channel, the molecular structure and function of channels gated by mechanical forces are poorly understood, unlike those of channels gated by voltage, external ligands, or internal messengers (35). It has been speculated that the actions of MS channels are the first events in animals' senses of touch, hearing, balance; in cardiac mechano-electric feedback, visceral movements, sphincter contractions, etc; and in plants' gravitropism and thigmomorphogenesis. Perhaps nearly all cells respond to the most fundamental mechanical forces, their turgor or membrane stretch derived from osmotic pressure. If so, studying certain stretch-detecting MS channels in microbes can be a step toward the studies of more complex systems.

## WHY *E. COLI*?

*E. coli* is the most thoroughly analyzed organism. The great wealth of genetic, physiological, and molecular-biological knowledge already accumulated in this species (62) provides a strong conceptual and technical basis for gaining more knowledge. The bacterium's short doubling time and prototrophic nature allow rapid and inexpensive accumulation of large masses of homogeneous cells of the same genotype and phenotype. Even fermentation-scale production of such biomass can be mounted, if necessary. There is, therefore, no limit to the amount of starting material in biochemical purification. As the tool organism, *E. coli* offers a myriad of compatible plasmids and phages for genetic engineering. Its genome has been thoroughly mapped both genetically and physically. The soon-to-be-finished sequencing project will log every single nucleotides of its genome. For MS channel research, there are also fortuitous advantages: These channels do exist in bacteria and can be reconstituted into artificial lipid bilayers, thereby allowing their activities to be followed in vitro. They can be easily recognized by their conspicuous mechanical activation and their characteristic kinetic fingerprints. They have enormous unit conductances, providing large signal-to-noise ratios for tracking during biochemical fractionation.

The immediate relevance of bacterial MS channels in human or animal biology is not obvious, given the evolutionary distance. However, a *shaker*-like $K^+$ channel gene has been encountered in *E. coli* (38, 59), and a gene that appears to encode an inward-rectifying channel has been found in *Streptomyces* (77). At this point, we do not know whether MscL is a structural homologue and/or a functional analogue to the rest of the MS channels in animals and plants. Given the dearth of knowledge in molecular terms, MscL seems useful as a simple-and-plain entity for molecular dissection in order to to understand the basic principles of how a mechanosensitive protein works.

## PATCH CLAMPING *E. COLI*

The technology of patch clamp is advanced (30, 74). Besides the methods in analyzing conductance, selectivity, and kinetics (65, 74), and methods of controlling voltage and pressure (60), methods have been devised to prepare various cell surfaces so that gigaohm seals can be formed. For reviews on how various microbial surfaces are prepared and the various currents encountered, see References 44, 51, 55, 56, 70–73, 81, 92.

### Giant Round-Up Cells with MS channels In Situ

*E. coli* is gram negative and has a complex cell envelope comprising an outer membrane, a peptidoglycan cell wall, and an inner membrane. The outer membrane is an atypical bilayer having mostly lipopolysaccharide in its outer leaflet. This membrane contains a large number of porins, the trimeric $\beta$-sheet barrels that are the subject of intensive biochemical and structural studies (15). The inner cytoplasmic membrane consists of a phospholipid bilayer containing crucial membrane proteins, such as those for electron transport, $H^+$ pumping, and various receptions and transports (49). When the peptidoglycan wall is degraded with lysozyme and EDTA (7), the rod turns into a sphere. The bacteriology literature distinguishes two types of round structures: spheroplasts, the two-membraned spheres; and protoplasts, spheres enclosed only by the inner membrane.

The patch-clamp pipette cannot be made to seal onto a normal *E. coli* cell, which is only ≈2 $\mu$m long and 1 $\mu$m in diameter. There are, however, different methods of producing giant *E. coli* cells using antibiotics (47, 66, 70) or mutations (4, 14) (Figure 1). For example, culturing *E. coli* in cephalexin, a penicillin analogue, allows DNA replication and cell elongation but blocks septation. Such growth results in multinucleated filaments, of tens to over a hundred micrometers in length, that can be collapsed into spheres 3 to 10 $\mu$m in diameter by the lysozyme-EDTA treatment. Viewed under a phase-contrast microscope, these objects show a range of refractivity, likely reflecting cell contents and different degrees of digestion and dishabille (4, 18, 41, 53, 54, 70). Suction on these objects through the patch-clamp electrodes can eventually lead to gigaohm seals (Figure 1, *top row*). Ion channel activities described below have been recorded from on-cell patches, excised inside-out patches, and in whole-cell mode, largely according to standard patch-clamp procedures (30, 74). Using such a preparation, Martinac et al encountered clear MS channel activities in the first patch-clamp survey of the *E. coli* surface in 1986 (53, 54). However, it was not clear whether the seal was formed with the outer or the inner membrane. While Kung and his co-workers (14) called these objects giant spheroplasts and argued for the MS channels' presence in the outer membrane based on enzyme-digestion experiments and on morphologic, electric, and theoretical grounds, Ghazi et al (5) showed that MS channel activities are predominantly associated with the inner-membrane fraction when different sucrose-gradient fractions were reconstituted (Figure 1, row 2). Recently, two independent biochemical investigations clearly associated the MscL with the inner-membrane and not the outer-membrane fraction (9, 33; below). Because the activities of MscL are readily registered in patches from giant round-up cells, it appears that during sustained suction, the pipette tip ruptures the remainder of the outer membrane and seals onto the inner membrane (4). Before the situation was clarified, attempts were made to further digest the giant round-up cells with lysozyme, as evidenced by the further changes in the refractivity of the objects. Some of the resulting gray objects were called giant protoplasts. They usually bore debris, consistent with the outer membrane having been shed but still adhering to the surface (18, 19, 41, 42). This preparation, although fragile, can form gigaseals and can be converted to the whole-cell recording mode relatively easily. The consensus of the field now is that these spherical objects are all giant round-up cells with different amounts of digestion remnants. Gigaohm seals are formed on the inner membrane where the MS channels of *E. coli* are located.

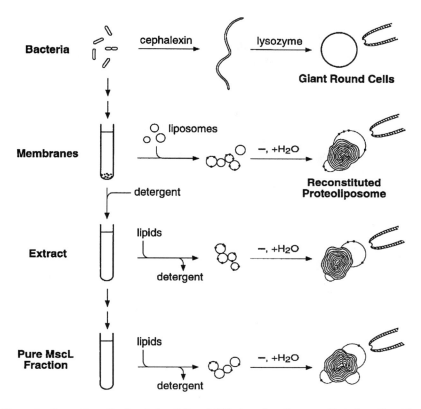

*Figure 1*   Preparations for the study of *E. coli* MS channels. *Top row*: Bacteria cultured in cephalexin grow into long unseptated filaments that are collapsed with lysozyme into giant round-up cells suitable for patch clamp. Here the MS channels are in their original inner-membrane location, i.e. in situ (see text and Reference 14; other variations can be found in References 4, 5, 18, 19, 41, 42, 84). *Row 2*: Pelleted membrane fraction can be fused with soybean azolectin liposomes through copelleting and de- and rehydration ($-$, $+H_2O$) cycle. The procedure converts the smaller fused liposomes into giant multilamellar ones, on which unilamellar blisters can be induced for patch-clamp study. Here the MS channels, greatly diluted into foreign lipids, remain functional in vitro (see text and References 5, 20, 82). *Row 3*: A mild detergent can be added to the membrane fractions to solubilize the membrane proteins. Adding such an extract into lipids followed by removal of the detergent by dialysis results in proteoliposomes that can be similarly treated for patch clamp. MS channels exposed to the detergent for some time, e.g. during biochemical fractionation, remain functional upon reconstitution in vitro, as judged by the patch-clamp assay (see text and References 74, 76, 77). *Bottom row*: Detergent extracts of membranes from *E. coli* strains containing the genetically tagged MscL are suitable for affinity purification. Nearly homogeneous fractions of MscL can also be reconstituted as above, and normal MscL activities are observed in patch-clamp assays (see text; Figure 2; References 9, 31).

## *Reconstituted Liposome: A Preparation In Vitro*

Some membrane proteins retain their functions after being removed from their native membranes and placed into foreign lipid bilayers. The bacterial MS channels are among those that survive such a reconstitution. Based largely on the procedure of Criado & Keller (16), liposomes are prepared by sonicating azolectin, a lipid mixture from soybean, and mixing it with *E. coli* membranes, in the form of small vesicles. The mixture is then pelleted by ultracentrifugation, and subjected to a dehydration and rehydration cycle, during which membrane fusion takes place. Addition of $MgCl_2$ collapses the fused multilamellar proteoliposomes and induces unilamellar blisters that are very suitable for patch-clamp studies (Figure 1, *row 2*) (5, 20, 70). Because there is no cell wall or other debris, liposome patches are more pliable and fragile than patches taken from giant round-up cells and the suction needed to open the same class of MS channels in liposome patches usually is lower than that needed to open MS channels in giant cells (82, 83). *E. coli* MS channels even survive extraction and solubilization by a mild detergent, e.g. 2% $\beta$-octylglucoside, as long as the membrane-detergent-lipid mixture is first dialyzed to remove the detergent before liposome formation (Figure 1, *row 3*) (83). In the most stringent case, column-purified MscL protein can be reconstituted into azolectin liposome by this method and show normal channel activity (Figure 1, *bottom row*). This figure also shows that MscL protein alone is sufficient for ion permeation, as well as for detection and response to mechanical forces. Other proteins, cytoskeletal or otherwise, are not needed to transmit the force to this channel protein (9, 31).

## ACTIVITIES OF *E. COLI* MECHANOSENSITIVE CHANNELS

### *MscL Activities*

MscL activity has been studied extensively (8–10, 31–34, 80–83) since the corresponding gene was cloned and the protein purified and reconstituted (Figure 2). This channel has a conductance of about 2,500 pS in buffer containing 200 mM KCl and 40 mM $MgCl_2$. It exhibits no current saturation up to 2 M KCl (S Sukharev, unpublished data) and no selectivity (82), all suggesting a wide water-filled pore. Multiple subconducting states, which are more pronounced at strong hyperpolarization ($-80$ to $-120$ mV) have been observed but not fully quantified. When standard pipettes of about 2 $\mu$m diameter are used, MscLs are activated at 100–200 mm Hg suction in patches from giant round-up cells and at 50–100 mm Hg in proteoliposome patches. The open probability versus pressure [$P_o(p)$] dependencies are steep sigmoidal curves, well fitted by Boltzmann distributions. Increase of pipette diameter, and consequently the

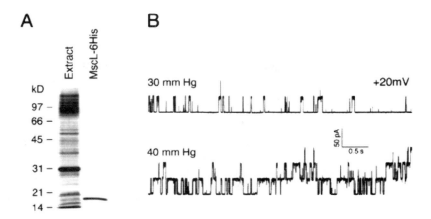

*Figure 2*   MscL protein alone accounts for the mechanosensitive conduction of ions. (*A*) One-step purification of 6His-tagged MscL on a Ni-NTA column results in >98% pure MscL protein, as shown by denaturing gel electrophoresis. Left lane shows total membrane protein extracted with 2% octylglucoside. Right lane shows the column-purified 6His-tagged MscL subunit protein at about 17 kDa. (*B*) MscL-channel activities observed by patch-clamp analysis of liposomes of phosphatidylcholine/phosphatidylserine (8:2) after reconstituting the purified protein, by the method outlined in Figure 1, *bottom row*. Excised liposome patch was examined in symmetric solutions of 200 mM KCl, 40 mM MgCl$_2$, 10 mM HEPES pH 7.4, at −20 mV pipette voltage, and the suctions marked. Note the obvious increase in open probability between 30 and 40 mm Hg; also that increased suction increases MscL open probability (from 9).

size of the patch, usually shifts the P$_o$(*p*) curve to the left, indicating that the actual parameter that gates the channel is the lateral membrane tension *T*, derived from the pressure gradient *p* by Laplace's law *T* = *pr*/2, where *r* is the radius of patch curvature. This is consistent with previous whole-cell recording of the MS channel activities in yeast (28).

Tension-dependent behavior of an MS channel may be explained by the simple two-state model first proposed by Howard et al (37a) for tip-link-gated channels, and then adapted for membrane stretch-activated channels by Sachs (68). Assuming that the channel may comply with the tension and experience transition-related expansion ΔA in the plane of the membrane, the work produced by the external force in this case would be TΔA. Thus following Boltzmann, P$_o$/(1 − P$_o$) = exp [(TΔA − ΔG)/kT], where ΔG is the free energy of channel transition from the closed to the open state in unperturbed membrane, which sets the midpoint for the activation curve, whereas ΔA, a factor by the tension, must determine the slope.

Recording of MscL activities at different pressures with simultaneous video imaging of the patch (79) allows direct assessment of the patch curvature and hence the actual tension $T$. The affinity-purified MscL reconstituted in liposomes displayed the $P_o(T)$ curve with the midpoint at 18 dynes/cm, which was fitted by Boltzmann curve with parameters $\Delta G = 16$ kT and $\Delta A = 3.5$ nm$^2$ (W Sigurdson & S Sukharev, unpublished observations). If the protein expansion is somehow related to the pore opening, then the large $\Delta A$ is consistent with the necessity of a wide, highly conducting pore. For comparison of MscL's $\Delta A$ with other MS channels, see a review by Hamill & McBride (30a). The relatively large $\Delta G$, the energy cost for MscL opening, ensures negligibly low $P_o$ at rest during normal cell cycle but an openable channel upon stressful conditions, as in abrupt osmotic downshock (see below).

The tension required to open MscL is about 1.4 times the tension required to activate MscS, a different MS conductance described below. For wild-type MscL, this ratio is highly reproducible from patch to patch, regardless of patch geometry. Thus MscS can be used as an internal control to study the relative mechanosensitivities of mutant MscLs (see below and 10).

MscL gates in a complex kinetic pattern. The mean open time depends on pipette pressure, as does $P_o$. Preliminary analyses of time distributions suggest more than one open state and more than one closed state. At low $P_o$ (around $10^{-3}$), the channels' open-time distribution can be fitted with three exponential components with characteristic times of $<0.3, 7$, and 30 ms (10). The activities of MscL at higher voltages have not been fully quantified, although they can be recognized in several studies (4, 5, 84). MscL displays little time-dependent behavior: No measurable delay in response as long as threshold is reached, and unlike MscS, MscL shows no obvious adaptation during sustained suctions.

Gd$^{3+}$ is commonly used to block the activities of MS channels (88). MscL currents are blocked by 0.3–1 mM Gd$^{3+}$ in situ as well as in reconstituted liposomes. The blocked channels can be reactivated by increasing the pressure gradient by a factor of 1.3 to 1.5. The results suggest that Gd$^{3+}$ shifts the equilibrium toward closed state and targets something other than the conductive pathway. Gd$^{3+}$ is known to induce phase separation in lipids (46). It is likely that Gd$^{3+}$ effects on these MS channel activities are mediated by modifying the mechanical properties of the lipid bilayer around the channel, thereby rendering the bilayer less effective in transmitting the stretch force or restraining the conformational transition in the protein (23).

## MscS Activities

The first MS activity of giant round-up *E. coli* cells described in 1986 (51, 52) is what we now call MscS, for mechanosensitive channel of smaller conductance (Figure 3A). This conductance can also be observed when total membranes (20, 80–83) or an inner-membrane fraction (4, 5) is reconstituted into liposomes (Figure 3B,D). This conductance is not a substate behavior of MscL

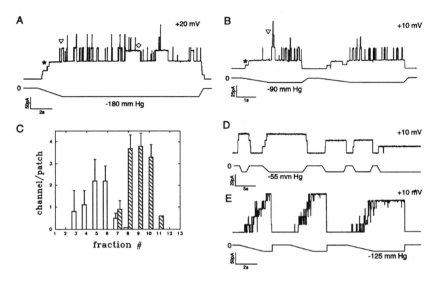

*Figure 3*    The two major *E. coli* MS channel activities and their separation by a sizing column. (*A*) The activities of MscL (*triangle*) and MscS (*asterisk*) recorded from a patch excised from a giant round-up cell, as diagrammed in Figure 1, *second row*. Note that MscS activities appear at lower suction than MscL activities. Substate behavior of MscL (*diamond*) is evident. (*B*) The same activities are observed in patches reconstituted with native-membrane vesicles as in Figure 1 (*second row*). (*C*) Separation of MscL and MscS activity by gel filtration on a Superose 6-HR column. Fractions were collected, and the aliquots were individually reconstituted into azolectin liposomes. Ten to 20 patches were sampled from each fraction, and the number of conducting units of each type found per patch were averaged. Bars show standard error of the means. Note that the activities of MscL (*hatched bars*) and those of MscS (*open bars*) show only a small overlap. (*D*) Activities of fraction 5. Only MscS conductances are seen. (*E*) Activities of fraction 9. Only MscL conductances are seen. (Modified from 82.)

because it remains intact in the *mscL* knock-out mutant, in which MscL conductances have been removed (80). MscS main conductance is 0.6 nS in 200 mM KCl and is therefore still highly conductive by the standard of most known channels. Both positive and negative pressure (suction) are effective in channel activation, although positive pressure tends to disrupt the seal and therefore the latter is preferred in experimentation. Changing the osmolarity of the bath solution can activate MscS, presumably by producing an osmotic force (19, 55). MscS's open probability change with pressure can be fitted with Boltzmann distributions. This channel also exhibits a voltage dependence; the more positive the voltage (membrane depolarization), the higher its open probability, as long as a suprathreshold suction is applied. MscS channel discriminates permeant ions poorly, with only a slight preference for anions, including $Cl^-$ and glutamate (54). At mild voltages, e.g. $\pm20$ mV, this channel displays kinetics that are relatively slow, dwelling in both its open and closed state for hundreds to thousands of milliseconds. Different permeant species often affect the kinetics differently (54). MscS kinetic behavior at higher voltages is complex (4, 5, 82, 83) and has not been fully explored. Its activities dissipate over sustained suction at moderate voltages. Adaptation appears to remain at strong polarization, where substate behavior is more prominent. Given that *E. coli* rests at $\approx-100$ mV (18, 24), such behavior should have physiological consequences. Similar to block in MscL, MscS can also be blocked by submillimolar $Gd3^+$ (4, 6). The above studies used on-cell or excised patches from giant round-up cells (giant spheroplasts) after limited lysozyme-EDTA treatment. Whole-cell recordings from further treated cells (giant protoplasts) (18, 19, 41, 42) show an activity of conductance, selectivity, mechanosensitivity, voltage dependence, $Gd3^+$ blockade, ionic effects, and kinetics that are similar to those described above. This MscS-like activity can be activated in whole-cell preparations by osmotic differences in the hypoosmotic bath on the order of tens to one hundred or more milliosmolal differences.

## Other Small MS Conductances

Conductances smaller than MscS are often encountered in various recordings from giant round-up cells. A 350-pS conductance (in 400 mM KCl) in whole-cell records from giant protoplasts has been described (18, 19). This activity appears less frequently than MscS under the same pressures and in the same cells, unless the cell is strongly depolarized. Like MscS conductance, the 350-pS conductance is activated by hypoosmotic solutions and reversibly blocked by $Gd3^+$. Since the *mscL*-disrupted mutant retains this conductance, it cannot be a subconducting state of MscL. Because *mscS* has not been cloned and disrupted for a comparable test, the possibility that this 350-pS conductance is an expression of MscS cannot be ruled out. However, patches taken from liposomes containing reconstituted inner membranes displayed slightly cation-selective, pressure-activated conductances of 100 and 150 pS in 100 mM KCl, which are nearly comparable to the 350-pS conductance in 400 mM KCl noted above. Because these conductances can be separated from those of MscS upon the dilution necessitated by the reconstitution procedure, they likely reflect a separate class of molecular entity, which Berrier et al (4, 5) named MscM for mechanosensitive channel mini.

## Other MS Activities?

In studies over a larger range of voltage (up to $\pm100$ mV), Berrier et al (4, 5) observed unit MS conductances of 100, 150, 300, 500, 950, 1500, and 2300 pS (in 0.1 M KCl) in giant round-up cells and in inner-membrane reconstitution experiments. Because the conducting events of the same magnitude tend to self-associate after dilution and reconstitution, it is attractive to regard each of the conductances as representing one class of channel molecules that tend to self-aggregate. These conductances have been sorted under three groups: 100–150 pS, 300 and 500 pS, and the 1000 pS or higher group, corresponding to MscM, MscS, and MscL (5). MscL and MscS activities are observed in every patch taken from giant spheroplasts examined under mild voltages ($\pm20$ mV). As reviewed above, MscM is encountered more rarely. The behavior of these three conductances at higher voltages appears to be more complex and has not been fully described. Subconducting states have been noted by various workers in the field (4, 5, 54, 82). Cooperative opening and closing of fully conducting units, if present, can be an additional complication (84). Whether two or three gene products account for all the MS conductances observed remains to be determined.

MscS is activated by forces smaller than those that activate MscL in both patches from cells and reconstituted liposomes (80–83). Interestingly, in the experiments of Berrier et al (4), where six distinct conductances are observed upon reconstitution, the size of the conductance parallels the pressure required to activate them.

## THE CLONING OF *mscL*

The way in which *mscL* was cloned was unusual. First, unlike most genes studied in *E. coli*, *mscL* was not discovered through mutations and phenotypes by the usual forward genetics approach in microbial research because mutants were unavailable. Second, the channel protein we needed to clone the gene through reverse genetics was identified in an unconventional manner. The channel protein was followed during purification not by its binding to any ligand, toxin, or other probes, but by the activity of the protein itself. The strategy of purifying the MscL protein was not unlike the one used in purifying an enzyme: Each enriched fraction during biochemical fractionation was assayed for its activity. Unlike an enzyme, however, each fraction had to be reconstituted into azolectin liposome and then assayed by patch clamp. No other ion channel proteins or genes have been discovered in this manner. However, even at the outset, the MscL channel's reconstitutability, its MS character, its unmistakably large conductance, and kinetic fingerprint, together with the unlimited starting material, spelled an auspicious presage. Although a laborious process, following a protein by its activity has an additional edge: The protein purified is active.

When total membrane proteins in a mild detergent were fractionated by gel-filtration chromatography and the fractions reconstituted and examined by patch clamp, it became clear that the activity of MscS and that of MscL can readily be separated (Figure $3C,D,E$). The peak fractions for MscL and MscS activity corresponded approximately to 60 to 70 and 200 to 400 kDa, respectively. Two series of fractionation were then performed to enrich for MscL: one through ion exchange, hydroxylapatite, gel filtration, and Mono-P columns; and one through ammonium-sulfate cut, then phenyl sepharose, and gel filtration. The two final active fractions each displayed a simple pattern in denaturing gel electrophoresis and both were highly enriched for a protein, the presumed MscL subunit protein, about $M_r$ 17,000. To find the corresponding gene, the N-terminal sequence of this putative MscL protein was determined. This sequence matched none of the full-length open reading frames (ORFs) in the *E. coli* genome known at the time. However, it perfectly matched the start of an unknown ORF 3' of a gene called *trkA* (29, 76) at minute 72 of the *E. coli* genetic map. The entire ORF was then retrieved from the proper fragment, subcloned, and sequenced (80).

Experiments were carried out to test whether the cloned gene indeed encodes the 17-kDa protein and the 2.5-nS mechano-activated conductance. Through homologous recombination, the chromosomal copy of the gene, *mscL*, was disrupted by the insertion of a selectable marker. Into this knock-out strain, a new copy of *mscL* was brought in through an inducible plasmid. The wild-type parent, the knock-out strain, and the restored strain were then examined. Both the 17-kDa protein and the 2.5-nS MS conductance (examined in patches from giant round-up cells and from reconstituted liposomes) were present in the parental and the restored strains, but lacking in the knock-out strain in repeated trials. Although these experiments showed *mscL* expression to be necessary for the MscL protein structure and function, they did not prove it to be sufficient. This sufficiency is suggested by the functional reconstitution of the enriched protein fractions prior to cloning, although not proven because the fractions, unlike the one shown in Figure 2, were not purified to homogeneity. Therefore, two additional experiments were performed to test whether *mscL* encodes the mechanosensitive pore-forming protein or a necessary regulator of the pore rather than the pore itself. First, a transcription-translation-coupled rabbit reticulocyte lysate supplemented with canine microsomes was used. After a properly subcloned *mscL* was allowed to express in this foreign and cell-free setting, the resulting material was reconstituted into azolectin liposomes, and typical MscL channel activities were observed as assayed by patch clamp (80). Second, a *E. coli*-yeast shuttle plasmid that has both the yeast and the bacterial origin of replication, as well as both selectable markers, was used in an attempt to express MscL in yeast. When the total membranes of the transformed yeast were reconstituted into liposomes, again the typical MscL channel activities were observed (83). These two results, in which the MscL conductance was observed in heterologous settings, leave little doubt that *mscL* indeed encodes the functional pore-forming protein, because it is unlikely that a putative bacterial regulator can activate in yeast and in mammalian microsomes an identical MS conductance of characteristics never seen in these organisms. The final proof that *mscL* alone encodes the MS channel came from the reconstitution of MscL purified by two different methods (9, 32; Figure 2) and from the fact that mutations in *mscL* result in specific changes in channel activities (below).

# THE MscL PROTEIN

## Primary Structure

MscL, conceptually translated from its gene, comprises 136 amino acid residues (80). Most are nonpolar residues, and there are no cysteines. Assuming no posttranslational modification, these amino acids have a mass of 15 kDa, agreeing with the ≈17-kDa experimental estimate. This value falls far short of 60 to 70 kDa of the functional channel estimated from gel filtration, thus suggesting oligomerization. As with many bacterial membrane proteins, it has no recognizable leader sequence. Hydropathy analyses showed an amphipathic N terminus (residues 1–15), followed by a strongly hydrophobic segment (19–49), a more hydrophilic segment (50–69), a second strongly hydrophobic segment (72–100), a cluster of five charged residues (104–108), and a hydrophilic C terminus (111–136) (Figure 4). The full sequence had no match in the databases at the time of discovery.

## Secondary Structure

MscL sequence does not show extended amphipathic arrangements for antiparallel $\beta$ sheets found in bacterial porins and mitochondrial voltage-dependent anion channels (VDACs). The two strongly hydrophobic segments can be modeled as transmembrane $\alpha$ helices (80, 81). For secondary structure and other studies, MscL protein has been produced in preparative scale and purified to homogeneity by using appropriate columns for either MscL attached to a cleavable glutathione-S-transferase domain (31) or six-histidine-tagged MscL (9). Both procedures yielded functional channel proteins. Purified six-histidine-tagged MscL was examined by circular dichroism (CD), transmission fast Fourier infrared (FTIR), and the attenuated total reflection FTIR spectroscopic techniques (1). The results indicated high helical content, with predominant *trans*-bilayer orientation of the helices. FTIR transmission spectra obtained upon solvent exchange from $H_2O$ to $D_2O$ suggested that two thirds of amide protons are exchangeable and therefore water accessible. At the same time the secondary structure of MscL was found to be exceptionally resistant to thermal denaturation (up to 95°C) even in the presence of SDS. The data are consistent with the general helix-loop-helix model of protein (see below),

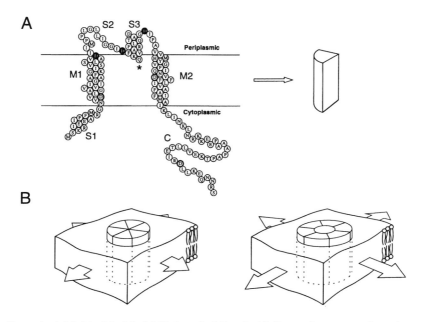

*Figure 4*  A Model of the MscL MS channel of *E. coli.* (*A*) Proposed structure and membrane topology of the MscL subunit peptide. For explanation and experimental evidence, see text and References 9, 10, 33, 80. (*B*) A diagram indicating the homohexameric nature of the functional unit capable of solute conduction and the detection and response to mechanical stretch force in the lipid bilayer (9, 10, 33, 52).

but the loop conformation investigated by independent techniques, in conjunction with the unusual stability of protein secondary structure, appears to be important.

## Membrane Topology

The hydropathy plot of MscL suggests that the polypeptide passes the membrane twice. Together with the $\alpha$ helicity of the transmembrane domains, this would model MscL like members of several families of channel subunit proteins such as the inward rectifier $K^+$ channels in animals (40). The PhoA-fusion method (22) was then used to test this model. The *E. coli* PhoA product, alkaline phosphatase, must be transported out of the cytoplasmic membrane before being posttranslationally processed into a mature functional enzyme. One can therefore fuse the *phoA* ORF at different locations of a gene whose product's membrane topology is under investigation and test for the chromogenic PhoA enzyme activity of the engineered bacteria. PhoA was attached individually to MscL at six of its aspartate residues (D18, D39, D53, D67, D84, D127), both in form of MscL-PhoA terminal fusions and in sandwich fusions. The results placed residue 39, 53, 67, and likely 84, outside and residues 18 and 127 inside the cytoplasmic membrane (9). These results fully support the model in which MscL traverses the membrane twice, with both its N and C termini in the cytoplasm and the central part between the two membrane spans facing the periplasm (Figure 4*A*). A result in the site-directed mutation analysis further supports this model (see Q56H mutant below).

These results led to a working model of a MscL subunit (Figure 4*A*) as follows: The N-terminal segment located in the cytoplasm forms a 3.5-turn amphipathic $\alpha$ helix called S1. S1 is followed by the first membrane-spanning 7.5 turn $\alpha$-helical segment, M1. A second 7.5 turn $\alpha$-helical segment, M2, returns the peptide to the cytoplasm, ending in the 40-residue C-terminal segment of unspecified structure. Between M1 and M2 is a loop that can be divided into two segments: a glycine- and proline-rich short segment, S2, and a short helical segment S3 that includes residue Q56. This model serves as a working hypothesis for further studies and will no doubt be modified in the future.

## *Multimerization*

Even when forced into a $\beta$ sheet, there would not be enough material for a single MscL polypeptide to enclose a pore that conducts at 2.5 nS. Furthermore, gel-filtration indicates the functional channel to be oligomeric (82). Two attempts have been reported to estimate the number of subunits in the functional MscL complex. In one study, MscL was specifically [35]S-labeled in live bacteria by using a T7-RNA-polymerase cassette. When these cells were treated with various cross-linkers, most of the labeled MscL remained monomeric in size in denaturing gels, although about 20% are in dimeric size, and even larger multimeric complexes are recognizable (33, 34). Purified functional MscL proteins or total *E. coli* membranes were examined in a separate study (9). A regular ladder of multimers up to hexamer was observed by silver stain of denaturing electrophoretic gels of cross-linker-treated pure MscL proteins. A similar ladder was seen when an anti-MscL antibody was used to recognize membrane proteins in gel blot after the membranes, known to contain active MscL channels, had been treated with cross-linker in situ. As expected, ladders missing the odd-numbered rungs were observed when the pure proteins or the total membranes were from bacteria with an engineered *mscL-mscL* tandem gene that still encodes functional MscL channels (9). Thus as diagrammed in Figure 4*B*, preassembled homohexamers are present in the native membrane and in purified MscL fractions. There must be monomers in the bacteria, even if only transiently during syntheses. Although not yet understood, ideas on how monomers assemble into functional channels in the bacteria have been posited (33).

## Location

Blount et al found that an anti-MscL antibody (9) specifically stained a band of the MscL molecular mass in a gel blot of proteins from the inner-membrane but not the outer-membrane fraction, separated by a sucrose gradient. Häse et al (33) showed that radioactivity of an engineered strain of *E. coli* in which MscL was specifically [35]S-labeled also fractionates with the inner and not the outer membrane. Together with previous functional assays of these fractions (5), the evidence strongly indicates that MscL resides in the inner membrane, the true cytoplasmic membrane of *E. coli*.

# MOLECULAR DISSECTION BEGINS

## Deletions

Blount et al engineered progressively larger deletions from the C-terminus of MscL (10). Deletion of up to 27 residues (Δ110–136) had little effect on mechanosensitivity, unit conductance, and kinetics. Deletion of six more residues (Δ104–136) extinguished all activities. These six, RKKEEP, form the charge cluster trailing the putative M2 (Figure 5). The C-terminal 27 residues that make up 20% of MscL form a sequence conserved among MscL homologues in gram-negative bacteria but not found in gram-positive ones (Figure 5). The function of this portion of the protein is presently unknown. Shortening of the N-terminal peptide is poorly tolerated. Deletion of four residues (Δ2–5) left the channel functional, albeit altered in gating and conductive properties

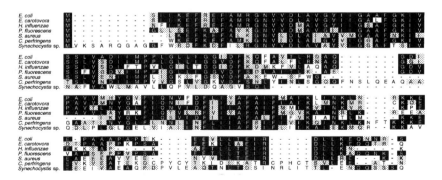

*Figure 5* Amino acid sequences of bacterial MscL homologues arranged from top to bottom in order of relatedness to *E. coli*. *Erwinia carotovora*, *Haemophilus influenzae*, and *Pseudomonas fluorescens* are gram-negative; *Staphylococcus aureus* and *Clostridium perfringens* are gram-positive; *Synechocystis* sp. is a cyanobacterium. Black squares: identical residues; shaded squares: similar residues; dashes: gaps introduced for fitting (P Moe et al, manuscript in preparation).

(32); a larger deletion (Δ2–12) resulted in no channel activity (33). These results suggest that a crucial channel function requires the putative cytoplasmic residues upstream of M1.

## Point Mutations

Mutations have been directed to different residues (10). Dramatic effects were observed after substitutions were placed in one of two residues: K31 and Q56, which are strategically located in the working model (Figure 4A). K31E greatly shortened the open time ($T_2$ about 1 ms, $T_3$ about 3 ms). Q56C, Q56F, Q56W, and Q56Y lengthened the open time ($T_3 > 150$ ms). Q56H significantly lengthened the open time ($T_2$ about 34 ms, $T_3$ 220 ms), but only when the pipette solution, which faced the putative periplasmic side of the excised inside-out patch, was at pH 7.5. At pH 5.5, the Q56H MscL kinetics was indistinguishable from that of the wild-type MscL. Interestingly, the Q56H channels in these patches were indifferent to the bath pH. Thus this engineered His56 apparently faces the outside and causes kinetic changes only when it is not protonated. That residue 56 faces outside supports the topological model shown in Figure 4A. Some mutations affect mechanosensitivity. In any given patch excised from wild-type giant round-up cells, MscL activity appears when the patch is subjected to a suction 1.4 times greater than that which activates MscS. Gauged by the ever-present MscS as an internal control, K31E, Q56R, and possibly Q56H mutant MscLs were found to be more mechanosensitive. The most dramatic change was found in Q56P, in which the mutated MscL became activated by suctions at or below the threshold of MscS activation. Although deletion of Q56 was tolerated, it made a channel that was less sensitive, requiring 2.2 times the MscS threshold suction for activation. These results indicate that the mutations studied have dramatic effects on equilibrium (pressure dependence of $P_o$) and/or kinetic parameters (mean open time) of the channel, changing both the free energy of channel activation (ΔG), as well as transition barriers. They also show that parts of M1 and the loop connecting M1 and M2 are intimately involved in channel gating. Interestingly, none of the mutations reported thus far altered the unit conductance.

## Gain-of-Function Mutants

The loss of MscL leads to no detectable effect on the growth of the bacterium, even in various adverse laboratory conditions. However, it is possible to mutagenize a plasmid-borne *mscL*, retransform *E. coli*, and select for mutants that show growth impairments afflicted by channels that are presumably inappropriately active. Such mutants harbored mutations that seem clustered in a limited region of the MscL molecule (X-R Ou et al, unpublished results).

## *mscL* HOMOLOGUES IN OTHER BACTERIA

Although *mscL* was unique at the time of its discovery, several homologues have recently been reported (Figure 5). A sequence similar to *E. coli* MscL exists in the completely sequenced genome of *Haemophilus influenzae* (25). Probes or oligonucleotide primers based on the *E. coli mscL* sequence have also been used to identify homologues in two other gram-negative bacteria, *Erwinia carotovora* and *Pseudomonas fluorescens*. An ORF that encodes a protein similar to the *E. coli* MscL has been recognized in *Clostridium perfringens* (58), a gram-positive bacterium. Degenerate oligonucleotides based on consensus sequences among these homologues have also been used successfully in cloning the homologue in *Staphylococcus aureus*, another gram-positive bacterium (P Moe et al, manuscript in preparation). Very recently an mscL homologue was reported in *Synechocystis* sp. strain PCC 6803 (38a). As shown in Figure 5, the MscL sequence is well conserved among diverse bacteria. Variations between the gram negatives and positives are largely at the C-terminal portion and at a region located at the junction between S3 and M2 in the model (Figure 4). The *mscL* homologues of *E. carotovora, P. fluorescens, S. aureus,* and *C. perfringens* have been subcloned and expressed in *E. coli*, in which the chromosomal *mscL* has been disrupted by insertion. Patch-clamp examination of these homologue-transformed *E. coli* strains of *mscL*-knock-out background showed MS activities reminiscent of *E. coli* MscL (P Moe et al, manuscript in preparation). It appears that the structurally conserved MscL homologues have conserved biophysical properties.

## MS CONDUCTANCES IN OTHER MICROBE

Patch-clamp surveys of the surfaces of several bacteria also showed MS channel activities. Zoratti and co-workers (92, 93) recorded multiple MS conductances in *Streptococcus faecalis* (86) and *Bacillus subtilis* (85, 94). Some of these conductances are in the range of nanoSiemens, as are those in *E. coli*, although the kinetics and mechanosensitivity often differ. Patch-clamp studies of fungi also revealed MS channel activities. After removal of the cell wall, gigaohm seals can be formed on various fungal plasma membranes. Gustin et al (27, 28) showed that the budding yeast *Saccharomyces cerevisiae* exhibits a 36-pS conductance activatable by pipette suction. Although impermeable to arginine$^+$ and glutamate$^-$, this conductance discriminates smaller cations and anions poorly. The gene that encodes this conductance has yet to be identified, although it is clearly not *ykc1*, which encodes a voltage-activated outwardly rectifying K$^+$-specific channel residing in the same membrane (91). Zhou and co-workers described a 180-pS MS conductance in the fission yeast

*Schizosaccharomyces pombe* (89) and a 600-pS (in 300 mM KCl) MS conductance in the germ-tube protoplasts of the bean-rust fungus *Uromyces appendiculatus* (90). Both are cation selective and can pass $Ca^{2+}$. The ciliate protist *Paramecium* has been studied extensively by using two-electrode voltage-clamp and piezoelectrically driven mechanical probes. Probing the cell anterior induces a cation-based inward current; probing the posterior induces a $K^+$ outward current. In unclamped specimens, the former results in a depolarizing receptor potential capable of triggering an action potential and therefore a transient ciliary reversal and a short back swim of the cell. The latter corresponds to a hyperpolarization, increased ciliary beat frequency, and a forward spurt (61, 75).

# THE MECHANICAL FORCE AND ITS TRANSMISSION

In yeast, whole-cell MS current activates uniformly after the applied pressure is normalized by the cell diameter (28). This is expected from Laplace's law for a thin-walled object if the sensors detect the stretch of the wall. Thus MS channels respond to stretch forces along the plane of the membrane and not pressure perpendicular to it. Even if the pressure can be clamped accurately and rapidly (60) and can be measured directly with a manometer, the stretch force cannot. Although the size of the patch can be estimated from the pipette bore (about 1-2 $\mu$m in diameter), unless one knows the degree of patch curvature and has assurance that the channels are situated in that curved surface (37, 79) and not at its edges, the pressure gauged by the manometer cannot be converted to the stretch force. Thus the actual stretch force that activates MscL or any MS channels remains unknown and can only be roughly estimated. An additional complication in dealing with patches taken from giant round-up cells is the degree of the parallel resistive element in the patches. These elements, formed of the remnant of the outer membrane and various amounts of peptidoglycan, greatly influence the measured threshold pressure for MscL, MscS, and MscM. Mutational changes in the nonchannel proteins in the inner membrane itself may also be expected to directly or indirectly change those thresholds (18, 43). Thus observed changes in threshold pressure between preparations or due to mutations, even if systematic, should be viewed with caution (18, 19).

How the stretch force is transmitted to the MS channel molecule has often been discussed in relation to the cytoskeleton. In the case of MscL, and likely MscS, there is little doubt that the stretch force is transmitted to the channels entirely through the lipid bilayer, because purified channel proteins reconstituted into artificial lipid bilayers are perfectly functional (Figure 2). Before this reductionistic proof, Martinac et al (52) had already shown that amphipathic molecules, expected to partition differentially into each of the two leaflets of a bilayer, can in fact activate MS channels, and that the effectiveness and time course of the activation parallel the lipid solubility of the amphipath in question. These results can be explained by the bilayer couple hypothesis (78) and are quantitatively fitted in a model in which the monolayer leaflet that has the higher tension gates the channel (50).

## THE ROLE(S) OF MS CHANNELS IN BACTERIA

The widespread, if not universal, presence of MS channels in the cytoplasmic membrane of both gram-positive and gram-negative bacteria is interesting. Homologous *mscL* genes in these bacteria are highly conserved in their sequences. MscL activities are observed in all patches taken from *E. coli*, which suggests that *mscL* may be expressed constitutively. That there are apparently redundant devices, e.g. MscS and perhaps MscM, also seems to support this view and explains why the MscL-null mutant has no growth defects in the laboratory. The ubiquitous presence of MS channels in plasma membranes indicates their importance. Yet the cytoplasmic membrane insulates the cytoplasm and partitions the proton motive force. A permanent leak in this membrane can collapse this gradient and eventually kill the bacterium. In the biological warfare among microbes, certain antibiotics and colicins kill their victims precisely by this mechanism (48, 57). The notion that this membrane naturally contains pores—large or somewhat smaller—that allow passive diffusion flies in the face of conventional wisdom in bacterial physiology. One way to reconcile this is to consider that these channels, although ever-present, are usually heavily guarded and are used only in a crisis. One possibility is that these MS channels are emergency valves for the release of turgor upon sudden osmotic downshock, e.g. in rain. *E. coli* have elaborate systems to deal with long-term and short-term osmotic stresses, both hyper- and hypotonic (for review, see 11, 17). Placing *E. coli* in distilled water causes it to jettison most of its solutes immediately, although the cell retains most of its macromolecules and remains viable for some time, capable of recolonizing in a hospitable environment (13, 87). Thus the proton motive force can apparently be collapsed without killing the cell immediately. This notion seems to have escaped some bacteriologists (49), although it is well known that *E. coli* can be frozen, even lyophilized, and remain viable. The pathway(s) through which solutes escape upon downshock have never been identified in the bacterial physiology literature. Thus it has been speculated, even at the time of their discovery, that these MS channels are used in osmoregulation and perhaps are these pathways (44, 45, 54, 71–73). Berrier et al (6) proposed that the MS channels are indeed such pathways and showed that submillimolar concentrations of $Gd3^+$, at concentrations that block the MS conductances in both gram-positive and -negative bacteria, also interfere with the hypoosmotically induced effluxes of lactose and even ATP from bacteria. The progressively larger conductance from MscM to MscS to MscL parallels the rise in threshold stretch force and can be seen as a highly evolved system providing graded responses to differing levels of hypoosmotic stress (4). However, recent experiments indicate that efflux of several osmo-protectants triggered by hypoosmotic shock are very similar in the wild-type and the *mscL*-null mutant. It is possible that the multiple MS channel types reflect a redundancy required by the importance of their function (4).

## PERSPECTIVE AND FUTURE DIRECTIONS

The cloning of *mscL* makes it possible to bring the modern tools of recombinant DNA and biochemistry to bear on the puzzle of mechanosensation. Three directions are indicated: For those interested in mechanosensation in plants and animals, the search for *mscL* homologues needs to be carried out; for those interested in bacterial physiology, the turgor-adjustment model or other models need to be further tested; and for those interested in the molecular basis of mechanosensation, further dissection of MscL will be necessary, regardless of whether MscL is a homologous third cousin of human touch receptors or an analogous model molecule that happens to be a small protein and is functional in simple foreign lipid bilayers.

ACKNOWLEDGMENTS

We thank Dr. Alexandre Ghazi for critical reading of the manuscript. Work in our laboratories was support in part by NASA grant NAGW-4934 to SS, a DOE-Energy Biosciences Research Fellowhip to PB, grants from the Australian Research Council A19332733 and the Raine Medical Research Foundation to BM, and NIH grant GM47856 to CK.

*Literature Cited*

1. Arkin IT, Sukharev SI, Blount P, Kung C, Brünger AT. 1996. Helicity, membrane incorporation, orientation, and thermal stability of the large conductance mechanosensitive ion channel from E. coli. *J. Biol. Chem.* Submitted
2. Awayda, MS, Ismailow, II, Berdiev BK, Benos DJ. 1995. A cloned renal epithelial Na+ channel protein displays stretch activation in planar lipid bilayers. *Am. J. Physiol.* 268:C1450–59
3. Bargmann CI. 1994. Molecular mechanisms of mechanosensation? *Cell* 78:729–31
4. Berrier C, Besnard M, Ajouz B,

Coulombe A. Ghazi A. 1996. Multiple mechanosensitive ion channels from *Escherichia coli*, activated at different thresholds of applied pressure. *J. Membr. Biol.* 151:175–87
5. Berrier C, Coulombe A, Houssin C, Ghazi A. 1989. A patch-clamp study of ion channels of inner and outer membranes and of contact zones of E. coli, fused into giant liposomes. Pressure-activated channels are located in the inner membrane. *FEBS Lett.* 259:27–32
6. Berrier C, Coulombe A. Szabò I, Zoratti M, Ghazi A. 1992. Gadolinium ion inhibits loss of metabolites induced by

osmotic downshock, and large stretch-activated channnels, in bacteria. *Eur. J. Biochem.* 206:559–65

7. Birdsell DC, Cotta-Robles EH. 1967. Production and ultrastructure of lysozyme and ethylenediaminetetraacetate-lysozyme spheroplasts of *Escherichia coli. J. Bacteriol.* 93:427–37

8. Blount P, Sukharev S, Schroeder M, Nagle, Kung C. 1996. Mutations that change gating properties of a mechanosensitive channel in *E. coli. Biophys. J.* 70:A366 (Abstr.)

9. Blount P, Sukharev SI, Moe PC, Schroeder MJ, Guy HR, Kung C. 1996. Membrane topology and multimeric structure of a mechanosensitive channel protein. *EMBO J.* In press

10. Blount P, Sukharev SI, Schroeder MJ, Nagle SK, Kung C. 1996 Mutational analyses and functional domains of a mechanosensitive channel protein. *Proc. Natl. Acad. Sci. USA.* In press

11. Booth IR, Douglas RM, Munro AW, Lamb AJ, Ritchie GY, et al. 1992. Regulated transport systems in bacteria. In *Molecular Mechanisms of Transport,* ed. E Quagliariello, F Palmieri, pp. 59–66. Amsterdam: Elsevier

12. Brehm P, Kullberg K, Moody-Corbett F. 1984. Properties of nonjunctional acetylcholine receptor channels on innervated muscle of *Xenopus laevis. J. Physiol.* 350:631–48

13. Britten RJ, McClure FT. 1962. The amino acid pool of *Escherichia coli. Bacteriol. Rev.* 26:292–335

14. Buechner M, Delcour AH, Martinac B, Adler J, Kung C. 1990. Ion channel activities in the *Escherichia coli* outer membrane. *Biochim. Biophy. Acta* 1024:111–21

15. Cowan SW, Schirmer T, Rummel G, Steiert M, Ghosh R, et al. 1992. Crystal structures explain functional properties of two *E. coli* porins. *Nature* 358:727–33

16. Criado M, Keller BU. 1987. A membrane fusion strategy for single-channel recordings of membranes usually non-accessible to patch-clamp pipette electrodes. *FEBS Lett.* 224:172–76

17. Csonka LN, Hanson AD. 1991. Prokaryotic osmoregulation: genetics and physiology. *Annu. Rev. Microbiol.* 45:569–606

18. Cui C, Adler J. 1996. Effect of mutation of potassium-efflux system, kefA, on mechanosensitive channels in the cytoplasmic membrane of *Escherichia coli. J. Membr. Biol.* 150:143–52

19. Cui C, Smith DO, Adler J. 1995. Characterization of mechanosensitive channels in *Escherichia coli* cytoplasmic membrane by whole-cell patch clamp recording. *J. Membr. Biol.* 144:31–42

20. Delcour AH, Martinac B, Adler J, Kung C. 1989. Modified reconstitution method used in patch-clamp studies of *Escherichia coli* ion channels. *Biophys. J.* 56:631–36

21. Driscoll M, Chalfie M. 1992. Developmental and abnormal cell death in *C. elegans. Trends Neurosci.* 15:15–19

22. Ehrmann M, Boyd D, Beckwith J. 1990. Genetic analysis of membrane protein topology by a sandwich gene fusion approach. *Proc. Natl. Acad. Sci. USA* 87:7574–78

23. Ermakov Yu-A, Averbakh AZ, Lobyshev VI, Sukharev SI. 1996. Effects of gadolinium on electrostatic and thermodynamic properties of lipid membranes. *Biophys. J.* 70:A96

24. Feller H, Porter JS, Slayman CL, Kaback HR. 1980. Quantitative measurement of membrane potential in *Escherichia coli. Biochemistry* 19:3585–90

25. Fleischmann RD, Adams MD, White O, Clayton RA, Kirkness EF. 1995. Whole-genome random sequencing and assembly of *Haemophilus influenzae* RD. *Science* 269:496–512

26. Guharay F, Sachs F. 1984. Stretch-activated single ion channel currents in tissue-cultured embryonic chick skeletal muscle. *J. Physiol.* 352:685–701

27. Gustin MC. 1992. Mechanosensitive ion channels in yeast. Mechanisms of activation and adaptation. In *Advances in Comparative and Environmental Physiology,* ed. F Ito, 10:19–38. Berlin: Springer-Verlag

28. Gustin MC, Zhou X-L, Martinac B, Kung C. 1988. A mechanosensitive ion channel in the yeast plasma membrane. *Science* 242:762–65

29. Hamann A, Bossenmeyer A, Bakker EP. 1987. Physical mapping of the $K^+$ transport trkA gene opf *Escherichia coli* and overproduction of the TrkA protein. *J. Bacteriol.* 169:3138–45

30. Hamill OP, Marty A, Neher E, Sakmann B, Sigworth FJ. 1981. Improved patch-clamp techniques for high-resolution current recording from cells and cell-free membrane patches. *Pflügers Arch.* 391:85–100

30a. Hamill OP, McBride DW Jr. 1994. The cloning of a mechano-gated membrane ion channel. *Trends Neurosci.* 17:439–43

31. Häse CC, Le Dain AC, Martinac B. 1995. Purification and functional reconstitution

of the recombinant large mechanosensitive ion channel (MscL) of *Escherichia coli. J. Biol. Chem.* 270:18329–34
32. Häse CC, Le Dain AC, Martinac B.1996. An N-terminal mutant of the large mechanosensitive ion channel (MscL) of *Escherichia coli* with an altered conductance. *Biophys. J.* 70:A346
33. Häse CC, Minchin RF, Martinac B. 1996. Cross-linking studies and membrane localization of radiolabelled large mechanosensitive ion channel (MscL) of *Escherichia coli. Proc. Natl. Acad. Sci. USA.* Submitted
34. Häse CC, Minchin RF, Martinac B. 1996. Cross-linking studies of radiolabeled wild-type and mutant large mechanosensitive ion channel (MscL) in *Escherichia coli. Biophys. J.* 70:A346
35. Hille B. 1992. *Ionic Channels of Excitable Membranes.* Sunderland, MA: Sinauer. 2nd ed.
36. Hoffmann EK, Kolb H-A. 1991. Volume and osmolality control in animal cells. In *Comparative and Environmental Physiology,* ed. R. Gilles, EK Hoffmann, L Bolis, 9:140–85. Berlin: Springer-Verlag
37. Hoerber JKH, Mosbacher J, Haeberle W. 1995. Force microscopy on membrane patches: a perspective. See Ref. 74, pp. 375–93
37a. Howard J, Roberts WM, Hudspeth AJ. 1988. Mechanelectrical transduction by hair cells. *Annu. Rev. Biophys. Biophys. Chem.* 17:99–124
38. Jan LY, Jan UN. 1994. Potassium channels and their evolving gates. *Nature* 371:119–22
38a. Kaneko T, Sato S, Kotani H, Tanaka A, Asamizu E, et al. 1996. Sequence analysis of the genome of the unicellular cyanobacterium *Synechocystis* sp. PCC6803. II Sequence determination of the entire genome and assignment of potential protein-coding regions. *DNA Res.* 3:109–36
39. Kernan M, Cowan D, Zuker C. 1994. Genetic dissection of mechanosensory transduction: mechanoreception defective mutants of *Drosophila. Neuron* 12:1195–2006
40. Kubo Y, Baldwin, TJ, Jan YN, Jan LY. 1993. Primary structure and functional expression of a mouse inward rectifier potassium channel. *Nature* 362:127–34
41. Kubalski A. 1995. Generation of giant protoplasts of *Escherichia coli* and an inner-membrane anion selective conductance. *Biochim. Biophy. Acta* 1238:117–82
42. Kubalski A, Martinac B, Adler J, Kung C.

1992. Patch clamp studies on *E. coli* inner membrane in vivo. *Biophys. J.* 61:A513
43. Kubalski A, Martinac B, Ling K-Y, Adler J, Kung C. 1993. Activities of a mechanosensitive ion channel in an *E. coli* mutant lacking the major lipoprotein. *J. Membr. Biol.* 131:151–60
44. Kung C, Saimi Y. 1995. Solute sensing vs. solvent sensing, a speculation. *J. Eukaryotic Microbiol.* 42:199–200
45. Kung C, Saimi Y, Martinac B. 1990 Mechanosensitive ion channels in microbes and the early evolutionary origin of solvent sensing in protein membrane interactions. In *Current Topics in Membranes and Transport,* ed. E Claudio, 36:145–53. New York: Academic
46. Li X-M, Zhang YF, Ni JZ, Chen JW, Hwang F. 1994. Effect of lanthanide ions on phase behavior of dipalmitoylphosphatidylcholine multilamellar liposomes. *J. Inorg. Biochem.* 53:139–49
47. Long WS, Slayman CL, Low KB. 1978. Production of giant cells of *Escherichia coli. J. Bacteriol.* 133:995–1007
48. Luria SE, Suist JL. 1987. Colicins and Col plasmids. See Ref. 62, pp. 1615–23
49. Maloney PC. 1987. Coupling to an energized membrane: role of ion-motive gradients in the transduction of metabolic energy. See Ref. 62, pp. 222–43
50. Markin VS, Martinac B. 1991. Mechanosensitive ion channels as reporters of bilayer expansion: a theoretical model. *Biophys. J.* 60:1120–27
51. Martinac B. 1993. Mechanosensitive ion channels: biophysics and physiology. In *Thermodynamics of Membrane Receptors and Channels,* ed. MB Jackson, pp.327–52. Boca Raton: CRC Press
52. Martinac B, Adler J, Kung C. 1990. Mechanosenistive ion channels of *E. coli* activated by amphipaths. *Nature* 348:261–63
53. Martinac B, Buechner M, Delcour AH, Adler J, Kung C. 1986. Pressure-sensitive ion channel in *Escherichia coli. Soc. Neurosci. Abstr.* 12:46
54. Martinac B, Buechner M, Delcour AH, Adler J, Kung C. 1987. Pressure-sensitive ion channel in *Escherichia coli. Proc. Natl. Acad. Sci. USA* 84:2297–301
55. Martinac B, Delcour AH, Buechner M, Adler J, Kung C. 1992. Mechanosensitive ion channels in bacteria. In *Advances in Comparative and Environmental Physiology,* ed. F Ito, 10:3–18. Berlin: Springer-Verlag
56. Martinac B, Zhou X-L, Kubalski A, Sukharev S, Kung C. 1994. Microbial channels. In *Handbook of Membrane*

*Channels: Molecular and Cellular Physiology,* ed. C Peracchia, pp. 447–59. New York: Academic

57. Martinac B, Zhu H, Kubalski A, Zhou X-L, Culbertson M, et al. 1990. Yeast K1 killer-toxin forms ion channels in sensitive yeast spheroplasts and in artificial liposomes. *Proc. Natl. Acad. Sci. USA* 87:6228–32

58. Matsushita O, Jung CM, Okabe A. 1995. Identification of the gene encoding a mechanosensitive channel MscL homologue in *Clostridium perfringens. Gene* 165:147–48

59. Milkman R. 1994. An *Escherichia coli* homologue of eukaryotic potassium channel proteins. *Proc. Natl. Acad. Sci. USA* 91:3510–14

60. McBride DW, Hamill OP. 1995. A fast pressure-clamp technique for studying mechanogated channels. See Ref. 74, pp. 329–40

61. Naitoh Y, Eckert R. 1972. Electrophysiolgy of ciliate protozoa. In *Experiments in Physiology and Biochemistry,* ed. GA Kerkut, 5:17038. New York: Academic

62. Neidhardt FC, ed. 1987. Escherichia coli *and* Salmonella typhimurium, *Cellular and Molecular Biology.* Washington, DC: Am. Soc. Microbiol. 1654 pp.

63. Petro AG, Usherwood PNR 1994. Mechanosensitivity of cell membranes. *Eur. Biophys.* 23:1–19

64. Plamer LG, Frindt G. 1996. Gating of Na channels in the rat cortical collecting tubule: effects of voltage and membrane stretch. *J. Gen. Physiol.* 107:35–45

65. Qin F, Auerbach A, Sachs F. 1996. Estimating single-channel kinetic parameters from idealized patch-clamp data containing missed events. *Biophys. J.* 70:264–80

66. Ruthe JJ, Adler J. 1985. Fusion of bacterial spheroplasts by electric fields. *Biochim. Biophys. Acta* 819:105–13

67. Sachs F. 1988. Mechanical transduction in biological systems. *CRC Crit. Rev. Biomed. Eng.* 16:141–69

68. Sachs F. 1992 Stretch-sensitive ion channels: an update. In *Sensory Transduction,* ed. D Corey, S Roper, pp. 241–60, New York: Rockefeller Univ. Press

69. Sackin H. 1995. Mechanosensitive channels. *Annu. Rev. Physiol.* 57:333–53

70. Saimi Y, Martinac B, Delcour AH, Minorsky PV, Gustin MC, et al. 1992. Patch-clamp studies of microbial ion channels. In *Methods in Enzymology: Ion Channels,* ed. B Rudy, LE Iverson, 207:681–91. New York: Academic

71. Saimi Y, Martinac B, Gustin MC, Culbertson MR, Adler J, Kung C. 1988.

72. Saimi Y, Martinac B, Gustin MC, Culbertson MR, Adler J, Kung C. 1988. Ion channels in *Paramecium,* yeast and *Escherichia coli.* In *The Molecular Biology of Signal Transduction,* 2:667–673. Cold Spring Harbor, NY: Cold Spring Harbor Press

73. Saimi Y, Martinac B, Preston RR, Zhou X-L, Sukharev SI, et al. 1994. Ion channels of microbes. In *Molecular Evolution of Physiological Processes,* ed. D Fambrough, pp. 179–95. New York: Rockefeller Univ. Press

74. Sakmann B, Neher E, eds. 1995. *Single-Channel Recording.* New York: Plenum. 2nd ed.

75. Satow Y, Murphy AD, Kung C 1983. The ionic basis of the depolarization mechanoreceptor potential of *Paramecium tetraurelia. J. Exp. Biol.* 103:253–64

76. Schlosser A, Hamann A, Bossemeyer A, Schneider E, Bakker EP. 1993 NAD$^+$ binding to the *Escherichia coli* K$^+$-uptake protein TrkA and sequence similarity between TrkA and domains of a family of dehydrogenases suggest a role for NAD$^+$ in bacterial transport. *Mol. Microbiol.* 9:533–43

77. Schrempf H, Schmidt O, Kuemmerlen R, Hinnah S, Mueller D, et al. 1993. A prokaryotic potassium ion channel with two predicted transmembrane segments from *Streptomyces lividans. EMBO J.* 14:5170–78

78. Sheetz MP, Singer SJ. 1974. Biological membranes as bilayer couples. A molecular mechanism of drug-erythrocyte interaction. *Proc. Natl. Acad. Sci. USA* 71:4457–61

79. Sokabe M, Sachs F. 1990. The structure and dynamics of patch-clamped membranes: a study using differential interference contrast light microscopy. *J. Cell Biol.* 111:599–606

80. Sukharev SI, Blount P, Martinac B, Blattner FR, Kung C. 1994. A large conductance mechanosensitive channel in *E. coli* encoded by mscL alone. *Nature* 368:265–68

81. Sukharev SI, Blount P, Martinac B, Guy HB, Kung C. 1996. MscL, a mechanosensitive channel in *E. coli.* In *Organellar Ion Channels and Transporters, Soc. Gen. Physiol. Series,* ed. DE Clapham, B Ehrlich, 51:133–41. New York: Rockefeller Univ. Press

82. Sukharev SI, Martinac B, Arshavsky VY,

Kung C. 1993. Two types of mechanosensitive channels in the *Escherichia coli* cell envelope: solubilization and functional reconstitution. *Biophys. J.* 654:1–7

83. Sukharev SI, Martinac B, Blount P, Kung C. 1994. Functional reconstitution as an assay for biochemical isolation of channel protein. Application to the molecular identification of a bacterial mechanosensitive channel. *Methods: Companion Methods Enzymol.* 6:51–59

84. Szabò I, Petronilli V, Guerra L, Zoratti M. 1990. Cooperative mechanosensitive ion channels in *Escherichia coli. Biochem. Biophys. Res. Comm.* 171:280–86

85. Szabò I, Petronilli V, Zoratti M. 1992. A patch-clamp study of *Bacillus subtilis. Biochim. Biophys. Acta* 1112:29–38

86. Szabò I, Petronilli V, Zoratti M. 1993. A patch-clamp investigation of the *Streptococcus faecalis* cell membrane. *J. Membr. Biol.* 131:203–18

87. Tsapis A, Kepes A. 1977. Transient breakdown of the permeability barrier of the membrane of *Escherichia coli* upon osmotic shock. *Biochim. Biophys. Acta* 469:1–12

88. Yang X-C, Sachs F. 1989 Block of stretch-activated ion channels in *Xenopus* oocytes by gadolinium and calcium ions. *Science* 243:1068–71

89. Zhou X-L, Kung C. 1992 A mechanosensitive ion channel in *Schizosaccharomyces pombe. EMBO J.* 11:2869–75

90. Zhou X-L, Stumpf MA, Hoch HC, Kung C. 1991. A mechanosensitive channel in whole cells and in membrane patches of the fungus *Uromyces. Science* 253:1415–17

91. Zhou X-L, Vaillant B, Loukin SH, Kung C, Saimi Y. 1995. YKC1 encodes the depolarization-activated $K^+$ channel in the plasma membrane of yeast. *FEBS Lett.* 373:170–76

92. Zoratti M, Ghazi A. 1993 Stretch-activated channels in prokaryotes. In *Alkali Transport Systems in Prokaryotes,* ed. EP Bakker, pp. 349–58. Boca Raton: CRC Press

93. Zoratti M, Petronilli M. 1988. Ion-conducting channels in a gram-positive bacterium. *FEBS Lett.* 240:105–109

94. Zoratti, M, Szabò I. 1991 Stretch-activated composite ion channels in *Bacillus subtilis. Biochem. Biophys. Res. Commun.* 168:443–50

*Annu. Rev. Physiol. 1997. 59:659–89*

# MOLECULAR MODELING OF MECHANOTRANSDUCTION IN THE NEMATODE *CAENORHABDITIS ELEGANS*

## Nektarios Tavernarakis and Monica Driscoll

Department of Molecular Biology and Biochemistry, Rutgers University, New Brunswick, New Jersey 08855

KEY WORDS:    touch transduction, degenerins, *mec* genes, stretch-sensitive ion channels, motor neurons

### ABSTRACT

Genetic and molecular studies of touch avoidance in the nematode *Caenorhabditis elegans* have resulted in a molecular model for a mechanotransducing complex. *mec-4* and *mec-10* encode proteins hypothesized to be subunits of a mechanically gated ion channel that are related to subunits of the vertebrate amiloride-sensitive epithelial Na$^+$ channel. Products of *mec-5*, a novel collagen, and *mec-9*, a protein that includes multiple Kunitz-type protease inhibitor repeats and EGF repeats, may interact with the channel in the extracellular matrix. Inside the cell, specialized 15-protofilament microtubules composed of *mec-12* α-tubulin and *mec-7* β-tubulin may be linked to the mechanosensitive channel by stomatin-homologous MEC-2. MEC-4 and MEC-10 are members of a large family of *C. elegans* proteins, the degenerins. Two other degenerins, UNC-8 and DEL-1, are candidate components of a stretch-sensitive channel in motor neurons. Implications for advancing understanding of mechanotransduction in other systems are discussed.

## INTRODUCTION

Despite the fundamental importance of mechanical signaling in a myriad of biological processes ranging from cell volume regulation to sensory transduction in touch and hearing (reviewed in 27, 66), remarkably little is known about the nature of the molecules that mediate mechanotransduction. Although elegant

659

0066-4278/97/0315-0659$08.00

electrophysiological studies have shown that mechanically gated ion channels play central roles in the conversion of mechanical forces into cellular responses, aspects of channel biology have rendered the genes encoding channel components elusive: Reagents that could facilitate protein isolation by specifically associating with channel subunits at high affinity are not available, and even in specialized mechanotransducing structures such as the vertebrate cochlea, mechanically gated channels are distributed at low concentrations. To date, biochemical purification and cloning of only one mechanosensitive channel, the *Escherichia coli* MscL, has been heroically accomplished (75).

An alternative approach toward isolating molecules involved in mechanotransduction is to isolate mutants defective in mechanosensitive behaviors and then to clone the identified genes by standard methods. Such a strategy has resulted in the isolation and characterization of several genes required for mechanosensitive behaviors in the nematode *C. elegans* (reviewed in 20, 22, 36). Here we review genetic and molecular studies in *C. elegans* that have culminated in a molecular model of body touch transduction and the identification of candidate mechanically gated ion channels.

## The C. elegans Experimental System

*C. elegans*, a small (1 mm) free-living nematode normally found in soil, is easily reared on an *E. coli* diet in the laboratory. The life cycle of this animal, which can be completed in just 2.5 days at 25°C, includes a period of embryonic development within an eggshell, four larval stages (L1–L4), and adulthood, which is distinguished by sexual maturity. The most common sexual form is the hermaphrodite (XX), although males (X0) can be easily propagated for use in genetic studies. *C. elegans* is fairly transparent such that the nucleus of every cell can be visualized using Normarski differential interference contrast microscopy. This feature enabled the complete sequence of cell divisions that occur as the fertilized egg develops into the 959-celled adult to be recorded (77, 78). Of these cells, 302 are neurons, and the pattern of synaptic connections made by each neuron has been determined using serial section electron microscopy (88). Knowledge of the complete wiring diagram of the animal has enabled neural circuits for specific mechanosensory behaviors to be predicted. Such predictions have been tested by laser ablation experiments in which individual cells are killed by a laser microbeam (15, 44).

A key advantage to investigating biological processes in *C. elegans* is its powerful genetic system (6). Thousands of mutations affecting development or behavior have been identified and assigned to complementation groups that are positioned on a detailed genetic map. Once genes are mapped, it is increasingly straightforward to clone them. A collection of overlapping cosmid and YAC clones that cover most of the six chromosomes (the physical map of the *C.*

*elegans* genome) is correlated with the genetic map (37, 84) so that the position of a mapped candidate gene can usually be restricted to a collection of cosmids spanning only a few hundred kilobases of DNA. Verification of gene identity is frequently accomplished by constructing transgenic lines and testing for complementation of identified mutations (26, 55). Sequence analysis of the *C. elegans* genome is underway (76, 91) with a projected completion date of 1998.

Taken together, the abilities to identify and experimentally verify individual neurons specialized for mechanosensation, to isolate mutations specifically affecting the function of these cells, and to clone the identified genes rapidly has led to significant insight into molecular mechanisms of mechanotransduction in *C. elegans*.

## *Mechanosensitive Behaviors in C. elegans*

Mechanical stimuli regulate many *C. elegans* behaviors including locomotion, foraging, egg laying, feeding (pharyngeal pumping), and defecation. The mechanosensitive response best characterized at the cellular, genetic, and molecular levels is the movement away from a light touch delivered to the body with an eyelash hair (14). Another behavioral paradigm elegantly utilized to study mechanosensory control of locomotion is the response to nose touch—the reversal of direction as a consequence of head-on collision or a light touch on the side of the nose (35, 44, 53; reviewed in 22). Other touch-mediated locomotory responses such as a reaction to harsh touch (a strong prod with a metal wire best assayed in the absence of gentle touch mechanosensory neurons; 86) or to tap (a diffuse stimulus as delivered by a tap on the plate on which worms are reared; 19, 60, 89, 90), have been less extensively studied at the genetic level. Here we review the molecular genetics of body touch, with an emphasis on a recently identified family of ion channel subunits postulated to function in mechanically gated ion channels.

## GENTLE BODY TOUCH

### *The Mechanosensory Touch Receptor Neurons*

In the laboratory, *C. elegans* moves through a bacterial lawn on a petri plate with a readily observed sinusoidal motion. When gently touched with an eyelash hair (typically attached to a toothpick) on the posterior, an animal will move forward; when touched on the anterior body, it will move backward. This gentle body touch is sensed by the touch receptor neurons ALML/R (anterior lateral microtubule cell left, right), AVM (anterior ventral microtubule cell), and PLML/R (posterior lateral microtubule cell left, right) (14, 15; see Figure 1). The touch receptors are situated so that their processes, embedded in the hypodermis adjacent to the cuticle, run longitudinally along the body wall.

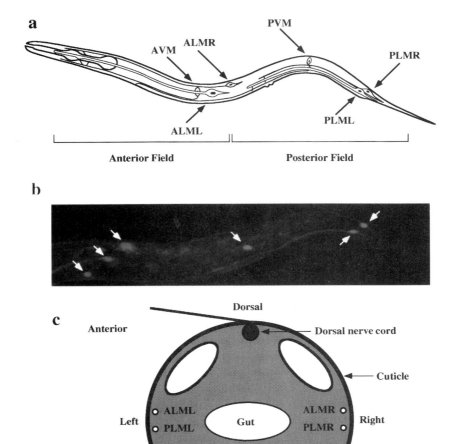

*Figure 1* The *C. elegans* touch receptor neurons. (*a*) Schematic diagram showing the position of the six touch receptor neurons in the body of the adult nematode. Note the two fields of touch sensitivity defined by the arrangement of these neurons along the body axis. The ALMs and AVM mediate the response to touch over the anterior field, whereas PLMs mediate the response to touch over the posterior field. (*b*) Visualization of touch receptors in living worms expressing the green fluorescent protein under the control of the *mec-4* promoter, which is active only in the six touch receptor neurons. Arrows indicate touch receptor cell bodies. Some touch receptor axons are apparent. (*c*) Schematic representation of a nematode in theoretical cross section. Position of the touch cell processes are depicted. Other landmarks of *C. elegans* anatomy are also shown.

The position of the processes along the body axis correlates with the sensory field of the touch cell. Laser ablation of AVM and the ALMs, which have sensory receptor processes in the anterior half of the body, eliminates anterior touch sensitivity, and laser ablation of the PLMs, which have posterior dendritic processes, eliminates posterior touch sensitivity (15). In addition to mediating touch avoidance, the touch receptor neurons appear to control the spontaneous rate of locomotion because animals that lack functional touch cells are lethargic. The mechanical stimuli that drive spontaneous locomotion are unknown but could include encounters with objects in their environment or body stretch induced by locomotion itself.

One additional neuron, PVM (posterior ventral microtubule cell) is also categorized as a touch cell because it is ultrastructurally similar to the others and its differentiation is controlled by the same genetic pathway (see below). Laser ablation studies have shown, however, that the PVM neuron does not play a critical role in gentle touch-modulated locomotion because it cannot mediate touch avoidance by itself (15).

## Distinguishing Ultrastructual Features of the Touch Receptor Neurons

TOUCH CELL-SPECIFIC MICROTUBULES    The touch receptor cell processes are distinguished by the presence of a bundle of wide-diameter [15-protofilament (pf)] microtubules (16, 17; see Figure 2). These 15-pf microtubules are only found in the six touch receptor neurons (microtubules in most *C. elegans* cells contain 11 protofilaments; those in most organisms contain 13 protofilaments). Individual microtubules do not span the full length (about 400—500 mm) of the touch cell processes. Rather, individual microtubules 10–20 mm in length overlap within the microtubule bundle to fill the process (16). Interestingly, microtubule ends appear structurally distinct in electron micrographs—the end proximal to the cell body is darkened and is preferentially found on the inside of a microtubule bundle, whereas the distal end is diffusely stained and is always situated outside of the microtubule bundle. It is particularly intriguing that the distal end of the microtubule is often situated adjacent to the plasma membrane; such an arrangement suggests a mechanical link could be formed between the microtubule network and mechanosensitive channels in the plasma membrane (16; see discussion of mechanotransduction model below). The integrity of the 15-pf microtubules is required for touch receptor neuron function. If touch cell microtubules are disrupted by low concentrations of colchicine or by mutation, touch sensitivity is lost (14, 17).

THE EXTRACELLULAR MANTLE    Touch receptor processes are surrounded by a specialized extracellular matrix referred to as the mantle (14; see Figure 2).

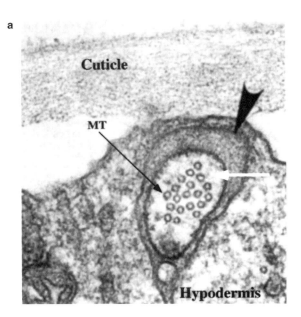

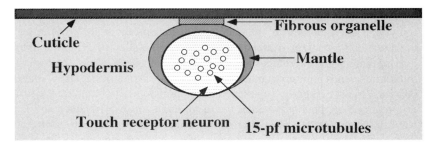

*Figure 2*    Ultrastructural features of the touch receptor neurons. (*a*) Electron micrograph of a touch receptor neuron process. The touch cell process (*white arrow*) is filled with 15-pf microtubules (MT, *thin black arrow*). The process is embedded in the hypodermis and surrounded by the mantle (*large black arrowhead*). (*b*) Schematic representation of a touch receptor neuron cross section. A darkly staining region labeled fibrous organelle is depicted here as a bar-shaded rectangle connecting the mantle and the cuticle. Such specializations appear periodically along the length of the touch receptor process and may serve to attach the process to the cuticle. This figure is adapted from Reference 36.

The mantle can be stained with peanut lectin and is most prominent on the side of the touch receptor neuron closest to the cuticle. Darkly staining cuticular specializations are positioned periodically along the length of the touch receptor process in close contact with the mantle. These cuticular specializations look similar to muscle attachment sites and thus may be sites at which the touch receptor process, via the mantle, is fixed to the cuticle. The integrity of the mantle appears important for touch receptor function (see below).

## Genetic and Molecular Analysis of Body Touch

To identify genes needed for function of the touch receptor neurons, Chalfie and colleagues mutagenized animals and screened their F2 progeny for the failure to respond to gentle touch. Mutants were retested by prodding with a wire (harsh touch) to confirm that although they were touch-insensitive, they were still capable of locomotion. Using this approach, more than 400 mutants that (more or less) specifically lack the ability to respond to gentle touch were identified (11, 14). Many of these were designated as *mec* mutants because the phenotype they confer is mechanosensory abnormal (Mec). The identified mutations define 16 genes that contribute in specific ways to touch cell development and function (summarized in Table 1).

## Transcription Factors Needed for Touch Cell Development

UNC-86 AND MEC-3    Touch cell development requires the combinatorial action of genes needed for appropriate execution of touch cell lineages, specification of touch cell fate, restricted cellular expression of structural genes, cell migration, and process outgrowth (10, 22). Two genes, *unc-86* and *mec-3*, are particularly important for differentiation of the touch receptor neurons.

UNC-86 is a POU homeodomain transcription factor needed for the proper differentiation of neuroblasts that generate all six touch receptor neurons (13, 25). A key function of UNC-86 in touch receptor development is to bind to DNA to stimulate transcription of *mec-3*, which encodes a LIM homeodomain protein (28) expressed in the six touch receptors (and in two other neurons that may be stretch sensitive, FLP and PVD; 44, 85–87, 92). *mec-3* is needed for the specification of touch cell fate. In the absence of *mec-3*, the lineages that generate the touch cells are executed normally and cells produced differentiate as neurons. However, the neurons generated fail to express touch cell–specific features such as the 15-pf microtubules and the mantle (14, 85). The MEC-3 homeodomain protein forms a heterodimer with UNC-86 and binds to well-defined sites in the *mec-3* promoter and in other touch cell–specific promoters (48, 93), thereby functioning as a transcriptional activator of touch cell–specific structural genes, including the *mec-7* $\beta$-tubulin and the *mec-4* channel subunit (33, 56, 87, 92). Once *mec-3* is expressed in the touch cells, it activates its own

**Table 1**    The touch cell genes of *C. elegans*

| Gene[a] | Encoded product | Likely function | References |
|---|---|---|---|
| *unc-86* | POU homeodomain transcription factor | Execution of cell lineage | 24, 25, 48, 92, 93 |
| *mec-3* | LIM homeodomain transcription factor | Specification of touch cell differentiation | 48, 85, 86, 87, 92, 93 |
| *mec-4* | Channel subunit | Mechanosensitive channel | 12, 21, 38, 39, 46 |
| *mec-10* | Channel subunit | Mechanosensitive channel | 12, 40 |
| *mec-2* | Stomatin-like protein | Channel-cytoskeleton linker | 41 |
| *mec-7* | β-tubulin | 15-pf microtubule formation | 33, 67, 68 |
| *mec-12* | α-tubulin | 15-pf microtubule formation | 32, 30 |
| *mec-5* | Collagen | Extracellular matrix | 23, 30 |
| *mec-9* | EGF and Kunitz repeats | Extracellular interactions | 23, 30 |
| *mec-8* | Likely RNA-binding protein | Splicing | 51, 52 |
| *mec-14* | Aldo-keto reductase | Channel activity | 11, 14, 54 |
| *mec-1*[b] | ? | Mantle | 11, 14 |
| *mec-6*[b] | ? | Channel activity | 11, 14 |
| *mec-17*[b] | ? | Maintenance of transcription | 11, 14 |
| *mec-15*[c] | ? | ? | 11, 14 |
| *mec-18*[c] | ? | ? | 11, 14 |

[a]Genes identified by mutations in *C. elegans* that are required for normal response to gentle body touch mediated by the six touch receptor neurons.
[b]Even though the molecular identity of these genes has yet to be established, genetic analysis suggests a function for their encoded products.
[c]Mutations in these genes disrupt or attenuate touch response, but the mode of action of the encoded proteins has not been determined.

transcription (86). Later in development, *mec-17* also contributes to maintenance of *mec-3* expression. The mechanism of action of *mec-17* is not known because the gene has not been characterized molecularly. *unc-86* continues to be expressed in differentiated touch receptors and is continuously needed for their function (24).

## Structural Genes Required for Touch Receptor Function

MEC-4 AND MEC-10 CHANNEL PROTEINS    Animals bearing loss-of-function mutations in *mec-4* or *mec-10* are touch insensitive despite the fact that in these mutant backgrounds, the touch receptor neurons develop normally and exhibit no apparent defects in ultrastructure (14). *mec-4* and *mec-10* encode homologous proteins related to subunits of the multimeric amiloride-sensitive $Na^+$ channel, which mediates $Na^+$ readsorption in vertebrate kidney, intestine, and lung epithelia (the ENaC channel; 7, 8, 12, 21, 40, 46). By analogy, MEC-4 and MEC-10 are likely ion channel subunits. Indeed, although channel activity has not yet been directly demonstrated for either MEC-4 or MEC-10, certain chimeric nematode/rat proteins function in *C. elegans* and in *Xenopus* oocytes, implying that the nematode and rat proteins are functionally similar (38, 82).

What is the role of the MEC-4/MEC-10 ion channel in the touch receptor neurons? Intriguingly, *mec-4* is expressed only in the six touch receptor neurons (56) and *mec-10* is expressed in the six touch receptor neurons and in two other neuron pairs that may mediate stretch-sensitive responses (FLPL/R and PVDL/R; 40). Because the MEC-4 and MEC-10 subunits are expressed exclusively in mechanosensitive neurons and are essential for the function of these neurons, it has been proposed that MEC-4 and MEC-10 coassemble into a mechanically gated ion channel that plays a central role in touch transduction. The relationship of these channel subunits to subunits of an amiloride-sensitive channel is also intriguing because amiloride is a general inhibitor of mechanosensitive ion channels (34). Experimental verification that the MEC-4/MEC-10 channel is mechanically gated remains a challenge for the future.

*MEC-4 primary sequence and transmembrane topology*    MEC-4 and MEC-10 are members of a superfamily of homologous proteins that includes additional members from *C. elegans* and vertebrates. Here we briefly describe features of MEC-4 (21, 46), most of which are also generally conserved in other *C. elegans* family members. MEC-4 is 768 amino acids in length and includes two membrane-spanning domains (MSDI, MSDII; Figure 3). Both predicted hydrophobic domains are slightly longer than required for a single transmembrane pass, and it has been proposed that MSDI and MSDII in other superfamily members may include residues that loop back into the membrane forming a pore, similar to H5 domains of several characterized channel types (29, 43, 61). MEC-4 also includes three cysteine-rich domains (CRDI, CRDII, CRDIII) and one region similar to venom neurotoxins (NTD) (N Tavernarakis & M Driscoll, submitted) situated between the two transmembrane domains.

Mechanically gated channels are thought to be tethered to proteins inside and outside the cell to provide gating tension (e.g. work on the hair cell channel reviewed in 42, 59). In MEC-4 the N- and C-termini are cytoplasmic and are thus candidate domains for interaction with the cytoskeleton; the central region of MEC-4 is extracellular and thus the CRD and NTD domains situated outside the cell are candidate regions for interaction with the extracellular matrix (46). Other superfamily members have the same transmembrane topology (8, 29, 61, 72).

*MEC-4 structure/activity relationships—toxic alleles*    Dominant gain-of-function *mec-4* alleles induce swelling and death of the touch receptor neurons (11, 14). These *mec-4(d)* alleles encode substitutions of large side chain amino acids (Val or Thr) for a conserved Ala residue (aa 713) situated adjacent to MSDII

**a**

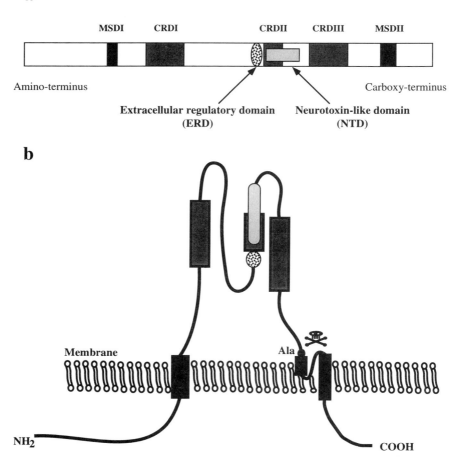

*Figure 3* Features of the MEC-4 protein. (*a*) Structural features of MEC-4. The two membrane-spanning domains (MSDI, II; *black boxes*) are shown together with the three cysteine-rich domains (CRDI, II, III; *gray boxes*). The putative extracellular regulatory domain (ERD) is depicted by the oval. The neurotoxin-related domain (NTD) is represented by the lightly shaded rectangle overlapping with CRDII. (*b*) Transmembrane topology of MEC-4. Both the amino- and carboxy-termini are intracellular; the central part of the protein, which includes the CRDs, ERD, and NTD, is extracellular. The second membrane-spanning domain is longer than required for a single transmembrane pass and may loop back to form a pore-lining structure. Ala713, which when replaced by a bulkier amino acid results in degenerative cell death, is indicated by the skull and cross-bones icon.

(see Figure 3; 21, 46). There is a correlation between the size of the amino acid side chain at position 713 and toxicity: Tests of *mec-4* mutant alleles engineered to include all possible amino acid substitutions established that a large side chain amino acid at this site is toxic to touch neurons, whereas a small side chain amino acid (Ala, Ser, Cys) is not lethal (21). These results suggest that steric hindrance plays a critical role in the degeneration mechanism. A working model for the initiation of cell death is that the presence of a bulky side chain at this site prevents the channel from closing effectively, resulting in an increased influx of ions that is toxic (Figure 4). Interestingly, small amino acid side chains are present at the position corresponding to MEC-4 (Ala713) in all superfamily members. Other *C. elegans* family members (e.g. *deg-1* and *mec-10*) can be altered by analogous amino acid substitutions to induce neurodegeneration, and thus the *C. elegans* branch of the gene family has been named the degenerin family. Strikingly, a mutant variant of neuronally expressed mammalian family member MDEG, engineered to encode Val or Phe at the corresponding position, induces swelling and death when introduced into *Xenopus* oocytes and hamster embryonic kidney cells (83).

An alternative way in which *mec-4* can be engineered to induce neurodegeneration has been determined based on studies of an unusual toxic recessive allele of degenerin *deg-1* (29). *mec-4* alleles harboring a missense mutation (A404T) or a small deletion ($\Delta$399–407) in the extracellular region induce degeneration in transgenic animals. Again, increased channel activity is thought to initiate degeneration. Thus these toxic alterations in degenerin proteins may disrupt an extracellular domain that functions in channel closing (the extracellular regulatory domain, ERD). Alternatively, death-inducing substitutions in the ERD could modify the MEC-4 tertiary structure to favor the open channel conformation. The ERD is highly conserved among *C. elegans* family members.

*MSDII is a predicted pore-lining domain*    The more C-terminal MEC-4 transmembrane domain MSDII is amphipathic. Amino acids on the hydrophilic face are highly conserved and essential for *mec-4* function (38). These observations underlie the hypothesis that MSDII forms part of the channel pore with polar residues projecting into the lumen to influence ion conductance. Consistent with this suggestion, amino acid substitutions in the candidate pore domain (designed to disrupt ion influx) block or delay neurodegeneration when present in *cis* to the channel-opening A713V substitution (38). Electrophysiological characterization of rat ENaC mutants and rat/nematode chimeras supports the hypothesis that specific polar residues in MSDII influence channel conductivity (82).

*Other regions important for MEC-4 function*    In the saturation genetic screen for touch-insensitive mutants, more than 50 *mec-4* loss-of-function alleles were

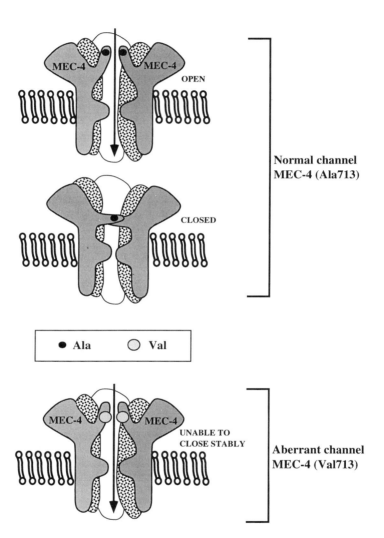

*Figure 4*  Model for *mec-4(d)*-induced toxicity. Gain-of-function mutations in *mec-4* encode substitutions for a conserved alanine adjacent to MSDII and result in neuronal degeneration. Amino acids with bulkier side chains at this position are thought to lock the channel in an open conformation by causing steric hindrance, resulting in Na$^+$ influx that triggers necrotic-like cell death.

isolated (11, 14). DNA sequence analysis of these alleles revealed that in addition to MSDII, there are three regions where single amino acid substitutions that inactivate MEC-4 are clustered (39). Two of the sites are in the extracellular domain, situated either near or within the extracellular CRDIII. The role of these regions in channel function remains to be determined but is speculated to be to facilitate protein interactions. One short stretch in the intracellular N-terminal domain (aa 87–95) may define a site of interaction of the MEC-4 subunit with an intracellular protein.

## Subunit Composition of the Candidate Mechanotransducing Channel

The subunit compositions and stoichiometries for DEG/ENaC channels have not been determined. Biochemical analyses suggest that the mammalian ENaC channel has as many as six different subunits (1, 4). Electrophysiological assays of the rat ENaC channel reconstituted in oocytes established that at least three homologous subunits ($\alpha$-, $\beta$-, and $\gamma$-rENaC) must be coexpressed to assemble an active channel with the pharmacological properties similar to the in vivo channel (9).

The touch receptor channel also appears to be multimeric. Evidence that MEC-4 and MEC-10 coassemble into the same channel complex include (*a*) MEC-4 and MEC-10 subunits are coexpressed in the touch receptor neurons, (*b*) MEC-4 and MEC-10 proteins translated in vitro in the presence of microsomes can coimmunoprecipitate (C Lai & M Driscoll, unpublished observations), and (*c*) genetic interactions between *mec-4* and *mec-10* have been observed (30, 40). For example, *mec-10* can be engineered to encode a death-inducing amino acid substitution *mec-10*(A673V) (40). However, if *mec-10*(A673V) is introduced into a *mec-4* loss-of-function background, neurodegeneration does not occur. This result is consistent with the hypothesis that MEC-10 cannot form a functional channel in the absence of MEC-4.

Genetic experiments also suggest that MEC-4 subunits interact with each other. The toxic protein MEC-4(A713V) can kill cells even if it is coexpressed with wild-type MEC-4(+) [as occurs in a *trans* heterozygote of genotype *mec-4(d)/mec-4(+)*]. However, if toxic MEC-4(A713V) is coexpressed with a specific *mec-4* allele that encodes a single amino acid substitution in MSDII, e.g. *mec-4(d)/mec-4*(E732K), neurodegeneration is partially suppressed (38; Figure 5). Because one MEC-4 subunit can interfere with the activity of another, it is likely that there may be more than one MEC-4 subunit in the channel complex. Interestingly, genetic experiments also suggest interactions between MEC-10 subunits (40). Thus a model for the minimum touch receptor channel is that the multimeric complex includes at least two MEC-4 and two MEC-10 subunits.

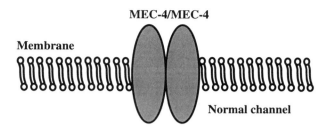

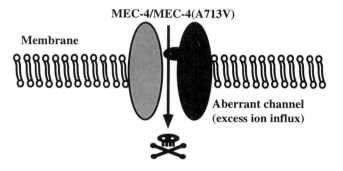

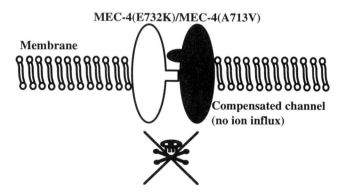

*Figure 5*   Multiple MEC-4 subunits are likely to participate in the formation of a touch receptor neuron channel.  Allele-specific compensatory mutations in *mec-4* can neutralize the deleterious effects of the toxic gain-of-function mutation.  Such an effect would be difficult to explain if only a single MEC-4 subunit were present in each channel complex and thus implies there is more than one MEC-4 molecule in each channel.

*mec-6* AND CHANNEL ACTIVITY    Recessive *mec-6* mutations disrupt touch sensitivity but do not cause detectable changes in touch cell ultrastructure (14). *mec-6* alleles have the interesting property that they completely block *mec-4(d)*- and *mec-10*(A673V)-induced touch cell degeneration, i.e. in *mec-6*; *mec-4(d)*, and *mec-6*; *mec-10*(A673V) double mutant strains, cell death is suppressed. How exactly *mec-6* acts to influence MEC-4/MEC-10 channel activity is unknown in part because the gene remains to be cloned. It appears that *mec-6* mutations do not affect *mec-4* transcription, although they do cause a *mec-4/lacZ* reporter fusion product to be rapidly degraded (N Tavernarakis et al, unpublished observations). Working hypotheses concerning the function of *mec-6* thus focus on the possibilities that *mec-6* could encode either another subunit needed for channel function/assembly or a protein that mediates localization or a posttranslational modification essential for MEC-4 and MEC-10 activity. It should be noted that *mec-6* action is not exclusive to the MEC-4/MEC-10 touch receptor channel. *mec-6* mutations also suppress deleterious consequences of vacuole-inducing mutations in other *C. elegans* degenerins, including *deg-1* (18), *unc-8* (80), and *unc-105* (N Tavernarakis & M Driscoll, unpublished).

## Intracellular Proteins Needed for Touch Transduction

As described above and shown in Figure 1, the touch receptor processes are filled with bundled 15-pf microtubules. Mutations in two genes, *mec-7* and *mec-12,* disrupt the production of these microtubules (11, 14). Interestingly, even in the absence of the 15-pf microtubules, the touch receptor processes grow out seemingly normally and become filled with 11-pf microtubules (17). Such touch receptors do not function, however, suggesting that the extensively cross-linked 15-pf microtubules contribute a specific role in touch transduction.

MEC-7    *mec-7* encodes a $\beta$-tubulin (68) expressed at high levels in the touch receptor neurons (33, 69). MEC-7 is highly conserved; apart from the C-terminal domain that is characteristically highly variable, only seven amino acids differ from other $\beta$-tubulins. It is not known whether any of the unique residues are instructive for the formation of 15-pf microtubules, although it is interesting that one of the amino acid differences affects a strictly conserved Cys residue (MEC-7 Cys293) that has been implicated in protofilament assembly by analysis of *Drosophila* mutants (64). *mec-7* mutations isolated in the screen for touch-insensitive mutants range in severity from recessive to strongly dominant, and most of the amino acid changes that disrupt MEC-7 function are known (67, 68). Domains affected by mutations include sites for GTP binding and hydrolysis, sites for heterodimerization with $\alpha$-tubulin, and sites for higher-order microtubule assembly.

MEC-12    *mec-12* encodes an $\alpha$-tubulin expressed at high levels in the touch receptor neurons but also expressed in several other neurons that do not assemble 15-pf microtubules (32). Thus the presence of the MEC-12 tubulin is not sufficient to nucleate assembly of the touch cell–specific microtubules. As is the case for *mec-7*, many *mec-12* mutations are semidominant or dominant and thus may disrupt subunit interactions or protofilament assembly. MEC-12 is the only *C. elegans* tubulin that is acetylated.

Taken together, studies of *mec-7* and *mec-12* strongly support that unique $\alpha$- and $\beta$-tubulins assemble to form the 15-pf microtubules required for touch receptor function. Whether these specialized microtubules play a direct role in the function of the mechanotransducing complex remains to be determined.

MEC-2, A CANDIDATE LINKER PROTEIN    How might the touch cell microtubule network influence the activity of a mechanically gated ion channel? Given that the specialized microtubules in the touch cells appear to associate with the plasma membrane at their distal ends, a simple hypothesis is that the 15-pf microtubules might contact the touch receptor channel directly to provide gating tension. There is some genetic evidence, however, that implicates another molecule, MEC-2, as a link between the microtubules and the touch receptor channel.

*mec-2*, required for the function of the touch receptors, encodes a predicted 481-amino acid protein expressed in the touch receptor neurons (and in a few additional neurons in the head) that appears to be localized all along the length of the touch receptor process, as well as in the cell body (41). The *mec-2* primary sequence features three candidate protein interaction domains (Figure 6a): (*a*) the carboxy-terminal domain includes a proline-rich region similar to SH3-binding domains; (*b*) the central MEC-2 domain (aa 114–363) includes a membrane-associated hydrophobic domain (aa 114–141) and a cytoplasmic hydrophilic domain that together exhibit 65% identity to the human red blood cell protein stomatin [stomatin is an integral membrane protein that associates with the cytoskeleton and affects ion balance via an unknown mechanism (74)]; and (*c*) part of the N-terminal domain (situated in part between aa 42–118) is needed for the localization of a MEC-2/LacZ fusion protein to the touch receptor process. Some of MEC-2 interactions appear to be with other MEC-2 proteins: Many of the 54 mutant *mec-2* alleles have dominant effects and exhibit a complex pattern of interallelic complementation (14). However, genetic data also suggest that MEC-2 interacts with the specialized touch cell microtubules (30, 41). Normally, a MEC-2/LacZ fusion protein is distributed along the touch receptor axon (41). The axonal distribution of a MEC-2/LacZ fusion protein is mildly disrupted in a *mec-7* null or *mec-12* strong loss-of-function background, implying that the 15-pf microtubules are not essential for the localization of

**a**

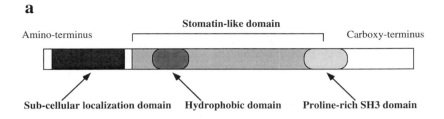

**b**

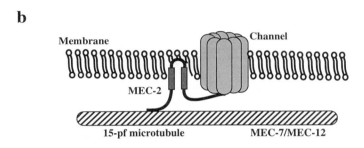

*Figure 6*   The MEC-2 protein and proposed interactions in the touch receptor neurons. (*a*) Structural features of the candidate linker protein MEC-2. The central region of the protein is similar to stomatin and contains a hydrophobic region capable of inserting into the membrane. A proline-rich SH3-binding domain partially overlaps with the stomatin-like region at the carboxy-terminus and may mediate interactions with channel subunits. Sequences in the N-terminus are needed for MEC-2 localization to neuronal processes. (*b*) Monotopic arrangement of MEC-2 with respect to the plasma membrane and predicted interacting proteins. Both N- and C-termini are intracellular with the amino-terminus hypothesized to interact with microtubules and the carboxy-terminus hypothesized to interact with the channel. This arrangement is reminiscent of a lever structure with the membrane attachment serving as a fulcrum to relay a mechanically induced microtubule deflection to the channel, pulling it open.

MEC-2 to the neuronal process. However, two specific *mec-12* missense alleles interfere dramatically with localization of MEC-2 fusion proteins, restricting the fusion proteins to the cell body (41). One of the *mec-12* alleles encodes a single amino acid substitution close to a MAP-binding region in other α-tubulins; the other affects a residue in the C-terminal domain. Taken together, analyses of the MEC-2/lacZ fusion protein suggest that residues in the MEC-2 N-terminus and the MEC-12 α-tubulin C-terminus could interact (Figure 6*b*).

There is also some evidence that the MEC-2 protein functionally interacts with the touch receptor channel. Certain *mec-2* alleles partially suppress *mec-10*(A673V)-induced death (40). In addition, some recessive *mec-2* alleles act as dominant enhancers of a weak *mec-4(ts)* allele (30, 41). In other words, when a temperature-sensitive *mec-4* mutant is reared at the maximum temperature at which the touch receptors still function, adding a single mutant copy of the *mec-2* gene to the strain background can push the touch receptor neuron over the threshold into a nonfunctional state. Although such genetic studies do not in any way prove a direct interaction, they are consistent with the simple hypothesis that MEC-2 may tether the 15-pf microtubules to the degenerin channel (Figure 6*b*; see below; 41). Clearly, it is imperative that the implied interactions be tested biochemically.

## *Proteins that Affect or Act in the Extracellular Matrix: MEC-1, MEC-5, and MEC-9*

MEC-1    In *mec-1* mutants, touch cells generally lack the mantle and associated periodic specializations of the overlying cuticle; the ALM processes are somewhat displaced and run along body wall musculature rather than within the hypodermis (14). However, where portions of the touch processes are embedded within the hypodermis in *mec-1* mutants, the mantle is present. Whether the mantle acts to position the touch cell processes or, alternatively, whether incorrect positioning of the process leads to the failure to produce the mantle remains to be determined. Cloning of *mec-1* and analysis of its expression pattern should aid in distinguishing between these possibilities.

MEC-5    *mec-5* mutations disrupt the extracellular matrix in a subtle manner; the mantle in a wild-type animal can be stained with peanut lectin, whereas the mantle in *mec-5* mutants cannot (14; E Hedgecock & M Chalfie, unpublished data). *mec-5* encodes a novel collagen type that is secreted by hypodermal cells (23). The central portion of the MEC-5 protein is made up of Pro-rich Gly-X-Y repeats. *mec-5* mutations (many of which are temperature sensitive) cluster toward the carboxy-terminus of the protein and affect these repeats. What role the unique sequences in the amino- and carboxy-termini contribute to MEC-5 function is not clear because no *mec-5* mutations map to these regions. Genetic interactions suggest that *mec-5* influences MEC-4/MEC-10 channel function (e.g. *mec-4* and *mec-10* mutations can enhance the *mec-5(ts)* mutant phenotype; 30). Thus a specialized collagen could interact with the touch receptor channel, perhaps acting to provide gating tension. The potential importance of collagen:degenerin interactions is underscored by studies of another degenerin family member, *unc-105*, that is expressed in muscle (50). Semidominant gain-of-function mutations in *unc-105* cause severe muscle hypercontraction (58). Specific alleles of *let-2/sup-20*, which encodes a type-IV basement membrane collagen, suppress the *unc-105(sd)* phenotype (50, 58). Thus although direct interactions of collagens and degenerin channels remain to be proven, such associations may emerge as a common theme in the function of this channel class.

MEC-9    *mec-9* mutations do not alter mantle ultrastructure in a detectable manner (14) despite the fact that *mec-9* encodes a protein that appears to be secreted from the touch receptor neurons (23). The *mec-9* gene actually encodes two transcripts, the larger of which encodes a 834 amino acid protein (MEC-9L) expressed only by the touch receptors. The predicted MEC-9L protein contains several domains related to the Kunitz-type serine protease inhibitor domain, the $Ca^{2+}$-binding EGF repeat, the non-$Ca^{2+}$-binding EGF repeat, and a glutamic acid–rich domain. Single amino acid substitutions that disrupt MEC-9 function affect the two $Ca^{2+}$-binding EGF repeats, the sixth EGF repeat, and the third Kunitz-type domain, thus implicating these regions as important in MEC-9 function. How MEC-9 is needed for touch cell activity is not clear, but it is interesting that MEC-9 appears specialized for protein interactions and that agrin, a protein that acts to localize acetylcholine receptors, has a domain structure similarly specialized (agrin features multiple EGF and Kazal-type serine protease inhibitor repeats; 65). *mec-9* mutations are dominant enhancers of a *mec-5(ts)* allele, suggesting that these proteins might interact in the unique mantle matrix outside the touch receptor neuron (23, 30).

## Molecular Biology of Other mec Genes

Two other genes needed for body touch sensitivity, *mec-14* and *mec-8*, have been cloned. *mec-14* mutations do not perturb touch receptor ultrastructure but can partially suppress *mec-10*(A673V)-induced death, suggesting that MEC-14 could influence channel function (40). *mec-14* encodes a member of the aldo-keto reductase superfamily (M Chalfie, personal communication). Interestingly, the β-subunit of the Shaker type $K^+$ channels, which modifies channel properties (62), is also a member of this superfamily (54).

*mec-8* is an example of a gene that affects touch cell function because it is needed for expression of at least one other *mec* gene. *mec-8* alleles disrupt touch sensitivity (14), but they also affect other sensory structures, attachment of body wall muscle to the hypodermis and cuticle, and embryonic and larval development (51). Molecular analysis has shown that the *mec-8* protein, which includes two RNA-binding motifs, is required for splicing of several messages, including that of the *mec-2* protein (41, 52).

The molecular identities of *mec-1, mec-6, mec-15, mec-17,* and *mec-18* remain to be determined to elaborate a more detailed understanding of touch transduction in *C. elegans*.

## A Model for Mechanotransduction in the Touch Receptor Neurons

The molecular features of cloned touch cell structural genes and genetic data suggesting interactions between them constitute the basis of a model of the touch receptor mechanotransducing complex (Figure 7a; see 23, 30, 41, 46 for discussion). The central component of this model is the candidate mechanosensitive ion channel that includes multiple MEC-4 and MEC-10 subunits. These subunits assemble to form a channel pore that is lined by hydrophilic residues in MSDII. Subunits adopt a topology in which the Cys-rich and NTD domains extend into the specialized extracellular matrix outside the touch cell and the amino- and carboxy-termini project into the cytoplasm. Although it is not known what type of protein *mec-6* encodes, available data are consistent with the hypothesis that it could encode another channel subunit.

Regulated gating is expected to depend on mechanical forces exerted on the channel. Tension is hypothesized to be delivered by tethering the extracellular channel domains to the specialized extracellular matrix and anchoring intracellular domains to the microtubule cytoskeleton. Outside the cell, channel subunits may contact MEC-5 and/or MEC-9 (MEC-5 and MEC-9 may associate with one another; 23) in the touch receptor mantle. Inside the cell, channel subunits may interact with MEC-2, which is proposed to link the channel to the distal ends of the 15-pf microtubules through an association with the MEC-12 $\alpha$-tubulin. A touch stimulus could deform the microtubule network or could perturb the mantle connections to deliver the gating stimulus. In either scenario, $Na^+$ influx would activate the touch receptor to signal the appropriate locomotory response (see below).

Interestingly, the model proposed for mechanotransduction in the touch receptor neurons shares features of the proposed gating mechanism of mechanosensory channels that respond to auditory stimuli in the hair cells of the vertebrate inner ear (Figure 7b; 42, 59). Stereocilia situated on the hair cell apical surface are connected at their distal ends to neighboring stereocilia by filaments called tip links. Directional deflection of the stereocilia relative to each other introduces tension on the tip links, which is proposed to open the mechanosensitive hair cell channels directly.

## Neuronal Circuitry for Body Touch Avoidance

Upon conversion of a mechanical stimulus into an electrochemical response, the touch receptor neurons activate a simple reflex circuit. Although the molecules involved in signaling to interneurons are not determined, the likely neuronal circuit has been identified (Figure 8; 15). The touch cells provide direct input to the interneurons that control locomotion. Two interneurons, AVD and PVC,

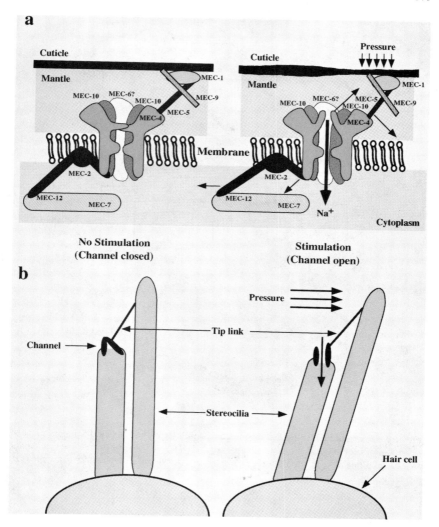

*Figure 7*  Models of mechanotransduction. (*a*) A touch-transducing complex in *C. elegans* touch receptor neurons (see text). In the absence of mechanical stimulation, the channel is closed and therefore the sensory neuron is idle. Application of a mechanical force to the body of the animal results in distortion of a network of interacting molecules that opens the channel. Na$^+$ influx depolarizes the neuron initiating the perceptory integration of the stimulus. (*b*) Model for mechanical gating of the channels in vertebrate hair cells. Mechanosensory channels situated at the stereocilia tips may be pulled open by the tip link when stereocilia are deflected. Note that although the channel is shown at only one end of the tip link, evidence suggests that channels can be situated at both ends (20a, 50a).

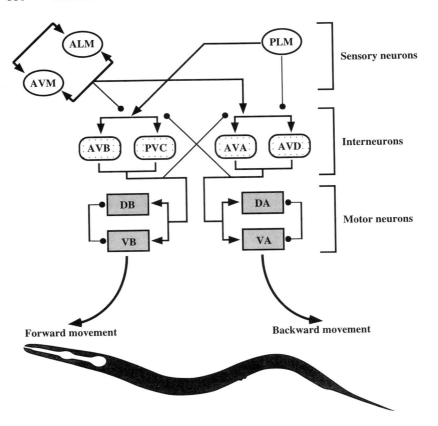

*Figure 8*   Neuronal circuitry for locomotion in response to gentle body touch. Interconnections between sensory neurons (*white ovals*), interneurons (*stippled*), and motor neurons (*gray rectangles*) are shown. Stimulatory connections are represented by arrowheads and inhibitory connections are represented by dark circles.

have been experimentally demonstrated to participate in touch circuits. The AVD interneuron promotes backward locomotion and is required for anterior touch sensitivy in larvae; when AVD is removed by laser microsurgery, larvae cannot back up (15). Likewise, the PVC interneuron promotes forward locomotion and is required for posterior touch sensitivity; animals that lack this neuron cannot move forward. (Two other interneurons that the touch cells contact, AVA and AVB, have a bit more complex involvement in locomotion). The anterior touch cells ALM and AVM form gap junctions with the backward interneuron AVD and provide synaptic input to the forward interneurons AVB and PVC. Conversely, PLMR forms gap junctions with the forward interneuron PVC and provides synaptic input to the backward interneurons AVA and AVD. In other words, the touch cells form gap junctions with agonist interneurons and apparent chemical synapses with the antagonist interneurons. This reciprocal pattern of connectivities enables locomotion in the appropriate direction to be stimulated at the same time that locomotion in the inappropriate direction is inhibited.

The connectivity of the touch receptors suggests roles in the regulation of multiple behaviors (88). Among the neurons the touch cells synapse onto are several putative sensory neurons, interneurons that connect the somatic nervous system with the pharyngeal nervous system, and motor neurons that control egg laying. Because body touch has been shown to regulate pharyngeal pumping (15), egg laying (B Sawin, personal communication), and defecation (81), at least some of the connections are likely to be functional. As noted above, the PVM touch receptor does not appear to play a role in the touch-mediated locomotory response (15). Possibly, PVM mediates mechanosensory control of some of these other behaviors.

## *C. ELEGANS* DEGENERINS AND STRETCH-SENSITIVE CHANNELS

The *C. elegans* degenerin gene family includes at least 15 members [the characterized *mec-4* (21, 46), *mec-10* (40), *deg-1* (18, 29), *unc-105* (50), *unc-8* and *del-1* (79) genes, as well as 9 additional members predicted by the *C. elegans* genome sequencing project]. The expression patterns of all these family members have been assayed (31, 40, 56, 79; N Tavernarakis & M Driscoll, unpublished data). In general, degenerin subunits are expressed in different combinations in different cell types, including neurons, muscle, and hypodermis (Table 2). Whether these degenerins actually function in mechanically gated ion channels remains to be determined. However, it has been suggested that at least three degenerins, *unc-105*, *unc-8*, and *del-1*, influence stretch-sensitive behaviors.

### *unc-105*

Semidominant *unc-105* alleles induce hypercontraction of body wall muscles (57) and encode amino acid substitutions in the extracellular domain (50). These substitutions are presumed to cause muscle hypercontraction because muscle cells are depolarized by inappropriate ion influx. Specific alleles of *sup-20/let-2*, an essential type-IV basement membrane collagen (71), suppress *unc-105(sd)* hypercontraction (50, 58). It has been proposed that *unc-105* may function in a stretch-responsive channel in body wall muscle that is gated via

**Table 2**   Characterized *C. elegans* degenerins[a]

| Protein | Cellular expression pattern | Postulated function | Reference |
|---------|----------------------------|---------------------|-----------|
| MEC-4 | Touch receptors | Touch-sensitive channel | 12, 21, 38, 39, 46 |
| MEC-10 | Touch receptors | Touch-sensitive channel | 12, 40 |
|  | Other sensory neurons |  |  |
| DEG-1 | Interneurons | ? | 18, 29 |
|  | Sensory neurons |  |  |
|  | Muscle |  |  |
|  | Hypodermis |  |  |
| UNC-105 | Muscle | Stretch-sensitive channel | 50 |
| UNC-8 | Motor neurons | Stretch-sensitive channel | 70, 79 |
|  | Interneurons |  |  |
|  | Sensory neurons |  |  |
| DEL-1[b] | Motor neurons | Stretch-sensitive channel | 79 |
|  | Sensory neurons |  |  |

[a]Except for DEL-1, all degenerins have been identified genetically.
[b]DEL for degenerin-like. This gene was identified by homology searches for new degenerins in the *C. elegans* genomic sequences database compiled by the *C. elegans* Genome Sequencing Consortium.

attachment to collagen in the extracellular matrix (50). Interestingly, *unc-105* null mutations have no apparent phenotype (58), suggesting that another degenerin coexpressed with *unc-105* could redundantly supply the same function in muscle. Another possibility is that, as is the case for *unc-8* null mutations (see below), the *unc-105* null phenotype may be a subtle behavioral defect that is difficult to detect.

## unc-8

Unusual semidominant gain-of-function *unc-8* alleles induce transient neuronal swelling (70) and severe uncoordination (6, 57). *unc-8* encodes a degenerin expressed in several motor neuron classes and in some interneurons and nose touch sensory neurons (80). Interestingly, semidominant *unc-8* alleles alter an amino acid in the region hypothesized to be an extracellular channel closing domain (80) defined in studies of *deg-1* and *mec-4* (29, 80). The genetics of *unc-8* are also similar to those of *mec-4* and *mec-10*: (*a*) Specific *unc-8* alleles can suppress or enhance *unc-8(sd)* mutations in *trans*, suggesting that UNC-8::UNC-8 interactions occur, and (*b*) *mec-6* mutations suppress *unc-8(sd)*-induced phenotypes (70), suggesting that MEC-6 is needed for UNC-8 channel function. Another degenerin family member, *del-1* (for degenerin-like) is coexpressed in a subset of neurons that express *unc-8* (the VA and VB motor neurons and the FLP nose touch neurons) and may assemble into a channel complex with UNC-8 in these cells (80).

What function does the UNC-8 degenerin channel serve in motor neurons? *unc-8* null mutants have a subtle locomotion defect (80). Wild-type *C. elegans*

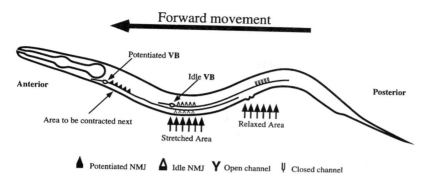

*Figure 9*  Model for modulation of locomotion by stretch-responsive channels in motor neurons. Two VB motor neurons in the ventral nerve cord are shown with stretch-sensitive channels situated in their undifferentiated processes. The anterior VB is potentiated by opening of ion channels during the process of stretch. This motor neuron will signal to the anterior muscles to then become fully contracted. At the same time another motor neuron in the middle of the body remains idle because its process does not receive a stretch stimulus. Sequential activation of motor neurons, which are distributed along the ventral nerve cord and signal non-overlapping groups of muscles, amplifies and propagates the sinusoidal body wave (neuromuscular junction, NMJ).

moves through an *E. coli* lawn with a characteristic sinusoidal pattern (this occurs by localized alternating contraction and relaxation of body wall muscles; see 22). *unc-8* null mutants inscribe a path in an *E. coli* lawn that is markedly reduced in both wavelength and amplitude as compared with wild-type worms. This phenotype suggests that the UNC-8 degenerin channel functions to modulate the locomotory trajectory of the animal.

How does the UNC-8 motor neuron channel influence locomotion? One highly interesting morphological feature of motor neurons (in particular, the VA and VB motor neurons that coexpress *unc-8* and *del-1*) is that their processes include extended regions that do not participate in neuromuscular junctions or neuronal synapses (Figure 9). These undifferentiated process regions have been hypothesized to be stretch sensitive (originally by RL Russell & L Byerly and discussed in Reference 88). Given the morphological features of certain motor neurons and the homology of UNC-8 and DEL-1 to candidate mechanically gated channels, it has been proposed that these subunits coassemble into a stretch-sensitive channel that might be localized to the undifferentiated regions of the motor neuron process. When activated by the localized body stretch that occurs during locomotion, this motor neuron channel can potentiate signaling at the neuromuscular junction, which is situated at a distance from the site of stretch stimulus. The stretch signal enhances motor neuron excitation of muscle, increasing the strength and duration of the pending muscle contraction and directing a full-size body turn. In the absence of the stretch activation, the body wave and locomotion still occur, but with significantly reduced amplitude because the potentiating stretch signal is not transmitted. Because *unc-8* is expressed in several motor neuron classes and there are no known mutations in *del-1*, it is not clear which (if any) are the critical motor neurons that mediate this stretch-sensitive behavior.

One important corollary of the *unc-8* mutant studies is that the UNC-8 channel does not appear to be essential for motor neuron function; if this were the case, animals lacking the *unc-8* gene would be severely paralyzed. This observation strengthens the argument that degenerin channels function directly in mechanotransduction rather than merely serving to maintain the osmotic environment so that other channels can function. Still, it cannot be ruled out that another yet-to-be-discovered degenerin family member that performs the same cellular function as *unc-8* is coexpressed with *unc-8* in motor neurons. As is true for MEC-4 and MEC-10, the model of UNC-8 and DEL-1 function based on mutant phenotypes, cell morphologies, and molecular properties of degenerins remains to be tested by determining subcellular channel localization, subunit associations and, most importantly, channel gating properties.

# CONCLUDING REMARKS AND FUTURE DIRECTIONS

## Limitations of Genetic Approaches

Genetic analyses in *C. elegans* have been highly successful in identifying genes needed for mechanosensitive behaviors. Still, limitations of the genetic approach to dissection of mechanotransduction mechanisms should be mentioned. Genes that encode products needed for the activities of mechanotransducing complexes in multiple cell types or that perform multiple cellular functions might have evaded genetic detection because mutations in such genes would be expected to be severely uncoordinated or even lethal. [Indeed, many mutations that affect mechanosensation in *Drosophila* render animals severely uncoordinated and nearly inviable (45)]. Moreover, genes whose functions are redundantly encoded cannot be readily identified in genetic screens. Thus additional cellular proteins essential for the mechanotransducing complex in the well-studied *C. elegans* body touch receptor neurons may remain to be identified. Alternative experimental approaches for isolating such genes, for example library screens for interacting proteins, should fill in gaps that genetic studies leave.

## Verification of the Model for the Touch-Transducing Complex

The detailed model for touch transduction in the *C. elegans* body touch receptor neurons accommodates genetic data and molecular properties of cloned *mec* genes. However, apart from unpublished findings that MEC-4 and MEC-10 coimmunoprecipitate in vitro, no direct interactions between proteins proposed to be present in the mechanotransducing complex have been demonstrated. Given that genes for candidate interacting genes are in hand, it should be possible to test hypothesized associations biochemically. More challenging and most critical, the hypothesis that a degenerin-containing channel is mechanically gated must be addressed. This may be particularly difficult because at present it is not straightforward to record directly from tiny *C. elegans* neurons (2). Expression of the MEC-4/MEC-10 or (UNC-8/DEL-1) channel in heterologous systems such as *Xenopus* oocytes will be complicated by the presence of the many endogenous mechanically gated ion channels (47) and by the likely possibility that not only the multimeric channel, but essential interacting proteins, will have to be assembled to gate the channel.

## A Global Role of Degenerins in Mechanotransduction?

A key question that remains regards how broadly DEG/ENaC superfamily members will prove to be involved in mechanotransduction. It should be noted that the *E. coli* mechanosensitive ion channel MscL is not homologous at the level of primary sequence to the *C. elegans* degenerins. Nonetheless, both subunit types share general structural features including similar transmembrane topologies (5, 29, 46) and participation in a multimeric complex. It has also been proposed that MscL and DEG/ENaC superfamily members could share a structurally related channel pore structure (43). Themes in the structures of mechanosensitive channels will be better elaborated as more are characterized at the molecular level.

Will any mammalian DEG/ENaC family members be mechanically gated? At present, although *C. elegans* degenerins share many sequence motifs and are approximately 20–30% identical to their cloned vertebrate counterparts, clear differences distinguish *C. elegans* and characterized mammalian family members. CRDI and the 22-amino acid region in the ecto-domain implicated in channel closing (29) are unique to the *C. elegans* proteins. In addition, the C-termini of *C. elegans* degenerins lack the Pro-rich regions important to the localization and turnover of the vertebrate proteins (63, 69, 73). Such distinctions may reflect true differences in functional specialization. Gating of at least one distant member of the DEG/ENaC superfamily, *Helix* FaNaC, is regulated by FMRF-amide (49), and thus it is clear that DEG/ENaC family members will not be exclusively mechanically gated.

On the other hand, analyses of the mammalian αENaC channel reconstituted in lipid bilayers suggest that its gating can be influenced by hydrostatic tension (3). This result should be considered tentative; see discussion in Reference 34a. One recently identified mammalian family member, MDEG, is expressed exclusively in the nervous system and behaves analogously to *C. elegans* degenerins in that it can be similarly altered to create a toxic form that induces cell degeneration (83). Given the strong implication of multiple *C. elegans* degenerin family members in stretch-sensitive behaviors and the large size of the *C. elegans* gene family, it is likely that mammalian members more closely related to *C. elegans* degenerins will be identified in the future. Such genes will be plausible candidate genes for the elusive mammalian stretch-sensitive channels.

ACKNOWLEDGMENTS

We thank our colleagues cited herein, especially M Chalfie, for communicating results prior to publication, and D Hall, for providing touch receptor electon micrographs. NT is supported by a fellowship from the Human Frontiers in Science Program Organization. MD is a fellow of the Alfred P. Sloan Foundation. Some of the work reviewed here was supported by the National Science Foundation (MCB-9205856, IBN-9209451, IBN-9511710) and the National Institutes of Health (NS34435).

*Literature Cited*

1. Ausiello DA, Stow JL, Cantiello HF, de Almeida JB, Benos D. 1992. Purified epithelial Na⁺ channel complex contains the pertussis toxin-sensitive Gαi-3 protein. *J. Biol. Chem.* 267:4759–65

2. Avery L, Raizen D, Lockery S. 1995. Electrophysiological methods. In *Methods in Cell Biology. Caenorhabditis elegans: Modern Biological Analysis of an Organism,* ed. HF Epstein, DC Shakes, 48:251–69. San Diego: Academic

3. Awayda MS, Ismailov II, Berdiev, BK, Benos DJ. 1995. A cloned renal epithelial Na⁺ channel protein displays stretch activation in planar lipid bilayers. *Am. J. Physiol.* 268:C1450–59

4. Benos DJ, Saccomani G, Sariban-Sohraby S. 1987. The epithelial sodium channel: subunit number and location of the amiloride binding site. *J. Biol. Chem.* 262:10613–18

5. Blount P, Sukharev SI, Moe PC, Schroeder MJ, Guy HR, Kung C. 1996. Membrane topology and multimeric structure of a mechanosensitive channel protein of *Escherichia coli. EMBO J.* 15:4798–1805

6. Brenner S. 1974. The genetics of *Caenorhabditis elegans. Genetics* 77:71–94

7. Canessa CM, Horsiberger J-D, Rossier BC. 1993. Functional cloning of the epithelial sodium channel: relation with genes involved in neurodegeneration. *Nature* 361:467–70

8. Canessa CM, Merillat AM, Rossier BC. 1994. Membrane topology of the epithelial sodium channel in intact cells. *Am. J. Physiol.* 267:C1682–90

9. Canessa CM, Schild L, Buell G, Thorens B, Gautschi I, et al. 1994. Amiloride-sensitive epithelial Na⁺ channel is made of three homologous subunits. *Nature* 367:463–67

10. Chalfie M. 1993. Touch receptor development and function in *Caenorhabditis elegans. J. Neurobiol.* 24:1433–41

11. Chalfie M, Au M. 1989. Genetic control of differentiation of the *Caenorhabditis elegans* touch receptor neurons. *Science* 243:1027–33

12. Chalfie M, Driscoll M, Huang M. 1993. Degenerin similarities. *Nature* 361:504

13. Chalfie M, Horvitz HR, Sulston JE. 1981. Mutations that lead to reiterations in the cell lineages of C. elegans. *Cell* 24:59–69

14. Chalfie M, Sulston J. 1981. Developmental genetics of the mechanosensory neurons of *Caenorhabditis elegans. Dev. Biol.* 82:358–70

15. Chalfie M, Sulston JE, White JG, Southgate E, Thomson JN, Brenner S. 1985. The neural circuit for touch sensitivity in *C. elegans. J. Neurosci.* 5:956–64

16. Chalfie M, Thomson JN. 1979. Organization of neuronal microtubules in the

nematode *C. elegans. J. Cell. Biol.* 82:278–89

17. Chalfie M, Thomson JN. 1982. Structural and functional diversity in the neuronal microtubules of *C. elegans. J. Cell. Biol.* 93:15–23

18. Chalfie M, Wolinsky E. 1990. The identification and suppression of neurodegeneration in *Caenorhabditis elegans. Nature* 345:410–16

19. Chiba CM, Rankin CS. 1990. A developmental analysis of spontaneous and reflexive reversals in the nematode *C. elegans. J. Neurobiol.* 21:543–54

20. Corey DP, García-Añoveros J. 1996. Mechanosensation and the DEG/ENaC ion channels. *Science* 273:323–24

20a. Denk W, Holt JR, Shepherd GMG, Corey DP. 1996. Calcium imaging of single stereocilia in hair cells: localization of both ends of the tip links. *Neuron* 15:1311–21

21. Driscoll M, Chalfie M. 1991. The *mec-4* gene is a member of a family of *Caenorhabditis elegans* genes that can mutate to induce neuronal degeneration. *Nature* 349:588–93

22. Driscoll M, Kaplan JM. 1997. Mechanotransduction. In *The Nematode C. elegans, II.* ed. D Riddle, Cold Spring Harbor, NY: Cold Spring Harbor Press. pp. 645–77

23. Du H, Gu G, William C, Chalfie M. 1996. Extracellular proteins needed for *C. elegans* mechanosensation. *Neuron* 16:183–94

24. Finney M, Ruvkun G. 1990. The *unc-86* gene product couples cell lineage and cell identity in C. elegans. *Cell* 63:895–905

25. Finney M, Ruvkun G, Horvitz HR. 1988. The C. elegans cell lineage and differentiation gene *unc-86* encodes a protein with a homeodomain and extended homology to transcription factors. *Cell* 55:757–69

26. Fire A. 1986. Integrative transformation of *C. elegans. EMBO J.* 5:2673–80

27. French AS. 1992. Mechanotransduction. *Annu. Rev. Physiol.* 54:135–52

28. Freyd G, Kim SK, Horvitz HR. 1990. Novel cysteine-rich motif and homeodomain in the product of the *Caenorhabditis elegans* cell lineage gene *lin-11. Nature* 344:876–79

29. Garcia-Añoveros J, Ma C, Chalfie M. 1995. Regulation of *Caenorhabditis elegans* degenerin proteins by a putative extracellular domain. *Curr. Biol.* 5:441–48

30. Gu G, Caldwell GA, Chalfie M. 1996. Genetic interactions affecting touch sensitivity in *Caenorhabditis elegans. Proc. Natl. Acad. Sci. USA* 93:6577–82

31. Hall DH, Gu G, García-Añoveros J, Gong L, Chalfie M, Driscoll M. 1996. Neuropathology of degenerative cell death in *C. elegans. J. Neurosci.* In press

32. Hamelin M, Chou M, Culotti JG. 1996. MEC-12 is an acetylated α-tubulin required for the assembly of large-diameter microtubules in *C. elegans.* Submitted

33. Hamelin M, Scott IM, Way JC, Culotti JG. 1992. The *mec-7* β-tubulin gene of *Caenorhabditis elegans* is expressed primarily in the touch receptor neurons. *EMBO J.* 11:2885–93

34. Hamill OP, Lane JW, McBride DW. Jr. 1992. Amiloride: a molecular probe for mechanosensitive channels. *Trends Pharmacol. Sci.* 13:373–76

34a. Hamill OP, McBride DW Jr. 1996. The pharmacology of mechanogated ion channels. *Pharmacol. Rev.* 48:231–52

35. Hart A, Sims S, Kaplan J. 1995. A synaptic code for sensory modalities revealed by analysis of the *C. elegans* GLR-1 glutamate receptor. *Nature* 378:82–85

36. Herman RK. 1996. Touch sensation in *Caenorhabditis elegans. BioEssays* 18:199–206

37. Hodgkin J, Plasterk RHA, Waterston RH. 1995. The nematode *Caenorhabditis elegans* and its genome. *Science* 270:410–14

38. Hong K, Driscoll M. 1994. A transmembrane domain of the putative channel subunit MEC-4 influences mechanotransduction and neurodegeneration in *C. elegans. Nature* 367:470–73

39. Hong K, Driscoll M. 1997. Structure/function analysis of *C. elegans mec-4,* a subunit of a candidate mechanosensitive ion channel. Submitted

40. Huang M, Chalfie M. 1994. Gene interactions affecting mechanosensory transduction in *Caenorhabditis elegans. Nature* 367:467–70

41. Huang M, Gu G, Ferguson EL, Chalfie M. 1995. A stomatin-like protein is needed for mechanosensation in *C. elegans. Nature* 378:292–95

42. Hudspeth AJ. 1989. How the ear's works work. *Nature* 341:397–404

43. Jan LY, Jan YN. 1994. Potassium channels and their evolving gates. *Nature* 371:119–22

44. Kaplan JM, Horvitz HR. 1993. A dual mechanosensory and chemosensory neuron in *C. elegans. Proc. Natl. Acad. Sci. USA* 90:2227–31

45. Kernan M, Cowan D, Zucker C. 1994. Genetic dissection of mechanosensory transduction: mechanoreception-

defective mutations of *Drosophila. Neuron* 12:1195–206

46. Lai CC, Hong K, Kinnell M, Chalfie M, Driscoll M. 1996. Sequence and transmembrane topology of MEC-4, an ion channel subunit required for mechanotransduction in *C. elegans. J. Cell Biol.* 133:1071–81

47. Lane JW, McBride DW, Hamill OP. 1991. Amiloride block of the mechanosensitive cation channel in *Xenopus* oocytes. *J. Physiol.* 441:347–66

48. Lichtsteiner S, Tjian R. 1995. Synergistic activation of transcription by unc-86 and mec-3 in *Caenorhabditis elegans* embryo extracts. *EMBO J.* 14:3937–45

49. Lingueglia E, Champigny G, Lazdunski M, Barbry P. 1995. Cloning of the amiloride-sensitive FMRFamide peptide-gated sodium channel. *Nature* 378:730–33

50. Liu J, Schrank B, Waterston R. 1996. Interaction between a putative mechanosensory membrane channel and a collagen. *Science* 273:361–64

50a. Lumpkin EG, Hudspeth AJ. 1995. Detection of $Ca^{2+}$ entry through mechanosensitive channels localizes the site of mechanoelectrical transduction in hair cells. *Proc. Natl. Acad. Sci. USA* 92:10297–10301

51. Lundquist EA, Herman RK. 1994. The *mec-8* gene of *Caenorhabditis elegans* affects muscle and sensory neuron function and interacts with three other genes: *unc-52, smu-1* and *smu-2. Genetics* 138:83–101

52. Lundquist EA, Herman RK, Rogalski TM, Mullen GP, Moerman DG, Shaw JE. 1996. The *mec-8* gene of *C. elegans* encodes a protein with two RNA recognition motifs and regulates alternative splicing of unc-52 transcripts. *Development* 122:1601–10

53. Maricq AV, Peckol E, Driscoll M, Bargmann C. 1995. Mechanosensory signalling in *C. elegans* mediated by the GLR-1 glutamate receptor. *Nature* 378:78–81

54. McCormack T, McCormack K. 1994. Shaker $K^+$ channel $\beta$ subunits belong to an NAD(P)H-dependent oxidoreductase superfamily. *Cell* 79:1133–35

55. Mello CC, Kramer JM, Stinchcomb D, Ambros V. 1992. Efficient gene transfer in *C. elegans:* extrachromosomal maintenance and integration of transforming sequences. *EMBO J.* 10:3959–70

56. Mitani S, Du H, Hall D, Driscoll M, Chalfie M. 1993. Combinatorial control of touch receptor neurons expression in *Caenorhabditis elegans. Development* 119:773–83

57. Park E-C, Horvitz HR. 1986. Mutations with dominant effects on the behavior and morphology of the nematode *C. elegans. Genetics* 113:821–52

58. Park E-C, Horvitz HR. 1986. *C. elegans* unc-105 mutations affect muscle and are suppressed by other mutations that affect muscle. *Genetics* 113:853–67

59. Pickles JO, Corey DP. 1992. Mechanoelectrical transduction by hair cells. *Trends Neurosci.* 15:254–59

60. Rankin CH. 1991. Interactions between two antagonistic reflexes in the nematode *C. elegans. J. Comp. Physiol.* 169:59–67

61. Renard SE, Lingueglia E, Voilley N, Lazdunski M, Barbry P. 1994. Biochemical analysis of the membrane topology of the amiloride-sensitive $Na^+$ channel. *J. Biol. Chem.* 269:12981–86

62. Rettig J, Heinemann SH, Wunder F, Lorra C, Parcej DN, et al. 1994. Inactivation properties of voltage-gated $K^+$ channels altered by the presence of $\beta$-subunit. *Nature* 369:289–94

63. Rotin D, Bar-Sagi D, O'Brodovich H, Merilainen J, Lehto VP, et al. 1994. An SH3 binding region in the epithelial $Na^+$ channel ($\alpha$rENaC) mediates its localization at the apical membrane. *EMBO J.* 13:4440–50

64. Rudolph JE, Kimble M, Hoyle HD, Subler MA, Raff EC. 1987. Three *Drosophila* $\beta$-tubulin sequences: a developmentally regulated isoform ($\beta3$), the testis-specific isoform ($\beta2t^8$) reveal both an ancient divergence in metazoan isotypes and structual contraints for $\beta$-tubulin function. *Mol. Cell Biol.* 7:2231–42

65. Rupp F, Payan DG, Magill-Solc C, Cowan DM, Scheller RH. 1991. Structure and expression of a rat agrin. *Neuron* 6:811–23

66. Sackin H. 1995. Mechanosensitive channels. *Annu. Rev. Physiol.* 57:333–53

67. Savage C, Hamelin M, Culotti JG, Coulson A, Albertson DG, Chalfie M. 1989. *mec-7* is a beta-tubulin gene required for the production of 15-protofilament microtubules in *Caenorhabditis elegans. Genes Dev.* 3:870–81

68. Savage C, Xue YZ, Mitani S, Hall D, Zakhary R, Chalfie M. 1994. Mutations in the *Caenorhabditis elegans* $\beta$-tubulin gene *mec-7*: effects on microtubule assembly and stability and on tubulin autoregulation. *J. Cell Sci.* 107:2165–75

69. Schild L, Canessa CM, Shimkets RA, Gautschi I, Lifton RP, Rossier BC. 1995.

A mutation in the epithelial sodium channel causing Liddle's disease increases channel activity in the *Xenopus laevis* oocyte expression system. *Proc. Natl. Acad. Sci. USA* 92:5699–703

70. Shreffler W, Margardino T, Shekdar K, Wolinsky E. 1995. The *unc-8* and *sup-40* genes regulate ion channel function in *Caenorhabditis elegans* motorneurons. *Genetics* 139:1261–72

71. Sibley MH, Johnson JJ, Mello CC, Kramer JM. 1993. Genetic identification, sequence, and alternative splicing of the *Caenorhabditis elegans* alpha2(IV) collagen gene. *J. Cell Biol.* 123:255–64

72. Snyder PM, McDonald FJ, Stokes JB, Welsh MJ. 1994. Membrane topology of the amiloride sensitive epithelial sodium channel. *J. Biol. Chem.* 269:24379–83

73. Snyder PM, Price MP, McDonald FJ, Adams CM, Volk KA, et al. 1995. Mechanisms by which Liddle's syndrome mutations increase activity of a human epithelial sodium channel. *Cell* 83:969–78

74. Stewart GW, Argent AC, Dash BCJ. 1993. Stomatin: a putative cation transport regulator in the red cell membrane. *Biochim. Biophys. Acta* 1225:15–25

75. Sukharev SI, Blount P, Martinac B, Blattner FR, Kung C. 1994. A large conductance mechanosensitive channel in *E. coli* encoded by *mscL* alone. *Nature* 368:265–68

76. Sulston J, Du Z, Thomas K, Wilson R, Hillier L, et al. 1992. The *C. elegans* genome sequencing project: a beginning. *Nature* 356:37–41

77. Sulston JE, Horvitz HR. 1977. Postembryonic cell lineages of the nematode, *Caenorhabditis elegans. Dev. Biol.* 56:110–56

78. Sulston JE, Schierenberg E, White JG, Thomson JN. 1983. The embryonic cell lineage of the nematode *Caenorhabditis elegans. Dev. Biol.* 100:64–119

79. Deleted in proof

80. Tavernarakis N, Shreffler W, Wang S, Driscoll M. 1996. *unc-8*, a member of the DEG/ENaC superfamily, encodes a subunit of a candidate stretch-gated motor neuron channel that modulates locomotion in *C. elegans. Neuron.* In press

81. Thomas JH. 1990. Genetic analysis of defecation in *Caenorhabditis elegans. Genetics* 124:855–72

82. Waldmann R, Champigny G, Lazdunski M. 1995. Functional degenerin-containing chimeras identify residues essential for amiloride-sensitive Na⁺ channel function. *J. Biol. Chem.* 270:11735–37

83. Waldmann R, Champigny G, Voilley N, Lauritzen I, Lazdunski M. 1996. The mammalian degenerin MDEG, an amiloride-sensitive cation channel activated by mutations causing neurodegeneration in *Caenorhabditis elegans. J. Biol. Chem.* 271:10433–36

84. Waterston R, Sulston J. 1995. The genome of *Caenorhabditis elegans. Proc. Natl. Acad. Sci USA* 92:0836–40

85. Way JC, Chalfie M. 1988. *mec-3*, a homeobox-containing gene that specifies differentiation of the touch receptor neurons in C. elegans. *Cell* 54:5–16

86. Way JC, Chalfie M. 1989. The *mec-3* gene of *Caenorhabditis elegans* requires its own product for maintained expression and is expressed in three neuronal cell types. *Genes Dev.* 3:1823–33

87. Way JC, Wang L, Run JQ, Wang A. 1991. The *mec-3* gene contains *cis*-acting elements mediating positive and negative regulation in cells produced by asymmetric cell division in *Caenorhabditis elegans. Genes Dev.* 5:2199–211

88. White JG, Southgate E, Thomson JN, Brenner S. 1986. The structure of the nervous system of *Caenorhabditis elegans. Philos. Trans. R. Soc. London Ser. B* 314:1–340

89. Wicks SR, Rankin CH. 1995. Integration of mechanosensory stimuli in *C. elegans. J. Neurosci.* 15:2434–44

90. Wicks SR, Roehrig C, Rankin CH. 1996. A dynamic network simulation of the nematode tap withdrawal circuit: predictions concerning synaptic function using behavioral criteria. *J. Neurosci.* 16:4017–31

91. Wilson R, Ainscough R, Anderson K, Baynes C, Berks M, et al. 1994. 2.2 Mb of contiguous nucleotide sequence from chromosome III of *C. elegans. Nature* 368:32–38

92. Xue D, Finney M, Ruvkun G, Chalfie M. 1992. Regulation of the *mec-3* gene by the C. elegans homeoproteins UNC-86 and MEC-3. *EMBO J.* 11:4969–79

93. Xue D, Tu Y, Chalfie, M. 1993. Cooperative interactions between the *Caenorhabditis elegans* homeoproteins UNC-86 and MEC-3. *Science* 261:1324–28

# SUBJECT INDEX

## A

Acetylcholine
  calcium-permeable channels
    and, 152
  ECL cell stimulation and,
    248–49
  parietal cell acid secretion and,
    244
  proglucagon-derived peptide
    secretion and, 261
  vasodilatory responses to
    pulmonary hypertension and,
    109
Acid-base regulation
  in fish
    gill chloride cells and,
      337–39
Acidic fibroblast growth factor
  (aFGF)
  endothelial cell proliferation in
    lung development and, 91
Acidosis
  fish gill chloride cells and,
    338–39
Acrosome reaction
  progesterone and, 375
Actin
  regulation of ion
    channels/transporters and,
      194
Actin cytoskeleton
  physical linkage of integrins to,
    586
Actomyosin ATPase activity
  modulation of adrenergic effect
    on, 518–19
Adhesion receptors
  as mechanoreceptors, 584
Adipocytes
  maturation of
    pulmonary lipofibroblast
      maturation compared,
      56–58
Adrenomedullin
  calcium-permeable channels
    and, 152
Airway cilia
  cathepsin S and, 82–83
Aldose reductase gene
  aberrant regulation in diabetes,
    441–42
  osmotic regulation and, 439–40
Aldose reductase osmotic
  response element, 440–41
Aldosterone

membrane-binding sites for,
  378–80
specific, nongenomic effects of,
  370–74
stimulatory effect of
  angiotensin on, 401–2
Alkalosis
  fish gill chloride cells and,
    337–38
Alpha-adrenergic agonists
  endothelial cells modulating,
    521
Amino acid receptors
  excitatory, 460–64
Amino acids
  cholecystokinin secretion and,
    235
Ammonia
  gastrin release and, 289–90
Androgens
  adipocyte maturation and, 57
  ovarian follicle atresia and, 356
  specific, nongenomic effects of,
    376–77
Angiotensin, 395–408
  kidney ontogeny and, 398–99
  pathogenic role in progressive
    renal disease, 397–98
  production and action in heart,
    399–401
  stimulatory effect on
    aldosterone, 401–2
Angiotensin II
  lung vascular development and,
    94–95
  pulmonary hypertension and,
    110
  stretch-induced cardiac
    hypertrophy and, 562–65
Angiotensinogen
  renin-angiotensin system and,
    403
Angiotensin receptors
  in renal cells, 395–96
*Anguilla rostrata*
  gill chloride cells of, 327
Anion channels
  cytoplasmic ATP and, 210
Anion exchange, 203–4
Antigen-presenting cells
  cathepsin S expression in, 77
Apoproteins
  lung-specific, 6
Apoptosis, 349–59
  in ovary, 351–58
  regulation of

hormonal mechanisms in,
  358–59
Apoptosis-regulating genes,
  350–51
Arachidonic acid
  adipocyte differentiation and,
    57–58
  M-current modulation and, 488
  renal potassium channels and,
    418
Atherosclerosis
  focal
    causative factors of, 528
Atomic force microscopy (AFM)
  endothelial surface geometry
    and, 532
ATP
  calcium-permeable channels
    and, 152
  cytoplasmic
    anion channels and, 210
    calcium channels and,
      209–10
    epithelial sodium channels
      and, 211
    potassium channels and,
      207–9
    nonselective cation channels
      and, 151
  polyvalent cation chelation by,
    198–99
  regulation of ion
    channels/transporters and,
      193–213
ATP-binding proteins
  ATP-dependent ion
    channels/transporters and,
      196–98
ATP receptors
  on sensory neurons, 465–66
Atrial natriuretic peptides
  endothelial cells modulating,
    521
Atropine
  gastrin release and, 289

## B

Bacteria
  mechanosensitive channels in
    roles of, 652–63
Barakat, A. I., 527–46
Barbee, K. A., 527–46
Basic fibroblast growth factor
  (bFGF)

691

# CUMULATIVE INDEXES

## CONTRIBUTING AUTHORS, VOLUMES 55–59

701

# CHAPTER TITLES, VOLUMES 55–59

704